CALCULUS AND ANALYTIC GEOMETRY

Prentice-Hall, Inc. Englewood Cliffs, N. J.

ROBERT C. FISHER

The Ohio State University

ALLEN D. ZIEBUR

Harpur College

CALCULUS

AND ANALYTIC GEOMETRY

 Printed in the United States of America. Library of Congress Catalog Card Number 61-8696

Calculus and Analytic Geometry

Robert C. Fisher and Allen D. Ziebur

Second printing..........July, 1962

PRENTICE-HALL MATHEMATICS SERIES

Dr. Albert A. Bennett, Editor

Design by Walter Behnke

Drawings by Felix Cooper

11226-C

PREFACE

This book is an introduction to calculus and analytic geometry and is designed primarily for college freshmen and sophomores. We have tried, by physical examples, geometric visualization, and the like, to make clear the basically reasonable nature of a subject that is sometimes technically difficult. This attitude contrasts with the idea that a mathematics textbook should consist only of the bare bones of "theorem . . . proof," leaving motivation and explanation to the instructor. Our feeling is that a student reads his textbook in his room, without an instructor on hand to translate it for him, and that in such circumstances a somewhat informal approach is more understandable than a strictly formal one.

Although we make no claims to complete rigor, we have made a real effort to prove most of our theorems in terms of a relatively small core of unproved, but geometrically reasonable, theorems, such as the Theorem of the Mean. We have also taken great pains with our notation and language in an attempt to make them clear and consistent.

The general plan of the book is the "natural" one. Thus in the first chapter we briefly discuss such ideas as functions, graphs, and slopes of lines, so that we may get into calculus quickly. Chapter 2 contains definitions and techniques of differentiation, and Chapter 3 consists of applications of the derivative. In Chapter 4 we study the conic sections. Chapters 5, 6, and 7 are devoted to integration, and thus by the end of Chapter 7 we have covered the basic theory and techniques of the calculus of functions of one variable. In Chapters 8 and 9 we interweave geometry and calculus. Here we place strong emphasis on the use of vectors and vector notation, both in the plane and space. Chapter 10 is a chapter on linear algebra. Strictly speaking, some of the sections on systems of linear equations may look out of place in a calculus book, but many students will have no other place to learn this important material. Diagonalizing matrices is not traditional fare for a textbook on this level, but it certainly has important applications, both in geometry, as we have indicated, and in other fields. Chapter 10 can be omitted without affecting the continuity of the book. Chapters 11 and 12 are devoted to the differential and integral calculus of functions of several variables with the emphasis on functions of two and three variables. Chapter 13 presents tools, such as l'Hospital's Rule and improper integrals, that are both important in themselves and useful for the final chapter, Chapter 14, on infinite series.

In a preliminary edition, this book was tested for two years on several thousand students at The Ohio State University. We have used it in both regular and accelerated classes. Our experience shows that it can be covered in a one-year course (at least with the better students), but that it is more realistic to expect it to take four quarters or three semesters.

In addition to the many students and teachers who used the preliminary edition and suggested improvements, we must thank a number of people for their contributions to this book. Mrs. Bette Martin and Mrs. Patricia Staley spent many nighttime hours typing the preliminary edition. Our editor, W. E. Mangas, shepherded both the preliminary and final editions through the press, in addition to acting as a third author. Chapter 10 was added at the suggestion of R. W. Hansen, Assistant Vice-President of Prentice-Hall, although he modestly declined our invitation to write it.

R.C.F.

A.D.Z.

TO THE STUDENT

Mathematics is a deductive science; that is, mathematical results are deduced by reasoning from first principles. Theoretically, therefore, we should develop our subject by first setting down a few axioms and then constructing, in a sequence of logical steps, the whole structure of calculus.

This procedure is not practical for a first approach to calculus. If we went through all the details that are necessary to develop calculus from scratch in a rigorous way, we wouldn't get very far into our subject. Therefore, mixed in with the mathematical arguments in this book you will find appeals to your geometrical imagination ("The figure shows . . . ") and even at times such authoritarian phrases as, "It is true that . . . ." Our intention is to make the ideas of calculus seem reasonable to you, and we have employed those arguments that seemed most suitable to that end. We hope you respond to this approach in the same spirit. Wherever possible you should try to understand how our theorems and techniques are deduced from previously developed facts. A sound geometric notion of what is going on will certainly help you feel more at home with calculus, since many of the concepts of calculus are easy to visualize in geometrical terms. Finally, you should not feel too badly if you simply have to accept some facts on faith. At this stage in your mathematical training you don't have the time, interest, or experience to prove every little detail. Needless to say, however, you should try to keep the number of things you must accept on faith to a minimum.

When we introduce a new idea in calculus we take up the questions:

What is it?
What are the calculation rules?
What is it good for?

in that order. No doubt you feel that the last question is the most important. For if the answer to that question is "nothing," then there is no reason to spend a lot of time answering the first two questions—we might as well drop the idea. In this book however, we haven't intentionally introduced any worthless ideas. So as we bring up concepts such as the derivative and the integral, we ask you to go through the definitions and learn the rules of calculations. Practical applications will appear in due time. And you will be much more skillful at applying the concepts of calculus if you have a fairly solid understanding of what they are and have had some experience calculating with them.

Calculus is a hard, but rewarding, subject. If you study this book thoroughly and conscientiously, you will acquire some understanding of one of the finest creations of the human mind. We wish you success!

CONTENTS

CALCULUS AND ANALYTIC GEOMETRY

1 BASIC CONCEPTS

Scientists and engineers study relationships. An engineer, for example, would be interested in the relationship between the thrust of a rocket engine and its rate of fuel consumption. If he can express this relationship in a quantitative way—the number of pounds of thrust that corresponds to the number of pounds of fuel burned per second, for example—so much the better. Calculus and analytic geometry are two of the most important mathematical tools used to study quantitative relationships. In calculus and analytic geometry we deal with such basic mathematical concepts as numbers, functions, graphs, and so on. These topics form the subject of this introductory first chapter. Although these topics are not part of calculus proper, experience shows that many students taking calculus have as much trouble with such things as absolute values, inequalities, factoring, and so on, as they do with calculus itself. So it will pay you to first master the material in this chapter (if you have not done so already) so that you will be ready to take up your actual study of calculus in Chapter 2.

1. The Real Numbers

It should not surprise you if a mathematics book starts with a discussion of numbers—a great deal of mathematics is based on numbers. In this section we will summarize some of the facts about the real number system that we will need to know in order to study calculus. You are probably familiar with most of this material; it is found in any elementary algebra and trigonometry text.

Any number that can be written as an infinite decimal is called a **real number.** Thus $\pi = 3.14159\ldots$, $2 = 2.00\ldots$, and $\frac{1}{3} = .333\ldots$ are real numbers. There is no real number whose square is -1, so $i = \sqrt{-1}$ is not a real number. If x and y are real numbers, $x + iy$ is a **complex number.** We will be mainly concerned with real numbers. Particular examples of real numbers are the **integers,** $\ldots\ -2,\ -1,\ 0,\ 1,\ 2,\ \ldots$ and the **rational numbers** such as $-\frac{3}{2}$, $\frac{22}{7}$, and $\frac{0}{3}$. By definition, a rational number can be written as a *ratio* of two integers. It is a fact that the decimal expansion of a rational number is "repeating"; that is, certain digits keep recurring in successive blocks, as in the number $23.46731731731\ldots$, where we assume that the block 731 is repeated indefinitely. We will assume that you are familiar with the rules of the arithmetic of real numbers.

The **number scale** provides a convenient geometrical representation of the real number system. To construct the number scale, we choose two points of a horizontal line and label the left-hand point 0 and the right-hand point 1. The point labeled 0 is called the **origin** and the point labeled 1 is the **unit point.** The distance between these two points is the unit of distance. You can readily see (Fig. 1-1) how points representing integers and rational numbers are located once the origin and

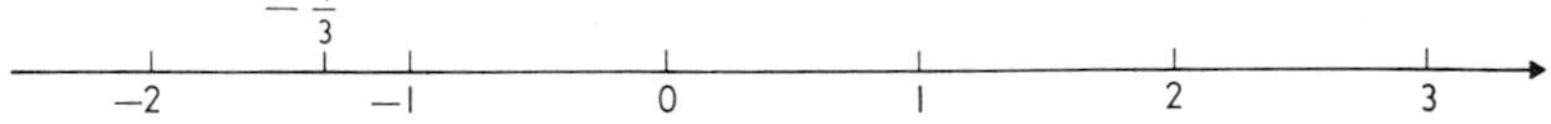

Figure 1-1

the unit point are chosen. For example, since $-\frac{4}{3} = -1 - \frac{1}{3}$, the point $-\frac{4}{3}$ is one-third of the way from -1 to -2.

It is not difficult to see how each point of the number scale determines an infinite decimal. For an example of the correspondence between points of a line and infinite decimals, let us look at Fig. 1-2. The point P lies between 2 and 3. If the segment between 2 and 3 is divided into 10 equal parts, then the points of division represent the numbers 2.1, 2.2, . . ., 2.9, and we see that P lies between 2.7 and 2.8. Now the segment between 2.7 and 2.8 is divided into 10 equal parts, and P is located in one of the subdivisions. Suppose that the point P lies between 2.72 and

Figure 1-2

2.73. Then to the first two decimal places, the decimal expansion associated with P is 2.72. Theoretically, we could continue this process indefinitely, if we agree that any segment of the number scale, no matter how small, can be divided into 10 equal parts. In this way we generate an infinite decimal expansion. (If P should be one of our points of division, we can regard all further digits in the expansion as 0.) The converse is also true; any infinite decimal determines a point of the number scale. Hence, *each point of the number scale is the graphical representation of a real number, and to each real number there corresponds a point of the number scale.*

Logically, a number and its corresponding point of the number scale should be distinguished as two different things. The number associated with a point is called the **coordinate** of the point. In practice, however, we will often refer to the "point" 5, and so on.

Any real number is either positive, or zero, or negative, and the sum and product of any two positive numbers are positive. On the basis of these facts, we construct an order relation among the real numbers.

DEFINITION 1-1. *We say* ***a is greater than b*** *($\boldsymbol{a > b}$) and* ***b is less than a*** *($\boldsymbol{b < a}$) if, and only if, $a - b$ is a positive number. The symbols $>$ and $<$ are called* ***inequality signs.***

According to this definition, the statement "a is positive" can be written as $a > 0$. Referring to the number scale, with the usual convention that the positive direction is to the right, the statement $a < b$ means that the point a is to the left of the point b. Thus $-5 < -3$ because $-3 - (-5)$ is positive, and we see that the point -5 lies to the left of the point -3 on the number scale. The notation $a < b < c$ means that $a < b$ *and* $b < c$, and the number b is said to be **between** a and c.

Thus the number 4 is between 2 and 7, since $2 < 4 < 7$. The following basic rules govern the usage of the inequality symbols:

(1-1) If $\boldsymbol{a < b}$ and $\boldsymbol{b < c}$, then $\boldsymbol{a < c}$.

(1-2) If $\boldsymbol{a < b}$, then $\boldsymbol{a + c < b + c}$ for any number $\boldsymbol{c}$, positive, negative, or zero.

(1-3) If $\boldsymbol{c > 0}$ and $\boldsymbol{a < b}$, then $\boldsymbol{ac < bc}$.

(1-4) If $\boldsymbol{c < 0}$ and $\boldsymbol{a < b}$, then $\boldsymbol{ac > bc}$.

The notation $a \leq b$ or $b \geq a$ means that a is a number that is either less than b or equal to b; that is, a is *not greater than* b. For example, $4 \leq 6$ and $6 \leq 6$, since neither 4 nor 6 is greater than 6. The basic rules that govern the use of the symbol $\leq$ are just like the rules we use with the symbol $<$.

The graphical representation of the system of real numbers as points of the number scale enables us to look at these numbers from a geometrical point of view. As a result, the geometrical concept of *distance* is introduced into our number system. Let x be a number that is represented by a point of the scale. Then the number of units between this point and the origin is called the **absolute value of $\boldsymbol{x}$** and is denoted by the symbol $|x|$. Thus $|2| = 2$, $|-3| = 3$, $|\pi| = \pi$, and so on. The absolute value of a number gives only its distance from the origin, not its direction. If $|x| = 5$, for example, we know that x is either the number 5 or the number -5, since both these numbers, and no others, are 5 units from the origin.

We can also formulate a definition of absolute value that does not rely on geometrical notions. In every case, this definition yields the same result as the geometrical definition.

DEFINITION 1-2. For any real number a

$$|a| = a \textit{ if } a \geq 0, \textit{ and } |a| = -a \textit{ if } a < 0.$$

From this definition we see that $|2| = 2$, since $2 > 0$, while $|-3| = -(-3) = 3$, since $-3 < 0$. These examples illustrate the fact that *the absolute value of a number is never negative.*

A glance at the number scale will show you that for any two numbers a and b, the number $|a - b|$ represents the distance between them. Notice that $|b - a| = |a - b|$, so the distance between any two points of the number scale is obtained by subtracting the coordinates in either order and taking the absolute value of the difference. If we want to find the distance without using absolute values, we should subtract the coordinate of the left point (smaller number) from the coordinate of the right point (larger number).

Example 1-1. Verify that the distance between the points $a = -3$ and $b = 2$ is given by the formula $|a - b| = |b - a|$.

Solution. The points -3 and 2 are shown on the number scale in Fig. 1-3. It is obvious that they are 5 units apart, and $5 = |2 - (-3)| = |(-3) - 2|$.

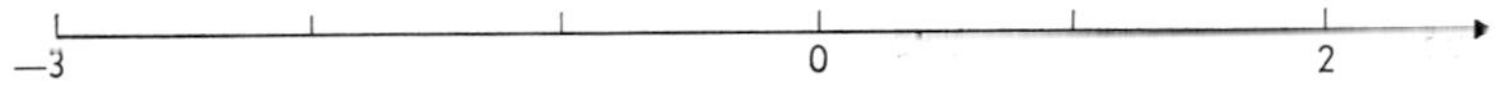

Figure 1-3

Notice that we determine the distance, 5, by subtracting the left number, -3, from the number on the right, 2.

Problems 1

1. On the number scale, what number is represented by the point that is:
(a) $\frac{1}{3}$ of the way from 2 to 3?
(b) $\frac{3}{4}$ of the way from -6 to -5?
(c) $\frac{1}{5}$ of the way from -5 to 10?
(d) midway between -3 and 4?

2. List all the integers between -2 and 3.

3. Suppose you know that a and b are numbers such that $a < b$. Which of the following inequalities do you then know are true?
(a) $3a < 3b$ (b) $a + 4 < b + 5$
(c) $a < \dfrac{a + b}{2} < b$ (d) $a^2 < b^2$
(e) $\sqrt{|a|} < \sqrt{|b|}$ (f) $a^{-1} < b^{-1}$

4. Use Definition 1-1 to prove Formula 1-1.

5. Use Definition 1-1 to prove Formula 1-2.

6. Use Definition 1-1 to prove Formulas 1-3 and 1-4.

7. What is the distance between $-\frac{7}{3}$ and $\frac{4}{7}$?

8. What can you say about the number x if:
(a) $|x| = 4$? (b) $|x - 1| = 3$?
(c) $|2x| = 2x$? (d) $|x - 1| = 1 - x$?

9. If $a \leq b$, is it true that:
(a) $ca \leq cb$? (b) $a - b \leq 0$? (c) $ab \leq b^2$?

10. Use absolute values and inequalities to express the following facts. (Assume the usual orientation of the number scale.)
(a) The point x is to the left of the point y.

(b) The point x is closer to the origin than is the point y.
(c) The distance between the point x and the point 3 is less than $\frac{1}{2}$.
(d) The distance between x and y is less than 1.

11. Find two rational numbers x and y such that
(a) $x < \pi < y$ and $y - x < .01$.
(b) $x < \sqrt{3} < y$ and $y - x < .1$.

12. Prove that if x is any number, then $x \leq |x|$ and $-x \leq |x|$.

13. If $a = .141414\ldots$, then $100a = 14.141414\ldots$ Therefore,

$$100a - a = 14.141414\ldots - .141414\ldots$$

or

$$99a = 14.$$

Thus, $a = \frac{14}{99}$. Use a similar argument to write $b = .142142\ldots$ and $c = 2.99999\ldots$ as fractions.

14. Show that $|a + b| \leq |a| + |b|$ for any pair of numbers a and b.

15. Show that $|a - b| \leq |a - c| + |b - c|$ for any three numbers a, b, and c.

16. Show that $|a| - |b| \leq |a - b|$ for any pair of numbers a and b.

2. Intervals

As we proceed with our study of calculus we will often refer to *sets of numbers*. For example, we might talk about the set of positive integers, the set of all rational numbers that are less than 5, and so on. Many times we will be talking about numbers that lie in some *interval* of the number scale; for example, the set of numbers between -3 and 7. In this section we introduce some of the terminology and notation connected with intervals.

Suppose that a and b are numbers and that $a < b$. Then the **open interval** (a, b) is the set of all numbers between a and b. Thus x is contained in the open interval (a, b) if, and only if, $a < x < b$. For example, the points 3, π, and $\sqrt{2}$ are contained in the open interval $(1, 5)$, but the points 0, -3, and 1 are not. The open interval (a, b) does not contain its end points a and b. The **closed interval** $[a, b]$ is the set of all points between a and b *and* the end points a and b also. Thus the only difference between the open interval $(-1, 3)$ and the closed interval $[-1, 3]$ is that the latter contains the points -1 and 3 as well as all the points between, whereas the former contains only the points which are less than 3 and greater than -1. Notice that we use *parentheses to denote an open interval*, and *brackets to denote a closed interval*. As a matter of convenience we will say that a single point is a closed interval. Thus $[5, 5]$ is simply the number 5. We sometimes speak of the "half-open" intervals $(a, b]$ and $[a, b)$ that include one end point and not the other.

For example, the interval $(-1, 2]$ contains each real number x such that $-1 < x \leq 2$.

Example 2-1. What points are common to the intervals $(-1, 3)$ and $[2, 5)$?

Solution. In order to solve this problem we use a simple sketch (Fig. 2-1). From the sketch it is clear that the interval $[2, 3)$ is common to the given

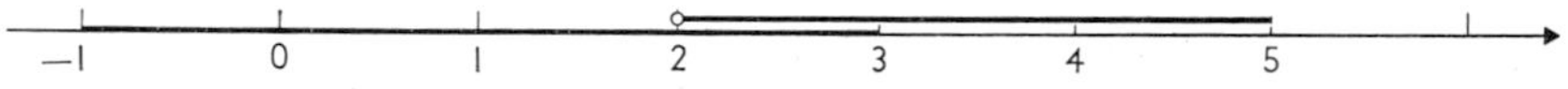

Figure 2-1

intervals; that is, each point x such that $2 \leq x < 3$ lies in both the given intervals.

Now let c be a real number and consider the set of all numbers greater than c. We will speak of this set as an interval whose left end point is c but *which does not have a right end point.* In order to use our regular interval notation we will use the symbol ∞ in place of the nonexistent right end point. Since we are talking about numbers *greater* than c, the left end point is not included in the interval, and the parenthesis symbol (rather than the bracket [is appropriate. Our interval has no right end point, so it makes no sense to ask whether or not the right end point is in the interval. We will simply adopt the convention that with the symbol ∞ we can use either the square bracket or the parenthesis, and either the word "closed" or the word "open." Thus the interval that consists of numbers greater than c is denoted either by $(c, \infty]$ or by (c, ∞). The symbol $-\infty$ is used in place of a nonexistent left end point. Thus the closed interval $[-\infty, 7]$ consists of all the numbers less than or equal to 7. The set of all real numbers can be represented as the closed interval $[-\infty, \infty]$, the open interval $(-\infty, \infty)$, or even as one of the half-open intervals $(-\infty, \infty]$ or $[-\infty, \infty)$. Notice that *the symbol* ∞ *does not stand for a number.*

Suppose that a and b are two numbers such that $a < b$. If these numbers are the end points of an interval, whether open, closed, or half-open, then the midpoint m and the length d of this interval are given by the formulas

$$m = \frac{a + b}{2} \tag{2-1}$$

and

$$d = b - a. \tag{2-2}$$

Example 2-2. Verify that Formulas 2-1 and 2-2 give the midpoint and length of the interval $(-3, 5]$.

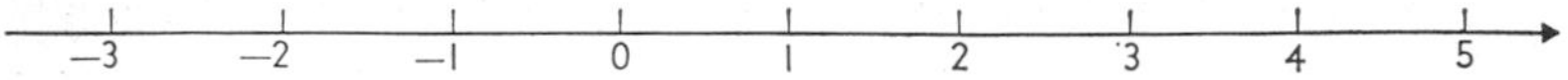

Figure 2-2

Solution. From Fig. 2-2 you can see that the interval $(-3, 5]$ is 8 units long and that its midpoint is 1. Since $1 = \dfrac{-3 + 5}{2}$ and $8 = 5 - (-3)$, we see that Formulas 2-1 and 2-2 give us the correct answer in this case.

Now let us suppose that m and d represent the midpoint and length of an interval (a, b). Then we have the following simple but useful theorem.

THEOREM 2-1. *A point x is contained in the interval (a, b) if, and only if,* $|x - m| < d/2$.

Proof. In Section 1 we said that the number $|x - m|$ measures the distance between x and m. So if we put our theorem entirely into words, it states the obvious fact that a point x is contained in the interval (a, b) if, and only if, the distance between x and the midpoint m is less than half the length of the interval.

Example 2-3. What can you say about the set that is made up of the numbers that satisfy the inequality $|x - 5| \leq 2$?

Solution. The numbers in question are no more than 2 units distant from the point 5. A simple sketch will easily convince you that these numbers are precisely the numbers in the interval $[3, 7]$. Algebraically, we have $|x - 5| \leq 2$ if, and only if,

$$-2 \leq x - 5 \leq 2,$$
$$3 \leq x \leq 7.$$

That is, x is in the interval $[3, 7]$.

A set of numbers is *contained in* an interval if every number in the set is contained in the interval. For example, the set of all rational numbers with numerator 1 is contained in the interval $[-1, 1]$. This same set is also contained in the intervals $[-7, 10]$ and $[-3, 2]$, for example. But it is clear that the *smallest closed interval* that contains the set of rational numbers with numerator 1 is the interval $[-1, 1]$.

As another example, consider the set of all positive rational numbers whose squares are less than 2. This set is contained in the intervals $[-1, 5]$, $[0, 2]$, and so on. The *smallest closed interval* containing this set is the interval $[0, \sqrt{2}]$. You might notice that neither 0 nor $\sqrt{2}$ belongs to the set of positive rational numbers whose squares are less than 2. But even though the end points of the interval $[0, \sqrt{2}]$ are not contained in our given set, you cannot find a smaller closed interval that contains this set.

The following property of the real numbers is basic to a theoretical discussion of calculus.

PROPERTY 2-1 (*the completeness of the real numbers*). *Every set of real numbers is contained in a smallest closed interval.*

The table below illustrates the completeness property of the real numbers.

Set of Real Numbers	Smallest Closed Interval Containing the Set
The positive integers	$[1, \infty]$
The number 3	$[3, 3]$
The interval $(-1, 5)$	$[-1, 5]$
The set of numbers belonging to one or the other of the intervals $(-1, 2]$ and $[5, 10]$	$[-1, 10]$
The rational numbers	$[-\infty, \infty]$
The reciprocals of the positive integers	$[0, 1]$

Problems 2

1. Find the midpoint and length of each of the following intervals. Use the number scale to illustrate.
   (a) $(0, 4)$ (b) $[-1, 3)$ (c) $(-5, -1]$ (d) $[\frac{11}{3}, \frac{9}{2}]$
2. Find points that divide the interval into three subintervals of equal length.
   (a) $[2, 8]$ (b) $(-4, 8)$ (c) $[2, 7)$ (d) (a, b)
3. State a theorem similar to Theorem 2-1 that involves a closed interval $[a, b]$.
4. In each case use inequalities to express the fact that x belongs to the interval.
   (a) $(0, \infty)$ (b) $[0, \infty]$ (c) $(-\infty, 2)$ (d) $[-3, \infty]$
5. Find the interval to which the number x must belong and illustrate with a sketch in each of the following cases.
   (a) $|x| \leq 1$ (b) $|x| < 2$
   (c) $|x - 3| < 1$ (d) $|x + 3| \leq 1$
   (e) $|2x + 3| < 1$ (f) $|x + 1| \leq 0$

6. Find the intervals to which x must belong if:

(a) $|x| > 3$ (b) $|x - 1| \geq 2$

(c) $|x + 3| \geq 2$ (d) $|2x - 4| > 8$

7. In each case use absolute values and inequalities to express the fact that x belongs to the interval.

(a) $(3, 5)$ (b) $(0, 7)$

(c) $(-1, 3)$ (d) $[4, 10]$

(e) $[-7, -2]$ (f) $[-2, 9]$

8. In each case determine the smallest closed interval that contains the set of numbers listed.

(a) The points common to the intervals $(-1, 3)$ and $[2, 5]$.

(b) The points contained in one or the other of the intervals $(-1, 3)$ and $[4, 5)$.

(c) The three points -1, 0, and 1.

(d) All possible values of $\sin t$.

(e) All possible values of $\tan t$.

(f) All numbers x such that $|x| > 1$.

3. Functions

According to Ohm's Law, if the voltage drop across a resistance of 5 ohms is E volts, then the current through the resistor is $I = E/5$ amperes. Thus if $E = 10$, $I = 2$; if $E = 20$, $I = 4$, and so on. We have here an example of a very simple quantitative relationship. The equation $I = E/5$ is a rule that assigns to each number representing voltage a number representing amperage. An engineer might look for a rule that tells him how many inches a certain beam bends when subjected to a certain number of pounds of load. The essential feature of our quantitative relationships is that we have (or seek) a rule that assigns to each number of a given set another number. A number in the original set represents a measurement of a certain physical quantity (voltage and pounds of load in our examples), and the corresponding number represents a measurement of some other physical quantity (amperes and inches of deflection). The study of calculus is primarily the study of certain mathematical aspects of quantitative relationships.

From the mathematical point of view, we need not be concerned with the laws of nature that give rise to the quantitative relationships we study. We simply suppose that we have a set of numbers and a rule of correspondence that associates a number with every number of the set. Together, the set and the rule comprise a **function;** the set is called the **domain** of the function. To each number x of the domain, the rule assigns a corresponding real number y. The set $\{y\}$ of all such numbers is called the **range** of the function. Let us take as an illustration the function whose domain consists of the set of numbers $\{1, 2, 3, 4\}$ and whose rule of correspondence is furnished by the table

Number in the domain	1	2	3	4
Corresponding real number	5	4	4	6

Thus with the number 2, our rule associates the number 4, and so on. The range of this function is the set of numbers $\{4, 5, 6\}$.

For our function above, the number y associated with a given number x in the domain is found from a table. For the functions you will encounter most often in this book, the rule of correspondence between x and y will be given by an equation. For example, we might consider the function whose domain is the set of all real numbers and whose rule of correspondence is given by the equation $y = x^4$. Thus to the number $x = 2$ there corresponds the number $y = 2^4 = 16$, to the number -3 there corresponds the number 81, and so on. The range of this function is the set of all non-negative numbers.

Functions are usually denoted by letters such as f, g, F, G, and ϕ. If x represents a number in the domain of a function f, then the corresponding number is often denoted by the symbol $f(x)$ rather than by the letter y. The symbol $f(x)$ is read "f of x" or "f at x." If f is the function whose rule of correspondence is given by the equation $y = x^4$, we write $f(-3) = 81$, which means the same thing as the phrase "in the function f, the number that corresponds to -3 is 81." For a given function f we shall use either a letter such as y or the symbol $f(x)$ to denote the number that corresponds to the number x in the domain. The number $f(x)$ is called the **value** of the function at x.

Example 3-1. Let f be the function whose domain is the set of all real numbers and whose rule of correspondence is given by the equation $y = x^2 + 2$. Find $f(0)$, $f(-1)$, and $f(2)$.

Solution. By definition, $f(0)$, $f(-1)$, and $f(2)$ are the numbers corresponding to 0, -1, and 2. Hence $f(0) = 0^2 + 2 = 2$, $f(-1) = (-1)^2 + 2 = 3$, and $f(2) = 2^2 + 2 = 6$.

The rule of correspondence of the function f in Example 3-1 is given by the equation $f(x) = x^2 + 2$. To find the number associated with any particular number in the domain, we merely replace the letter x wherever it appears in the equation $f(x) = x^2 + 2$ by the given number. We followed this procedure in solving Example 3-1. Suppose, for instance, that a, $|a|$, and $(2 + h)$ represent numbers in the domain of the function in Example 3-1. Then the corresponding numbers are $f(a) = a^2 + 2$, $f(|a|) = |a|^2 + 2 = a^2 + 2$, and $f(2 + h) = (2 + h)^2 + 2 = 6 + 4h + h^2$. It is sometimes helpful to think of the correspondence in this case as being defined by the equation $f(\ ) = (\ )^2 + 2$, where any symbol representing a number in the domain of f may be inserted in both parentheses.

Although the domain is an essential part of a function, we frequently do not mention it explicitly, especially when the rule of correspondence is given by a formula and the domain consists of all numbers for which the formula yields real numbers. Thus, for example, we may say that g is the function defined by the equation $g(x) = \sqrt{1 - x^2}$ (or $y = \sqrt{1 - x^2}$). Then we assume that a number x is in the domain of the function g if the number $1 - x^2$ is not negative. Therefore, a number x is in the domain of g if, and only if, it satisfies the inequalities $-1 \leq x \leq 1$. Thus the domain of g is the interval $[-1, 1]$.

Example 3-2. The function f is defined by the equation $f(x) = \dfrac{x}{|x|}\cdot$ What is the domain, and what is the range of f?

Solution. We can replace x in the formula $\dfrac{x}{|x|}$ with any number except 0, so the domain of f is the set of non-zero numbers. In other words, the domain of f consists of the points in the two intervals $(-\infty, 0)$ and $(0, \infty)$. If x is negative, then $f(x) = -1$; and if x is positive, then $f(x) = 1$. So the range of f is the set consisting of the two numbers -1 and 1.

We will now give several illustrations of functions.

Illustration 3-1. Suppose c is a given real number. Let f be the function such that for each real number x we have $f(x) = c$. The domain of f is the set of all real numbers and we see, for example, that $f(-1) = c, f(0) = c, f(\pi) = c$, and so on. The range of this function is the set consisting of the single number c. This function is called the **constant function with value c.**

Illustration 3-2. Another function that is frequently encountered is the **identity function j.** The domain of j is the set of all real numbers, and its rule of correspondence is simply $j(x) = x$. Thus, $j(7) = 7$, $j(\sqrt{2}) = \sqrt{2}$, and so on.

Illustration 3-3. The symbol $[\![x]\!]$ denotes the greatest integer n such that $n \leq x$. Thus $[\![\pi]\!] = 3$, $[\![\sqrt{2}]\!] = 1$, $[\![3]\!] = 3$, $[\![-3]\!] = -3$, and $[\![-\frac{1}{2}]\!] = -1$. We may define a function f, the **greatest integer function,** by the equation $f(x) = [\![x]\!]$. The domain of this function is the set of all real numbers, and its range is the set of all integers. Almost every time you state your age you are using the greatest integer function. You say you are 18, for example, when you are actually $18\frac{1}{4}$, and $18 = [\![18\frac{1}{4}]\!]$. When a dealer prices a certain item at \$4.95, he hopes you will read the tag as $[\![4.95]\!] = 4$ dollars. If x is a given real number, then $[\![x]\!]$ can be determined graphically by locating x on the number scale and choosing the first integer at or to the left of this point.

Illustration 3-4. Let us assume that the materials used in making a cylindrical tin can cost .012¢ per square inch for the sides and .021¢ per square inch for the top or bottom. Suppose we want to make a can with a capacity of 54π cubic inches. But the volume alone does not completely determine the dimensions of the can; it may be tall and thin, or short and squat. We may select any positive number r and make the radius of the base of the can r inches. Since the volume is already fixed, the choice of r determines the height of the can, and hence the dimensions of the can are then completely determined. The cost of the can depends on its dimensions, so we see that the cost of the can depends on our choice of the base radius r. Let us suppose that a can of base radius r inches costs c cents, and find a formula that expresses c in terms of r.

Clearly, $c =$ (area of sides) $\times$ .012 + (area of ends) $\times$ .021. If the can is h inches high and has a base radius of r inches, the area of the sides is $2\pi rh$ square inches and the area of the top (or bottom) is πr^2 square inches. Therefore

$$c = (2\pi rh)(.012) + (2\pi r^2)(.021). \tag{3-1}$$

We have now expressed the cost of the can in terms of the dimensions r and h, but we wanted to express c in terms of r alone. We therefore write a formula for h in terms of r. Since the volume of the can is 54π cubic inches, $\pi r^2 h = 54\pi$ and hence $h = 54/r^2$. Now we replace h in Equation 3-1 by $54/r^2$ and get the equation

$$c = \frac{108\pi}{r}(.012) + (2\pi r^2)(.021). \tag{3-2}$$

This equation defines a function. As far as the equation is concerned, the domain of the function could be the set of all non-zero numbers, but in terms of the original problem, we see that we must take $r > 0$. Thus the domain in which we are interested is the interval $(0, \infty)$.

Illustration 3-5. Let f be the function whose domain is the interval $(0, 1)$ and whose rule of correspondence is expressed as follows:
(i) If we can write a decimal expansion of x in which, after some point, all the digits are 0 (for example, $x = .13500\ldots$), then $f(x) = 0$.
(ii) Otherwise, $f(x) = 1$.
Thus we have $f(\frac{1}{4}) = 0$, $f(\frac{1}{3}) = 1$, $f(\frac{1}{2}) = 0$, and so on. Notice that if x is an irrational number, then $f(x) = 1$.

Problems 3

1. Each of the statements below determines a function. In each case, designate the function by a letter, determine its domain and range, and find a formula that gives its rule of correspondence.
   (a) To each positive integer n let there correspond the next largest integer.
   (b) To each real number x let there correspond three times its square.
   (c) To each positive real number x let there correspond the sum of its square and its principal square root.
2. Each of the following equations defines a function. In each case write a word statement that defines the function.
   (a) $y = x^2$ (b) $y = 1/x$ (c) $y = x$ (d) $y = |[x]|$
3. Determine the domains of the functions defined by the following equations.
   (a) $f(x) = \sqrt{x^{-1}}$ (b) $g(x) = \log x$
   (c) $H(x) = \dfrac{x-1}{x+1}$ (d) $u(t) = \dfrac{|t|}{t}$
   (e) $F(x) = \log \dfrac{x+1}{x-1}$ (f) $G(z) = \sqrt{\dfrac{z+1}{z-1}}$
4. Find $f(-2)$ if:
   (a) $f(x) = x^3 - x$ (b) $f(x) = \sqrt{x^2}$ (c) $f(t) = 2^t$
5. If $f(x) = x^2$, find:
   (a) $f(3 - 2)$ (b) $f(3) - f(2)$
   (c) $f(3 \cdot 2)$ (d) $3f(2)$
   (e) $f(\sqrt{2})$ (f) $\sqrt{f(2)}$
6. Find $f(x^2)$ if:
   (a) $f(x) = 2x$ (b) $f(x) = \sqrt{x}$ (c) $f(t) = t^t$
7. If $f(x) = |x| + x$, evaluate each of the following:
   (a) $f(2)$ (b) $f(-2)$ (c) $2f(-1)$ (d) $f(2)\,f(-2)$
8. Find examples of constant functions for which the following statements are not true.
   (a) $f(x^2) = [f(x)]^2$ (b) $f(|x|) = |f(x)|$
   (c) $f(x + y) = f(x) + f(y)$
9. Let $f(k)$ denote the number of "n's" that occur in the kth word of the sentence in the preceding question. What is the domain of f? Find $f(1)$, $f(4)$, and $f(5)$. What is the range of f?
10. A box with a square base x inches by x inches has a volume of 25 cubic inches. Express the area of the box in terms of x.
11. A cubical box is constructed with wooden sides that cost 5¢ per square foot and with a cardboard top and bottom that cost 1¢ per square foot. Express the cost of the box in terms of the length of a side of the box.
12. The rates for delivering a package by a certain delivery firm are as follows. A flat fee of \$3 is charged, plus 50¢ per pound, where any fraction of a pound is counted as 1 pound. (For example, the charge for delivering a $3\frac{1}{7}$ pound package is \$5.) Suppose it costs d dollars to have a package weighing p pounds delivered. Express d in terms of p.

13. A conical cup is to be made of paper costing .01¢ per square inch and is to be fitted with a circular cardboard lid costing .1¢ per square inch. The volume of the container is to be 3π cubic inches. If the radius of the cone is r inches and the cost is c cents, express c in terms of r. (The volume and lateral surface area of a cone are given by the formulas $V = \pi r^2 h/3$, $S = \pi r \sqrt{r^2 + h^2}$.)

4. Cartesian Coordinates and the Distance Formula

In Section 1, we discussed the manner in which real numbers are associated with points of a line. In this section, we will consider the corresponding procedure in two dimensions.

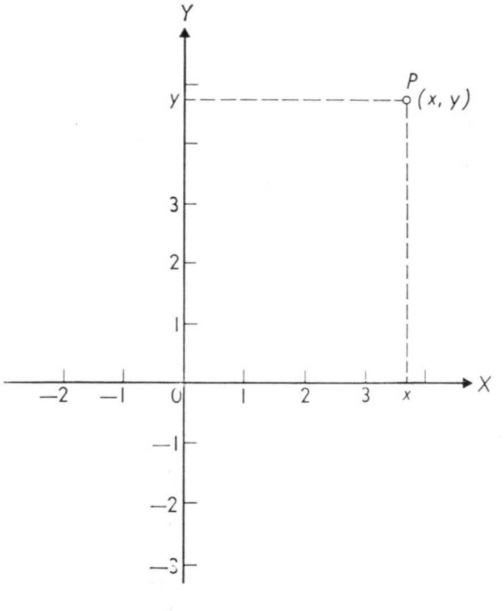

Figure 4-1

Let us begin by drawing two number lines meeting at right angles at their origins with the positive direction upward on one line and to the right on the other (see Fig. 4-1). These number lines are called **coordinate axes.** The horizontal line is the **X-axis,** and the vertical line is the **Y-axis.** Let P be any point of the plane and construct through P lines that are perpendicular to the axes. If x is the number represented by the foot of the perpendicular to the X-axis and y is the corresponding number on the Y-axis, then the pair of numbers (x, y) is associated with P. Conversely, let (x, y) be any pair of numbers. Then construct a line perpendicular to the X-axis at the point x, and construct a line perpendicular to the Y-axis at the point y. The intersection of these two lines will determine exactly one point, P, to be associated with the pair of numbers (x, y). In summary, with each point of the plane there is associated a pair of numbers (x, y), and with each pair of numbers there is associated a point P of the plane. The numbers x and y are the **coordinates** of P.

We have just described a **cartesian coordinate system** (named after the seventeenth century French philosopher and mathematician René Descartes). We have established a correspondence between a geometric system (points) and an algebraic system (pairs of numbers). This correspondence makes it possible to solve certain geometric problems algebraically and certain algebraic problems by means of geometry. We sometimes ignore the logical distinction between a point and its coordinates, and no confusion will arise if we speak of the "point" (x, y).

The points (3, 1), (−2, 3), (−2, −1), and (4, −2) are shown in Fig. 4-2. Notice carefully that the first number of the number pair (a, b)

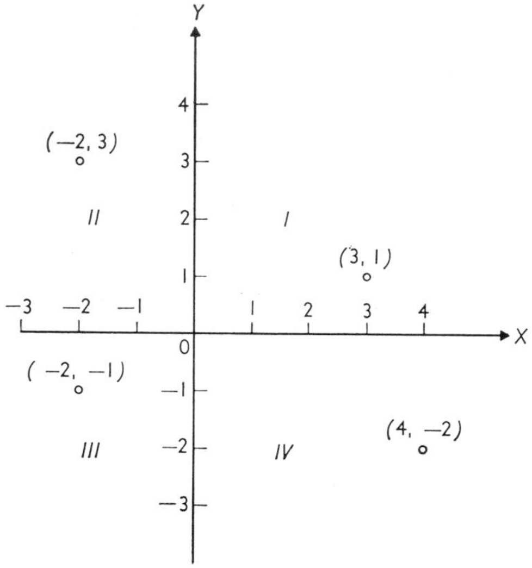

Figure 4-2

is the X-coordinate, and the second is the Y-coordinate. The two axes divide the plane into four regions, or **quadrants.** These quadrants are numbered I, II, III, and IV, as shown in Fig. 4-2. For example, the point (−2, 3) is in the second quadrant.

We have seen that the distance between the points of the number scale that represent the two real numbers a and b is $|a - b|$. We can also calculate the distance between two points of the plane.

Example 4-1. The point P_1 has coordinates (−2, −1), and the point P_2 has coordinates (2, 2). Find the distance $\overline{P_1P_2}$ between these points.

Solution. The points P_1 and P_2 are plotted in Fig. 4-3. Let P_3 be the point whose coordinates are (2, −1). It is apparent that the points P_1, P_2, and P_3 are the vertices of a right triangle, with the right angle at P_3. Since the points P_2 and P_3 lie in the same vertical line, you can easily see that the distance between them is 3 units. Similarly, the distance $\overline{P_1P_3} = 4$. Now according to the Pythagorean Theorem,

$$\overline{P_1P_2^2} = \overline{P_1P_3^2} + \overline{P_3P_2^2} = 16 + 9 = 25.$$

It follows that $\overline{P_1P_2} = 5$.

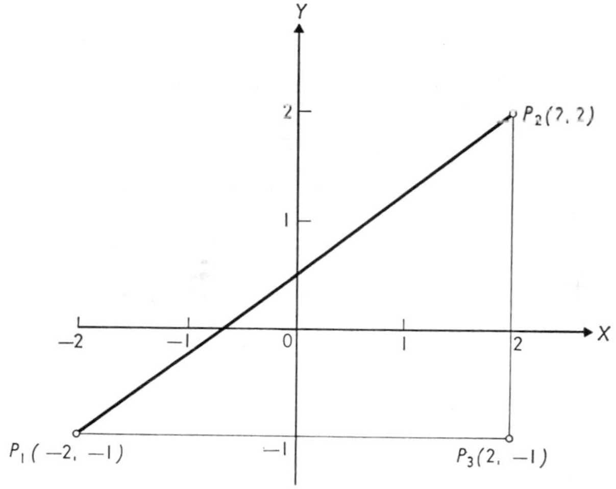

Figure 4-3

The concept of distance between two points is so important that we shall develop a formula for it. The arguments we use are the same as the ones we used in Example 4-1.

THEOREM 4-1. *Let P_1 and P_2 with coordinates (x_1, y_1) and (x_2, y_2) be any two points of the plane. Then the distance $\overline{P_1P_2}$ is given by the formula*

(4-1) $$\overline{\mathbf{P_1P_2}} = \sqrt{(x_2 - x_1)^2 + (y_2 - y_1)^2}.$$

Proof. As in Example 4-1, the auxiliary point P_3 with coordinates (x_2, y_1) is introduced (see Fig. 4-4) in such a way that the points P_1, P_2, and P_3 form a right triangle with the right angle at P_3. The lengths of the legs of this triangle are the distances $\overline{P_1P_3}$ and $\overline{P_2P_3}$, while the length of the hypotenuse, $\overline{P_1P_2}$, is the distance we wish to find. Again, according to the Pythagorean Theorem,

(4-2) $$\overline{P_1P_2^2} = \overline{P_1P_3^2} + \overline{P_2P_3^2}.$$

Since the points P_1 and P_3 have the same Y-coordinate, you can easily convince yourself that $\overline{P_1P_3} = |x_2 - x_1|$. Hence

$$\overline{P_1P_3^2} = |x_2 - x_1|^2 = (x_2 - x_1)^2.$$

Similarly,

$$\overline{P_2P_3}^2 = |y_2 - y_1|^2 = (y_2 - y_1)^2.$$

We can therefore write Equation 4-2 as

$$\overline{P_1P_2}^2 = (x_2 - x_1)^2 + (y_2 - y_1)^2,$$

which is equivalent to Equation 4-1.

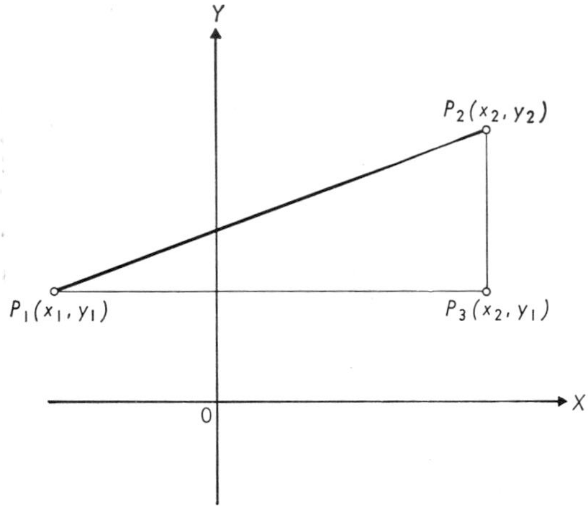

Figure 4-4

You will use the distance formula so often that you should memorize it.

Example 4-2. Find the distance between the points $(-3, 2)$ and $(2, -3)$.

Solution. You should realize that it makes no difference which point is designated P_1. If the first point is labeled P_2 and the second P_1, the distance formula yields

$$\overline{P_1P_2} = \sqrt{(-3 - 2)^2 + (2 + 3)^2} = 5\sqrt{2}.$$

Example 4-3. Find the distance between the point (x, y) and the origin.

Solution. Let P_1 be the point $(0, 0)$ and P_2 be the point (x, y) and apply the distance formula. The distance turns out to be

$$\sqrt{(x - 0)^2 + (y - 0)^2} = \sqrt{x^2 + y^2}.$$

If P_1, P_2, and P_3 are any three points, then

$$\overline{P_1P_3} \leq \overline{P_1P_2} + \overline{P_2P_3}, \tag{4-3}$$

and the equality sign holds if, and only if, the point P_2 belongs to the line segment joining P_1 and P_3. This important property of distance is called the **triangular inequality,** for reasons that will be obvious to you from a glance at Fig. 4-5. The truth of this property is apparent from the

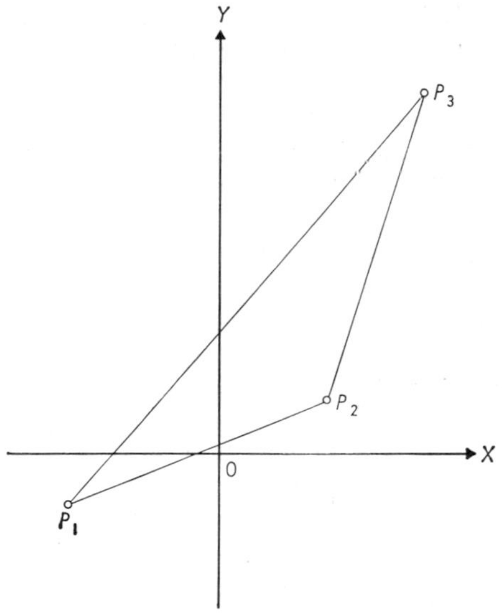

Figure 4-5

geometry of the situation, but we can check it by using Formula 4-1 and considerable algebra.

Problems 4

1. Sketch the following pairs of points in a cartesian coordinate system and find the distance between them.
   (a) $(1, 2)$ and $(3, 7)$ (b) $(2, -1)$ and $(-2, 1)$
   (c) $(1, 1)$ and $(-3, -2)$ (d) $(x, |x|)$ and $(x, -|x|)$
   (e) $(-\sqrt{2}, 2)$ and $(\sqrt{5}, 5)$ (f) $(x, \cos x)$ and $(x, \sin x)$
2. In each case determine the quadrant in which the point lies.
   (a) $(1, 3)$ (b) $(1, -4)$ (c) $(-\pi, 2)$ (d) $(-1, -\pi)$
3. Find the distance between the following pairs of points.
   (a) $(a + b, a - b)$ and $(b - a, b + a)$.
   (b) $(\sqrt{a}, \sqrt{b})$ and $(-a^{1/2}, -b^{1/2})$.
4. Verify Inequality 4-3 in case $P_1 = (0, 0)$, $P_2 = (1, 1)$, and $P_3 = (1, 2)$.
5. Use the distance formula to determine if the triangle with vertices $(1, 1)$, $(3, 2)$, and $(2, 12)$ is a right triangle.

6. Two vertices of a square are $(-3, 2)$ and $(-3, -6)$. Find three sets of other possible vertices.
7. Without using the distance formula, find the point midway between the points $(-7, -1)$ and $(3, -1)$.
8. Prove that the point $(\sqrt{2}, 2)$ is a point of the circle whose center is the origin and which passes through the point $(-1, \sqrt{5})$.
9. Find the point of the X-axis that is equidistant from the points $(0, -2)$ and $(6, 4)$.
10. Find the equation that must be satisfied by the coordinates of every point (x, y) that is equidistant from the origin and the point $(1, 1)$.
11. Use Inequality 4-3 to determine whether or not the following points are collinear.
    (a) $(4, -3)$, $(-5, 4)$, and $(0, 0)$.
    (b) $(3, 2)$, $(-\frac{4}{3}, \frac{5}{9})$ and $(6, 3)$.

5. Graphs of Functions

A coordinate system permits us to construct geometric representations of functions. With each number in the domain of a function there is associated a number in the range. This pair of numbers can be represented as a point in the plane. For example, let f be the function determined by the equation $f(x) = x^2 - 1$. This equation associates with the number 2 the number $f(2) = 3$. Then the pair of numbers $(2, 3)$ may be plotted as a point in the cartesian plane. If this same procedure is followed for every number in the domain of f, the resulting collection of points forms the *graph* of the function f.

DEFINITION 5-1. *The* ***graph*** *of a function f is a set of points in the plane. A point (x, y) belongs to the graph of f if, and only if, x is a number in the domain of f and $y = f(x)$.*

In other words, the graph of a function f consists of all points of the form $(\boldsymbol{x}, \boldsymbol{f(x)})$, where x is a number in the domain of f.

Example 5-1. What is the graph of the function f whose domain is the set of integers $\{1, 2, 3, 4\}$ and whose rule of correspondence is stated by the equations $f(1) = 5$, $f(2) = 4$, $f(3) = 4$, and $f(4) = 6$?

Solution. Since the domain consists of only four numbers, this function is easy to graph. There are only four points of the form $(x, f(x))$, and they are $(1, 5)$, $(2, 4)$, $(3, 4)$, and $(4, 6)$. These four points comprise the graph of f, which is shown in Fig. 5-1.

The domains of the functions that we meet in calculus do not consist of merely a finite number of points, as was the case in Example 5-1. For example, the function f determined by the equation $f(x) = x^2$ has for its domain the set of all real numbers. For each number of the domain there is a number in the range, and hence a point of the graph of f. The

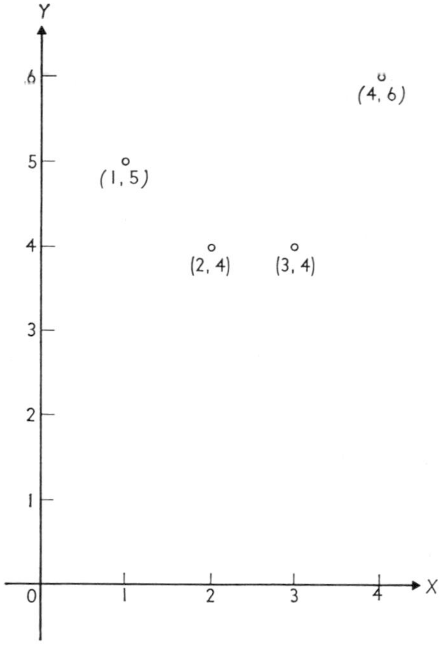

Figure 5-1

graph of f therefore consists of an infinite number of points, and it is clearly impossible to plot them individually. We take what we think is a representative sample of the points of the graph and plot them. If this collection of points seems to determine a curve, we draw it in and hope that its points are the remaining points of the graph of our function. As we get to know more about functions through our study of calculus, we will find that the process of graphing a function is not, as the preceding sentences seem to indicate, entirely a matter of guesswork. We will be able to draw quite accurate graphs even though we plot only a few points.

Example 5-2. Sketch the graph of the constant function f defined by the equation $f(x) = 2$.

Solution. Clearly every point (x, y) of the graph of this constant function has a Y-coordinate equal to 2. Thus the graph of f is a horizontal straight line 2 units above the X-axis, as shown in Fig. 5-2.

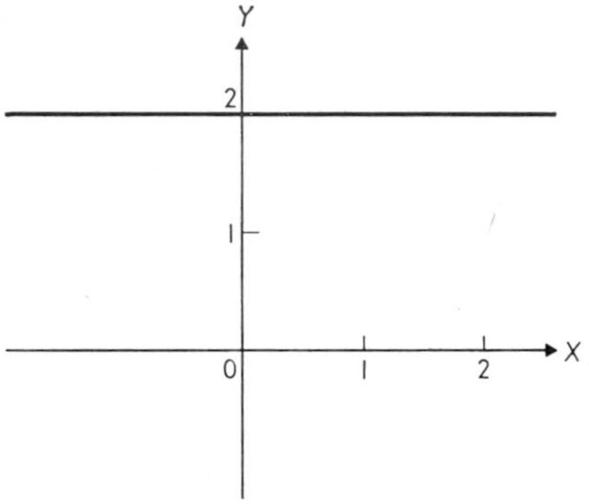

Figure 5-2

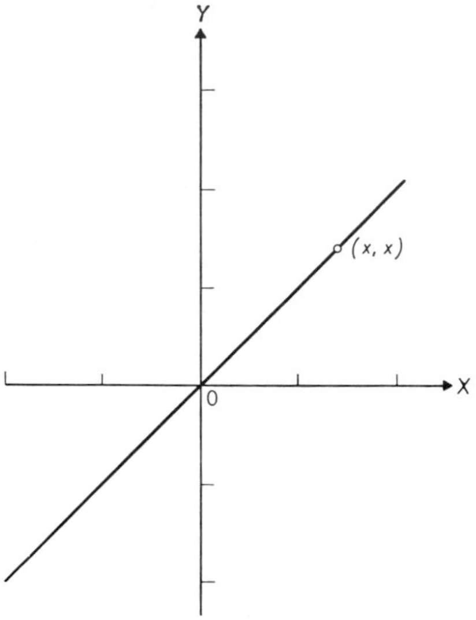

Figure 5-3

Example 5-3. Sketch the graph of the identity function j.

Solution. Since $j(x) = x$, we see that each point $(x, j(x))$ of the graph of j is of the form (x, x). Thus $(0, 0)$, $(1, 1)$, $(-3, -3)$, and so on, are points of the graph of the identity function. If you plot a few of these points, you can easily convince yourself that the graph of j is the straight line bisecting quadrants I and III that is shown in Fig. 5-3.

Example 5-4. Sketch the graph of the function f determined by the equation $f(x) = x^2$.

Solution. To find our "representative sample" of points of the graph of f, we make several choices for the number x and for each choice calculate the corresponding number $f(x)$. The table for Fig. 5-4 gives the calculated points from which the graph of f shown in Fig. 5-4 is sketched. You might calculate a few more points of this curve and show that they are contained in the arc we have drawn.

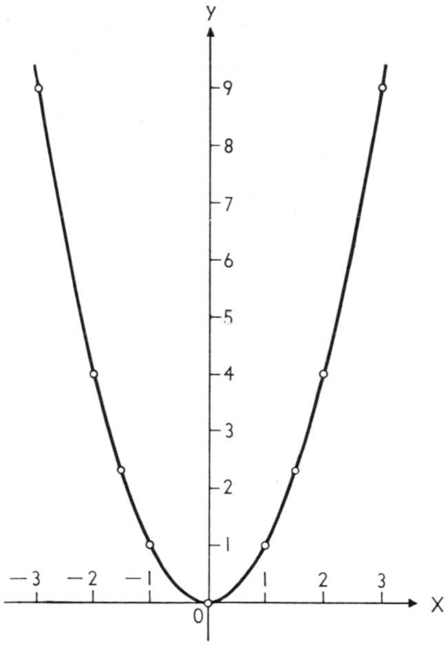

x	$f(x) = x^2$
0	0
1	1
−1	1
$\frac{3}{2}$	$\frac{9}{4}$
2	4
−2	4
3	9
−3	9

Figure 5-4

Example 5-5. Sketch the graph of the greatest integer function determined by the equation $f(x) = [\![x]\!]$.

Solution. First, we make up a table showing a few points of the graph of this function, and then we plot these points. You can convince yourself that Fig. 5-5 really does represent the graph of the greatest integer function.

Although the next example may appear artificial to you, we shall see in Chapter 2 that functions defined by a formula such as the one below do arise when we try to solve quite practical and reasonable problems.

Example 5-6. Plot the graph of the function g defined by the equation $g(x) = (x^2 - 1)/(x - 1)$.

Solution. In the expression $(x^2 - 1)/(x - 1)$, the letter x can be replaced with any number except the number 1. So the domain of g consists of all numbers except $x = 1$. If x is any number other than 1, we see that $\dfrac{x^2 - 1}{x - 1} = \dfrac{(x - 1)(x + 1)}{x - 1} = x + 1$, so $g(x) = x + 1$. When we make up a table of values and plot a few points, we obtain the graph shown in Fig. 5-6. Since 1 is not in the domain of our function g, there is no point of the graph above the number 1 of the X-axis. (We have exaggerated this omission in the picture.)

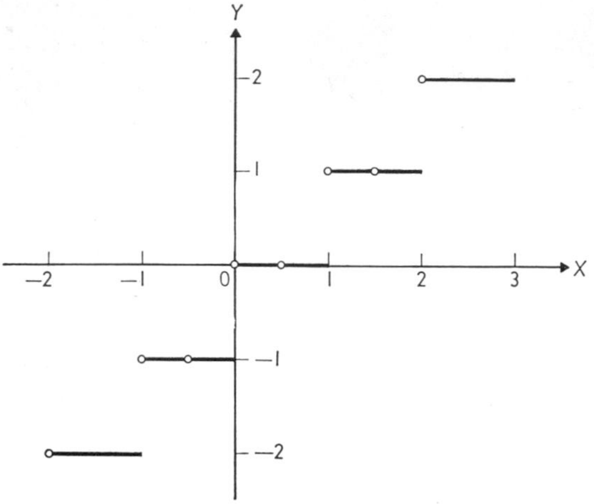

x	$f(x) = [x]$
0	0
$\frac{1}{2}$	0
1	1
$\frac{3}{2}$	1
2	2
$-\frac{1}{2}$	−1
−1	−1
−2	−2

Figure 5-5

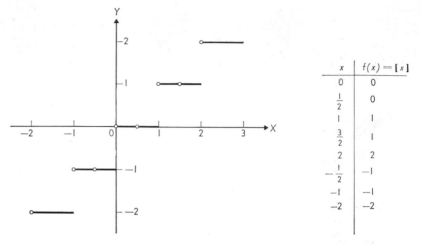

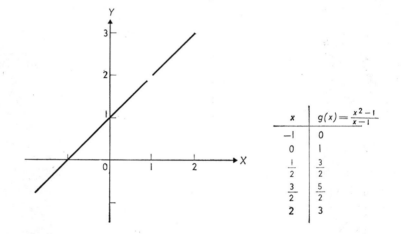

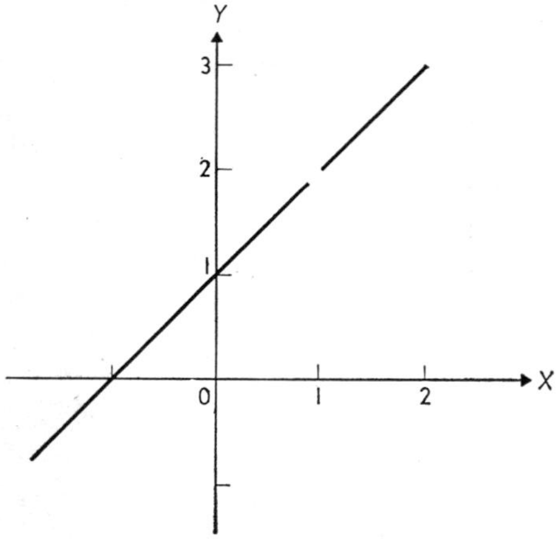

x	$g(x) = \frac{x^2-1}{x-1}$
−1	0
0	1
$\frac{1}{2}$	$\frac{3}{2}$
$\frac{3}{2}$	$\frac{5}{2}$
2	3

Figure 5-6

Problems 5

1. Plot 7 points of the graphs of the functions defined by the following equations and sketch what appear to be the graphs.

(a) $f(x) = -3$ (b) $f(x) = 4$
(c) $f(x) = 2x$ (d) $F(x) = 3x + 1$
(e) $G(x) = -3x + 2$ (f) $g(x) = |x|$
(g) $h(x) = 2x^2 - 1$ (h) $u(x) = 1 - x^2$

2. Plot the graph of the function f.
(a) $f(x) = [\![2x]\!]$
(b) $f(x) = 2[\![x]\!]$
(c) $f(x) = [\![|x|]\!]$
(d) $f(x) = |[\![x]\!]|$
(e) $f(x) = \dfrac{|x|}{x}$
(f) $f(x) = \dfrac{x^2 - 3x + 2}{x - 2}$
(g) $f(x) = \dfrac{x^3 - 1}{x - 1}$
(h) $f(x) = [\![\cos \pi x]\!]$
(i) $f(x) = [\![\sin \pi x]\!]$
(j) $f(x) = [\![x - \cos \pi x]\!]$
(k) $f(x) = x - [\![x]\!]$
(l) $f(x) = [\![2x]\!] - 2[\![x]\!]$

3. Let $f(x) = \frac{1}{2}(1 - x)$ and $g(x) = -x - 1$. Plot the graphs of the functions f and g on the same coordinate axes and locate a point that belongs to both the graph of f and the graph of g. Check your answer algebraically.

4. Sketch the graph of the function defined in (a) Question 1a of Problems 3, (b) Question 9 of Problems 3, and (c) Question 11 of Problems 3.

5. If $g(x) = 2x^2 + 1$, what is the distance between the points of the graph of g that correspond to the numbers $x = 1$ and $x = 2$?

6. Let $f(x) = \sqrt{x^2 + 1}$. If the point (a, b) is a point of the graph of f, which of the following points are also points of the graph of f?
(a) (b, a) (b) $(-a, b)$ (c) $(-a, -b)$

7. Define the function f as follows: To a number x let there correspond the length of the line segment joining the points $(x, 1)$ and $(-1, 3)$. Sketch the graph of f. What is the range of f?

8. Plot 5 points of the graph of the function defined by the equation $f(x) = \sqrt{4 - x^2}$. Show that these points are points of a semicircle with radius 2 and center the origin. Show that any point of the graph of f is a point of this semicircle. What is the domain of f? What is the range of f?

6. Graphs of Equations

We have used either the letter y or the symbol $f(x)$ to denote the number that corresponds to the number x in the domain of a function f. The fact that y and $f(x)$ represent the same number is expressed by the equation $y = f(x)$. A point (a, b) belongs to the graph of the function f if, and only if, $b = f(a)$; that is, if, and only if, the equals sign is valid when x is replaced with a and y with b in the equation $y = f(x)$. The *graph of the equation* $y = f(x)$ consists of precisely those points whose coordinates have this property.

Example. 6-1. Let f be the function defined by the equation $f(x) = x^2 - 3x + 2$. Does the graph of the equation $y = f(x)$ contain the points $(1, 0)$ and $(2, 3)$?

Solution. The equation $y = f(x)$ is $y = x^2 - 3x + 2$. The graph of this equation contains the point $(1, 0)$ since $0 = 1 - 3 + 2$, whereas the point $(2, 3)$ does not belong to the graph since $3 \neq 4 - 6 + 2$.

Example 6-2. Graph the equation $y = |x| + x$.

Solution. We construct a line of the table for Fig. 6-1 by choosing a number x and calculating the corresponding number y. Thus if $x = -1$, then $y = |-1| + (-1) = 0$, and so forth. We plot and join the resulting points to construct the graph shown.

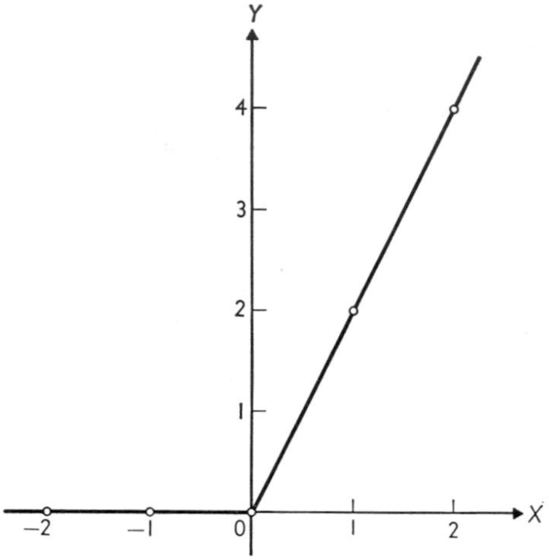

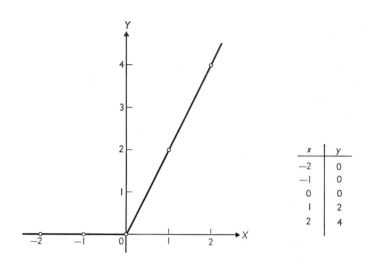

x	y
−2	0
−1	0
0	0
1	2
2	4

Figure 6-1

Sometimes in our mathematical work we encounter equations that are not of the form $y = f(x)$. The equation $x^2 - y^2 = 1$ is an example. We wish to consider the graphs of such equations as well as those equations of the form $y = f(x)$. When we speak of the **graph of an equation,** *we simply mean the set of all points whose coordinates satisfy the equation.*

Example 6-3. Sketch the graph of the equation $x^2 - y^2 = 1$.

Solution. The graph of this equation consists of precisely those points whose coordinates satisfy the equation. To find a point of the graph of this equation we write $y^2 = x^2 - 1$, choose a number x, and calculate a corresponding number y. For example, if $x = 2$, then $y^2 = 3$ so that $y = \sqrt{3}$ or $y = -\sqrt{3}$. Thus $(2, \sqrt{3})$ and $(2, -\sqrt{3})$ are two points of the graph. A more complete table of points accompanies the graph in Fig. 6-2.

Instead of being asked to find the geometrical representation of a given equation, we are sometimes faced with the converse problem; we

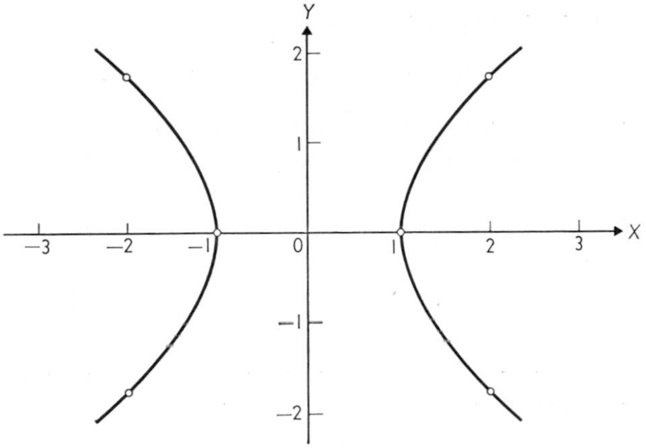

x	y
−2	$-\sqrt{3}$
−2	$\sqrt{3}$
−1	0
1	0
2	$\sqrt{3}$
2	$-\sqrt{3}$

Figure 6-2

may be given a figure and instructed to find the equation of which it is the graph.

Example 6-4. What is the equation satisfied by the coordinates of any point (x, y) of the circle of radius 2 whose center is the point $(2, -1)$? (See Fig. 6-3.)

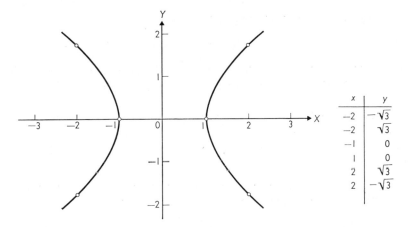

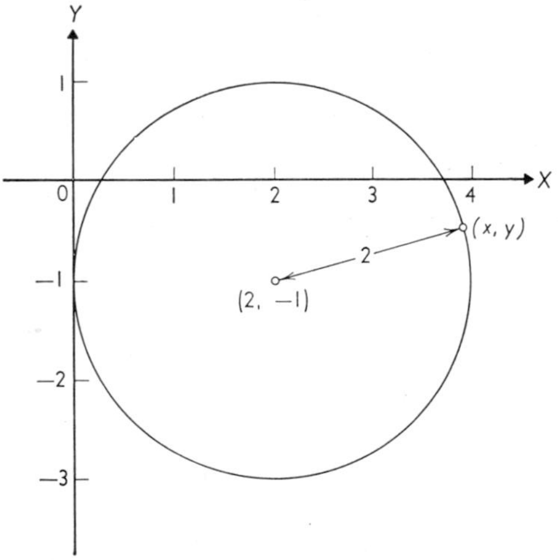

Figure 6-3

Solution. Since any point (x, y) of the circle and the point $(2, -1)$ are 2 units apart, we may use the distance formula (Equation 4-1) to get the equation

$$\sqrt{(x-2)^2 + (y+1)^2} = 2.$$

We now square both sides and we have

$$(x - 2)^2 + (y + 1)^2 = 4.$$

This equation is satisfied by the coordinates of every point of the circle and by the coordinates of no other points. It is the equation of the circle.

A point belongs to the graphs of two equations if its coordinates satisfy both equations. To find the points of intersection of two graphs, then, we must solve their equations simultaneously.

Example 6-5. Find the points at which the circle in the last example intersects the graph of the equation $y = x - 5$.

Solution. We must solve the equations $y = x - 5$ and $(x - 2)^2 + (y + 1)^2 = 4$ simultaneously. On substituting the number $x - 5$ for y in the second equation, we find

$$\begin{aligned} (x - 2)^2 + (x - 4)^2 &= 4, \\ 2x^2 - 12x + 20 &= 4, \\ x^2 - 6x + 8 &= 0, \\ (x - 4)(x - 2) &= 0. \end{aligned}$$

It then follows (since $y = x - 5$) that the only points common to the two graphs are the points $(4, -1)$ and $(2, -3)$.

Problems 6

1. Sketch the graphs of the following equations.
(a) $y = |2x| + 2x$ (b) $y = |x| + 2x$
(c) $y = x^2 - 2$ (d) $y = \sqrt{x}$
(e) $y = x|x|$ (f) $y = \log |x|$
(g) $y = |\sin x|$ (h) $y = |\cos x|$

2. Sketch the graphs of the following equations.
(a) $y^2 - x^2 = 1$ (b) $x^2 + y^2 = 16$
(c) $x^2 + 4y^2 = 4$ (d) $4y^2 - x^2 = 4$
(e) $|x| + |y| = 1$ (f) $|x + y| = 1$
(g) $\log x + \log y = 0$ (h) $|x| + |y| = 0$

3. The graph of the equation $(x + 3)^2 + (y - 1)^2 = 1$ is a circle. What is its center and what is its radius?

4. Sketch the graphs of the equations of Example 6-5.

5. How far apart are the points of intersection of the graphs of the equations $y = x^2$ and $x = y^2$?

6. In each case find the points of intersection of the graphs of the given pair of equations.
   (a) $y - 3x = 1$ and $x + 3y = 1$.
   (b) $x^2 + y^2 = 5$ and $y = 4x$.
   (c) $y = \sin x$ and $y = \tan x$.
   (d) $y = x^2$ and $2y - x = 4$.
7. The graph of an equation may consist of a two-dimensional region in the plane. In each case shade the region in the plane that is the graph of the equation. Indicate which points on the boundary of the region belong to the graph.
   (a) $[x] + [y] = 0$ (b) $[x + y] = 0$
   (c) $|[x] + [y]| = 1$ (d) $[\log xy] = 1$
8. The graph of an inequality consists of precisely those points whose coordinates satisfy the inequality. In each case shade the region in the plane that is the graph of the inequality. Indicate which points on the boundary of your region belong to the graph.
   (a) $x < y$ (b) $y \leq 2x + 1$
   (c) $|x| + |y| < 1$ (d) $|x + y| \leq 1$
   (e) $[x] + [y] \geq 1$ (f) $[x + y] < 1$

7. Direct and Inverse Variation

Among the simplest types of functions are the ones that are determined by equations of the form $y = mx$, where m is a given number. Such functions have many scientific applications: distance = rate × time (constant rate), work = force × distance (constant force), force = mass × acceleration (constant mass), energy = mass × c^2 (c^2 is a constant), and many others.

DEFINITION 7-1. *To say that* ***y is directly proportional to x*** *or that* ***y varies directly as x*** *means that there is a number m such that $y = mx$ for every related pair (x, y). The number m is called the* ***constant of proportionality.***

Example 7-1. Express y in terms of x if y is directly proportional to x and $y = 2$ when $x = 3$.

Solution. We are told that y is directly proportional to x and therefore, from Definition 7-1, we know that $y = mx$, so the problem is to find the number m. If we substitute 3 for x and 2 for y in the equation $y = mx$, we find that $2 = 3m$, and hence $m = \frac{2}{3}$. It follows that y and x satisfy the equation $y = \frac{2}{3}x$.

Example 7-2. The velocity of a body falling from rest is directly proportional to the time it falls. If a body attains a speed of 48 feet per second after falling $1\frac{1}{2}$ seconds, how fast will it be falling 2 seconds later?

Solution. If the body reaches a velocity of v feet per second at the end of t seconds, then, by the assumption of direct proportionality, $v = mt$. Since $v = 48$ when $t = \frac{3}{2}$, $48 = 3m/2$ and hence $m = 32$. Therefore, $v = 32t$, and from this equation we find that $v = 112$ feet per second when $t = \frac{7}{2}$.

If f is a given function, we cannot assume that $f(2x)$ and $2f(x)$ are the same number for every number x. Nor is it generally true that $f(2 + 3)$ and $f(2) + f(3)$ are the same. We will now prove that both these statements are true for a function f that is defined by an equation of the form $f(x) = mx$.

THEOREM 7-1. *If m is a given number and the function f is defined by the equation $y = mx$, then $f(ax) = af(x)$ for any two numbers a and x.*

Proof. Since $f(x) = mx$,

$$f(ax) = m(ax) = a(mx) = af(x).$$

Theorem 7-1 states that if $f(x) = mx$, then $f(ax) = af(x)$ for any two numbers a and x. In the problems for this section you will be asked to show that conversely, if f is a function such that $f(ax) = af(x)$, then f is defined by an equation of the form $f(x) = mx$.

THEOREM 7-2. *If m is a given number and the function f is defined by the equation $f(x) = mx$, then $f(x_1 + x_2) = f(x_1) + f(x_2)$ for any two numbers x_1 and x_2.*

Proof. Since $f(x) = mx$, then

$$f(x_1 + x_2) = m(x_1 + x_2) = mx_1 + mx_2 = f(x_1) + f(x_2).$$

No other function you are likely to encounter has the property described in Theorem 7-2.

The terminology of direct variation is also associated with the function determined by the equation $y = mx^2$. In this case, *y is directly proportional to x^2, or y varies directly as x^2.* Common examples of this type of variation are found in area formulas. The area A of a circle, for instance, is directly proportional to the square of its radius, r. Thus $A = mr^2$. If we measure the radius in certain units (inches, yards, and so forth) and the area in square units of the same type (square inches, square yards, and the like), then the constant of proportionality is, of course, π. We also use the language of variation if y is a multiple of other powers of x. For example, *y is directly proportional to $x^{1/2}$ or to the square root of x if $y = mx^{1/2}$.*

In addition to the concept of direct variation, there is also the concept of inverse variation.

DEFINITION 7-2. *To say that* **y is inversely proportional to x** *or that* **y varies inversely as x** *means that there is a number k such that $y = k/x$ for every related pair (x, y).*

Example 7-3. Express y in terms of x if y is inversely proportional to x and $y = 2$ when $x = 3$.

Solution. Since we are told that y is inversely proportional to x, we know from Definition 7-2 that $y = k/x$. Our problem will be solved when we determine the number k. If we substitute 3 for x and 2 for y in the equation $y = k/x$, we find $2 = k/3$ and hence $k = 6$. It follows that y and x satisfy the equation $y = 6/x$.

Example 7-4. The electrical resistance of a wire of given length and material is inversely proportional to its cross-sectional area. The resistance in a circuit composed of wire that has a cross section of 82 square millimeters is 210 ohms. What would the resistance be if we rewire the circuit using wire with a cross section of 70 square millimeters?

Solution. Let R denote the resistance in ohms corresponding to wire with a cross-sectional area of A square millimeters. Then $R = k/A$. Now $R = 210$ when $A = 82$, so $210 = k/82$ and hence $k = 82 \cdot 210$. The equation determining R is therefore $R = 82 \cdot 210/A$. It is now clear that $R = 82 \cdot 210/70 = 246$ when $A = 70$.

Example 7-5. Sketch the graph of the equation $y = \dfrac{2}{x}$.

Solution. The graph is shown in Fig. 7-1, and is an example of an "equilateral hyperbola." Notice the appearance of the graph when x is near 0 (x cannot be 0, since $\frac{2}{0}$ is not defined). What can you say about $|y|$ when $|x|$ is very large?

The terminology of inverse variation is also applied to functions that are determined by equations of the type $y = k/x^p$. Thus if $y = k/x^2$, we say that y is inversely proportional to the square of x; if $y = k/\sqrt[3]{x}$, we say that y is inversely proportional to the cube root of x, and so on.

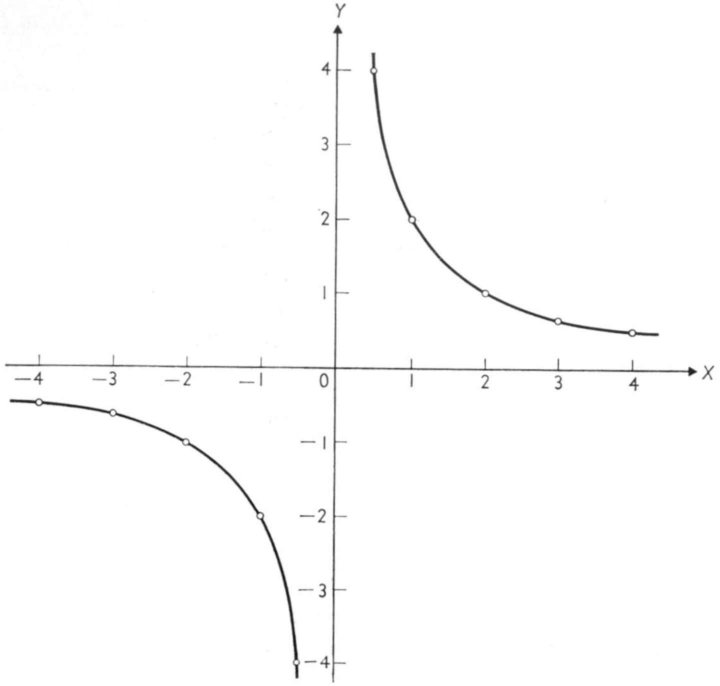

Figure 7-1

Problems 7

1. Find the equation satisfied by x and y if y is directly proportional to x and if the graph of the equation contains the following point.
   (a) (2, 3) (b) (−1, 7) (c) (4, −3)
2. Find the equation satisfied by x and y if y is inversely proportional to x^2 and if the graph of the equation contains the following point.
   (a) (2, 3) (b) (1, −2) (c) (−3, 1)
3. Let y be directly proportional to x, and let $y = f(x)$.
   (a) Show that $f(x_1)/f(x_2) = x_1/x_2$ for any two numbers x_1 and x_2 (such that $f(x_2) \neq 0$).
   (b) Is it always true that $f(1/a) = 1/f(a)$?
   (c) Is it always true that $f(ab) = f(a)\,f(b)$?
   (d) Is it always true that $f(a + 1) = f(a) + 1$?
   (e) Is it always true that $f(x^2) = [f(x)]^2$?
4. Suppose that y is inversely proportional to x and that $y = f(x)$. Answer questions (b), (c), (d), and (e) in the preceding problem.

5. An automobile travels 115 miles in 2 hours and 40 minutes. Assuming constant velocity:
   (a) How far will it go in 3 hours?
   (b) How long will it take to make a trip of 200 miles?
6. If $y = (mx)^{-1}$, is y inversely proportional to x?
7. A lamp post h feet high is placed on top of a wall 6 feet high. A man 6 feet tall stands 4 feet from the base of the wall. Show that the length of his shadow is inversely proportional to h, and calculate h if his shadow is 12 feet long.
8. If a and b are two positive numbers, then $\log_a x$ is directly proportional to $\log_b x$. What is the constant of proportionality?
9. If $\log y$ is directly proportional to $\log x$, what is the relation between y and x?
10. Suppose that f is a function with the property that for each pair of numbers a and x, $f(ax) = af(x)$. Show that if we set $m = f(1)$, then $f(x) = mx$ for each x.

8. **Linear Functions**

A function defined by an equation $y = mx + b$, where m and b are given numbers, is called a **linear function.** In the last section, we considered functions defined by equations of the form $y = mx$, which are simply linear functions for which $b = 0$. Linear functions are so named because the graph of a linear function is a straight line. The proof of this assertion will be easier to follow if we first consider an example.

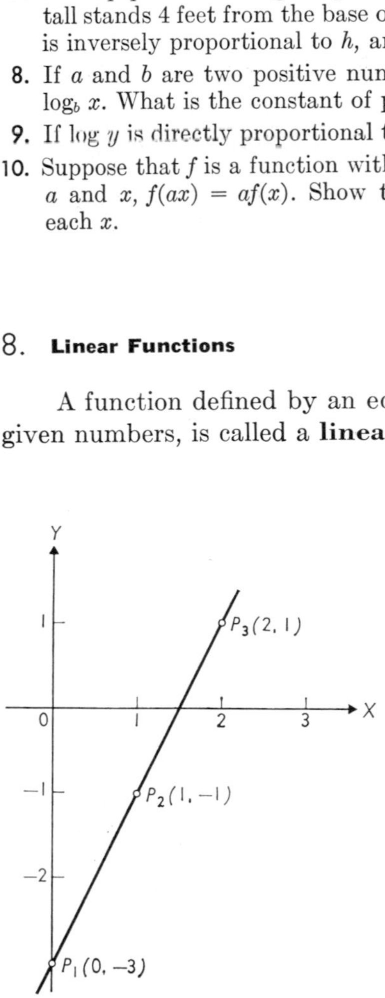

Figure 8-1

Example 8-1. Suppose the function f is defined by the equation $y = 2x - 3$. Choose any three points of the graph of f and show that they lie in a line.

Solution. We were asked to choose any three points, so let us arbitrarily take $x = 0$, $x = 1$, and $x = 2$. Thus we find the three points $P_1(0, -3)$, $P_2(1, -1)$, and $P_3(2, 1)$ of the graph of f (see Fig. 8-1). The points will lie in a line if the distance $\overline{P_1P_3}$ is equal to the sum of the distances $\overline{P_1P_2}$ and $\overline{P_2P_3}$. (The shortest path between two points is a straight line; see Inequality

4-3.) Now

$$\overline{P_1P_3} = \sqrt{2^2 + 4^2} = \sqrt{20} = 2\sqrt{5}, \quad \overline{P_1P_2} = \sqrt{1^2 + 2^2} = \sqrt{5},$$
$$\overline{P_2P_3} = \sqrt{1^2 + 2^2} = \sqrt{5},$$

and therefore

$$\overline{P_1P_3} = \overline{P_1P_2} + \overline{P_2P_3}.$$

We shall now apply the same argument to the general linear function.

THEOREM 8-1. *The graph of a linear function f is a straight line.*

Proof. Since f is a linear function, it is defined by an equation of the form $y = mx + b$. We have to show that any three points of the

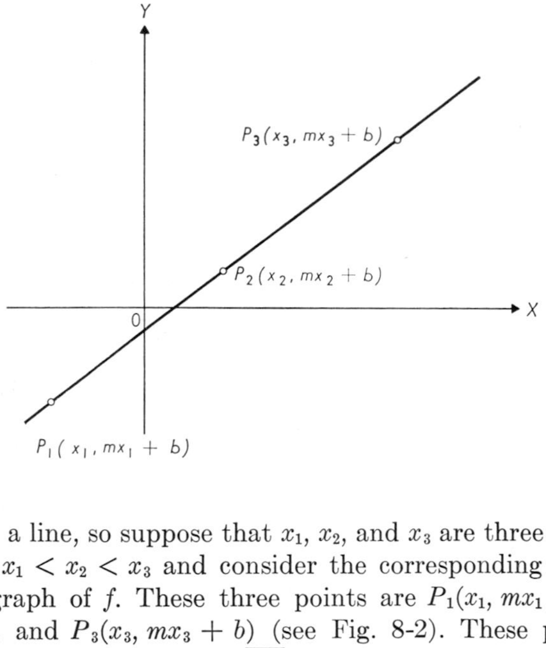

Figure 8-2

graph of f lie in a line, so suppose that x_1, x_2, and x_3 are three numbers such that $x_1 < x_2 < x_3$ and consider the corresponding three points of the graph of f. These three points are $P_1(x_1, mx_1 + b)$, $P_2(x_2, mx_2 + b)$, and $P_3(x_3, mx_3 + b)$ (see Fig. 8-2). These points lie in a straight line if the distance $\overline{P_1P_3}$ is equal to the sum of the distances $\overline{P_1P_2}$ and $\overline{P_2P_3}$.

Now
$$\begin{aligned}\overline{P_1P_3} &= \sqrt{(x_3 - x_1)^2 + [(mx_3 + b) - (mx_1 + b)]^2} \\ &= \sqrt{(x_3 - x_1)^2 + m^2(x_3 - x_1)^2} \\ &= \sqrt{(x_3 - x_1)^2(1 + m^2)} \\ &= \sqrt{(x_3 - x_1)^2}\sqrt{1 + m^2}.\end{aligned}$$

Since $x_3 > x_1$, $x_3 - x_1$ is positive, and hence

$$\sqrt{(x_3 - x_1)^2} = x_3 - x_1.$$

We therefore have

$$\overline{P_1P_3} = (x_3 - x_1)\sqrt{1 + m^2}.$$

In exactly the same way we could calculate

$$\overline{P_1P_2} = (x_2 - x_1)\sqrt{1 + m^2},$$

and

$$\overline{P_2P_3} = (x_3 - x_2)\sqrt{1 + m^2}.$$

We can therefore write

$$\begin{aligned}\overline{P_1P_2} + \overline{P_2P_3} &= (x_2 - x_1)\sqrt{1 + m^2} + (x_3 - x_2)\sqrt{1 + m^2} \\ &= [(x_2 - x_1) + (x_3 - x_2)]\sqrt{1 + m^2} \\ &= (x_3 - x_1)\sqrt{1 + m^2} = \overline{P_1P_3}\end{aligned}$$

and the theorem is proved.

Example 8-2. Sketch the graph of the equation $y = 3x - 5$.

Solution. The graph in question is a straight line, and therefore it is only necessary to find two points of the graph in order to draw it. Two points are (2, 1) and (1, −2), and the graph is shown in Fig. 8-3.

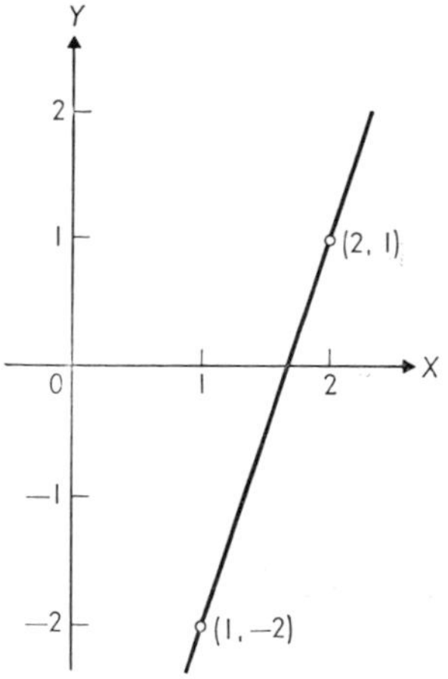

Figure 8-3

Example 8-3. What can we say about a linear function f if $f(3) = f(1) + f(2)$?

Solution. Since f is a linear function, it must be defined by an equation of the form $y = mx + b$. Therefore $f(3) = 3m + b$, $f(1) = m + b$, and $f(2) = 2m + b$. The equation $f(3) = f(1) + f(2)$ is valid only if $3m + b = (m + b) + (2m + b)$; that is, $3m + b = 3m + 2b$. But this equation means that $b = 2b$, and hence $b = 0$. Therefore the function f is defined by an equation of the form $y = mx$.

Example 8-4. If the temperature of a body is C degrees Centigrade and if the corresponding Fahrenheit reading is F degrees, then the relation between these numbers is a linear one. Find it.

Solution. Since the relation is linear, we know that $F = mC + b$, so our problem is to determine the numbers m and b. Now $F = 32$ when $C = 0$, and $F = 212$ when $C = 100$; and therefore $32 = b$ and $212 = 100m + b$. Thus $212 = 100m + 32$, and we see that $m = \frac{9}{5}$. The formula connecting the two units of temperature measurement is therefore $F = \frac{9}{5}C + 32$.

The graph of an equation of the form $y = mx + b$ is a line. The question of whether or not every line must be the graph of such an equation is answered by the following theorem.

THEOREM 8-2. *Any line not parallel to the Y-axis is the graph of an equation $y = mx + b$. A line parallel to the Y-axis is the graph of an equation $x = a$.*

Proof. First, let us consider the case of a line parallel to the Y-axis. A line parallel to the Y-axis must intersect the X-axis at some point $(a, 0)$. Then the X-coordinate of every point of the line must be $x = a$, which is the equation of the line. If a line is not parallel to the Y-axis, then it must intersect that axis and every line parallel to that axis. Suppose such a line intersects the Y-axis at the point $(0, b)$ and the line $x = 1$ at the point $(1, c)$, and let $c - b = m$. (See Fig. 8-4.) A given line therefore determines the numbers m and b, and we shall show that the equation of the line is $y = mx + b$. We already know that the graph of the equation $y = mx + b$ is a line. Furthermore, it is easy to establish that the graph of this equation contains the points $(0, b)$ and $(1, c)$. Since there is only one line containing these points, it follows that the graph of the equation $y = mx + b$ must be the line we started with.

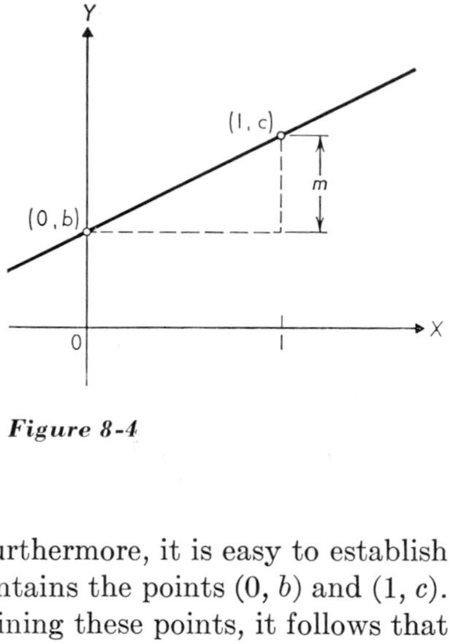

Figure 8-4

Problems 8

1. Suppose f is a linear function. Determine the formula for $f(x)$ if the graph of f contains the points:
   (a) $(1, 1)$ and $(2, 4)$
   (b) $(0, 1)$ and $(1, 0)$
   (c) $(1, 0)$ and $(-2, \pi)$
   (d) (r, r) and $(2r, 3r)$

2. Graph the following equations.

(a) $y = 4x - 7$ (b) $y = -2x + 3$

(c) $y = 2$ (d) $x = -4$

(e) $2x - 3y + 13 = 0$ (f) $y - 1 = \log 2^x$

3. What can you say about a linear function f if:

(a) $2f(x) = f(2x)$ for every number x?

(b) $f(x + 1) = f(x) + 1$ for every number x?

(c) $f(2x + 1) = 2f(x) + 1$ for every number x?

(d) $f(3) = 2$?

(e) $f(3) = 2$ and $f(-1) = 1$?

(f) $f(2) = -4$ and $f(-1) = -f(2)$?

4. The equations $f(x) = 2x + 3$ and $g(x) = \frac{1}{2}(x + 3)$ define linear functions f and g. At what point do the graphs of these functions intersect? Check your result graphically.

5. If the quantity of heat in calories required to change 1 gram of solid ice at 0° C to water at T°C is denoted by Q, then the associated function is linear when $0 \leq T \leq 100$. If $Q = 90$ when $T = 10$, and $Q = 150$ when $T = 70$, what is the quantity of heat required to transform ice into 0° water?

6. Suppose that $x_1 \neq x_2$ and that $y_1 \neq y_2$. Let $x_3 = x_1 + r(x_2 - x_1)$ and $y_3 = y_1 + s(y_2 - y_1)$. Show that the point (x_3, y_3) is a point of the line determined by the points (x_1, y_1) and (x_2, y_2) if, and only if, $r = s$.

7. Graph the two equations $y = 2x + 3$ and $y = 2x - 2$. Can you say anything about these two lines?

9. More about Lines. Slope

We have just seen that the graph of an equation of the form

$$y = mx + b \tag{9-1}$$

is a line not parallel to the Y-axis. The two numbers m and b determine this line. Since the point $(0, b)$ is a point of the line, we see that the number b is the Y-coordinate of the point of intersection of the line with the Y-axis. The number b is called the **Y-intercept** of the line. Next we will find a geometric interpretation of the number m.

Suppose that (x_1, y_1) and (x_2, y_2), where $x_1 \neq x_2$, are two points of our line. Then both these pairs of numbers satisfy Equation 9-1, so that

$$y_1 = mx_1 + b$$

and

$$y_2 = mx_2 + b.$$

If we subtract the first of these equations from the second, we get $y_2 - y_1 = m(x_2 - x_1)$. Hence

$$\boldsymbol{m = \frac{y_2 - y_1}{x_2 - x_1}.} \tag{9-2}$$

Equation 9-2 shows that the number m in the equation $y = mx + b$ is the ratio of the difference of the Y-coordinates to the difference of the X-coordinates of any two points of the line which forms the graph of the equation. The number m is called the **slope** of this line. We also say that the slope of any line segment containing the points (x_1, y_1) and (x_2, y_2) is m. Equation 9-2 is meaningless if the points (x_1, y_1) and (x_2, y_2) lie in a line (or line segment) parallel to the Y-axis. We shall simply say that such lines (or segments) have *no slope*.

Figure 9-1 shows that if we move along our line from the point (x_1, y_1) to the point (x_2, y_2), then we move $y_2 - y_1$ units in the Y direction and $x_2 - x_1$ units in the X direction. Therefore, the quotient $m = (y_2 - y_1)/(x_2 - x_1)$ is the number of units moved in the Y direction, for each unit moved in the X direction or, as we say, the **rate** at which the line rises. You will also note from elementary trigonometry that $m = \tan \alpha$, where α is the angle between the line and the positive X-axis (see Fig. 9-1). The angle α is called the **angle of inclination** of the line. Notice that α is a nonnegative angle that measures less than 180°.

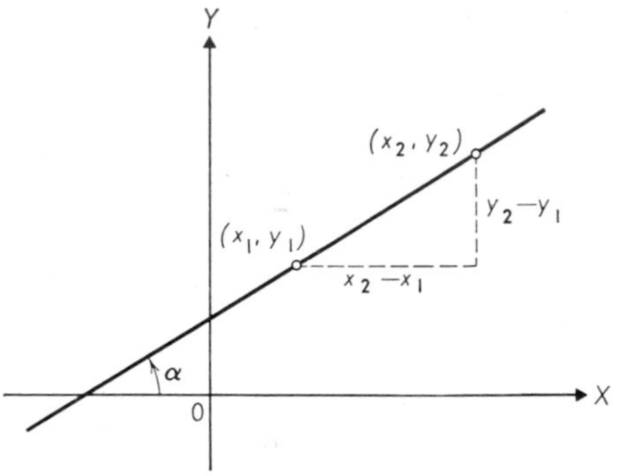

Figure 9-1

Example 9-1. The graph of the equation $F = \frac{9}{5}C + 32$ that relates Fahrenheit and Centigrade temperatures is a line. What is the slope of this line?

Solution. If we plot C along the horizontal axis, we see that $m = \frac{9}{5}$. So if a body's temperature increases 1° C, then it increases $m = \frac{9}{5}$ degrees F. Similarly, if a body's temperature increases $-10°$ (decreases 10°) C, then it increases $\frac{9}{5}(-10°) = -18°$ F.

Lines parallel to the Y-axis have equations of the form $x = a$, and lines not parallel to the Y-axis have equations of the form $y = mx + b$. Both of these equations are of the general form $Ax + By + C = 0$. Conversely, we have the following theorem.

THEOREM 9-1. *If A, B, and C are three real numbers such that A and B are not both 0, then the points whose coordinates (x, y) satisfy the equation $Ax + By + C = 0$ form a line.*

Proof. (i) Suppose $B \neq 0$ and (x, y) is a pair of numbers such that $Ax + By + C = 0$. Then $y = (-A/B)x - C/B$. Thus every pair of coordinates that satisfies the given equation satisfies the equation $y = mx + b$, where $m = -A/B$ and $b = -C/B$. We know that this latter equation is the equation of a line, so the points whose coordinates satisfy the given equation lie in a line.

(ii) If $B = 0$, then $A \neq 0$, since we have assumed that A and B are not both 0. The equation $Ax + By + C = 0$ then reduces to the equation $x = -C/A$, which we know is the equation of a line parallel to the Y-axis.

Example 9-2. Find the slope and Y-intercept of the line whose equation is $2x + 3y + 4 = 0$.

Solution. If we write this equation in the form $y = mx + b$, then we can read off the slope m and the Y-intercept b. Thus from the equation $y = -\frac{2}{3}x - \frac{4}{3}$, we see that $m = -\frac{2}{3}$ and $b = -\frac{4}{3}$.

Now let us consider two simple but important theorems about lines.

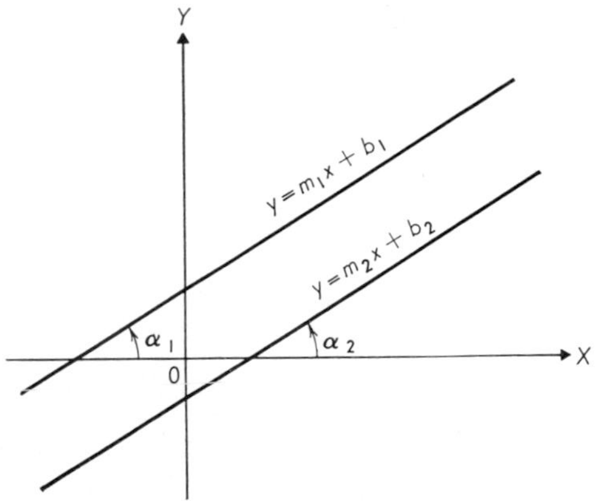

Figure 9-2

THEOREM 9-2. *Two lines $y = m_1x + b_1$ and $y = m_2x + b_2$ are parallel if, and only if, $m_1 = m_2$.*

Proof. Figure 9-2 shows our lines with their angles of inclination labeled α_1 and α_2. The lines are parallel if, and only if, $\alpha_1 = \alpha_2$. But these angles are equal if, and only if, their tangents are equal; that is, if, and only if, $m_1 = m_2$.

THEOREM 9-3. *Two lines* $y = m_1x + b_1$ *and* $y = m_2x + b_2$ *are perpendicular if, and only if,* $m_1m_2 = -1$.

Proof. Figure 9-3 shows the two lines intersecting at a point $P(x, y)$. If we move along the line $y = m_1x + b_1$ one unit to the right, then

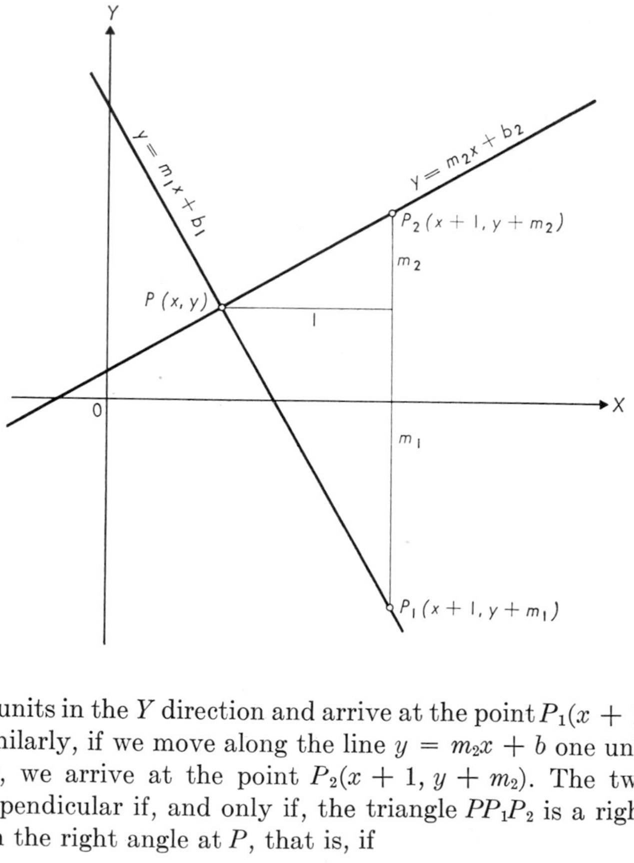

Figure 9-3

we move m_1 units in the Y direction and arrive at the point $P_1(x + 1, y + m_1)$. Similarly, if we move along the line $y = m_2x + b$ one unit to the right, we arrive at the point $P_2(x + 1, y + m_2)$. The two lines are perpendicular if, and only if, the triangle PP_1P_2 is a right triangle with the right angle at P, that is, if

$$\overline{P_1P}_2^2 = \overline{PP}_1^2 + \overline{PP}_2^2. \tag{9-3}$$

It is clear that

$$\overline{P_1P}_2^2 = [(y + m_2) - (y + m_1)]^2 = (m_2 - m_1)^2.$$

From the distance formula we have

$$\overline{PP}_1^2 = [(x+1) - x]^2 + [(y+m_1) - y]^2 = 1 + m_1^2$$

$$\overline{PP}_2^2 = [(x+1) - x]^2 + [(y+m_2) - y]^2 = 1 + m_2^2$$

so that Equation 9-3 becomes

$$(m_2 - m_1)^2 = 1 + m_1^2 + 1 + m_2^2.$$

Simplifying this equation we find

$$-2m_2m_1 = 2.$$

That is,

$$m_1m_2 = -1.$$

Example 9-3. Find the equation of the line that is perpendicular to the line $3x - y + 5 = 0$ at the point $(-1, 2)$.

Solution. The desired equation will have the form $y = mx + b$; we must find the numbers m and b. We find the slope of the given line by writing its equation as $y = 3x + 5$, and taking the coefficient of x. Thus the slope of the original line is 3 and, according to Theorem 9-3, $3m = -1$. So $m = -\frac{1}{3}$. Hence the equation of our desired line is $y = (-\frac{1}{3})x + b$. This line must contain the point $(-1, 2)$, and therefore to find b we solve the equation $2 = (-\frac{1}{3})(-1) + b$. Thus $b = \frac{5}{3}$, and we obtain the equation $y = (-\frac{1}{3})x + \frac{5}{3}$. If we prefer, we can write the equation of our desired line as $x + 3y - 5 = 0$.

We have seen that the equation of any line can be written in the form $Ax + By + C = 0$, where A and B are not both zero. If a line has slope m, then the equation of the line can be written as $\boldsymbol{y = mx + b}$. This form is called the **slope-intercept** form of the equation of a line. Another form of the equation of a line that is useful to know is the **point-slope** form,

$$\boldsymbol{y - y_1 = m(x - x_1)}. \tag{9-4}$$

Equation 9-4 may be written as $y = mx + b$, where $b = y_1 - mx_1$. Therefore it is the equation of the line with slope m and Y-intercept $y_1 - mx_1$. By substituting in Equation 9-4, we see that this line contains the point (x_1, y_1). Hence *Equation 9-4 is the equation of the line with slope m that contains the point* (x_1, y_1).

Example 9-4. Write the equation of the line with slope π that contains the point $(1, 2)$.

Solution. Using Equation 9-4 with $m = \pi$, $x_1 = 1$, and $y_1 = 2$, we find that

$$y - 2 = \pi(x - 1).$$

That is,

$$y = \pi x + (2 - \pi).$$

Notice that the Y-intercept $b = 2 - \pi$. The graph of this line is shown in Fig. 9-4.

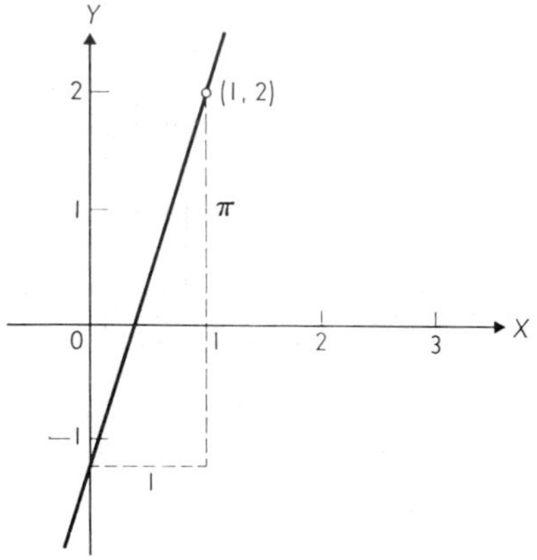

Figure 9-4

Problems 9

1. Find the slope and Y-intercept of each of the following lines. Sketch the graphs.
   (a) $y = 3x - 1$ (b) $y = 1 - 4x$
   (c) $2y = 4x + 7$ (d) $2y = 5 - 4x$
   (e) $3x + y - 7 = 0$ (f) $2x - y + 5 = 0$
   (g) $2x + 4y + 1 = 0$ (h) $x + 4y + \pi = 0$
2. Explain why Theorem 9-3 does not apply to the case of one horizontal line and one vertical line.
3. Write the equation of the line of slope m that contains the point listed.
   (a) $m = 4$, $(1, 3)$ (b) $m = 7$, $(1, 7)$
   (c) $m = -1$, $(2, 0)$ (d) $m = -4$, $(-3, 3)$
   (e) $m = 2$, $(1, 2)$ (f) $m = 5$, $(-1, 6)$
   (g) $m = \frac{22}{7}$, $(1, \pi)$ (h) $m = \sqrt{2}$, $(1, 1.414)$
4. Is the Y-intercept positive or negative in the case of the line given in 3(g)? in 3(h)?
5. Find the slope of the line containing the points given.
   (a) $(1, 2)$ and $(3, 4)$ (b) $(-1, 2)$ and $(-3, 4)$
   (c) $(2, 1$ and $(-2, 3)$ (d) $(-2, 1)$ and $(2, 3)$
   (e) $(4, 1)$ and $(\pi, 1)$ (f) $(-4, 1)$ and $(-\pi, 1)$
   (g) $(1, 5)$ and $(1, \sqrt{2})$ (h) $(-1, 5)$ and $(\pi, \sqrt{2})$

6. Write the equation of each of the lines in the preceding question.
7. Write the equation of the line that contains the point $(-1, 2)$ and is parallel to the line $3x + 5y - 4 = 0$.
8. Use the idea of slope to determine if the triangle with vertices $(1, 1)$, $(3, 2)$, and $(2, 12)$ is a right triangle.
9. A circle has a radius of 2 units and its center is the origin. Find the equation of the line tangent to this circle at the point $(1, \sqrt{3})$.
10. Use the concept of slope to determine whether or not the points are collinear.
    (a) $(4, -3)$, $(-5, 4)$, and $(0, 0)$.
    (b) $(3, 2)$, $(-\frac{4}{3}, \frac{5}{9})$, and $(6, 3)$.
11. Show that the equation of a line whose Y-intercept is $b \neq 0$ and whose X-intercept is $a \neq 0$ may be written as

$$\frac{x}{a} + \frac{y}{b} = 1.$$

This equation is called the **intercept form** of the equation of a line.
12. Use the equation in the preceding question to write the equation of the line that contains the points $(7, 0)$ and $(0, 11)$.
13. A circle is to be drawn so that it is tangent to the line $y = \frac{3}{4}x + 5$ at the point $(0, 5)$ and also tangent to the line $y = -4$. There are two possible choices for the center of such a circle. Find them.
14. Suppose that A and B are real numbers, not both 0, and that C and D are any real numbers. Show that the lines $Ax + By + C = 0$ and $Bx - Ay + D = 0$ are perpendicular.

10. The Trigonometric Functions

We assume that you have studied trigonometry and are familiar with the trigonometric functions—sine, cosine, tangent, and so on. However, when you studied elementary trigonometry you probably were primarily concerned with angles and triangles. In calculus we need to adopt a numerical as well as a geometrical point of view of the trigonometric functions. In order to orient ourselves to this numerical point of view, we present a brief review of the numerical aspects of trigonometry.

First, we will discuss the sine and cosine functions. When we define a trigonometric function, as with any function, we must specify a set of numbers as its domain and a rule that assigns a number to each number of the domain set. The set of all real numbers is the domain of both the sine and cosine functions. The number assigned to a real number t by the sine function is denoted by $\mathbf{\sin t}$. Similarly, $\mathbf{\cos t}$ is the number associated with the number t by the cosine function. The numbers $\cos t$ and $\sin t$ are determined in the following way. We draw the circle whose center is the origin and whose radius is 1 (Fig. 10-1). Starting at the point

(1, 0), we proceed $|t|$ units along the circumference of this **unit circle**—counterclockwise if t is positive, and clockwise if t is negative. In this way we reach a point P. *The X-coordinate of P is the number cos t, and the Y-coordinate of P is the number sin t.*

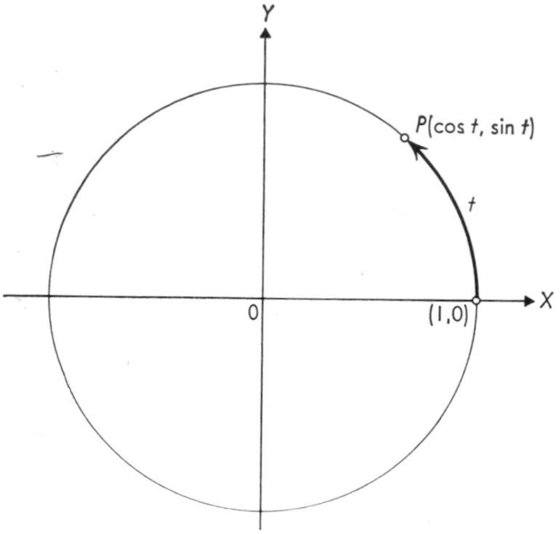

Figure 10-1

Example 10-1. Find the numbers $\cos \pi$, $\sin(-\pi/2)$ and $\sin 3\pi/4$.

Solution. The circumference of our unit circle is 2π. Thus if we proceed π units along the circle in the counterclockwise direction from the point (1, 0), we will arrive at the point $(-1, 0)$. Since $\cos \pi$ is the X-coordinate of this point, $\cos \pi = -1$. Similarly, if we proceed $\pi/2$ units in the clockwise direction, we arrive at the point $(0, -1)$. It follows that $\sin(-\pi/2) = -1$. If we proceed $3\pi/4$ units along the circle in the counterclockwise direction from (1, 0), we will arrive at a point P midway along that portion of the circle that lies in the second quadrant (see Fig. 10-2). Let us denote the coordinates of P by (x, y). Then, according to the definition of the sine function, we have $\sin 3\pi/4 = y$, so we must find the number y. It is apparent that for our point P, $x = -y$. Further, since P is one unit from the origin, $x^2 + y^2 = 1$. Thus $(-y)^2 + (y)^2 = 1$, or $y^2 = \frac{1}{2}$. Since y is positive in Quadrant II, we obtain $y = \dfrac{1}{\sqrt{2}}\cdot$ Finally, then,

$$\sin \frac{3\pi}{4} = \frac{1}{\sqrt{2}} = \frac{\sqrt{2}}{2}.$$

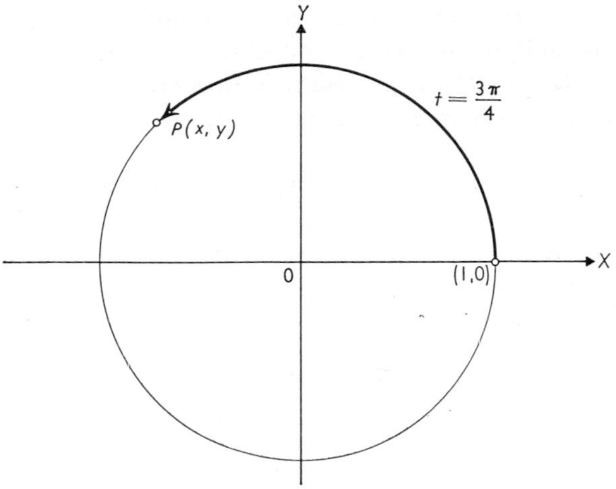

Figure 10-2

The other trigonometric functions—tangent, cotangent, cosecant, and secant—are defined by the equations

$$\textbf{tan}\ t = \frac{\sin t}{\cos t}$$

$$\textbf{cot}\ t = \frac{\cos t}{\sin t}$$

(10-1)
$$\textbf{csc}\ t = \frac{1}{\sin t}$$

$$\textbf{sec}\ t = \frac{1}{\cos t}.$$

The sine and cosine functions as defined in this section can be related to the same functions defined in terms of angles in the following way. With an angle θ in standard position (vertex at the origin and initial side

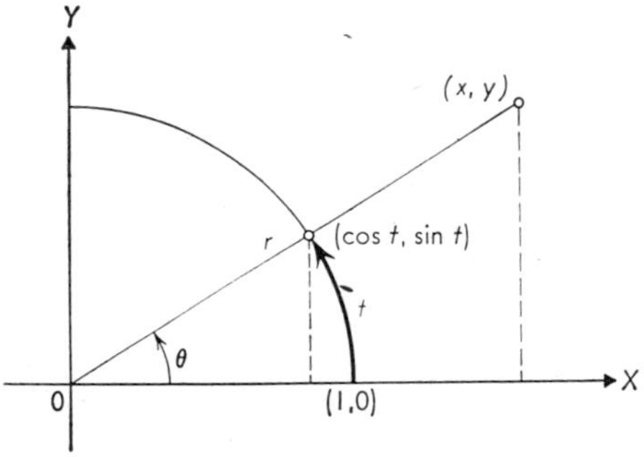

Figure 10-3

along the X-axis), we can associate a number t, the directed distance along the unit circle from the initial side to the terminal side of the angle. This number t is then the **radian measure** of the angle θ (Fig. 10-3). The definitions of the trigonometric functions are such that if T is any trigonometric function, $T(\theta) = T(t)$. Thus, for example, the sine of the *angle* θ is the same as the sine of the *number* t that is the radian measure of θ. If (x, y) is any point on the terminal side of θ, and if $r = \sqrt{x^2 + y^2}$, we can use similar triangles (See Fig. 10-3) to derive the fundamental equations

$$\begin{aligned} \sin\theta &= \frac{y}{r} \\ \cos\theta &= \frac{x}{r} \\ \tan\theta &= \frac{y}{x} \\ \cot\theta &= \frac{x}{y} \\ \csc\theta &= \frac{r}{y} \\ \sec\theta &= \frac{r}{x}. \end{aligned} \tag{10-2}$$

We shall assume that you are familiar with a number of standard trigonometric identities and formulas, several of which are listed in Appendix A.

Example 10-2. Find the distance between the points $(\cos t, \sin t)$ and $(1, 0)$ shown in Fig. 10-1.

Solution. If we use d to denote the desired distance, the distance formula (Equation 4-1) gives us

$$\begin{aligned} d^2 &= (\cos t - 1)^2 + \sin^2 t \\ &= \cos^2 t - 2\cos t + 1 + \sin^2 t \\ &= 2 - 2\cos t \\ &= 2(1 - \cos t) \\ &= 4\sin^2 t/2. \end{aligned}$$

Therefore,

$$\begin{aligned} d &= \sqrt{4\sin^2 \tfrac{1}{2}t} \\ &= 2|\sin \tfrac{1}{2}t|. \end{aligned}$$

Figures 10-4, 10-5, and 10-6 show the graphs of the sine, cosine, and tangent functions.

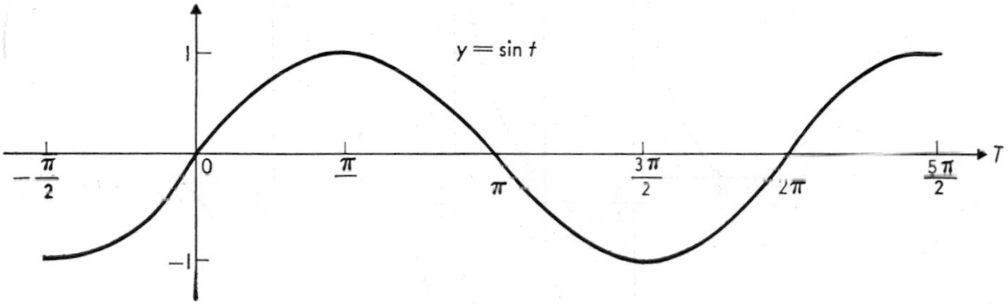

Figure 10-4

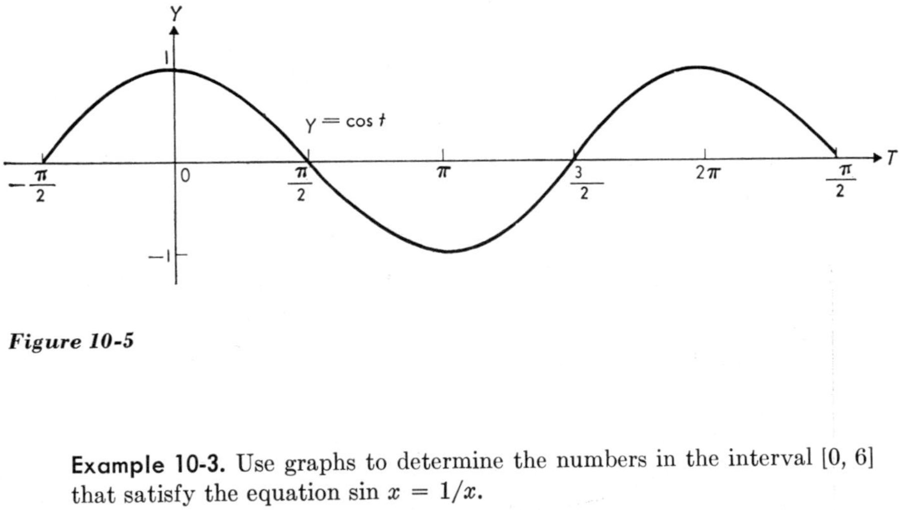

Figure 10-5

Example 10-3. Use graphs to determine the numbers in the interval [0, 6] that satisfy the equation $\sin x = 1/x$.

Solution. In Fig. 10-7 we have graphed the equations $y = 1/x$ and $y = \sin x$ on the same coordinate axes for the interval in question. The solutions to our equation are the X-coordinates of the points of intersection of these curves. There are two solutions in the interval [0, 6], and they appear to be approximately equal to 1.1 and 2.8.

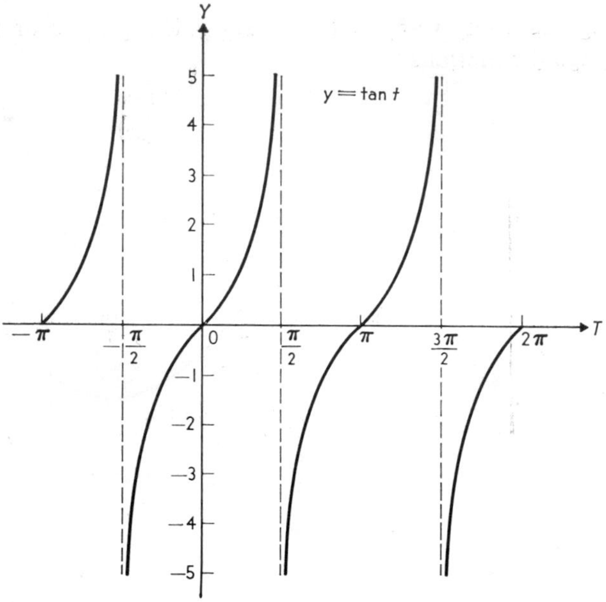

Figure 10-6

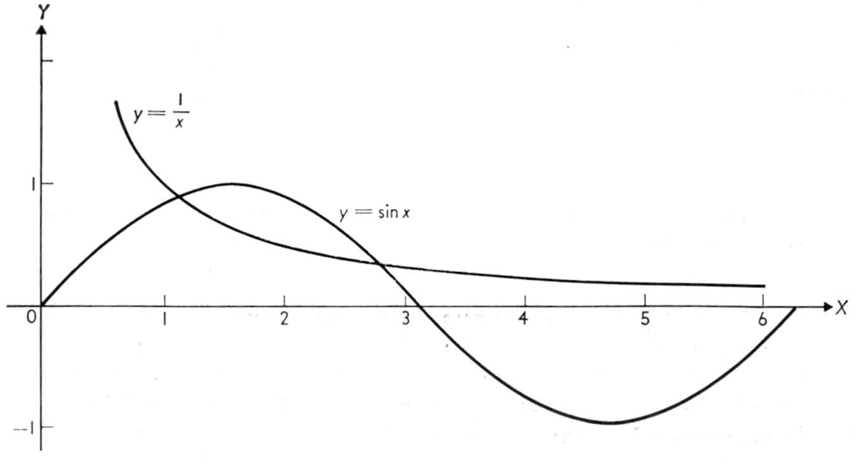

Figure 10-7

Problems 10

1. Use a sketch of the unit circle to estimate each of the following numbers.
   (a) $\sin 1$ (b) $\cos 1$ (c) $\cot 1.5$ (d) $\sin \frac{1}{2}$
2. Use a sketch of the unit circle to determine which of the following inequalities are true.
   (a) $\sin 2 < \sin 3$ (b) $\cos 2 < \cos 3$
   (c) $\cos 3 < \sin 3$ (d) $\cos 3 < \sin 2$
   (e) $\sin 3 < \cos 2$ (f) $|\cos 3| < |\cos 2|$
3. Use a sketch of the unit circle to find the following numbers.
   (a) $\sin \pi/4$ (b) $\cos \pi/4$
   (c) $\tan \pi/4$ (d) $\sin \pi/3$
   (e) $\cos \pi/3$ (f) $\sin \pi/6$
4. The symbol $\sin 2°$ stands for the sine of an angle that measures 2°. Use a sketch of the unit circle to determine which of the following inequalities are true.
   (a) $\sin 2 < \sin 2°$ (b) $\cos 2 < \cos 2°$
   (c) $\tan 2 < \tan 2°$ (d) $\cos 3 < \cos 3°$
5. Which of the following numbers are positive?
   (a) $\sin 2$ (b) $\tan 3$
   (c) $\cos 1.5$ (d) $\csc 4$
   (e) $\cot 5$ (f) $\sec 6$
   (g) $\cos 820°$ (h) $\sin(-460°)$
6. Graph the following equations for the interval $[0, \pi]$.
   (a) $y = \sin 2x$ (b) $y = 2 \cos x$ (c) $y = \frac{1}{2} \tan 2x$
7. Find the following numbers.
   (a) $\sec(-31\pi/4)$ (b) $\cos 31\pi/6$
   (c) $\csc(-31\pi/4)$ (d) $\sin 19\pi/3$
   (e) $\cot(-31\pi/4)$ (f) $\tan 22\pi/3$
8. Show that $\sqrt{1 + \sin 2x} = |\sin x + \cos x|$.
9. Simplify:
   (a) $(\sin x + \cos x)^2 - \sin 2x$

   (b) $\dfrac{\sin^2 2t}{(1 + \cos 2t)^2} + 1$

   (c) $\sin^2 2t - \cos^2 2t$

   (d) $(\sin 2t)(\cos 2t)$

   (e) $\dfrac{2 \sin^2 t - 1}{\sin t \cos t} + \cot 2t$

   (f) $\dfrac{\sec t + \tan t}{\cos t - \tan t - \sec t}$

   (g) $\dfrac{\sin t \cot t (\sec t - 1)}{1 - \cos t}$

(h) $\dfrac{\sin x}{\sec x + 1} + \dfrac{\sin x}{\sec x - 1}$

10. If a central angle θ in a circle of radius r measures t radians, then $s = rt$, where s is the directed length of the intercepted arc. A circle with a radius of 2 contains a central angle θ that intercepts an arc 5 units long. What is the measure of θ in radians? In degrees?

11. The radius of the front wheel of a child's tricycle is 10 inches and the rear wheels each have a radius of 6 inches. The pedals are fastened to the front wheel by arms that are 7 inches long. How far does a pedal travel when the rear wheels make 1 revolution?

Review Problems, Chapter One

You can use the following problems to test yourself on the material covered in this chapter.

1. Give an example of a rational number r such that $2 < r < 3$.

2. What can you say about the relative position of the points a and b of the number scale if $a < b$? If $|a - b| < 1$? If $|a| < |b|$?

3. What can you say about the location of the point x of the number scale if $|x| < 3$? If $|x - 1| > 3$? If $|x + 1| \leq 3$?

4. Is the inequality $|x| \geq x$ true for every number x? Explain.

5. Use inequalities to express the fact that a number is in the interval $(-1, 7]$.

6. Let f be a function whose domain is the set of all real numbers. Which of the following statements are surely true?

(a) $f(3 - 2) = f(3) - f(2)$ (b) $f(3 - 2) = f(1)$

(c) $f(\sqrt{2}) = \sqrt{f(2)}$ (d) $f(|-3|) = f(3)$

(e) $f(2)f(3) = f(6)$ (f) $f(x^2) = f(x)f(x)$

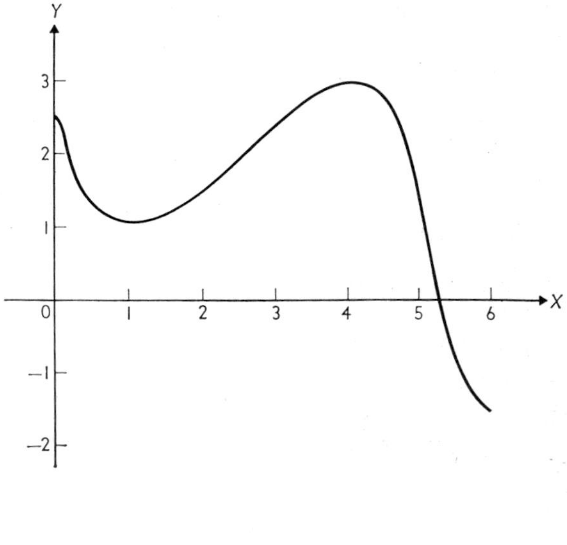

Figure I-1

7. The graph of a function f is shown in Fig. I-1.
   (a) What is the domain of f?
   (b) What is the range of f?
   (c) Find $f(2)$ and $f(\pi)$
   (d) If $f(x) = 2$, what is x?
8. The perimeter of a Norman window (rectangle surmounted by a semi-circle) is 240 inches. The vertical side of the window is h inches. Find a formula that expresses the area A in square inches in terms of h.
9. The graph of a linear function f contains the points (0, 1) and (2, 5). Find a formula that determines f, and find the point where the graph intersects the X-axis.
10. Find a formula for the distance d between two points whose X-coordinates are the same if one point is a point of the graph of the equation $y = x^2$ and the other point is a point of the graph of the equation $y = x^3$.
11. Let $f(x) = x^2$. Sketch the graph of the equation $y = \dfrac{f(1 + h) - f(1)}{h}$.
12. If y is directly proportional to x, is x directly proportional to y? If z is inversely proportional to x, is x inversely proportional to z?
13. A perpendicular is dropped from the point (1, 4) to the line $2y - 4x + 16 = 0$. Find the coordinates of the foot of the perpendicular.
14. Graph the equation $y = \sqrt{1 - \sin^2 x}$.
15. A Ferris wheel with a radius of 12 feet revolves at the rate of 3 revolutions per minute. Assume that the rays of the sun are parallel, and that the sun is directly overhead. Find a formula that gives the position of the shadow of a rider t minutes after he passes the lowest point of the wheel. Find the formula if the sun is not directly overhead but makes a 45° angle with the horizontal.
16. Solve for x:
   (a) $\sin [\sin (\sin x)] = 0$
   (b) $\cos (\cos x) = 0$.
17. Show that $\cos 2t = \cos^4 t - \sin^4 t$.
18. Show that the area of a regular polygon with n sides each of length a is $\frac{1}{4}na^2 \cot (\pi/n)$.

2 THE DERIVATIVE

The material concerning functions, graphs, slopes and other fundamental concepts that we covered in Chapter 1 forms a necessary groundwork for the study of calculus and has numerous applications in the development of the basic ideas of calculus. One of the basic concepts of calculus, the derivative, will be introduced in this chapter. We can gain some insight into the nature of the derivative by considering the following two problems.

Problem 1. A bottle is dropped into a stream that is flowing 3 miles per hour. Plot a graph showing the relationship between the distance the bottle has drifted and the time it has been drifting.

Problem 2. A bottle is dropped from rest in a vacuum. Plot a graph showing the relationship between the distance the bottle falls and the time during which it falls.

In order to solve these problems we need only to recall a little elementary science. If S denotes the number of miles that the bottle in Problem 1 has drifted in t hours, then by applying the formula *distance = rate · time* we obtain the equation $S = 3t$. The graph of this equation (Fig. II-1) is a straight line with slope 3. The *slope of the line is the velocity of the bottle.*

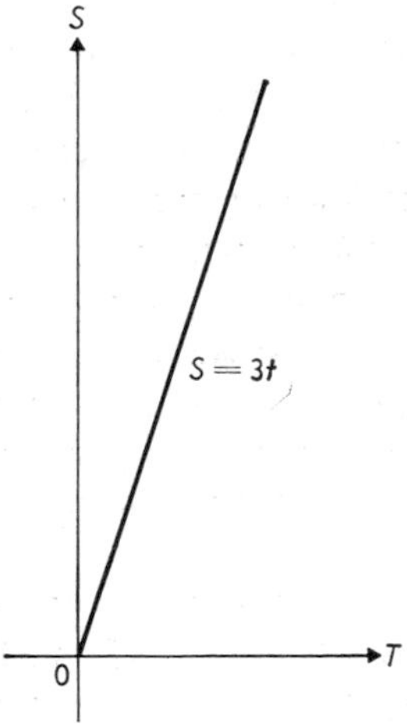

Figure II-1

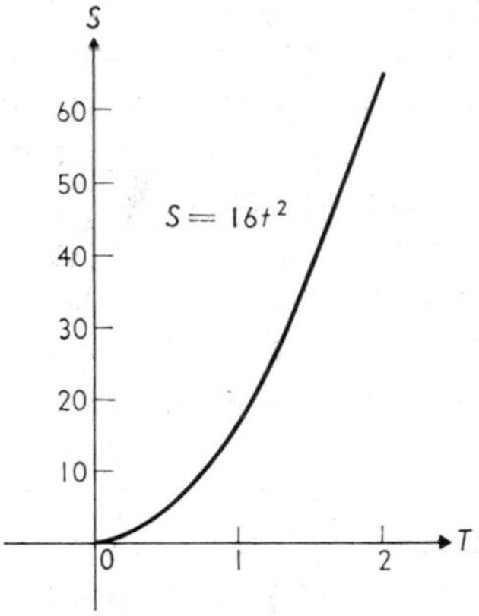

Figure II-2

To solve Problem 2 let us recall from elementary physics that the relation between the number of units S of distance that a body falls from rest in t units of time is expresssed by the equation $S = \frac{1}{2}gt^2$, where g is a number denoting the acceleration due to gravity. If we measure distance in feet and time in seconds, then g is equal to 32 (approximately), and the relationship between S and t is expressed by the equation $S = 16t^2$. The graph of this equation is shown in Fig. II-2.

One obvious difference between the graph in Fig. II-1 and the graph in Fig. II-2 is that one is a straight line and the other isn't. The fact that the slope of the graph (line) in Fig. II-1 represents the velocity of the bottle in Problem 1 leads us to ask if the slope of the graph in Fig. II-2 represents the velocity of the bottle in Problem 2. But then we are faced with the question, "What do we mean by the 'slope of the graph'"?, since we have formerly only talked about slope in connection with lines. In this chapter we will answer this last question, and we will also learn how to calculate the slope of the graphs of many of the elementary functions with which you are acquainted.

Later we will find that the concept of the slope of a graph has many applications in science. In particular, it does give us the velocity of our falling bottle.

11. A Geometrical Approach to the Derivative

How, then, shall we define the slope of the graph of a function f? To each point $(x, f(x))$ of the graph we wish to assign a number m that we can call the slope of the curve *at the point*. If the graph of f is a straight line, its slope at any point will turn out to be the slope of the line. Thus the slope of a line at one point is the same as its slope at any other point. For other curves, though, the slope will be different at different points.

Since we have already defined the slope of a straight line, we might try to obtain the slope of a curve at a point by first associating with the point of the curve a line that best "fits" the curve at the point and then assigning the slope of this line as the slope of the curve at the point. The line that best "fits" the curve at a point is called the **tangent line** to the curve at the point. The *slope of the curve* at a point is the *slope of this tangent line.*

Suppose we have a function f and that at each point of the graph of f the slope of the graph is obtained in the manner we have just indicated. Then with each number x of the domain of f we associate the number m, the slope of the graph of f at the point $(x, f(x))$. We now have a new function. Its rule of correspondence is simple: To the number x there corresponds the number m. This new function is *derived* from f. We call it the **derived function** of f and designate it by the symbol $\boldsymbol{f'}$. The value of the derived function at x is therefore denoted by $f'(x)$. Thus $f'(x) = m$, where m is the slope of the graph of f at the point $(x, f(x))$. The number $\boldsymbol{f'(x)}$ is called the **derivative of** $\boldsymbol{f(x)}$.

Our geometrical definition of the derivative is not very precise. For one thing, we have not been very explicit about what a tangent line to a curve is. Nevertheless, we shall proceed with a few examples, using intuitive ideas concerning tangent lines, in order to illustrate the basic ideas involved. We will give a more precise definition of the derivative in the next section.

Example 11-1. Let $f(x) = \sqrt{4 - x^2}$. Find the derivative $f'(x)$.

Solution. We first graph the equation $y = f(x)$—that is $y = \sqrt{4 - x^2}$. If (x, y) is a point of the graph of this equation, then x lies in the interval $[-2, 2]$, $y \geq 0$, and $\sqrt{x^2 + y^2} = 2$. Thus each point of the graph is two units from the origin and lies above the X-axis. The graph of f is therefore the upper semi-circle whose radius is 2 and whose center is the origin (Fig. 11-1).

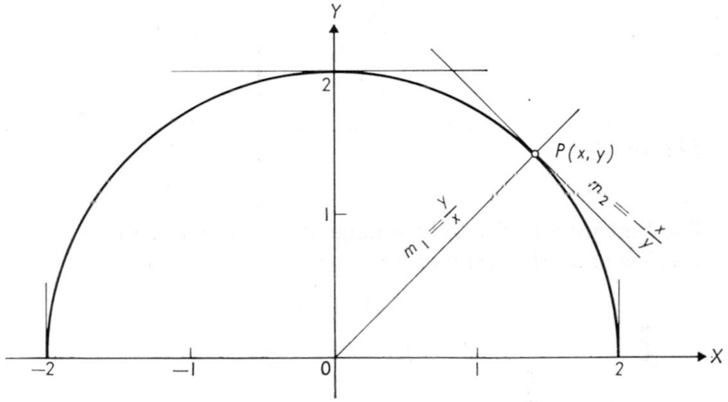

Figure 11-1

Let us use this graph to find some values of the derived function f'. According to our definition of f', the number $f'(0)$ is the slope of the line tangent to the graph at the point $(0, f(0)) = (0, 2)$. The tangent line at this point is horizontal and has slope 0. Therefore $f'(0) = 0$. When $x = 2$ or $x = -2$, the tangent line to the graph is vertical, and the slope of such a line is undefined (see Section 9). Thus the numbers 2 and -2 are not in the domain of the derived function f', though they are in the domain of f.

Now let us find a formula that gives us the number $f'(x)$ for any number x in the interval $(-2, 2)$. Suppose that (x, y) is a point of our graph. We know that the tangent line to a circle at a given point is perpendicular to the radius to that point; hence the slope of the tangent line is the negative reciprocal of the slope of the radius (Theorem 9-3). The slope of the radius to the point (x, y) is y/x (Why?), and so we see that the slope of the tangent line is $-x/y$. Therefore, $f'(x) = -x/y$, or since $y = \sqrt{4 - x^2}$,

$$f'(x) = \frac{-x}{\sqrt{4 - x^2}}.$$

Example 11-2. If $f(x) = |x|$, find the derivative $f'(x)$.

Solution. The graph of f is shown in Fig. 11-2. It is clear that for $x > 0$ the line tangent to the graph of f at the point $(x, |x|)$ is simply the line $y = x$. This line has slope $m = 1$. If $x < 0$, the equation of the tangent line is $y = -x$. The slope of this line is $m = -1$. At the point (0, 0) there is no

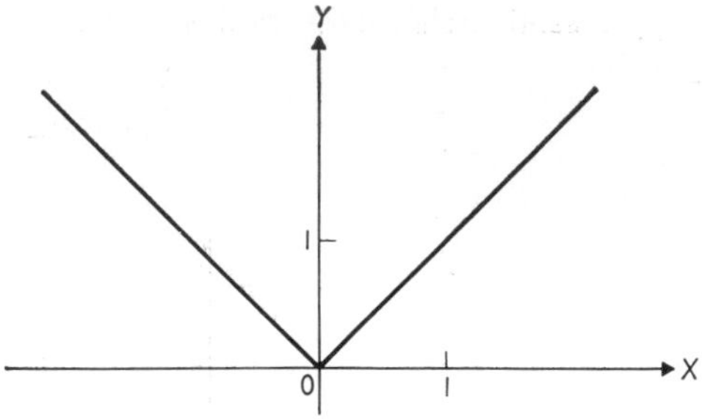

Figure 11-2

line that we consider to be a tangent line. It follows that the domain of f' consists of all the real numbers except $x = 0$, and that

$$f'(x) = 1 \text{ if } x > 0$$
$$f'(x) = -1 \text{ if } x < 0.$$

We shall use Fig. 11-3 to illustrate a number of points that we have considered in this section. The curve is the graph of a certain function f. (If you like, you may consider the curve as defining the function f.) From the figure we see that the domain of f is the interval $[-1, 8]$, and we can read off some values of the function; for example, $f(-1) = 1$, $f(1) = 3$, $f(5) = 5$, and so on. We have sketched in "tangent lines" at various

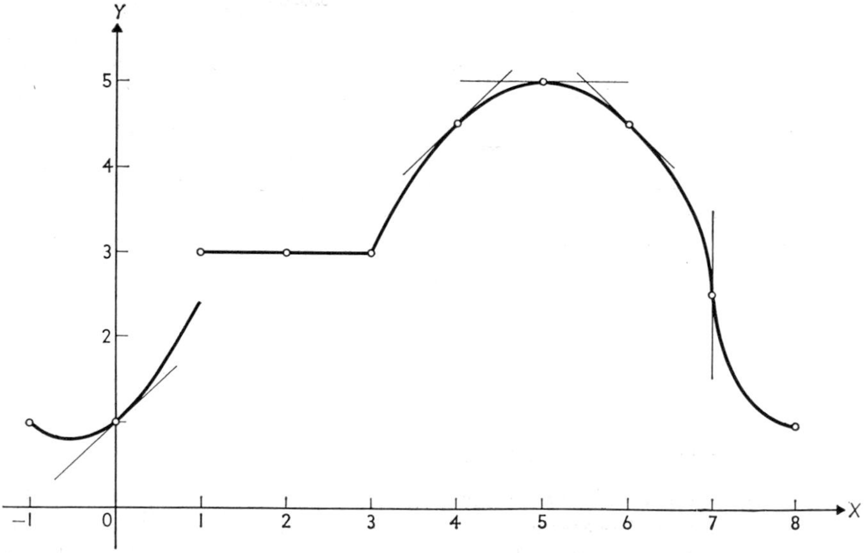

Figure 11-3

points of the graph. The derivative $f'(x)$ at such a point is the slope of the tangent line. We read from the figure the following approximate values: $f'(2) = 0$, $f'(4) = 1$, $f'(5) = 0$, and $f'(6) = -1$. When $x = 7$, the curve has a vertical tangent; but since a vertical line has no slope assigned to it, we see that the number 7 is not in the domain of f'. Finally, we see that there is no tangent line at either the point (1, 3) or at the point (3, 3). Thus we conclude that the numbers 1 and 3 are not in the domain of the derived function.

Example 11-3. If $f(x) = \sin x$, sketch the graph of the derived function f' for the interval [0, 1.6].

Solution. In Fig. 11-4 we have sketched the graph of the equation $y = \sin x$ in the interval [0, 1.6] as a solid curve, using the points in the accompanying table. We approximate the value of the derived function at each of these points by taking the slope of the segment joining that point to the next point listed in the table. Thus the derivative at $x = 0$ is approximated by the number

$$\frac{.0998 - 0}{.1 - 0} = .998;$$

$f'(.1)$ is approximately

$$\frac{.1987 - .0998}{.2 - .1} = .989,$$

and so on. The approximate values thus obtained are given in the third column of the table. The dashed curve in Fig. 11-4 is (approximately) the graph of the derived function.

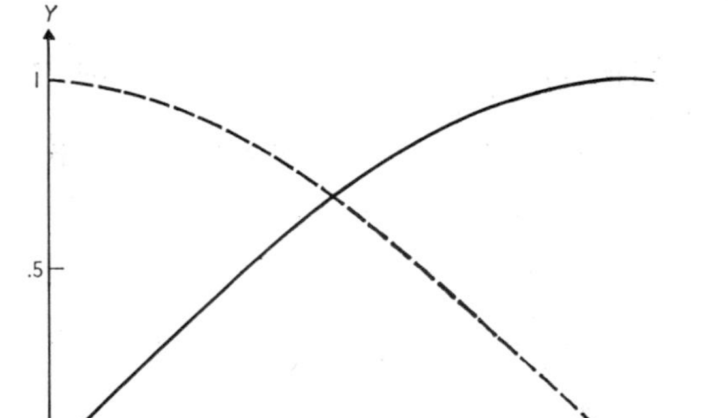

x	$f(x) = \sin x$	$f'(x)$
.0	.0000	.998
.1	.0998	.989
.2	.1987	.968
.3	.2955	.939
.4	.3894	.900
.5	.4794	.852
.6	.5646	.796
.7	.6442	.732
.8	.7174	.659
.9	.7833	.582
1.00	.8415	.497
1.10	.8912	.408
1.20	.9320	.316
1.30	.9636	.218
1.40	.9854	.121
1.50	.9975	.021
1.60	.9996	......

Figure 11-4

There are many notations commonly used in connection with the derivative. We shall use the "prime" notation for the present and introduce other notations later. If f is a function and x is a number in its domain, then we use either the symbol $f(x)$ or simply the letter y to represent the number that is made to correspond to x by the function f. Similarly, the derived function of f is a function f', and the number that is made to correspond to x by the derived function f' is denoted either by $f'(x)$ or by y'. The number y' is called the **derivative of y.** Thus, for example, the result of Example 11-1 can be written:

If $$y = \sqrt{4 - x^2}, \quad \text{then } y' = \frac{-x}{\sqrt{4 - x^2}}.$$

Problems 11

1. In each case make a careful sketch of the graph of the function f for the interval $[0, 3]$ and use tangent lines drawn in "by eye" to calculate $f'(1)$ and $f'(2)$.
   (a) $f(x) = x^2 - 4$
   (b) $f(x) = 3 - x^2$
   (c) $f(x) = (1 - x^3)/5$
   (d) $f(x) = \sin \pi x$
   (e) $f(x) = .1x^4 - .3x^3$
   (f) $f(x) = \cos \frac{1}{2}\pi x$
2. Let $f(x) = \tan x$. From the graph of f, estimate $f'(0)$. To check your estimate, compute the slopes of several chords that join the point $(0, f(0))$ to nearby points of the graph of f.
3. What is the derived function f' if f is a constant function?
4. Let f be the function defined by the graph in Fig. 11-3. Use this graph to find (approximately) the following numbers.
   (a) $f'(0)$
   (b) $f'(4.5)$
   (c) $f'(2.5)$
   (d) $f'(7.5)$
5. Let $f(x) = \cos x$. Use the procedure followed in Example 11-3 to sketch the graph of the derived function f' for the interval $[0, 1.6]$.
6. Draw a solid-line graph of the function f and a dashed-line graph of the derived function f' if:
   (a) $f(x) = 2x - 3$
   (b) $f(x) = 4 - x$
   (c) $f(x) = [\![x]\!]$
   (d) $f(x) = |x - 1|$
   (e) $f(x) = x - [\![x]\!]$
   (f) $f(x) = |x| + |x - 2|$
7. For each function f of Exercise 1 of these problems, compute approximations to the number of $f'(1)$ by computing $\dfrac{f(1.1) - f(1)}{1.1 - 1}$.
8. Let $f(x) = |x| + |x - 1| + |x - 2| + |x - 3|$. What numbers are not in the domain of the derived function f'?
9. Find the number y' if
   (a) $y = \frac{1}{2}(x - 1)$
   (b) $3y = x - 4$
   (c) $2y = 4x - 7$
   (d) $1 - y = 2 - x$

12. Definition of the Derivative

Now we will explore more thoroughly the question of defining the derivative of $f(x)$. According to the remarks we made in the preceding section, if we want to calculate $f'(1)$, for example, we should sketch the graph of f and then draw the tangent line to this curve at the point where $x = 1$. The slope of this tangent line is then $f'(1)$. The device of using graphs and sketching in tangent lines "by eye" is useful for introducing the notion of derivative, but it is not a very precise description of a mathematical concept. One obvious drawback to the graphical method is the fact that no two people are likely to get the same value of a derived function at a given point, since the tangent line that one person sketches "by eye" will probably not be exactly the same line that the other person sketches "by eye." Let us look for a method of calculating derivatives that will at least enable everyone to get the same answer.

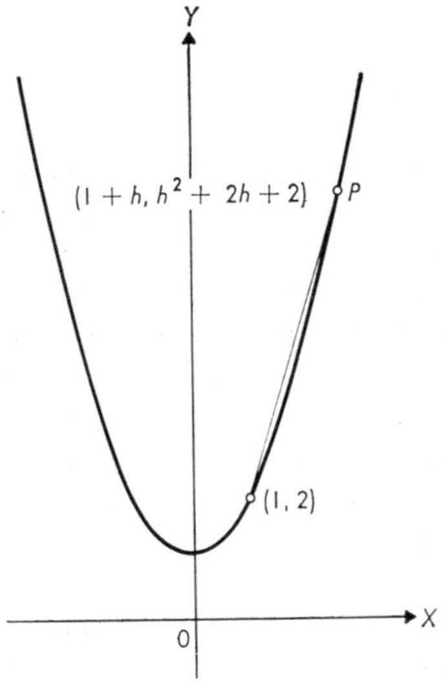

Figure 12-1

For a clue to a "numerical" approach to the concept of derivative, we return to Example 11-3. There we approximated the derivative at a point by finding the slope of the "chord" joining that point and a nearby point. It is certainly true that this chord is not the tangent line at the point, but we took the slope of the chord to be a satisfactory *approximation* to the slope of the tangent line. Notice that we assumed that there was a tangent line, that it had a slope, and it was this perfectly definite number (the slope of the tangent line) that we approximated.

Let us apply this same idea to find $f'(1)$ when the function f is defined by the equation $f(x) = x^2 + 1$. We will arrive at the number $f'(1)$ indirectly. We will calculate approximations of $f'(1)$ and by looking at these approximations decide what number they approximate. Figure 12-1 shows the graph of f.

The number $f'(1)$ (the slope of the tangent line at the point $(1, 2)$) is approximated by the slope of the chord joining the point $(1, 2)$ and a second point P of the graph of the equation $y = x^2 + 1$; and if we want a "good" approximation, we should choose the second point P so that it is close to the point $(1, 2)$. In order to simplify the algebraic expressions that will arise, we denote the X-coordinate of P by $1 + h$. Then the Y-coordinate of P is $(1 + h)^2 + 1 = h^2 + 2h + 2$. The number h may be positive or negative; we have shown h as a positive number in Fig. 12-1. The slope of the chord joining the points $(1, 2)$ and P is given by the formula (see Equation 9-2)

$$\text{(12-1)} \qquad \frac{(h^2 + 2h + 2) - 2}{(1 + h) - 1} = \frac{h^2 + 2h}{h}.$$

Since $h \neq 0$, Formula 12-1 reduces to

$$\text{(12-2)} \qquad 2 + h.$$

Formula 12-2 yields an approximation of the number $f'(1)$ for each choice of the number h. For example, we obtain the approximations 3, 1, and $\frac{5}{2}$ by taking $h = 1$, -1, and $\frac{1}{2}$. We have said that we will consider an approximation to be "good" if the point P is near the point $(1, 2)$, and P will be near $(1, 2)$ if h is near zero. Thus we see that $2 + h$ is a good approximation of $f'(1)$ if h is near zero. Now it is perfectly obvious that the number approximated by Formula 12-2 for h close to zero is the number 2. Thus if $f(x) = x^2 + 1$, we can define $f'(1) = 2$. We have obtained this choice of $f'(1)$ by considering numbers that approximate it.

The geometrical argument we used to get our approximating numbers suggests that we consider the line through the point $(1, 2)$ with slope 2 as the line tangent to our graph at that point. We find the equation of this line to be $y = 2x$. We have shown this line in Fig. 12-2, and you will probably agree that the name "tangent line" is appropriate.

Notice that we said $2 + h$ is *near* 2 when h is *near* 0, not $2 + h$ *equals* 2 when h *equals* 0. The reason we don't set $h = 0$ is simple. Our basic formula for the approximations of $f'(1)$ is really Formula 12-1, not Formula 12-2. Formula 12-2 is a consequence of Formula 12-1 only under the assumption that $h \neq 0$; Formula 12-1 is meaningless for $h = 0$. But even though we shouldn't set $h = 0$, it is perfectly clear that 2 is the number that $2 + h$ approximates if h is close to 0.

Let us continue to suppose that $f(x) = x^2 + 1$. If x is any real number, we can calculate $f'(x)$ by the same procedure we just used to determine $f'(1)$. We consider (Fig. 12-3) the chord joining two distinct points $(x, x^2 + 1)$ and $P(x + h, (x + h)^2 + 1)$. The slope of this chord is given by the formula

$$\text{(12-3)} \qquad \frac{(x + h)^2 + 1 - (x^2 + 1)}{(x + h) - x} = \frac{2xh + h^2}{h},$$

where $h \neq 0$, since the two points do not coincide. Thus we may divide the numerator and denominator of Formula 12-3 by h to see that the slope of the chord is

$$(12\text{-}4) \qquad 2x + h.$$

When the point P in Fig. 12-3 is close to $(x, x^2 + 1)$—that is, when h is

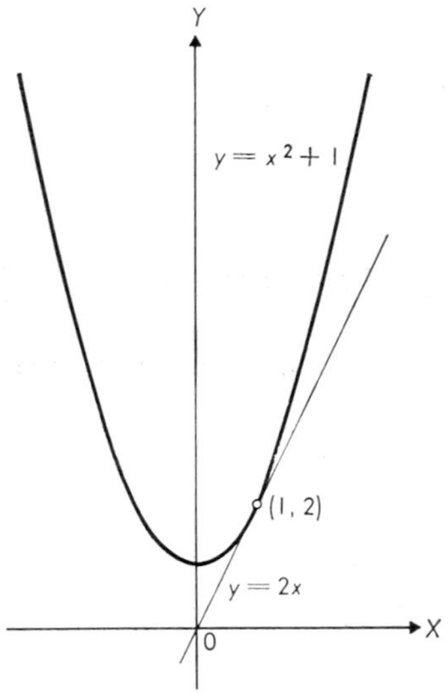

Figure 12-2

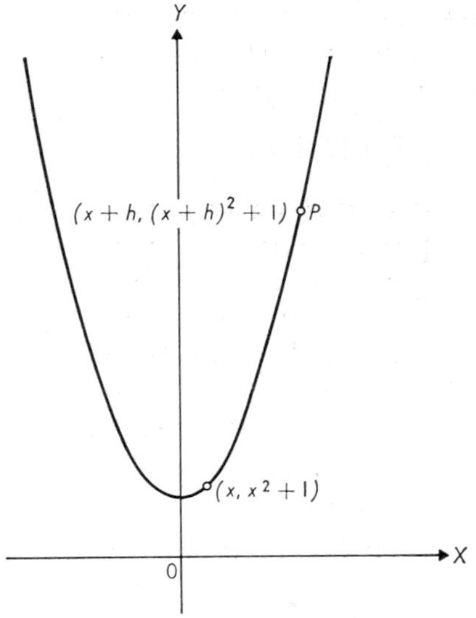

Figure 12-3

close to 0—Formula 12-4 tells us that the slope of the chord is close to $2x$. Thus *if* $f(x) = x^2 + 1$, *then we define* $f'(x) = 2x$.

If you read the preceding sentence carefully, you noticed that we *defined* $f'(x)$ to be $2x$. We have reversed the position that we took in Section 11. There we said that in order to calculate a derivative we should *first* draw a tangent line and *then* calculate its slope. Here we calculated a derivative without drawing the tangent line. And now we will *define* the tangent line to be the line through our point with the calculated derivative as its slope. This procedure eliminates the guesswork involved in fitting a tangent line to the curve "by eye" and gives us just one tangent line.

The number $2x$ is called the **limit** of $2x + h$ as h approaches 0. We shall have more to say about the concept of a limit later. For now we trust that you will develop enough intuitive feeling about this concept to enable you to handle the simple limits that we will meet in our beginning study of the derivative. In rough terms, the statement that the limit of $2x + h$ as h approaches 0 is $2x$ means that $2x$ is the number approximated by $2x + h$ for h close to, but not equal to, 0. We write this statement in symbols as follows:

$$\lim_{h\to 0} (2x + h) = 2x.$$

As a particular example of the use of the limit language, we found that $f'(1) = 2$ by finding that the limit of $2 + h$, as h approaches 0, is 2; that is

$$\lim_{h\to 0} (2 + h) = 2.$$

Now that we have introduced the notation of limits, we are in a position to formulate the concept of the derivative in general terms. Let f be a given function. We obtain the derived function f' by assigning to a number x the number $f'(x)$ in exactly the same manner as we did in the example we have just considered. Thus we compute the slope of the chord joining the point $(x, f(x))$ to a second point $(x + h, f(x + h))$ (see Fig. 12-4) by means of the formula

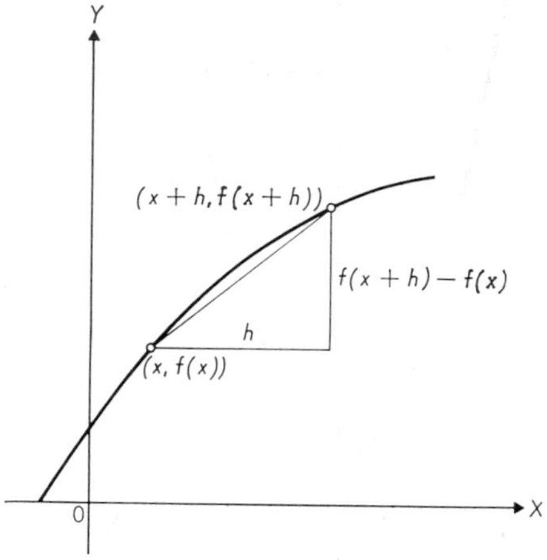

Figure 12-4

$$\frac{f(x + h) - f(x)}{h}. \tag{12-5}$$

Then we define the derivative $f'(x)$ as the limit, as h approaches 0, of the **Difference Quotient** 12-5 (if the limit exists, of course).

DEFINITION 12-1. *If x is a number in the domain of a function f for which the following limit exists, then*

$$f'(x) = \lim_{h\to 0} \frac{f(x + h) - f(x)}{h}. \tag{12-6}$$

The above limit need not exist at every (or, indeed, any) point in the domain of a given function f. If it does exist at a particular number x, then we say that f is ***differentiable*** *at x. The process of finding the derivative $f'(x)$ is* *called* ***differentiation.*** *Thus differentiation means finding the limit of the difference quotient.*

Definition 12-1 tells us how to calculate the number $f'(x)$. The Difference Quotient 12-5 approximates $f'(x)$ when h is close to 0. But the difference quotient is the slope of the chord joining the points $(x, f(x))$ and $(x + h, f(x + h))$. So if these two points are close together, the slope of the segment joining them is approximately the number $f'(x)$. It is natural to say that this number $f'(x)$ is the slope of the line tangent to the graph of f at the point $(x, f(x))$. Hence we make the following definition.

DEFINITION 12-2. *If a function f is differentiable at a point x, then the* ***tangent line*** (*or simply,* ***tangent***) *to the graph of f at the point $(x, f(x))$ is the line that contains the point $(x, f(x))$ and has slope $f'(x)$.*

The two foregoing definitions form the basis for our beginning study of calculus. It will pay you to read them carefully.

Example 12-1. The function f is defined by the equation $f(x) = 5x^2 - 3x$. Find $f'(x)$.

Solution. The difference quotient for f is

$$\begin{aligned}\frac{f(x+h) - f(x)}{h} &= \frac{5(x+h)^2 - 3(x+h) - (5x^2 - 3x)}{h} \\ &= \frac{5(x^2 + 2xh + h) - 3x - 3h - 5x^2 + 3x}{h} \\ &= \frac{10xh + 5h^2 - 3h}{h} \\ &= 10x - 3 + 5h.\end{aligned}$$

Therefore, according to Definition 12-1,

$$\begin{aligned}f'(x) &= \lim_{h \to 0} \frac{f(x+h) - f(x)}{h} \\ &= \lim_{h \to 0} (10x - 3 + 5h).\end{aligned}$$

It is clear that the number approximated by $10x - 3 + 5h$ when h is close to 0 is $10x - 3$; that is,

$$\lim_{h \to 0} (10x - 3 + 5h) = 10x - 3.$$

Therefore, $f'(x) = 10x - 3$.

Example 12-2. What is the equation of the tangent line to the graph of the function in Example 12-1 at the point (1, 2)?

Solution. In Example 12-1 we found that $f'(x) = 10x - 3$, and therefore $f'(1) = 10 - 3 = 7$. The slope of the tangent to the curve at the given point is therefore 7. Using the point-slope form of the equation of a line (Equation 9-4), we get the equation of our tangent line: $y - 2 = 7(x - 1)$ or $y = 7x - 5$.

To find the derivatives called for in the problems at the end of this section, you should use the following **Two-Step Rule:**

(i) *Set up the difference quotient*

$$\frac{f(x+h) - f(x)}{h} \quad \textit{and}$$

(ii) *"Manipulate" this quotient according to the rules of elementary mathematics until the number approximated by the quotient when h is near 0 becomes apparent.*

Example 12-3. If $f(x) = \sqrt{x}$, find $f'(x)$.

Solution. We will follow the two steps outlined above. First

(i) $$\frac{f(x+h) - f(x)}{h} = \frac{\sqrt{x+h} - \sqrt{x}}{h}.$$

(ii) It is not easy to see what this last quotient approximates when h is close to zero, nor is it easy to see what to do about it. Experience shows that the proper approach is to "rationalize the numerator." If we multiply the numerator and denominator by $\sqrt{x+h} + \sqrt{x}$, we get

$$\frac{f(x+h) - f(x)}{h} = \frac{\sqrt{x+h} - \sqrt{x}}{h} \cdot \frac{\sqrt{x+h} + \sqrt{x}}{\sqrt{x+h} + \sqrt{x}}$$

$$= \frac{(x+h) - x}{h(\sqrt{x+h} + \sqrt{x})}$$

$$= \frac{1}{\sqrt{x+h} + \sqrt{x}}.$$

Since $\sqrt{x+h}$ approximates $\sqrt{x}$ when h is close to zero, this last fraction approximates $1/2\sqrt{x}$ when h is close to zero. Thus

$$f'(x) = \frac{1}{2\sqrt{x}}.$$

Problems 12

1. Draw the graph of the function f if $f(x) = 1 - x^2$. Compute the slopes of and sketch the chords joining the point $(1, 0)$ to the following points: $(0, f(0))$; $(\frac{1}{2}, f(\frac{1}{2}))$; $(\frac{3}{2}, f(\frac{3}{2}))$. On the basis of your chord-slope calculations, estimate the slope of the tangent line at the point $(1, 0)$.
2. Follow the procedure outlined in the preceding question if $f(x) = 1 - x^3$.
3. Use the Two-Step Rule to find $f'(x)$ if:
   (a) $f(x) = 2x - 3$ (b) $f(x) = 4 - x$
   (c) $f(x) = x^2 - 4x$ (d) $f(x) = x^3 - 7x$
   (e) $f(x) = (x - 1)^2$ (f) $f(x) = \dfrac{1 - x}{1 + x}$
4. Use the Two-Step Rule to find the derivatives in Exercise 1, Problems 11.
5. Find the equation of the tangent line to the graph of f at the point $(1, 0)$ if:
   (a) $f(x) = x - x^2$ (b) $f(x) = 1 - x^2$
   (c) $f(x) = x - x^3$ (d) $f(x) = 1 - x^4$
   (e) $f(x) = 3x^3 - 4x^2 + 1$ (f) $f(x) = x - x^{-1}$
6. Use the Two-Step Rule to find $f'(x)$ if:
   (a) $f(x) = \sqrt{x + 1}$ (b) $f(x) = \sqrt{2x}$
   (c) $f(x) = \sqrt{x^2 + 1}$ (d) $f(x) = \sqrt[3]{x}$
7. Let $f(x) = |x|$.
   (a) Compute the difference quotient for $x = 0$ and $h > 0$. What number does this difference quotient approximate when h is close to zero?
   (b) Compute the difference quotient for $x = 0$ and $h < 0$. What number does this difference quotient approximate when h is close to zero?
   (c) What do you conclude about $f'(0)$?
8. Set up the difference quotient associated with f and notice that the limit of the difference quotient as h approaches zero is not "apparent"!
   (a) $f(x) = \sin x$ (b) $f(x) = \log x$ (c) $f(x) = 2^x$
9. Answer the questions in Exercise 7 if $f(x) = x|x|$.
10. Answer the questions in Exercise 7 if $f(x) = [x]$.
11. Answer the questions in Exercise 7 if f is the function defined as follows:

$$f(x) = \begin{matrix} x^2 \text{ if } x \geq 0 \\ x^3 \text{ if } x < 0. \end{matrix}$$

13. **Limits**

The problem of finding a derivative leads us to one of the basic concepts of mathematics, the concept of a limit. In the preceding section we made use of an intuitive idea of limit, and now we shall carry our discussion somewhat further. When we calculate the derivative $f'(x)$ for a given function f at a given point x, we set up the difference quotient

$$\frac{f(x + h) - f(x)}{h},$$

where h is a number that is close to 0 but different from 0. We can think of the difference quotient as a formula that defines a function q whose domain consists of all points, except 0, of some interval that contains 0. We call q the **quotient function associated with f at x,** and say that its domain is a **deleted interval about 0.** The rule of correspondence of the quotient function is given by the equation

$$q(h) = \frac{f(x + h) - f(x)}{h}.$$

Geometrically speaking, we might call q the "chord-slope" function, since $q(h)$ is the slope of a chord.

Example 13-1. Let $f(x) = x^2/3$. Find the formula that defines the quotient function q that is associated with f at 2 and draw the graph of q.

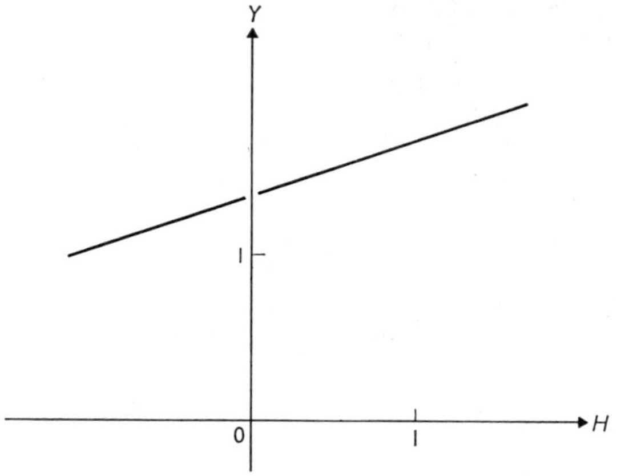

Figure 13-1

Solution. The equation that defines q is

$$q(h) = \frac{f(2 + h) - f(2)}{h} = \frac{\dfrac{(2 + h)^2}{3} - \dfrac{2^2}{3}}{h}$$

$$= \frac{4h + h^2}{3h} = \frac{4}{3} + \frac{h}{3}.$$

The graph of q is shown in Fig. 13-1. It is a "straight line with the Y-intercept missing."

The derivative $f'(x)$ is given by the equation

$$\lim_{h\to 0} \frac{f(x+h) - f(x)}{h} = \lim_{h\to 0} q(h) = f'(x).$$

We say that $f'(x)$ is the **limit at 0 of the function q.** Thus the problem of finding a derivative is the problem of finding the limit at 0 of a certain function, and it is this concept, the concept of the limit of a function at a point, that we will discuss in this section.

Let us begin by considering the quotient function q that we found in Example 13-1. There we had $q(h) = \frac{4}{3} + \frac{1}{3}h$ for $h \neq 0$. Although $h \neq 0$, it is clear from the formula that the number that $q(h)$ approximates when h is near 0 is the number $\frac{4}{3}$. In general, for any function g, we say that *the number L is the limit at* 0 *of* g, in symbols,

$$\lim_{h\to 0} g(h) = L,$$

if L is the number that is approximated by $g(h)$ for h close to, but not equal to, 0. As a beginner, you will probably do best to think of the concept of limit as it is described in the preceding statement. This statement, however, is not precise enough (what does "h close to 0" mean?) to enable us to prove theorems about limits. We shall give a precise definition shortly, but first let us look at the limit concept from a geometrical point of view.

Figure 13-1 is the graph of the quotient function q that is defined by the equation $q(h) = \frac{4}{3} + \frac{1}{3}h$ for $h \neq 0$. The graph of q does not intersect the Y-axis (because $h = 0$ is not in the domain of q), but Fig. 13-1 indicates that the graph "should" intersect the Y-axis at the point whose Y-coordinate is $\frac{4}{3}$. This number is the limit at 0 of the function q. Thus we are led to the geometrical definition of the limit at 0 of a function as the Y-coordinate of the point at which the graph of the function "should" intersect the Y-axis. Although this definition of limit is still not precise (the meaning of the phrase "should intersect the Y-axis" is not spelled out), it does furnish us with another intuitive idea of what a limit is; and we can use the geometric definition to suggest the precise analytic definition that we shall now give.

Let g be a function whose domain contains a deleted interval I about 0. To each number h of the deleted interval I there corresponds a number $y = g(h)$ (see Fig. 13-2). The collection of all such numbers is a certain set of numbers, and there is a smallest closed interval $J(I)$ that contains this set (see Property 2-1). Thus, corresponding to a deleted interval I of the H-axis we obtain an interval $J(I)$ of the Y-axis that contains each number $y = g(h)$ for h in I. From Fig. 13-2 it is evident that if we let the deleted interval I of the H-axis "squeeze down" on the point 0, then the interval $J(I)$ will "squeeze down" on the point at which the graph of g "should intersect the Y-axis." The Y-coordinate of this point is the limit of g at 0. We therefore make the following definition, which is mathematically satisfactory even if it seems less intuitive

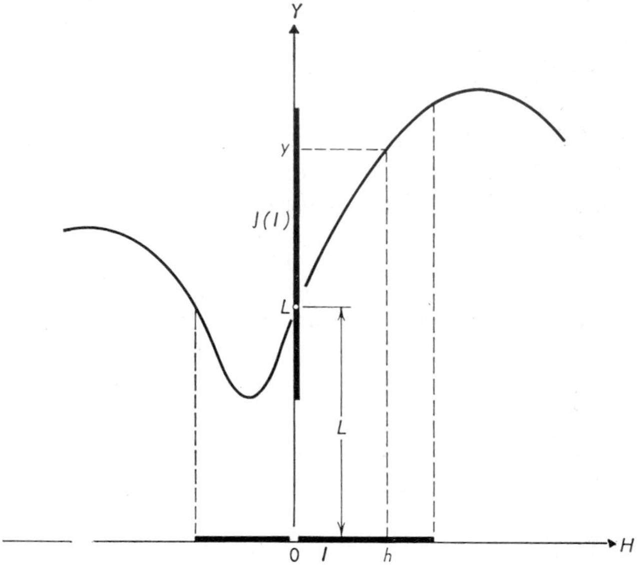

Figure 13-2

than our preceding definitions. It says the same thing that we said before, but more precisely.

DEFINITION 13-1. *The number* **L** *is the limit at* 0 *of the function* **g**, *in symbols,*

$$\lim_{h \to 0} g(h) = L,$$

if, and only if,

(i) *For each choice of deleted interval* I *about* 0 *the number* L *is contained in the corresponding interval* $J(I)$.
(ii) L *is the only number that is contained in all the* J*-intervals.*

Example 13-2. Let $f(x) = |x|$, and let q be the quotient function associated with the function f at 1. Draw a graph of q and determine $\lim_{h \to 0} q(h)$.

Solution. The equation that defines q is

$$q(h) = \frac{f(1 + h) - f(1)}{h} = \frac{|1 + h| - |1|}{h}.$$

From this equation it follows that if $h \geq -1$ and $h \neq 0$, then $q(h) = 1$, and if $h < -1$, then $q(h) = -1 - \frac{2}{h}$. The graph of q is shown in Fig. 13-3. Now it is clear from Fig. 13-3 that to any "I-interval" whose left endpoint

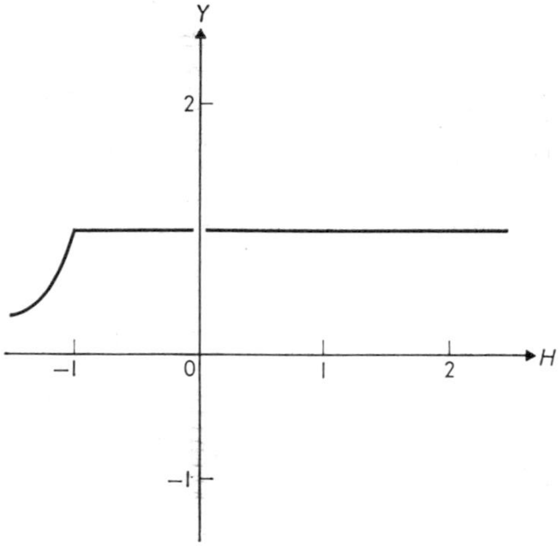

Figure 13-3

is to the right of -1 there corresponds the "J-interval" $[1, 1]$. The number 1 belongs to each "J-interval," and the only number that is contained in all "J-intervals" is the number 1. Thus $\lim_{h \to 0} q(h) = 1$.

If in Definition 13-1 of the limit we replace the deleted intervals with intervals that lie to the right of 0—that is, with intervals of the form $I = (0, r)$—then the number L is said to be the **limit at 0 from the right.** In this case we write

$$\lim_{h \to 0^+} g(h) = L.$$

Similarly, if we replace the deleted intervals with intervals of the form $I = (-r, 0)$, then L is said to be the **limit at 0 from the left,** and we write

$$\lim_{h \to 0^-} g(h) = L.$$

Intuitively, the limit from the right is the number that is approximated by $g(h)$ when h is a positive number close to 0, and the limit from the left is the number that is approximated by $g(h)$ when h is a negative number close to 0. *The function g has a limit at 0 if, and only if, the right and left limits of g at 0 are equal.*

Example 13-3. Let $f(x) = |x|$, and let q be the quotient function associated with the function f at 0. Draw a graph of q and discuss $\lim_{h \to 0^+} q(h)$, $\lim_{h \to 0^-} q(h)$, and $\lim_{h \to 0} q(h)$.

Solution. The equation that defines q is

$$q(h) = \frac{|0 + h| - |0|}{h} = \frac{|h|}{h}.$$

From this equation it follows that if $h > 0$, then $q(h) = 1$, and if $h < 0$, then $q(h) = -1$. The graph of q is shown in Fig. 13-4. If we let h approach 0

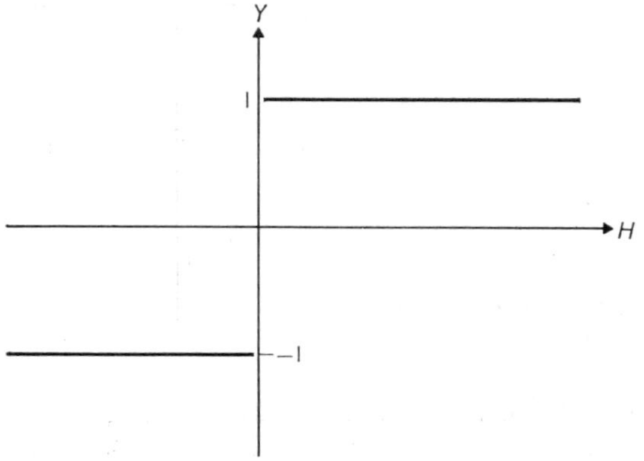

Figure 13-4

from the right, it appears that the graph "should" intersect the Y-axis at the point 1 on the Y-axis. Thus $\lim_{h \to 0^+} q(h) = 1$. If we let h approach 0 from the left, it appears that the graph "should" intersect the Y-axis at the point -1 on the Y-axis. Thus $\lim_{h \to 0^-} q(h) = -1$. Since the limits at 0 from the right and from the left are not equal, there is no limit at 0 of this function q.

It is possible to use Definition 13-1 to prove the following theorems about limits. In this introductory section we will omit the proofs of these theorems and simply accept them as true. If you are interested in the proofs (or become interested later) you should refer to Appendix B.

THEOREM 13-1. *The limit at* 0 *of the identity function* j *is* 0. *Since* $j(h) = h$, *we may write*

(13-1) $$\lim_{h \to 0} h = 0.$$

THEOREM 13-2. *If f is the constant function with value c, then the limit at 0 of f is c. Since $f(h) = c$, we write*

$$\lim_{h \to 0} \mathbf{c} = \mathbf{c}. \tag{13-2}$$

Note: In many of our applications of Theorem 13-2 we will be dealing with constant functions whose value is expressed in terms of an unspecified number x. Thus we might encounter the function f defined by the equation $f(h) = 2x$ in a context such that we would consider it the constant function with value $2x$. Then

$$\lim_{h \to 0} 2x = 2x.$$

THEOREM 13-3. *If f and g are functions with limits at 0, then*

$$\lim_{h \to 0} [f(h) + g(h)] = \lim_{h \to 0} f(h) + \lim_{h \to 0} g(h), \tag{13-3}$$

$$\lim_{h \to 0} f(h)g(h) = \lim_{h \to 0} f(h) \lim_{h \to 0} g(h), \tag{13-4}$$

and

$$\lim_{h \to 0} \frac{f(h)}{g(h)} = \frac{\lim_{h \to 0} f(h)}{\lim_{h \to 0} g(h)} \quad (\textit{if } \lim_{h \to 0} g(h) \neq 0). \tag{13-5}$$

THEOREM 13-4. *If f is a function with limit at 0 and p is a number such that the expression $[f(h)]^p$ is defined in a deleted neighborhood of zero (we don't want to take square roots of negative numbers, for example), then*

$$\lim_{h \to 0} [f(h)]^p = [\lim_{h \to 0} f(h)]^p. \tag{13-6}$$

Each of the preceding theorems about limits remains valid if we replace the limit with the limit from the right or the limit from the left.

We now illustrate these theorems by using them to calculate some derivatives.

Example 13-4. If $f(x) = 3x^2$, find $f'(2)$.

Solution. According to Definition 12-1, $f'(2)$ is the limit as h approaches 0 of $q(h)$, where

$$q(h) = \frac{f(2 + h) - f(2)}{h} = \frac{3(2 + h)^2 - 3 \cdot 2^2}{h}$$

$$= \frac{12h + 3h^2}{h} = 12 + 3h.$$

Then

$$
\begin{aligned}
f'(2) &= \lim_{h\to 0} q(h) = \lim_{h\to 0} (12 + 3h) && \text{(Def. 12-1)}\\
&= \lim_{h\to 0} 12 + \lim_{h\to 0} 3h && \text{(Eq. 13-3)}\\
&= \lim_{h\to 0} 12 + \lim_{h\to 0} 3 \lim_{h\to 0} h && \text{(Eq. 13-4)}\\
&= 12 + 3 \lim_{h\to 0} h && \text{(Eq. 13-2)}\\
&= 12 + 3 \cdot 0 = 12 && \text{(Eq. 13-1).}
\end{aligned}
$$

Example 13-5. If $y = 1/x$, find y'.

Solution. Here our quotient function q is given by the equation

$$q(h) = \frac{\dfrac{1}{x+h} - \dfrac{1}{x}}{h}.$$

We first simplify this expression:

$$q(h) = \frac{\dfrac{-h}{x(x+h)}}{h} = \frac{-1}{x(x+h)}.$$

Now we find y' by finding the limit of $q(h)$ as h approaches zero:

$$
\begin{aligned}
y' &= \lim_{h\to 0} \frac{-1}{x(x+h)} && \text{(Def. 12-1)}\\
&= \frac{\lim_{h\to 0} (-1)}{\lim_{h\to 0} x(x+h)} && \text{(Eq. 13-5)}\\
&= \frac{\lim_{h\to 0} (-1)}{\lim_{h\to 0} x(\lim_{h\to 0} x + \lim_{h\to 0} h)} && \text{(Eq. 13-3 and 13-4)}\\
&= \frac{-1}{x(x+0)} = \frac{-1}{x^2} && \text{(Eq. 13-1 and 13-2).}
\end{aligned}
$$

We will now use our theorems about limits to prove the following important theorem.

THEOREM 13-5. *If a function f is differentiable at a point x, then*

(13-7) $$\lim_{h\to 0} f(x+h) = f(x).$$

Proof. Since f is differentiable at x, then

$$\lim_{h\to 0}\frac{f(x+h)-f(x)}{h}=f'(x). \tag{13-8}$$

Let us write $f(x+h)$ in a way that will enable us to determine $\lim_{h\to 0} f(x+h)$ rather easily. Clearly,

$$f(x+h)=f(x)+[f(x+h)-f(x)].$$

For $h \neq 0$ we may multiply and divide the last term on the right by h to obtain

$$f(x+h)=f(x)+\frac{f(x+h)-f(x)}{h}h.$$

Now we apply Equations 13-1, 13-2, 13-4, and 13-8 to get

$$\begin{aligned}\lim_{h\to 0} f(x+h) &= \lim_{h\to 0} f(x)+\lim_{h\to 0}\frac{f(x+h)-f(x)}{h}\lim_{h\to 0} h\\ &= f(x)+[f'(x)]\cdot 0\\ &= f(x).\end{aligned}$$

A function that satisfies Equation 13-7 is said to be **continuous** at x. Thus Theorem 13-5 states that *if a function f is differentiable at a point x, then f is continuous at x.*

In addition to speaking of the limit at 0 of a function f, we can talk about the limit of f at a point a other than 0. The number $\boldsymbol{\lim_{x\to a} f(x)}$ is the number that is approximated by $f(x)$ when x is close to, but not equal to, a, and it is formally defined by the equation

$$\boldsymbol{\lim_{x\to a} f(x)=\lim_{h\to 0} f(a+h).}$$

Thus, for example,

$$\lim_{x\to 3} x^2=\lim_{h\to 0}(3+h)^2=9.$$

Using this limit notation, we see that a function f is continuous at a point a if, and only if,

$$\lim_{x\to a} f(x)=f(a).$$

In other words, *f is continuous at a if the number that is approximated by $f(x)$ when x is close to a is the value of f at a.*

Finally, we mention that both the concept of continuity and the concept of the derivative can be modified either by the phrase "from the right" or by the phrase "from the left." Thus, for example, the

derivative from the right $f'_+(x)$ is defined by the equation

$$f'_+(x) = \lim_{h \to 0^+} \frac{f(x+h) - f(x)}{h}.$$

If $f(x) = |x|$, then $f'_+(0) = 1$, and $f'_-(0) = -1$ (see Examples 11-2 and 13-2), but $f'(0)$ is not defined.

Problems 13

1. Graph the quotient function q associated with the function f at 1 if:
   (a) $f(x) = 1 - 4x$ (b) $f(x) = x^2 - 2$
   (c) $f(x) = |x + 1|$ (d) $f(x) = x^3$
2. Let $f(x) = 1 - |x|$. Establish that f is not differentiable at 0.
3. Use the graphs in Exercise 1 to find $f'(1)$ in each case.
4. Use the theorems about limits to find $f'(2)$ if:
   (a) $f(x) = 1 - x^2$ (b) $f(x) = x + x^2$
   (c) $f(x) = x^3 - x$ (d) $f(x) = x + 3x^3$
   (e) $f(x) = x^2 + 3x - 7$ (f) $f(x) = x|x|$
   (g) $f(x) = x|x - 1|$ (h) $f(x) = |x - 1|^2$
   (i) $f(x) = x + |x - 1|$ (j) $f(x) = [\![x + \frac{1}{2}]\!]$
   (k) $f(x) = [\![x - \frac{1}{2}]\!]$ (l) $f(x) = x[\![x - \frac{1}{2}]\!]$
5. Use the theorems about limits to find y' if:
   (a) $y = (x - 2)^2$ (b) $y = x^2 - 2$
   (c) $y = \dfrac{1}{x^2}$ (d) $y = \dfrac{1}{x^2 + 1}$
   (e) $y = \dfrac{1 + x}{1 - x}$ (f) $y = \dfrac{1 + x^2}{1 - x^2}$
   (g) $y = x^4 + 2x^2 + 1$ (h) $y = x(x^3 + 2)$
6. Use the graph of the quotient function associated with f at 2 to determine whether or not f is differentiable at 2 if:
   (a) $f(x) = x|x - 2|$ (b) $f(x) = (x - 2)^{-1}$
   (c) $f(x) = 1 - |x - 2|$ (d) $f(x) = (x - 2)[\![x - 2]\!]$
7. Let $f(x) = \sin x$ and graph the quotient function associated with f at 0. From your graph find the number $f'(0)$.
8. In each case state what the domain of the function g is, tell where the graph of g "should" intersect the line $x = 3$, and hence find $\lim_{x \to 3} g(x)$.
   (a) $g(x) = \dfrac{x^2 - 9}{x - 3}$ (b) $g(x) = \dfrac{x^2 - 5x + 6}{x - 3}$
   (c) $g(x) = \dfrac{2x^2 - 5x - 3}{x - 3}$ (d) $g(x) = \dfrac{x^3 - 3x^2 + 9x - 27}{x - 3}$
9. Let $f(x) = x[\![x]\!]$. Let q be the quotient function associated with f at 0.
   (a) Find $\lim_{h \to 0^+} q(h)$ (b) Find $\lim_{h \to 0^-} q(h)$ (c) Does $f'(0)$ exist?

10. Let $f(x) = x[\![1 - x^2]\!]$. Determine from the graph of f the points in the interval $(-2, 2)$ at which the function is not continuous (that is, is **discontinuous**).

11. Let $f(x) = x - [\![x]\!]$.
(a) Find $\lim_{x \to 0^+} f(x)$ (b) Find $f'_+(0)$.

12. Let $f(x) = [\![1 - x]\!] + [\![x - 1]\!]$. Find $\lim_{x \to 0^+} f(x)$ and $\lim_{x \to 0^-} f(x)$. Does $\lim_{x \to 0} f(x)$ exist? Is f continuous at 0?

14. The Rate of Change

We interpret the slope m of the line $y = mx + b$ as the rate at which the line rises. Now the tangent line to a point of the graph of a function f is the line that best "fits" the graph at the point, so it is natural to say that the slope of the tangent line measures the rate at which the graph of the function rises. The slope of the tangent line at a point $(x, f(x))$ is the derivative $f'(x)$. Thus we shall use the derivative $f'(x)$ to measure the rate at which the graph of f rises; that is, the rate at which the values of f change. In this connection it is customary to use a new notation for derivatives. If $y = f(x)$, then in addition to the notations y' and $f'(x)$ for the derivative of $f(x)$ we also write $D_x y$. We call $D_x y$ *the derivative of y with respect to x*. Thus

$$\boldsymbol{D_x y = f'(x) = y'}.$$

The way we use $D_x y$ to measure rate of change can be illustrated by considering the concept of velocity. When you ask the driver of a car, "How fast are we going now?" you are using a concept of velocity that is an extension of the concept of velocity ordinarily used in elementary science. A difficulty in answering your question arises from the use of the word "now." In elementary science you computed the velocity of a body by dividing the distance traveled by the time elapsed. Thus, if a car travels 100 miles in 2 hours, the velocity of the car is calculated as 50 miles per hour. The velocity of the car thus calculated is an *average* velocity, and it certainly does not imply that the speedometer of the car will register 50 miles per hour at all times during the trip.

We define the velocity that the speedometer measures at a given instant in the following way. Let t denote the number of hours elapsed since the beginning of the trip, and s the number of miles traveled during this time. Then the relationship between s and t defines a function f so that $s = f(t)$. Let us now attempt to answer the question, "What is the velocity *at* $t = 1$"? The average velocity over any time interval beginning or ending at $t = 1$ can be calculated in the usual way. Thus we find the average velocity over the time interval from 1 to $1 + h$ by dividing the distance traveled by the time elapsed. The distance traveled is $f(1 + h) - f(1)$; that is, the distance traveled in $1 + h$ hours minus the distance traveled in 1 hour. The time elapsed is h hours, so the average velocity is given by the difference quotient

$$\frac{f(1 + h) - f(1)}{h}. \tag{14-1}$$

We cannot set $h = 0$, for then the average velocity is not defined. But, as in the problem involving the slope of a curve, it is perfectly clear that the velocity when $t = 1$ should be the number that is approximated by the difference quotient in Formula 14-1 when h is a number near 0. Thus, using our limit notation, we *define* the velocity when $t = 1$ to be the number

$$\lim_{h\to 0} \frac{f(1 + h) - f(1)}{h} = f'(1).$$

In general, *if $s = f(t)$, then the* ***velocity*** *v at any time t is defined by the equation*

$$\boldsymbol{v = D_t s = f'(t).} \tag{14-2}$$

In order to distinguish this velocity from the average velocity, the velocity defined in Equation 14-2 is sometimes called the **instantaneous velocity.**

Example 14-1. We have already noticed in the introduction to this chapter that if a body falls from rest in a vacuum a distance of s feet in t seconds, then the relationship between s and t is given by the equation $s = 16t^2$. How fast is the body falling at the end of 5 seconds?

Solution. According to Equation 14-2, we have to calculate $f'(5)$, where $f(t) = 16t^2$. To find $f'(t)$ we form the difference quotient

$$\begin{aligned}\frac{f(t + h) - f(t)}{h} &= \frac{16(t + h)^2 - 16t^2}{h} \\ &= \frac{32th + 16h^2}{h} \\ &= 32t + 16h,\end{aligned}$$

and then calculate its limit:

$$f'(t) = \lim_{h\to 0} (32t + 16h) = 32t.$$

Thus $f'(5) = 32 \cdot 5 = 160$, so that the velocity of the body at the end of 5 seconds is 160 feet per second.

In Example 14-1 we measured distance in feet and time in seconds; hence the velocity is measured in feet per second. If distance had been measured in kilometers and time in hours, then velocity would be measured in kilometers per hour, and so on.

We use the concept of rate even though distance and time are not involved. For example, if y ergs of work are required to move a certain object x centimeters, then we say $D_x y$ is the number of ergs per centimeter (or dynes) of force applied at a given point during the motion. Similarly, if a house can be heated to a temperature of T degrees by burning p pounds of coal, then the number $D_p T$ measures the rate of change of temperature in degrees per pound.

Example 14-2. Boyle's Law says that the pressure P and the volume V of a gas at constant temperature are related by the equation $PV = k$, where k is some number. Find the rate of change of volume with respect to pressure.

Solution. We have said that if $V = f(P)$, then $D_P V = f'(P)$ measures the rate of change of volume with respect to pressure. According to Boyle's Law, we can write $V = f(P)$, where

$$f(P) = \frac{k}{P}.$$

To calculate $D_P V$ we first form the difference quotient

$$\frac{f(P+h) - f(P)}{h} = \frac{\dfrac{k}{P+h} - \dfrac{k}{P}}{h} = \frac{kP - k(P+h)}{hP(P+h)};$$

that is,

$$\frac{f(P+h) - f(P)}{h} = \frac{-k}{P(P+h)}.$$

Now we use our theorems about limits to find the limit of this difference quotient as h approaches zero:

$$D_P V = f'(P) = \lim_{h \to 0} \frac{-k}{P(P+h)} = \frac{-k}{P^2}.$$

If volume is measured in cubic inches and pressure is measured in pounds, then $D_P V = \dfrac{-k}{P^2}$ cubic inches per pound.

Problems 14

1. Use the "two-step" rule and the theorems about limits to find $D_x y$ if:
   (a) $y = 3x^2$ (b) $y = 1 - x^3$
   (c) $y = 1/(1 + x)$ (d) $y = \sqrt{1 + x}$
   (e) $y = \sqrt{1 + x^2}$ (f) $y = x\sqrt{x}$

2. A block slides down an inclined plane. At the end of t seconds the block is s feet from its starting point. Find the average velocity of the block for the first two seconds and its instantaneous velocity at $t = 2$ if:
   (a) $s = 3t^2$ (b) $s = t^2 + t$ (c) $s = t^2 + \sqrt{t}$
3. A mass is connected to a certain spring. The mass moves along a line so that it is s inches from the equilibrium position t seconds after some moment, where $s = \sin t$. Use the graphs in Fig. 11-4 to estimate the velocity of the mass when $t = 0$, $t = .5$, and $t = 1$.
4. A steel ball is dropped in a glass tube that contains heavy oil. Suppose that the ball is s centimeters above the base of the tube t seconds after the ball enters the oil. The observed values of s and t are contained in the following table. From this table estimate the velocity of the ball when it strikes the bottom of the tube.

t	0	1	2	3	4	5
s	4	2.5	1.5	.75	.25	0

5. A penny expands when heated. Find the expression for the rate of change of the area of one side with respect to the radius.
6. At t minutes after noon the radius of a melting snowball is $60 - 3t$ inches. How fast is the volume changing at 12:10?
7. A point moves along a line so that it is s feet from the origin t seconds after some moment. Find the velocity if:
   (a) $s = \dfrac{1}{t+1}$ (b) $s = t + \dfrac{1}{t}$
   (c) $s = 1 - \dfrac{1}{(t+1)^2}$ (d) $s = \dfrac{t+1}{t+2}$
8. By examining the algebraic signs of s and v, determine the time intervals during which the point in Question 7 is moving toward the origin if $s = t^2 - 4t + 5$.

15. The Differentiation Formula for $D_x x^r$

The routine of setting up a difference quotient and then finding its limit every time we wish to calculate a derivative soon becomes unduly time consuming, so it is worth while to establish (and memorize) certain differentiation rules. These rules are of two types—specific and general. The specific rules are formulas for derivatives for certain basic functions. The general rules enable us to find derivatives for complicated functions that are built up out of basic functions. In this section we will begin the task of finding derivatives for some basic functions. In particular, we will be concerned with the formulas for $D_x x^n$ and $D_x x^{1/n}$, where n is a positive integer.

Example 15-1. Find $f'(x)$ if f is the constant function with value c.

Solution. We have already used a graphical approach to find this derivative (see Question 3, Problems 11). Now let us calculate it from its definition.

At each point x the difference quotient is

$$\frac{f(x+h) - f(x)}{h} = \frac{c - c}{h} = 0.$$

Now according to Equation 13-1, $\lim_{h \to 0} 0 = 0$, so $f'(x) = 0$ for every number x.

The preceding example tells us that the derived function of any constant function is the constant function whose value is 0; in other words,

$$\textbf{(15-1)} \qquad D_x c = 0.$$

As a special case, notice that $D_x x^0 = D_x 1 = 0$. We will now state a fundamental differentiation rule that includes this result:

If r is a positive integer, or the reciprocal of a positive integer, or $r = 0$, then

$$\textbf{(15-2)} \qquad D_x x^r = r x^{r-1}.$$

As we have noticed, if $r = 0$, then Rule 15-2 is a special case of Rule 15-1. We will prove that Rule 15-2 is correct if r is a positive integer or the reciprocal of a positive integer after we have considered some examples.

If we let $r = 3$, then Rule 15-2 reads

$$D_x x^3 = 3x^2.$$

If we let $r = \frac{1}{3}$, then Rule 15-2 reads

$$D_x x^{1/3} = \tfrac{1}{3} x^{-2/3};$$

that is,

$$D_x \sqrt[3]{x} = \frac{1}{3\sqrt[3]{x^2}}.$$

Example 15-2. Find the equation of the tangent line to the graph of the function f at the point $(-1, f(-1))$ if $f(x) = x^4$.

Solution. The slope of the tangent line at the point $(-1, f(-1)) = (-1, 1)$ is $f'(-1)$. Using Rule 15-2,

$$f'(x) = D_x x^4 = 4x^3,$$

so that

$$f'(-1) = -4.$$

Thus the equation of our tangent line is $y - 1 = -4(x + 1)$.

Example 15-3. Show that the tangent line to the graph of the equation $y = x^5$ at the point (2, 32) is parallel to the tangent line to the graph of the equation $y = x^{80}$ at the point (1, 1).

Solution. On applying Rule 15-2, we see that if $y = x^5$, then $D_x y = 5x^4$, and if $y = x^{80}$, then $D_x y = 80x^{79}$. Thus the slope of the tangent to the curve $y = x^5$ at a point (x, y) is $5x^4$, and therefore at the point (2, 32) the slope of the tangent line is $5 \cdot 2^4 = 80$. Similarly, the slope of the tangent to the curve $y = x^{80}$ at the point (1, 1) is $80 \cdot 1^{79} = 80$. Since the two tangent lines have the same slope, 80, they are parallel (Theorem 9-2).

Let P be a point of the graph of a function f. The line that contains P and is perpendicular to the tangent line to the graph of f at P is called the **normal line** (or **normal**) to the graph at the point P.

Example 15-4. Find the equation of the normal line to the graph of the equation $y = \sqrt{x}$ at the point (9, 3).

Solution. Since $y = x^{1/2}$, the slope of the tangent line at a point is given by

$$D_x y = \frac{1}{2} x^{-1/2} = \frac{1}{2\sqrt{x}}.$$

When $x = 9$, we see that the slope of the tangent line is $\frac{1}{6}$. Thus the slope of the normal line at the point (9, 3) is -6, and its equation is $y - 3 = -6(x - 9)$.

Although we stated Rule 15-2 in terms of the letters x and r, it is clear that the same formula is applicable if other letters are used. For example:

$$D_y y^s = s y^{s-1};$$
$$D_u u^7 = 7u^6;$$
$$D_t \sqrt[5]{t} = \frac{1}{5\sqrt[5]{t^4}}.$$

Example 15-5. Suppose a body moves s feet in t seconds, where s and t are related by the equation $s = t^2$. At what time is the velocity equal to 10 feet per second?

Solution. We use Rule 15-2 to find that $v = D_t s = 2t$. Now we must find the number t such that $2t = 10$, and that number clearly is $t = 5$. Thus, 5 seconds after the start of the motion the body is moving with the velocity of 10 feet per second.

We will now prove that Rule 15-2 is correct if r is a positive integer n. If $f(x) = x^n$, then

$$\frac{f(x+h) - f(x)}{h} = \frac{(x+h)^n - x^n}{h}. \tag{15-3}$$

To simplify this difference quotient we can expand $(x+h)^n$ by the Binomial Formula as follows:

$$(x+h)^n = x^n + nx^{n-1}h + \frac{n(n-1)}{2}x^{n-2}h^2 + \cdots + h^n. \tag{15-4}$$

For our purposes here we do not need to know the exact form of any term beyond the second one, except that h^2 is a factor of each such term, so we will write Equation 15-4 as

$$(x+h)^n = x^n + nx^{n-1}h + h^2E, \tag{15-5}$$

where E is an expression involving x and h. Now, using Equation 15-5, we can write the difference quotient in Equation 15-3 as

$$\frac{f(x+h) - f(x)}{h} = \frac{nx^{n-1}h + h^2E}{h} = nx^{n-1} + hE.$$

Since

$$\lim_{h\to 0} hE = \left(\lim_{h\to 0} h\right)\left(\lim_{h\to 0} E\right) = 0 \cdot \left(\lim_{h\to 0} E\right) = 0 \quad \text{(see Equation 13-1)},$$

we see that

$$f'(x) = \lim_{h\to 0} \frac{f(x+h) - f(x)}{h} = nx^{n-1}.$$

Thus Rule 15-2 is verified if r is a positive integer.

Finally, we prove that Rule 15-2 is correct if $r = 1/n$, where n is a positive integer. If $f(x) = x^{1/n}$, then

$$\frac{f(x+h) - f(x)}{h} = \frac{(x+h)^{1/n} - x^{1/n}}{h}. \tag{15-6}$$

Since $1/n$ is not a positive integer, we cannot expand $(x+h)^{1/n}$ by the Binomial Formula as we did in the preceding proof. However, we can note that

$$[(x+h)^{1/n}]^n - [x^{1/n}]^n = h. \tag{15-7}$$

Now let us factor the difference in Equation 15-7 by using the formula

$$b^n - a^n = (b-a)(b^{n-1} + b^{n-2}a + b^{n-3}a^2 + \cdots + a^{n-1}).$$

(You may check this formula by multiplying out the right-hand side.)

If we let $b = (x + h)^{1/n}$ and $a = x^{1/n}$, we can write Equation 15-7 as

$$(15\text{-}8) \quad h = \{(x + h)^{1/n} - x^{1/n}\}\{[(x + h)^{1/n}]^{n-1} + [(x + h)^{1/n}]^{n-2}x^{1/n} + \cdots + [x^{1/n}]^{n-1}\}$$

where there are n terms in the last sum. By means of Equation 15-8, the difference quotient in Equation 15-6 can be written

$$\frac{f(x + h) - f(x)}{h} = \frac{1}{(x + h)^{(n-1)/n} + (x + h)^{(n-2)/n}x^{1/n} + \cdots + x^{(n-1)/n}}.$$

From the theorems about limits in Section 13, it then follows that each term in the sum in the denominator approaches $x^{(n-1)/n}$ as a limit as h approaches zero, and since there are n terms in this sum we have

$$f'(x) = \lim_{h \to 0} \frac{f(x + h) - f(x)}{h} = \frac{1}{nx^{(n-1)/n}},$$

or

$$f'(x) = \frac{1}{n}\, x^{(1/n)-1}.$$

Thus Rule 15-2 is proved if $r = 1/n$, where n is a positive integer.

Problems 15

1. Find y' if:
   (a) $y = x^7$
   (b) $y = \sqrt[4]{x}$
   (c) $y = \sqrt[5]{t}$
   (d) $y = u^3$
   (e) $y = \sqrt[6]{v}$
   (f) $y = (w^3)^3$
2. Suppose that n and m are positive integers and $n > m$. Does $D_x(x^n \cdot x^m) = (D_x x^n)(D_x x^m)$? Does $D_x\left(\frac{x^n}{x^m}\right) = \frac{D_x x^n}{D_x x^m}$?
3. Find the equation of the tangent line at the point (1, 1) if:
   (a) $y = \sqrt[3]{x}$
   (b) $y = x^3$
   (c) $y = x^4$
   (d) $y = \sqrt[4]{x}$.
4. Find the points of the graphs of the two equations listed that have the same X-coordinate and at which the tangent lines are parallel.
   (a) $y = x^2$ and $y = x^3$
   (b) $y = \sqrt{x}$ and $y = \sqrt[3]{x}$
   (c) $y = \sqrt{x}$ and $y = x^2$
5. Prove that if n is an odd positive integer, the lines tangent to the graph of the equation $y = x^n$ at the points (1, 1) and $(-1, -1)$ are parallel.
6. Prove that if n is an even positive integer, the line tangent to the graph of the equation $y = \sqrt[n]{x}$ at the point (1, 1) is perpendicular to the line tangent to the graph of the equation $y = x^n$ at the point $(-1, 1)$.

7. In each case write the equation of the normal line to the curve at the point (1, 1).
(a) $y = \sqrt[3]{x}$ (b) $y = x^3$
(c) $y = x^4$ (d) $y = \sqrt[4]{x}$
8. Show that the tangent line to the graph of the equation $y = x^r$ (r a positive integer or the reciprocal of a positive integer) at the point (1, 1) intersects the Y-axis at a point that is $|r - 1|$ units away from the origin.
9. Show that the Y-intercept of the tangent line to the graph of the equation $y = x^r$ (r a positive integer or the reciprocal of a positive integer) at the point (a, b) is $(1 - r)a^r$.
10. Suppose that the tangent line to the graph of the equation $y = x^2$ at the point (a, b) intersects the Y-axis at the point P and that the normal line to the graph at the point (a, b) intersects the Y-axis at the point Q. Show that the coordinates of P are $(0, -b)$ and that the distance between the points P and Q is $2b + \frac{1}{2}$.
11. What is the distance between the points P and Q in the preceding question if you consider the graph of the equation $y = x^r$ (r a positive integer or the reciprocal of a positive integer)?

16. General Laws of Differentiation

In the preceding section we learned the specific differentiation rule that gives the derivatives of certain powers of x. For example, we now know how to find y' if $y = x^3$, or if $y = \sqrt{x}$, and so on. Later we shall show that the same rule also applies to other powers of x, to $x^{3/5}$ and x^π, for example. But before we go farther with specific rules, we shall develop some general laws of differentiation that apply to all differentiable functions.

Our first general theorem shows us that the "differential operator" D_x commutes with every number c; for example, $D_x 4\sqrt{x} = 4D_x\sqrt{x}$.

THEOREM 16-1. *If f is a differentiable function and c is a number, then*

$$D_x[cf(x)] = cD_x[f(x)]. \tag{16-1}$$

Proof. We have

$$\begin{aligned} D_x[cf(x)] &= \lim_{h\to 0} \frac{cf(x+h) - cf(x)}{h} && \text{(Def. 12-1)} \\ &= \lim_{h\to 0} c \cdot \frac{f(x+h) - f(x)}{h} && \text{(factoring)} \\ &= c \lim_{h\to 0} \frac{f(x+h) - f(x)}{h} && \text{(Eqs. 13-2 and 13-4)} \\ &= cD_x f(x) && \text{(Def. 12-1).} \end{aligned}$$

Example 16-1. If $y = 4\sqrt{x}$, find D_xy.

Solution. Using Equation 16-1 and Rule 15-2, we have

$$D_x(4\sqrt{x}) = 4D_xx^{1/2} = 4 \cdot \tfrac{1}{2}x^{-1/2}.$$

Thus

$$D_xy = \frac{2}{\sqrt{x}}.$$

Our next general theorem states that the differential operator D_x is distributive with respect to addition. Thus it is immaterial whether we first add and then apply the operator D_x or first apply the operator and then add. We get the same result in either case. For example,

$$D_x(\sqrt{x} + 3x^2) = D_x\sqrt{x} + D_x3x^2.$$

THEOREM 16-2. *If f and g are differentiable functions, then*

$$D_x[f(x) + g(x)] = D_xf(x) + D_xg(x). \tag{16-2}$$

Proof. We have

$$\begin{aligned} D_x[f(x) + g(x)] &\\ &= \lim_{h\to 0} \frac{[f(x+h) + g(x+h)] - [f(x) + g(x)]}{h} && \text{(Def. 12-1)}\\ &= \lim_{h\to 0} \left(\frac{f(x+h) - f(x)}{h} + \frac{g(x+h) - g(x)}{h}\right)\\ &= \lim_{h\to 0} \frac{f(x+h) - f(x)}{h} + \lim_{h\to 0} \frac{g(x+h) - g(x)}{h} && \text{(Eq. 13-3)}\\ &= D_xf(x) + D_xg(x) && \text{(Def. 12-1).} \end{aligned}$$

Example 16-2. Find $D_x(\sqrt{x} + 3x^2)$.

Solution.

$$\begin{aligned} D_x(\sqrt{x} + 3x^2) &= D_x\sqrt{x} + D_x3x^2 && \text{(Eq. 16-2)}\\ &= D_x\sqrt{x} + 3D_xx^2 && \text{(Eq. 16-1)}\\ &= \frac{1}{2\sqrt{x}} + 3 \cdot (2x) && \text{(Rule 15-2)}\\ &= \frac{1}{2\sqrt{x}} + 6x. \end{aligned}$$

Example 16-3. Show that

$$D_x[f(x) - g(x)] = D_xf(x) - D_xg(x).$$

Solution. Since $f(x) - g(x) = f(x) + (-1) \cdot g(x)$, we may use Equations 16-1 and 16-2 to write

$$\begin{aligned} D_x[f(x) - g(x)] &= D_xf(x) + D_x[(-1)g(x)] \\ &= D_xf(x) + (-1)D_xg(x) \\ &= D_xf(x) - D_xg(x). \end{aligned}$$

The rule for differentiating products is more complicated than the rule for differentiating sums. It is not true, in general, that the derivative of a product is the product of the derivatives of its factors. Instead we have the following theorem.

THEOREM 16-3. *If f and g are differentiable functions, then*

$$\mathbf{D_x[f(x) \cdot g(x)] = f(x) \cdot D_xg(x) + g(x) \cdot D_xf(x).} \tag{16-3}$$

Proof. The derivative of the product $f(x)g(x)$ is the limit, as h approaches 0, of the difference quotient

$$\frac{f(x + h)g(x + h) - f(x)g(x)}{h}.$$

It will make it easier to see what the limit is if we first use a little algebra. We subtract and add the quantity $f(x + h)g(x)$ in the numerator, and our difference quotient becomes

$$\begin{aligned} &\frac{f(x + h)g(x + h) - f(x + h)g(x) + f(x + h)g(x) - f(x)g(x)}{h} \\ &\qquad = f(x + h)\frac{g(x + h) - g(x)}{h} + \frac{f(x + h) - f(x)}{h}g(x). \end{aligned}$$

According to our rules of limits, the limit of this last sum is

$$\left[\lim_{h\to 0} f(x + h)\right] \cdot \left[\lim_{h\to 0} \frac{g(x + h) - g(x)}{h}\right] + \left[\lim_{h\to 0} \frac{f(x + h) - f(x)}{h}\right] g(x).$$

But this expression is the right-hand side of Equation 16-3, since according to Theorem 13-5, $\lim_{h\to 0} f(x + h) = f(x)$, and the other two limits are, by definition, the derivatives of $f(x)$ and $g(x)$.

Example 16-4. Find $D_x[x(4x + 3)]$.

Solution. We may proceed in either of two ways. We can perform the indicated multiplication first and obtain

$$D_x(4x^2 + 3x) = D_x(4x^2) + D_x(3x) = 8x + 3,$$

or we may use Theorem 16-3 to get

$$\begin{aligned} D_x[x(4x + 3)] &= xD_x(4x + 3) + (4x + 3)D_x x \\ &= x \cdot 4 + (4x + 3) \cdot 1 = 8x + 3. \end{aligned}$$

Example 16-5. Find $D_x x^{7/2}$.

Solution. We write $x^{7/2} = x^{3+1/2} = x^3 \cdot x^{1/2}$.
Then using Equation 16-3 and Rule 15-2, we obtain

$$\begin{aligned} D_x x^{7/2} &= D_x(x^3 \cdot x^{1/2}) = x^3 D_x x^{1/2} + (D_x x^3)x^{1/2} \\ &= x^3 \cdot \tfrac{1}{2}x^{-1/2} + 3x^2 \cdot x^{1/2} \\ &= \tfrac{1}{2}x^{5/2} + 3x^{5/2} \\ &= \tfrac{7}{2}x^{5/2}. \end{aligned}$$

Notice that this example shows that Rule 15-2 is valid if $r = \frac{7}{2}$. In Section 18 we will show that Rule 15-2 is valid if r is any rational number.

Let us write the general differentiation laws stated in Equations 16-1, 16-2, and 16-3 in our other notations. Let $u = f(x)$ and $v = g(x)$. Then the laws read

(16-4) $$\boldsymbol{D_x cu = cD_x u}$$

or $$\boldsymbol{(cu)' = cu'}$$

(16-5) $$\boldsymbol{D_x(u + v) = D_x u + D_x v}$$

or $$\boldsymbol{(u + v)' = u' + v'}$$

(16-6) $$\boldsymbol{D_x(uv) = uD_x v + (D_x u)v}$$

or $$\boldsymbol{(uv)' = uv' + u'v.}$$

The rules stated in Theorems 16-2 and 16-3 can be extended to cases in which more than two functions are involved. Although we will not take the time to prove them, we will use these extensions freely. For example, if we consider three functions—f, g, and h—then Rule 16-3 becomes

$$D_x[f(x)g(x)h(x)] = f(x)g(x)[D_x h(x)] + f(x)[D_x g(x)]h(x) + [D_x f(x)]g(x)h(x).$$

Example 16-6. If $y = 3x^7 - 2x^3 + 4x - 14$, find y'.

Solution. According to the rules of this and the preceding section,

$$\begin{aligned} y' &= D_x(3x^7 - 2x^3 + 4x - 14) \\ &= 3D_xx^7 - 2D_xx^3 + 4D_xx - D_x14 \\ &= 3 \cdot 7x^6 - 2 \cdot 3x^2 + 4 \cdot 1 - 0 \\ &= 21x^6 - 6x^2 + 4. \end{aligned}$$

Problems 16

1. Find y' if:
   (a) $y = \frac{1}{2}x^2$ (b) $y = 3\sqrt{x}$ (c) $y = 3x^2 + 1$
   (d) $y = 2\sqrt{x} + 1$ (e) $y = 2t^3 + t$ (f) $y = \sqrt{2}\,x$
   (g) $y = \sqrt{2x}$ (h) $y = (3x)^2$ (i) $y = \frac{1}{2}v^4 - v$
   (j) $y = x^2 + x + 1$ (k) $y = 3\sqrt[3]{x} - x$ (l) $y = x^2 + \sqrt{x} + 2x$
2. Find $f'(-2)$ if:
   (a) $f(x) = \frac{1}{2}x^2$ (b) $f(x) = 2x^2 - 1$ (c) $f(x) = x^3 - x$
   (d) $f(x) = x^2 + x^4$ (e) $f(x) = |x| + x^2$ (f) $f(x) = \sqrt[5]{x}$
   (g) $f(x) = \sqrt[3]{8x}$ (h) $f(x) = 8\sqrt[3]{x}$ (i) $f(x) = 3\sqrt[3]{x} + 5\sqrt[5]{x}$
   (j) $f(x) = x^2 + x + 1$ (k) $f(x) = \sqrt{x^2}$ (l) $f(x) = \sqrt{4x^2}$
3. Compute:
   (a) $D_x(x^4 - \sqrt[4]{x}/3 + 17x + 4)$ (b) $D_x(\sqrt{2x} + \sqrt{2}x + \sqrt{3x} + \sqrt{3}x)$
   (c) $D_t(2t^3 - 3t^2 + 7t - 1)$ (d) $D_u(u^3 + 2u^2 - \sqrt{u} + 4u + 7)$
4. Use Theorem 16-3 (the Product Rule) to find D_xx^2 by writing $D_xx^2 = D_x(x \cdot x)$.
5. Find the listed derivative by two methods: First, expand and then differentiate; second, use the Product Rule (see Example 16-4).
   (a) $D_x(x + 2)^2$ (b) $D_xx(x + 1)$
   (c) $D_t(t^2 + 1)^2$ (d) $D_uu^2(u^2 + 1)$
   (e) $D_x(x + 1)^3$ (f) $D_uu(u - 1)(u - 2)$
   (g) $D_x(x^2 + 3x - 1)^2$ (h) $D_x(x - 1)(x^2 + x + 1)$
6. Write the equation of the tangent line to the graph of the equation at the point whose X-coordinate is 4.
   (a) $y = x + \sqrt{x}$ (b) $y = 4x - 2$
   (c) $y = x^3 - 4x^2 - 1$ (d) $y = x^4 - \sqrt{x}$
7. Write the equation of the normal line to the graph of the equation at the point whose X-coordinate is -2.
   (a) $y = 3x^2 - 1$ (b) $y = \sqrt[3]{x} + x$ (c) $y = x^2 - \sqrt{x^2}$
8. What is the rate of change of volume with respect to the radius:
   (a) of a sphere? (b) of a cylinder with fixed height?
   (c) of a cone with fixed height?
9. Find the points of the graphs of the following equations at which the tangent lines are perpendicular to the line $4y + x - 8 = 0$.
   (a) $y = x^2 - 5x + 1$ (b) $y = x^3 - 23x + 7$
   (c) $y = x^5/5 + 2x^3/3 + x + 9$ (d) $y = 3 - 2\sqrt{x}$

10. A rocket is fired directly upward. It is s feet high t seconds after the firing. Find the velocity of the rocket 1 second after firing, and determine the time when the rocket reaches its maximum height if $s = 480t - 16t^2$.

17. The Chain Rule

The general differentiation laws that we developed in Section 16, together with the Power Formula, Equation 15-2, enable us to find the derivatives with respect to x of sums and products of powers of x if the exponent is a positive integer, zero, or the reciprocal of a positive integer. For example, we can find D_xy if $y = 3x^2 - 2x^3\sqrt{x}$. But we cannot write an expression such as $\sqrt{x^2+1}$ as a sum of products of powers of x, so if we want its derivative we must find another way to make the Power Formula apply. To find D_xy in case $y = \sqrt{x^2+1}$ we introduce an intermediate step. We write

$$y = \sqrt{u}, \text{ where } u = x^2 + 1.$$

We may then use the following theorem to find D_xy.

THEOREM 17-1. (**The Chain Rule.**) *If*

$$y = f(u), \textit{ where } u = g(x),$$

then

$$\mathbf{D_xy = D_uy \cdot D_xu.} \tag{17-1}$$

We will delay the proof of this theorem until after we have looked at some examples of how to use it.

Example 17-1. Find D_xy if $y = \sqrt{x^2+1}$.

Solution. Here we take

$$y = \sqrt{u}, \text{ where } u = x^2 + 1.$$

We then calculate D_uy and D_xu from these equations and substitute the results in the Chain Rule Equation 17-1. Thus we have

$$D_uy = D_u\sqrt{u} = \frac{1}{2\sqrt{u}}, \text{ and } D_xu = D_x(x^2+1) = 2x.$$

Equation 17-1 therefore becomes

$$D_xy = \frac{1}{2\sqrt{u}} \cdot 2x = \frac{x}{\sqrt{u}}.$$

Since $u = x^2 + 1$, we can write our final result as:

$$D_x y = \frac{x}{\sqrt{x^2 + 1}}.$$

We see that the Chain Rule involves the following 4 steps:
Step 1. Express y in terms of u and u in terms of x.
Step 2. Find $D_u y$ and $D_x u$.
Step 3. Substitute the derivatives found in Step 2 in the Chain Rule Equation $D_x y = D_u y D_x u$.
Step 4. Replace u in the result obtained in Step 3 by its expression in terms of x as given in Step 1.

Example 17-2. If $f(x) = \sqrt{2x^2 - 3}$, find $f'(x)$.

Solution. Following the four steps above we have:

(1) $y = \sqrt{u},\ u = 2x^2 - 3$

(2) $D_u y = \dfrac{1}{2\sqrt{u}},\ D_x u = 4x$

(3) $D_x y = D_u y D_x u = \dfrac{1}{2\sqrt{u}} 4x$

(4) $D_x y = \dfrac{2x}{\sqrt{2x^2 - 3}}.$

Example 17-3. If $s = \dfrac{1}{t^3 + 1}$, find $D_t s$.

Solution. To find $D_t s$ we follow the four steps for using the Chain Rule (with obvious modifications because of the different letters):

(1) $s = \dfrac{1}{r},\ r = t^3 + 1$

(2) $D_r s = -\dfrac{1}{r^2}$ (Ex. 13-5)

$D_t r = 3t^2$ (Eq. 15-2)

(3) $D_t s = D_r s D_t r = -\dfrac{1}{r^2} 3t^2 = -\dfrac{3t^2}{r^2}$

(4) $D_t s = -\dfrac{3t^2}{(t^3 + 1)^2}.$

If $y = f(u)$, where $u = g(x)$, then $y = f[g(x)]$. Thus, corresponding to each number x in the domain of g (for which $g(x)$ is a number in the domain of f) we obtain a number y. This correspondence determines a new function, p, that is "composed" of the functions f and g by means of the equation

$$\boldsymbol{p}(\boldsymbol{x}) = \boldsymbol{f}[\boldsymbol{g}(\boldsymbol{x})].$$

We call $\boldsymbol{p}$ the **composite function** formed by the composition of g by f. The Chain Rule tells us how to express the derivative $p'(x)$ in terms of values of the functions f' and g'. We simply replace, in Equation 17-1, D_xy with $p'(x)$, D_uy with $f'(u)$, and D_xu with $g'(x)$, and we have the equation

$$\boldsymbol{p}'(\boldsymbol{x}) = \boldsymbol{f}'(\boldsymbol{u})\boldsymbol{g}'(\boldsymbol{x}) \tag{17-2}$$

or

$$\boldsymbol{p}'(\boldsymbol{x}) = \boldsymbol{f}'[\boldsymbol{g}(\boldsymbol{x})]\boldsymbol{g}'(\boldsymbol{x}). \tag{17-3}$$

Example 17-4. Calculate $p'(0)$ if $p(x) = \sqrt[3]{x^2 + 1}$.

Solution. We write

$$p(x) = f(u) = \sqrt[3]{u}, \text{ where } u = g(x) = x^2 + 1.$$

Then

$$f'(u) = \frac{1}{3\sqrt[3]{u^2}} \text{ and } g'(x) = 2x.$$

If we substitute these results in Equation 17-2 we get

$$p'(x) = \frac{1}{3\sqrt[3]{u^2}} \cdot 2x.$$

Thus

$$p'(x) = \frac{2x}{3\sqrt[3]{(x^2+1)^2}}$$

and so

$$p'(0) = 0.$$

Let us now indicate how the proof of the Chain Rule proceeds. Equations 17-1, 17-2, and 71-3 express the Chain Rule in different notation. For the purposes of this proof we find the notation of Equation 17-2 most useful. We suppose that x is a point in the domain of the composite function p and that the function g is differentiable at x and the function f is differentiable at u, where $u = g(x)$. We must show that p is differentiable at x and that $p'(x)$ is given by Equation 17-2. Therefore, we try to write the difference quotient

$$\frac{p(x+h) - p(x)}{h} = \frac{1}{h}\left(f[g(x+h)] - f[g(x)]\right) \tag{17-4}$$

in such a way that we can see what its limit is. To this end we introduce an auxiliary function q defined by the equations

$$q(k) = \frac{f(u+k) - f(u)}{k} \text{ for } k \neq 0 \text{ and } q(0) = f'(u).$$

Since the value of q at 0 is its limit at 0, we see that q is continuous at 0. We use our function q to express the difference $f(u+k) - f(k)$; thus $f(u+k) - f(u) = kq(k)$. In this equation we now replace k with the difference $g(x+h) - g(x)$ and we have

$$f[u + g(x+h) - g(x)] - f(u) = (g(x+h) - g(x))q[g(x+h) - g(x)].$$

Since $u = g(x)$, the left side of this equation is simply $f[g(x+h)] - f[g(x)]$, and so the difference quotient in Equation 17-4 takes the form

$$\frac{p(x+h) - p(x)}{h} = \frac{g(x+h) - g(x)}{h} q[g(x+h) - g(x)],$$

and now we can see what its limit is. The first factor on the right,

$$\frac{g(x+h) - g(x)}{h},$$

approaches $g'(x)$ as h approaches 0. To find the limit of the second factor we make use of the facts that the function q is continuous at 0 and that $\lim_{h \to 0} [g(x+h) - g(x)] = 0$. It follows that the limit of the second factor as h approaches 0 is $q(0) = f'(u)$, and so our difference quotient approaches $g'(x)f'(u)$, as asserted by Equation 17-2.

Problems 17

1. Use the "four-step method" with the Chain Rule to find y' if
   (a) $y = \sqrt{x+1}$ (b) $y = \sqrt[3]{4-x}$
   (c) $y = \sqrt{2x-7}$ (d) $y = \sqrt[4]{1-2x}$
   (e) $y = (x^2 + 2x - 1)^3$ (f) $y = \sqrt[3]{x^2 - 3}$
   (g) $y = (2 - x^2)^4$ (h) $y = \sqrt{25 - x^2}$
   (i) $y = 3(1 - x + x^3)^4$ (j) $y = \sqrt{x - x^2}$
2. Write the equation of the tangent line to the graph of f at the point $(1, f(1))$ if:
   (a) $f(x) = \sqrt{x^2 + 3}$ (b) $f(x) = \sqrt[3]{x^2 + 3x + 4}$
3. Let $y = \sqrt{F(x)}$. Find $D_x y$ if:
   (a) $F(x) = x^2 + 4x - 3$ (b) $F(x) = x(x^2 - 5)$
   (c) $F(x) = (x-1)(x^2+1)$ (d) $F(x) = \sqrt{x} + 1$
4. Write the equation of the normal line to the graph of f at the point $(1, f(1))$ if:
   (a) $f(x) = \sqrt{x^2 + 3}$ (b) $f(x) = \sqrt[3]{x^2 + 3x + 4}$

5. Use the "four-step method" to compute:

(a) $D_x(x\sqrt{x^2+1})$ (b) $D_t(\sqrt{1-t}\sqrt{1+t})$

(c) $D_x(\sqrt{x^2+7}-\sqrt{x^2-7})$ (d) $D_t[t^2(t^2-1)^4]$

(e) $D_x[(2x-1)^3(2x+1)^2]$ (f) $D_x[\sqrt{1-x^2}+\sqrt{1+x^2}]$

6. Compute $f[g(2)]$ if:

(a) $f(x)=\sqrt{x}$ and $g(x)=2x$ (b) $f(x)=\sin x$ and $g(x)=x^2$

(c) $f(x)=\log x$ and $g(x)=10^x$ (d) $f(x)=\cos x$ and $g(x)=\sin x$

7. Use the Chain Rule to compute $f'(\frac{3}{2})$ if:

(a) $f(x)=\sqrt{3x^2-1}$ (b) $f(x)=\sqrt{11-4x^2}$

(c) $f(x)=\sqrt[3]{x^2}$ (d) $f(x)=x^{3/4}$

8. Which of the following are correct statements of the Chain Rule Equation? $D_yx=D_uxD_yu$; $D_uy=D_xyD_xu$; $D_xu=D_xvD_vu$.

9. At each of the following points find the slope of the line tangent to the graph of the equation $y=x\sqrt{1-x^2}$, and then sketch this graph: $(-1,0)$, $(-\sqrt{2}/2,-\frac{1}{2})$, $(0,0)$, $(\sqrt{2}/2,\frac{1}{2})$, $(1,0)$.

10. Show that if $y=\sqrt{3-x^2}$, then $yy'+x=0$.

11. Suppose that $D_tx=4$ when $x=1$. Find D_ty when $x=1$ if:

(a) $y=x^3$ (b) $y=\sqrt{x}$

(c) $y=\sqrt{x^2+3}$ (d) $y=\sqrt[3]{5x^2+3}$

12. A point moves along a line and is s feet away from the origin t seconds after some given moment. If $s=\sqrt{t^2-t+1}$, find out when the velocity is zero.

18. Rational Exponents

In Section 15 we derived the Power Rule $D_xx^r=rx^{r-1}$ if r is a nonnegative integer or the reciprocal of a positive integer. Now we will use the Chain Rule to show that this rule is valid if r is any rational number. Thus we will show, for example, that $D_xx^{5/3}=\frac{5}{3}x^{2/3}$.

Let us suppose first that r is a positive rational number. Then we can write $r=p/q$, where p and q are positive integers. To find D_xy if $y=x^r=x^{p/q}$, we will use the Chain Rule and follow the usual four steps:

(1) $y=u^p,\ u=x^{\frac{1}{q}}$;

(2) $D_uy=pu^{p-1},\ D_xu=\frac{1}{q}x^{\frac{1}{q}-1}$; (Rule 15-2)

(3) $D_xy=D_uyD_xu=pu^{p-1}\dfrac{x^{\frac{1}{q}-1}}{q}$;

(4) $D_xy=\dfrac{p}{q}x^{\frac{p-1}{q}}\cdot x^{\frac{1}{q}-1}=\dfrac{p}{q}x^{\frac{p}{q}-1}$.

Since $r=p/q$,

$$D_xx^r=rx^{r-1},$$

and thus the Power Rule is verified for positive rational exponents.

Next we suppose that r is a negative rational number. Then we can write $r = -s$, where s is a positive rational number, and so

$$y = x^r = x^{-s} = (x^{-1})^s.$$

When we use the usual four-step method with the Chain Rule,

(1) $y = u^s$, $u = x^{-1}$;

(2) $D_u y = su^{s-1}$; (Preceding paragraph)

$D_x u = -x^{-2}$; (Example 13-5)

(3) $D_x y = D_u y D_x u = (su^{s-1})(-x^{-2})$;

(4) $D_x y = -s(x^{-1})^{s-1}x^{-2} = rx^{-s-1} = rx^{r-1}$.

Thus the Power Rule is valid for negative rational exponents, and so we may now use it to calculate the derivatives of all rational powers of x.

Example 18-1. Find $D_x(2x)^{\frac{5}{3}}$.

Solution. We can proceed in either of two ways, both of which are correct.

Method 1. Since $(2x)^{\frac{5}{3}} = 2^{\frac{5}{3}}\, x^{\frac{5}{3}}$,

$D_x(2x)^{\frac{5}{3}} = 2^{\frac{5}{3}}\, D_x x^{\frac{5}{3}} = 2^{\frac{5}{3}} \cdot \frac{5}{3} \cdot x^{\frac{2}{3}}$.

Method 2. We may also use the Chain Rule:

(1) $y = u^{\frac{5}{3}}$, $u = 2x$;

(2) $D_u y = (\frac{5}{3})u^{\frac{2}{3}}$, $D_x u = 2$;

(3) $D_x y = D_u y D_x u = \frac{5}{3}\, u^{\frac{2}{3}} \cdot 2$;

(4) $D_x y = 2 \cdot (\frac{5}{3}) \cdot (2x)^{\frac{2}{3}} = 2^{\frac{5}{3}} \cdot (\frac{5}{3}) \cdot x^{\frac{2}{3}}$.

Example 18-2. Find $D_x\left(\sqrt{x} + \dfrac{1}{\sqrt{x}}\right)$.

Solution.

$$D_x\left(\sqrt{x} + \frac{1}{\sqrt{x}}\right) = D_x(x^{\frac{1}{2}} + x^{-\frac{1}{2}}) = D_x x^{\frac{1}{2}} + D_x x^{-\frac{1}{2}}$$

$$= \tfrac{1}{2}x^{-\frac{1}{2}} - \tfrac{1}{2}x^{-\frac{3}{2}}$$

$$= \frac{1}{2\sqrt{x}}\left(1 - \frac{1}{x}\right).$$

When we write one of our specific differentiation formulas, such as the Power Formula, we usually "incorporate" it in the Chain Rule.

Thus if $y = u^r$, where $u = g(x)$, the Power Formula yields $D_u y = ru^{r-1}$, and hence the Chain Rule Equation, $D_x y = D_u y D_x u$, reads

(18-1) $$\boldsymbol{D_x u^r = ru^{r-1} D_x u.}$$

Example 18-3. Find $D_x(x^2 + 1)^{\frac{3}{2}}$.

Solution. Here we let $r = \frac{3}{2}$ and $u = x^2 + 1$. Hence $D_x u = 2x$, and Equation 18-1 becomes

$$D_x(x^2 + 1)^{\frac{3}{2}} = \frac{3}{2}(x^2 + 1)^{\frac{1}{2}} \cdot 2x = 3x(x^2 + 1)^{\frac{1}{2}}.$$

We can use the rule for differentiating a product (Equation 16-6) and Equation 18-1 to find the derivative of a quotient u/v, where $u = f(x)$, $v = g(x)$, and $v \neq 0$. Thus

(18-2) $$D_x\left(\frac{u}{v}\right) = D_x(uv^{-1}) = uD_x v^{-1} + v^{-1} D_x u.$$

If we replace r with -1 and u with v, Equation 18-1 yields $D_x v^{-1} = -v^{-2} D_x v$. Equation 18-2 then yields the **Quotient Rule**

$$D_x\left(\frac{u}{v}\right) = -\frac{u}{v^2} D_x v + \frac{1}{v} D_x u,$$

that is,

(18-3) $$\boldsymbol{D_x\left(\frac{u}{v}\right) = \frac{vD_x u - uD_x v}{v^2}.}$$

Example 18-4. Find $D_x\left(\dfrac{x^2}{2x + 1}\right)$.

Solution. Let $u = x^2$ and $v = 2x + 1$. Then $D_x u = 2x$, $D_x v = 2$, and Equation 18-3 becomes

$$D_x\left(\frac{x^2}{2x + 1}\right) = \frac{(2x + 1) \cdot 2x - x^2 \cdot 2}{(2x + 1)^2} = \frac{2x(x + 1)}{(2x + 1)^2}.$$

Let us pause here and gather together all the rules and formulas of differentiation that we have encountered so far. At this stage in our study we have developed one specific differentiation formula; namely, the Power Formula,

(18-4) $\boldsymbol{D_x u^r = ru^{r-1} D_x u}$ (r any rational number, and $u = g(x)$).

In addition, we have the following general formulas. If $u = f(x)$ and $v = g(x)$, then

(18-5) $$\boldsymbol{D_x(cu) = cD_xu}$$ (c any real number),

(18-6) $$\boldsymbol{D_x(u + v) = D_xu + D_xv}$$ (Sum Rule),

(18-7) $$\boldsymbol{D_x(uv) = uD_xv + vD_xu}$$ (Product Rule),

(18-8) $$\boldsymbol{D_x\left(\frac{u}{v}\right) = \frac{vD_xu - uD_xv}{v^2}}$$ (Quotient Rule).

Finally, the important Chain Rule states:

If $y = f(u)$ and $u = g(x)$, then

(18-9) $$\boldsymbol{D_xy = D_uyD_xu.}$$

We conclude this section with two examples illustrating uses of the rules we have developed thus far.

Example 18-5. Find $D_x\left(\frac{x^3}{x^2 + 3}\right)$.

Solution. Using our rules of differentiation,

$$D_x\left(\frac{x^3}{x^2 + 3}\right) = \frac{(x^2 + 3)D_xx^3 - x^3D_x(x^2 + 3)}{(x^2 + 3)^2}$$

$$= \frac{(x^2 + 3)3x^2 - x^3 \cdot 2x}{(x^2 + 3)^2}$$

$$= \frac{x^4 + 9x^2}{(x^2 + 3)^2} = \frac{x^2(x^2 + 9)}{(x^2 + 3)^2}.$$

Example 18-6. If $y = \frac{x - 1}{\sqrt{x + 1}}$, find y'.

Solution. Using the rules listed above,

$$D_x\left(\frac{x - 1}{\sqrt{x + 1}}\right) = \frac{(\sqrt{x + 1})D_x(x - 1) - (x - 1)D_x\sqrt{x + 1}}{x + 1}$$

$$= \frac{\sqrt{x + 1} - \dfrac{x - 1}{2\sqrt{x + 1}}}{x + 1}$$

$$= \frac{x + 3}{2(x + 1)^{\frac{3}{2}}}.$$

Problems 18

1. Find y' if:
   (a) $y = x^{5/7}$
   (b) $y = 10x^{2/5}$
   (c) $y = \sqrt[4]{x^3}$
   (d) $y = \sqrt[3]{2z^2}$
   (e) $y = 1/\sqrt[3]{x^2}$
   (f) $y = 3t^{-4/9}$
   (g) $y = (1 - x)^{3/2}$
   (h) $y = 1/\sqrt[3]{(1 - w)^2}$
   (i) $y = (1 - x^2)^{-1/2}$
   (j) $y = (5x^2 + 7)^{-3}$
2. Compute:
   (a) $D_x \dfrac{x + 1}{x - 1}$
   (b) $D_t \dfrac{1 + t^2}{1 - t^2}$
   (c) $D_x \dfrac{2(1 + x^2)}{(1 - x^2)^2}$
   (d) $D_z \dfrac{z^2 + z}{1 - 2z}$
   (e) $D_y \dfrac{(y + 5)^2}{8y}$
   (f) $D_x \left(1 + \dfrac{2}{x}\right)^{3/2}$
3. Find $f'(2)$ if:
   (a) $f(x) = \left[\dfrac{x^2 + 1}{x^2 - 1}\right]^2$
   (b) $f(x) = \dfrac{x}{\sqrt{16 - x^2}}$
   (c) $f(x) = \sqrt{\dfrac{x}{1 + x}}$
   (d) $f(s) = \sqrt{\dfrac{9 - s^2}{9 + s^2}}$
4. Write the equations of the tangent line and normal line to the graph of the equation $y = \sqrt[3]{-x}$ at the point $(-1, f(-1))$.
5. Find y' if:
   (a) $y = \sqrt{(1 + x)(1 - x)}$
   (b) $y = (t + \sqrt{t^2 + 4})^{1/2}$
   (c) $y = (1 - x^{2/3})^{3/2}$
   (d) $y = \sqrt{(2x + 1)/(x^2 - 3)}$
6. The electric field intensity E on the axis of a uniformly charged ring at a point x units from the center of the ring is given by the equation

$$E = \frac{Qx}{(r^2 + x^2)^{3/2}} \quad (Q \text{ and } r \text{ certain numbers}).$$

   What is the rate of change of field intensity with respect to distance along the axis at a point on the axis 5 units from the center?
7. A point moves along a line and is s feet from the origin t seconds after a given moment. Find the equation defining the velocity of the moving point if:
   (a) $s = \dfrac{1 + t + t^2}{\sqrt{t}}$
   (b) $s = \dfrac{1 - \pi t + t^2}{t}$
8. Use two different methods to compute $D_x y$ if:

$$y = \frac{1 - u}{1 + u} \quad \text{and} \quad u = \frac{2 - x}{2 + x}.$$

9. Find the points of the graph of the given equation at which the tangent line is parallel to the X-axis.
   (a) $y = \dfrac{8}{4 + x^2}$
   (b) $y = \dfrac{x}{x^3 - 2}$

10. Write the equation of the line tangent to the graph of the equation $y = \sqrt{\dfrac{x}{x-3}}$ at the point where $x = 4$.

19. The Derivative of Sin x

So far we have developed only one differentiation formula that deals with specific functions; namely, the Power Formula 18-1 for rational exponents. This one formula, together with the general differentiation rules, makes it possible for us to find the derived functions of a great many functions. But it does not help us to find the derived functions of the familiar trigonometric, exponential, and logarithmic functions. In this section we shall find the formula for the derivative of $\sin x$.

To compute $D_x \sin x$, we write $f(x) = \sin x$ and form the difference quotient

$$\frac{f(x+h) - f(x)}{h} = \frac{\sin(x+h) - \sin x}{h}.$$

The derivative of $\sin x$ is the limit of this difference quotient as h approaches 0. In order to reduce this difference quotient to a more manageable form, we replace $\sin(x+h)$ with $\sin x \cos h + \cos x \sin h$ (See Formula A-2 in Appendix A). Our difference quotient then becomes

$$\frac{\sin x \cos h + \cos x \sin h - \sin x}{h} = \cos x\left(\frac{\sin h}{h}\right) - \sin x\left(\frac{1 - \cos h}{h}\right).$$

Therefore, according to the definition of a derivative, and our theorems about limits,

$$D_x \sin x = \cos x \cdot \lim_{h \to 0} \frac{\sin h}{h} - \sin x \cdot \lim_{h \to 0} \frac{1 - \cos h}{h}. \tag{19-1}$$

Thus in order to calculate $D_x \sin x$, we need to calculate the two limits that appear in Equation 19-1. Our next two examples are devoted to finding these limits.

Example 19-1. Show that $\lim_{h \to 0} \dfrac{1 - \cos h}{h} = 0$.

Solution. From the definition of the derivative, we see that the derivative of $\cos x$ at $x = 0$ is the number

$$\lim_{h \to 0} \frac{\cos h - \cos 0}{h} = \lim_{h \to 0} \frac{\cos h - 1}{h}.$$

Thus the limit we are to find is the negative of the derivative of $\cos x$ at $x = 0$. From the graph of the cosine curve, it appears that the slope of the cosine curve at the point where $x = 0$ is zero, so we have a graphical verification that our desired limit is 0. We will give an analytic verification of this fact, too.

In Fig. 19-1 we have sketched a portion of the unit circle showing the points $R(1, 0)$ and $P(\cos h, \sin h)$. Although the figure shows $h > 0$, we must also consider the possibility that $h < 0$; the absolute value signs in our equations take care of this possibility. The length d of the chord

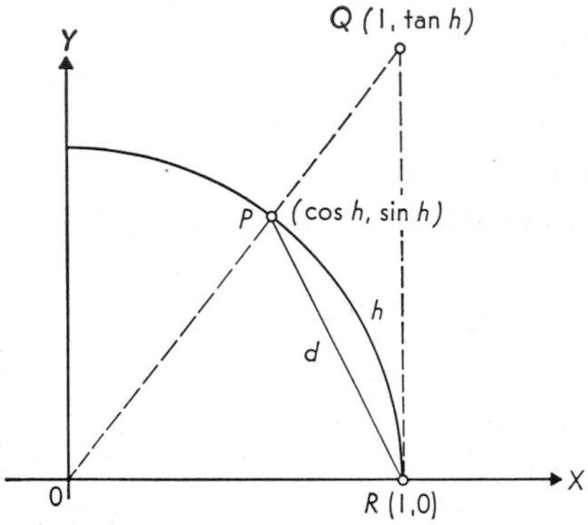

Figure 19-1

joining the two points P and R can be found (see Example 10-2) from the equation

(19-2) $$d^2 = 2(1 - \cos h).$$

Therefore we have

$$\left|\frac{1 - \cos h}{h}\right| = \left|\frac{d^2}{2h}\right|.$$

It is clear that $d < |h|$ (see Fig. 19-1), so

$$\left|\frac{1 - \cos h}{h}\right| < \left|\frac{h^2}{2h}\right| = \frac{|h|}{2}.$$

Therefore if h is close to 0, $\frac{1 - \cos h}{h}$ also must be close to 0; that is,

$$\lim_{h \to 0} \frac{1 - \cos h}{h} = 0.$$

In the preceding example we noticed that the limit we found was the negative of the derivative of $\cos x$ at $x = 0$, so that the cosine function is differentiable at $x = 0$. According to Theorem 13-5, a function that is differentiable at a point is continuous at that point, so the cosine function is continuous at $x = 0$. This statement means that its limit at 0 is its value at 0, in symbols,

$$\lim_{h \to 0} \cos h = 1. \tag{19-3}$$

Example 19-2. Show that $\lim_{h \to 0} \dfrac{\sin h}{h} = 1$.

Solution. In geometric terms, we are to show that the derivative of $\sin x$ at $x = 0$ is 1, and this fact will probably seem reasonable to you from an inspection of the sine curve. Analytically, we proceed as follows (refer to Fig. 19-1). For $0 < |h| < \pi/2$,

$$\text{area } \Delta OPR < \text{area sector } OPR < \text{area } \Delta OQR. \tag{19-4}$$

You can easily show that:

$$\begin{aligned} \text{area } \Delta OPR &= \tfrac{1}{2}|\sin h|, \\ \text{area sector } OPR &= \tfrac{1}{2}|h| \text{ (see Appendix A)}, \\ \text{area } \Delta OQR &= \tfrac{1}{2}|\tan h|. \end{aligned}$$

Therefore, Inequalities 19-4 become

$$\tfrac{1}{2}|\sin h| < \tfrac{1}{2}|h| < \tfrac{1}{2}|\tan h|.$$

Now we divide by $\frac{1}{2}|\sin h|$ and note that $\dfrac{|h|}{|\sin h|} = \dfrac{h}{\sin h}$ and $|\cos h| = \cos h$, and we have

$$1 < \frac{h}{\sin h} < \frac{1}{\cos h}.$$

These inequalities are equivalent to the inequalities

$$\cos h < \frac{\sin h}{h} < 1.$$

Thus the quotient $\dfrac{\sin h}{h}$ is "trapped" between the numbers $\cos h$ and 1. Since (Equation 19-3) the limit of $\cos h$ as h approaches 0 is 1, it is apparent that $\lim_{h \to 0} \dfrac{\sin h}{h} = 1$.

We can now complete the differentiation formula for the sine function. Using the results of Examples 19-1 and 19-2, we see from Equation 19-1 that

$$D_x \sin x = (\cos x) \cdot 1 - (\sin x) \cdot 0;$$

that is,

(19-5) $$\mathbf{D_x \sin x = \cos x.}$$

This formula is our second differentiation formula that deals with a specific basic function. It says that the derived function of the sine function is the cosine function. We used a geometrical argument to obtain the rough sketch of the equation $y = D_x \sin x$ shown as the dashed curve in Fig. 11-4. You might re-examine that graph in light of Equation 19-5.

Now we will incorporate in the Chain Rule our specific differentiation formula for the sine function. If $y = \sin u$, where $u = g(x)$, then according to Equation 19-5, $D_u y = \cos u$. Therefore the Chain Rule Equation $D_x y = D_u y D_x u$ becomes $D_x y = \cos u\, D_x u$. Thus we can write our specific differentiation formula for the sine function in the form

(19-6) $$\mathbf{D_x \sin u = \cos u\, D_x u.}$$

Notice that if $u = x$, then Equation 19-6 reduces to Equation 19-5.

Example 19-3. Find $D_x \sin (2x + 3)$.

Solution. Here we let $u = 2x + 3$, so that $D_x u = 2$, and Equation 19-6 becomes

$$D_x \sin (2x + 3) = 2 \cos (2x + 3).$$

Example 19-4. Find $D_x \sin^2 x$.

Solution. Here we use the Power Formula $D_x u^r = r u^{r-1} D_x u$, with $u = \sin x$ and $r = 2$. Thus

$$D_x(\sin x)^2 = 2 \sin x D_x \sin x = 2 \sin x \cos x = \sin 2x.$$

Example 19-5. Show that the slope of the graph of the equation $y = x - \sin x$ is never negative.

Solution. Since the slope of the graph of an equation $y = f(x)$ at any point (x, y) is given by $y' = f'(x)$, we must compute y':

$$y' = D_x(x - \sin x) = 1 - \cos x.$$

Since $\cos x \leq 1$, $y' = 1 - \cos x \geq 0$.

Problems 19

1. Find y' if:

(a) $y = \sin \sqrt{x}$ (b) $y = \sin x^2$

(c) $y = \sqrt{\sin x}$ (d) $y = \sin (x^2 + 1)$

(e) $y = \sin (3t + 2)$ (f) $y = \sin \pi(2t - 1)$

(g) $y = \sin \sqrt{2t + 3}$ (h) $y = \sin \sqrt[3]{2t^2 + 1}$
(i) $y = \sin 2x + \sin x$ (j) $y = (\sin 2x)(\sin x)$
(k) $y = \sin 3x + \sin 2$ (l) $y = \sin \dfrac{1}{x^2}$

2. Use trigonometric formulas to express $f(x)$ in terms of values of the sine function and then find $f'(\pi/3)$.
(a) $f(x) = 2 \sin x \cos x$ (b) $f(x) = \cos^2 x - \cos 2x$
(c) $f(x) = \cos^2 x$ (d) $f(x) = \csc^2 x$
(e) $f(x) = \tan x \cos x$ (f) $f(x) = \tan^2 x$
(g) $f(x) = \cot x \sec x$ (h) $f(x) = (1 + \cos 2x)$

3. Find

$$\lim_{h \to 0} \frac{\sin\left(\frac{3\pi}{2} + h\right) + 1}{h}.$$

(*Hint:* Let $f(x) = \sin x$, and write out the definition of $f'(3\pi/2)$.)

4. Find the equations of the tangent line and normal line to the sine curve at the point: (a) $(0, 0)$; (b) $\left(\frac{\pi}{4}, \frac{\sqrt{2}}{2}\right)$; (c) $\left(\frac{\pi}{2}, 1\right)$.

5. Find a point of the sine curve at which the tangent line is parallel to the line $x + 2y + 3 = 0$.

6. Find a point of the sine curve at which the normal line is parallel to the line $2x + y + 3 = 0$.

7. Let c be any number and $y = \sin(x + c)$. Show that $(y')^2 + y^2 = 1$.

8. If the displacement of a body is related to the time by the equation $s = A \sin(bt + c)$, then the motion of the body is termed *simple harmonic motion* (A, b, and c are given numbers). Find the velocity in simple harmonic motion.

9. Let $f(x) = |\sin x|$. Discuss the derived function f' for x in the interval $(-\pi/2, \pi/2)$.

10. The sine function is a periodic function with period 2π. Notice that the derived function of the sine function (the cosine function) is again a periodic function with the same period. In general, suppose f is a differentiable periodic function with period p. Show that $f'(x + p) = f'(x)$.

11. The sine function is an odd function, and its derived function is an even function. Suppose that f is an odd function; that is, $f(-x) = -f(x)$ for each number x, and that g is an even function; that is, $g(-x) = g(x)$ for each number x. Show that f' is an even function and that g' is an odd function.

12. Let $\sin \theta°$ and $\cos \theta°$ denote the sine and cosine of an angle that measures θ degrees. Show that $D_\theta \sin \theta° = \dfrac{\pi}{180} \cos \theta°$.

20. Differentiation Formulas for the Trigonometric Functions

In the preceding section we found that

$$\mathbf{D_x \sin u = \cos u \, D_x u.} \tag{20-1}$$

We can use this formula, various trigonometric identities, and some of our general rules of differentiation to find the derived functions of the other trigonometric functions.

To find the derivative of $\cos x$ we use the identity

$$\cos x = \sin\left(\frac{\pi}{2} - x\right).$$

Therefore $D_x \cos x = D_x \sin\left(\frac{\pi}{2} - x\right)$, and we can find the derivative on the right by setting $u = \frac{\pi}{2} - x$ in Equation 20-1. Thus we have

$$D_x \cos x = \cos\left(\frac{\pi}{2} - x\right) D_x\left(\frac{\pi}{2} - x\right) = -\cos\left(\frac{\pi}{2} - x\right).$$

Since $\cos\left(\frac{\pi}{2} - x\right) = \sin x$,

(20-2) $$\boldsymbol{D_x \cos x = -\sin x.}$$

Now that we have found the derivatives of $\sin x$ and $\cos x$, it is a simple matter to find the derivatives of $\tan x$, $\cot x$, $\sec x$, and $\csc x$. For example, we find the derivative of $\tan x$ by applying the rule for differentiating a quotient (Equation 18-8) to the right side of the trigonometric identity $\tan x = \frac{\sin x}{\cos x}$.

Thus

$$\begin{aligned} D_x \tan x &= D_x\left(\frac{\sin x}{\cos x}\right) \\ &= \frac{\cos x D_x \sin x - \sin x D_x \cos x}{\cos^2 x} \\ &= \frac{\cos^2 x + \sin^2 x}{\cos^2 x} = \frac{1}{\cos^2 x}. \end{aligned}$$

So we find that

(20-3) $$\boldsymbol{D_x \tan x = \sec^2 x.}$$

It is easy to derive the following formulas by the same kind of reasoning:

(20-4) $$\boldsymbol{D_x \cot x = -\csc^2 x,}$$

(20-5) $$\boldsymbol{D_x \sec x = \sec x \tan x,}$$

(20-6) $$\boldsymbol{D_x \csc x = -\csc x \cot x.}$$

For example, we find the derivative of $\sec x$ by first writing $D_x \sec x = D_x(\cos x)^{-1}$. Then we apply the Power Formula $D_x u^r = ru^{r-1}D_x u$, with $r = -1$ and $u = \cos x$. We have just seen that $D_x \cos x = -\sin x$, so the Power Formula gives us

$$D_x(\cos x)^{-1} = -(\cos x)^{-2}(-\sin x) = \frac{\sin x}{\cos^2 x} = \frac{\tan x}{\cos x} = \sec x \tan x,$$

as stated in Equation 20-5.

We may incorporate these new differentiation formulas into the Chain Rule. Thus, for example, if $y = \cos u$, where $u = g(x)$, we have $D_u y = -\sin u$, so the Chain Rule Equation $D_x y = D_u y D_x u$ becomes

(20-7) $$\boldsymbol{D_x \cos u = -\sin u\, D_x u.}$$

The corresponding formulas for our other differentiation rules are

(20-8) $$\boldsymbol{D_x \tan u = \sec^2 u\, D_x u,}$$

(20-9) $$\boldsymbol{D_x \cot u = -\csc^2 u\, D_x u,}$$

(20-10) $$\boldsymbol{D_x \sec u = \sec u \tan u\, D_x u,}$$

(20-11) $$\boldsymbol{D_x \csc u = -\csc u \cot u\, D_x u.}$$

Example 20-1. If $f(x) = \csc \frac{1}{x}$, find $f'\left(\frac{2}{\pi}\right)$.

Solution. According to Equation 20-11, with $u = \frac{1}{x}$, we have

$$D_x \csc \frac{1}{x} = -\csc \frac{1}{x} \cot \frac{1}{x} D_x \frac{1}{x} = -\left(\csc \frac{1}{x} \cot \frac{1}{x}\right)\left(-\frac{1}{x^2}\right).$$

Therefore, $f'(x) = \frac{1}{x^2} \csc \frac{1}{x} \cot \frac{1}{x}$, and so

$$f'\left(\frac{2}{\pi}\right) = \left(\frac{\pi}{2}\right)^2 \csc \frac{\pi}{2} \cot \frac{\pi}{2} = 0.$$

Example 20-2. Find the points of the graph of the equation $y = x + \cot x$ at which the tangent line is horizontal.

Solution. With the help of our differentiation formulas, we see that

$$y' = 1 - \csc^2 x = -\cot^2 x.$$

The slope of the tangent line is y', so the tangent line is horizontal at those points where $y' = 0$. To find those points, we must therefore solve the equation

$$-\cot^2 x = 0.$$

The solutions to this last equation are $x = \pi/2 + k\pi$, where k can be any integer—positive, negative or zero. Thus the points where the tangent line is horizontal are the points

$$(\pi/2 + k\pi, \pi/2 + k\pi).$$

A graph of the equation $y = x + \cot x$ is shown in Fig. 20-1.

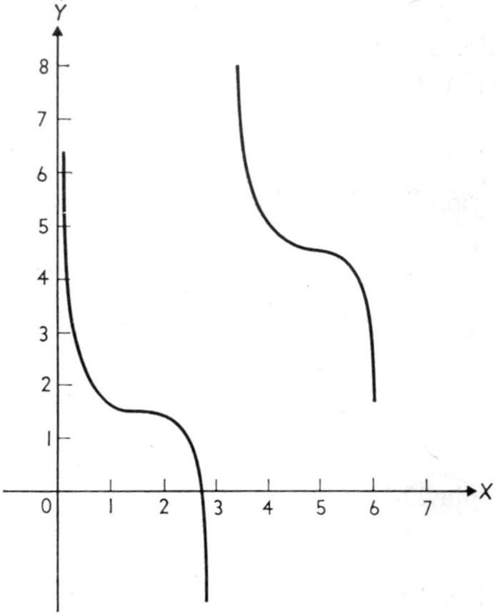

Figure 20-1

Problems 20

1. Find $D_x y$ if:
   (a) $y = \cos(2x - 3)$
   (b) $y = \tan^2 x$
   (c) $y = \sec x^2$
   (d) $y = \tan x^2$
   (e) $y = \cot \sqrt{x}$
   (f) $y = \sqrt{\cot x}$
   (g) $y = \sec x \tan x$
   (h) $y = \sec^2 x \tan^3 x$
   (i) $y = 2 \cos 3x - 3 \cos 2x$
   (j) $y = (\cos 3x)(\cos 2x)$
   (k) $y = \tan 2x \sin^2 x$
   (l) $y = \cot 2x \cos x^2$
   (m) $y = \sqrt{\cos 2x}$
   (n) $y = \sqrt[3]{\sec^2 2x}$
   (o) $y = \csc^2 x^2$
   (p) $y = \cot^2 x^3$
   (q) $y = x \sin x + \cos x$
   (r) $y = x^2 \sin \pi x^2$
   (s) $y = \sin(\cos x)$
   (t) $y = \sin^2(\cos^2 x^2)$
2. Derive Formula 20-4.
3. Derive Formula 20-6.
4. Show that there are no points of the graph of the equation $y = \sec x - \tan x$ at which the tangent line is horizontal.

5. Calculate each of the following derivatives in two ways:
   (a) $D_x(\cos^2 x + \sin^2 x)$ (b) $D_x(\sin^2 x - 1)$
   (c) $D_x \tan 2x$ (d) $D_x \cos 2x$
6. Differentiate both sides of the identity $\sin 2x = 2 \sin x \cos x$ to obtain an identity involving $\cos 2x$.
7. Show that if $y = \tan x$, then $y' \sin 2x = 2y$.
8. Find the points of the graph of the equation $y = \tan(\pi x - 4)$ at which the tangent line is parallel to the line $y = \pi x - 4$.
9. A point P moves along a circle of radius 1 whose center is the origin at the rate of 1 rpm. Let Q denote the point at which the tangent to the circle at P intersects the X-axis. How fast is the point Q moving along the X-axis when Q is 2 units to the right of the origin?

21. The Theorem of the Mean

There are all kinds of functions, and their graphs can have all sorts of shapes. The graph of the function of Example 5-1 (Fig. 5-1) consists of just 4 points; the graph of the greatest integer function (Fig. 5-5) is a series of steps, and so on. Most of the time in our study of calculus we will be concerned with functions whose graphs are "smooth" (see Fig. 21-1, for example). In this section we will state some properties possessed by the graphs of the "well-behaved" functions we study in calculus.

In Section 13 we saw that a function f **is continuous at a point** x of its domain if

$$\lim_{h \to 0} f(x + h) = f(x). \tag{21-1}$$

The function f is **continuous in an interval** if it is continuous at every point in the interval. If the point x is an end-point of an interval, the limit in Equation 21-1 is understood to be a limit from the right or from the left, whichever is appropriate.

These analytic definitions of continuity do not convey a great deal of meaning to the beginning student of calculus. But we can give a rough geometrical description of how the continuity of a function shows up in its graph. Roughly speaking, *the graph of a function that is continuous in an interval has no "breaks" in the interval.* Thus the greatest integer function is not continuous in the interval (0, 2)—its graph has a break at $x = 1$. But the greatest integer function *is* continuous in the interval $[\frac{1}{4}, \frac{3}{4}]$—its graph in that interval has no breaks. The function whose graph is shown in Fig. 21-3 is discontinuous at $x = 0$, and we notice that its graph has a break there. We shall have to use many properties of continuous functions in this book. One of the most important is stated in the following theorem.

THEOREM 21-1 (**The Intermediate Value Theorem**). *If a function f is continuous in an interval $[a, b]$ and if $f(a)$ and $f(b)$ have opposite signs, then there is at least one number c in the interval (a, b) such that $f(c) = 0$.*

An analytic proof of this theorem is somewhat complicated. Graphically, the theorem simply says that if the points $(a, f(a))$ and $(b, f(b))$ are on opposite sides of the X-axis, and if the graph of f has no breaks, then the graph must intersect the X-axis at some point between a and b.

We saw (Theorem 13-5) that if a function f is differentiable at a point, then it is continuous at the point. So the graphs of differentiable functions have no breaks. But we can say more about the graph of a differentiable function. The **Theorem of the Mean** (also called the **Mean Value Theorem**), which we will now state, is one of the most useful theorems in calculus. Like Theorem 21-1, the Theorem of the Mean is "obvious" on geometrical grounds and its analytic proof can well be left to a course in advanced calculus.

THEOREM 21-2 (**The Theorem of the Mean**). *Suppose a function f is differentiable in an open interval (a, b) and continuous in the closed interval $[a, b]$. Then there exists at least one point c in the interval (a, b) such that*

$$\frac{f(b) - f(a)}{b - a} = f'(c). \qquad (21\text{-}2)$$

Figure 21-1 will help us interpret this theorem. In this figure the graph of a function f is shown for an interval $[a, b]$. The quotient on the left side of Equation 21-2 is the slope of the chord joining the end points $(a, f(a))$ and $(b, f(b))$ of the graph. The number $f'(c)$ is the slope of the tangent line at the point of the graph of f where $x = c$. Thus the Theorem of the Mean asserts that there is at least one point at which the slope of the tangent line to the graph is equal to the slope of the chord joining the end points of the graph. In short, *there exists a point at which the tangent line is parallel to this chord.* In Fig. 21-1 we see that there are *two* points at which the tangent line is parallel to the

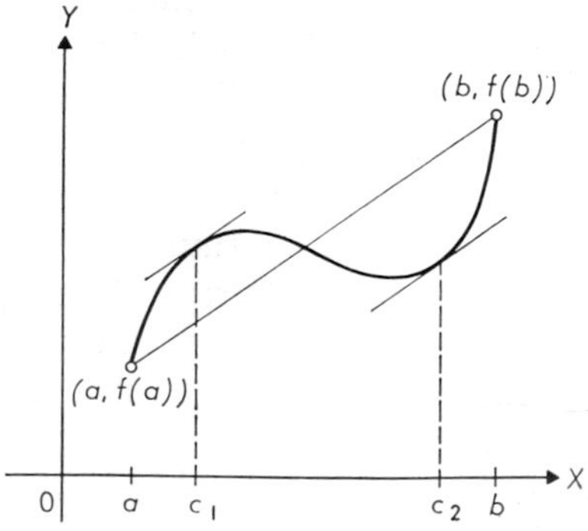

Figure 21-1

chord joining the end points, and hence we can choose either c_1 or c_2 for the number c. For other functions there may be 5, 100, or even infinitely many choices for c. But if the conditions of the Theorem of the Mean are satisfied, then there must be *at least one choice for c.*

You might look at a few familiar graphs, such as the graphs of the trigonometric functions, to see how the Theorem of the Mean applies to them. Figures 21-2 and 21-3 illustrate cases in which the Theorem of the Mean does not apply. In Fig. 21-2 we have drawn the graph of the

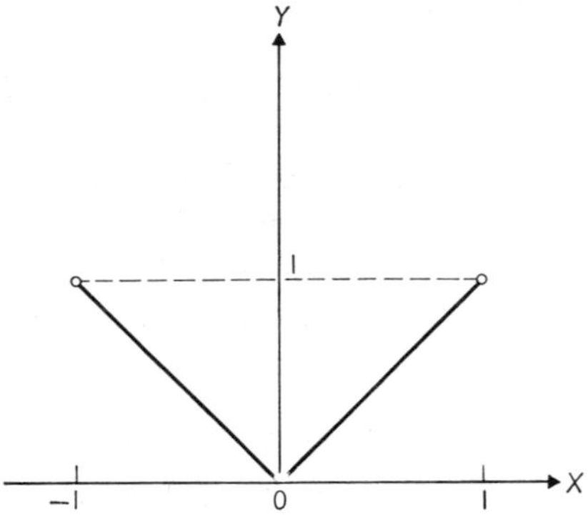

Figure 21-2

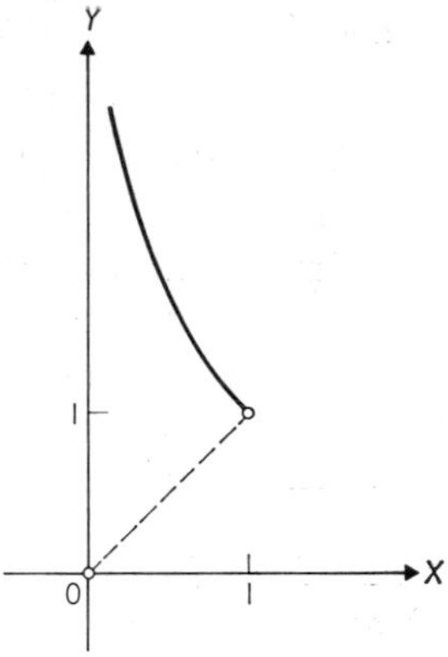

Figure 21-3

absolute value function ($f(x) = |x|$) in the interval $[-1, 1]$. The line joining the end points of this curve is parallel to the X-axis, but the curve has no tangent line parallel to the X-axis. This fact does not contradict the Theorem of the Mean since the absolute value function doesn't satisfy the hypotheses. Specifically, the hypotheses require that $f'(x)$ exist everywhere in the interval (a, b), and for the absolute value function $f'(0)$ does not exist. If we let $g(x) = 1/x$ for $0 < x \leq 1$ and $g(0) = 0$, we have defined the function g whose graph is shown in Fig. 21-3. This function is differentiable at every point in the open interval $(0, 1)$, but g is not continuous at $x = 0$. The hypotheses of Theorem 21-2 are not fulfilled, and the conclusion doesn't hold as you can see by trying to imagine a line tangent to the curve and parallel to the line joining $(0, 0)$ and $(1, 1)$.

Now let us look at an example to which the Theorem of the Mean does apply.

Example 21-1. Let $f(x) = x^3$, $a = 1$, and $b = 3$. Find a number c in the interval $(1, 3)$ such that Equation 21-2 is satisfied.

Solution. Here the number c must satisfy the equation

$$\frac{f(3) - f(1)}{3 - 1} = f'(c). \tag{21-3}$$

Since $f(x) = x^3$, we have $f'(x) = 3x^2$, and therefore Equation 21-3 becomes

$$\frac{3^3 - 1^3}{3 - 1} = 3c^2.$$

Thus

$$\tfrac{26}{2} = 3c^2$$

and

$$c^2 = \tfrac{13}{3}.$$

It follows that the only choice of c in the interval $(1, 3)$ is $c = \sqrt{\frac{13}{3}} = 2.08$.

An important special case of the Theorem of the Mean arises when a and b are points at which the value of the function is the same; that is, $f(a) = f(b)$. In this case the left side of Equation 21-2 is zero, so $f'(c) = 0$. This special case of the Theorem of the Mean is known as **Rolle's Theorem.**

THEOREM 21-3 (**Rolle's Theorem**). *If f is differentiable in the interval (a, b) and continuous in the closed interval $[a, b]$, and if $f(a) = f(b)$, then there exists at least one number c in the interval (a, b) such that $f'(c) = 0$.*

Rolle's Theorem is an obvious consequence of the Theorem of the Mean. Although it is not so obvious, it is nevertheless easy to show (if you know the trick) that the Theorem of the Mean is a consequence of Rolle's Theorem (see Exercise 10 at the end of this section).

Example 21-2. If $f(x) = \sqrt{x}\,(x^3 - 1)$, then $f(0) = f(1) = 0$. Find a number c such that $0 < c < 1$ and $f'(c) = 0$.

Solution. Since we may write

$$f(x) = x^{7/2} - x^{1/2},$$

we see that

$$f'(x) = \tfrac{7}{2}x^{5/2} - \tfrac{1}{2}x^{-1/2}.$$

Thus we seek a solution to the equation

$$\tfrac{7}{2}c^{5/2} - \tfrac{1}{2}c^{-1/2} = 0.$$

This equation simplifies to $c^3 = \frac{1}{7}$, and the only real number that satisfies this last equation is $c = \sqrt[3]{\frac{1}{7}} = .52$. This number lies in the interval $(0, 1)$, as it should.

Example 21-3. Use the Theorem of the Mean to find an approximate value of $\sqrt{101}$.

Solution. Let $f(x) = \sqrt{x}$, and let $a = 100$ and $b = 101$ in Equation 21-2. Here $f'(x) = \dfrac{1}{2\sqrt{x}}$, so the Theorem of the Mean tells us that there is a number c such that $100 < c < 101$ and

$$\frac{\sqrt{101} - \sqrt{100}}{101 - 100} = \frac{1}{2\sqrt{c}}.$$

On simplifying this last equation we have

$$\sqrt{101} = 10 + \frac{1}{2\sqrt{c}}.$$

Now since $100 < c < 101$, then $10 < \sqrt{c} < \sqrt{101}$, so that

$$20 < 2\sqrt{c} < 2\sqrt{101} = \sqrt{404} < \sqrt{441} = 21.$$

Therefore

$$\frac{1}{21} < \frac{1}{2\sqrt{c}} < \frac{1}{20}.$$

Thus $\sqrt{101}$ is a number between $10 + \frac{1}{21}$ and $10 + \frac{1}{20}$, or in terms of decimals,

$$10.047 < \sqrt{101} < 10.050.$$

So we know that if we take $\sqrt{101} = 10.05$, our error will be less than .003.

Example 21-4. Show that the equation $x^5 + 2x^3 - 5x - 10 = 0$ has exactly one solution that lies in the interval $(1, 2)$.

Solution. Let $f(x) = x^5 + 2x^3 - 5x - 10$. We are to show that f has one zero, and no more, in the interval $(1, 2)$. To show that f has at least one zero, we will use Theorem 21-1. Our function is continuous, and we readily see that $f(1) = -12$ and $f(2) = 28$. Therefore, according to Theorem 21-1, there must be at least one number a between 1 and 2 such that $f(a) = 0$. Thus we infer that f has *at least one* zero in the interval $(1, 2)$. Actually, our function has *just one zero*. For suppose that there are two numbers a and b, where $1 < a < b < 2$ such that $f(a) = f(b) = 0$. Then, according to Rolle's Theorem, there is a number c, between a and b and hence between 1 and 2 such that $f'(c) = 5c^4 + 6c^2 - 5 = 0$. But you can easily see that if $c > 1$, then $5c^4 + 6c^2 - 5 > 0$. Hence there is no number c for which $f'(c) = 0$. Therefore we must reject the possibility that f has two zeros in the interval $(1, 2)$.

If f is a constant function, then it is easy to show that f' is the constant function with value zero (See Section 15). Thus, regardless of what the number k is, *if* $f(x) = k$ for every number x in some interval, *then* $f'(x) = 0$. Now let us look at the converse of this statement. Suppose we know that $f'(x) = 0$ for every number x in some interval. Can we therefore assert that f is a constant function; that is, that there is a number k such that $f(x) = k$ for every number x in the interval? The following theorem tells us that the answer to this question is yes.

THEOREM 21-4. *If $f'(x) = 0$ in some interval, then f is a constant function in that interval.*

Proof. To show that f is a constant function in our interval, we have to show that the value of f at any one point in the interval is the same as its value at any other point. Thus, if a and b are any two distinct points in our interval, we must show that $f(a) = f(b)$. Now according to the Theorem of the Mean, there is always a point c between the points a and b such that

$$\frac{f(b) - f(a)}{b - a} = f'(c).$$

But we are assuming that the only value of f' in the interval under consideration is the number 0. Hence $f'(c) = 0$, and therefore $f(b) = f(a)$.

Theorem 21-4 states that if $f'(x) = 0$ in some interval, then there is a number k such that $f(x) = k$ in that interval. From this fact it is easy to prove the following theorem.

THEOREM 21-5. *If f and g are two functions whose common domain is some interval, and at every point x in that interval $f'(x) = g'(x)$, then there is a number k such that $f(x) = g(x) + k$.*

Proof. Let $F(x) = f(x) - g(x)$. Then $F'(x) = f'(x) - g'(x) = 0$. Therefore it follows from Theorem 21-4 that there is a number k such that $F(x) = k$. Thus $f(x) - g(x) = k$, or $f(x) = g(x) + k$, as was to be shown.

The preceding theorem says that if two functions have equal derived functions, then they differ by a constant function. We shall make use of this theorem in an important way in our later work. The statement that $f'(x) = g'(x)$ means that the graphs of the functions f and g are "parallel." Any vertical line cuts the two graphs in points at which they have the same slope. Theorem 21-5 tells us that the two graphs therefore cut segments of equal lengths from such vertical lines (See Fig. 21-4).

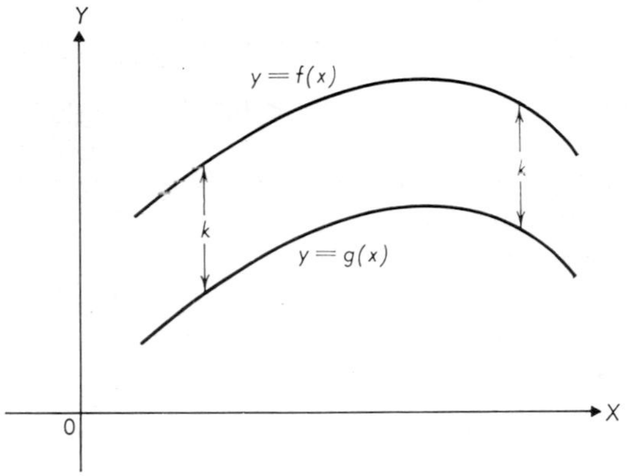

Figure 21-4

Problems 21

1. Use a graph to determine whether or not f is a continuous function in the interval $(-1, 1)$ if:
   (a) $f(x) = x\,|x|$ (b) $f(x) = x + |x|$
   (c) $f(x) = x - [\![x]\!]$ (d) $f(x) = [\![1 - |x|]\!]$
2. Find a number that can be chosen as the number c in the Theorem of the Mean if $f(x)$ and the interval $[a, b]$ are:
   (a) $f(x) = \sin x$, $[0, \pi]$ (b) $f(x) = x$, $[0, 1]$
   (c) $f(x) = x^2$, $[0, 1]$ (d) $f(x) = x^3$, $[0, 2]$
   (e) $f(x) = x^3 + 2x^2 + 1$, $[0, 3]$ (f) $f(x) = \sin x + \cos x$, $[0, 2\pi]$
3. In each of the following cases show that $f'(x) = g'(x)$. What is the relation between $f(x)$ and $g(x)$?
   (a) $f(x) = \sin^2 x$, $g(x) = -(\cos 2x)/2$
   (b) $f(x) = (x - 2)^2$, $g(x) = x(x - 4)$
   (c) $f(x) = x/(1 + x)$, $g(x) = -1/(1 + x)$
   (d) $f(x) = x(1 + x + x^2)$, $g(x) = (1 - x^4)/(1 - x)$
   (e) $f(x) = \sec^2 x$, $g(x) = \tan^2 x$
4. Suppose $f(x) = \log x$ and $g(x) = \log 3x$. What is the relation between $f'(x)$ and $g'(x)$?
5. Suppose that for every number x in the interval $(-2, 2)$ we know that $f'(x) = 0$. If $f(1) = 3$, what is $f(\frac{1}{2})$?
6. Suppose that, for every number $x \geq 0$, $D_x[10^x f(x)] = 0$. If $f(0) = 3$, what is $f(x)$?

7. Does the Theorem of the Mean apply to the tangent function in the interval $[0, \pi]$? Use a sketch to illustrate that the conclusion of the Theorem of the Mean is not true in this case.

8. Let $f(x) = [\![1 - |x|]\!]$ (see Exercise 1(d)). Does the Theorem of the Mean apply for the interval $[-1, 1]$? Is the conclusion of the Theorem of the Mean true in this case?

9. In Example 21-3 we showed that (i) $\sqrt{101} = 10 + \dfrac{1}{2\sqrt{c}}$, where c is a number such that (ii) $100 < c < 101$. We concluded that (iii) $10 + \frac{1}{21} < \sqrt{101} < 10 + \frac{1}{20}$. Now (ii) says that $10 < \sqrt{c} < \sqrt{101}$, and if we use Inequalities (iii) we see that $10 < \sqrt{c} < 10 + \frac{1}{20}$. From these inequalities and Equation (i) show that $10 + \frac{10}{201} < \sqrt{101} < 10 + \frac{1}{20}$. Thus $10.0497 < \sqrt{101} < 10.05$.

10. Let f be a function that satisfies the hypothesis of the Theorem of the Mean. Define the function G by means of the equation

$$G(x) = x[f(b) - f(a)] - f(x)[b - a].$$

Show that G satisfies the hypothesis of Rolle's Theorem, and apply Rolle's Theorem to obtain the Theorem of the Mean applied to f.

22. Derivatives of Higher Order

With a differentiable function f we associate its derived function f'. Now f' may very well be a differentiable function itself. That is, we may be able to associate with it another function $(f')'$—the derived function of f'. The derived function of f' is the **second derived function of f** and is denoted by f''. We have called $f'(x)$ the derivative of $f(x)$. We can call **$f'(x)$ the first derivative of $f(x)$** to distinguish it from the **second derivative $f''(x)$**. Just as we use the notation D_xy for the first derivative of y with respect to x, so the symbol D_x^2y represents the second derivative of y with respect to x, and so on.

Example 22-1. If $y = x^2 + \sin x$, find y''.

Solution. We calculate $y' = 2x + \cos x$ in the usual way. To find y'' we simply differentiate $2x + \cos x$. Thus $y'' = 2 - \sin x$.

We don't stop with the concept of second derivative, but consider third, fourth, and higher derivatives, as well. The derivative of $f''(x)$ is the third derivative of $f(x)$, which we write as $f'''(x)$. Similarly, $f^{\text{iv}}(x)$ is the fourth derivative of $f(x)$ (and, incidentally, the second derivative of $f''(x)$), and so on. The notation $f^{(n)}$ is also used to denote the derived function of order n of a given function f. Thus we obtain $f^{(12)}(x)$ by differentiating $f(x)$, differentiating the result, and so on, for a total of 12 differentiations.

Example 22-2. Find $D_x^4(x^2 \sin x)$.

Solution. We must perform four successive differentiations. First we find that

$$D_x(x^2 \sin x) = 2x \sin x + x^2 \cos x.$$

Then

$$\begin{aligned} D_x^2(x^2 \sin x) &= D_x(2x \sin x + x^2 \cos x) \\ &= 2 \sin x + 2x \cos x + 2x \cos x - x^2 \sin x \\ &= 2 \sin x + 4x \cos x - x^2 \sin x. \end{aligned}$$

Now

$$\begin{aligned} D_x^3(x^2 \sin x) &= D_x(2 \sin x + 4x \cos x - x^2 \sin x) \\ &= 2 \cos x + 4 \cos x - 4x \sin x - 2x \sin x - x^2 \cos x \\ &= 6 \cos x - 6x \sin x - x^2 \cos x. \end{aligned}$$

And finally,

$$\begin{aligned} D_x^4(x^2 \sin x) &= D_x(6 \cos x - 6x \sin x - x^2 \cos x) \\ &= -6 \sin x - 6 \sin x - 6x \cos x - 2x \cos x + x^2 \sin x \\ &= -12 \sin x - 8x \cos x + x^2 \sin x. \end{aligned}$$

Example 22-3. Find $D_x^{27} \sin x$.

Solution. Let us look at the first four of the indicated 27 differentiations.

$$\begin{aligned} D_x \sin x &= \cos x, \\ D_x^2 \sin x &= D_x \cos x = -\sin x, \\ D_x^3 \sin x &= D_x(-\sin x) = -\cos x, \\ D_x^4 \sin x &= D_x(-\cos x) = \sin x. \end{aligned}$$

These four differentiations lead us back to our starting point. Hence we conclude that $D_x^8 \sin x = \sin x$, $D_x^{12} \sin x = \sin x$, and so on, till finally $D_x^{24} \sin x = \sin x$. Now it is clear that $D_x^{27} \sin x = D_x^3 \sin x = -\cos x$.

In Section 14 we used the first derivative to measure rate of change. In particular, if a moving point is displaced s units of distance from a given reference point t time units from some initial instant, then D_ts measures the rate of change of distance with respect to time; that is, D_ts measures the velocity of the moving point. So we write $v = D_ts$. Now the second derivative of s with respect to t, D_t^2s, is equal to $D_t(D_ts) = D_tv$. Thus *D_t^2s measures the rate of change of velocity with respect to time.* This rate is called the **acceleration of the moving point.** For example, in the formula $s = 16t^2$ (the relation between displacement measured in feet and time measured in seconds for a body falling from rest near the surface of the earth) we see that $v = D_t s = 32t$ and $D_t^2 s = 32$. Thus the number 32 measures the acceleration of the body. Acceleration is measured in units of velocity per unit of time, so the acceleration of our falling body is 32 feet per second per second.

Example 22-4. If a point moves along a line in such a way that its displacement s from some reference point after t units of time have elapsed is given by the formula $s = A \sin (at + b)$, then we call the motion of the point **simple harmonic motion.** Show that the acceleration of the point is proportional to its displacement.

Solution. We are to show that the acceleration $D_t^2 s$ and the displacement s are related by an equation of the form $D_t^2 s = ks$, for some number k. You may readily verify that $D_t s = aA \cos (at + b)$, and $D_t^2 s = -a^2 A \sin (at + b)$. Thus $D_t^2 s = -a^2 s$, so the number $-a^2$ is our constant of proportionality and our assertion is verified.

Example 22-5. Let $y = \sin x^2$. Show that $xy'' - y' + 4x^3 y = 0$. (This latter equation is called a **differential equation,** and we say that if $y = \sin x^2$, then y *satisfies* the given differential equation.)

Solution. We have $y' = 2x \cos x^2$, and $y'' = 2 \cos x^2 - 4x^2 \sin x^2$. Thus

$$\begin{aligned} xy'' - y' + 4x^3 y &= x(2 \cos x^2 - 4x^2 \sin x^2) - 2x \cos x^2 + 4x^3 \sin x^2 \\ &= 0. \end{aligned}$$

Problems 22

1. Find y'' if:

   (a) $y = x^3 - 2x^2 + 5$ (b) $y = x + \dfrac{1}{x}$

   (c) $y = \dfrac{1 - x}{1 + x}$ (d) $y = \dfrac{1 - x^2}{1 + x^2}$

   (e) $y = (1 - \sqrt{x})^2$ (f) $y = \cos x^2$

   (g) $y = \sqrt{x} + \dfrac{1}{\sqrt{x}}$ (h) $y = \sqrt[3]{x^2 + 1}$

   (i) $y = \dfrac{x^3}{x^2 - 1}$ (j) $y = \sec^2 x^2$

   (k) $y = \dfrac{x}{\sqrt{x - 1}}$ (l) $y = \sqrt{\cot x^3}$

2. Find $f''(x)$ if:

   (a) $f(x) = \sin 2x$ (b) $f(x) = \cos^2 x$
   (c) $f(x) = x^3 \cos x$ (d) $f(x) = (\sin x)/x$
   (e) $f(x) = x \sin (1/x)$ (f) $f(x) = x^2 \sin (1/x^2)$

3. Let $f(x) = x^{13}$. Show that

$$f^{(n)}(x) = \frac{13!}{(13-n)!}\,x^{13-n} \quad \text{for } n \leq 13.$$

Show that $f^{(n)}(x) = 0$ if $n > 13$.

4. Theorem 21-4 says that if $f'(x) = 0$ in some interval, then f is a constant function in that interval. Show that if $f''(x) = 0$ in an interval, then f is a linear function in the interval. What can you say if $f'''(x) = 0$ in an interval?

5. Show that $y = 3x^2 + 2x$ satisfies the differential equation $x^2y'' - 2xy' + 2y = 0$.

6. Determine k so that $y = \sec kx$ satisfies the differential equation $y'' + y = 2y^3$.

7. Show that if A and b are any numbers and $y = A \sin(x + b)$, then $y'' + y = 0$.

8. Show that if $y = t \sin t$, then $y^{\text{iv}} - y = -4 \cos t$.

9. State Rolle's Theorem as it applies to a derived function f'.

10. Show that $D_x^n \cos x = \cos(x + n\pi/2)$.

11. Show that $D_x^n \sin x = \sin(x + n\pi/2)$.

12. Show that $(uv)'' = u''v + 2u'v' + uv''$, and

$$(uv)''' = u'''v + 3u''v' + 3u'v'' + uv'''.$$

Do these formulas remind you of the Binomial Theorem? If so, see if you can guess the formula for $(uv)^{\text{iv}}$.

13. Suppose that $f(a) = f(b) = f'(a) = f'(b) = 0$. Show that there are at least two points in the interval (a, b) that are solutions to the equation $f''(x) = 0$. Illustrate this result with the function defined by the equation $f(x) = (x^2 - 1)^2$, in the interval $[-1, 1]$.

23. Increasing Functions. Concavity

Some students get little more from their study of calculus than an ability to find the derivatives of complicated expressions. But differentiation formulas, though important, are really little more than technical details. We study calculus in order to gain a better understanding of functional relationships, and one of the best ways to increase this understanding is to apply our knowledge of calculus to the graphs of functions. We will devote this section to some geometrical consequences of the Theorem of the Mean and a geometrical interpretation of the second derivative.

Figure 23-1 shows the graph of a function f, typical of the kind of functions we have in mind. Let us consider the motion of a point traveling along this curve from left to right. The point goes up as its X-coordinate increases from 0 to 2, and then down as its X-coordinate increases from 2 to 5. We say that f is *increasing* in the interval $(0, 2)$ and *decreasing* in the interval $(2, 5)$. We have the following formal definition.

Definition 23-1. *A function f is* **increasing in an interval** *if for any pair of points c and d in the interval such that $c < d$, we have $f(c) < f(d)$. Similarly, f is* **decreasing in the interval** *if for every pair of points c and d in the interval such that $c < d$, we have $f(c) > f(d)$.*

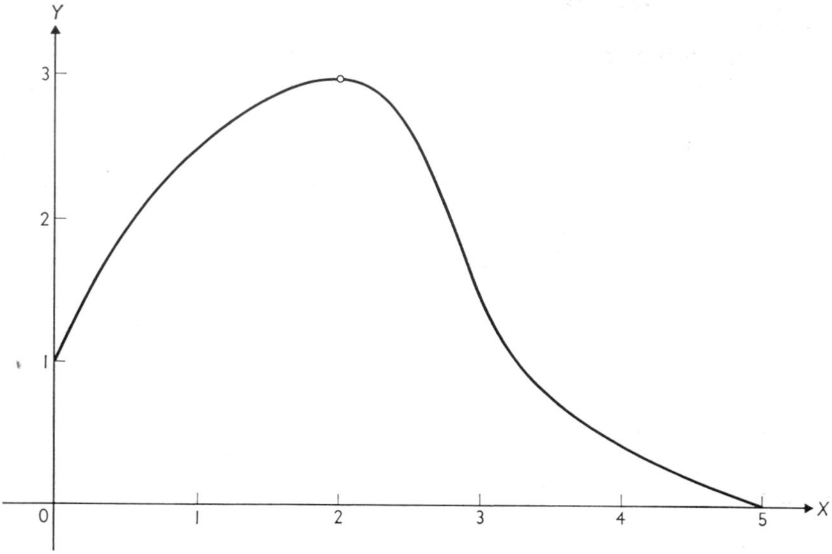

Figure 23-1

A glance at Fig. 23-1 shows that, according to this definition, f is increasing in the interval $(0, 2)$ and decreasing in the interval $(2, 5)$. Notice that if we consider the whole interval $(0, 5)$ we cannot say that f is either increasing or decreasing.

In more informal terms than we used in Definition 23-1, we say that *f is increasing if the graph of f "rises to the right," and f is decreasing if the graph of f "falls to the right."*

Now we will develop a simple test that shows if a given function f is increasing or decreasing. We first recall that the graph of a linear function f is a straight line, and we see immediately that if the line has a positive slope, then f is increasing. If the line has a negative slope, then f is decreasing. This same rule applies to functions in general, as we see from the following theorem.

Theorem 23-1. *If $f'(x) > 0$ at every point x in an interval (a, b), then f is increasing in (a, b). If $f'(x) < 0$ at every point x in an interval (a, b), then f is decreasing in (a, b).*

Proof. We shall only write out the proof for the first case and leave the other case for the problems. Thus we are assuming that $f'(x) > 0$ for every number x in our interval (a, b) and we are to show that this condition implies that if c and d are two numbers in (a, b) such that $c < d$, then $f(c) < f(d)$. Now, according to the Theorem of the Mean, there is a number k between c and d such that

$$\frac{f(d) - f(c)}{d - c} = f'(k).$$

Therefore, $f(d) - f(c) = f'(k)(d - c)$. We are assuming that all values of f' are positive and that $d - c$ is positive. Therefore the product $f'(k)(d - c) > 0$, and we see that $f(d) - f(c) > 0$; that is, $f(d) > f(c)$.

Example 23-1. Show that if $f(x) = 3x^3 + 2x - 7$, then f is increasing in any interval.

Solution. Since $f'(x) = 9x^2 + 2 > 0$ for any real number x, it follows from Theorem 23-1 that f is an increasing function in any interval.

Example 23-2. Determine the interval in which f is decreasing if $f(x) = 2x^3 + 3x^2 - 12x + 5$.

Solution. Here we have $f'(x) = 6x^2 + 6x - 12 = 6(x - 1)(x + 2)$. So Theorem 23-1 tells us that f is decreasing in intervals in which

$$(x - 1)(x + 2) < 0.$$

The product $(x - 1)(x + 2)$ is negative if, and only if, the factors $(x - 1)$ and $(x + 2)$ have opposite signs. Thus we are looking either for an interval in which $(x - 1)$ is positive and $(x + 2)$ is negative, or an interval in which $(x - 1)$ is negative and $(x + 2)$ is positive. We must rule out the first possibility, for if there were a number x such that $(x - 1)$ is positive and $(x + 2)$ is negative, then x would be both greater than 1 and less than -2. There is no such number x. However, we *can* find an interval in which $(x - 1) < 0$ and $(x + 2) > 0$. These two inequalities are equivalent to the inequalities $x < 1$ and $x > -2$, which hold when x is a number in the interval $(-2, 1)$. Thus we conclude that f is decreasing in the interval $(-2, 1)$.

Now let us see what information $f''(x)$ gives us. Since $f''(x)$ is the derivative of $f'(x)$, we know that it is the slope of the line tangent at the point $(x, f'(x))$ to the graph of f'. Therefore, according to Theorem 23-1, if $f''(x) > 0$ in some interval, then f' is increasing in that interval; that is, the graph of f' rises to the right. But what does the inequality $f''(x) > 0$ tell us about the graph of f itself? Figure 23-2 is meant to suggest an answer. Suppose that the points P_1, P_2, and P_3 are the points of the graph of f that correspond to numbers x_1, x_2, and x_3 such that $x_1 < x_2 < x_3$. Then, since f' is increasing, the tangent line at P_2 has a larger slope than the tangent line at P_1, and the tangent line at P_3 has a still larger slope. The segments we have drawn through P_1, P_2, P_3 show this behavior. Since a curve is closely approximated in a neighborhood of one of its points by the tangent line at the point, Fig. 23-2 suggests that our function f has a graph of the form shown in Fig. 23-3.

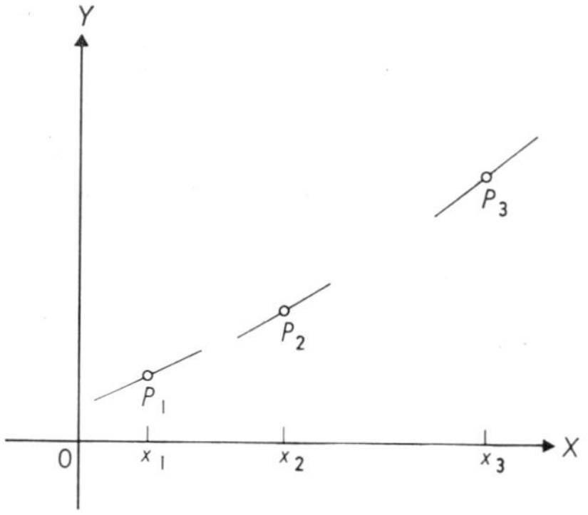

Figure 23-2

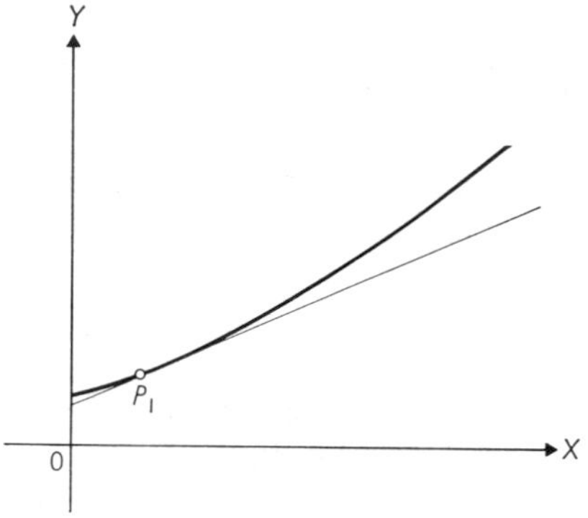

Figure 23-3

The arc in Fig. 23-3 has the following property: If we draw the tangent line at any point of the arc, then the entire arc (with the exception of the point of tangency) lies above the tangent line. Such an arc is said to be **concave up.** If an arc lies below every tangent line, then we say that the arc is **concave down.** The part of the curve in Fig. 23-1 for which $0 < x < 3$, for example, is concave down.

We were led to the arc shown in Fig. 23-3 by trying to find the geometrical implications of the inequality $f''(x) > 0$. Our informal analysis above suggests that the inequality implies that the graph of f is concave up, and the following theorem confirms this result. The proof of the theorem is rather long, but it gives us good practice in dealing with some of the fundamentals of calculus.

THEOREM 23-2. *If $f''(x) > 0$ at every point x in an interval (a, b), then the graph of f is concave up in (a, b). If $f''(x) < 0$ at every point x in an interval (a, b), then the graph of f is concave down in (a, b).*

Proof. We shall only write out the proof for the case $f''(x) > 0$. The case $f''(x) < 0$ is similar. You will want to refer to Fig. 23-4 as we proceed with the proof. We are to show that if we draw the tangent line at any point $(h, f(h))$, then the curve lies above this line. That is, a vertical line at a point k in our interval (a, b) will intersect the tangent line at a point P and the curve at a point Q, and we must show that P lies below Q. So if y_P is the Y-coordinate of P and y_Q is the Y-coordinate of Q, our goal is to demonstrate the truth of the inequality

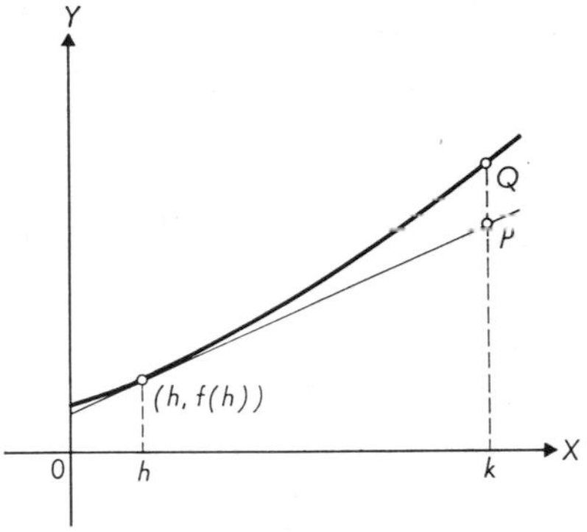

Figure 23-4

(23-1) $$y_P < y_Q.$$

Clearly $y_Q = f(k)$. To find y_P, we observe that the slope of the line joining P and $(h, f(h))$ is

$$\frac{y_P - f(h)}{k - h}.$$

But this line is the *tangent line* at $(h, f(h))$, so its slope is $f'(h)$. Therefore,

$$\frac{y_P - f(h)}{k - h} = f'(h),$$

and hence

$$y_P = f(h) + f'(h)(k - h).$$

Thus Inequality 23-1 becomes

$$f(h) + f'(h)(k - h) < f(k).$$

So our theorem will be proved if we can show that

(23-2) $$f'(h)(k - h) < f(k) - f(h).$$

Now, according to the Theorem of the Mean, there is a number c between h and k such that

(23-3) $$f(k) - f(h) = f'(c)(k - h).$$

Thus we must show that

(23-4) $$f'(h)(k - h) < f'(c)(k - h),$$

where c is a number between h and k. We must consider two possibilities. First, we suppose (as shown in Fig. 23-4) that $k > h$. Then we have $h < c < k$. But since $f''(x) > 0$, f' is increasing and therefore $f'(h) < f'(c)$. It follows that Inequality 23-4 is valid in this case. If, on the other hand, $k < h$, we have $k < c < h$, so $f'(c) < f'(h)$. Now multiplication by the negative number $k - h$ reverses this last inequality, and again we have Inequality 23-4.

Our results concerning the increasing and decreasing nature of a function and the concavity of its graph are summed up in the following table:

$f'(x) > 0$	f increasing
$f'(x) < 0$	f decreasing
$f''(x) > 0$	graph of f concave up
$f''(x) < 0$	graph of f concave down

Example 23-3. Discuss the graph of the equation $y = \frac{1}{2}x + \sin x$ for x in the interval $[0, 2\pi]$.

Solution. We can get quite a bit of information about our graph by considering the derivatives

$$D_xy = \tfrac{1}{2} + \cos x \quad \text{and} \quad D_x^2y = -\sin x.$$

From the first of these equations we find that for $0 < x < 2\pi/3$ and for

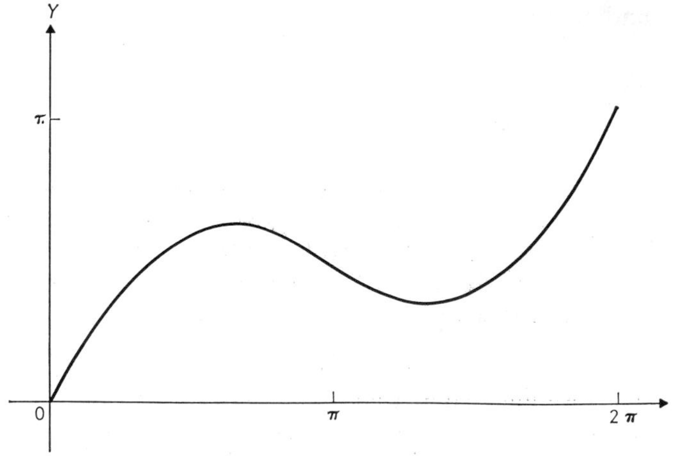

Figure 23-5

$4\pi/3 < x < 2\pi$ we have $D_x y > 0$, so the curve rises to the right. For $2\pi/3 < x < 4\pi/3$ the derivative is negative and the curve falls to the right. We see that $D_{xy}^2 y < 0$ in the interval $(0, \pi)$, and so the curve is concave down. For the interval $(\pi, 2\pi)$ we see that $D_{xy}^2 y > 0$, and so the curve is concave up. Using the preceding information and plotting a few points enables us to sketch the graph of our equation as shown in Fig. 23-5.

Example 23-4. Discuss the graph of the equation $y = x/(x + 1)$ for $x \geq 0$.

Solution. Here we find that $y' = (x + 1)^{-2}$ and $y'' = -2(x + 1)^{-3}$. Since $y' > 0$ and $y'' < 0$ for all $x \geq 0$, we see that the graph rises to the right and is concave down. Clearly, when $x = 0$, $y = 0$, and $y < 1$ for all values of x under consideration. If x is a large number, though, y is a number nearly equal to 1. The graph of our equation is shown in Fig. 23-6.

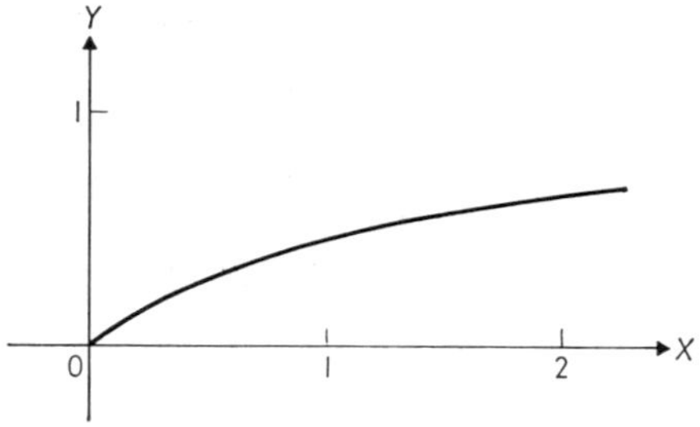

Figure 23-6

Problems 23

1. Find the intervals in which f is increasing and the intervals in which f is decreasing if:
   (a) $f(x) = x^3 - 6x^2 + 9x + 3$ (b) $f(x) = x^2 - 2x + 5$
   (c) $f(x) = \sin x \cos x$ (d) $f(x) = \cos^2 \frac{1}{2}\pi x$
   (e) $f(x) = \dfrac{1}{x}$ (f) $f(x) = \dfrac{1}{x^2}$
   (g) $f(x) = \tan 2x$ (h) $f(x) = \cot 2x$
   (i) $f(x) = x + \dfrac{1}{x}$ (j) $f(x) = x + \dfrac{4}{x^2}$
   (k) $f(x) = (x + 1)^2(x - 2)$ (l) $f(x) = |x| + |x - 1| + |x - 2|$
2. If $f''(x) > 0$ for every number x in the interval $[a, b]$, then we know from Theorem 23-2 that the graph of f lies above any tangent line. Show that the graph lies below the chord joining the points $(a, f(a))$ and $(b, f(b))$.

3. Discuss the concavity of the graphs of the following equations.

(a) $y = x^3 - 2x^2 + 5$ (b) $y = \sin x$

(c) $y = x^4 - 4x^3 + 6x^2 + 12x$ (d) $y = \dfrac{1}{x}$

(e) $y = x^4 - 2x^2$ (f) $y = \tan x$

(g) $y = x^4 - 4x^3 - 18x^2 + 12x - 9$ (h) $y = |x^2 - 1|$

4. In each case (i) find the intervals in which the function f is decreasing and the intervals in which it is increasing; (ii) investigate the concavity of the graph; (iii) sketch the graph of f.

(a) $f(x) = \sqrt[3]{x}$ (b) $f(x) = x^3 - 3x^2 - 9x + 1$

(c) $f(x) = -\sqrt{4 - x^2}$ (d) $f(x) = 24x^2 - x^4$

(e) $f(x) = x\sqrt{1 - x^2}$ (f) $f(x) = x^2 + \dfrac{1}{x}$

(g) $f(x) = \sin x + \sin 2x$ (h) $f(x) = \dfrac{6x}{x^2 + 3}$

5. Prove Theorem 23-1 when $f'(x) < 0$.

6. Prove Theorem 23-2 when $f''(x) < 0$.

Review Problems, Chapter Two

You can use the following problems to test yourself on the material covered in this chapter.

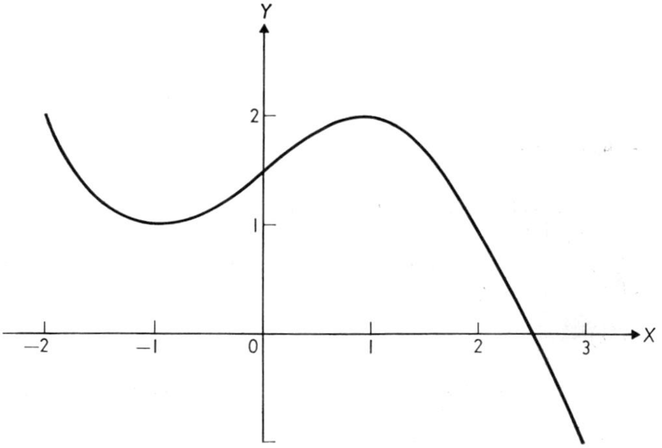

Figure II-3

The graph of a function f is shown in Fig. II-3. In the first four multiple-choice questions choose the answer that seems most nearly correct according to the figure.

1. The number $f'(2)$ is equal to:
(a) -2, (b) -1, (c) 0, (d) 1, (e) 2.
2. If $f'(x) \geq 0$, then x is in the interval
(a) [0, 3)], (b) $[-1, 1]$, (c) [1, 3], (d) $[-2, 2.5]$, (e) [2.5, 3].
3. If $f'(x) = 1$, then x is equal to
(a) -2, (b) -1, (c) 0, (d) 1, (e) 2.
4. If $f'(x) = 0$, then $|x|$ is equal to
(a) -2, (b) -1, (c) 0, (d) 1, (e) 2.
5. Let $f(x) = |x| + |x + 1|$. From the graph of f determine the points at which f is not differentiable.
6. Let $f(x) = \sqrt[3]{x^2}$. Write out the definition of $f'(x)$ in symbols. With the aid of this definition, find

$$\lim_{h \to 0} \frac{\sqrt[3]{(8 + h)^2} - 4}{h}.$$

7. If y is directly proportional to x^2, then y' is
(a) directly proportional to x, (b) inversely proportional to x,
(c) directly proportional to x^2, (d) inversely proportional to x^2,
(e) directly proportional to x^3.
8. If $f(u) = \dfrac{u^3}{1 - u}$, find $f'(2)$.
9. Find the best approximation to the slope of the tangent line to the sine curve at the point (1, sin 1) among the following numbers.
(a) $-.1$, (b) .1, (c) 1, (d) .5, (e) .8.
10. A point moving along a number scale is $s = 3 \sin (2t - 1)$ feet from the origin t seconds after some initial instant. Which of the following numbers most closely approximates the acceleration of the point when $t = 1$?
(a) 0, (b) -1, (c) 1, (d) -10, (e) 10
11. Find $D_t \sqrt{2t^{2/3} - 1}$.
12. Which of the following is an example of the Chain Rule Equation?
(a) $D_x y = D_x u\, D_y x$, (b) $D_u y = D_y u\, D_x y$, (c) $D_x y = D_y u\, D_u x$,
(d) $D_y x = D_u x\, D_y u$, (e) $D_x u = D_y u\, D_u x$.
13. Show that the rule $D_x(cu) = cD_x u$ is a consequence of the rule for differentiating a product and the fact that $D_x c = 0$.
14. Find the equation of the normal line at the origin to the curve $y = \sin x^4$.
15. Rolle's Theorem says that if f is a differentiable function in the interval (a, b) and is continuous in the interval $[a, b]$, and if _____, then there is a number c in the interval (a, b) such that _____.
16. Compute $D_x^2 \tan^2 x$.
17. If $y = \sqrt{\cos x}$, find y''.
18. If $f'(x) = g'(x)$ and $f(0) = g(0) + 1$, then $f(1) - g(1) =$ _____.
19. Find the interval(s) in which the function defined by the equation $y = \sqrt{1 - x^3}$ is a decreasing function. In what intervals is the graph of this equation concave down? Sketch the graph of the equation for the interval $[-2, 1]$.
20. Answer the questions in the preceding problem if $y = \frac{1}{5}(x^3 - 9x^2 + 24x - 7)$.

3 APPLICATIONS OF THE DERIVATIVE

Attempts to solve the problems that arise in natural science, from Newton's study of gravity to the present research in atomic physics, have required the development of suitable mathematical tools. Calculus ranks high among these mathematical tools, and it is easy to see why. In science we study relationships. For example, we might be interested in the relationship between the velocity of an earth satellite and its distance from the earth. We would ask such questions as, "At what distances is the velocity increasing, at what distances is it decreasing?" "At what distances is the velocity greatest, at what distances is it least?" Calculus can help us answer such questions.

In this chapter we will look at some of the simpler applications of calculus to geometry, and to some problems in natural science. Our object, obviously, is not to teach physics but to increase your understanding of calculus and its applications.

24. Curve Sketching

Calculus is a study of functions, and functions are represented geometrically by means of graphs. It helps us visualize the concepts of calculus if we use them in sketching the graphs of equations. So in this section we are going to see what some facts we already know can tell us about curves. These facts are:

(1) *The number y' is the slope of the tangent to the graph of the equation $y = f(x)$ at the point (x, y);*

(2) *The graph of f rises to the right in an interval in which $f'(x) > 0$ and falls to the right in an interval in which $f'(x) < 0$;*

(3) *The graph of f is concave up in an interval in which $f''(x) > 0$ and concave down in an interval in which $f''(x) < 0$.*

Example 24-1. Sketch the graph of the function f defined by the equation

$$f(x) = \frac{x^2}{8} - \frac{1}{x}.$$

Solution. For a given number x we calculate both the number

$$y = \frac{x^2}{8} - \frac{1}{x},$$

and the number

$$y' = \frac{x}{4} + \frac{1}{x^2}.$$

We have tabulated the results of some of these calculations in Fig. 24-1. In the coordinate system on the left side of Fig. 24-1 we have plotted the points in the table. In the coordinate system on the right we have drawn through each of the points (x, y) a short segment with slope y'. These segments are tangent to the graph of our function.

Next we calculate

$$y'' = \frac{1}{4} - \frac{2}{x^3} = 2\left(\frac{1}{8} - \frac{1}{x^3}\right).$$

From this equation we find that $y'' < 0$ if $0 < x < 2$, while $y'' > 0$ if $x < 0$ or if $x > 2$. Thus our curve will be concave up when $x < 0$ or when $x > 2$, and it will be concave down when x is in the interval $(0, 2)$. The curve therefore lies above the tangent lines for points to the left of the Y-axis and for points to the right of the vertical line $x = 2$. The curve lies below the tangent lines for points between the Y-axis and the vertical line $x = 2$. Figure 24-2 shows the graph of our function.

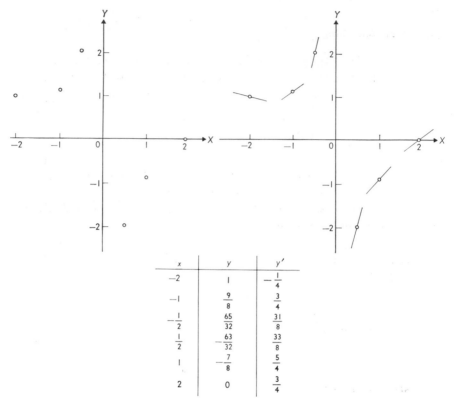

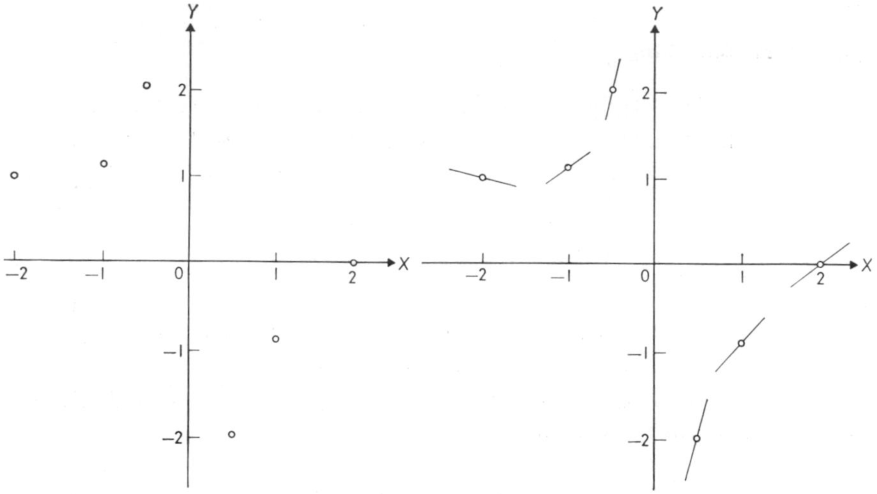

x	y	y'
-2	1	$-\frac{1}{4}$
-1	$\frac{9}{8}$	$\frac{3}{4}$
$-\frac{1}{2}$	$\frac{65}{32}$	$\frac{31}{8}$
$\frac{1}{2}$	$-\frac{63}{32}$	$\frac{33}{8}$
1	$-\frac{7}{8}$	$\frac{5}{4}$
2	0	$\frac{3}{4}$

Figure 24-1

In Fig. 24-2 we have labeled one point of the curve P. This point is "lower" (has a smaller Y-coordinate) than any other point "near" it. We call such a point a **minimum point.** Notice that we are only comparing the Y-coordinate of our minimum point with the Y-coordinates of points whose X-coordinates approximate the X-coordinates of P. There are points of the graph that are lower than P—for example, the point $(2, 0)$.

Now let us find the coordinates of our minimum point P. We see from the graph in Fig. 24-2 that the tangent line at P is horizontal; that is, has slope zero. Thus if the coordinates of P are (x, y), we see that $f'(x) = 0$. But $f'(x) = \frac{x}{4} + \frac{1}{x^2}$, so x satisfies the equation

$$\frac{x}{4} + \frac{1}{x^2} = 0.$$

It follows that $x^3 = -4$, and therefore $x = -\sqrt[3]{4} = -1.6$. Since

$f(-1.6) = \frac{(-1.6)^2}{8} + \frac{1}{1.6} = .95$, we see that the coordinates of P are $(-1.6, .95)$.

We have called the point P of Fig. 24-2 a minimum point because its Y-coordinate is smaller than the Y-coordinate of any point with a nearby X-coordinate. More precisely, we call a point (x_0, y_0) a **minimum point** of the graph of a function f if the following criterion is satisfied: *There must be an open interval of the X-axis that contains the point x_0, and for each number x different from x_0 in this interval, $f(x) > y_0$.* The number y_0 is called a *minimum value* of f. Similarly, we call a point (x_0, y_0) a **maximum point** of the graph of a function f if *there is an open interval of the X-axis that contains the point x_0, and for each number x different from x_0 in this interval, $f(x) < y_0$.* The number y_0 is called a *maximum value* of f. The point P of Fig. 24-2 is a minimum point according to this definition. For the open interval $(-2, -1)$ of the X-axis clearly contains the X-coordinate of P, and it is plain that the Y-coordinate of P is the smallest functional value that corresponds to any point x in the interval $(-2, -1)$. Of course, we could use other intervals, too; even the interval $(-\infty, 0)$ would do. All that we require is that we be able to find *some* open interval in which our inequality holds.

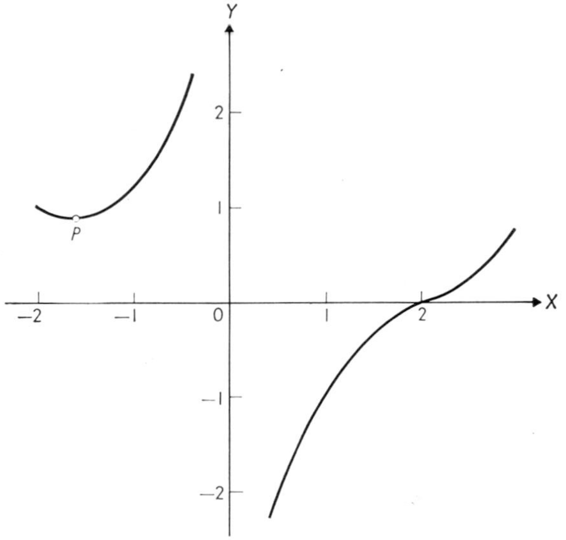

Figure 24-2

In Fig. 24-3 we have sketched the graph of a function f whose domain is the interval $(1, 6]$. This graph illustrates the "kinds" of maximum and minimum point you will meet. The points P and S are maximum points, and the points Q and T are minimum points. We will have more to say about how to find maximum and minimum points in the next section, but for now let us just see what the graph suggests.

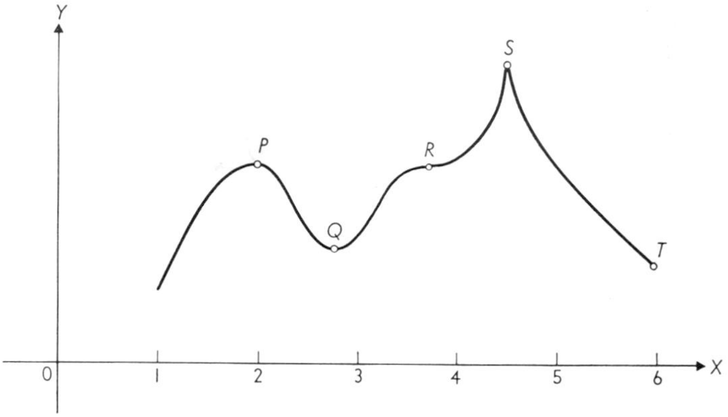

Figure 24-3

At the maximum point P and the minimum point Q the slope of the curve is 0. Thus the X-coordinates of these points satisfy the equation $f'(x) = 0$. So when we look for maximum or minimum points, we will certainly want to consider those points whose X-coordinates satisfy the equation $f'(x) = 0$. We mustn't jump to the conclusion that just because the X-coordinate of a point satisfies the equation $f'(x) = 0$, then the point is either a maximum or a minimum point; for example, the slope of our curve is 0 at the point R, even though R is neither a maximum nor a minimum point. If we confined our search for maximum and minimum points to those points whose X-coordinates satisfy the equation $f'(x) = 0$, we would miss the maximum point S and the minimum point T. The graph doesn't have a slope at S (so it cannot have slope 0 there), and the point T is an "end point."

The preceding remarks suggest that we look for maximum and minimum points of the graph of a function f among those points (x, y) such that

(1) $f'(x) = 0$,
(2) $f'(x)$ does not exist, or
(3) (x, y) is an end point of the curve.

Not all the points that satisfy one of the conditions (1), (2), or (3) need be maximum or minimum points; we have to test each point to see. These facts will become clearer to you as you study the examples that follow.

Example 24-2. Let $f(x) = 2x^2 - 8x + 1$. If the function f has maximum or minimum values, find them.

Solution. The domain of f is the open interval $(-\infty, \infty)$, and $f'(x)$ exists for all x. Thus there are no points satisfying conditions (2) or (3). Therefore, if f has maximum or minimum values, they occur at the points whose X-coordinates satisfy the equation $f'(x) = 4x - 8 = 0$. So the only possible maximum or minimum point occurs when $x = 2$. Since $f(2) = -7$, the point $(2, -7)$ is the only possible maximum or minimum point; but for all we know now, it may be either or neither. We have to check and see. In the next section we will develop criteria that make this check easier, but here we will show directly that we actually have a minimum point. We will show that there is an open interval that contains the point 2, and for each number x different from 2 in this interval, $2x^2 - 8x + 1 > -7$. It so happens that in this case *any* open interval that contains 2 will do. For suppose that x is any number other than 2. The $2x^2 - 8x + 1 = 2(x^2 - 4x + 4) + 1 - 8 = 2(x - 2)^2 - 7 = -7 + 2(x - 2)^2$. Since we are assuming that $x \neq 2$, we have $f(x) = -7 +$ (a positive number), and hence $f(x) > -7$. So we see that $(2, -7)$ is a minimum point of our graph and that the graph has no maximum points.

Example 24-3. Determine whether or not the graph of the equation $y = x^3 + 1$ has any maximum or minimum points.

Solution. Since the derivative y' exists at each point x, the maximum and minimum points, if any, occur among the points where $y' = 3x^2 = 0$. Thus the only possible maximum or minimum point is the point $(0, 1)$. Any open interval of the X-axis that contains the point 0 contains both positive and negative numbers. If x is a negative number, then $y = 1 + x^3 = 1 +$ (a negative number), so $y < 1$. On the other hand, if x is a positive number, then $y = 1 + x^3 = 1 +$ (a positive number), so $y > 1$. It follows that the point $(0, 1)$ is neither a maximum nor a minimum point of our graph, and hence the graph of the equation $y = x^3 + 1$ has no maximum or minimum points. The graph of this equation is shown in Fig. 24-4.

Example 24-4. Find the maximum and minimum points and sketch the graph of f if $f(x) = 2\sqrt{x} - x$.

Solution. We note that the domain of f consists of the interval $[0, \infty)$. The derivative exists at all points in $(0, \infty)$ and

$$f'(x) = \frac{1}{\sqrt{x}} - 1.$$

We see that the only solution to the equation $f'(x) = 0$ is $x = 1$, so the only possible maximum or minimum points are the points (0, 0) and (1, 1). We see that $f''(x) = -x^{-3/2}/2 < 0$, so the curve is concave down. These facts enable us to sketch the graph of f as shown in Fig. 24-5. It is clear from this graph that (0, 0) is a minimum point and (1, 1) is a maximum point.

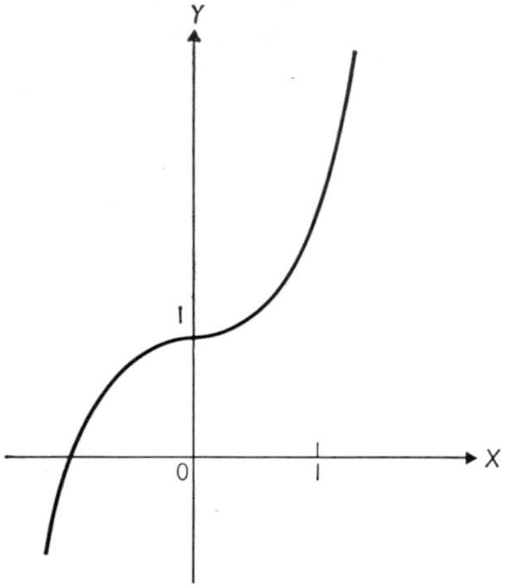

Figure 24-4

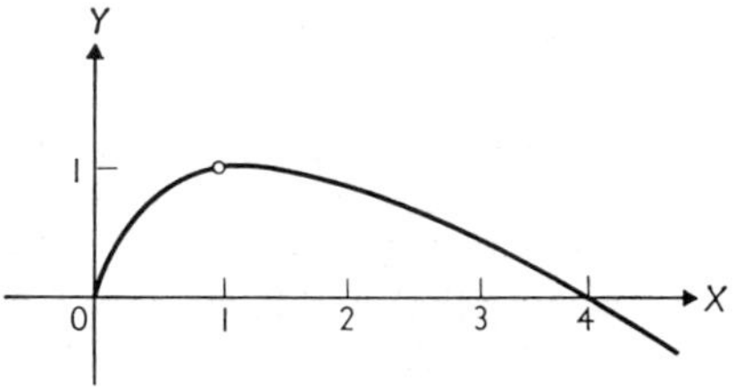

Figure 24-5

Problems 24

1. Let $y = x + \dfrac{1}{x}\cdot$ (a) Complete the following table.

x	-2	-1	$-\frac{1}{2}$	$\frac{1}{2}$	1	2
y						
y'						
y''						

(b) Discuss the concavity of the graph of the equation.
(c) Find the maximum and minimum points.
(d) Sketch the graph of the equation, showing the tangent lines at the points in the table.

2. Find the maximum and minimum points of the graphs of the following equations.
(a) $y = 3x^2 + 2x - 4$ (b) $y = x^2 - 1$
(c) $y = |x^2 - 1|$ (d) $y = |\sin x|$

3. Sketch the graphs of the following equations, making use of maximum and minimum points and information about concavity.

(a) $y = \sqrt{\dfrac{x^3}{2 - x}}$ (b) $y = x^2 + \dfrac{2}{x}$

(c) $y = (x - 1)^3(x - 3)$ (d) $y = 3x^4 - 4x^3 + 1$

(e) $y = \dfrac{x(x - 2)}{(x + 1)^2}$ (f) $y = (x - 1)^{2/3}$

4. Are there any points of the graph of the equation $y = 1 - (x - 1)^{4/5}$ at which the tangent line is horizontal? Are there any end points? Are there any maximum or minimum points?

5. Sketch the graphs of the following equations making use of maximum and minimum points and information about the concavity for x in the interval $[0, 2\pi]$.

(a) $y = (\sin x + 1)^2 - 1$ (b) $y = \cos^2 x + 2 \cos x$

6. Discuss completely the graph of the general quadratic equation $y = ax^2 + bx + c$.

7. Show that the graph of the equation $y = 3 \sin 2x + 5 \cos 2x$ is concave up when y is negative and concave down when y is positive.

8. Find the maximum and minimum points, discuss the concavity, and graph the equation

$$y = x^4 - 2x^3 - 12x^2 + 26x - 13.$$

25. First and Second Derivative Tests for Maxima and Minima

After studying Fig. 24-3, we concluded that if (x, y) is a maximum or a minimum point of the graph of a function f, then one of the following conditions must be true

(1) $f'(x) = 0$,

(2) $f'(x)$ does not exist, or

(3) (x, y) is an end point of the arc.

We will call a point at which one of conditions (1), (2), or (3) is satisfied a **critical point** of the graph of f. Maximum and minimum points must be critical points, but not every critical point need be a maximum or a minimum point.

The point P is a minimum point and Q is a maximum point of the graph shown in Fig. 25-1. The slope of the graph is negative at points just to the left of P and positive at points just to the right of P. The situation is reversed at the maximum point Q. The slope of the curve changes from positive to negative as we move to the right through the point Q. The slope of the curve is 0 at the point R, but it is negative for all other points near R. The point R is neither a maximum nor a minimum point. These simple observations suggest the following theorem.

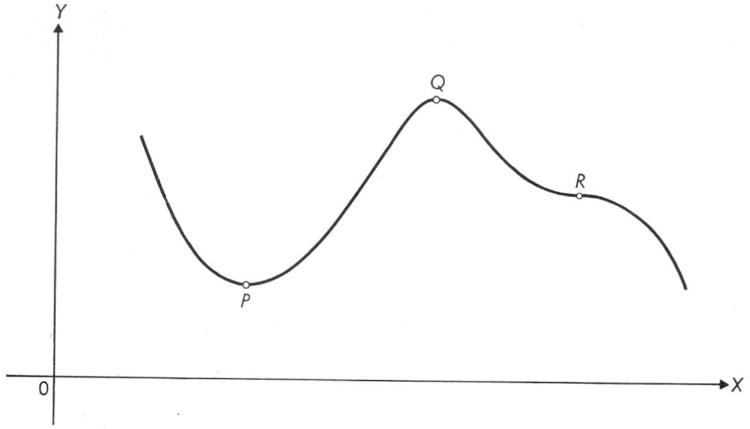

Figure 25-1

THEOREM 25-1. *Suppose that the function f is continuous at every point of an interval (a, b) and that $f'(x)$ exists at all points of (a, b), with the possible exception of one point x_0. Then*

(i) *$f(x_0)$ is a maximum value of f if $f'(x)$ is positive for x in the interval (a, x_0), and $f'(x)$ is negative for x in the interval (x_0, b).*

(ii) *$f(x_0)$ is a minimum value of f if $f'(x)$ is negative for x in the interval (a, x_0), and $f'(x)$ is positive for x in the interval (x_0, b).*

(iii) *$f(x_0)$ is neither a maximum nor a minimum value of f if $f'(x)$ has the same sign in the two intervals (a, x_0) and (x_0, b).*

We will call Theorem 25-1 the **First Derivative Test** for maximum and minimum points. Notice that we can apply this test at a point $(x_0, f(x_0))$ even when our function f is not differentiable there. We will delay the proof of this theorem until after we have looked at some examples of its application.

Example 25-1. Apply the First Derivative Test to the critical points of the graph of the function f, where $f(x) = 2x^2 - 8x + 1$.

Solution. In Example 24-2 we found that the point $(2, -7)$ is the only critical point of this graph. Since $f'(x) = 4x - 8 = 4(x - 2)$, we see that $f'(x) < 0$ when $x < 2$ and $f'(x) > 0$ when $x > 2$. These inequalities tell us that Statement (ii) of Theorem 25-1 applies. The point $(2, -7)$ is a minimum point.

Example 25-2. Use the First Derivative Test to examine the critical points of the graph of the equation $y = x^3 + 1$ (see Example 24-3).

Solution. Since $y' = 3x^2$, the only critical point of this graph is the point (0, 1). Now $3x^2 > 0$ when $x < 0$ or when $x > 0$, so Statement (iii) of Theorem 25-1 applies. The point (0, 1) is neither a maximum nor a minimum point.

Example 25-3. Find the maximum and minimum values of the function f if $f(x) = x^3 - 2x^2 + x$.

Solution. Here we have $f'(x) = 3x^2 - 4x + 1 = (x - 1)(3x - 1)$. The X-coordinates of the critical points satisfy the equation $f'(x) = 0$, and we see that they are the numbers $x = 1$ and $x = \frac{1}{3}$. You can easily verify that

(25-1) $$f'(x) = (x - 1)(3x - 1) > 0$$

when

$$x > 1 \quad \text{or} \quad x < \tfrac{1}{3},$$

and

$$f'(x) = (x - 1)(3x - 1) < 0$$

when

$$\tfrac{1}{3} < x < 1.$$

In Fig. 25-2 we have expressed in graphical form the information that Inequalities 25-1 furnish us about the sign of $f'(x)$. From Fig. 25-2 we immediately see that $f'(x)$ is positive for x just to the left of $\frac{1}{3}$ and

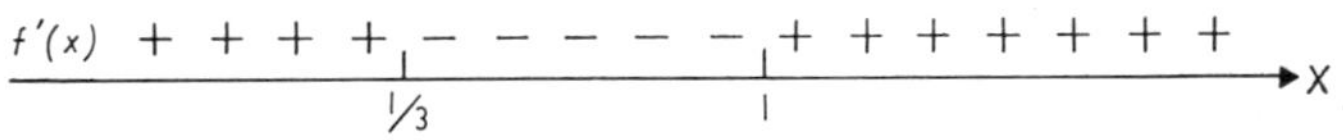

Figure 25-2

that $f'(x)$ is negative for x just to the right of $\frac{1}{3}$. Statement (i) of Theorem 25-1 therefore applies and tells us that $f(\frac{1}{3}) = \frac{4}{27}$ is a maximum value of f. The situation at the point $x = 1$ is just the opposite, and Satement (ii) of Theorem 25-1 says that $f(1) = 0$ is a minimum value of f.

Example 25-4. Examine the absolute value function f for maximum and minimum values.

Solution. Here $f(x) = |x|$ and so $f(x) = x$ when $x > 0$, and $f(x) = -x$ when $x < 0$. We therefore see that

$$f'(x) = 1 \text{ for } x > 0, \text{ and } f'(x) = -1 \text{ for } x < 0.$$

So $f'(x)$ is positive for x just to the right of 0, and $f'(x)$ is negative for x just to the left of 0. Statement (ii) of Theorem 25-1 applies and tells us that $f(0) = 0$ is a minimum value of the absolute value function.

Now we return to the proof of Theorem 25-1.

Proof. We shall prove only Statement (i) of Theorem 25-1; the proofs of Statements (ii) and (iii) follow the same pattern. To show that $f(x_0)$ is a maximum under the stated conditions, we will show that if x is a number such that $a < x < x_0$ or $x_0 < x < b$, then

$$f(x) < f(x_0). \tag{25-2}$$

Inequality 25-2 is, of course, equivalent to the inequality

$$f(x_0) - f(x) > 0. \tag{25-3}$$

Now let x be any number in the interval (a, x_0). According to the Theorem of the Mean, there is a number c such that $a < c < x_0$ for which $f(x_0) - f(x) = f'(c)(x_0 - x)$. We are assuming that the conditions of Statement (i) are fulfilled—in particular, that all values of f' corresponding to numbers in the interval (a, x_0) are positive. Since c is in this interval, $f'(c) > 0$. Also, $x_0 - x > 0$, so we have $f(x_0) - f(x) = f'(c)(x_0 - x) > 0$. It follows that Inequality 25-3 is satisfied. If x is a number in the interval (x_0, b), then, according to the Theorem of the Mean, there is a number d between x_0 and x such that $f(x) - f(x_0) = f'(d)(x - x_0)$. Since the conditions of Statement (i) are fulfilled, $f'(d) < 0$, and hence $f'(d)(x - x_0) < 0$. Thus $f(x) - f(x_0) < 0$, and again Inequality 25-3 is verified.

Another useful theorem that provides us with criteria for determining whether or not we have a maximum or minimum is the **Second Derivative Test.**

THEOREM 25-2. *If $f'(x_0) = 0$, then*
(i) *$f(x_0)$ is a maximum value of f if $f''(x_0) < 0$, and*
(ii) *$f(x_0)$ is a minimum value of f if $f''(x_0) > 0$.*
If $f''(x_0) = 0$, this test does not apply.

Example 25-5. Show how the Second Derivative Test applies to the function f of Example 25-3.

Solution. Here $f(x) = x^3 - 2x^2 + x$, $f'(x) = 3x^2 - 4x + 1$, and $f''(x) = 6x - 4$. Since $f'(1) = 0$ and $f''(1) = 6 - 4 = 2 > 0$, we see that Statement (ii) of Theorem 25-2 applies and tells us that $f(1)$ is a minimum value of f. We also see that $f'(\frac{1}{3}) = 0$ and $f''(\frac{1}{3}) = 2 - 4 = -2 < 0$, so Statement (i) of Theorem 25-2 tells us that $f(\frac{1}{3}) = \frac{4}{27}$ is a maximum value of f.

We shall just discuss the basic ideas of the proof of Theorem 25-2, leaving out the technical details (and we shall only discuss Statement (i) because the proof of Statement (ii) follows the same lines). From the definition of the derivative of $f'(x)$;

$$f''(x_0) = \lim_{h \to 0} \frac{f'(x_0 + h) - f'(x_0)}{h}.$$

We are assuming that $f'(x_0) = 0$, so this equation says, roughly, that for h close to 0, the quotient $f'(x_0 + h)/h$ approximates $f''(x_0)$. We are also assuming that $f''(x_0)$ is negative, and therefore if $|h|$ is small enough so that the quotient $f'(x_0 + h)/h$ is a good approximation to $f''(x_0)$, it must be true that $f'(x_0 + h)/h$ is also negative. Thus for h close to 0 (h may be positive or negative), we have $f'(x_0 + h)/h < 0$. If $h > 0$, then $f'(x_0 + h) < 0$, while if $h < 0$, then $f'(x_0 + h) > 0$. Thus for points slightly to the right of x_0 the values of f' are negative, and for points slightly to the left of x_0 the values of f' are positive. Therefore Statement (i) of Theorem 25-1 tells us that $f(x_0)$ is a maximum point of f, as Statement (i) of Theorem 25-2 asserts.

In summary, to find the maximum and minimum points of the graph of a function f we

(i) Locate the critical points of the graph, and

(ii) Test each critical point—making use of the First Derivative Test or the Second Derivative Test when these are applicable.

As a closing remark, notice that a slight modification of the First Derivative Test makes it applicable to end points. Suppose a function f is continuous in the interval $[a, b]$. If $f'(x)$ is positive in the interval (a, b), then $f(b)$ is a maximum value, and $f(a)$ is a minimum value. If $f'(x)$ is negative in the interval (a, b), then $f(a)$ is a maximum value and $f(b)$ is a minimum value.

Problems 25

1. In each case find all critical points of the graph of f; indicate graphically, as in Fig. 25-2, the sign of $f'(x)$; and use the First Derivative Test to determine the maximum and minimum values of f.
   (a) $f(x) = 4x^3 + 9x^2 - 12x + 5$ (b) $f(x) = \cos x$
   (c) $f(x) = |x - 1|$ (d) $f(x) = \tan x$
   (e) $f(x) = 3x^5 - 5x^3 - 8$ (f) $f(x) = 1 - (x - 2)^{2/3}$
2. Use the Second Derivative Test to help you find the maximum and minimum points of the graph of f if:
   (a) $f(x) = x^2 + x - 1$ (b) $f(x) = 3x^3 - 4x + 1$
   (c) $f(x) = \sin x \cos x$ (d) $f(x) = 2x^3 - 3(kx)^2 + k^6$

(e) $f(x) = \dfrac{-3x}{x^2 + 9}$ (f) $f(x) = x^2 - a^4x^{-2}$

3. Find each number x such that $f(x)$ is a maximum or a minimum value if:
(a) $f(x) = (x - 1)^2(x + 1)^3$ (b) $f(x) = 2x^3 + 3x^2 + 12x$
(c) $f(x) = \tan x - x$ (d) $f(x) = \dfrac{x^{3/2}}{\sqrt{x - 18}}$

4. Find the maximum and minimum values of the function f if:
(a) $f(x) = \sin x^2$ (b) $f(x) = \sqrt{1 - x^2}$
(c) $f(x) = \sin x \tan x$ (d) $f(x) = -\sqrt{4 - x^2}$
(e) $f(x) = \sqrt{2x^3 + 3x^2 - 12x + 128}$ (f) $f(x) = x^{1/2} + x^{-1/2}$
(g) $f(x) = x(x^2 + 1)^{-1}$ (h) $f(x) = x\sqrt{1 - x^2}$

5. (a) Prove Statement (ii) of Theorem 25-1.
(b) Prove Statement (iii) of Theorem 25-1.

6. Let $f(x) = x - \sin x$. Does f have any maximum or minimum values?

7. Let $f(x) = \dfrac{x}{\sin x}\cdot$ Does f have any maximum or minimum values in the open interval $(0, \pi/2)$?

8. Let $f(x) = (x - a)^m(x - b)^n$, where m and n are positive integers, and $a \neq b$. Discuss the maximum and minimum points of the graph of f, considering the different cases that occur when m and n are even or odd integers.

26. Problems Involving Maxima and Minima

Some of the most important problems in mathematics and in the applications of mathematics can be solved by finding maximum or minimum values of functions. We will devote this section to some examples.

In Section 3 (Illustration 3-4) we showed that if a cylindrical tin can with a capacity of 54π cubic inches is constructed from material costing .012¢ per square inch for the sides and .021¢ per square inch for the top and bottom, then the relation between the cost c in cents and the base radius r in inches is given by the equation

$$c = \frac{108\pi}{r}(.012) + 2\pi r^2(.021). \tag{26-1}$$

For each choice of r we obtain a number c. Thus, for example, if we select $r = 2$, we obtain $c = 2.57$, so a can with a 2-inch base radius costs 2.57 cents; a can with a base radius of 3 inches costs 2.54 cents, and so on. Since each different choice of a number r as radius yields a different number c as cost, a natural question to ask is, "What choice of r results in the *smallest* number c?"—that is, "What is the radius of the cheapest can?"

Our knowledge of the maximum and minimum points of graphs will help us answer this question. Figure 26-1 shows the graph of Equation

26-1 for $r > 0$. If (r, c) is a point of this graph, then a can with a radius of r inches costs c cents. The point labeled P in Fig. 26-1 has the smallest C-coordinate of any point of the graph. Therefore the R-coordinate of P represents the radius, and the C-coordinate of P represents the cost of

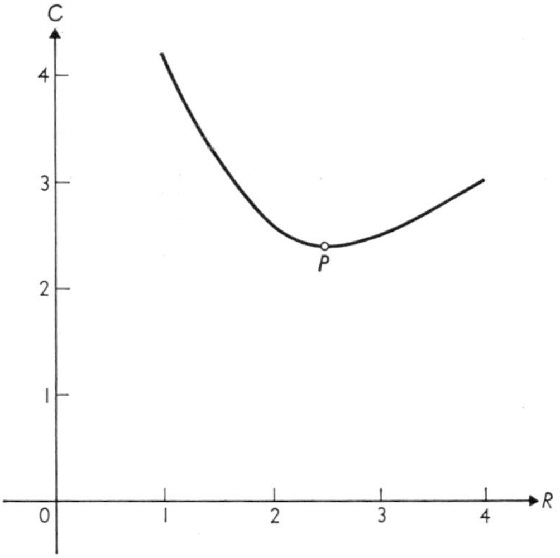

Figure 26-1

the cheapest can. So our question, "What is the radius of the cheapest can?" will be answered when we find the R-coordinate of the minimum point P.

It is clear from Fig. 26-1 that we can find the R-coordinate of P by solving the equation $D_r c = 0$. From Equation 26-1 we find that

$$D_r c = -\frac{108\pi(.012)}{r^2} + 4\pi r(.021). \tag{26-2}$$

Therefore, the equation $D_r c = 0$ becomes

$$4\pi r(.021) - \frac{108\pi}{r^2}(.012) = 0.$$

It is a simple matter to solve this last equation for r:

$$r = \sqrt[3]{\frac{108\pi(.012)}{4\pi(.021)}} = 2.49.$$

Thus the radius of the cheapest can is 2.49 inches. To find its cost, we simply replace r in Equation 26-1 with 2.49, and find that $c = 2.45$. The cheapest can has a radius of 2.49 inches and costs 2.45 cents.

Notice that we only used the graph in Fig. 26-1 to convince ourselves that we could find the coordinates of the minimum point P by solving the equation $D_r c = 0$. Actually, we could have relied on our previous theory and dispensed altogether with drawing the picture. The only critical points of the graph of Equation 26-1 are those at which $D_r c = 0$. If we have any doubts whether such a critical point is a maximum point, or a minimum point, or neither, we can consider the second derivative. It is easy to see that

$$D_r^2 c = 4\pi(.021) + (216\pi)(.012)/r^3.$$

Thus $D^2 c > 0$ for every $r > 0$. It follows that the graph of Equation 26-1 is concave up, and hence it is clear that a point at which $D_r c = 0$ is a minimum point. The First Derivative Test or The Second Derivative Test could also be used to verify that we have a minimum point.

In order to solve the "word problems" of this section, it will pay you to proceed according to the following steps:

(i) Read the problem carefully, and draw a sketch to illustrate it if you can.

(ii) Determine exactly what quantity you want to be a maximum or a minimum.

(iii) Use the data of the problem to express the quantity to be maximized or minimized in terms of some one other quantity, thus obtaining an equation of the form $y = f(x)$, $A = g(r)$, or the like.

(iv) Find the critical points of the graph of the equation found in the preceding step and determine the nature of these critical points—maximum points, minimum points, or neither.

(v) Re-read the problem to see explicitly what question was asked and then see if you can answer the question with the information you now have.

We will devote the remainder of this section to examples that show how to use these steps in solving maximum and minimum problems.

Example 26-1. A farmer has 100 yards of fencing. He wishes to construct a rectangular enclosure along a long stone wall, using the wall as one side of the enclosure and fencing in the other three sides. What is the largest area he can enclose?

Solution. We follow the five steps listed above.

(i) From the description we sketch the drawing of the enclosure shown in Fig. 26-2.

(ii) We wish to find the maximum area.

(iii) If the side of the enclosure perpendicular to the wall is x yards long, then the side parallel to the wall is $100 - 2x$ yards long. So if the area is A square yards, then

$$A = x(100 - 2x) = 100x - 2x^2. \tag{26-3}$$

(iv) From the nature of the problem we see that x must be a number satisfying the inequalities $0 < x < 50$ in order to obtain a proper rectangle. So there are no end points to consider and the X-coordinate of the critical point is found from the equation

$$D_xA = 100 - 4x = 0.$$

Thus $x = 25$. We see that $D_x^2A = -4 < 0$, and hence The Second Derivative Test tells us that we have found a maximum point.

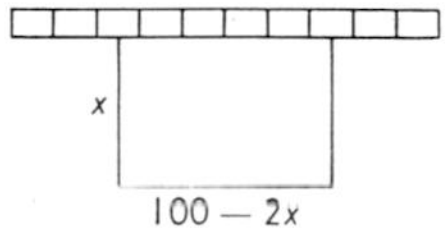

Figure 26-2

(v) Finally, the question asked us to find the maximum area. We know that the maximum area is attained when $x = 25$. So we set $x = 25$ in Equation 26-3 to find that

$$A_{\max} = 25(100 - 50) = 1{,}250 \text{ square yards.}$$

Example 26-2. Find the dimensions of the right triangle with a hypotenuse 10 units long whose area is a maximum.

Solution. Again we follow Steps (i) to (v).

(i) In Fig. 26-3 we have drawn a sketch that shows a right triangle with a hypotenuse 10 units long.

(ii) We wish to maximize the area of the triangle.

(iii) If t is the radian measure of one of the angles of our triangle, then the two sides are $10 \sin t$ and $10 \cos t$ units long, so if the area is A square units, then

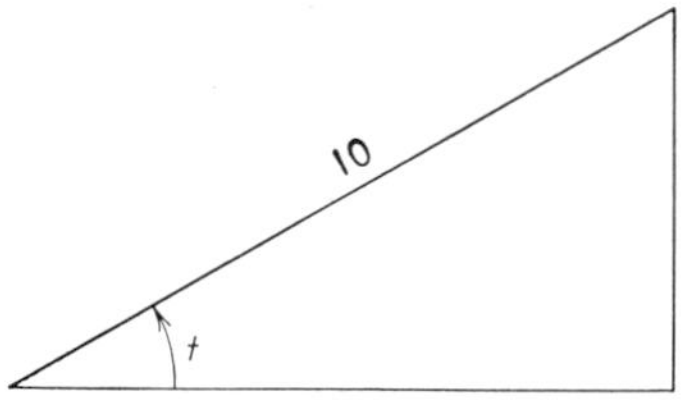

Figure 26-3

$$A = 50 \sin t \cos t.$$

(iv) In order to have a proper triangle, t must be a number in the open interval $(0, \pi/2)$, so we have no end points to consider. The critical points are the points at which

$$D_tA = 50(\cos^2 t - \sin^2 t) = 0.$$

It follows from this equation that $\cos^2 t = \sin^2 t$; that is, $\tan^2 t = 1$. Since $0 < t < \pi/2$, we therefore have $t = \pi/4$. Thus the point with T-coordinate $\pi/4$ is a critical point of the graph of the equation $A = 50 \sin t \cos t$. We have

$$\begin{aligned} D_t^2A &= 50(-2 \cos t \sin t - 2 \sin t \cos t) \\ &= -200 \sin t \cos t. \end{aligned}$$

Thus the second derivative is negative when $t = \pi/4$ and The Second Derivative Test tells us that our critical point is a maximum point.

(v) The question asked for the dimensions of the triangle of maximum area. The lengths of the sides of our maximum triangle are $10 \cos \frac{\pi}{4}$ and $10 \sin \frac{\pi}{4}$, so we see that the triangle of maximum area is an isosceles triangle with legs of length

$$10 \cos \frac{\pi}{4} = 10 \sin \frac{\pi}{4} = 5\sqrt{2} \text{ units.}$$

Example 26-3. A man who can swim 18 feet per second and run 25 feet per second stands at the edge of a circular swimming pool. He wishes to reach a point $\frac{1}{4}$ of the way around the pool in the least possible time. He plans to run along the edge of the pool for a ways and then to swim straight to his destination. How far should he run before diving in?

Solution. Again we follow our five steps.

(i) In Fig. 26-4 we have sketched a quarter circle with a radius of r feet representing the perimeter of the pool. The man will run along the circle from A to P, a distance of s feet, and then swim from P to B, a distance of c feet.

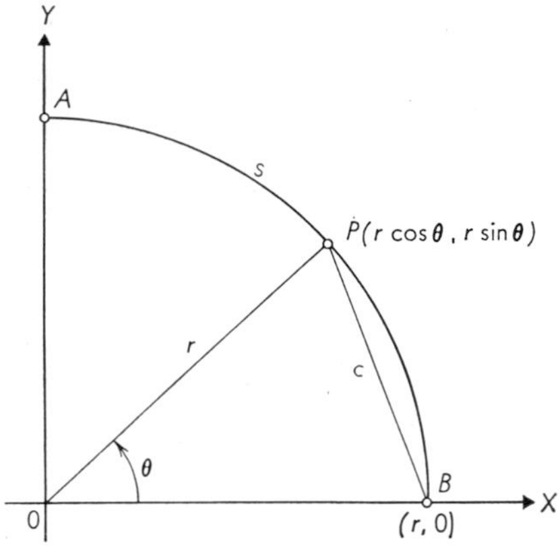

Figure 26-4

(ii) We wish to minimize the time that it takes him to get from A to B.

(iii) The total number of seconds, t, that it takes our man to go from A to B is the sum of the time required to go from A to P and the time required to go from P to B. Hence

$$t = \frac{s}{25} + \frac{c}{18}. \qquad (26\text{-}4)$$

If θ denotes the radian measure of the angle POB, then the coordinates of P are $(r \cos \theta, r \sin \theta)$. The distance from P to the point $B(r, 0)$ is given by the Distance Formula 4-1 (see Example 10-2) as

$$\begin{aligned} c &= \sqrt{(r\cos\theta - r)^2 + (r\sin\theta)^2} \\ &= r\sqrt{\cos^2\theta - 2\cos\theta + 1 + \sin^2\theta} \\ &= r\sqrt{2(1-\cos\theta)} \\ &= r\sqrt{4\sin^2\theta/2} \\ &= 2r\sin\theta/2. \end{aligned}$$

Further, since angle $AOP = \frac{\pi}{2} - \theta$, we have $s = r\left(\frac{\pi}{2} - \theta\right)$. Now we replace s and c in Equation 26-4 with their expressions in terms of θ, so that we have t in terms of θ:

$$t = \frac{r\left(\frac{\pi}{2} - \theta\right)}{25} + \frac{r\sin\frac{\theta}{2}}{9}. \tag{26-5}$$

It follows from the statement of the problem that $0 \leq \theta \leq \frac{\pi}{2}$.

(iv) The critical points of the graph of Equation 26-5 are the end points—the points at which $\theta = 0$ and $\theta = \pi/2$—and the points at which $D_\theta t = 0$. Now

$$D_\theta t = \frac{-r}{25} + \frac{r\cos\frac{\theta}{2}}{18}$$

and

$$D_\theta^2 t = -\frac{r\sin\frac{\theta}{2}}{36}.$$

Thus we see that $D_\theta^2 t < 0$ for $0 < \theta \leq \pi/2$, and therefore our curve is concave down. Hence the only minimum points must be the end points of the arc.

(v) From Equation 26-5 we find that $t = \pi r/50$ when $\theta = 0$, and $t = \sqrt{2}\,r/18$ when $\theta = \pi/2$. Since $\sqrt{2}\,r/18 > \pi r/50$, we see that the minimum time occurs when $\theta = 0$. Our man should run all the way, and not swim at all!

Problems 26

1. A box with a square base and no top is to be made from 300 square inches of tin. Find the dimensions of such a box with the largest volume.

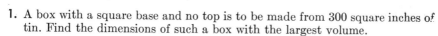

2. A box with a square base and a top is to be made from 300 square inches of tin. Find the dimensions of such a box with the largest volume.
3. Equal squares are cut from each corner of a piece of tin measuring 6 inches by 6 inches, and the edges are then turned up to form a rectangular box with no lid. What is the volume of the largest such box?
4. A triangle whose base angles are acute has an altitude of h inches and a base of b inches. A rectangle is placed inside the triangle with one side on the base of the triangle. Show that the maximum possible area of such a rectangle is one-half the area of the triangle.
5. The area of a cylindrical tin can with a top and bottom is fixed at S square inches. If the can is H inches tall and has a base radius of R inches, show that the can has a maximum volume if $2R = H$.
6. A rectangular wall is to have an area of 12 square yards. What should be the height and width of the wall so that a brace from one base corner to the midpoint of the opposite vertical side is of minimum length?
7. An irrigation ditch is to have a cross section the shape of an isosceles trapezoid with a horizontal base. The bottom and equal sides of the trapezoid are each to be L feet long. Let θ denote the angle that the side of the ditch makes with the horizontal.
   (a) Show that the cross sectional area of the ditch is given by the equation $A = L^2(\sin\theta + \sin\theta\cos\theta)$.
   (b) For what angle θ will the carrying capacity of the ditch be a maximum?
8. An E-volt battery has an internal resistance of r ohms. If a resistor of R ohms is connected across the battery terminals, then a current of I amps will flow and generate P watts of power, where

$$I = \frac{E}{R + r}, \qquad \text{and} \qquad P = I^2R.$$

   For what resistance R will the power generated be a maximum?
9. A page is to contain 24 square inches of print. The margins at the top and bottom are each to be one and a half inches. Each margin at the side is to be 1 inch. What are the dimensions of the smallest such page?
10. While driving through the north woods, Bill runs out of gas. He can reach the nearest gas station either by walking 1 mile north and 10 miles east along paved roads, or by walking through the woods in a north-easterly direction until he reaches the paved road and then proceeding east along the road to the gas station. Suppose he can walk 5 miles per hour along the paved roads, and 3 miles per hour through the woods. Describe the path he should follow in order to reach the gas station in the shortest time.
11. Find the area of the largest isosceles triangle that can be drawn with equal sides k inches long.
12. An experiment is performed n times, and n numbers (measurements) x_1, x_2, . . ., x_n are obtained. In order to obtain an "average" number, we choose the number x that makes the sum of the squares of the differences between x and each x_i the least; that is, we choose the number x that makes $s = (x - x_1)^2 + (x - x_2)^2 + \cdots + (x - x_n)^2$ a minimum. Show that we get the usual arithmetic mean as our "average" number.

13. A wall h feet high stands d feet away from a tall building. A ladder L feet long reaches from the ground outside the wall to the building. Let θ be the angle between the ladder and the horizontal.
(a) Show that if the ladder touches the top of the wall, $L = h \csc \theta + d \sec \theta$.
(b) Find the shortest ladder that will reach the building if $h = 8$ and $d = 24$.

27. Linear Motion

If a projectile fired vertically upward with an initial velocity of 96 feet per second reaches a height of s feet above its launching site after t seconds, then the numbers s and t are related by the formula

$$s = -16t^2 + 96t. \tag{27-1}$$

We have already defined velocity as the rate of change of distance with respect to time (Section 14), so that $v = D_t s$. Therefore, for our projectile, v is expressed in terms of t by the equation

$$v = -32t + 96. \tag{27-2}$$

Here we are measuring distance in feet and time in seconds, so velocity is measured in feet per second. The absolute value $|v|$ is called the **speed** of the projectile.

We saw in Section 23 that the inequality $D_t s > 0$ implies that distance is increasing, and the inequality $D_t s < 0$ implies that distance is decreasing. In our present example, then, we see that when $v > 0$, the distance between the projectile and the launching site is increasing (the projectile is moving up) while if $v < 0$ the distance is decreasing (the projectile is moving down).

The number $a = D_t v$ measures the rate of change of velocity with respect to time; that is, the **acceleration** of the projectile. For our projectile

$$a = -32. \tag{27-3}$$

Acceleration is measured in units of velocity per unit of time. Here it is measured in feet per second per second.

Since $a = D_t v$, Equation 27-3 tells us that the derivative $D_t v$ is negative. Hence the velocity of our projectile is decreasing with time. The projectile starts at a velocity of 96 feet per second and slows down to 0 feet per second. Then it begins to fall, *but its velocity continues to decrease* through negative values. The *speed* of the projectile increases as the body falls.

Example 27-1. For the projectile whose motion is described by Equation 27-1 find the maximum height, the total time of flight, and the maximum velocity.

Solution. The projectile reaches its maximum height when $D_t s = v = -32t + 96 = 0$; that is, 3 seconds after launching. According to Equation 27-1, $s = -16 \cdot 3^2 + 96 \cdot 3 = 144$ feet at that moment. We will assume that a projectile fired vertically upward will return to its starting point. Hence the duration of its flight is found by solving the equation $s = 0$; that is $-16t^2 + 96t = 0$. There are two solutions to this equation: $t = 0$ and $t = 6$. When $t = 0$, the projectile is at its launching point at the start of the flight, and when $t = 6$ the projectile is at its launching point after completing its flight. Thus its total time of flight is 6 seconds. The projectile's velocity is decreasing during its flight, so the maximum value of the velocity occurs when $t = 0$, and is 96 feet per second.

In general we will picture a body moving along a line as a point moving along a number scale (Fig. 27-1). Let s denote the coordinate

Figure 27-1

of the point t seconds after some initial instant of time. The number s is positive if the point is on the positive side of the origin. In our projectile problem we placed the number scale so that the "up" direction was positive, and $s = 0$ when $t = 0$. In general we do not insist that s be 0 when $t = 0$. If the velocity of our moving point is measured by the number v, the acceleration by the number a, and the speed by the number r, then, by definition,

$$\text{(27-4)} \qquad \begin{aligned} \boldsymbol{v} &= \boldsymbol{D_t s}, \\ \boldsymbol{a} &= \boldsymbol{D_t v} = \boldsymbol{D_t^2 s}, \\ \boldsymbol{r} &= |\boldsymbol{v}|. \end{aligned}$$

Example 27-2. Discuss the motion of a point that moves along the number scale of Fig. 27-1 in accordance with the equation $s = t + \frac{1}{t}$ for $t > 0$.

Solution. We have

$$s = t + \frac{1}{t},$$

$$v = D_t s = 1 - \frac{1}{t^2},$$

$$a = D_t^2 s = \frac{2}{t^3}.$$

For t close to 0, the number s is very large, and hence our point is very far from the origin. For t in the interval (0, 1), v is negative, and hence s is decreasing. Thus the particle moves to the left. When $t = 1$, $v = 0$, and for $t > 1$, $v > 0$. Thus our particle stops and reverses direction when $t = 1$. At this instant $s = 2$, so the closest the particle comes to the origin is the point two units to the right of it. For $t > 1$, the particle moves to the right, and as time goes on it recedes indefinitely. The acceleration is always positive; that is, the velocity is continually increasing. However, notice that the velocity always remains less than 1.

The following example will test your understanding of the concept of absolute value as well as the concepts of linear motion that we have discussed in this section.

Example 27-3. Suppose that during some time interval the velocity and acceleration of a moving point are such that $v < 0$ and $a < 0$. Show that the speed of the point is increasing during the interval.

Solution. Using the notation of Equations 27-4 we see that the problem will be solved if we show that $D_t r > 0$. We know that $r = |v|$, and since $v < 0$, $r = -v$. Hence $D_t r = D_t(-v) = -D_t v = -a$. But since $a < 0$, we have $-a > 0$. Thus $D_t r > 0$, and hence the speed of the point is increasing.

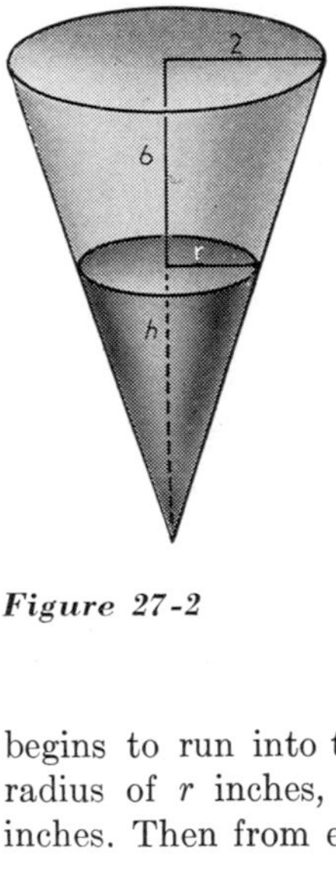

Figure 27-2

Example 27-4. A soda jerk fills a conical soda cup that is 4 inches across the top and 6 inches deep at the rate of 1 cubic inch per second. What is the vertical velocity of a fly sitting on top of the liquid when the soda is half way to the top?

Solution. Suppose that t seconds after the soda begins to run into the cup, the soda is h inches deep, the surface has a radius of r inches, and the volume of the soda in the cup is V cubic inches. Then from elementary geometry (See Fig. 27-2) we see that

$$r = \frac{h}{3}, \text{ and } V = \frac{\pi}{3} r^2 h.$$

On the other hand, we know that $V = 1 \cdot t$, so we have

$$t = \frac{\pi}{3}\left(\frac{h}{3}\right)^2 h,$$

(27-5) $$h^3 = \frac{27t}{\pi}.$$

Thus

$$h = 3\sqrt[3]{\frac{t}{\pi}}.$$

We were asked to find the vertical velocity $D_t h$ when $h = 3$, so we first calculate

(27-6)
$$D_t h = \left(\frac{1}{\pi t^2}\right)^{1/3}.$$

From Equation 27-5 we see that $t = \pi$ when $h = 3$, so from Equation 27-6 we find that the vertical velocity, when $h = 3$, is $(1/\pi)$ inches per second.

Problems 27

1. For the indicated time find the velocity, speed, and acceleration of a point moving along a number scale if:
(a) $s = t^3 + 2t^2$; $t = 2$
(b) $s = t + 2/t^2$; $t = \frac{1}{2}$
(c) $s = \cos(\pi t/3)$; $t = 1$
(d) $s = t \sin t$; $t = 1$
2. Discuss the motion of a point that moves along the number scale in accordance with the given equation.
(a) $s = 9t + \frac{4}{t}$, $t > 0$ (b) $s = t^2 + \frac{4}{t^2}$, $t > 0$
(c) $s = \sin t + \csc t$, $0 < t < \pi$ (d) $s = \sin\sqrt{1 - t^2}$, $0 < t < 1$.
3. A projectile is fired from a balloon in such a way that it is s feet above the ground t seconds after firing and $s = -16t^2 + 96t + 256$.
(a) How high was the balloon when the projectile was fired?
(b) What is the maximum height reached by the projectile?
(c) How fast is the projectile going when it hits the earth?
4. During a certain time interval, the velocity and acceleration of a given moving body are such that v and a have opposite signs. Show that the speed of the body is decreasing during the interval.
5. A rocket travels upward from the surface of the earth and is s miles high t minutes after take-off. Suppose that $s = 200 + 100 \sec(2t + 2\pi/3)$.
(a) How high does the rocket go?
(b) How fast is the rocket going when it hits the earth?
(c) What is the duration of the flight?
(d) What is the maximum speed of the rocket?
6. A point moves along the number scale in accordance with the equation $s = 3t^4 - 4t^3 + 2$. How close does the point come to the origin? What is its minimum speed? What is its minimum velocity?
7. How is the velocity of a freely falling body dropped from rest near the surface of the earth related to the distance fallen? What is the rate of change of velocity with respect to distance fallen? (Assume distance is measured in feet and velocity in feet per second).

8. Find the vertical velocity of the fly in Example 27-4 when $h = 3$ if the soda cup has a leak in it that allows the soda to run out at the rate of $\frac{1}{8}$ cubic inches per second while it is being filled.
9. A body is displaced from the origin according to the law

$$s = 4(1 + t^2)^{1/2} - t^2 \quad \text{for } t \geq 0.$$

Find the time intervals during which the body is moving toward the origin.
10. A boat is moored to a dock by a 13-foot rope fastened 5 feet above the bow of the boat. A man pulls in the rope at the rate of 1 foot per second. What is the horizontal velocity of the boat at the instant he starts pulling?
11. A marble is dropped from a tall building and T seconds later a second marble is dropped. Does the distance between the marbles remain constant? What is the rate of change of distance between the marbles?

28. Related Rates

The straightforward way to find the velocity of a moving point is to express s in terms of t and then calculate D_ts as we did in the preceding section. But sometimes we have to find the rate of change of a quantity even though we don't have an equation that explicitly relates that quantity and time. An example will illustrate the type of problem we wish to discuss.

Let us suppose that a spherical snowball melts in such a way that at the instant its radius is 4 inches its volume is decreasing at the rate of 2 cubic inches per minute. How fast is the radius changing at that instant? If the snowball has a radius of r inches t minutes after some initial time, the problem amounts to finding the number D_tr when $r = 4$. So if we could express r in terms of t, then the problem would simply become a problem in differentiation. But we are not given enough information to write r in terms of t, and therefore we must attack the problem in a different manner.

We are told that at the instant we are interested in the volume of the snowball is decreasing at the rate of 2 cubic inches per minute. Therefore if the volume is V cubic inches at t minutes after some initial time, then $D_tV = -2$ at our given instant. (The negative sign indicates that the volume is decreasing then.) Thus we are given D_tV, and we are asked to find D_tr. The basic problem is to find the relation between these two rates. This relation is furnished by the Chain Rule equation

$$D_tV = D_rVD_tr. \tag{28-1}$$

Since we know D_tV, we will be able to find D_tr as soon as we know D_rV. We calculate D_rV as follows. Because the snowball is spherical, the relation between V and r is

$$V = \frac{4\pi r^3}{3}. \tag{28-2}$$

Hence $D_rV = 4\pi r^2$, and therefore Equation 28-1 becomes

$$D_tV = 4\pi r^2 D_tr. \tag{28-3}$$

Since we are interested in the value of D_tr when $r = 4$, we replace r with 4 and D_tV with -2 in Equation 28-3 and obtain the equation

$$-2 = 64\pi D_tr.$$

It follows that

$$D_tr = -\frac{1}{32\pi} \text{ inches per minute when } r = 4, \tag{28-4}$$

which answers our original question.

You may find it helpful to follow the same sequence of steps each time you solve a problem concerning related rates. In such problems one of two rates, D_ty or D_tx, is given and we are asked to find the other at some particular instant of time. (Of course we may use letters other than x and y as, for example, we used V and r in the problem above.) We follow these steps:

(i) Find an equation that expresses y in terms of x—a figure is often helpful. (This step gave us Equation 28-2.)

(ii) From the equation found in Step (i) calculate D_xy and substitute in the Chain Rule Equation $D_ty = D_xyD_tx$. (This step led us to Equation 28-3.)

(iii) Substitute in the equation found in Step (ii) the data given in the problem and evaluate the unknown rate. (This step led us to our solution, Equation 28-4.)

Example 28-1. A television cameraman is televising a 100-yard dash. He is located 10 yards away from the track in line with the finish line (Fig. 28-1).

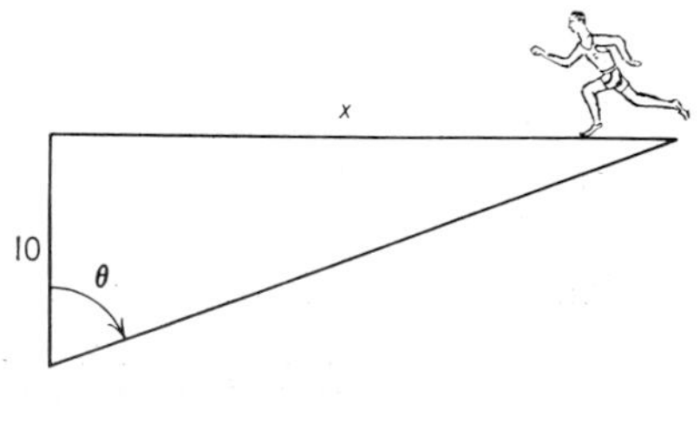

Figure 28-1

When the runners are 10 yards from the finish line, his camera is turning at the rate of $\frac{3}{5}$ radians per second. How fast are the runners moving at that instant?

Solution. Figure 28-1 shows the situation at the instant the runners are x yards from the finish line, at which time θ is the radian measure of the angle between the line joining the camera and the runners and the finish line extended to the camera. We are told that $D_t\theta = -\frac{3}{5}$ radians per second (θ is decreasing, so we use the minus sign) when $x = 10$. Our steps in the solution are:

(i) From Fig. 28-1 we see that $x = 10 \tan \theta$.

(ii) Therefore $D_\theta x = 10 \sec^2 \theta$, and we substitute this value in the Chain Rule Equation $D_tx = D_\theta x D_t\theta$. The relation between the rates D_tx and $D_t\theta$ is therefore

$$D_tx = 10 \sec^2 \theta D_t\theta. \tag{28-5}$$

(iii) We are interested in the speed of the runners when $x = 10$. At that point we clearly have $\theta = \pi/4$, and therefore $\sec \theta = \sqrt{2}$. So Equation 28-5 becomes $D_tx = 10(\sqrt{2})^2(-\frac{3}{5}) = -12$, and we see that our runners are approaching the finish line at the rate of 12 yards per second.

The next example is very similar to Example 27-4. However, the method used to solve it here is different.

Example 28-2. A freshman is drinking a soda through a straw from a conical cup 8 inches deep and 4 inches in diameter at the top. At the instant the soda is 5 inches deep, he is drinking at the rate of 3 cubic inches per second. How fast is the level of the soda dropping at that time?

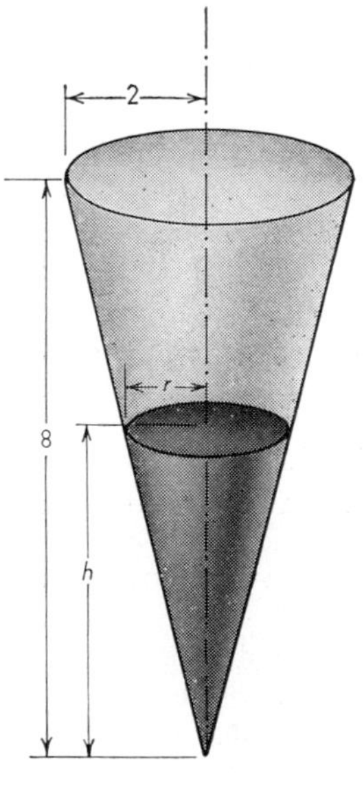

Figure 28-2

Solution. Suppose that t seconds after the freshman starts drinking, the soda is h inches deep and V cubic inches in volume. We know that $D_tV = -3$ when $h = 5$ and we are asked to find D_th. Our three steps become:

(i) In Fig. 28-2 we have illustrated the situation at some instant of time. We now want to find the relationship between V and h. According to the formula for the volume of a cone, $V = \frac{\pi r^2 h}{3}$. However, this equation gives us V in terms of *both* h and r, instead of just h. We must eliminate r. From the similar triangles in Fig. 28-2 we see that $\frac{r}{2} = \frac{h}{8}$, so $r = \frac{h}{4}$. Therefore we can eliminate r in our expression for V and write

$$V = \pi \left(\frac{h^2}{16}\right) \frac{h}{3} = \frac{\pi h^3}{48}. \tag{28-6}$$

(ii) From Equation 28-6 we find that $D_hV = \dfrac{\pi h^2}{16}$, and we then use the Chain Rule Equation $D_tV = D_hVD_th$ to obtain the equation

$$D_tV = \frac{\pi}{16} h^2 D_th. \tag{28-7}$$

(iii) But $D_tV = -3$ when $h = 5$, so Equation 28-7 becomes

$$-3 = \frac{\pi}{16} 5^2 D_th.$$

Hence $D_th = -\dfrac{48}{25\pi}$; the level of the soda is dropping at the rate of $\dfrac{48}{25\pi}$ inches per second.

Problems 28

1. A horizontal eaves trough 10 feet long has a triangular cross section 4 inches across the top and 4 inches deep. During a rainstorm the water in the trough is rising at the rate of $\frac{1}{4}$ inch per minute when the depth is 2 inches. How fast is the volume of water in the trough increasing? After the rain has stopped, the water drains out of the trough at the rate of 40 cubic inches per minute. How fast is the surface of the water falling when the depth is 1 inch?
2. A man climbs a pole while holding one end of a rope that is wound around a spindle located 15 feet from the base of the pole. If he climbs at the rate of 1 foot per second, how fast is the rope coming off the spindle when he is twenty feet high?
3. A 13-foot ladder leans against the wall of a house. Someone pulls the base of the ladder away from the house at the rate of 2 feet per second. How fast is the top of the ladder sliding down the wall when it is 5 feet from the ground?
4. Use the methods of this section to answer Question 10, Problems 27.
5. An airplane is flying at an altitude of 10,000 feet directly toward an observer on the ground. The observer notes that the angle between his line of sight to the plane and the horizontal measures $\pi/3$ radians and is increasing at the rate of .06 radians per second. How fast is the plane flying? How fast is the distance between the plane and the observer changing?
6. The area of a rectangle is decreasing at the constant rate of 9 square inches per second and at any instant the height of the rectangle is decreasing twice as fast as the width. At a certain instant the rectangle is a 1 inch by 1 inch square. At what rate is the width decreasing at that instant.
7. A man 6 feet tall walks at the rate of 5 feet per second directly away from a lamp 15 feet above the ground. Find the rate at which the end of his shadow is moving and the rate at which his shadow is lengthening when he is 20 feet away from the lamp post.

8. The radius of the base of a cone is increasing at the rate of 4 inches per minute while the altitude of the cone is decreasing at the rate of 7 inches per minute. Is the volume of the cone increasing or decreasing at the instant that the altitude and radius are equal?
9. A penny is heated so that its radius is expanding at the rate of .01 inch per minute. At what rate is the surface of one side expanding when the radius is $\frac{7}{16}$ inch?
10. A lightplane whose groundspeed is 120 miles per hour is in level flight at an altitude of 2,640 feet above the ground. The plane passes directly over a car traveling 50 miles per hour on a road that is at right angles to the plane's path. How fast are the car and plane separating 1 minute after the plane is directly over the car?
11. A circular cylinder whose radius is r inches and whose height is h inches is surmounted by a hemisphere whose radius is r inches. If the radius decreases at the rate of 2 inches per minute, at what rate must the height increase so that the volume does not change at the moment when $h = 2r$?
12. Show that the relation between the rate of change of volume and the rate of change of surface area of a sphere is given by the equation $D_tV = \frac{r}{2} D_tS$.

29. Approximations. Newton's Method

We first introduced the concept of the derived function in connection with the problem of drawing the line tangent to the graph of a function at a point. We will now return to this idea as we study problems such as the following two: (1) Find $\sqrt{10}$, approximately; (2) Find an approximate solution to the equation $\sin x - \frac{1}{x} = 0$.

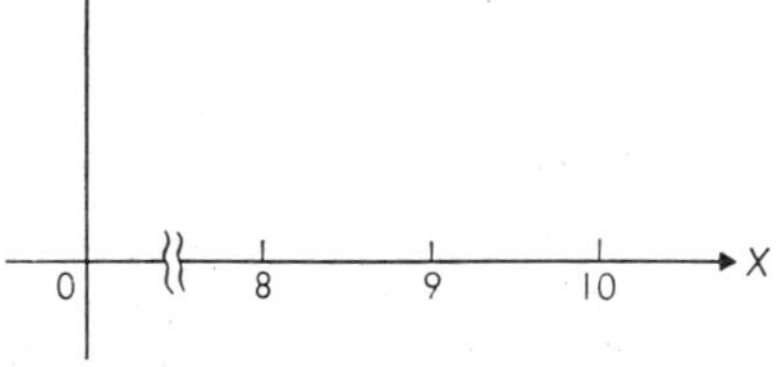

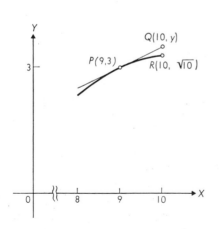

Figure 29-1

In Fig. 29-1 we have drawn a somewhat exaggerated view of the graph of the function f defined by the equation $f(x) = \sqrt{x}$. In geometrical language, the problem of finding $\sqrt{10}$ amounts to finding the Y-coordinate of the point $R(10, \sqrt{10})$ of this graph. We have drawn the line tangent to our graph at the point $P(9, 3)$, and this tangent line approximates the graph of the function for nearby points. In particular, we might agree that the Y-coordinate of the point labeled $Q(10, y)$ of the tangent line is a close approximation of the Y-coordinate of the point $R(10, \sqrt{10})$. In other words, we may be satisfied to call this number y an approximation of $\sqrt{10}$.

This number y is easy to calculate. The line containing P and Q is tangent to the graph of the equation $y = f(x)$ at the point $P(9, 3)$, so its slope is $f'(9)$. On the other hand, the slope of the line PQ is given (see Equation 9-2) by the quotient

$$\frac{y-3}{10-9} = y - 3.$$

Thus we have

$$y - 3 = f'(9). \tag{29-1}$$

Since $f(x) = \sqrt{x}$, we find that $f'(x) = \dfrac{1}{2\sqrt{x}}$, and so $f'(9) = \frac{1}{6}$. Therefore Equation 29-1 becomes $y - 3 = \frac{1}{6}$, and hence $y = \frac{19}{6}$. To two decimal places, the actual value of $\sqrt{10}$ is 3.16, so our approximate value of $\frac{19}{6} = 3.17$ is quite close.

Example 29-1. Find an approximation of sin 3.

Solution. Figure 29-2 shows a portion (somewhat exaggerated) of the graph of the equation $y = \sin x$ for x near $\pi = 3.14$. We have also drawn the line tangent to the graph at the point $(\pi, 0)$. We will take the Y-coordinate of the point of this tangent line that corresponds to $x = 3$ as an approximation of the Y-coordinate of the point of the curve that corresponds to $x = 3$. To find the number y, we calculate the slope of the tangent line in two ways. On one hand, we have $D_x y = \cos x$, so the slope of the tangent line at $x = \pi$ is $\cos \pi = -1$. On the other hand, the slope of the line joining the points $(3, y)$ and $(\pi, 0)$ is the quotient $\dfrac{y-0}{3-\pi}$. Thus $\dfrac{y}{3-\pi} = -1$, and hence $y = \pi - 3 = 3.14 - 3 = .14$. Our approximate value of sin 3 is therefore .14. This number is actually the value of sin 3 correct to two decimal places.

We will now use the same arguments that we used in the preceding specific examples to develop a general approximation formula. Suppose we know the value of a given function f at a point a and wish to approximate its value at another point b. Figure 29-3 shows the arc of the graph of f that joins the points $(a, f(a))$ and $(b, f(b))$. We will approximate the number $f(b)$ by the Y-coordinate of the point (b, y) of the tangent line at the point $(a, f(a))$. To calculate this approximation y we will equate two expressions for the slope of the line joining $(a, f(a))$ and (b, y). First we note that the slope of this line is $f'(a)$, since it is the tangent line at

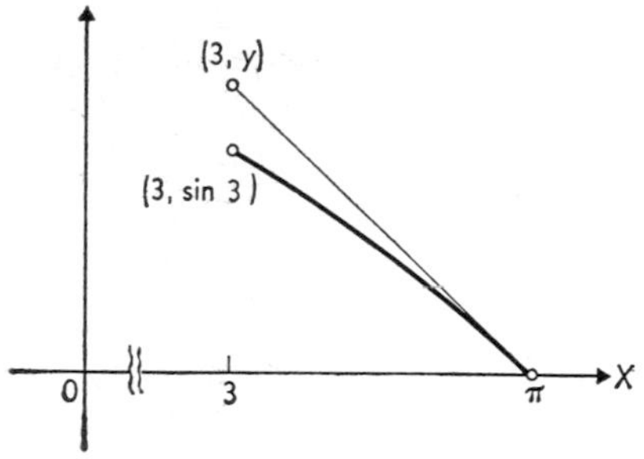

Figure 29-2

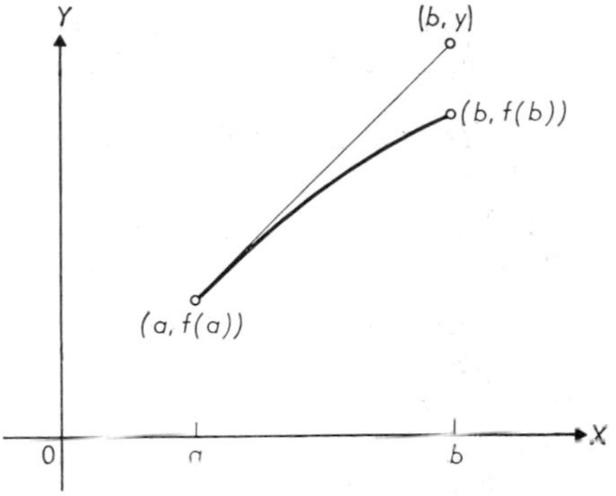

Figure 29-3

$(a, f(a))$. But the slope is also given by the quotient $\frac{y - f(a)}{b - a}$. Thus

$$\frac{y - f(a)}{b - a} = f'(a),$$

from which we have

$$y = f(a) + f'(a)(b - a).$$

To indicate that $f(b)$ is approximated by this number y we write

$$\text{(29-2)} \qquad \boldsymbol{f(b) \approx f(a) + f'(a)(b - a).}$$

Formula 29-2 is our desired approximation formula. If we let $b = \boldsymbol{a + h}$, we can also write our approximation formula as

$$\boldsymbol{f(a + h) \approx f(a) + f'(a)h.}$$

Example 29-2. A cubical box with inside dimensions $4'' \times 4'' \times 4''$ is made of lead $\frac{1}{32}$ inch thick. If lead weighs 5 pounds per cubic inch, approximately how much does the box weigh?

Solution. We will define the function f by means of the equation $f(x) = x^3$. Then the exterior of our box encloses a volume of

$$(4\tfrac{1}{16})^3 = f(4\tfrac{1}{16}) \text{ cubic inches.}$$

On the other hand, the volume of the interior of the box is $4^3 = f(4)$ cubic inches. Therefore the volume of lead used to make our box is

$$f(4\tfrac{1}{16}) - f(4) \text{ cubic inches.}$$

Now according to Formula 29-2, we see that

$$\begin{aligned} f(4\tfrac{1}{16}) - f(4) &\approx f'(4) \cdot \tfrac{1}{16} \\ &= 3 \cdot 4^2 \cdot \tfrac{1}{16} = 3. \end{aligned}$$

Our box is made out of about 3 cubic inches of lead and therefore weighs approximately 15 pounds.

If the number A is an approximation of a number N, then we shall call the number $E = N - A$ the **error** of the approximation, and the number $|E|$ the **absolute error** of the approximation. The number $R = |E/N|$ is called the **relative error,** and $100R\%$ is termed the **percentage error.** In practice, of course, we usually do not know the number N that we approximate with a number A. Hence the error is not known. What we try to do is to find a **bound** on $|E|$; that is, a number that we know is not exceeded by $|E|$.

Let us find a bound on the error involved in considering the right-hand side of Formula 29-2 as the number A that approximates the number $N = f(b)$. Thus in this case the equation $N = A + E$ is

(29-3) $$f(b) = f(a) + f'(a)(b - a) + E,$$

and we want to obtain an estimate of the size of $|E|$. We first rewrite Equation 29-3 in the form

(29-4) $$f(b) - f(a) = f'(a)(b - a) + E.$$

Now according to the Theorem of the Mean, there is a number c between a and b such that $f(b) - f(a) = f'(c)(b - a)$. Therefore we can write Equation 29-4 as

$$f'(c)(b - a) = f'(a)(b - a) + E;$$

that is,

(29-5) $$E = [f'(c) - f'(a)](b - a).$$

If we assume that the Theorem of the Mean applies to the derived function f', then we know that there is a number d between a and c such that $f'(c) - f'(a) = f''(d)(c - a)$. Therefore Equation 29-5 becomes

$$E = f''(d)(c - a)(b - a),$$

and hence

(29-6) $$|E| = |f''(d)|\,|(c - a)|\,|(b - a)|.$$

Now suppose that M is a number such that $|f''(x)| \leq M$ for every number between a and b. (We call such a number an **upper bound** for the second derivative.) Then, since $|c - a| < |b - a|$, we finally have

$$|E| \leq M(b - a)^2.$$

By a somewhat more "sophisticated" argument (see Problem 11 at the end of the section) we can even show that

(29-7) $$\boldsymbol{|E| \leq (M/2)(b - a)^2.}$$

Let us see what Inequality 29-7 tells us about the accuracy of our computation in Example 29-2.

Example 29-3. Find a bound on the accuracy of our approximation of the volume of lead used to construct the box in Example 29-2.

Solution. In Example 29-2 we dealt with the function f for which $f(x) = x^3$, with x in the interval $[4, 4\frac{1}{16}]$. In this case

$$|f''(x)| = |6x| \leq 6 \cdot 4\tfrac{1}{16} = \tfrac{195}{8}.$$

So Equation 29-7 becomes

$$|E| \leq \tfrac{195}{16}(\tfrac{1}{16})^2 = \tfrac{195}{4096} < .05.$$

The absolute error in our calculation is less than .05 cubic inches, and our relative error is bounded by $\frac{.05}{3}$; that is, we are in error by no more than about .02 or 2%.

The problem of solving equations is an important one in mathematics and its applications. Some equations, for example, linear and quadratic equations, can be solved by straightforward methods. Other equations, such as

$$\text{(29-8)} \qquad \sin x - \frac{1}{x} = 0,$$

cannot be solved by simple formulas. If we define the function f by means of the equation $f(x) = \sin x - 1/x$, then Equation 29-8 is the equation $f(x) = 0$. The solutions to this equation are called **zeros** of the function f. One useful method for finding an approximation to a zero of a function is known as **Newton's Method.**

Newton's Method is best described in geometrical language. A zero of a function f is the X-coordinate of a point at which the graph of the equation $y = f(x)$ cuts the X-axis. Thus the point r is a zero of the function whose graph appears in Fig. 29-4. We will suppose that we don't know r, but that graphically, or by using tables, we have found a number x_0 that approximates r. We wish to improve upon this approximation. From Fig. 29-4 we see that the tangent line at $(x_0, f(x_0))$ intersects the X-axis at a point x_1 that is a closer approximation of r than is x_0. We find the number x_1 in much the same way that we derived Equation 29-2. Thus the slope of the line joining $(x_0, f(x_0))$ and $(x_1, 0)$ is

$$\frac{f(x_0) - 0}{x_0 - x_1}.$$

On the other hand, this line is the tangent line at $(x_0, f(x_0))$, so its slope is $f'(x_0)$. Hence we have

$$f'(x_0) = \frac{f(x_0)}{x_0 - x_1},$$

from which it follows that

(29-9) $$x_1 = x_0 - \frac{f(x_0)}{f'(x_0)}.$$

From Fig. 29-4 it is apparent that we can find a still closer approximation

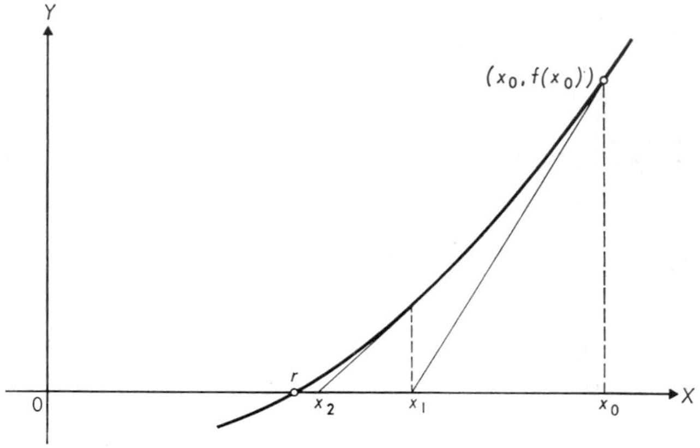

Figure 29-4

of r by locating the point at which the tangent line at the point $(x_1, f(x_1))$ intersects the X-axis. We follow the exact steps we used to find x_1 and arrive at the equation

(29-10) $$x_2 = x_1 - \frac{f(x_1)}{f'(x_1)}.$$

We can repeat this procedure as often as we please and obtain a sequence of numbers $x_1, x_2, x_3, \ldots$, each number being a closer approximation of r than the preceding number.

We based our discussion of Newton's Method on Fig. 29-4, which shows a somewhat special graph. Our arguments don't apply to graphs that are too "wiggly." To be sure that Newton's Method will always yield a sequence of numbers such that x_2 is a closer approximation of the desired zero than is x_1, x_3 is a closer approximation than is x_2, and so on, we should stay in an interval in which $f'(x) \neq 0$ and every number $f''(x)$ has the same sign. Then the curve is either concave up (as in Fig. 29-4) or concave down. You might experiment with a few graphs to see how the sequence of numbers $x_1, x_2, \ldots$ "converges" toward r.

Example 29-4. Use Newton's Method to find a solution to the equation $\sin x - 1/x$ that is near $x_0 = \pi$.

Solution. Here we have $f(x) = \sin x - 1/x$ and $x_0 = \pi = 3.142$. Equation 29-9 gives us the first approximation

$$x_1 = \pi - \frac{\sin \pi - 1/\pi}{\cos \pi + (1/\pi)^2} = 2.789.$$

A second approximation follows from Equation 29-10:

$$x_2 = 2.789 - \frac{\sin 2.789 - 1/2.789}{\cos 2.789 + (1/2.789)^2} = 2.776.$$

Additional approximations could be found in the same manner.

We can get an idea of how the accuracy of our approximations $x_1, x_2, \ldots$ is improved at each step by means of the following analysis. If we replace b with r and a with x_1 in Equation 29-3, we obtain the equation

$$f(r) = f(x_1) + f'(x_1)(r - x_1) + E. \tag{29-11}$$

Since $f(r) = 0$, we can solve Equation 29-11 for r to obtain the equation

$$r = x_1 - \frac{f(x_1)}{f'(x_1)} - \frac{E}{f'(x_1)}.$$

Now from Equation 29-10 we see that this last equation can be written

$$r = x_2 - \frac{E}{f'(x_1)},$$

and so

$$|r - x_2| = \frac{|E|}{|f'(x_1)|}.$$

Now from Inequality 29-7 we have

$$|r - x_2| \leq \frac{M}{2|f'(x_1)|}(r - x_1)^2,$$

where M is a number such that $|f''(x)| \leq M$ for every number x between r and x_1. If we can find a positive number m such that $|f'(x)| \geq m$ for every number x in the interval in which we are working, then we will have $|f'(x_1)| \geq m$, and therefore $\frac{M/2}{|f'(x_1)|} \leq \frac{M}{2m}$. So the absolute errors $|r - x_2|$ and $|r - x_1|$ are related by the inequality

$$\boldsymbol{|r - x_2| \leq \frac{M}{2m}|r - x_1|^2.} \tag{29-12}$$

Example 29-5. To two decimal places $\sqrt{45} = 6.71$. Use Newton's Method to find a closer approximation.

Solution. The number $\sqrt{45}$ is a zero of the function f defined by the equation $f(x) = x^2 - 45$. Here $f'(x) = 2x$, and if we use $x_0 = 6.71$, Equation 29-9 gives us

$$x_1 = 6.71 - \frac{(6.71)^2 - 45}{2(6.71)} = 6.70820.$$

Since $f''(x) = 2$, $M = 2$. Surely we need only consider numbers greater than $x = 6$, so that $f'(x) = 2x > 2 \cdot 6 = 12$. Therefore we can take $m = 12$, and Inequality 29-12 (with x_1 and x_2 replaced by x_0 and x_1) reads

$$|\sqrt{45} - x_1| \leq (\tfrac{1}{12})|\sqrt{45} - 6.71|^2.$$

We said that 6.71 approximates $\sqrt{45}$ to two decimal places, and that statement means that

$$|\sqrt{45} - 6.71| \leq .005 = (\tfrac{1}{2})10^{-2}.$$

Therefore

$$|\sqrt{45} - 6.71|^2 \leq (\tfrac{1}{4})10^{-4},$$

and we have

$$|\sqrt{45} - x_1| \leq (\tfrac{1}{12}) \cdot (\tfrac{1}{4}) \cdot 10^{-4} < (\tfrac{1}{4})10^{-5}.$$

We can conclude from this last inequality and our expression for x_1 that to five decimal places $\sqrt{45} = 6.70820$.

Problems 29

1. Use Formula 29-2 to find approximations of the following numbers.

(a) $\sqrt{26}$ (b) $\sqrt{120}$

(c) $\sqrt[5]{34}$ (d) $\sqrt[3]{9}$

(e) $\dfrac{1}{\sqrt[3]{65}}$ (f) $\sin 1°$

(g) $\dfrac{1}{\sqrt[4]{85}}$ (h) $\cos 1°$

2. A flat circular ring with an outside radius of b inches and an inside radius of a inches has an area of A square inches. Let $f(r) = \pi r^2$, and use Formula 29-2 to find a formula for a number A_1 that is an approximation to A. What is the formula for A? Show that $A_1 < A$. If $b = 10$ and $a = 9$, compute the percentage error of the approximation.

3. Use $\sqrt{2} = 1.4142$ and $\pi/4 = .7854$ to compute an approximation to $\sin .78$ with the aid of Formula 29-2.

4. Find a formula for the approximate volume of material in a thin cylindrical shell h inches tall with an inside radius of r inches and a wall thickness of t inches.
5. Find a formula for the approximate volume of material in a thin spherical shell with an inside radius of r inches and a wall thickness of t inches.
6. In each case use Newton's Method to find a solution to the given equation.

(a) $x^3 - 12x^2 + 45x - 35 = 0$	(b) $x^3 + x - 1 = 0$
(c) $x + \cos 2x = 0$	(d) $x + 1 = \tan x$
(e) $3 \sin x = x^2$	(f) $x^2 = 2 \cos x$
(g) $x - 2 \sin x = 0$	(h) $\cos t = \sin 3t$

7. A limber stick 8 feet long is bent into a circular arc by tying the ends together with a piece of string 6 feet long. What is the radius of the arc?
8. Suppose you let the number x_1 be an approximation of the number $\sqrt{a}$. Show that Newton's Method leads you to take $(x_1^2 + a)/2x_1$ as your next approximation.
9. Generalize the result in the preceding problem when you are approximating $\sqrt[n]{a}$.
10. Find the point of the graph of the equation $y = x^2$ that is closest to the point $(1, 0)$.
11. Fill in the details of the following sketch of the derivation of Inequality 29-7. Let $G(x) = f(x) + f'(x)(b - x) + E(b - x)^2/(b - a)^2$. With the aid of Equation 29-4, it is easy to see that $G(b) = G(a) = f(b)$. Therefore, according to Rolle's Theorem, there is a number c between a and b such that $G'(c) = 0$. When we calculate $G'(x)$ and replace x with c, we find that the equation $G'(c) = 0$ becomes $f'(c) - f'(c) + f''(c)(b - c) - 2E(b - c)/(b - a)^2 = 0$. We solve this equation for E. Thus $E = f''(c)(b - a)^2/2$. Since $|f''(c)| \leq M$, Equation 29-7 follows immediately.
12. We say that a number A approximates a number N to **within p decimal places** if $|N - A| \leq (\frac{1}{2})10^{-p}$ (why?). Use Inequality 29-12 to show that if f is a function for which $M/m \leq 4$, and if x_1 approximates r to within p decimal places, then x_2 will approximate r to within $2p$ decimal places.

30. Implicit Differentiation

The equation

$$y = \sqrt{1 - x^2} \tag{30-1}$$

defines a differentiable function f in the interval $(-1, 1)$. We can use our differentiation rules to find the derivative $D_x y$:

$$D_x y = D_x(1 - x^2)^{1/2} = \frac{-x}{\sqrt{1 - x^2}}. \tag{30-2}$$

Another way to find $D_x y$ is the following. If y is given by Equation 30-1, then the equation

$$x^2 + y^2 = 1 \tag{30-3}$$

is an identity. Hence

$$D_x(x^2 + y^2) = D_x 1;$$

that is,

$$D_x x^2 + D_x y^2 = 0,$$

(30-4) $$2x + D_x y^2 = 0.$$

To find $D_x y^2$, we note that $y = f(x)$, so that we can use the Power Formula (incorporated in the Chain Rule):

$$D_x y^2 = 2y D_x y.$$

When we substitute this result in Equation 30-4, we get the equation

$$2x + 2y D_x y = 0.$$

From this equation we see that

(30-5) $$D_x y = \frac{-x}{y}.$$

Notice that Equation 30-5 is the same as Equation 30-2 (recall that $y = \sqrt{1 - x^2}$). The second method we used to find $D_x y$ is called **implicit differentiation.**

In the example above we wanted to find y', and we had an explicit equation (Equation 30-1) for y. We can use either the explicit Equation 30-1 or the implicit Equation 30-3 to find $D_x y$. In the examples that follow we will be given only an implicit equation. For example, we might consider the equation

(30-6) $$x^2 + y^5 - 4y = 0.$$

We cannot find a simple explicit expression for y in terms of x, but we will assume that there is a differentiable function f such that if we set $y = f(x)$ in the left side of Equation 30-6, we obtain the identity

(30-7) $$x^2 + [f(x)]^5 - 4f(x) = 0.$$

We then use implicit differentiation to find $D_x y$. We first differentiate both sides of Identity 30-7, or what amounts to the same thing, both sides of Equation 30-6:

(30-8) $$2x + D_x y^5 - 4D_x y = 0.$$

We use the Power Rule to find $D_x y^5 = 5y^4 D_x y$. Therefore, Equation 30-8 becomes

$$2x + (5y^4 - 4)D_x y = 0.$$

We then solve this equation for $D_x y$ and find that

$$D_x y = \frac{2x}{4 - 5y^4}.$$

The justification for assuming that there is a differentiable function f such that Equation 30-7 is an identity can best be left to a more advanced course. Here we will be content to give examples of how implicit differentiation works and the kind of results we can expect from it. The main point to keep in mind is that a derivative of the form $D_x f(y)$ *is a derivative with respect to* x. Therefore, we must use the Chain Rule:

$$D_x f(y) = f'(y) D_x y.$$

We used this rule when we calculated $D_x y^5$ in the preceding example.

Example 30-1. Use implicit differentiation to find $D_x y$ if $y^3 - 3 \sin x = 2$, and verify your answer.

Solution. We differentiate both sides of our given equation with respect to x:

$$D_x y^3 - 3D_x \sin x = D_x 2.$$

According to the Power Formula, $D_x y^3 = 3y^2 D_x y$, so

$$3y^2 D_x y - 3 \cos x = 0.$$

From this equation we get

$$D_x y = \frac{\cos x}{y^2}.$$

The only real solution to our original equation is

$$y = \sqrt[3]{2 + 3 \sin x}.$$

Then

$$D_x y = \tfrac{1}{3}(2 + 3 \sin x)^{-2/3}(3 \cos x)$$
$$= \frac{\cos x}{\left(\sqrt[3]{2 + 3 \sin x}\right)^2} = \frac{\cos x}{y^2},$$

so implicit differentiation gave us the correct derivative.

Example 30-2. The point $(\sqrt{2}, \pi/4)$ is a point of the graph of the equation $x \sin y = 2x^2 - 3$. Find the slope of the line tangent to the graph at this point.

Solution. We differentiate both sides of our given equation with respect to x:

$$D_x(x \sin y) = D_x(2x^2 - 3). \tag{30-9}$$

The right side of this last equation is clearly $4x$. To calculate the left side we use the Product Rule. Thus

$$D_x(x \sin y) = (D_x x) \sin y + x D_x \sin y$$
$$= \sin y + x \cos y D_x y.$$

Equation 30-9 now becomes

$$\sin y + x \cos y D_x y = 4x.$$

We are interested in the point $(\sqrt{2}, \pi/4)$, so we substitute these coordinates in this equation to obtain the equation

$$\frac{1}{\sqrt{2}} + \frac{\sqrt{2}}{\sqrt{2}} D_x y = 4\sqrt{2}.$$

This equation yields

$$D_x y = 4\sqrt{2} - \frac{1}{\sqrt{2}} = \frac{7}{\sqrt{2}}.$$

Example 30-3. At what points of the graph of the equation $\frac{x^2}{4} - y^2 = 1$ are the tangent lines parallel to the line $y = x + 3$?

Solution. Since the slope of the line $y = x + 3$ is 1, we are looking for those points of the graph at which the tangent lines have slope 1. If we differentiate both sides of our given equation with respect to x, we obtain the equation

$$D_x\left(\frac{x^2}{4} - y^2\right) = D_x 1.$$

As we perform the various differentiations, this equation becomes

$$D_x\left(\frac{x^2}{4}\right) - D_x y^2 = 0,$$

and then

$$\frac{x}{2} - 2y\, D_x y = 0,$$

so the tangent line at a point (x, y) has slope

$$D_x y = \frac{x}{4y}.$$

We are interested in finding those points at which the slope is 1. If (x, y) is such a point, $x/4y = 1$, or

(30-10) $$x = 4y.$$

But those points must also belong to our curve, and so their coordinates must satisfy the equation of the curve

(30-11) $$\frac{x^2}{4} - y^2 = 1.$$

Equations 30-10 and 30-11 form a system of simultaneous equations whose solutions are the answers to our original question. You may verify that the solutions to this system are the points $(4/\sqrt{3}, 1/\sqrt{3})$ and $(-4/\sqrt{3}, -1/\sqrt{3})$.

Example 30-4. Sketch the graph of the equation

$$y^2 = 2x^2 - x^4 + 8.$$

Solution. When $x = 0$, we have $y = \sqrt{8}$ or $y = -\sqrt{8}$. The X-coordinates of the points at which $y = 0$ satisfy the equation $2x^2 - x^4 + 8 = 0$. It is easy to solve this equation and find that $x = 2$ or $x = -2$ when $y = 0$. We find D_xy by implicit differentiation:

$$2yD_xy = 4x - 4x^3$$

and hence

$$D_xy = \frac{2x(1 - x^2)}{y}.$$

We see that $D_xy = 0$ when $x = 0, 1,$ or -1. Our results are summarized in the table in Fig. 30-1.

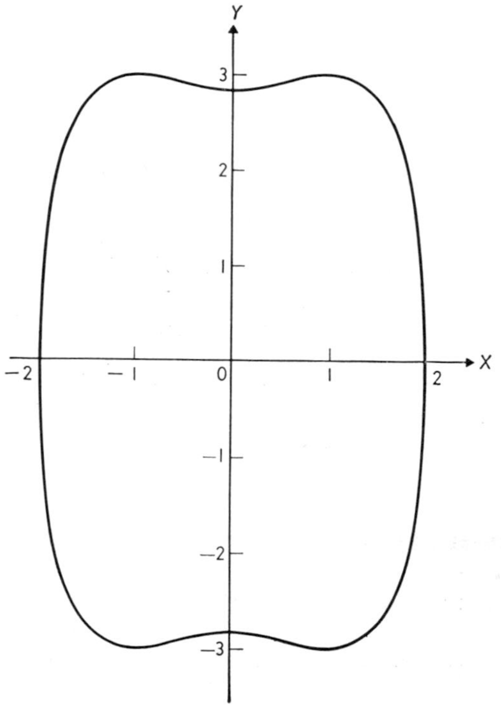

x	y	D_xy
0	$\sqrt{8}$	0
0	$-\sqrt{8}$	0
−1	3	0
−1	−3	0
1	3	0
1	−3	0
−2	0	—
2	0	—

Figure 30-1

Problems 30

1. Use implicit differentiation to compute $D_x y$ if:
   (a) $3y^5 + 5y^3 + 15y = 15x$
   (b) $2x^2 - 5y^2 - 8 = 0$
   (c) $x^3 + y^3 - 20x = 5$
   (d) $x^2y + y^3 - 4 = 0$
   (e) $xy^3 - 2xy + y^2 = 7$
   (f) $\sqrt{xy} + x^4y = 3$
   (g) $x^2 = (x - y)/(x + y)$
   (h) $y^2 = x^2 + 1/x^2$
   (i) $x^2y^2 = x^2 + y^2$
   (j) $y^2 = x^2 - x$
2. Find the slope of each of the following curves at the given point.
   (a) $x^2 + xy + 2y^2 = 28$; $(2, 3)$
   (b) $x^3 - 3xy^2 + y^3 = 1$; $(2, -1)$
   (c) $b^2x^2 + a^2y^2 = a^2b^2$; (x_0, y_0)
   (d) $(x - y)/(x - 2y) = 2$; $(3, 1)$
3. Show that the graph of the equation $y^2 = 6x + 9$ intersects the graph of the equation $y^2 = 9 - 6x$ at right angles.
4. Find the equation of the tangent to the graph of the equation $x^my^n = a^{m+n}$ at the point (x_0, y_0) of the graph.
5. Show that the graphs of the equations $x^2 - y^2 = 5$ and $4x^2 + 9y^2 = 72$ intersect at right angles.
6. Find the equations of the two tangents to the graph of the equation $4x^2 + y^2 = 72$ that contain the point $(4, 4)$.
7. (a) Show that if (i) $x^2 - 2y^2 = 4$, then (ii) $D_x y = x/2y$.
   (b) Differentiate both sides of Equation (ii) to obtain

   (iii) $D_x^2 y = \dfrac{y - xD_x y}{2y^2}.$

   (c) Use Equation (ii) to transform Equation (iii) into the equation

$$D_x^2 y = -1/y^3.$$

8. Use the method employed in Problem 7 to compute $D_x^2 y$ if:
   (a) $x^2 + y^2 = 1$
   (b) $x^3 + y^3 = 1$
   (c) $y^2 = 4ax$
   (d) $x^4 + 2x^2y^2 = \pi$
9. Sketch the graphs of the following equations.
   (a) $y^2(2 - x) = x^3$
   (b) $x^2y^2 = (y + 1)^2(4 - y^2)$
   (c) $x\sqrt{1 + y} = x^2 - y$
   (d) $(x^2 + y^2)^2 = (x^2 - y^2)$
   (e) $x^{2/3} + y^{2/3} = 1$
   (f) $y + \sqrt{xy} = x^2$

Review Problems, Chapter Three

You can use the following problems to test yourself on the material covered in this chapter.

1. Sketch the graph of the equation $y = 1 + \sqrt[3]{x - 3}$.
2. Sketch the graph of the equation $y = \dfrac{x^2}{x^2 - 9}$.

3. Let $f(x) = x^3 - 3x$. Find the maximum and minimum values of f on the interval $[-3, 2]$. Find the interval(s) in which the graph of f is concave down.
4. A can with no top is to be made in the form of a cylinder with a circular base, and its volume is to be V cubic inches. If the can is h inches tall and has a base radius of r inches, then the can with the least surface area has dimensions such that
(a) $r = h^2$, (b) $r^2 = h$, (c) $r = 2h$, (d) $r = h$, (e) $2r = h$.
5. Use information about maximum and minimum points and concavity to make a graph of the equation $y = -x\sqrt{3 - x^2}$.
6. Suppose you are told that there are no maximum or minimum points of the graph of the equation $y = ax^3 + bx^2 + cx + d$. What can you conclude about the numbers a, b, and c?
7. A rectangle is to have one side along the X-axis and two vertices on the circle with a radius of 5 whose center is the origin. What is the largest possible perimeter that such a rectangle can have?
8. One end of a 40-foot rope is fastened to a weight and the other end is passed through a pulley 25 feet above the ground to a man who holds it 5 feet above the ground. The man walks directly away from the spot under the weight at the rate of 5 feet per second. How fast is the weight being raised when it is 10 feet above the ground?
9. Find y' if $x^2y^2 = 4 + y$. Are there any maximum or minimum points of the graph of this equation?
10. A line segment is to join the point $(0, \frac{1}{2})$ to a point P in the first quadrant that is a point of the graph of the equation $y = 1/x^2$. Locate P so that the line segment is as short as possible.
11. Find the slope of the tangent to the graph of the equation $x^2 - x\sqrt{xy} - 2y^2 = 6$ at the point $(4, 1)$.
12. An open trough is to be made in the form of a half-cylinder. The trough is to hold 1000 cubic feet when full. Determine the radius and length of the trough that requires the least material to construct.
13. Find the point of the unit circle whose center is the origin that is closest to the point $(3, 4)$.
14. Suppose that during some time interval the velocity v and acceleration a of a point moving along a number scale are such that $v > 0$ and $a < 0$. What can you conclude about the speed of the moving point?
15. A particle moves along a line in such a way that its acceleration is given by the equation $a = \sin t^2$. At what times $(t > 0)$ is the velocity a maximum?
16. A man in a rowboat is 2 miles off a straight shoreline, directly out from a large rock on the beach. He wishes to reach a point that is 5 miles down the shore from the rock. He can row at the rate of 3 miles per hour and run at the rate of 9 miles per hour. How many miles from the rock should he dock his boat in order to reach his destination as quickly as possible?
17. A cylindrical tin can, closed at the top and bottom, is to be made to contain a volume of 24 cubic inches. No waste is involved in cutting the tin for the vertical side of the can, but each circular end piece is to be stamped from a square, and the "corners" of the square are wasted. Find the radius of the most economical can that can be manufactured in this way.

18. A wire 2 feet long is to be cut into two pieces. One piece is then used to form a circle, and the other piece is used to form a square. How much wire should be used to form the square if the sum of the areas enclosed by the circle and the square is to be a minimum?
19. Use Approximation Formula 29-2 to find an approximation of the number cos 3.
20. Sketch the graph of the equation $y^2 + x^4 = x^2$.
21. Town B is 10 miles upstream from Town A. The current in the stream is 3 miles per hour. The rate of fuel consumption (in gallons per hour) of a certain boat is proportional to the cube of its velocity. What is the most economical cruising speed for the boat to maintain when it makes a trip from Town A to Town B? from Town B to Town A?

4 THE CONICS

The graph of an equation consists of exactly those points whose coordinates satisfy the equation. Certain figures—lines and circles, for example, occur frequently in mathematics and its applications, and it is very useful to have analytical representations of such figures in terms of equations. We have already discussed the equations of lines, and now we are ready to take up more complicated curves—the circle, the ellipse, the hyperbola, and the parabola. We will first treat these curves individually. Then in Section 35 we shall show how the last three, which are collectively known as *conics*, are related.

31. The Circle. Translation of Axes

We have already dealt with equations of circles in certain special cases. In Example 6-4, for instance, we found that the equation of the circle with a radius of 2 and whose center is the point $(2, -1)$ is $(x - 2)^2 + (y + 1)^2 = 4$. Let us recall the steps that we followed in deriving that equation. First, we knew the geometrical definition of a circle—a circle with a radius of 2 is the set of all points that are 2 units distant from the center. Next, we used the distance formula to write an equation that expressed this geometrical condition, and this equation was the equation of the circle. In the general case of the circle with a radius of r and with the point (h, k) as center, we proceed in the same way. If (x, y) is any point of this circle, then it is r units from the point (h, k) (see Fig. 31-1). Therefore, the distance formula yields the equation

$$\sqrt{(x - h)^2 + (y - k)^2} = r.$$

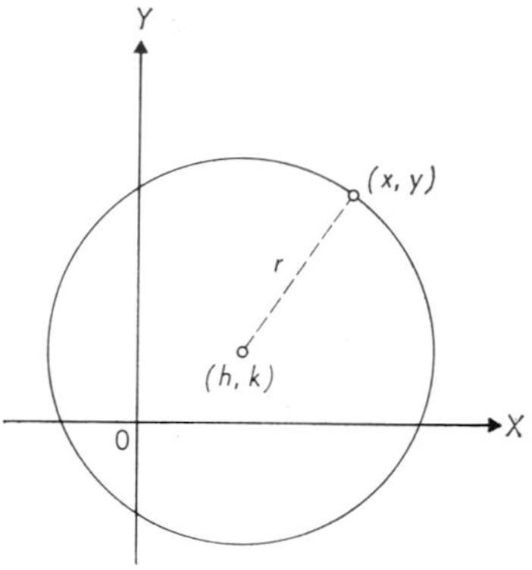

Figure 31-1

Conversely, if the numbers x and y satisfy this equation, then the point (x, y) belongs to the circle. We square both sides of this equation and get the following result: *The equation of the circle with radius r whose center is the point (h, k) is*

$$(31\text{-}1) \qquad (\mathbf{x} - \mathbf{h})^2 + (\mathbf{y} - \mathbf{k})^2 = \mathbf{r}^2.$$

For example, the equation of the circle with a radius of 3 whose center is the point $(0, -1)$ is $x^2 + (y + 1)^2 = 9$; that is, $x^2 + y^2 + 2y - 8 = 0$.

Example 31-1. Find the center and radius of the circle whose equation is

$$x^2 - 4x + y^2 + 8y - 5 = 0.$$

Solution. We can find the radius and the coordinates of the center by inspection (and, incidentally, verify the fact that the given equation *is* a circle) if we write the equation in the form of Equation 31-1. In order to do so, we "complete the square" as follows:

$$\begin{aligned}(x^2 - 4x \qquad) + (y^2 + 8y \qquad) &= 5,\\ (x^2 - 4x + 4) + (y^2 + 8y + 16) &= 5 + 4 + 16,\\ (x - 2)^2 + (y + 4)^2 &= 25.\end{aligned}$$

From our final form of the given equation, we see that its graph is the circle with a radius of 5 and with the point $(2, -4)$ as its center.

Example 31-2. Find the center of the circle that contains the following three points: (0, 0), (1, 0), and (1, 4).

Solution. If we denote the coordinates of the center of the circle containing these points by (h, k) and its radius by r, then its equation will be Equation 31-1. We are to find the numbers h and k. Since the three given points are to be points of the circle, the coordinates of each must satisfy this equation. So we substitute the coordinates of our three points in Equation 31-1 to obtain the three equations

$$(0 - h)^2 + (0 - k)^2 = r^2,$$

$$(1 - h)^2 + (0 - k)^2 = r^2,$$

and

$$(1 - h)^2 + (4 - k)^2 = r^2.$$

In other words,

$$h^2 + k^2 = r^2,$$

$$1 - 2h + h^2 + k^2 = r^2,$$

and

$$1 - 2h + h^2 + 16 - 8k + k^2 = r^2.$$

Now we subtract the first equation from the second and the second equation from the third and find that

$$1 - 2h = 0$$

and

$$16 - 8k = 0.$$

Thus $h = \frac{1}{2}$ and $k = 2$, so the center of our circle is the point $(\frac{1}{2}, 2)$.

For the circle with a radius of r whose center is the origin, Equation 31-1 reduces to

(31-2) $$x^2 + y^2 = r^2.$$

This equation is "simpler" than Equation 31-1. When dealing with geometrical problems in terms of coordinates, it is wise to choose the coordinate axes in order to make your equation as simple as possible. Sometimes it is even convenient to change coordinate axes in order to simplify things. One method of changing the coordinate axes is to perform a *translation of axes,* as we shall now illustrate.

Let us suppose that we have chosen a set of coordinate axes, shown in Fig. 31-2 by solid lines. We have labeled these axes the X-axis and Y-axis. Let us now select another set of coordinate axes, shown in Fig. 31-2 by dashed lines. We have labeled these axes the $\overline{X}$-axis and the $\overline{Y}$-axis. The $\overline{X}$-axis is parallel to the X-axis and $\frac{1}{2}$ unit above it. The $\overline{Y}$-axis is parallel to the Y-axis and 1 unit to the left of it. We say we have obtained the $\overline{X}\overline{Y}$-axes from the XY-axes by a **translation.** Any point P

in the plane can be described by either its XY-coordinates (x, y) or its $\overline{X}\overline{Y}$-coordinates $(\bar{x}, \bar{y})$. From Fig. 31-2 we see that the relation between the numbers x and $\bar{x}$ is $\bar{x} = x + 1$ and between the numbers y and $\bar{y}$ is

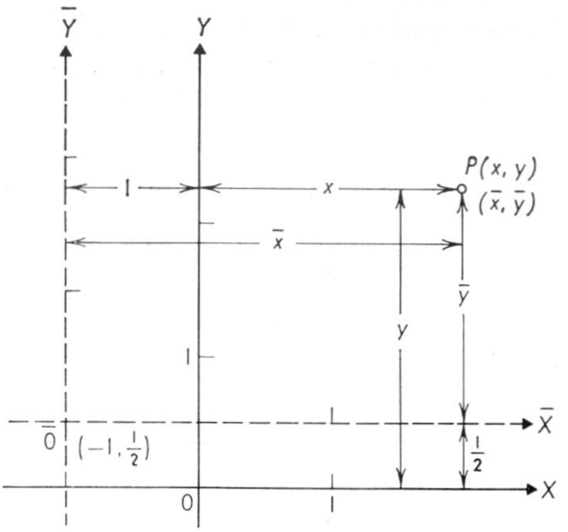

Figure 31-2

$\bar{y} = y - \frac{1}{2}$. Let us write these equations in the form

(31-3)
$$\bar{x} = x - (-1)$$
$$\bar{y} = y - \tfrac{1}{2}.$$

In particular, we notice that the origin of the $\overline{X}\overline{Y}$-coordinate system has $\overline{X}\overline{Y}$-coordinates $(0, 0)$ and XY-coordinates $(-1, \frac{1}{2})$. Thus to obtain the $\overline{X}\overline{Y}$-coordinates of a point P, we subtract the XY-coordinates of the origin of the $\overline{X}\overline{Y}$-coordinate system from the XY-coordinates of P.

Now let us consider a coordinate change in which we obtain new coordinates $(\bar{x}, \bar{y})$ for a point with original coordinates (x, y) by using the formulas

(31-4)
$$\boldsymbol{\bar{x} = x - h}$$
$$\boldsymbol{\bar{y} = y - k},$$

in which h and k are given numbers. It is clear from Equations 31-4 that the origin of the $\overline{X}\overline{Y}$-coordinate system—that is, the point whose $\overline{X}\overline{Y}$-coordinates are $(0, 0)$—is the point whose XY-coordinates are (h, k). Furthermore, every point whose $\overline{X}$-coordinate is zero belongs to the line $x = h$; that is, *the line $x = h$ is the $\overline{Y}$-axis*. Similarly, *the line $y = k$ is the $\overline{X}$-axis*. Thus we see that the coordinate change described by Equations 31-4 is a translation; the $\overline{X}$ and $\overline{Y}$ axes are parallel to the X and Y axes and have the same directions, and their intersection is the point whose XY-coordinates are (h, k). Equations 31-4 are called the **transformation of coordinates equations** for a **translation** of axes.

The equation of a graph depends not only on the set of points comprising the graph but also on the coordinate system we choose. Thus, for example, the same line may be represented by different equations in different coordinate systems.

Example 31-3. Suppose the coordinate axes are translated so that the origin of the $\bar{X}\bar{Y}$-coordinate system is the point whose XY-coordinates are $(2, -3)$. Write the equation of the line $3x - 2y + 7 = 0$ in terms of $\bar{x}$ and $\bar{y}$.

Solution. In this example, $h = 2$ and $k = -3$, so Equations 31-4 become

$$\bar{x} = x - 2 \quad \text{and} \quad \bar{y} = y + 3.$$

Thus we can replace x with $\bar{x} + 2$ and y with $\bar{y} - 3$ in the given equation of the line to obtain the equation $3(\bar{x} + 2) - 2(\bar{y} - 3) + 7 = 0$; that is, the equation of our line is $3\bar{x} - 2\bar{y} + 19 = 0$.

Now if we replace $x - h$ and $y - k$ in Equation 31-1 with the numbers $\bar{x}$ and $\bar{y}$ taken from the Translation Equations 31-4, we get

$$\bar{x}^2 + \bar{y}^2 = r^2. \tag{31-5}$$

So we see that with the aid of a suitable translation of the axes, the equation of a circle can always be reduced to the simple form of Equation 31-2.

Example 31-4. Find the translation of axes that will reduce the equation

$$3x^2 + 3y^2 + 7x - 9y + 2 = 0$$

to the form of Equation 31-5.

Solution. We could complete the square, as we did in Example 31-1, to find the center of our circle and then translate our axes so that the $\bar{X}\bar{Y}$-axes have their origin as this center. Instead we shall use an alternative method. We will replace x with $\bar{x} + h$ and y with $\bar{y} + k$ in our given equation and then choose h and k so that the resulting equation has the desired form. When we make the replacement, we obtain the equation

$$3(\bar{x} + h)^2 + 3(\bar{y} + k)^2 + 7(\bar{x} + h) - 9(\bar{y} + k) + 2 = 0.$$

Then we expand and collect terms:

$$3\bar{x}^2 + 3\bar{y}^2 + (6h + 7)\bar{x} + (6k - 9)\bar{y} = 9k - 7h - 3h^2 - 3k^2 - 2. \tag{31-6}$$

This equation can be put in the form of Equation 31-5 if we first make the coefficients of $\bar{x}$ and $\bar{y}$ equal to zero; that is,

$$6h + 7 = 0,$$
$$6k - 9 = 0.$$

Thus, $h = -\frac{7}{6}$ and $k = \frac{3}{2}$, and Equation 31-6 reduces to

$$3\bar{x}^2 + 3\bar{y}^2 = \tfrac{53}{6}.$$

We obtain an equation of the form of Equation 31-5 by dividing both sides of this last equation by 3. So the translation whose transformation of coordinates equations are

$$\bar{x} = x + \tfrac{7}{6},$$
$$\bar{y} = y - \tfrac{3}{2},$$

reduces our given equation to

$$\bar{x}^2 + \bar{y}^2 = \tfrac{53}{18}.$$

This equation, and hence the given equation, represents a circle with a radius of

$$r = \sqrt{\tfrac{53}{18}}.$$

Problems 31

1. Find the equations of the circles with the following points as centers and the given numbers as radii.
(a) $(3, -2)$, 5 (b) $(2, -1)$, 3
(c) $(-1, -1)$, 2 (d) $(3, 0)$, 3
(e) $(0, 0)$, $\frac{1}{2}$ (f) $(0, -4)$, 4

2. "Complete the square" to find the center and radius of each of the following circles.
(a) $x^2 + y^2 - 4x + 2y - 4 = 0$ (b) $x^2 - 2x + y^2 = 0$
(c) $x^2 + y^2 + 6x + 5 = 0$ (d) $x^2 + y^2 - 4y = 0$
(e) $x^2 + y^2 + 4x - 4y = 0$ (f) $4x^2 + 4y^2 - 4x - 3 = 0$
(g) $9x^2 + 9y^2 - 18x + 36y + 44 = 0$ (h) $x^2 + y^2 - \frac{2}{3}x - 2y = \frac{8}{9}$

3. Find the equation of the circle that:
(a) Contains the points $(0, 0)$, $(0, 1)$, and $(1, 0)$.
(b) Has the point $(2, 3)$ as its center and contains the origin.
(c) Has its center on the X-axis, contains the point $(0, 1)$, and has a radius of $\sqrt{17}$.

4. We construct an $\bar{X}\bar{Y}$-coordinate system from an XY-coordinate system by translating the axes so that the origin is translated to the point $(2, -3)$. What are the $\bar{X}\bar{Y}$-coordinates of the points whose XY-coordinates are:
(a) $(0, 0)$ (b) $(1, 3)$
(c) $(-5, 1)$ (d) $(-4, -4)$
(e) $(2, -3)$ (f) $(-2, 3)$

5. What are the XY-coordinates of the points whose $\bar{X}\bar{Y}$-coordinates (after the translation of Problem 4) are:
(a) $(0, 0)$ (b) $(1, 3)$
(c) $(-5, 1)$ (d) $(-4, -4)$
(e) $(2, -3)$ (f) $(-2, 3)$

6. Find one pair of numbers h and k so that after a translation of axes that translates the origin to the point (h, k) the equation $y = 3x - 2$ becomes $\bar{y} = m\bar{x}$. Find this number m.
7. Find a translation of axes such that the lines whose equations are $x - 3y + 7 = 0$ and $2x - y + 4 = 0$ intersect at the new origin. What are the equations of the lines in the $\bar{X}\bar{Y}$-coordinate system?
8. Find a translation of axes that reduces the equation $4x^2 + 4y^2 + 12x - 8y + 11 = 0$ to $\bar{x}^2 + \bar{y}^2 = r^2$.
9. A point moves so that it is always three times as far from the point $(0, -4)$ as it is from the point $(0, 4)$. Find the equation of the curve traced out by the point, sketch the curve, and perform a translation so as to simplify the equation of the curve.
10. Generalize the situation in the preceding problem by replacing "three" with r, where r is any positive number. Describe the path of the point in each of the following cases: $0 < r < 1$; $r = 1$; $r > 1$.
11. What relation among the coefficients a, b, and c is necessary in order that the graph of the equation $x^2 + y^2 + ax + by + c = 0$ be a circle?

32. The Ellipse. Symmetry

A circle can be considered as a special case of a curve known as an **ellipse.** Ellipses occur quite frequently in nature; satellites, for example, move in elliptical orbits. Although there are various geometrical definitions of an ellipse, we have chosen to start with the following one.

DEFINITION 32-1. *An **ellipse** is the set of points, the sum of whose distances from two given points is a given positive number.*

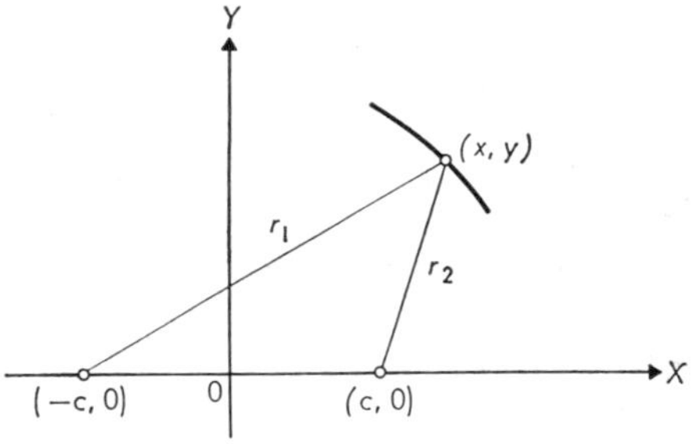

Figure 32-1

We shall use Fig. 32-1 to illustrate our definition. Here we have labeled our points in terms of a conveniently introduced coordinate system. The "two given points" mentioned in Definition 32-1 are the points $(-c, 0)$ and $(c, 0)$. They are called the **foci** of the ellipse. For each point (x, y) of the ellipse, the sum of the distances r_1 and r_2 to the foci is a "given positive number." It will simplify our later algebra if we use $2a$ to designate this number rather than a single letter. Thus Definition 32-1 says that

$$r_1 + r_2 = 2a \tag{32-1}$$

for each point (x, y) of the ellipse. The foci are $2c$ units apart, so since the sum of the lengths of two sides of a triangle is greater than the length of the third side, $r_1 + r_2 > 2c$. For our ellipse, therefore, $2a > 2c$; that is, $a > c$.

A simple mechanical procedure to follow in constructing an ellipse is to stick thumbtacks into each focus and then place a loop of string $2a + 2c$ units long around the tacks. Now put your pencil point inside the loop of string and draw it taut, thus obtaining the triangle shown in Fig. 32-1. As you move your pencil, keeping the string taut, you will trace out an ellipse.

To find the equation of the ellipse, we use the distance formula to express r_1 and r_2:

$$r_1 = \sqrt{(x + c)^2 + y^2} \quad \text{and} \quad r_2 = \sqrt{(x - c)^2 + y^2}.$$

When we substitute these numbers in Equation 32-1, we find that a point (x, y) is one of the points of our ellipse if, and only if, its coordinates satisfy the equation

$$\sqrt{(x + c)^2 + y^2} + \sqrt{(x - c)^2 + y^2} = 2a. \tag{32-2}$$

We could consider Equation 32-2 as the equation of our ellipse, but a little algebra enables us to reduce this equation to a much simpler form. To eliminate radicals we transpose the term

$$\sqrt{(x - c)^2 + y^2}$$

and square, thus obtaining

$$(x + c)^2 + y^2 = 4a^2 - 4a\sqrt{(x - c)^2 + y^2} + (x - c)^2 + y^2.$$

When we simplify the last equation, we have

$$a\sqrt{(x - c)^2 + y^2} = a^2 - cx,$$

so we square again to get

$$a^2[(x - c)^2 + y^2] = a^4 - 2a^2cx + c^2x^2.$$

Simplification now yields

$$(a^2 - c^2)x^2 + a^2y^2 = a^2(a^2 - c^2).$$

We noticed that $a > c$, so $a^2 - c^2 > 0$. We can therefore introduce the number $\boldsymbol{b = \sqrt{a^2 - c^2}}$, and our equation becomes

$$b^2x^2 + a^2y^2 = a^2b^2.$$

Now we divide both sides of this equation by a^2b^2 to get the final form of the equation of our ellipse:

$$\frac{x^2}{a^2} + \frac{y^2}{b^2} = 1. \tag{32-3}$$

The graph of this equation is shown in Fig. 32-2. We see from Equation

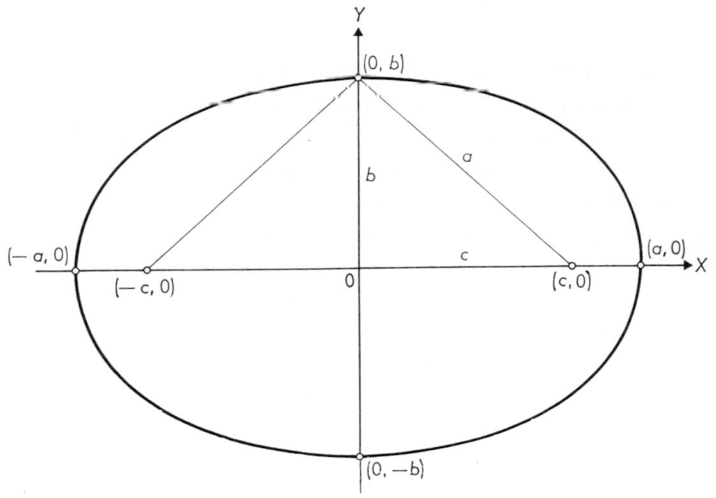

Figure 32-2

32-3 that a circle whose center is the origin and whose radius is r is the graph of the special case of Equation 32-3 in which $a = b = r$.

An ellipse is a highly symmetrical figure, and this fact is very useful in constructing its graph. Before we discuss the symmetry of the ellipse in particular, let us say a few words about the symmetry of graphs in general.

A graph is **symmetric with respect to a line** L if for every point P of the graph there is a point Q of the graph such that the line L is the perpendicular bisector of the segment PQ. In particular, *a graph is symmetric with respect to the Y-axis if for each point* (x, y) *of the graph the point* $(-x, y)$ *also belongs to the graph* because, as you can see, the Y-axis is the perpendicular bisector of the segment joining the points (x, y) and $(-x, y)$. Similarly, *a graph is symmetric with respect to the X-axis if for each point* (x, y) *of the graph, the point* $(x, -y)$ *also belongs to the graph.*

A graph is **symmetric with respect to a point** Q if for each point P of the graph there is a point R of the graph such that the point Q is the mid-point of the segment PR. In particular, *a graph is symmetric with* *respect to the origin if for each point* (x, y) *of the graph the point* $(-x, -y)$ *also belongs to the graph.*

We may replace x with $-x$, and y with $-y$, separately or together, in Equation 32-3 and obtain Equation 32-3 again, so our ellipse is symmetric with respect to the Y-axis, the X-axis, and the origin. The point of symmetry of an ellipse (here the origin) is called the **center** of the ellipse. An ellipse has two lines of symmetry, and the four points of intersection of the ellipse with its lines of symmetry are called the **vertices** of the ellipse. The vertices of the ellipse whose equation is Equation 32-3 are the points $(a, 0)$, $(-a, 0)$, $(0, b)$, and $(0, -b)$. A line segment that contains the center of an ellipse and joins a pair of points of the ellipse is called a **diameter** of the ellipse. The longest diameter of an ellipse is called its **major diameter,** and the shortest diameter is called its **minor diameter.** The major diameter of the ellipse in Fig. 32-2 joins the vertices $(a, 0)$ and $(-a, 0)$ and is $2a$ units long, whereas the minor diameter of this ellipse joins the vertices $(0, b)$ and $(0, -b)$ and is $2b$ units long (see Problem 7 of this section). Notice that the foci are points of the major diameter.

The graph of Equation 32-3 is also an ellipse if $b > a$. In that case

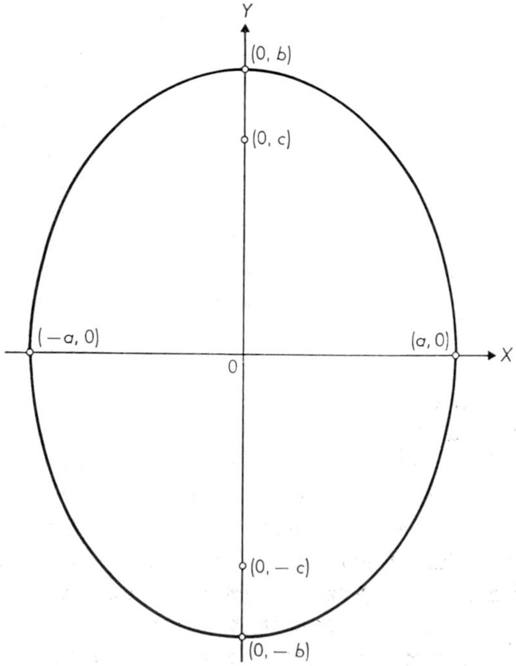

Figure 32-3

the major diameter of the ellipse joins the vertices $(0, -b)$ and $(0, b)$, whereas the minor diameter is the segment joining the points $(-a, 0)$ and $(a, 0)$. The "given positive number" in the definition of the ellipse is $2b$ in this case. The foci lie on the Y-axis. They are the points $(0, -c)$ and $(0, c)$, where c is the positive number that satisfies the equation $a^2 = b^2 - c^2$. Figure 32-3 shows an ellipse whose equation takes the form of Equation 32-3, with $b > a$.

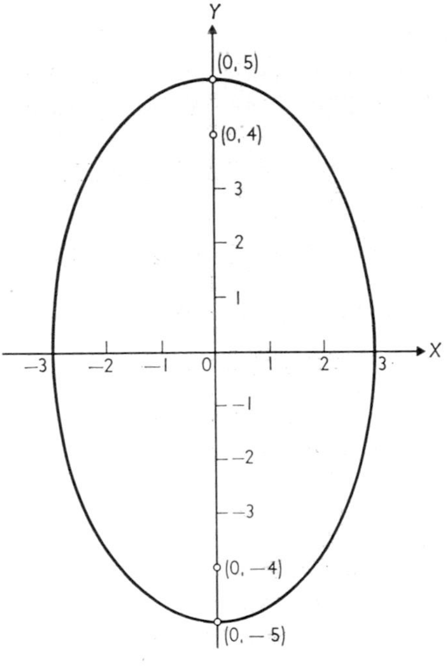

Figure 32-4

Example 32-1. Find the equation of the ellipse whose foci are the points $(0, 4)$ and $(0, -4)$ and which has $(0, 5)$ and $(0, -5)$ as vertices.

Solution. The desired equation takes the form of Equation 32-3; we are to find the numbers a and b. Because the foci lie on the Y-axis, $b > a$. Here $b = 5$ and $c = 4$, and we determine a from the equation $a^2 = b^2 - c^2$. Thus $a = \sqrt{25 - 16} = 3$. The equation of our ellipse is

$$\frac{x^2}{9} + \frac{y^2}{25} = 1,$$

and a sketch is shown in Fig. 32-4.

Equation 32-3 represents an ellipse whose center is the origin. Now let us suppose that we have an ellipse whose center is the point (h, k). We still assume that the major and minor diameters of the ellipse are parallel to the coordinate axes. If we choose a translated $\bar{X}\bar{Y}$-coordinate system whose origin is the point (h, k), then the equation of the ellipse relative to this new coordinate system takes the form of Equation 32-3; that is,

$$\frac{\bar{x}^2}{a^2} + \frac{\bar{y}^2}{b^2} = 1.$$

When we use the translation equations $\bar{x} = x - h$ and $\bar{y} = y - k$, the equation of our ellipse in the XY-coordinate system is

$$\frac{(x - h)^2}{a^2} + \frac{(y - k)^2}{b^2} = 1. \tag{32-4}$$

Example 32-2. Write the equation of the ellipse whose vertices are the points $(1, 1)$, $(5, 1)$, $(3, 6)$, and $(3, -4)$, and sketch its graph.

Solution. We first plot the given vertices (Fig. 32-5). These four points are the ends of the major and minor diameters of the ellipse. The diameter that is parallel to the Y-axis is 10 units long, and the diameter that is parallel to the X-axis is 4 units long. Thus $a = 2$ and $b = 5$. The center of an ellipse is the point where its major and minor diameters intersect. In this case the center is the point $(3, 1)$. Thus $h = 3$ and $k = 1$, and Equation 32-4 becomes

$$\frac{(x - 3)^2}{4} + \frac{(y - 1)^2}{25} = 1.$$

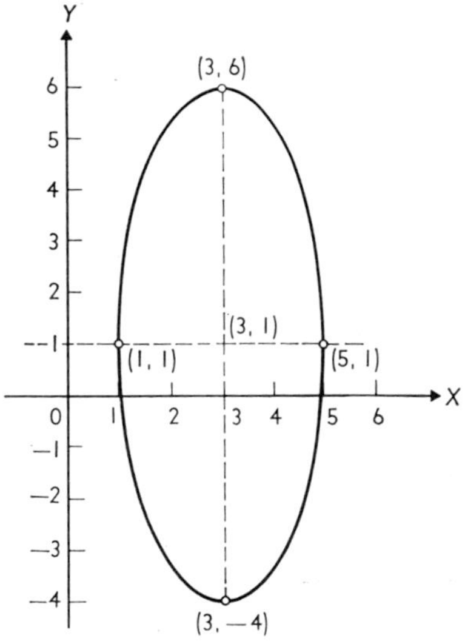

Figure 32-5

Example 32-3. Reduce the equation

$$9x^2 + 4y^2 + 18x - 16y - 11 = 0$$

to a simpler form by a translation of axes. What can you say about its graph?

Solution. The relations between the coordinates (x, y) of a point relative to the original XY-coordinate system and the coordinates $(\bar{x}, \bar{y})$ of the same point relative to a translated $\overline{X}\overline{Y}$-coordinate system are given by the Transformation Equations 31-4. So we replace x with $\bar{x} + h$ and y with $\bar{y} + k$ in our given equation and obtain the equation

$$9(\bar{x} + h)^2 + 4(\bar{y} + k)^2 + 18(\bar{x} + h) - 16(\bar{y} + k) - 11 = 0.$$

Now we will choose the numbers h and k to make this equation "simpler." When we multiply out and collect terms, we get

$$9\bar{x}^2 + 4\bar{y}^2 + (18h + 18)\bar{x} + (8k - 16)\bar{y} + 9h^2 + 4k^2 + 18h - 16k - 11 = 0.$$

If we choose $h = -1$ and $k = 2$, this equation becomes $9\bar{x}^2 + 4\bar{y}^2 - 36 = 0$, which immediately reduces to the standard form (relative to the $\overline{X}\overline{Y}$-coordinate system) of the equation of an ellipse:

$$\frac{\bar{x}^2}{4} + \frac{\bar{y}^2}{9} = 1.$$

So now we know that the graph of the given equation is an ellipse. Here $a = 2$, $b = 3$, and $c = \sqrt{b^2 - a^2} = \sqrt{5}$. The coordinates of the vertices of our ellipse in the $\overline{X}\overline{Y}$-coordinate system are $(-2, 0)$, $(2, 0)$, $(0, -3)$, and $(0, 3)$, and its foci are the points with $\overline{X}\overline{Y}$-coordinates $(0, -\sqrt{5})$ and $(0, \sqrt{5})$. Since $h = -1$ and $k = 2$, the XY- and $\overline{X}\overline{Y}$-coordinates are related by the equations $x = \bar{x} - 1$ and $y = \bar{y} + 2$. Therefore the $\overline{X}\overline{Y}$-coordinates of the vertices are $(-3, 2)$, $(1, 2)$, $(-1, -1)$, and $(-1, 5)$. The foci are the points $(-1, 2 - \sqrt{5})$ and $(-1, 2 + \sqrt{5})$.

Example 32-4. At what point in the first quadrant is the tangent to the ellipse

$$\frac{x^2}{16} + \frac{y^2}{9} = 1$$

parallel to the chord that contains the vertices $(4, 0)$ and $(0, 3)$?

Solution. To find the slope of the tangent at a point (x, y), we use implicit differentiation. Thus we will differentiate both sides of the equation $\frac{x^2}{16} + \frac{y^2}{9} = 1$ with respect to x to obtain the equation

$$\frac{2x}{16} + \frac{2yy'}{9} = 0,$$

from which we see that

$$y' = \frac{-9x}{16y}.$$

The slope of the chord joining the vertices (4, 0) and (0, 3) is $-\frac{3}{4}$. Since this chord is parallel to the tangent line, their slopes are equal. Therefore the coordinates (x, y) of our desired point satisfy the equation

$$\frac{-9x}{16y} = \frac{-3}{4};$$

that is,

$$y = 3x/4.$$

The numbers x and y also satisfy the equation of the ellipse, so

$$\frac{x^2}{16} + \frac{(3x/4)^2}{9} = 1,$$

and hence

$$x^2 = 8.$$

Thus (since (x, y) is in the first quadrant) $x = 2\sqrt{2}$, and $y = 3x/4 = 3\sqrt{2}/2$.

Problems 32

1. Find the equation of, and then sketch, the ellipse whose:
   (a) center is (0, 0), major diameter is along the X-axis and is 6 units long, and minor diameter is 4 units long.
   (b) center is (1, 3), major diameter is parallel to Y-axis and is 8 units long, and minor diameter is 2 units long.
   (c) center is (2, -1), major diameter is parallel to X-axis and is 4 units long, minor diameter is 2 units long.
   (d) center is (-3, 1), major diameter is parallel to Y-axis and is 5 units long, and minor diameter is 1 unit long.
2. An ellipse is to be constructed on an $8\frac{1}{2}''$ by $11''$ sheet of paper by the string and thumbtack method so that its major diameter is parallel to the $11''$ edge. Where should we place the tacks and how long a piece of string should we use in order to draw the largest possible ellipse on the paper?
3. Find the equations of the ellipses whose foci are the given points and whose lengths of major diameters are the given numbers.
   (a) (-2, 0), (2, 0), 8
   (b) (0, -1), (0, 1), 6
   (c) (1, 4), (3, 4), 4
   (d) (-1, -1), (-1, 7), 16
4. Find the equations of the ellipses whose vertices are:
   (a) (-3, 0), (3, 0), (0, -5), (0, 5)
   (b) (1, 2), (5, 2), (3, -1), (3, 5)
   (c) (0, -1), (12, -1), (6, -4), (6, 2)
   (d) (0, $\frac{1}{2}$), (2, $\frac{1}{2}$), (1, 0), (1, 2)
5. Find the foci of each of the following ellipses.
   (a) $9x^2 + 25y^2 - 18x + 100y - 116 = 0$
   (b) $5x^2 + y^2 + 20x - 2y + 16 = 0$
   (c) $x^2 + 2y^2 + 6x + 7 = 0$
   (d) $16x^2 + 4y^2 - 32x - 4y + 13 = 0$

6. Find the equations of the tangent and normal lines to the given ellipses at the indicated points.
(a) $4x^2 + 9y^2 = 72$, (3, 2). (b) $4x^2 + y^2 = 4$, (1, 0).
(c) $\dfrac{(x+1)^2}{8} + \dfrac{(y-2)^2}{2} = 1$, $(-3, 1)$.
(d) $x^2 + 2y^2 + 6x + 7 = 0$, $(-3, -1)$.
7. Use the methods described in Chapter 3 for finding maximum and minimum values to show that the ellipse whose equation is Equation 32-3, with $a > b$, has a major diameter (the diameter of maximum length) $2a$ units long and a minor diameter (the diameter of minimum length) $2b$ units long.
8. The segment that an ellipse cuts from a line that contains a focus and is perpendicular to the major diameter is called a **latus rectum** of the ellipse. Show that the length of a latus rectum of the ellipse whose equation is Equation 32-3 and whose major diameter lies along the X-axis is $\dfrac{2b^2}{a}$.
9. Consider an ellipse whose center is the origin and whose major diameter lies along the X-axis. Find the slope of the tangent line to the ellipse at the end-point of the latus rectum (see preceding problem) that lies in the first quadrant. Show that this tangent line cuts off a segment on the positive Y-axis that is half as long as the major diameter.
10. Equation 32-3 is the equation of an ellipse. A rectangle is to be inscribed in the ellipse so that its sides are parallel to the major and minor diameters of the ellipse. Show that the largest area that such a rectangle can have is $2ab$.
11. A point moves so that the line segments joining it to two given points are always perpendicular. Describe the path of the point.
12. What relations among the coefficients a, b, c, d, and e are necessary for the graph of the equation $ax^2 + by^2 + 2cx + 2dy + e = 0$ to be an ellipse?
13. Let us generalize the property in Problem 11 in the following way. A point moves so that the product of the slopes of the line segments joining it to two given points is $-k^2$ (-1 is a special case). Describe the path of the point. (Use the points $(-a, 0)$ and $(a, 0)$ as the given points and write the equation of the path.)

33. The Hyperbola

Our geometrical definition of a hyperbola is similar to our geometrical definition of an ellipse.

DEFINITION 33-1. *A **hyperbola** is the set of points, the difference of whose distances from two given points is a given positive number.*

We shall use Fig. 33-1 to illustrate this definition. In that figure we have referred all points to a conveniently chosen cartesian coordinate system. The "two given points" mentioned in Definition 33-1 are the points $(-c, 0)$ and $(c, 0)$; they are called the **foci** of the hyperbola. For each point (x, y) of the hyperbola, the difference between the distances r_1 and r_2 to the foci is a "given positive number." It will simplify our later algebra if we denote this number by $2a$. Thus if $r_1 > r_2$, then $r_1 - r_2 = 2a$, whereas if $r_1 < r_2$, then $r_2 - r_1 = 2a$. Both these cases are covered when we say that (x, y) is a point of our hyperbola if, and only if,

$$|r_1 - r_2| = 2a. \tag{33-1}$$

The sides of the triangle whose vertices are the points $(-c, 0)$, $(c, 0)$, and (x, y) have lengths of $2c$, r_1, and r_2. Since the difference in the lengths of two sides of a triangle is less than the length of the third side, $|r_1 - r_2| < 2c$. But $|r_1 - r_2| = 2a$, so in the case of the hyperbola, $a < c$.

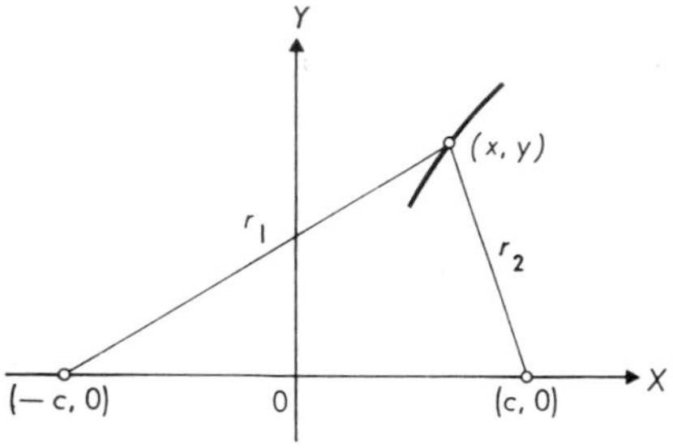

Figure 33-1

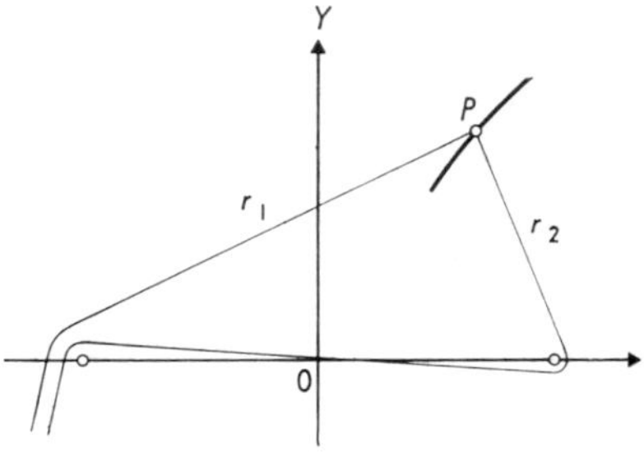

Figure 33-2

Just as in the case of the ellipse, we can construct an arc of a hyperbola by using a pencil, some string, and two thumbtacks. The tacks are placed at the foci, and the pencil is tied in the middle of the string. Then the string is looped around the tacks as shown in Fig. 33-2 (the pencil point is at P). We keep the string taut and move the pencil, paying out both strands of the string together. Thus the difference $r_1 - r_2$ is the same for any two points of the arc traced out by the pencil, so the arc must be part of a hyperbola.

We see that Equation 33-1 is equivalent to the equation

$$(r_1 - r_2)^2 = 4a^2.$$

Since

$$r_1 = \sqrt{(x + c)^2 + y^2} \quad \text{and} \quad r_2 = \sqrt{(x - c)^2 + y^2},$$

we find (after a little simplification) that a point (x, y) is one of the points of our hyperbola if, and only if, its coordinates satisfy the equation

$$x^2 + y^2 + c^2 - 2a^2 = \sqrt{(x + c)^2 + y^2}\sqrt{(x - c)^2 + y^2}.$$

Now we square and simplify to find that

$$(c^2 - a^2)x^2 - a^2y^2 = a^2(c^2 - a^2). \tag{33-2}$$

Since $c > a$, we may define the number $\boldsymbol{b} = \sqrt{\boldsymbol{c}^2 - \boldsymbol{a}^2}$. Therefore Equation 33-2 becomes $b^2x^2 - a^2y^2 = a^2b^2$, that is,

$$\frac{\boldsymbol{x}^2}{\boldsymbol{a}^2} - \frac{\boldsymbol{y}^2}{\boldsymbol{b}^2} = \mathbf{1}. \tag{33-3}$$

Replacing x with $-x$ and y with $-y$, separately or together, in Equation 33-3 does not alter the equation, so we see that our hyperbola is symmetric

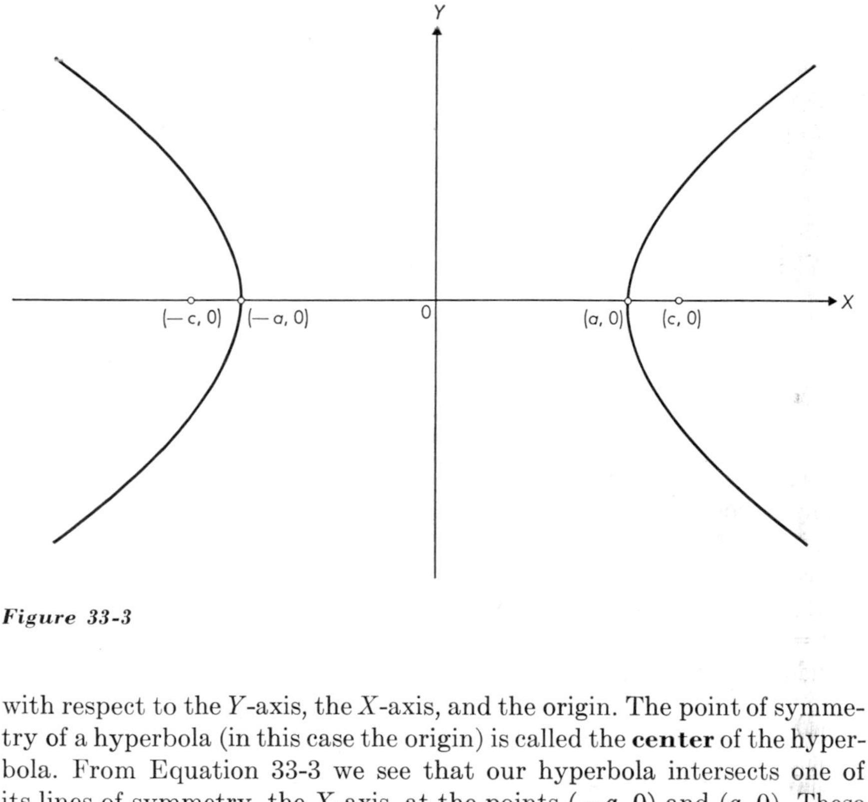

Figure 33-3

with respect to the Y-axis, the X-axis, and the origin. The point of symmetry of a hyperbola (in this case the origin) is called the **center** of the hyperbola. From Equation 33-3 we see that our hyperbola intersects one of its lines of symmetry, the X-axis, at the points $(-a, 0)$ and $(a, 0)$. These points are called the **vertices** of the hyperbola. The line segment joining the two vertices is called the **transverse diameter** of the hyperbola. Since there is no real number y that satisfies Equation 33-3 when $x = 0$, we see that our hyperbola does not intersect its other line of symmetry, the Y-axis. Figure 33-3 shows the graph of Equation 33-3.

Let us suppose for the moment that we consider only points in the first quadrant and solve Equation 33-3 for y to obtain $y = \frac{b}{a}\sqrt{x^2 - a^2}$, or the equivalent equation

(33-4) $$y = \frac{bx}{a}\sqrt{1 - \frac{a^2}{x^2}}.$$

Since $\sqrt{1 - a^2/x^2} < 1$, we see that $y < bx/a$. Hence the arc of the hyperbola that lies in the first quadrant is below the line whose equation is $y = bx/a$ (see Fig. 33-4). But if x is very large, $\sqrt{1 - (a^2/x^2)}$ is close to 1, and Equation 33-4 suggests that the equation of our hyperbola does not

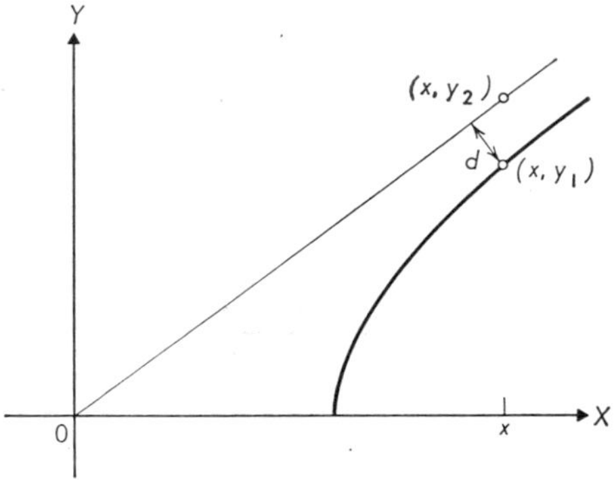

Figure 33-4

differ a great deal from the linear equation $y = (b/a)x$. Let us show that the hyperbola does in fact approximate (for large x) the line whose equation is $y = (b/a)x$. Let x be a large number and suppose that (x, y_1) is the corresponding point of the hyperbola. We wish to show that the (perpendicular) distance d between this point and the line whose equation is $y = (b/a)x$ is small. Now if (x, y_2) is the point of the line that corresponds to x, it is clear (Fig. 33-4) that

(33-5) $$d < y_2 - y_1.$$

We have $y_2 = (b/a)x$ and, according to Equation 33-4,

(33-6) $$y_1 = \frac{b}{a}\sqrt{x^2 - a^2}.$$

Hence

$$\begin{aligned} y_2 - y_1 &= \frac{b}{a}(x - \sqrt{x^2 - a^2}) \\ &= \frac{b}{a}(x - \sqrt{x^2 - a^2})\left[\frac{x + \sqrt{x^2 - a^2}}{x + \sqrt{x^2 - a^2}}\right] \end{aligned}$$

$$= \frac{b}{a}\frac{x^2 - (x^2 - a^2)}{x + \sqrt{x^2 - a^2}}$$

$$= \frac{ab}{x + \sqrt{x^2 - a^2}} < \frac{ab}{x}.$$

Therefore, $d < ab/x$, and we see that d is small when x is large. Thus for points in the first quadrant far to the right on our graph, the hyperbola practically coincides with the line $y = (b/a)x$. This line is called an **asymptote** of the hyperbola. It is not hard to see that for points in the third quadrant remote from the origin, the hyperbola also practically coincides with the line $y = (b/a)x$, whereas for points in the second and fourth quadrants, the line $y = -(b/a)x$ is an asymptote of the hyperbola.

The rectangle whose sides are parallel to the axes and contains the points $(-a, 0)$, $(a, 0)$, $(0, -b)$, and $(0, b)$ is called the **auxiliary rectangle** of our hyperbola. The asymptotes of the hyperbola are extensions of the diagonals of this rectangle. Our hyperbola, with the asymptotes drawn in, is the curve on the left in Fig. 33-5. If the auxiliary rectangle is a square, then the hyperbola is called an **equilateral hyperbola.**

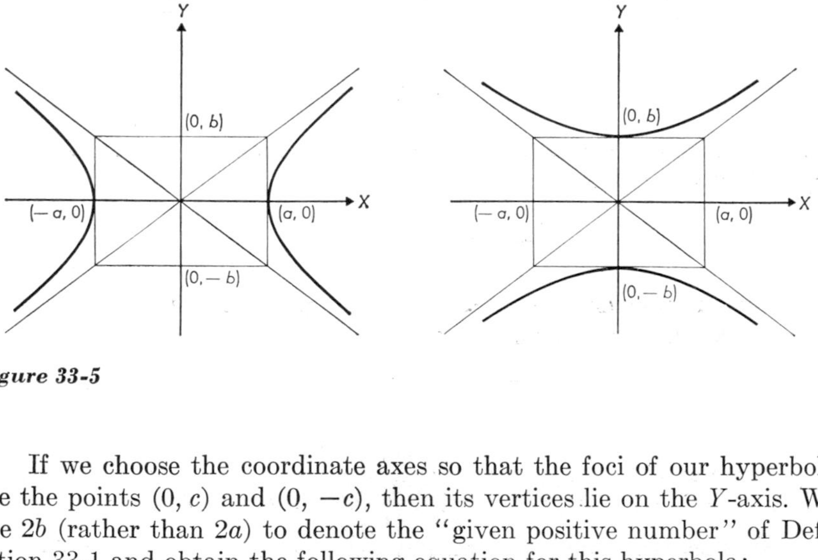

Figure 33-5

If we choose the coordinate axes so that the foci of our hyperbola are the points $(0, c)$ and $(0, -c)$, then its vertices lie on the Y-axis. We use $2b$ (rather than $2a$) to denote the "given positive number" of Definition 33-1 and obtain the following equation for this hyperbola:

(33-7) $$\frac{y^2}{b^2} - \frac{x^2}{a^2} = 1,$$

where again $a^2 + b^2 = c^2$. In this case the points $(0, -b)$ and $(0, b)$ belong to the hyperbola; they are the vertices of the hyperbola. We also see that there is no number x for which $y = 0$; that is, the curve does not intersect the X-axis. The graph of Equation 33-7 is shown on the right in Fig. 33-5. The asymptotes of both the hyperbolas in Fig. 33-5 are the same lines, and we say that these hyperbolas form a pair of **conjugate hyperbolas.**

Example 33-1. Find the equation of the hyperbola whose foci are the points (5, 0) and (−5, 0), and whose vertices are (4, 0) and (−4, 0).

Solution. We obtain the equation of this hyperbola by setting $c = 5$, $a = 4$, and $b = \sqrt{c^2 - a^2} = 3$ in Equation 33-3. Thus the equation of our hyperbola is

$$\frac{x^2}{16} - \frac{y^2}{9} = 1.$$

Its asymptotes are the lines $y = \frac{3}{4}x$ and $y = -\frac{3}{4}x$, and it looks like the hyperbola on the left in Fig. 33-5.

Now let us suppose that we have a hyperbola whose center is the point (h, k) and whose transverse diameter is parallel to the X-axis. If we choose a translated $\bar{X}\bar{Y}$-coordinate system whose origin is the point (h, k), then the equation of the hyperbola (according to Equation 33-3) is

$$\frac{\bar{x}^2}{a^2} - \frac{\bar{y}^2}{b^2} = 1.$$

Now since $\bar{x} = x - h$ and $\bar{y} = y - k$, the equation of the hyperbola in the XY-coordinate system is

$$\text{(33-8)} \qquad \boldsymbol{\frac{(x - h)^2}{a^2} - \frac{(y - k)^2}{b^2} = 1.}$$

In a similar manner, the equation of a hyperbola whose center is the point (h, k) and whose transverse diameter is parallel to the Y-axis is

$$\text{(33-9)} \qquad \boldsymbol{\frac{(y - k)^2}{b^2} - \frac{(x - h)^2}{a^2} = 1.}$$

Example 33-2. The foci of an equilateral hyperbola are the points (−3, 4) and (−3, −2). Find the equation of the hyperbola and sketch its graph.

Solution. We are to replace the letters a, b, h, and k in Equation 33-9 with appropriate numbers. The center of the hyperbola is midway between the two foci, so it is the point (−3, 1); hence $h = -3$ and $k = 1$ (Fig. 33-6). Since the hyperbola is equilateral, $a = b$. Now c is the distance between the center of the hyperbola and a focus, so in the present case, $c = 3$. Hence the equation $c^2 = a^2 + b^2$ becomes $9 = 2a^2$, and therefore $a^2 = b^2 = \frac{9}{2}$. The equation of our hyperbola is

$$\frac{2(y-1)^2}{9} - \frac{2(x+3)^2}{9} = 1;$$

its graph is shown in Fig. 33-6.

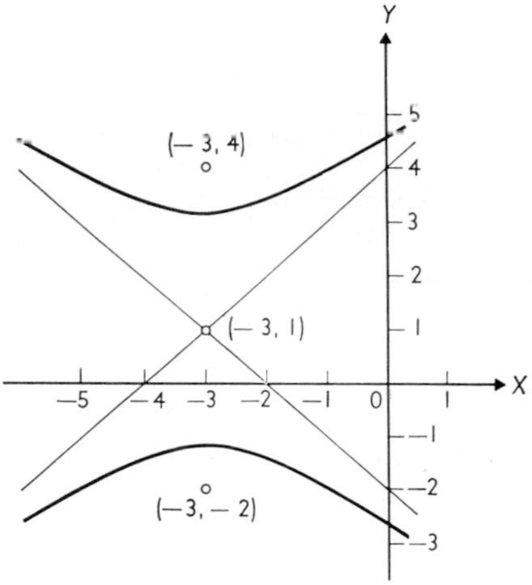

Figure 33-6

Example 33-3. Use a translation of axes to show that the graph of the equation $x^2 - 4y^2 - 4x - 8y - 4 = 0$ is a hyperbola.

Solution. In accordance with the Translation Equations 31-4, we will replace x with $\bar{x} + h$ and y with $\bar{y} + k$ to obtain

$$(\bar{x} + h)^2 - 4(\bar{y} + k)^2 - 4(\bar{x} + h) - 8(\bar{y} + k) - 4 = 0,$$
$$\bar{x}^2 - 4\bar{y}^2 + (2h - 4)\bar{x} - (8k + 8)\bar{y} + h^2 - 4k^2 - 4h - 8k - 4 = 0.$$

If we take $h = 2$ and $k = -1$, this equation becomes simply

$$\bar{x}^2 - 4\bar{y}^2 - 4 = 0;$$

that is,

$$\frac{\bar{x}^2}{4} - \frac{\bar{y}^2}{1} = 1.$$

This last equation is the standard form of the equation of a hyperbola in the $\overline{XY}$-coordinate system. Since $h = 2$ and $k = -1$, then $\bar{x} = x - 2$ and $\bar{y} = y + 1$, so the equation of our hyperbola relative to the XY-coordinate system is

$$\frac{(x-2)^2}{4} - \frac{(y+1)^2}{1} = 1.$$

This equation, of course, is simply the factored form of the given equation.

Problems 33

1. Find the foci, vertices, and asymptotes of the following hyperbolas and sketch them.
   (a) $x^2 - 4y^2 = 4$ (b) $4x^2 - y^2 = 4$
   (c) $x^2 - 4y^2 = -4$ (d) $4x^2 - y^2 = -4$
   (e) $\frac{(x+1)^2}{16} - \frac{(y-2)^2}{9} = 1$ (f) $4x^2 - y^2 = 1$
   (g) $\frac{(y+2)^2}{9} - \frac{(x-1)^2}{16} = 1$ (h) $y^2 - 9x^2 = 1$
2. Find the equation of the hyperbola whose foci are the vertices of the ellipse
$$\frac{x^2}{a^2} + \frac{y^2}{b^2} = 1$$
and whose vertices are the foci of this ellipse (assume that $a > b$).
3. Find the equation of the ellipse whose vertices are the foci of the hyperbola $11x^2 - 7y^2 = 77$ and whose foci are the vertices of this hyperbola.
4. Find the equation of the hyperbola whose foci and vertices are the points:
   (a) Foci: $(-3, 0)$, $(3, 0)$, Vertices: $(-2, 0)$, $(2, 0)$
   (b) Foci: $(0, -1)$, $(0, 1)$, Vertices: $(0, -\frac{1}{2})$, $(0, \frac{1}{2})$
   (c) Foci: $(-5, 1)$, $(7, 1)$, Vertices: $(-3, 1)$, $(5, 1)$
   (d) Foci: $(0, -2)$, $(0, 6)$, Vertices: $(0, -1)$, $(0, 5)$
5. Are there points of the graph of a hyperbola at which the tangent line is parallel to an asymptote?
6. Find the tangent and normal lines to the hyperbolas at the given point.
   (a) $8x^2 - 6y^2 = 48$, $(3, 2)$ (b) $9y^2 - 4x^2 = 32$, $(-1, -2)$
   (c) $(y-1)^2 - 12(x+2)^2 = 24$, $(-1, 7)$ (d) $x^2 - 4x - y^2 - 2y = 0$, $(0, 0)$
7. Find the equation of the hyperbola whose asymptotes are the given lines and which contains the given point.
   (a) $y = 2x$ and $y = -2x$, $(1, 1)$ (b) $y = 2x$ and $y = -2x$, $(0, 1)$
   (c) $y = x + 1$ and $y = -x + 3$, $(2, 4)$ (d) $y = x + 1$ and $y = -x + 1$, $(0, 0)$
8. The segment cut by a hyperbola from a line that contains a focus and is perpendicular to the transverse diameter is called a **latus rectum** of the hyperbola. Show that the length of a latus rectum of the hyperbola whose equation is Equation 33-3 is $\frac{2b^2}{a}$.
9. Find the slope of the tangent line at the end point of the latus rectum that is in the first quadrant if the equation of the hyperbola is Equation 33-3. Show that this tangent line cuts off a segment on the negative Y-axis half as long as the transverse diameter.
10. A point moves so that the product of the slopes of the line segments that join it to two given points is k^2. Describe the curve traced out by the point.

11. Consider the tangent to the hyperbola $\frac{x^2}{a^2} - \frac{y^2}{b^2} = 1$ at a point (h, k) of the hyperbola. Show that this tangent line intersects the asymptotes of the hyperbola at the points $\left(\frac{bh + ak}{b}, \frac{bh + ak}{a}\right)$ and $\left(\frac{bh - ak}{b}, \frac{ak - bh}{a}\right)$.

12. Use the result of the preceding question to prove the following theorem. If the tangent to a hyperbola at a point A intersects the asymptotes of the hyperbola at the points P and Q, then A is the midpoint of the line segment PQ.

34. The Parabola

As in our discussion of the ellipse and the hyperbola, we shall first give a geometrical definition of the parabola.

DEFINITION 34-1. *A parabola is a set of points, each of which is equidistant from a given point and a given line.*

The "given point" of Definition 34-1 is called the **focus** of the parabola; the "given line" is called the **directrix.**

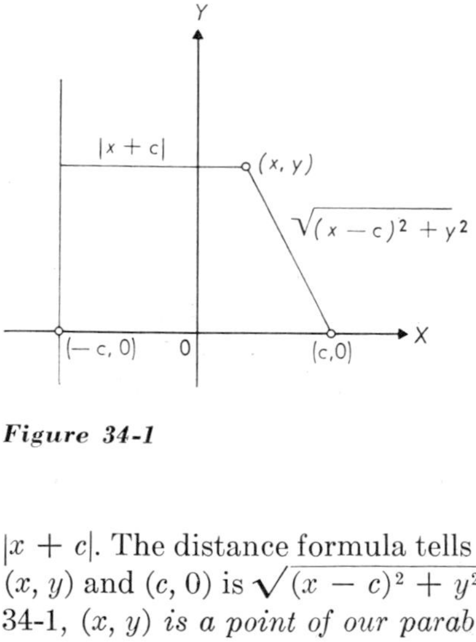

Figure 34-1

In order to obtain one form of the equation of a parabola, let us choose our coordinate axes so that the focus is the point $(c, 0)$ and the directrix is the line whose equation is $x = -c$. In Fig. 34-1 we have shown the focus and directrix if $c > 0$, but our discussion is valid if c is either positive or negative. The distance between a point (x, y) and the line $x = -c$ is the length of the perpendicular dropped from the point to the line and is equal to $|x + c|$. The distance formula tells us that the distance between the points (x, y) and $(c, 0)$ is $\sqrt{(x - c)^2 + y^2}$, so we see that, according to Definition 34-1, *(x, y) is a point of our parabola if, and only if,*

$$\sqrt{(x - c)^2 + y^2} = |x + c|.$$

When we square both sides of this equation and simplify, we get the equation

(34-1) $$\mathbf{y^2 = 4cx.}$$

Since we can replace y with $-y$ without changing Equation 34-1, we see that our parabola is symmetric with respect to the X-axis. The line of symmetry of a parabola (in this case the X-axis) is called the **axis** of the parabola. The axis of a parabola contains the focus and is perpendicular to the directrix.

The point of intersection of a parabola with its axis (in this case the origin) is the **vertex** of the parabola. The **focal length** of the parabola is the distance between the vertex and the focus (in this case $|c|$).

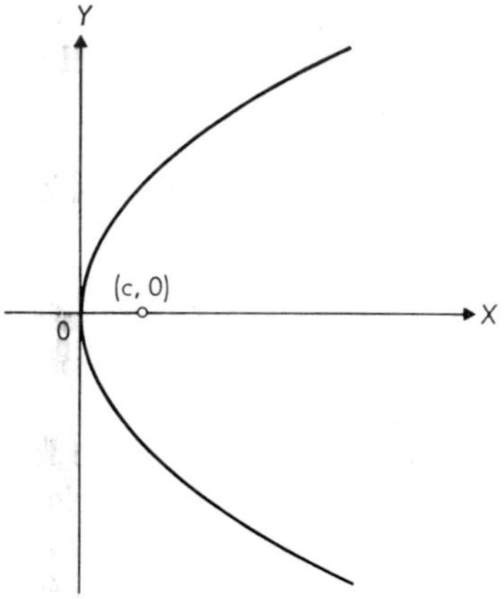

Figure 34-2

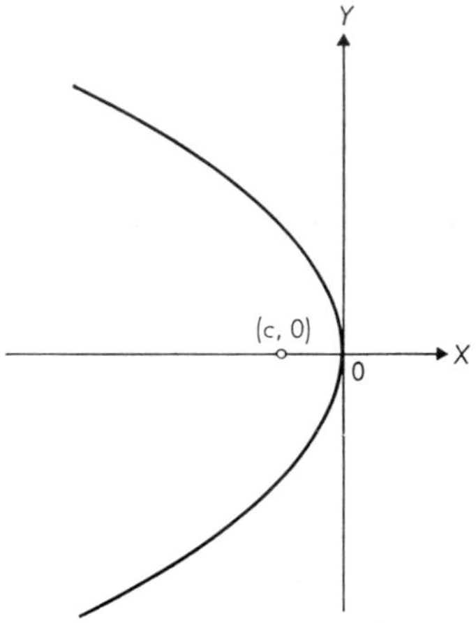

Figure 34-3

We shall now draw the parabola whose equation is Equation 34-1. Let us suppose for the moment that $c > 0$. Since the curve is symmetric about the X-axis, we need only sketch in those points for which $y > 0$, for we can obtain the remainder of the graph by reflecting this part about the X-axis. So we can suppose that

$$y = 2\sqrt{cx}.$$

Then it is easy to calculate that

$$y' = \sqrt{\frac{c}{x}} \quad \text{and} \quad y'' = -\frac{1}{2x}\sqrt{\frac{c}{x}}.$$

From the equation for y', we see that the slope is always positive (except where it is undefined at the origin), so the curve rises to the right. On the other hand, $y'' < 0$, so our parabola is concave down. Its graph is shown in Fig. 34-2.

When we sketched the parabola in Fig. 34-2, we assumed that $c > 0$. If $c < 0$, the parabola opens to the left, rather than to the right. The graph in this case is shown in Fig. 34-3.

If we choose the coordinate axes so that the focus of the parabola is the point $(0, c)$ of the Y-axis and the directrix is the line $y = -c$ parallel

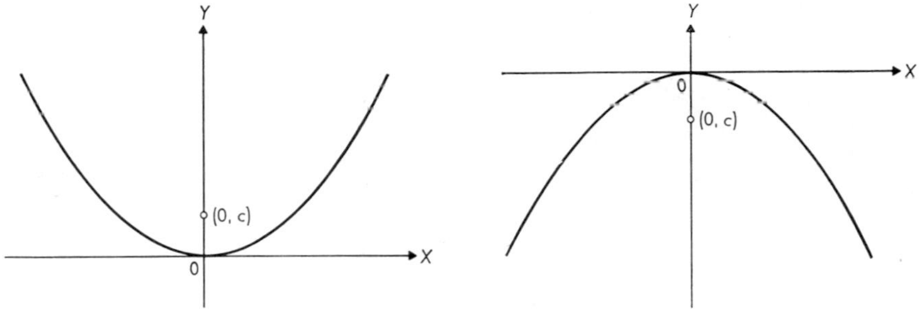

Figure 34-4

to the X-axis, then the vertex of the parabola is again the origin. However, the roles of x and y are now interchanged, so the line of symmetry of the parabola is the Y-axis, and its equation is

$$x^2 = 4cy. \tag{34-2}$$

If $c > 0$, the parabola opens upward as shown on the left in Fig. 34-4. If $c < 0$, the parabola opens downward as shown on the right in Fig. 34-4.

Example 34-1. Two parabolas intersect at the point (2, 2). The vertex of each parabola is the origin; one opens upward whereas the other opens to the right. Show that the product of the slopes of the curves at the point (2, 2) is 1.

Solution. The forms of the equations of the parabolas are

$$y^2 = 4c_1x \quad \text{and} \quad x^2 = 4c_2y.$$

We determine the numbers c_1 and c_2 by utilizing the fact that (2, 2) is a point of both parabolas. Hence $4 = 4c_1 \cdot 2$, so $c_1 = \frac{1}{2}$. In like manner, we find that $c_2 = \frac{1}{2}$, and so the equations of our parabolas are

$$y^2 = 2x \quad \text{and} \quad x^2 = 2y.$$

From the first of these equations we obtain the equation $2yy' = 2$, and therefore we see that $y' = \frac{1}{2}$ at the point (2, 2). From the equation $x^2 = 2y$ we calculate $y' = x$, and therefore $y' = 2$ at the point (2, 2). Thus the product of the slopes of the parabolas at the point (2, 2) is $\frac{1}{2} \cdot 2 = 1$.

Now let us suppose that we have a parabola whose vertex is the point (h, k) and whose directrix is the line $x = d$. If we choose a translated $\bar{X}\bar{Y}$-coordinate system whose origin is the point (h, k) and let $c = h - d$, then we can write the equation of our parabola as $\bar{y}^2 = 4c\bar{x}$. The graph of this parabola is shown in Fig. 34-5 (when $h > d$). Since

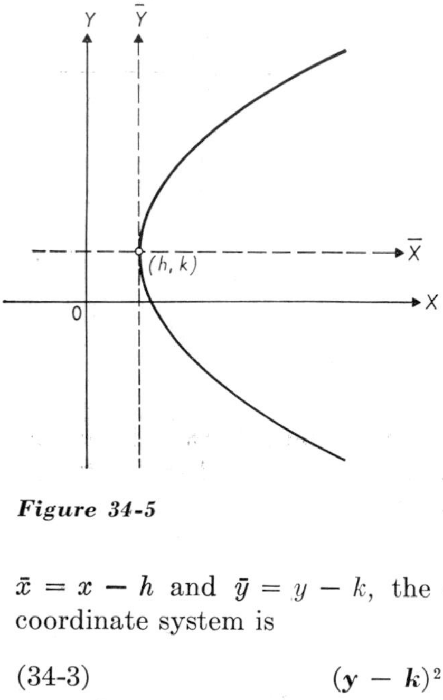

Figure 34-5

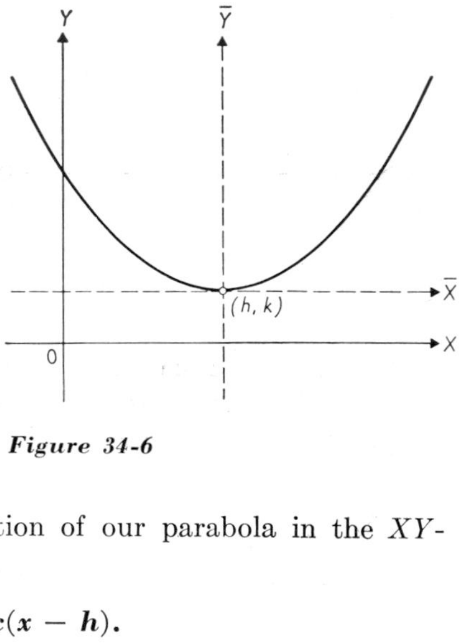

Figure 34-6

$\bar{x} = x - h$ and $\bar{y} = y - k$, the equation of our parabola in the XY-coordinate system is

(34-3) $$(y - k)^2 = 4c(x - h).$$

Similarly, if the vertex of a parabola is the point (h, k) and the directrix is the line $y = d$, and if we let $c = k - d$, then we can write the equation of the parabola as

(34-4) $$(x - h)^2 = 4c(y - k).$$

The graph of this parabola is shown in Fig. 34-6 (when $k > d$).

Example 34-2. Write the equation of the parabola whose directrix is the line $y = -5$ and whose focus is the point $(4, -1)$.

Solution. The axis of the parabola contains the point $(4, -1)$ and is perpendicular to the line $y = -5$, so the equation of the axis is $x = 4$. The vertex of a parabola is mid-way between the focus and the point of intersection of the axis and the directrix. In this case the vertex is the point $(4, -3)$. Clearly (see Fig. 34-7), the focal length is $c = 2$. Thus, we obtain

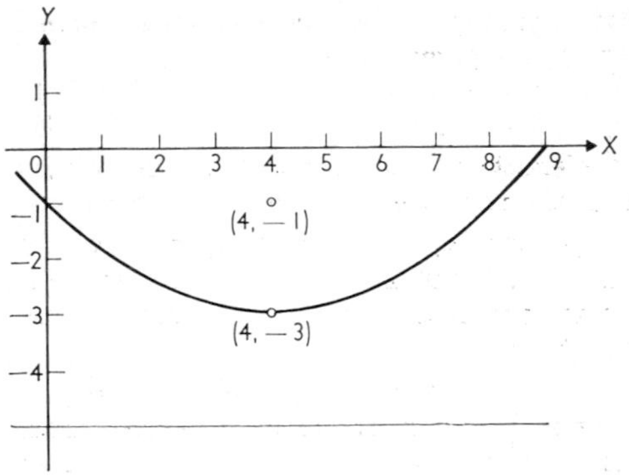

Figure 34-7

the equation of our parabola from Equation 34-4 by taking $h = 4$, $k = -3$, and $c = 2$; that is,

$$(x - 4)^2 = 8(y + 3).$$

This equation can also be written

$$x^2 - 8x - 8y - 8 = 0.$$

Example 34-3. Show that the graph of the equation $y = ax^2 + bx + c$ is a parabola if $a \neq 0$.

Solution. We replace x with $\bar{x} + h$ and y with $\bar{y} + k$, where h and k are numbers to be determined, and obtain the equation

$$\begin{aligned}\bar{y} + k &= a(\bar{x} + h)^2 + b(\bar{x} + h) + c \\ &= a\bar{x}^2 + (2ah + b)\bar{x} + ah^2 + bh + c.\end{aligned}$$

Now if we let $h = -b/2a$ and then $k = ah^2 + bh + c = \dfrac{4ac - b^2}{4a}$, we obtain the standard form of the equation of a parabola,

$$\bar{x}^2 = \frac{1}{a}\,\bar{y}.$$

If $a > 0$, the parabola opens upward; if $a < 0$, the parabola opens downward.

Problems 34

1. Find the focus and directrix of each of the following parabolas and sketch.
   (a) $y^2 = 8x$ (b) $x^2 = -16y$
   (c) $(x + 3)^2 = 24(y - 2)$ (d) $y^2 = 3(x + 2)$
   (e) $x^2 - 2x + 4y + 5 = 0$ (f) $y^2 - 12x + 2y + 1 = 0$

2. Find the equation of the parabola whose focus is the given point and whose directrix is the given line.
   (a) $(3, 0)$, $x = -3$ (b) $(0, 4)$, $y = 0$
   (c) $(1, 3)$, $x = -5$ (d) $(-3, 2)$, $y = -4$
3. Find the equation of the parabola whose axis is parallel to the Y-axis, whose vertex is the point $(-1, 3)$, and which contains the point $(1, 1)$.
4. Let (x_1, y_1) and (x_2, y_2) be any two points of the parabola whose equation is $x^2 = 4cy$. Show that the chord joining these two points is parallel to the tangent to the parabola at the point whose X-coordinate is the midpoint of the interval $[x_1, x_2]$.
5. The axis of the parabola whose equation is $y = ax^2 + bx + c$ is parallel to the Y-axis. Therefore its vertex is a maximum or a minimum point. Use derivatives to find the vertex of the parabola and compare your result with the result in Example 34-3. Use the second derivative to discuss the concavity of the parabola.
6. The segment that a parabola cuts off the line that contains the focus and is perpendicular to the axis is called the **latus rectum** of the parabola. Show that the length of the latus rectum of a parabola whose focal length is c is $4c$.
7. Determine the length of the latus rectum for each of the parabolas in the second question of these problems.
8. Find the slopes of the tangents to the parabola at the end points of the latus rectum of the parabola $y^2 = 4cx$. What is the angle between these tangents? Show that these tangents intersect on the directrix of the parabola.
9. Find the equation of the circle that contains the vertex and the two endpoints of the latus rectum of the parabola $y^2 = 4cx$.
10. The vertex of the parabola $x^2 = 4cy$ is the center of an ellipse, and the focus of the parabola is an end-point of the minor diameter of the ellipse. The parabola and ellipse intersect at right angles. Find the equation of the ellipse in terms of c.
11. One focus and one vertex of the hyperbola $b^2x^2 - a^2y^2 = a^2b^2$ belong to the positive X-axis. Find the equation of the parabola with the same vertex and focus.
12. Show that the parabola in the preceding problem is "contained in" the right-hand branch of the hyperbola of the problem.
13. Let $a > b$ so that one focus and one vertex of the ellipse $b^2x^2 + a^2y^2 = a^2b^2$ belong to the positive X-axis. Find the equation of the parabola with the same vertex and focus.
14. Show that the parabola in the preceding problem "contains" the ellipse in that problem.

35. Conics

We have defined a parabola as the set of points, each of which is equidistant from a given point (the focus) and a given line (the directrix). Another way to word this definition is to say that the ratio of the distance between a point of our parabola and the focus to the distance between the point and the directrix is 1 for each point of the parabola.

A similar property is possessed by ellipses and hyperbolas. Associated with each focus of an ellipse or a hyperbola is a line (called a *directrix*) such that the ratio of the distance between a point of the curve and the focus to the distance between the point and the directrix is a number e that is the same for every point of the curve.

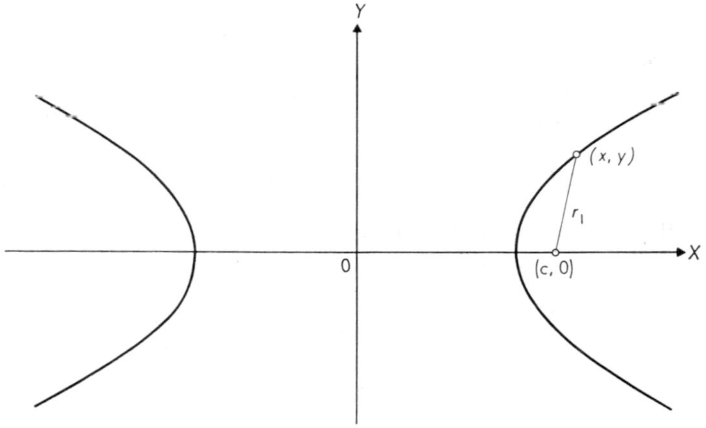

Figure 35-1

Let us look at a hyperbola to see exactly what we mean. In Fig. 35-1 we have drawn the hyperbola whose equation is

(35-1) $$\frac{x^2}{a^2} - \frac{y^2}{b^2} = 1.$$

We have also shown the focus $(c, 0)$, where

(35-2) $$c = \sqrt{a^2 + b^2}.$$

Let us compute the number r_1^2, where r_1 is the distance between a point (x, y) of our hyperbola and the focus $(c, 0)$. Even though we have shown (x, y) as a point of the "right branch" in our figure, it could be a point of either branch of the hyperbola. According to the distance formula,

$$r_1^2 = (x - c)^2 + y^2 = x^2 - 2cx + c^2 + y^2.$$

In this equation we may replace y^2 with $\dfrac{b^2x^2}{a^2} - b^2$ (from Equation 35-1), and get

$$\begin{aligned} r_1^2 &= x^2 - 2cx + c^2 + \frac{b^2x^2}{a^2} - b^2 \\ &= \left(\frac{a^2 + b^2}{a^2}\right) x^2 - 2cx + c^2 - b^2. \end{aligned}$$

Equation 35-2 tells us that $a^2 + b^2 = c^2$, and $c^2 - b^2 = a^2$, so

$$r_1^2 = \frac{c^2}{a^2}x^2 - 2cx + a^2$$

$$= \frac{c^2}{a^2}\left(x^2 - \frac{2a^2}{c}x + \frac{a^4}{c^2}\right)$$

$$= \frac{c^2}{a^2}\left(x - \frac{a^2}{c}\right)^2.$$

Thus we see that

(35-3) $$r_1 = \frac{c}{a}\left|x - \frac{a^2}{c}\right|.$$

The number $\left|x - \frac{a^2}{c}\right|$ is the distance r_2 between the point (x, y) and the line parallel to the Y-axis and a^2/c units to the right of it (Fig. 35-2).

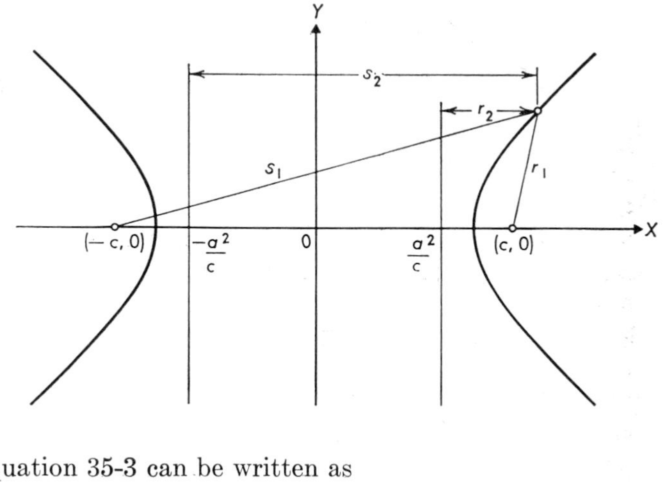

Figure 35-2

Therefore, Equation 35-3 can be written as

(35-4) $$\frac{\boldsymbol{r_1}}{\boldsymbol{r_2}} = \frac{\boldsymbol{c}}{\boldsymbol{a}}.$$

Thus, associated with the focus $(c, 0)$ we have found a line, $x = a^2/c$, such that the ratio of the distance between a point of our hyperbola and the focus to the distance between the point and the line is a number, $\frac{c}{a}$, that is independent of the choice of the point of the hyperbola. It is easy to show that the line a^2/c units to the left of the Y-axis is associated with the focus $(-c, 0)$ in the same way. That is, if s_1 is the distance between the point (x, y) and the focus $(-c, 0)$ and s_2 is the distance between the point and the associated line, then the ratio s_1/s_2 is again the number c/a. The lines $\boldsymbol{x} = \boldsymbol{a^2/c}$ and $\boldsymbol{x} = \boldsymbol{-a^2/c}$ are called the **directrices** of the hyperbola, and the ratio $\boldsymbol{e} = \boldsymbol{c/a}$ is the **eccentricity** of the hyperbola.

The same reasoning that we used above leads to similar results in the case of an ellipse. Let us consider the ellipse whose equation is

$$\frac{x^2}{a^2} + \frac{y^2}{b^2} = 1, \tag{35-5}$$

where $a > b$. This ellipse is shown in Fig. 35-3. Associated with the focus

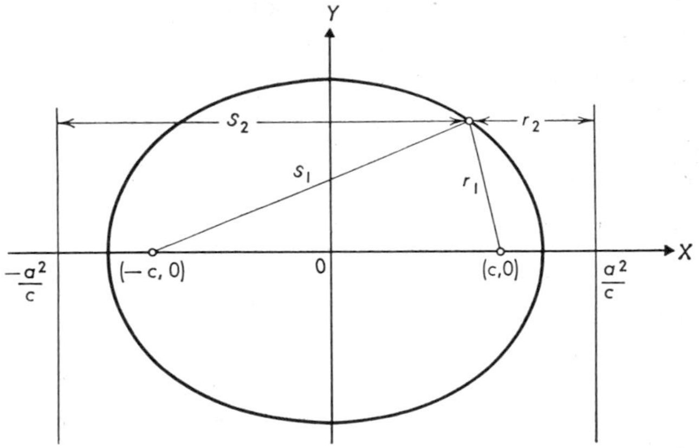

Figure 35-3

$(c, 0)$ is the directrix parallel to the Y-axis and a^2/c units to the right of it. The directrix a^2/c units to the left of the Y-axis is associated with the focus $(-c, 0)$. If (x, y) is any point of our ellipse, then the ratio r_1/r_2 of the distance between (x, y) and $(c, 0)$ to the distance between (x, y) and the associated directrix is the eccentricity $e = c/a$ (see Problem 12 of this section). The ratio s_1/s_2 of the distances to the other focus and directrix is also e.

We have shown that the ellipse, parabola, and hyperbola all share a common "ratio" property. Associated with a focus of one of these curves is a line, called a directrix, such that the ratio of the distance between a point of the curve and the focus to the distance between the point and the directrix is a number e (the eccentricity) that is independent of the choice of the point of the curve. In the case of our ellipse and hyperbola, we saw that the number e was given by the formula $e = c/a$. Since $c < a$ for the ellipse and $c > a$ for the hyperbola, we see that *the eccentricity of the ellipse is a number that is less than 1, the eccentricity of the hyperbola is greater than 1*, and *the eccentricity of the parabola is equal to 1*.

Ellipses, parabolas, and hyperbolas make up the family of curves known as *conics*. The members of this family can be defined as follows.

DEFINITION 35-1. *A* ***conic*** *is determined by a given point F (a* ***focus***), *a given line d not containing F (the* ***directrix associated with F***), *and a number e (the* ***eccentricity***). *The conic contains a point P if, and only if, the ratio of the distance $\overline{FP}$ to the distance between P and the line d is the number e.*

A conic is an ellipse, parabola, or hyperbola depending on whether $e < 1$, $e = 1$, or $e > 1$. In the case of our hyperbola of Equation 35-1 and of our ellipse of Equation 35-5 (in which $a > b$), the directrices are the lines

$$x = \frac{-a^2}{c} \quad \text{and} \quad x = \frac{a^2}{c}, \tag{35-6}$$

and the eccentricity is the number

$$e = \frac{c}{a}. \tag{35-7}$$

If a hyperbola or ellipse has a different orientation, these formulas must be modified accordingly. For example, if $b > a$ in Equation 35-5 of the ellipse, then $e = c/b$, and the directrices are the lines $y = -b^2/c$ and $y = b^2/c$.

Example 35-1. Find the equation of the conic that has an eccentricity of 2 and has the point (3, 0) as a focus for which the corresponding directrix is the Y-axis.

Solution. In Fig. 35-4 we show the typical point (x, y) of our conic and also the focus (3, 0). According to Definition 35-1, $r_1/r_2 = 2$; that is,

$$r_1^2 = 4r_2^2.$$

Since $r_1^2 = (x - 3)^2 + y^2$ and $r_2^2 = x^2$, the equation of our conic is

$$(x - 3)^2 + y^2 = 4x^2.$$

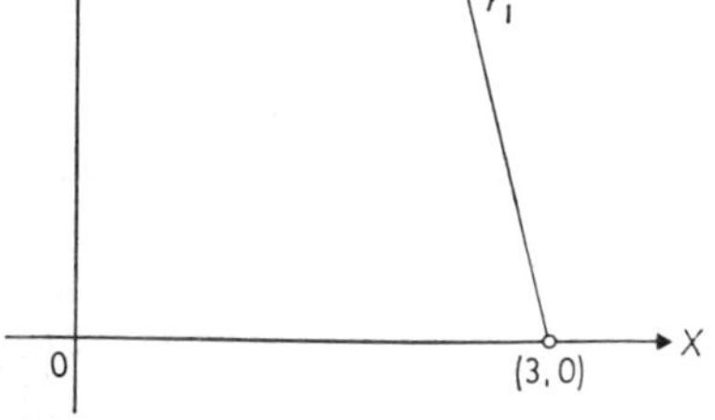

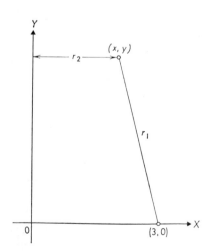

Figure 35-4

This equation can be written as

$$3x^2 - y^2 + 6x - 9 = 0,$$

or, after completing the square,

$$\frac{(x+1)^2}{4} - \frac{y^2}{12} = 1.$$

As you can see, our conic is a hyperbola; its eccentricity is $e = 2 > 1$.

Example 35-2. Find the eccentricity and locate the directrices of the conic whose equation is $9x^2 + 25y^2 = 1$.

Solution. If we write this equation as

$$\frac{x^2}{\frac{1}{9}} + \frac{y^2}{\frac{1}{25}} = 1,$$

we recognize it as the standard form of the equation of an ellipse for which $a^2 = \frac{1}{9}$ and $b^2 = \frac{1}{25}$. Hence

$$c = \sqrt{a^2 - b^2} = \sqrt{\tfrac{1}{9} - \tfrac{1}{25}} = \sqrt{\tfrac{16}{225}} = \tfrac{4}{15}.$$

Equation 35-7 gives the eccentricity of our ellipse as $e = \dfrac{c}{a} = \dfrac{\frac{4}{15}}{\frac{1}{3}} = \dfrac{4}{5}$, and we see from Equations 35-6 that the directrices are the lines with equations $x = -\frac{15}{36}$ and $x = \frac{15}{36}$.

The use of the word "focus" for certain points connected with the conics is related to the fact that these points play the role of focal points in a physical sense. To demonstrate this fact in the case of the parabola, we find it convenient to choose the coordinate axes so that the equation of the parabola is $y^2 = 4cx$, with $c > 0$. Figure 35-5 shows the upper half of the parabola; the point $F(c, 0)$ is its focus. If the figure represents the

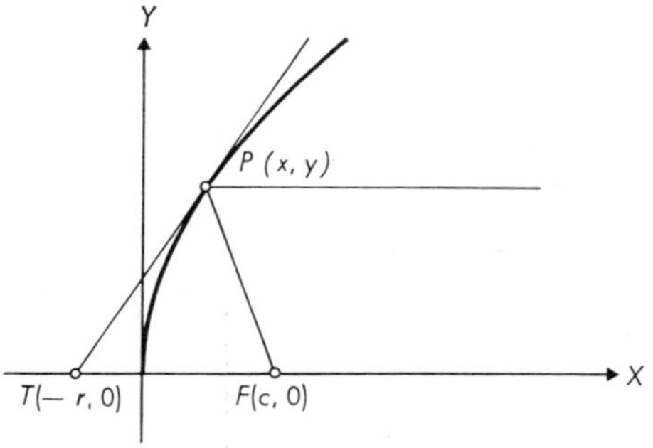

Figure 35-5

upper half of the cross section of a parabolic reflector, then we will show that a ray of light parallel to the X-axis will strike a point P of the parabola and be reflected to the focus F. The tangent to the parabola at P is the line TP in Fig. 35-5, and it is a law of optics that the reflected beam and the incident beam will make equal angles with this line. From elementary geometry, we see that the acute angle between the incident beam and the tangent line is equal to $\angle PTF$. The reflected beam will travel the path PF if, and only if, $\angle FPT = \angle PTF$. These angles will be equal if, and only if, the triangle TFP is an isosceles triangle with $\overline{PF} = \overline{TF}$. It is this equation that we shall now verify.

If the coordinates of P are (x, y), then the distance formula yields

$$\overline{PF} = \sqrt{(x-c)^2 + y^2} = \sqrt{x^2 - 2cx + c^2 + y^2}.$$

Since P is a point of our parabola, $y^2 = 4cx$, and hence we may replace y^2 with $4cx$ in the last radical to obtain

$$\overline{PF} = \sqrt{x^2 + 2cx + c^2} = x + c. \tag{35-8}$$

Calculating the distance $\overline{TF}$ is somewhat more complicated. The tangent line at P intersects the X-axis at the point T with coordinates $(-r, 0)$, where r is a positive number that we wish to find. On one hand, the slope of the segment TP is $y/(x + r)$. On the other hand, the slope of this segment may be found from the equation $y^2 = 4cx$ by implicit differentiation: $2yy' = 4c$. Hence $y' = 2c/y$, and we equate these two expressions for the slope of the segment TP to obtain the equation

$$\frac{y}{x+r} = \frac{2c}{y}.$$

Then

$$x + r = \frac{y^2}{2c} = \frac{4cx}{2c} = 2x,$$

and so $r = x$. It then follows that

$$\overline{TF} = c + r = c + x.$$

When we compare this equation with Equation 35-8, we see that $\overline{PF} = \overline{TF}$, and our result is proved.

We won't go into quite so much detail with regard to the focusing property of the ellipse. Figure 35-6 shows an ellipse whose equation has the standard form

$$\frac{x^2}{a^2} + \frac{y^2}{b^2} = 1,$$

with $a > b$. We have drawn a line tangent to the curve at an arbitrary point P of the ellipse. Now we assert that the segments SP and RP (S and R are the foci of the ellipse) make equal angles with the tangent line at P (or, equivalently, with the normal line QP). Thus, if our figure is the cross section of an elliptical reflector, we are saying that a ray of light emanating from the focus S will be reflected at P to the other focus R.

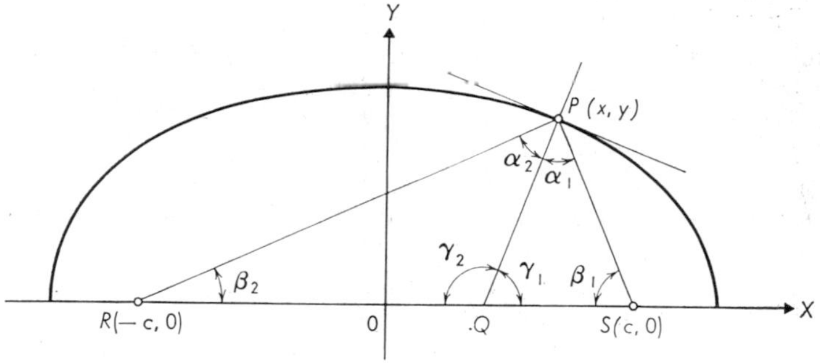

Figure 35-6

To prove this assertion, we must show that the angles α_1 and α_2 of Fig. 35-6 are equal. These angles will be equal if $\beta_1 + \gamma_1 = \beta_2 + \gamma_2$, and in this situation this equation is equivalent to the equation

$$\tan(\beta_1 + \gamma_1) = \tan(\beta_2 + \gamma_2).$$

We can verify the preceding equation by first expanding the two sides to obtain the equation

$$\frac{\tan\beta_1 + \tan\gamma_1}{1 - \tan\beta_1\tan\gamma_1} = \frac{\tan\beta_2 + \tan\gamma_2}{1 - \tan\beta_2\tan\gamma_2},$$

and then calculating these tangents in terms of the coordinates of P. For example, $\tan\beta_2 = y/(x + c)$ and $\tan\gamma_1$ is the negative reciprocal of the slope of the line tangent to the ellipse at P. We will leave the details of verifying this equation for the problems.

Problems 35

1. What is the formula for the eccentricity of the hyperbola whose equation is $a^2y^2 - b^2x^2 = a^2b^2$?
2. What are the equations of the directrices of the hyperbola whose equation is given in the preceding question?

3. Use Definition 35-1 to find the equation of the conic with a focus, corresponding directrix, and eccentricity as given.
(a) Focus (2, 0), directrix: $x = -2$, $e = 2$.
(b) Focus (2, 0), directrix: $x = -2$, $e = 1$.
(c) Focus (2, 0), directrix: $x = -2$, $e = \frac{1}{2}$.
(d) Focus (1, 0), directrix: $x = 2$, $e = 1$.
(e) Focus (0, 4), directrix: $y = 0$, $e = 3$.
(f) Focus (1, 0), directrix: $x = 4$, $e = \frac{1}{2}$.
(g) Focus (1, 2), directrix: $y = -2$, $e = \frac{1}{3}$.
(h) Focus (0, 4), directrix: $y = 1$, $e = 2$.

4. Find the eccentricity and the directrices of each of the following conics.
(a) $3x^2 + 4y^2 = 12$
(b) $3y^2 = 2x$
(c) $4x^2 - 3y^2 = 36$
(d) $5x^2 = y + 1$
(e) $y^2 - 2x^2 + 8 = 0$
(f) $x^2 + 4y^2 = 1$
(g) $x^2 + 2y^2 = 16$
(h) $4x^2 + y^2 = 1$

5. Find the eccentricity and the equations of the directrices of the ellipse whose equation is $3x^2 + 4y^2 + 6x + 24y - 9 = 0$.

6. (a) Discuss the way in which the shape of an ellipse changes as the eccentricity varies from near 0 to near 1.
(b) Discuss the way in which the shape of a hyperbola changes as the eccentricity varies from near 1 to a very large number.

7. Find the eccentricity of an equilateral hyperbola.

8. Fill in the details concerning the focusing property of the ellipse.

9. The vertex of the parabola $x^2 = 4cy$ is the center of an ellipse. The focus of the parabola is the endpoint of the minor diameter of the ellipse, and the parabola and ellipse intersect at right angles. Find the eccentricity of the ellipse (see Question 10 of Problems 34).

10. What is the eccentricity of an ellipse in which the distance between its foci is one-half the distance between its directrices?

11. The vertex of the parabola $y^2 = 4cx$ is the center of an ellipse. The latus rectum of the parabola is a latus rectum of the ellipse. What is the eccentricity of the ellipse?

12. Use algebra to show that the distance d between a point (x, y) of the ellipse $\dfrac{x^2}{a^2} + \dfrac{y^2}{b^2} = 1$ (with $a > b$) and the focus $(c, 0)$ is given by the equation $d = e\left|x - \dfrac{a^2}{c}\right|$.

13. The vertex of the parabola $y^2 = 4cx$ is the center of a hyperbola. The latus rectum of the parabola is a latus rectum of the hyperbola. What is the eccentricity of the hyperbola?

Review Problems, Chapter Four

You can use the following problems to test yourself on the material covered in this chapter.

1. An ellipse is tangent to the circle $x^2 + y^2 = 4$ at the points of intersection of the circle and the Y-axis, and its foci are the points of intersection of the circle and the X-axis. Find the equation of the ellipse. What is its eccentricity?

2. Sketch the graph of the conic whose equation is $9y^2 - 16x^2 = 144$. Label the foci and the directrices of the conic. Find the slope of the tangent at the point $(4, \frac{20}{3})$.

3. Find the equation of the circle whose points $(-1, 2)$ and $(5, 10)$ are the end-points of a diameter.

4. Find the coordinates of the vertex and focus of the parabola $x^2 + 4x - 4y + 8 = 0$.

5. Sketch the ellipse whose equation is $9x^2 + 4y^2 = 1$. Label the foci, vertices, and directrices. Find the length of the major diameter and the eccentricity of this ellipse.

6. Find the coordinates of the foci of the conic whose equation is $4x^2 - 9y^2 - 16x - 18y - 29 = 0$.

7. The vertex of a parabola is the origin and its focus is the point $(1, 1)$. What is the equation of the directrix of this parabola?

8. An artificial earth satellite moves in an elliptical orbit with the center of the earth as one focus. The minimum distance from the center of the earth to the satellite's path is d_1 miles, and the maximum distance is d_2 miles. Find the formula for the eccentricity of the elliptical path in terms of d_1 and d_2.

9. Find the slope of the line tangent to the ellipse $b^2x^2 + a^2y^2 = a^2b^2$ (where $a > b$) at the endpoint of the latus rectum that lies in the first quadrant. How is this slope related to the eccentricity of the ellipse?

10. Consider a hyperbola whose transverse diameter lies along the X-axis. Show that the slope of a tangent at an endpoint of a latus rectum is either e or $-e$.

11. Show that the point (h, k) is outside the ellipse $\frac{x^2}{a^2} + \frac{y^2}{b^2} = 1$ if, and only if, $\frac{h^2}{a^2} + \frac{k^2}{b^2} > 1$.

5 THE INTEGRAL

Two of the most important concepts in calculus can be introduced by a study of geometrical problems. We have seen how the concept of the *derivative* arose when we considered the problem of finding the line tangent to a curve at a point. In this chapter we shall see how the problem of finding the area of a plane region with a given curve as part of its boundary leads us to a second important concept of calculus—the *integral.*

Of course, we don't restrict our interpretation of the derivative to the geometrical idea of slope. A derivative is a rate, and as such we can use it to discuss problems involving the velocity and acceleration of moving bodies, and so on. Similarly, although we shall introduce the integral as a solution to the problem of finding the areas of certain regions, we shall also see that other interpretations are possible. Our applications of integrals will range from finding the work required to pump out a tank of water to providing a new approach to the definition of logarithms.

36. Approximating Areas

Before we introduce the concept of the integral of a function on an interval, let us briefly reconsider how we introduced the concept of the derivative of a function at a point. In geometrical terms, the derivative $f'(x)$ of a function f at the point x is the slope of the line that is tangent to the graph of f at the point $(x, f(x))$. Thus our first method of calculating the derivative $f'(x)$ was to draw "by eye" a line for which the name "tangent line" seemed appropriate and then measure its slope. This procedure suffers because the phrase "by eye" is vague; it is not good practice to define a mathematical concept such as the tangent line to a graph as the "line that seems to the eye to best fit the curve at the given point." Therefore, we turned to an analytical approach as follows.

(i) We *assumed* that there was a line tangent to the graph of the given function f at the given point.

(ii) Then we used geometrical reasoning to convince ourselves that the slope of that line was approximated by some slopes that we could calculate analytically—namely, the slopes of certain chords. These slopes are calculated from our difference quotient $\dfrac{f(x + h) - f(x)}{h}$.

(iii) Next, we examined these approximating slopes to see what number they approximated; that is, we found the limit of the difference quotient. This number we took to be the number $f'(x)$ that we were seeking.

(iv) Finally, we did away with all vagueness about just what a tangent line is by *defining* the tangent line as the line with slope $f'(x)$ that contains the given point $(x, f(x))$.

We will follow a similar sequence of steps as we introduce the integral of a function on an interval $[a, b]$. As a first geometrical approach to this concept, we will think of the integral as the area A of the region that is bounded by the graph of f, the X-axis, and the lines $x = a$ and $x = b$—the shaded region in Fig. 36-1. (For the moment, we will consider regions that lie wholly above the X-axis.) We could calculate the integral A by sketching the graph of f on graph paper and counting the squares that are contained in the shaded region. In general, the curve would cut some of the squares, so we would have to estimate "by eye" the fractions of squares that lie under the curve. Thus this graphical calculation of A suffers from difficulties that are similar to those we encountered when we tried to calculate $f'(x)$ by sketching a tangent line "by eye." To avoid these difficulties, we proceed as follows. First of all,

(i) We *assume* that there is a number A that we can say is the area of our region.

(ii) Then we use geometrical reasoning to develop an analytical method of calculating approximations of this number A.

(iii) Next, we examine these approximations to find the number that they approximate; that is, we find their limit.

(iv) Finally, we remove any vagueness about just what the area of a region with a curved boundary is by *defining* the area under our graph to be the limit found in step (iii).

In this section we will concentrate on step (ii), approximating the number that we think should measure the area of a region such as the one shown in Fig. 36-1.

Figure 36-2 shows how we make the approximations. We have drawn some rectangles in the figure in such a way that the sum of their areas seems to approximate the area A we seek. To construct these approximating rectangles, we simply chose three points, x_1, x_2, and x_3 between a and b. In this way the interval $[a, b]$ is divided into four smaller intervals called **subintervals** of $[a, b]$. In each subinterval we erected a vertical segment from the X-axis to the curve. The lengths of these segments

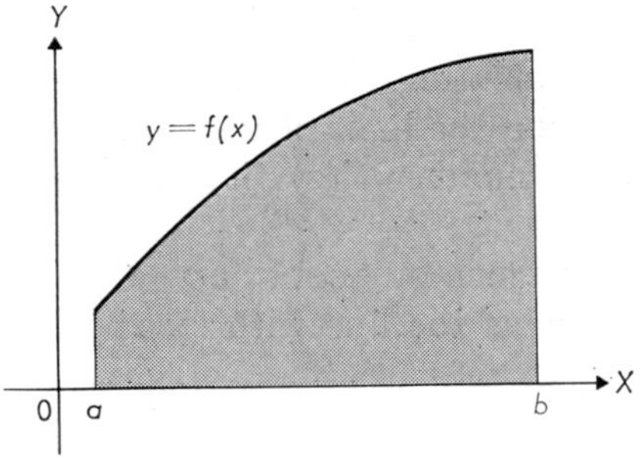

Figure 36-1

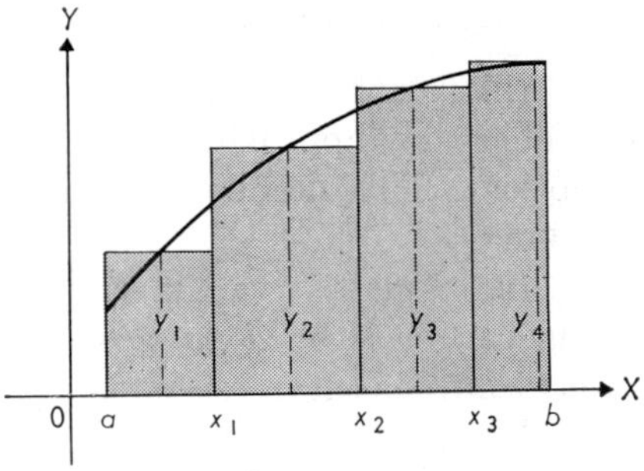

Figure 36-2

are y_1, y_2, y_3, and y_4. The areas of our four rectangles are $y_1(x_1 - a)$, $y_2(x_2 - x_1)$, $y_3(x_3 - x_1)$, and $y_4(b - x_3)$. From the figure, it appears that the sum of these areas, the number

$$S = y_1(x_1 - a) + y_2(x_2 - x_1) + y_3(x_3 - x_2) + y_4(b - x_3),$$

approximates our desired area A.

Example 36-1. Suppose that

$$f(x) = \frac{1}{1 + x^2}.$$

Approximate the area A of the region bounded by the graph of f, the X-axis, and the lines $x = 0$ and $x = 1$.

Solution. Fig. 36-3 shows the graph of f in the interval [0, 1]. Let us divide this interval into the two subintervals $[0, \frac{1}{2}]$ and $[\frac{1}{2}, 1]$, and then construct rectangles with these subintervals as bases. The bases of these rectangles

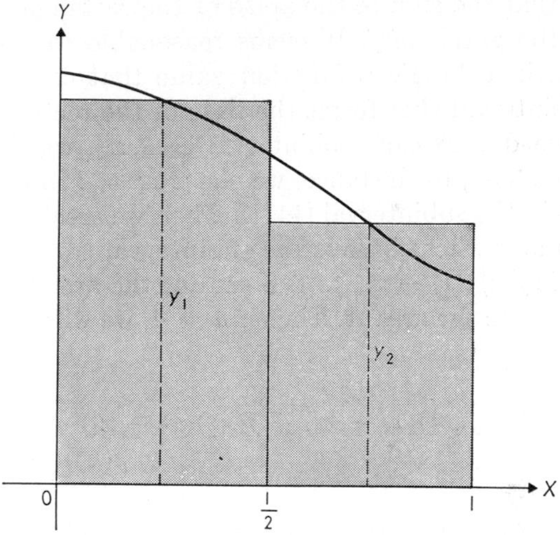

Figure 36-3

are each $\frac{1}{2}$ unit long. For the altitudes of the rectangles, we will arbitrarily choose the values of f at the midpoints of the subintervals. Thus

$$y_1 = f\left(\frac{1}{4}\right) = \frac{1}{1 + \frac{1}{16}} = \frac{16}{17}$$

and

$$y_2 = f(\tfrac{3}{4}) = \tfrac{16}{25}.$$

The area A is therefore approximated by the sum

$$S = \tfrac{16}{17} \cdot \tfrac{1}{2} + \tfrac{16}{25} \cdot \tfrac{1}{2} = .79.$$

Later we shall find that $A = \pi/4 \approx .78$, so our approximation is quite close.

Now let us go into a little more detail on how we calculate the sums that approximate the area of a region such as is illustrated in Fig. 36-1.

First we divide our basic interval $[a, b]$ into a number of subintervals. To form n subintervals we choose $n - 1$ points $x_1, x_2, \ldots, x_{n-1}$ lying between a and b such that $a < x_1 < x_2 < \cdots x_{n-1} < b$. These points determine a **partition** of (that is, a "division of") the interval $[a, b]$ into the subintervals $[a, x_1]$, $[x_1, x_2]$, $\ldots$, $[x_{n-1}, b]$. In order to simplify notation, we write $x_0 = a$ and $x_n = b$, so that we can talk about a subinterval $[x_{i-1}, x_i]$, where i is one of the numbers $1, 2, \ldots, n$. In Example 36-1, we chose $n = 2$, $x_0 = 0$, $x_1 = \frac{1}{2}$, and $x_2 = 1$; and these division points determined the subintervals $[0, \frac{1}{2}]$, and $[\frac{1}{2}, 1]$.

Now we construct a rectangle on each of the subintervals in such a way that the sum of the areas of the rectangles approximates the area under the graph of f. It seems reasonable to choose as the altitude of each such rectangle a function value that corresponds to a number in the subinterval that forms the base of the rectangle. And that is exactly what we do. In each subinterval $[x_{i-1}, x_i]$, we choose a number x_i^*. (In Example 36-1, for instance, we chose $x_1^* = \frac{1}{4}$ in the subinterval $[0, \frac{1}{2}]$ and $x_2^* = \frac{3}{4}$ in the subinterval $[\frac{1}{2}, 1]$.) Then we erect a rectangle whose altitude is $f(x_i^*)$ and whose base is the subinterval $[x_{i-1}, x_i]$. The area of this rectangle is $f(x_i^*)(x_i - x_{i-1})$. The sum of the areas of all the rectangles will approximate the area A. Thus if $n = 4$, we will have the **approximating sum**

$$(36\text{-}1) \quad S = f(x_1^*)(x_1 - x_0) + f(x_2^*)(x_2 - x_1) + f(x_3^*)(x_3 - x_2) + f(x_4^*)(x_4 - x_3).$$

If we had partitioned the interval $[a, b]$ into 104 subintervals, our number S would have been the sum of 104 terms. In order to condense our formulas for approximating sums to a manageable length when n is a large number, we must introduce some notation. The sum in Equation 36-1 may be obtained by carrying out the following directions: "Replace the letter i in the expression $f(x_i^*)(x_i - x_{i-1})$ with each of the numbers 1, 2, 3, and 4 in turn, and add up the terms that result." Directions such as these occur so often in mathematics that we have a special symbol for them. If $P(i)$ is some mathematical expression and n is a positive integer, then the symbol

$$\sum_{i=1}^{n} P(i)$$

means, "Successively replace the letter i in the expression $P(i)$ with the numbers $1, 2, 3, \ldots n$ and add up the resulting terms." The symbol Σ is the Greek letter **sigma,** and it is used to suggest "sum" since we are to add a number of terms. Thus, for example,

$$\sum_{i=1}^{6} i^2 = 1^2 + 2^2 + 3^2 + 4^2 + 5^2 + 6^2 = 91;$$

$$\sum_{i=1}^{5} 2^i = 2^1 + 2^2 + 2^3 + 2^4 + 2^5 = 62.$$

In this Σ-notation, Equation 36-1 can be written as

$$S = \sum_{i=1}^{4} f(x_i^*)(x_i - x_{i-1}).$$

The letter i is called the **index of summation,** and in the above sum the numbers 1, 2, 3, and 4 constitute the **range** of i. Other letters may be used as indices of summation, and the range of the index need not start at 1. Thus, for example,

$$\sum_{r=3}^{5} \log r = \log 3 + \log 4 + \log 5 = \log 60,$$

and so on. In the Σ-notation, an approximating sum based on a partition of the interval into n subintervals takes the form

$$\mathbf{S = \sum_{i=1}^{n} f(x_i^*)(x_i - x_{i-1}).} \tag{36-2}$$

There is one more notation that we will introduce in connection with writing approximating sums. The length of an interval $[a, b]$ is $b - a$. Similarly, the length of the subinterval $[x_{i-1}, x_i]$ is the number $x_i - x_{i-1}$, and it is customary to abbreviate this difference as follows:

$$\mathbf{\Delta x_i = x_i - x_{i-1}.}$$

The symbol $\mathbf{\Delta}$ is the Greek letter **delta,** and it is supposed to suggest the word "difference." In this Δ-notation, Equation 36-2 for an approximating sum becomes

$$\mathbf{S = \sum_{i=1}^{n} f(x_i^*)\, \Delta x_i.} \tag{36-3}$$

Example 36-2. Approximate the area of the region under the graph of the equation $y = \sin x$ for x in the interval $[0, \pi/2]$.

Solution. We first partition the interval $[0, \pi/2]$ into $n = 2$ subintervals by selecting the point $x_1 = \pi/4$. So $x_0 = 0$, $x_1 = \pi/4$, and $x_2 = \pi/2$. Hence $\Delta x_1 = \pi/4 - 0$, and $\Delta x_2 = \pi/2 - \pi/4 = \pi/4$. Let us arbitrarily select the point $x_1^* = \pi/6$ in the interval $[0, \pi/4]$ and $x_2^* = \pi/3$ in the interval

$[\pi/4, \pi/2]$. So Equation 36-3 becomes in this case

$$S = \left(\sin\frac{\pi}{6}\right)\cdot\left(\frac{\pi}{4}\right) + \left(\sin\frac{\pi}{3}\right)\cdot\left(\frac{\pi}{4}\right)$$
$$= \left(\frac{1}{2}\right)\left(\frac{\pi}{4}\right) + \left(\frac{\sqrt{3}}{2}\right)\left(\frac{\pi}{4}\right) \approx 1.1.$$

It appears from Fig. 36-4 that our approximation is probably a number that

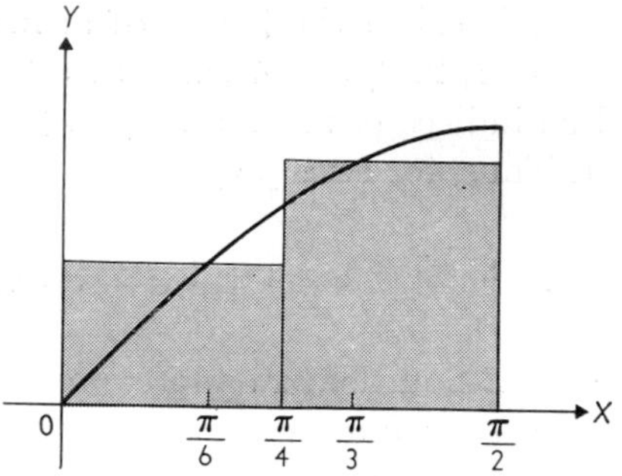

Figure 36-4

is too large. Later we will find that half the area bounded by an arch of the sine curve and the X-axis is 1 square unit.

In both Example 36-1 and 36-2 we partitioned the interval into subintervals of equal length. Thus in Example 36-1, $\Delta x_1 = \Delta x_2 = \frac{1}{2}$; and in Example 36-2, $\Delta x_1 = \Delta x_2 = \pi/4$. Choosing equal subintervals may make it easier to calculate an approximating sum, but it is not necessary to make such a choice. In fact, in some cases it is not even desirable. We conclude this section with an example of such a case.

Example 36-3. Approximate the area of the region under the graph of f in the interval $[0, 4]$ if $f(x) = 2x^4/(1 + x^4)$.

Solution. Figure 36-5 is a sketch of the graph of f for the interval $[0, 4]$. This graph suggests that we partition the basic interval $[0, 4]$ into subintervals that are shortest when the graph is steepest. So let us partition the interval $[0, 4]$ by means of the following points: $0, \frac{1}{2}, \frac{3}{4}, 1, \frac{5}{4}, \frac{3}{2}, 2$, and 4. If we then pick the number x_i^* to be the midpoint of the subinterval $[x_{i-1}, x_i]$, our approximating sum is

$$S = \tfrac{1}{2}f(\tfrac{1}{4}) + \tfrac{1}{4}f(\tfrac{5}{8}) + \tfrac{1}{4}f(\tfrac{7}{8}) + \tfrac{1}{4}f(\tfrac{9}{8}) + \tfrac{1}{4}f(\tfrac{11}{8}) + \tfrac{1}{2}f(\tfrac{7}{4}) + 2f(3) \approx 5.84.$$

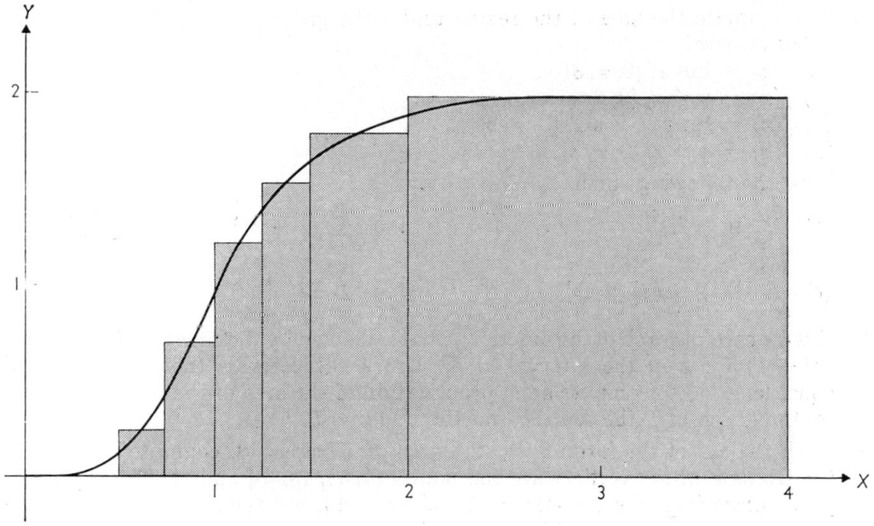

Figure 36-5

Problems 36

1. Find the points that partition the following intervals into 5 equal subintervals:
(a) [2, 12] (b) [−5, 10] (c) [−3, 5]

2. Approximate the area of the region bounded by the graph of f, the X-axis, and the lines $x = 2$ and $x = 10$ by partitioning the interval [2, 10] into 4 equal subintervals and using rectangles based on these subintervals with altitudes equal to the values of f at the midpoints of the subintervals.
(a) $f(x) = x$ (b) $f(x) = 1 - x$ (c) $f(x) = 20 - 2x$
(d) $f(x) = x^2$ (e) $f(x) = (x - 6)^2$ (f) $f(x) = x^3$

3. The area of the region bounded by the circle $x^2 + y^2 = 1$ is π square units. It follows that the area of the region in the first quadrant bounded by the X-axis, the Y-axis, and the graph of the equation $y = \sqrt{1 - x^2}$ is $\pi/4$ square units. Partition the interval [0, 1] into 4 equal subintervals and erect altitudes at the midpoints of the subintervals so as to obtain an approximating sum of 4 terms that approximates the area of this region, and hence obtain an approximation of the number π.

4. The area under the graph of the given function f and above the given interval is π square units. By calculating approximations of these areas, find approximations of π.
(a) $f(x) = 2\sqrt{1 - x^2}$, $[-1, 1]$
(b) $f(x) = 2/(1 + x^2)$, $[-1, 1]$
(c) $f(x) = 6/\sqrt{1 - x^2}$, $[0, \frac{1}{2}]$

5. Approximate the area of the region under the graph of f and above the indicated interval.
   (a) $f(x) = \tan x$, $[0, \pi/3]$
   (b) $f(x) = \cos^2 x$, $[0, 2\pi]$
   (c) $f(x) = \sin x + \cos x$, $[0, \pi/2]$
   (d) $f(x) = \sec^2 x$, $[0, \pi/3]$
6. Find the following sums.
   (a) $\sum_{i=1}^{4} \sin(\pi/i)$ (b) $\sum_{i=2}^{5} (1 + i)^2$
   (c) $\sum_{i=1}^{100} [F(i) - F(i-1)]$ (d) $\sum_{i=1}^{100} (3i + 2)$
7. Draw a careful graph of the function f that is defined by the equation $f(x) = 10x/(x^2 + 1)$ for x in the interval $[0, 5]$. Use 4 subintervals (not necessarily of equal lengths) to compute an approximation of the area of the region bounded by the graph of f, the X-axis, and the line $x = 5$.
8. With the aid of the formula for the area of a trapezoid, compute the area of the triangle whose vertices are the points (1, 1), (3, 5), and (7, 3). (Drop perpendiculars from the vertices to the X-axis and find the algebraic sum of the areas of the three trapezoids that are formed.)
9. Let $n = 3$, $x_0 = 0$, $x_i = 2^i$ for $i = 1, 2, 3$, $x_i^* = \frac{1}{2}(x_i + x_{i-1})$ and $f(x) = x^2$. Find $\sum_{i=1}^{n} f(x_i^*)\,\Delta x_i$.

37. The Integral

In the preceding section we saw how sums of the form

$$S = \sum_{i=1}^{n} f(x_i^*)\,\Delta x_i$$

approximate the area A of the region bounded by the graph of a function f that takes positive values, the X-axis, and the lines $x = a$ and $x = b$. When we look at the figures in that section, it appears that we can get a close approximation of the area A by choosing the partition points $x_1, x_2, \ldots x_{n-1}$ to be close together. Then the rectangles that approximate the region under the graph of f will be narrow, and we feel that the narrower the rectangles, the more nearly they "fill up" the region. Thus a "fine" partition of the interval $[a, b]$ should lead to a close approximation of the area, regardless of our choice of the points $x_1^*, x_2^*, \ldots, x_n^*$ at which we compute the functional values $f(x_1^*), f(x_2^*), \ldots, f(x_n^*)$ that serve as the altitudes of our approximating rectangles.

We measure the "fineness" of a partition by means of a number called the **norm** of the partition, which is the largest of the numbers Δx_i, $i = 1, 2, \ldots, n$. Thus the norm of a partition of the interval $[a, b]$ is the length of the longest subinterval into which the interval is divided.

For example, the norm of the partition in Example 36-3 is 2, and the norm of the partition in Example 36-2 is $\pi/4$. If the norm of a partition is small, then *all* the subintervals into which the basic interval is divided are short.

These remarks suggest that, intuitively speaking, *the area of the region under the graph of f is approximated by the sum*

$$S = \sum_{i=1}^{n} f(x_i^*)\, \Delta x_i,$$

and a close approximation can be assured by using a partition with a small norm when we form this approximating sum.

The number S is not determined simply by specifying the norm of the partition that we use when we calculate it. For one thing, we may choose many different partitions with the same norm. Secondly, even after the partition is fixed, we must choose a number x_i^* in each subinterval $[x_{i-1}, x_i]$, and in general we should not expect to get the same number S for each choice. Still it seems reasonable to suppose that if f is a moderately "well-behaved" function, we can get a close approximation to the area by choosing any approximating sum computed from a partition with a small norm.

Now let us take the next step in our introduction of the integral, finding the limit of our approximating sums. We seek a number A that is approximated by every approximating sum S formed by using a partition with a small norm. This number will be the *limit of S as the norm of our partition approaches 0;* we now wish to define what we mean by this limit. Since the norm of a partition is a positive number, our limit will be a "limit from the right," as we used the term in Section 13.

We proceed just as we did in Section 13. First, we choose an interval to the right of 0, $I = (0, r)$. Then we let $J(I)$ denote the smallest closed interval that contains every approximating sum S that can be formed by using a partition whose norm is a number in the interval I. Thus if h is any number in the interval I, the set of all approximating sums that can be formed using partitions of norm h belongs to our interval $J(I)$. If I is a very short interval, then every norm h is small. Thus as I "squeezes down" on 0, we expect $J(I)$ to "squeeze down" on the limit of our approximating sums. If $J(I)$ does "squeeze down" on a number A, then we call this limit A the *integral* of the function f on the interval $[a, b]$. Our formal definition of the integral follows.

DEFINITION 37-1. *If there is exactly one number A that is contained in every interval J(I) described above, then we say that the function f is* ***integrable*** *on the interval* $[a, b]$ *and that the number* ***A is the integral*** *of f on this* *interval. In symbols we write*

$$A = \int_a^b f(x)\,dx. \tag{37-1}$$

Before we say any more about the meaning of the integral, let us discuss the symbols used in Equation 37-1. The symbol $\int$ is an elongated S and is called an **integral sign.** It suggests that the integral is the limit of "sums." The numbers a and b are called, respectively, the **lower and upper limits of integration.** Here the word "limit" is used in an entirely new sense. The limits of integration are analogous to the numbers determining the range of the index in a summation; for example, the numbers r and n in the sum

$$\sum_{i=r}^{n} P(i). \tag{37-2}$$

The letter x in Equation 37-1 plays a role that is similar to the role played by the index of summation. Thus the letter i in Sum 37-2 is the index of summation, and it can be replaced by any other letter without altering the sum. The letter x in Equation 37-1 is called the **variable of integration,** and it can be replaced by any other letter without altering the integral. Thus, for example,

$$\int_a^b f(x)\,dx = \int_a^b f(t)\,dt = \int_a^b f(z)\,dz.$$

The "dx," or "dt," or "dz" tells us what the variable of integration is. For example,

$$\int_0^1 x^2t\,dx \quad \text{and} \quad \int_0^1 x^2t\,dt$$

are different integrals. Finally, we refer to $f(x)$ as the **integrand** of the integral in Equation 37-1. Thus $\sqrt{x}$ is the integrand of $\int_2^3 \sqrt{x}\,dx$.

In general, it is very difficult to use our definition directly to calculate an integral. We shall develop methods of evaluating integrals later. However, in order to illustrate Definition 37-1, we will now calculate the following simple integral.

Example 37-1. Use Definition 37-1 to evaluate $\int_a^b 1\,dx$.

Solution. Here we are dealing with the constant function with a value of 1; that is, $f(x) = 1$. Its graph appears in Fig. 37-1. Suppose we consider any subinterval $[x_{i-1}, x_i]$ of a partition of the interval $[a, b]$. If x_i^* is any number in this subinterval, then $f(x_i^*) = 1$. Therefore, any approximating sum S that is formed with any partition is

$$S = 1(x_1 - x_0) + \cdots + 1(x_n - x_{n-1})$$
$$= (x_n - x_0) = b - a.$$

Thus when we restrict ourselves to partitions with norms in a particular interval I, we shall obtain only the one sum $S = b - a$. Hence, the interval $J(I)$ in Definition 37-1 is the interval $[b - a, b - a]$ for each interval I. Thus the number $b - a$, and no other number, is contained in each interval $J(I)$, and

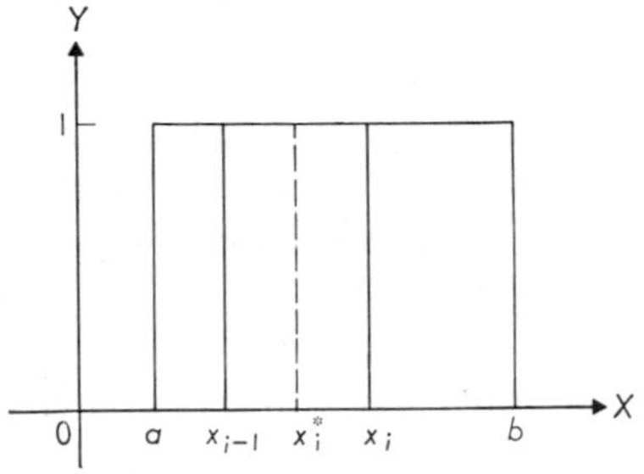

Figure 37-1

(37-3) $$\int_a^b 1\, dx = b - a.$$

This number is the area of a rectangle whose base is $b - a$ and whose altitude is 1, so our computation provides the answer we would expect from geometrical considerations.

We motivated the definition of the integral of a function f on an interval $[a, b]$ by supposing that $f(x) > 0$ at each point in the interval and then attempting to calculate the area under the graph of f. We now see that our analytical definition of the integral permits us to talk about $\int_a^b f(x)\, dx$ even though the graph of f crosses the X-axis between a and b. We shall interpret such an integral in terms of area later.

Definition 37-1 deals with an integral $\int_a^b f(x)\, dx$ in which the upper limit b is larger than the lower limit a. In order to complete our definition of the integral, we must add the following definitions.

DEFINITION 37-2. *For any number a and any function f,*

(37-4) $$\int_a^a f(x)\, dx = 0.$$

If $a < b$, and if f is integrable on the interval $[a, b]$, then

(37-5) $$\int_b^a f(x)\, dx = -\int_a^b f(x)\, dx.$$

Definition 37-1 is a formal and quite precise definition of the integral. The beginning student, however, also should keep the intuitive concept of an integral clearly in mind. Intuitively, the integral $\int_a^b f(x)\, dx$ is the number that is approximated by every sum $\sum_{i=1}^{n} f(x_i^*)\,\Delta x_i$, in which the largest of the numbers $\Delta x_1, \Delta x_2, \ldots, \Delta x_n$ is small. And as our earlier remarks suggest, we are going to define areas of plane regions in terms of integrals. Therefore, we have the geometrical interpretation of the number $\int_a^b f(x)\,dx$ as the area under the graph of f to help us get a clearer understanding of the concept of the integral.

To prove the following theorems on integrals, we should use such precise definitions of the integral concept as Definitions 37-1 and 37-2. However, these theorems will probably seem reasonable to you on an intuitive basis, and we shall accept them on this basis.

THEOREM 37-1. *If f is an integrable function on an interval $[a, b]$ and if $f(x) \geq 0$ for every number x in the interval, then* $\int_a^b f(x)\,dx \geq 0$.

This theorem follows from the fact that if $f(x) \geq 0$ for every number x in the interval, then for each x_i^*, $f(x_i^*) \geq 0$. Since each $\Delta x_i > 0$, each term of any approximating sum is non-negative so that each approximating sum is non-negative. It follows that the number that these sums approximate, $\int_a^b f(x)\,dx$, cannot be negative. Thus $\int_a^b f(x)\,dx \geq 0$.

THEOREM 37-2. *If f and g are integrable functions on the interval $[a, b]$, then*

$$\int_a^b [f(x) + g(x)]\,dx = \int_a^b f(x)\,dx + \int_a^b g(x)\,dx. \tag{37-6}$$

The key idea in the proof of this theorem is the following: The number $\int_a^b [f(x) + g(x)]\,dx$ is the number that is approximated by sums of the form $\sum_{i=1}^{n} [f(x_i^*) + g(x_i^*)]\,\Delta x_i$. It is easy to see that

$$\sum_{i=1}^{n} [f(x_i^*) + g(x_i^*)]\,\Delta x_i = \sum_{i=1}^{n} f(x_i^*)\,\Delta x_i + \sum_{i=1}^{n} g(x_i^*)\,\Delta x_i.$$

But the sums $\sum_{i=1}^{n} f(x_i^*)\,\Delta x_i$ and $\sum_{i=1}^{n} g(x_i^*)\,\Delta x_i$ approximate the integrals $\int_a^b f(x)\,dx$ and $\int_a^b g(x)\,dx$, so the sum $\sum_{i=1}^{n} [f(x_i^*) + g(x_i^*)]\,\Delta x_i$ approximates the number $\int_a^b f(x)\,dx + \int_a^b g(x)\,dx$, and hence we have Equation 37-6. Equation 37-6 can be generalized for integrands that are sums of more than two terms.

THEOREM 37-3. *If f is an integrable function on the interval [a, b] and c is any number, then*

(37-7) $$\int_a^b cf(x)\,dx = c\int_a^b f(x)\,dx.$$

Here the proof utilizes the fact that if $\sum_{i=1}^{n} f(x_i^*)\,\Delta x_i$ approximates $\int_a^b f(x)\,dx$, then $c\sum_{i=1}^{n} f(x_i^*)\,\Delta x_i$ approximates $c\int_a^b f(x)\,dx$. But

$$c\sum_{i=1}^{n} f(x_i^*)\,\Delta x_i = \sum_{i=1}^{n} cf(x_i^*)\,\Delta x_i,$$

so we see that $\sum_{i=1}^{n} cf(x_i^*)\,\Delta x_i$ approximates $c\int_a^b f(x)\,dx$. Since, by definition, the number approximated by $\sum_{i=1}^{n} cf(x_i^*)\,\Delta x_i$ is $\int_a^b cf(x)\,dx$, we see that Equation 37-7 is true.

THEOREM 37-4. *If f is a function and a, b, and c are any numbers for which the following integrals exist, then*

(37-8) $$\int_a^c f(x)\,dx = \int_a^b f(x)\,dx + \int_b^c f(x)\,dx.$$

If $f(x) > 0$ and $a < b < c$, then we can use our interpretation of the integral as an area to give a very simple geometrical expression of the content of Theorem 37-4. For in that case Equation 37-8 simply states that the areas of the regions R_1 and R_2 of Fig. 37-2 add up to the area of the entire shaded region. The theorem is true, however, even if f takes on negative values and if the numbers a, b, and c are not arranged in the order $a < b < c$.

To illustrate how we use the above theorems to prove other properties of integrals, we will now offer a careful proof of the following theorem.

THEOREM 37-5. *If f and g are integrable functions on the interval [a, b] and if $f(x) \geq g(x)$ for x in this interval, then*

(37-9) $$\int_a^b f(x)\,dx \geq \int_a^b g(x)\,dx.$$

Proof. By hypothesis, $f(x) - g(x) \geq 0$ for each x in the interval $[a, b]$. Therefore, according to Theorem 37-1,

(37-10) $\int_a^b [f(x) - g(x)]\, dx \geq 0.$

But $\int_a^b [f(x) - g(x)]\, dx = \int_a^b f(x)\, dx + \int_a^b (-1)g(x)\, dx$

(Theorem 37-2)

$= \int_a^b f(x)\, dx - \int_a^b g(x)\, dx$

(Theorem 37-3)

Substituting this result in Inequality 37-10 yields Inequality 37-9.

Finally, we will state an important theorem that applies to the integral of a continuous function. Geometrically, we interpret the integral $\int_a^b f(x)\, dx$ of the function f whose graph is shown in Fig. 37-3 as the area of the shaded region. From the figure it seems reasonable to conclude

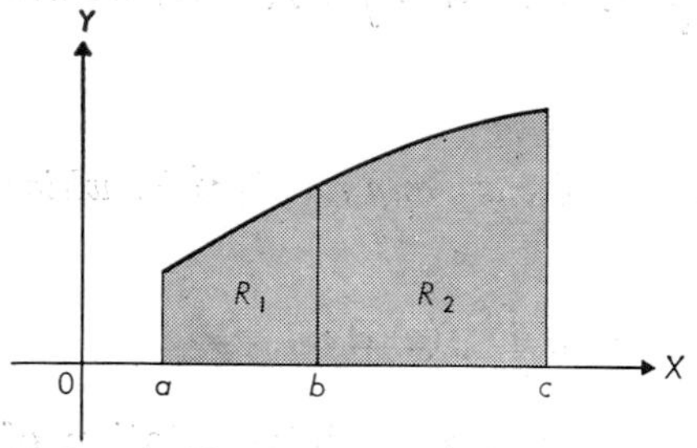

Figure 37-2

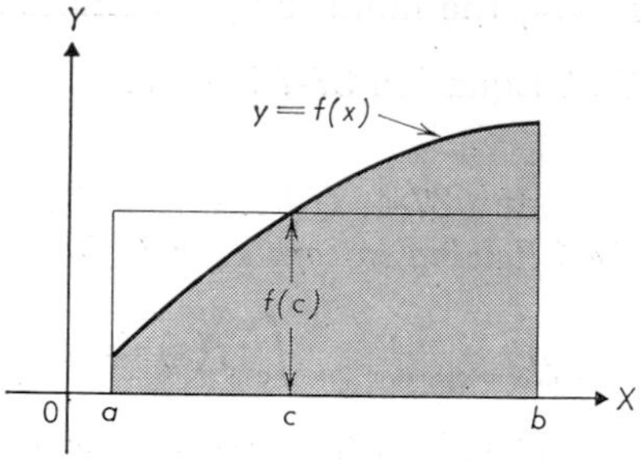

Figure 37-3

that there is a number c in the interval (a, b) such that the area of the rectangle of altitude $f(c)$ whose base is the interval $[a, b]$ (and hence is $b - a$ units long) has the same area as our shaded region. Thus we have

$$f(c)(b - a) = \int_a^b f(x)\, dx.$$

The number $f(c)$ is in a sense the **mean** or **average value of f** in the interval $[a, b]$. If f is any continuous function, then there is a point c such as we have described, and we shall state this result as a theorem.

THEOREM 37-6. (**A Mean Value Theorem for Integrals.**) *If f is continuous in the interval $[a, b]$, then there is a number c in the interval (a, b) such that*

(37-11) $$\mathbf{f(c) = \frac{1}{b - a} \int_a^b f(x)\, dx.}$$

An analytical proof of this theorem requires some facts from advanced calculus, so we shall omit it. Let us remark, however, that Theorem 37-6 merely tells us that there *is* a point c as described. It does not provide a simple way of finding this point!

Problems 37

1. Draw a graph of the function f defined by the equation $f(x) = x/3$ for the interval $[1, 4]$. Partition the interval into 3 equal subintervals. What is the norm of the partition? What numbers x_1^*, x_2^*, and x_3^* should be chosen to make the approximating sum based on your partition a minimum? What is this minimum sum? How should the numbers x_1^*, x_2^*, x_3^* be chosen to make the approximating sum a maximum? What is this maximum sum? Can you convince yourself that any approximating sum based on a partition with a norm equal to 1 satisfies the inequalities $2 \leq S \leq 3$? What inequalities are satisfied by an approximating sum S based on a partition whose norm is $\frac{1}{3}$? What number would you expect as the limit of S as the norm of the partition approaches zero?

Use the theorems in this section to solve the following problems.

2. Show that $\int_a^b 0\, dx = 0$.
3. Show that $\int_0^3 (4 + 3x - x^2)\, dx \geq 0$.
4. Show that $\int_{-1}^0 (z^3 - z^2 - 2z)\, dz \geq 0$.
5. Show that $\int_0^1 (t - \sin t)\, dt \geq 0$.
6. Prove: If f is an integrable function on an interval $[a, b]$ and if $f(x) \leq 0$ for every number x in the interval $[a, b]$, then $\int_a^b f(x)\, dx \leq 0$. [Let $g(x) = -f(x)$].
7. Show that $\int_1^2 (2 - 3x + x^2)\, dx \leq 0$.
8. Show that $\int_0^1 x^2\, dx \leq \int_0^1 x\, dx$.
9. Show that $\int_0^1 x^4\, dx \leq \int_0^1 y^2\, dy$.
10. Show that $\int_0^1 (x^2 - 2x - 3)\, dx \leq \int_0^{-1} (t^2 - 2t - 3)\, dt$.
11. Use the interpretation of the integral as an area to find the number c mentioned in Theorem 37-6 if $f(x) = x$, $a = 0$, and $b = 2$.
12. Use Definition 37-2 and a geometrical argument to show that Equation 37-8 is correct if $a < c < b$.

38. Integrals of Some Particular Functions

Now that we have defined the concept of the integral of a function, we want to apply it to some particular functions. When we are dealing with a function f defined on an interval $[a, b]$, we ask two questions: "Is f integrable on $[a, b]$; that is, do the approximating sums have a limit?" and "If f is integrable on $[a, b]$, then what is its integral; that is, what is the limit of the approximating sums?" Generally speaking, it is difficult to use Definition 37-1 to find out whether or not a given function f is integrable on a given interval. The fact is, however, that practically all functions you will deal with are integrable. For example, every function f that is continuous on an interval $[a, b]$ is integrable on that interval. The most common non-integrable functions that you will encounter are the unbounded functions. For example, if $f(x) = 1/x$, then f is unbounded in any interval containing 0, and f is not integrable on such an interval. Similarly, the tangent function is unbounded in any interval containing $\pi/2$, and it is not integrable on an interval containing this point. But it is safe to assume that most of the bounded functions you will meet are integrable. The function described in Illustration 3-5 is an example of a non-integrable bounded function.

If we know that a certain function f is integrable on an interval $[a, b]$, we can often use the following theorem, or later refinements, to evaluate its integral. The statement that f is integrable means that there is only one number that belongs to every "J-interval," and that number is $\int_a^b f(x)\,dx$. Suppose we can find a number A such that for every partition of $[a, b]$ there is a choice of the numbers $x_1^*, x_2^*, \ldots, x_n^*$ that makes the approximating sum equal to A. Then the number A belongs to every J-interval and therefore must be the limit of the approximating sums. We state this fact as a theorem.

THEOREM 38-1. *Suppose that the function f is integrable on the interval $[a, b]$. Suppose also that there is a number A such that for every partition of the interval it is possible to choose the numbers $x_1^*, x_2^*, \ldots, x_n^*$ to form an approximating sum that is equal to A. Then this number A is the integral of f; in symbols,*

$$\int_a^b f(x)\,dx = A.$$

We will now apply Theorem 38-1 to some important integrals.

Example 38-1. Verify that, for an arbitrary interval $[a, b]$,

$$\int_a^b x\,dx = \frac{b^2}{2} - \frac{a^2}{2}. \tag{38-1}$$

Solution. According to Theorem 38-1, we need only show that for each partition of the interval $[a, b]$ there is an approximating sum

$$S = \frac{b^2}{2} - \frac{a^2}{2}.$$

So suppose we have a partition of the interval $[a, b]$ determined by the points $x_0 = a, x_1, x_2, \ldots, x_{n-1}, x_n = b$. Every approximating sum will take the form

$$S = \sum_{i=1}^{n} f(x_i^*)\,\Delta x_i = \sum_{i=1}^{n} x_i^*\,\Delta x_i,$$

and we must show that a suitable choice of the numbers $x_1^*, x_2^*, \ldots, x_n^*$ will give us $S = \frac{b^2}{2} - \frac{a^2}{2}$. In this example the "suitable choice" consists of taking x_i^* to be the midpoint of the interval $[x_{i-1}, x_i]$, that is, $x_i^* = (x_i + x_{i-1})/2$. For then

$$\begin{aligned} S &= \sum_{i=1}^{n} \tfrac{1}{2}(x_i + x_{i-1})(x_i - x_{i-1}) \\ &= \sum_{i=1}^{n} \left(\frac{x_i^2}{2} - \frac{x_{i-1}^2}{2}\right) \\ &= \left(\frac{x_1^2}{2} - \frac{x_0^2}{2}\right) + \left(\frac{x_2^2}{2} - \frac{x_1^2}{2}\right) + \cdots + \left(\frac{x_n^2}{2} - \frac{x_{n-1}^2}{2}\right) \\ &= \frac{x_n^2}{2} - \frac{x_0^2}{2} = \frac{b^2}{2} - \frac{a^2}{2}. \end{aligned}$$

Example 38-2. Verify that, for an arbitrary interval $[a, b]$,

$$\int_a^b x^2\,dx = \frac{b^3}{3} - \frac{a^3}{3}. \tag{38-2}$$

Solution. For a given partition of the interval $[a, b]$, each approximating sum takes the form

$$S = \sum_{i=1}^{n} f(x_i^*)\,\Delta x_i = \sum_{i=1}^{n} x_i^{*2}\,\Delta x_i.$$

We shall pick the numbers $x_1^*, x_2^*, \ldots, x_n^*$ so that

$$S = \frac{b^3}{3} - \frac{a^3}{3}.$$

In Example 38-1 we chose the number x_i^* to be the midpoint of the interval $[x_{i-1}, x_i]$. Here we make a more complicated choice. We choose x_i^* to be a number in the interval $[x_{i-1}, x_i]$ such that

$$x_i^{*2} = \tfrac{1}{3}(x_i^2 + x_i x_{i-1} + x_{i-1}^2).$$

(In Question 12 in the Problems of this section we ask you to show that such a choice is possible.) Then

$$\begin{aligned} S &= \sum_{i=1}^{n} \left(\frac{x_i^2 + x_i x_{i-1} + x_{i-1}^2}{3}\right)(x_i - x_{i-1}) \\ &= \sum_{i=1}^{n} \left(\frac{x_i^3}{3} - \frac{x_{i-1}^3}{3}\right) \\ &= \left(\frac{x_1^3}{3} - \frac{x_0^3}{3}\right) + \left(\frac{x_2^3}{3} - \frac{x_1^3}{3}\right) + \cdots + \left(\frac{x_n^3}{3} - \frac{x_{n-1}^3}{3}\right) = \frac{x_n^3}{3} - \frac{x_0^3}{3} = \frac{b^3}{3} - \frac{a^3}{3}. \end{aligned}$$

We have shown that for every partition of the interval $[a, b]$, we can form an approximating sum $S = \dfrac{b^3}{3} - \dfrac{a^3}{3}$, and so Theorem 38-1 tells us that this number must be the integral of our function.

Together, the *specific* Integration Formulas 37-3, 38-1, and 38-2, and the *general* Integration Formulas 37-6 and 37-7 furnish the tools we need to evaluate the integral of any function f defined by an equation of the form $f(x) = Ax^2 + Bx + C$.

Example 38-3. Evaluate $\int_2^3 (6x^2 + 2x - 5)\,dx$.

Solution. Using Equation 37-6, we can write

$$\int_2^3 (6x^2 + 2x - 5)\,dx = \int_2^3 6x^2\,dx + \int_2^3 2x\,dx + \int_2^3 (-5)\,dx.$$

Now we use Equation 37-7 to obtain the equation

$$\int_2^3 (6x^2 + 2x - 5)\,dx = 6\int_2^3 x^2\,dx + 2\int_2^3 x\,dx - 5\int_2^3 1\,dx.$$

We use Equations 37-3, 38-1, and 38-2 to evaluate the integrals on the right:

$$\int_2^3 (6x^2 + 2x - 5)\,dx = 6\left(\frac{3^3}{3} - \frac{2^3}{3}\right) + 2\left(\frac{3^2}{2} - \frac{2^2}{2}\right) - 5(3 - 2) = 38.$$

Example 38-4. Show that

$$\text{(38-3)} \quad \int_a^b (Ax^2 + Bx + C)\,dx = \frac{b-a}{6}\left[g(a) + 4g\left(\frac{a+b}{2}\right) + g(b)\right],$$

where $g(x) = Ax^2 + Bx + C$. (We shall use this result in Section 39.)

Solution. We can evaluate the given integral just as we did the integral in the last example. Thus

$$\int_a^b (Ax^2 + Bx + C)\,dx = A\int_a^b x^2\,dx + B\int_a^b x\,dx + C\int_a^b 1\,dx,$$

and hence

$$\text{(38-4)}\quad \int_a^b (Ax^2 + Bx + C)\,dx = A\left(\frac{b^3}{3} - \frac{a^3}{3}\right) + B\left(\frac{b^2}{2} - \frac{a^2}{2}\right) + C(b - a).$$

Using algebra we can show that the right sides of Equations 38-3 and 38-4 are the same. Thus since

$$\begin{aligned} 4g\left(\frac{a+b}{2}\right) &= 4A\left(\frac{a+b}{2}\right)^2 + 4B\left(\frac{a+b}{2}\right) + 4C \\ &= A(b^2 + 2ab + a^2) + 2B(b + a) + 4C, \end{aligned}$$

you can easily verify that

$$g(a) + 4g\left(\frac{a+b}{2}\right) + g(b) = 2A(b^2 + ab + a^2) + 3B(b + a) + 6C.$$

So

$$\begin{aligned} &\frac{(b-a)}{6}\left[g(a) + 4g\left(\frac{a+b}{2}\right) + g(b)\right] \\ &\qquad = \frac{A(b^3 - a^3)}{3} + \frac{B(b^2 - a^2)}{2} + C(b - a), \end{aligned}$$

and therefore Equation 38-4 can be expressed in the form of Equation 38-3.

Problems 38

1. In Examples 38-1 and 38-2 we verified Formulas 38-1 and 38-2 when $b > a$. With the aid of Definition 37-2, show that these formulas are valid if $b \leq a$.
2. Compute the following integrals.
   (a) $\int_{-1}^{7} x\,dx$ (b) $\int_{-3}^{-1} t\,dt$
   (c) $\int_{-3}^{1} t\,dt$ (d) $\int_{5}^{3} x\,dx$
   (e) $\int_{-2}^{4} z^2\,dz$ (f) $\int_{-3}^{-5} x^2\,dx$
   (g) $\int_{-1}^{3} u^2\,du$ (h) $\int_{1}^{-1} t^2\,dt$
3. Compute the following integrals.
   (a) $\int_0^2 (x - 4x^2)\,dx$ (b) $\int_0^1 (x^2 - 4x)\,dx$

(c) $\int_1^4 (3t^2 - 6t + 7)\,dt$ (d) $\int_1^0 (t - 3t^2)\,dt$

(e) $\int_{-1}^0 (1 - r^2)\,dr$ (f) $\int_0^{-1} (1 - u^2)\,du$

(g) $\int_6^6 (s^2 + 6s - 7)\,ds$ (h) $\int_{-5}^{-5} (u^2 - 1)\,du$

4. Compute the following integrals.

(a) $\int_1^2 (2z - 4)^2\,dz$ (b) $\int_{-1}^0 x(x - 1)\,dx$

(c) $\int_0^3 (t + 1)^2\,dt$ (d) $\int_2^{-1} 2y(y + 1)\,dy$

(e) $\int_0^1 (x + a)^2\,dx - \int_0^1 (x - a)^2\,dx$

(f) $\int_0^1 x^2\,dx - \int_1^0 x^2\,dx$

(g) $\int_1^2 (x + 7)^2\,dx + \int_2^1 (y + 7)^2\,dy$

(h) $\int_1^2 x^3\,dx + \int_2^3 t^3\,dt + \int_3^1 u^3\,du$

5. Follow the method used in Example 38-2 and choose x_i^* to be the point such that

$$(x_i^*)^3 = \tfrac{1}{4}(x_i^3 + x_i^2 x_{i-1} + x_i x_{i-1}^2 + x_{i-1}^3)$$

to show that if $b > a$, then

$$\int_a^b x^3\,dx = \frac{b^4}{4} - \frac{a^4}{4}.$$

6. With the aid of Definition 37-2, show that the formula in the preceding question is valid if $b \leq a$.

7. Use the formula in Question 5 to compute the following integrals.

(a) $\int_1^6 x^3\,dx$ (b) $\int_{-1}^0 t^3\,dt$

(c) $\int_{-1}^1 w^3\,dw$ (d) $\int_3^{-1} x^3\,dx$

8. Compute $\int_0^2 f(x)\,dx$ if:

(a) $f(x) = x^3 - x$ (b) $f(x) = x^3 - 2x^2 - 1$

(c) $f(x) = 2x^3 + 7x^2 - 4$ (d) $f(x) = 4x^3 - 6x^2 + 2x - 1$

9. Compute

(a) $\int_0^2 (x - 1)(x^2 + x + 1)\,dx$

(b) $\int_{-1}^0 (t + 2)(t^2 - 2t + 4)\,dt$

10. Verify Formula 38-3 if $a = 0$, $b = 2$, $A = 3$, $B = 4$, and $C = 5$.

11. In Example 38-4 we showed that

$$\int_a^b g(x)\,dx = \frac{b-a}{6}\left[g(a) + 4g\left(\frac{a+b}{2}\right) + g(b)\right]$$

when $g(x) = A^2 + Bx + C$. Show that this equation is valid when $g(x) = Ax^3 + Bx^2 + Cx + D$.

12. Verify that a point x_i^* can be chosen as stated in Example 38-2.

39. Calculating Integrals. Approximation Formulas

We used Theorem 38-1 to develop Integration Formulas 38-1 and 38-2. In the next section we shall use this theorem to derive a valuable analytical method of calculating integrals. But before discussing this analytical method, we want to describe various geometrical approaches to the problem of evaluating an integral.

In Section 36 we said that we would introduce the concept of the integral in four steps. In step (i) we think of the integral of f as the area under the graph of f (in order to motivate our later analytical definition); in step (ii) we set up sums that seem to approximate this area; and in step (iii) we define the integral as the limit of these sums. Now we come to step (iv), the analytic definition of area. We can form approximating sums as we did in step (ii) and take their limit as we did in step (iii) without any reference to area whatever. Thus our definition of the integral is a purely analytical one that is independent of any vague intuitive ideas about the area of a region with curved boundaries. In fact, to avoid such vagueness, we may *define* the area under the graph of f to be the integral of f.

DEFINITION 39-1. *If a function f is integrable on an interval $[a, b]$, and if $f(x) \geq 0$ on that interval, then the* **area** *of the region under the graph of f, and bounded by the X-axis and vertical lines through a and b, is the number* $\int_a^b f(x)\,dx$.

The difference in our points of view in steps (i) and (iv) is this: In step (i) we regard the integral as the area (intuitive area), whereas in step (iv) we *define* the area to be the integral. In both cases we are saying that the area and the integral are the same. The concept of area as expressed in Definition 39-1 has all the properties that we would expect of an "area." Furthermore, Definition 39-1 yields the correct area of familiar figures such as rectangles (Example 37-1), triangles, and so on. We may therefore interpret the integral as an area and use this interpretation to calculate integrals.

Example 39-1. Suppose that a is a positive number. Evaluate

$$\int_0^a \sqrt{a^2 - x^2}\,dx.$$

Solution. You can easily verify that the graph of the equation

$$y = \sqrt{a^2 - x^2}$$

is the semicircle with a radius of a units whose center is the origin. The area of the region beneath the curve $y = \sqrt{a^2 - x^2}$ in the interval $[0, a]$ is therefore just one-half the area of the region under this semicircle; that is, $\pi a^2/4$ square units. Thus

$$\text{(39-1)} \qquad \int_0^a \sqrt{a^2 - x^2}\, dx = \pi a^2/4.$$

Except for special functions, we cannot calculate the exact value of an integral by a graphical method such as we used in the preceding example. However, we can use graphical methods to *approximate* any integral with as much accuracy as we may desire.

Example 39-2. Find an approximation to $\int_0^4 \sqrt{x}\, dx$.

Solution. Figure 39-1 shows the graph of the equation $y = \sqrt{x}$ if $0 \leq x \leq 4$. At the points $x = 1, 2, 3,$ and 4, we have erected vertical line segments with lengths of $\sqrt{1} = 1$, $\sqrt{2} \approx 1.4$, $\sqrt{3} \approx 1.7$, and $\sqrt{4} = 2$. When we

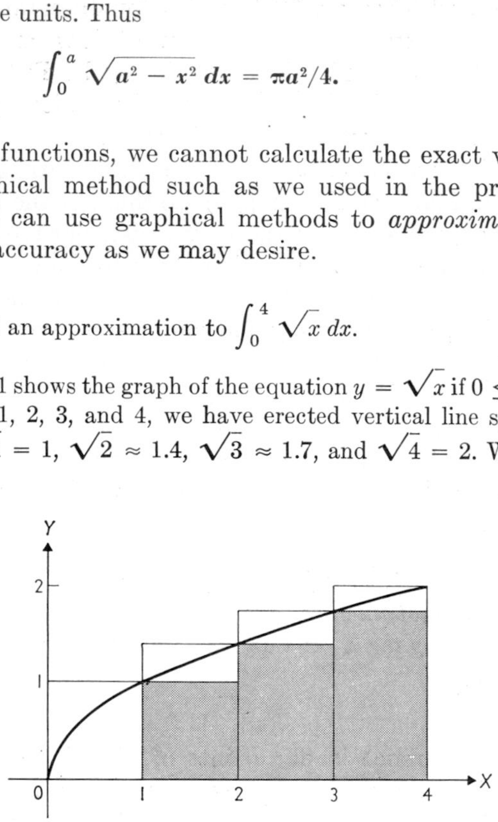

Figure 39-1

compute the area of the shaded "step region" contained in the region under the curve, we see that

$$\int_0^4 \sqrt{x}\, dx > 1 + 1.4 + 1.7 = 4.1.$$

Furthermore, if we compute the area of the "step region" that contains the region under the curve, we see that

$$\int_0^4 \sqrt{x}\, dx < 1 + 1.4 + 1.7 + 2 = 6.1.$$

The numbers 4.1 and 6.1 are rather crude approximations of the integral $\int_0^4 \sqrt{x}\, dx$, but we have at least found that

$$4.1 < \int_0^4 \sqrt{x}\, dx < 6.1. \tag{39-2}$$

So we will make an error of less than 1 unit if we take the average value $(4.1 + 6.1)/2 = 5.1$ as an approximation of this integral. Later we will be able to show that the actual value of the integral is $\frac{16}{3} \approx 5.3$.

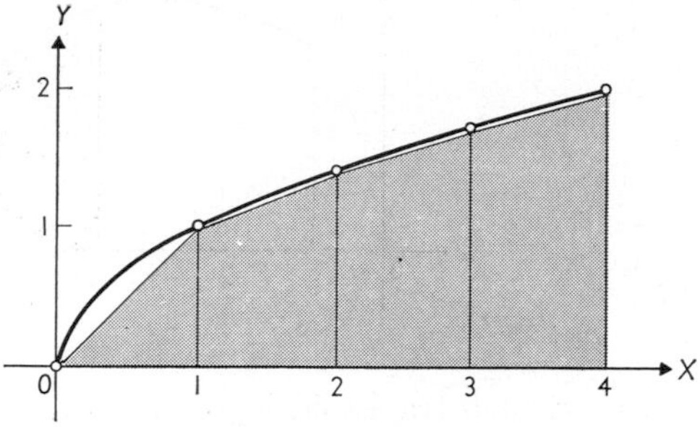

Figure 39-2

Instead of approximating the area by the sum of the areas of rectangles, we can use the sum of the areas of the shaded trapezoidal regions of Fig. 39-2. Here we use the formula for the area A of a trapezoid with an altitude of h and parallel sides a and b: $A = \dfrac{(a+b)}{2} h$. We find that the area of the entire shaded region in the figure is approximately

$$\frac{1+0}{2} \cdot 1 + \frac{1.4+1}{2} \cdot 1 + \frac{1.7+1.4}{2} \cdot 1 + \frac{2+1.7}{2} \cdot 1 = 5.1,$$

so we have the approximation

$$\int_0^4 \sqrt{x}\, dx \approx 5.1. \tag{39-3}$$

(Of course it is not a coincidence that the trapezoidal approximation is the average of the rectangular ones.)

We can employ exactly the same argument that we used in the preceding example to develop a general formula for a trapezoidal approximation of an integral

$$\int_a^b f(x)\, dx.$$

We first select a positive integer n. Then we divide the interval $[a, b]$ into

n subintervals, each $h = (b - a)/n$ units long, by means of the points

$$x_0 = a,\ x_1 = a + h,\ x_2 = a + 2h,\ \ldots,\ x_n = a + nh = b.$$

At each point x_i of this partition we erect a perpendicular with a height of $y_i = f(x_i)$, and then we form trapezoids like the one shown in Fig. 39-3.

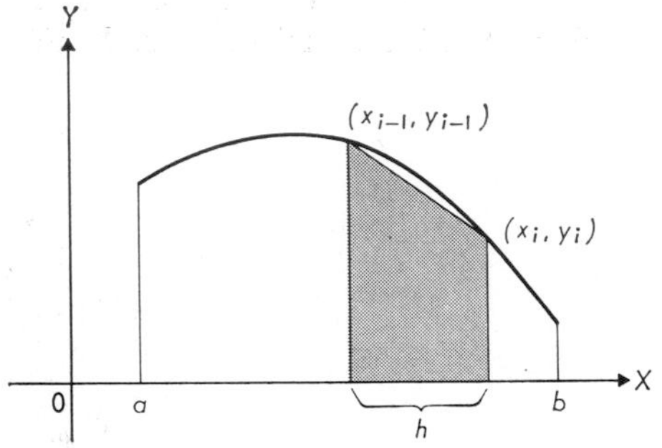

Figure 39-3

The area of each such trapezoid is given by a formula

$$\frac{y_{i-1} + y_i}{2} h,$$

where i is one of the numbers 1, 2, 3, ..., n. The sum of these areas approximates the integral of f. The sum is

$$\begin{aligned} &\frac{y_0 + y_1}{2} h + \frac{y_1 + y_2}{2} h + \cdots + \frac{y_{n-2} + y_{n-1}}{2} h + \frac{y_{n-1} + y_n}{2} h \\ &= \left(\frac{y_0}{2} + \frac{y_1}{2} + \frac{y_1}{2} + \frac{y_2}{2} + \cdots + \frac{y_{n-2}}{2} + \frac{y_{n-1}}{2} + \frac{y_{n-1}}{2} + \frac{y_n}{2}\right) h \\ &= \left(\frac{y_0}{2} + y_1 + y_2 + \cdots + y_{n-1} + \frac{y_n}{2}\right) h. \end{aligned}$$

Thus we have the following theorem.

THEOREM 39-1 (**The Trapezoidal Rule**). *Let n be a positive integer and take $h = (b - a)/n$. If we write $y_i = f(a + ih)$ for $i = 0, 1, 2, \ldots, n$, then*

$$(39\text{-}4) \qquad \int_a^b f(x)\, dx \approx \left(\frac{y_0}{2} + y_1 + y_2 + \cdots + y_{n-1} + \frac{y_n}{2}\right) h.$$

Example 39-3. Use the Trapezoidal Rule with $n = 4$ to approximate the integral $\int_1^2 \frac{1}{x}\, dx$.

Solution. We divide the basic interval [1, 2] into 4 parts, each with a length of $h = (2 - 1)/4 = \frac{1}{4}$, by means of the points $x_0 = 1$, $x_1 = \frac{5}{4}$, $x_2 = \frac{3}{2}$, $x_3 = \frac{7}{4}$, and $x_4 = 2$. Since $y_i = 1/x_i$, then $y_0 = 1$, $y_1 = \frac{4}{5}$, $y_2 = \frac{2}{3}$, $y_3 = \frac{4}{7}$, and $y_4 = \frac{1}{2}$. Thus, according to Formula 39-4,

$$\int_1^2 \frac{1}{x}\,dx \approx \left(\frac{1}{2} + \frac{4}{5} + \frac{2}{3} + \frac{4}{7} + \frac{1}{4}\right)\frac{1}{4}$$

$$= \tfrac{1171}{1680} \approx .697. \tag{39-5}$$

The actual value of this integral, correct to 3 decimal places, is .693.

The Trapezoidal Rule is based on the following simple procedure. We pick a number of points of the graph of a given function f and join

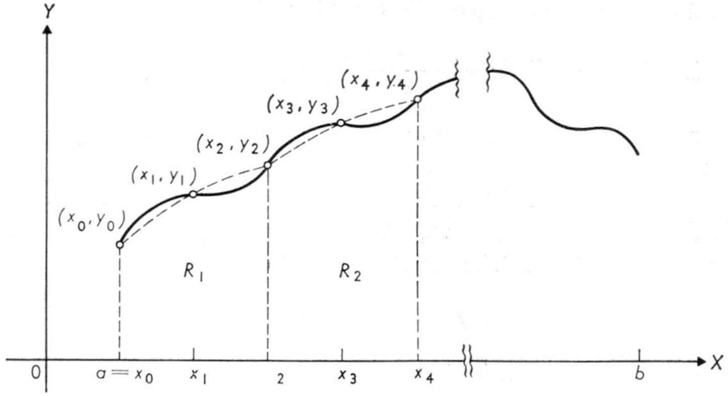

Figure 39-4

them by straight lines to form a polygonal graph. Then to approximate the integral of f, we calculate the area of the region under this polygonal graph and use this area as an approximation to the area of the region under the graph of f itself. Essentially what we have done is to divide our given interval $[a, b]$ into subintervals and to replace our original function with a function that is linear over each of the subintervals. Often we get an even closer approximation of the integral by replacing f with a function that is a quadratic function over certain subintervals of the given interval $[a, b]$.

To approximate the number $\int_a^b f(x)\,dx$ by this method, we divide the interval $[a, b]$ into an *even* number n of equal subintervals, each with a length of $h = \dfrac{b-a}{n}$ (Fig. 39-4). Suppose that the points of subdivision are $x_0 = a$, $x_1 = a + h$, $x_2 = a + 2h$, and so on, and that we denote the corresponding function values by y_0, y_1, y_2, and so on. It is a matter of simple algebra to find numbers A, B, and C such that the graph of the equation $y = Ax^2 + Bx + C$ contains the points (x_0, y_0), (x_1, y_1), and (x_2, y_2). Since this graph is a parabola (Example 34-3), we say that we have "passed a parabola through the points." Through the points (x_2, y_2), (x_3, y_3), and (x_4, y_4) we pass another parabola whose equation is $y = Dx^2 + Ex + F$, and so on, for each successive group of three points. Then the area of the region under the graph of f will be approximated by the sum of the areas of the regions $R_1, R_2 \ldots$ under the parabolas.

Now we will find formulas for the areas of the regions under these parabolas. The equation of the first parabola is $y = g(x) = Ax^2 + Bx + C$ for x in the interval $[x_0, x_2]$. We will find the area of R_1 by integrating this function g. Formula 38-3 gives us the value of this integral:

$$\int_{x_0}^{x_2} (Ax^2 + Bx + C)\, dx = \frac{x_2 - x_0}{6}\left[g(x_0) + 4g\left(\frac{x_0 + x_2}{2}\right) + g(x_2)\right].$$

We are supposing that $x_2 - x_0 = 2h$ and $(x_0 + x_2)/2 = x_1$, so the area of the region R_1 is given by the formula $(h/3)[g(x_0) + 4g(x_1) + g(x_2)]$. Finally, since the graph of the function g contains the three points (x_0, y_0), (x_1, y_1), and (x_2, y_2), we have $g(x_0) = y_0$, $g(x_1) = y_1$, and $g(x_2) = y_2$. Thus the formula for the area of R_1 reduces to

(39-6) $$(h/3)(y_0 + 4y_1 + y_2).$$

In exactly the same way we find that the area of R_2 is

(39-7) $$(h/3)(y_2 + 4y_3 + y_4).$$

Then we find the area of the combined regions R_1 and R_2 by adding Expressions 39-6 and 39-7:

$$(h/3)(y_0 + 4y_1 + 2y_2 + 4y_3 + y_4).$$

We add together the areas of all the regions $R_1, R_2, \ldots$ to get an approximation of the area of the region under the graph of f and state our result as a theorem.

THEOREM 39-2 (**Simpson's Parabolic Rule**). *Let n be a positive even integer and take $h = (b - a)/n$. Then*

(39-8) $$\int_a^b f(x)\, dx \approx (h/3)(y_0 + 4y_1 + 2y_2 + 4y_3 + \cdots + 2y_{n-2} + 4y_{n-1} + y_n),$$

where $y_i = f(a + ih)$, $i = 0, 1, \ldots, n$. *Notice that inside the parentheses,* *the numbers y_0 and y_n are multiplied by 1, whereas the other y's with even subscripts are multiplied by 2. All the y's with odd subscripts are multiplied by 4.*

Example 39-4. Use Simpson's Rule with $n = 4$ to approximate $\int_1^2 \frac{1}{x}\,dx$.

Solution. We use the numbers y_0, y_1, y_2, y_3, and y_4 that we calculated in Example 39-3, together with Formula 39-8, to get

$$\int_1^2 \frac{1}{x}\,dx \approx \frac{(\frac{1}{4})}{3}\left[1 + 4\cdot\left(\frac{4}{5}\right) + 2\cdot\left(\frac{2}{3}\right) + 4\cdot\left(\frac{4}{7}\right) + \frac{1}{2}\right]$$
$$= \tfrac{1747}{2520} \approx .6933.$$

The value of the integral, correct to 4 decimal places, is .6931. Our new approximation is somewhat more accurate than the result we obtained with the Trapezoidal Rule in Example 39-3.

Problems 39

1. The three points (0, 0), (1, 3), and (4, 0) determine a triangle. Use integration and integration formulas to find the area of the triangle.
2. The points (0, 0), (6, 0), (0, 3), and (6, 5) determine a trapezoid. Use integration and integration formulas to find the area of the trapezoid.
3. Use the area interpretation of the integral to compute the following integrals.
   (a) $\int_1^3 [\![x]\!]\,dx$ (b) $\int_0^{3/2} [\![x]\!]\,dx$
   (c) $\int_{-3}^5 |x|\,dx$ (d) $\int_{-1}^3 (2x + 3)\,dx$
   (e) $\int_{-1}^2 (|x| + x)\,dx$ (f) $\int_0^4 (|x - 1| + |x - 2|)\,dx$
4. Compare your results when you compute $\int_0^2 (2x - x^2 + 1)\,dx$ using (a) integration formulas and (b) the Trapezoidal Rule with $n = 4$. Sketch a figure showing the curve and the trapezoids involved.
5. Compute an approximation to the integral using the Trapezoidal Rule with the number n as indicated.
   (a) $\int_0^2 (1 + x^3)\,dx$; $n = 4$
   (b) $\int_1^2 x^{-2}\,dx$; $n = 2$
   (c) $\int_0^2 \sqrt{x}\,dx$; $n = 4$
   (d) $\int_1^5 \sqrt{126 - x^3}\,dx$; $n = 4$.

6. Compute $\int_0^1 x^3\,dx$ using (a) the integration formula in Question 5, Problems 38; (b) the Trapezoidal Rule with $n = 4$; (c) Simpson's Parabolic Rule with $n = 4$.

7. Compute an approximation of the integral using Simpson's Parabolic Rule with the number n as indicated.

(a) $\int_0^{\pi} \sin x\,dx;\ n = 4$

(b) $\int_0^{\pi} (2 + \cos x)^{-1}\,dx;\ n = 4$

(c) $\int_0^{1} (1 + x^2)^{-1}\,dx;\ n = 2$

(d) $\int_2^{8} x(4 + x^2)^{-1/3}\,dx;\ n = 6$

(e) $\int_0^{\pi/2} (1 - \frac{1}{2}\sin^2 x)^{-1/2}\,dx;\ n = 4$

(f) $\int_2^{10} (1 + x)^{-1}\,dx;\ n = 8.$

8. Find $\int_0^{\pi} [\![2 \sin x]\!]\,dx.$

9. Show that the equation of the parabola that contains the points (x_0, y_0), (x_1, y_1), and (x_2, y_2) is

$$y = \frac{y_0(x - x_1)(x - x_2)}{(x_0 - x_1)(x_0 - x_2)} + \frac{y_1(x - x_0)(x - x_2)}{(x_1 - x_0)(x_1 - x_2)} + \frac{y_2(x - x_0)(x - x_1)}{(x_2 - x_0)(x_2 - x_1)}$$

10. Find $\int_0^{4} |x^2 + 2x - 3|\,dx.$

11. Find $\int_1^{3} [\![\frac{1}{3}(-2x^2 + 11x - 9)]\!]\,dx.$

40. The Fundamental Theorem of Calculus

The concepts of the derivative and the integral (two of the fundamental concepts of calculus) were known long before the development of calculus by Isaac Newton and Gottfried Wilhelm Leibnitz in the seventeenth century. What these men discovered was that the processes of integration and differentiation are in a sense inverses of one another. Let us first write the relationship between the derivative and the integral as a formal theorem, and then we will discuss what this theorem says. We will delay the proof of the theorem until the end of the section.

THEOREM 40-1 (**The Fundamental Theorem of Calculus**). *If a function f is integrable on the interval $[a, b]$ and if F is a function that is con-*

tinuous in $[a, b]$ *and is such that* $D_xF(x) = f(x)$ *for* x *in the interval* (a, b), *then*

$$\int_a^b f(x)\, dx = F(b) - F(a). \tag{40-1}$$

We can make the connection between differentiation and integration seem more direct if we write Equation 40-1 in a different form. We are supposing that $D_xF(x) = f(x)$, and hence Equation 40-1 can be written as

$$\int_a^b D_xF(x)\, dx = F(b) - F(a).$$

This equation shows us how integration "undoes" the operation of differentiation. When you remember that we introduced the process of differentiation in terms of finding tangent lines to a curve and the process of integration in terms of the apparently unrelated problem of finding the area under a curve, you will probably agree that the Fundamental Theorem is not an obvious result!

Now let us see how we can use our theorem to calculate integrals. In essence, the Fundamental Theorem tells us that we can evaluate integrals very simply if we know our rules of differentiation backwards as well as forwards. For to evaluate the integral $\int_a^b f(x)\, dx$, we need only to find any function F such that $D_xF(x) = f(x)$ and then compute the number $F(b) - F(a)$. Of course, it is not always a simple matter to solve the equation $D_xF(x) = f(x)$ for $F(x)$, but we shall find that in many cases our familiarity with the rules of differentiation will enable us to solve this equation by inspection. If $D_xF(x) = f(x)$, then $f(x)$ is called the derivative of $F(x)$, and $F(x)$ is called an **antiderivative** of $f(x)$. The Fundamental Theorem tells us how to evaluate integrals of a function f if we can find an antiderivative of $f(x)$. It is customary to use the notation

$$F(x)\Big|_a^b = F(b) - F(a).$$

In that notation Equation 40-1 becomes

$$\int_a^b f(x)\, dx = F(x)\Big|_a^b. \tag{40-2}$$

Now let us apply the Fundamental Theorem to derive a most useful integration formula. In the notation of Equation 40-2, our earlier integration formulas can be written as

$$\text{(40-3)}\qquad \begin{aligned} \int_a^b 1\,dx &= x\Big|_a^b, \\ \int_a^b x\,dx &= \frac{x^2}{2}\Big|_a^b, \\ \int_a^b x^2\,dx &= \frac{x^3}{3}\Big|_a^b. \end{aligned}$$

These equations suggest that

$$\text{(40-4)}\qquad \int_a^b \boldsymbol{x^r\,dx} = \frac{\boldsymbol{x^{r+1}}}{\boldsymbol{r+1}}\Big|_a^b,$$

where r is any rational number other than -1. It is an easy matter to *verify* Equation 40-4. For according to the Fundamental Theorem, we need only show that $\frac{x^{r+1}}{r+1}$ is an antiderivative of x^r; that is, that the derivative of $\frac{x^{r+1}}{r+1}$ is x^r. Our rules of differentiation immediately yield

$$D_x\left(\frac{x^{r+1}}{r+1}\right) = \left(\frac{r+1}{r+1}\right)x^r = x^r,$$

and so the verification of Formula 40-4 is complete. When we see how easily the Fundamental Theorem yields Equation 40-4 (which includes Formulas 40-3 that we so laboriously derived, as well as many others) we begin to see what a valuable tool it really is.

We will now apply Equation 40-4 to some examples.

Example 40-1. Evaluate the integral $\int_0^4 \sqrt{x}\,dx$.

Solution. Our given integral can be written as $\int_0^4 x^{1/2}\,dx$, so we apply Formula 40-4 with $r = \frac{1}{2}$:

$$\int_0^4 x^{1/2}\,dx = \frac{x^{3/2}}{\frac{3}{2}}\Big|_0^4 = \frac{2}{3}(4^{3/2} - 0^{3/2}) = \frac{2}{3}\cdot 8 = \frac{16}{3}.$$

Example 40-2. Evaluate the integral $\int_{-1}^8 \sqrt[3]{t^2}\,dt$.

Solution. Since $\sqrt[3]{t^2} = t^{2/3}$, we can apply Formula 40-4 with $r = \frac{2}{3}$ to obtain

$$\int_{-1}^8 \sqrt[3]{t^2}\,dt = \frac{t^{5/3}}{\frac{5}{3}}\Big|_{-1}^8 = \frac{3}{5}[8^{5/3} - (-1)^{5/3}] = \frac{99}{5}.$$

When we combine Formula 40-4 with general integration rules such as Equations 37-6 and 37-7, we find that we have a way to evaluate a large class of integrals.

Example 40-3. Evaluate the integral $\int_1^2 (2z^3 - 3/z^2)\,dz$.

Solution. We have

$$\begin{aligned}\int_1^2 \left(2z^3 - \frac{3}{z^2}\right) dz &= \int_1^2 (2z^3 - 3z^{-2})\,dz \\ &= 2\int_1^2 z^3\,dz - 3\int_1^2 z^{-2}\,dz \\ &= 2\left(\frac{z^4}{4}\right)\Big|_1^2 - 3\left(\frac{z^{-1}}{-1}\right)\Big|_1^2 \\ &= 2[(\tfrac{16}{4}) - (\tfrac{1}{4})] - 3\left[\left(\frac{2^{-1}}{-1}\right) - \left(\frac{1}{-1}\right)\right] = 6.\end{aligned}$$

We conclude this section with a proof of the Fundamental Theorem of Calculus.

Proof. According to Theorem 38-1, the number $F(b) - F(a)$ is the integral of f on the interval $[a, b]$ if for *each* partition of the interval $[a, b]$ we can find an approximating sum such that

$$\sum_{i=1}^{n} f(x_i^*)\,\Delta x_i = F(b) - F(a). \tag{40-5}$$

So our problem is to find numbers $x_1^*, x_2^*, \ldots, x_n^*$ for which Equation 40-5 is valid. We are assuming that F is continuous in every interval $[x_{i-1}, x_i]$ and that $F'(x)$ is defined at each point in the open interval (x_{i-1}, x_i). Therefore, according to the Theorem of the Mean (Theorem 21-2), there is a number c_i in the interval (x_{i-1}, x_i) such that

$$F(x_i) - F(x_{i-1}) = F'(c_i)(x_i - x_{i-1}). \tag{40-6}$$

Since $F'(x) = f(x)$ by assumption, $F'(c_i) = f(c_i)$. Also, $x_i - x_{i-1} = \Delta x_i$, so Equation 40-6 can be written as

$$F(x_i) - F(x_{i-1}) = f(c_i)\,\Delta x_i. \tag{40-7}$$

Therefore, if we choose $x_i^* = c_i$, the left side of Equation 40-5 becomes

$$\begin{aligned}\sum_{i=1}^{n} f(c_i)\,\Delta x_i &= \sum_{i=1}^{n} [F(x_i) - F(x_{i-1})] \\ &= [F(x_1) - F(x_0)] + [F(x_2) - F(x_1)] + \cdots + [F(x_n) - F(x_{n-1})] \\ &= F(x_n) - F(x_0) = F(b) - F(a).\end{aligned}$$

We have found numbers $x_1^*, x_2^*, \ldots, x_n^*$ for which Equation 40-5 is valid, and have thereby completed the proof of the Fundamental Theorem of Calculus.

Problems 40

1. Compute.
   (a) $\int_0^2 10x^4\,dx$ (b) $\int_0^1 \sqrt[4]{t^3}\,dt$
   (c) $\int_{-4}^{-2} \frac{1}{t^2}\,dt$ (d) $\int_0^{-1} \sqrt[3]{z}\,dz$
   (e) $\int_1^4 \frac{1}{\sqrt{z}}\,dz$ (f) $\int_1^8 \frac{1}{3\sqrt[3]{x^2}}\,dx$
   (g) $\int_1^{32} \frac{\sqrt[5]{x^2}}{\sqrt[3]{x}}\,dx$ (h) $\int_0^1 \frac{\sqrt[4]{x^3}}{\sqrt[3]{x^2}}\,dx$
2. Compute.
   (a) $\int_0^1 (w^4 - \sqrt{w})\,dw$ (b) $\int_0^a (a^2x - x^3)\,dx$
   (c) $\int_{-1}^3 (3 + 2x - x^2)\,dx$ (d) $\int_0^{-4} x(\sqrt[3]{x} + x^3)\,dx$
   (e) $\int_{-2}^2 x(x^2 + 3x)\,dx$ (f) $\int_1^4 (\sqrt{t} + 2)(2t - 1)\,dt$
   (g) $\int_0^8 (2 - \sqrt[3]{x})^2\,dx$ (h) $\int_1^{64} (\sqrt{x} - \sqrt[3]{x})^2\,dx$
3. Compute.
   (a) $\int_0^4 |4 - x^2|\,dx$ (b) $\int_0^2 x|1 - x|\,dx$
   (c) $\int_{-1}^1 \sqrt{|x| + x}\,dx$ (d) $\int_{-1}^5 \sqrt[3]{4(|x| - x)}\,dx$
4. Find the area of the region bounded by the X-axis and the curve whose equation is given.
   (a) $y = 16 - x^2$ (b) $y = 64 - x^3$
   (c) $y = 2x^2 - x^3$ (d) $y = 4a^3x - 6a^2x^2 + 4ax^3 - x^4$
5. Find a positive number x such that

$$\int_0^x (2 - t + t^2)\,dt = \tfrac{14}{3}.$$

   Interpret this problem geometrically.
6. Let $a = 1$, $b = 3$, and $f(x) = x^3$. Find a number that will serve as the number c in the Mean Value Theorem 37-6.
7. Are there any positive rational numbers r and s such that

$$\int_0^1 x^r\,dx \cdot \int_0^1 x^s\,dx = \int_0^1 x^r \cdot x^s\,dx?$$

8. Compute.

(a) $\int_0^1 D_x \sqrt{x^2 + 8}\, dx$ (b) $\int_{-1}^1 D_t \sin t^2\, dt$

(c) $\int_0^{\pi/4} D_t \tan t\, dt$ (d) $\int_2^8 D_x \log x\, dx$

41. Integration Formulas

The Fundamental Theorem of Calculus tells us that

$$\int_a^b f(x)\, dx = F(x)\Big|_a^b \tag{41-1}$$

if $D_xF(x) = f(x)$. For example,

$$\int_a^b 6x^5\, dx = x^6\Big|_a^b \quad \text{since} \quad D_x x^6 = 6x^5.$$

The limits of integration a and b are arbitrary. They could be the numbers 2 and 3, $-\pi$ and π, or any other pair of real numbers. Thus

$$\int_2^3 6x^5\, dx = x^6\Big|_2^3 = 665, \qquad \int_{-\pi}^{\pi} 6x^5\, dx = x^6\Big|_{-\pi}^{\pi} = 0,$$

and so on. Since Equation 41-1 is independent of the limits of integration, we drop them and simply write

$$\int f(x)\, dx = F(x) \tag{41-2}$$

whenever $D_xF(x) = f(x)$. The Integration Formula 41-2 is simply an abbreviated form of Equation 41-1. We can get Equation 41-1 from Equation 41-2 by replacing the limits a and b. When we drop the limits of integration, our integral becomes "indefinite." You will sometimes encounter the statement that $F(x)$ is an "indefinite integral" of $f(x)$.

Equation 41-2 follows from the equation $D_xF(x) = f(x)$. We can therefore associate a specific integration formula with each of our specific differentiation formulas. Thus, because

$$D_x \frac{x^{r+1}}{r+1} = x^r,$$

we have the integration formula that we introduced in the preceding section,

$$\int \boldsymbol{x^r\, dx} = \frac{\boldsymbol{x^{r+1}}}{\boldsymbol{r+1}} \quad (r \text{ a rational number, not equal to } -1). \tag{41-3}$$

Our differentiation formulas for the various trigonometric functions lead to the following integration formulas:

$$\int \sin x\,dx = -\cos x \tag{41-4}$$

$$\int \cos x\,dx = \sin x \tag{41-5}$$

$$\int \sec^2 x\,dx = \tan x \tag{41-6}$$

$$\int \csc^2 x\,dx = -\cot x \tag{41-7}$$

$$\int \sec x \tan x\,dx = \sec x \tag{41-8}$$

$$\int \csc x \cot x\,dx = -\csc x \tag{41-9}$$

To verify one of these formulas, we need only show that the expression on the right is an antiderivative of the integrand. Thus, for example, Equation 41-8 is valid because $D_x \sec x = \sec x \tan x$. You should memorize these integration formulas and realize that they are nothing but our old differentiation formulas written in a new form.

Example 41-1. Find the area of the region bounded by an arch of the sine curve and the X-axis.

Solution. If we look at the graph of the equation $y = \sin x$, we see that the area we seek is given by the integral $\int_0^\pi \sin x\,dx$. This integral is evaluated by inserting the limits 0 and π into Formula 41-4:

$$\int_0^\pi \sin x\,dx = -\cos x \Big|_0^\pi = (-\cos \pi) - (-\cos 0)$$
$$= 2.$$

(In Example 36-2 we used rectangles to find an approximation of the area of one-half of this region.)

In addition to the integration formulas listed above, which deal with specific functions, there are a number of general integration formulas, two of which are

$$\int_a^b [mf(x) + ng(x)]\,dx = m\int_a^b f(x)\,dx + n\int_a^b g(x)\,dx \tag{41-10}$$

and

$$\int_a^c f(x)\,dx = \int_a^b f(x)\,dx + \int_b^c f(x)\,dx. \tag{41-11}$$

In these formulas, f and g are assumed to be integrable functions, and m and n are real numbers (see Theorems 37-2, 37-3, and 37-4).

The best way to become familiar with integration formulas is to use them.

Example 41-2. Evaluate the integral $\int_0^{\pi/2} (\cos x + 1)\,dx$.

Solution. Here we use the general Equation 41-10 before applying the appropriate specific integration formulas:

$$\int_0^{\pi/2} (\cos x + 1)\, dx = \int_0^{\pi/2} \cos x\, dx + \int_0^{\pi/2} 1\, dx \qquad \text{(Eq. 41-10)}$$

$$= \sin x \Big|_0^{\pi/2} + x \Big|_0^{\pi/2} \qquad \text{(Eq. 41-5 and Eq. 41-3 with } r = 0)$$

$$= \sin \frac{\pi}{2} - \sin 0 + \frac{\pi}{2} - 0$$

$$= 1 + \frac{\pi}{2}.$$

Example 41-3. Evaluate the integral $\int_0^1 (8t^3 - \sec^2 t)\, dt$.

Solution. Here we have

$$\int_0^1 (8t^3 - \sec^2 t)\, dt = 8 \int_0^1 t^3\, dt - \int_0^1 \sec^2 t\, dt \qquad \text{(Equation 41-10)}$$

$$= 8 \frac{t^4}{4} \Big|_0^1 - \tan t \Big|_0^1 \qquad \text{(Formulas 41-3 and 41-6)}$$

$$= 8(\tfrac{1}{4} - 0) - (\tan 1 - \tan 0)$$

$$= 2 - \tan 1.$$

From Table I we find that $\tan 1 = 1.557$, so

$$\int_0^1 (8t^3 - \sec^2 t)\, dt = .443.$$

Example 41-4. Evaluate the integral $\int_{-3}^1 |x|\, dx$.

Solution. None of the Formulas 41-3 to 41-9 applies directly to this case. However, since $|x| = -x$ when $-3 \leq x \leq 0$ and $|x| = x$ when $0 \leq x \leq 1$, we first apply Equation 41-11:

$$\int_{-3}^1 |x|\, dx = \int_{-3}^0 |x|\, dx + \int_0^1 |x|\, dx \qquad \text{(Eq. 41-11)}$$

$$= -\int_{-3}^0 x\, dx + \int_0^1 x\, dx \qquad \text{(replace } |x| \text{ with } -x \text{ in the first integral and with } x \text{ in the second)}$$

$$= -\frac{x^2}{2}\Big|_{-3}^0 + \frac{x^2}{2}\Big|_0^1 \qquad \text{(Formula 41-3)}$$

$$= \tfrac{9}{2} + \tfrac{1}{2} = 5.$$

You will often find the following generalizations of Formulas 41-4 and 41-5 useful. If a and b are any numbers ($a \neq 0$), then

(41-12) $$\int \cos (ax + b)\, dx = \frac{1}{a} \sin (ax + b)$$

and

(41-13) $$\int \sin (ax + b)\, dx = -\frac{1}{a} \cos (ax + b).$$

We verify these integration formulas by using our rules of differentiation to show that

$$D_x[(1/a) \sin (ax + b)] = \cos (ax + b),$$

and

$$D_x[(-1/a) \cos (ax + b)] = \sin (ax + b).$$

It is not hard to write similar generalizations of the other formulas on our list.

Finally, notice that the Fundamental Theorem tells how to evaluate the integral of a function f by using any antiderivative of $f(x)$. We get the value of the integral no matter which of the antiderivatives of $f(x)$ we choose. For example, if we evaluate the integral $\int_a^b \cos x\, dx$ by choosing the antiderivative $\sin x$, we obtain the number $\sin b - \sin a$. On the other hand, since $D_x(\sin x + 7) = \cos x$, we see that $\sin x + 7$ is also an antiderivative of $\cos x$ and hence

$$\int_a^b \cos x\, dx = (\sin x + 7)\Big|_a^b = (\sin b + 7) - (\sin a + 7)$$
$$= \sin b - \sin a.$$

Since it makes no difference which of the antiderivatives of $f(x)$ we use when we apply the Fundamental Theorem, we normally choose the "simplest" antiderivative when we state an integration formula. Thus we write $\int \cos x\, dx = \sin x$, for example, although it would be equally correct to write $\int \cos x\, dx = \sin x + 7$.

Problems 41

1. Compute.

(a) $\int_0^{\pi/2} (\sin x + 2 \cos x)\, dx$ (b) $\int_{-\pi/4}^{0} \sec^2 x\, dx$

(c) $\int_0^1 (x + \sin x)\, dx$ (d) $\int_{1/2}^{1} (2x + \csc^2 x)\, dx$

(e) $\int_{-1}^{1} \sec t \tan t\, dt$ (f) $\int_{\pi/4}^{3\pi/4} \csc z \cot z\, dz$

2. Compute.

(a) $\int_0^{\pi/4} \sin 2x\, dx$ (b) $\int_0^{\pi/6} \cos 3t\, dt$

(c) $\int_0^2 \cos (t/2 - 1)\, dt$ (d) $\int_0^{5\pi} \cos \left(\frac{x+1}{2}\right) dx$

3. Suppose n is an integer. Compute.

(a) $\int_0^{\pi/2} \sin (x + n\pi)\, dx$ (b) $\int_{-\pi/2}^{\pi/2} \sin nx\, dx$

(c) $\int_0^{n/2} \cos (\pi x + n\pi/2)\, dx$ (d) $\int_0^{n\pi} \cos (x + \pi)\, dx$

4. Find the area of the region bounded by the X-axis and an arch of the curve whose equation is given.

(a) $y = 2 \cos x$ (b) $y = \sin (\pi x/2)$

(c) $y = \sin (x/2 - \pi)$ (d) $y = \cos (2x - \pi/6)$

5. Compute.

(a) $\int_{-\pi/2}^{\pi/2} |\sin x|\, dx$ (b) $\int_{-\pi/2}^{\pi/2} |\cos x|\, dx$

(c) $\int_{-\pi/4}^{\pi/3} |\sec x \tan x|\, dx$ (d) $\int_0^{-\pi/2} |\sin x|\, dx$

6. Determine the position of a vertical line so that the regions under the cosine curve and the curve $y = 2 \sin 2x$ in the first quadrant between the Y-axis and the line have the same area.

7. Verify the following integration formulas.

(a) $\int \sin^2 x \cos x\, dx = \frac{\sin^3 x}{3}$

(b) $\int \cos^3 x \sin x\, dx = -\frac{\cos^4 x}{4}$

(c) $\int \sec^2 (ax + b)\, dx = \frac{1}{a} \tan (ax + b)$

(d) $\int (x + a)^r\, dx = \frac{(x + a)^{r+1}}{r + 1}$

(e) $\int \sqrt[n]{x + c}\, dx = \frac{n}{n + 1} (x + c)^{\frac{n+1}{n}}$

(f) $\int \sqrt{ax + b}\, dx = \frac{2}{3a} (ax + b)^{3/2}$.

8. What is the mean value of the sine function for the interval $[0, \pi]$ as given by the Mean Value Theorem 37-6?

9. State and prove two general integration formulas suggested by formulas (a) and (b) in Question 7.

42. Area

We introduced the concept of the integral in connection with the problem of finding the area of the region between the graph of a function f and an interval of the X-axis. In this section we will have more to say about the relationship of integrals to areas of plane regions.

Definition 39-1 tells us that if $f(x) \geq 0$ in the interval $[a, b]$, then the area A of the region bounded by the graph of a function f, the X-axis, and the lines $x = a$ and $x = b$ is given by the formula

$$A = \int_a^b f(x)\, dx. \tag{42-1}$$

In the graphical argument that suggests this definition we divide the basic interval $[a, b]$ into a set of subintervals of lengths $\Delta x_1, \Delta x_2, \ldots, \Delta x_n$,

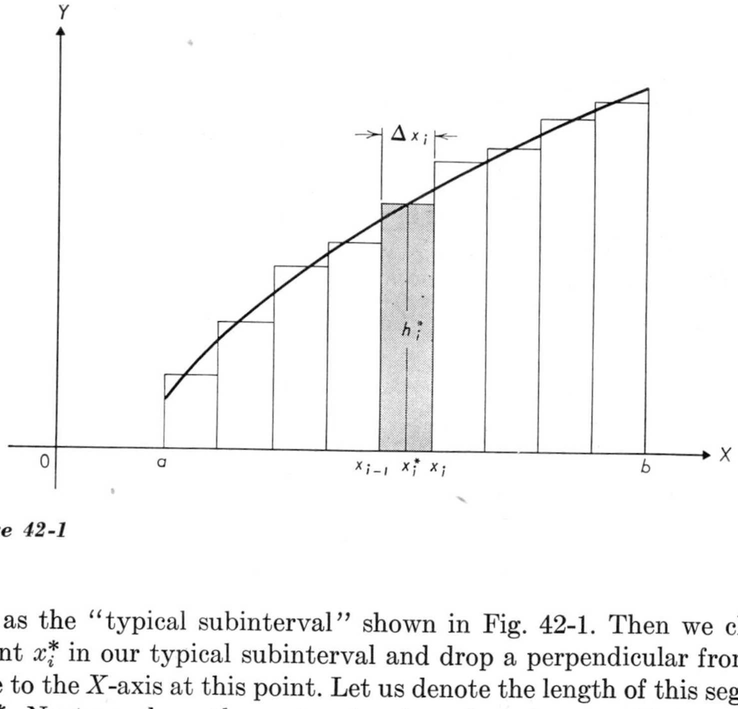

Figure 42-1

such as the "typical subinterval" shown in Fig. 42-1. Then we choose a point x_i^* in our typical subinterval and drop a perpendicular from the curve to the X-axis at this point. Let us denote the length of this segment by h_i^*. Next we draw the rectangle whose base is our subinterval and whose altitude is this perpendicular. The area of this rectangle is $h_i^* \Delta x_i$. Since $h_i^* = f(x_i^*)$, the formula for the area of our typical rectangle can be written as $f(x_i^*) \Delta x_i$. The sum of the areas of all the rectangles,

$$\sum_{i=1}^{n} f(x_i^*) \Delta x_i,$$

approximates the area of our region R. This sum also approximates the integral

$$\int_a^b f(x)\,dx,$$

which *is* the area of R.

Whenever we use integrals to compute areas, we shall follow the sequence of steps that we used in the example above:

(i) Draw a figure that shows the region whose area we are to find.

(ii) In the figure show a typical subinterval with a length of Δx_i on the X-axis and a point x_i^* in this subinterval.

(iii) Find the segment with a length of h_i^* that is perpendicular to the X-axis at x_i^* and which serves as the altitude of our typical rectangle; then draw in the typical rectangle.

(iv) Express h_i^* in terms of x_i^*, and hence derive an expression for the area $h_i^* \Delta x_i$ of our typical rectangle.

(v) Form the sum of these areas and then write down the integral that this sum suggests.

(vi) Evaluate this integral to determine the area of the region.

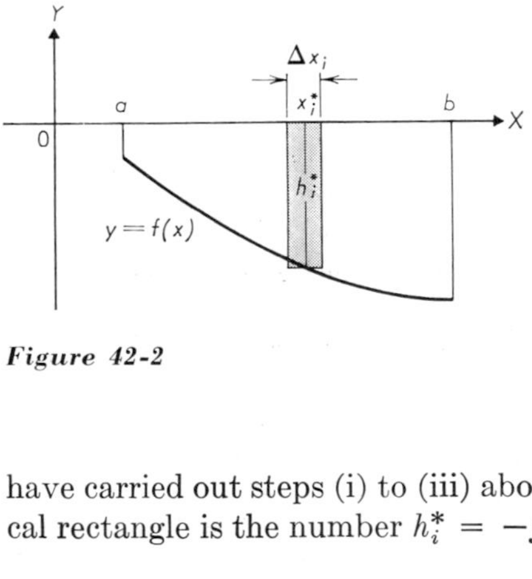

Figure 42-2

Let us see how these steps apply to a region such as the one shown in Fig. 42-2. Here we are considering a function f that takes only negative values in the interval $[a, b]$, and we wish to find the area of the region R that is bounded by the graph of f, the X-axis, and the lines $x = a$, $x = b$. Figure 42-2 shows how we have carried out steps (i) to (iii) above. Clearly the altitude h_i^* of our typical rectangle is the number $h_i^* = -f(x_i^*)$. Thus our approximating sum is

$$\sum_{i=1}^{n} - f(x_i^*)\,\Delta x_i,$$

and this sum suggests that the area A of our region is given by the equation

$$A = \int_a^b -f(x)\,dx = -\int_a^b f(x)\,dx. \tag{42-2}$$

Equation 42-1 applies when f is a function whose graph lies above the X-axis, and Equation 42-2 applies when f is a function whose graph lies below the X-axis. The formula

(42-3) $$A = \int_a^b |f(x)|\,dx$$

covers both cases. Furthermore, Equation 42-3 gives us the area of the region bounded by the graph of a function f, the X-axis, and the lines $x = a$, and $x = b$ even when this region lies partly above and partly below the X-axis. Thus if f is the function whose graph is shown in Fig. 42-3, then

$$\int_a^c |f(x)|\,dx = \int_a^b |f(x)|\,dx + \int_b^c |f(x)|\,dx.$$

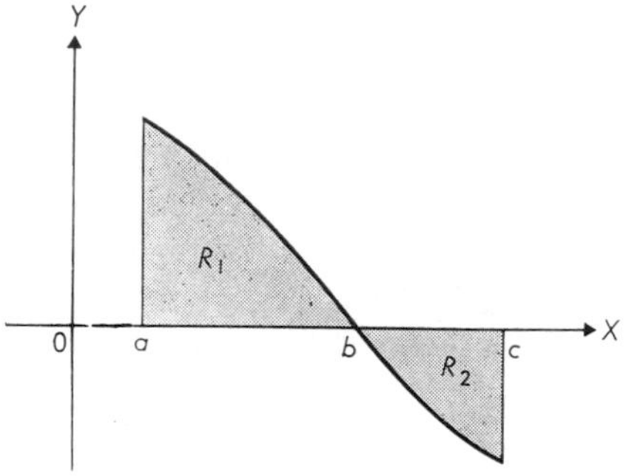

Figure 42-3

The first integral on the right in this equation gives us the area of the region R_1; the second integral gives us the area of R_2, and so their sum is the area of the region that is bounded by the graph of f, the X-axis, and the lines $x = a$ and $x = c$.

The graphical interpretation of the integral $\int_a^c f(x)\,dx$ for the function whose graph appears in Fig. 42-3 is the following. We have

$$\int_a^c f(x)\,dx = \int_a^b f(x)\,dx + \int_b^c f(x)\,dx.$$

The first integral on the right side of this equation gives us the area of the region R_1. The second integral is the *negative* of the area of R_2, since $f(x) \leq 0$ for x in the interval $[b, c]$. Therefore, the integral $\int_a^c f(x)\,dx$ represents the *difference* in the areas of the regions R_1 and R_2. In general, the integral $\int_a^b f(x)\,dx$ represents the number of square units by which the part of the region bounded by the graph of f, the X-axis, and the lines $x = a$ and $x = b$ that lies above the X-axis exceeds the part that lies below the X-axis. In other words, $\int_a^b f(x)\,dx$ represents a "net" area.

Example 42-1. Compute the area of the region between the X-axis and the graph of the function defined by the equation $f(x) = \frac{1}{4}(x^3 + x - 2)$ in the interval $[0, 2]$.

Solution. The graph of the given function is shown in Fig. 42-4. Because the curve lies below the X-axis for x in the interval (0, 1), the area A_1 of the

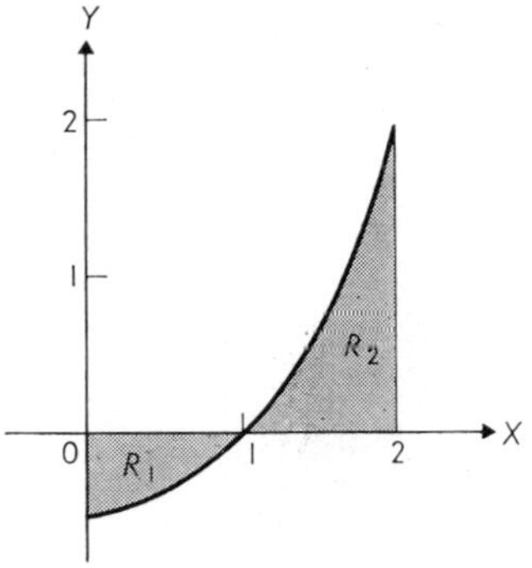

Figure 42-4

region R_1 is

$$A_1 = \int_0^1 |f(x)|\,dx = -\tfrac{1}{4}\int_0^1 (x^3 + x - 2)\,dx = \tfrac{5}{16}.$$

The area of the region R_2 is

$$A_2 = \int_1^2 |f(x)|\,dx = \tfrac{1}{4}\int_1^2 (x^3 + x - 2)\,dx = \tfrac{13}{16}.$$

Hence the area of the shaded region is the number

$$A_1 + A_2 = \tfrac{5}{16} + \tfrac{13}{16} = \tfrac{9}{8}.$$

Notice that

$$\tfrac{1}{4}\int_0^2 (x^3 + x - 2)\,dx = \tfrac{1}{2}.$$

This number is the amount by which A_2 exceeds A_1; that is,

$$A_2 - A_1 = \tfrac{13}{16} - \tfrac{5}{16} = \tfrac{1}{2}.$$

Instead of Equation 42-3, we frequently write the formula for the area of the region between the graph of the equation $y = f(x)$ and the interval $[a, b]$ of the X-axis as

(42-4) $$\boldsymbol{A = \int_a^b |y|\,dx}$$

or, if $f(x) \geq 0$ in the interval $[a, b]$, simply as

(42-5) $$\boldsymbol{A = \int_a^b y\,dx.}$$

We understand, of course, that we must replace y with $f(x)$ when we evaluate the integral.

Example 42-2. Find the area of the region interior to an ellipse whose diameters have lengths of $2a$ and $2b$.

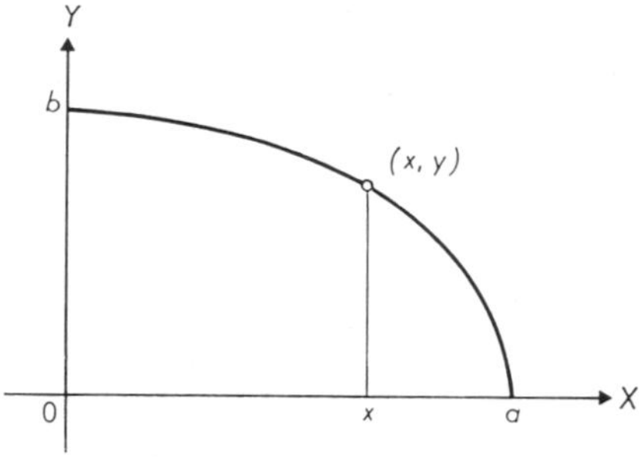

Figure 42-5

Solution. Figure 42-5 shows one quarter of our ellipse; so Formula 42-5 gives us

$$\frac{A}{4} = \int_0^a y\, dx.$$

Since the equation of our ellipse is $\frac{x^2}{a^2} + \frac{y^2}{b^2} = 1$, we have $y = \frac{b}{a}\sqrt{a^2 - x^2}$. Hence

$$A = \frac{4b}{a}\int_0^a \sqrt{a^2 - x^2}\, dx.$$

We have already seen (Equation 39-1) that $\int_0^a \sqrt{a^2 - x^2}\, dx = \frac{\pi a^2}{4}$, and therefore the area of the region bounded by the ellipse is $\frac{4b}{a}\frac{\pi a^2}{4}$; that is,

$$A = \pi ab.$$

When we use our six steps to find an area by integration, we usually use a simplified notation in which we write Δx rather than Δx_i for the length of our typical subinterval; x rather than x_i^* for a point in the subinterval; and h rather than h_i^* for the altitude of our typical rectangle. The next example illustrates this simplified notation.

Example 42-3. Find the area of the region between the sine and cosine curves in the interval $[\pi/4, 5\pi/4]$.

Solution. Figure 42-6 shows the region whose area we are to find. A typical rectangle whose altitude is h and base is Δx is also shown. Now we must express h in terms of x and substitute the result in the formula $h\,\Delta x$ for the area of the typical rectangle. Since the upper boundary of our region is an arc of the sine curve and the lower boundary is an arc of the cosine curve, $h = \sin x - \cos x$. Therefore, the area of our typical rectangle is

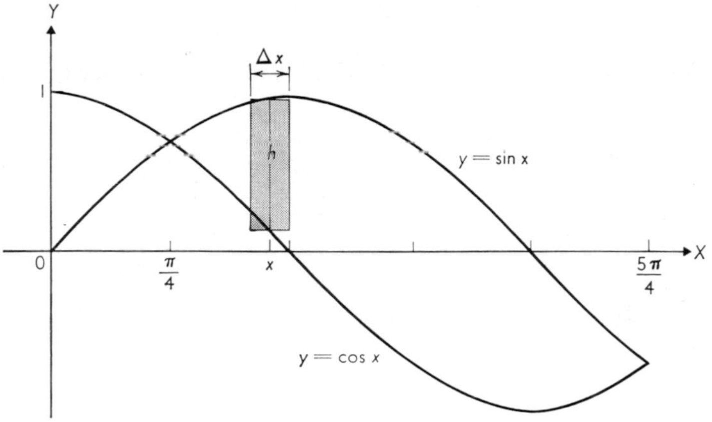

Figure 42-6

$(\sin x - \cos x)\,\Delta x$, and a sum of such terms, indicated as

$$\Sigma(\sin x - \cos x)\,\Delta x,$$

approximates the area of our region. This indicated sum is the simplified notation for the sum

$$\sum_{i=1}^{n} (\sin x_i^* - \cos x_i^*)\,\Delta x_i,$$

and this latter sum suggests the integral that gives us the actual area:

$$\int_{\frac{\pi}{4}}^{\frac{5\pi}{4}} (\sin x - \cos x)\,dx = -\cos x\,\Big|_{\frac{\pi}{4}}^{\frac{5\pi}{4}} - \sin x\,\Big|_{\frac{\pi}{4}}^{\frac{5\pi}{4}} = 2\sqrt{2}.$$

Example 42-4. Find the area A of the region bounded by the Y-axis and the curve whose equation is $y^2 - 4y + 2x = 0$.

Solution. Figure 42-7 shows the region whose area we are to find. A typical rectangle is also shown, and now we must express the altitude h of this rectangle in terms of x. In this case $h = y_2 - y_1$, where y_2 is the larger and y_1 is the smaller solution to the equation $y^2 - 4y + 2x = 0$. Thus

$$y_2 = \frac{4 + \sqrt{16 - 8x}}{2} = 2 + \sqrt{4 - 2x},$$

and

$$y_1 = 2 - \sqrt{4 - 2x}.$$

Therefore, $h = y_2 - y_1 = 2\sqrt{4 - 2x}$, so the area of our typical rectangle

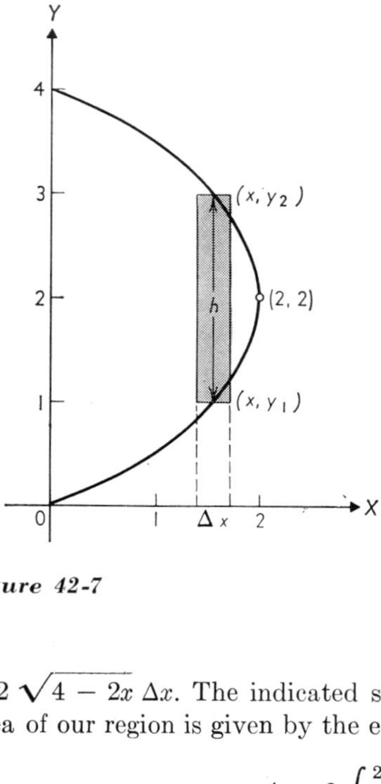

Figure 42-7

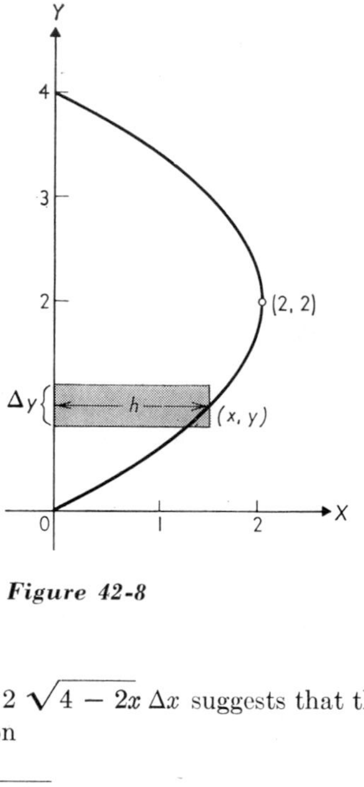

Figure 42-8

is $2\sqrt{4 - 2x}\,\Delta x$. The indicated sum $\Sigma\, 2\sqrt{4 - 2x}\,\Delta x$ suggests that the area of our region is given by the equation

$$A = 2\int_0^2 \sqrt{4 - 2x}\,dx.$$

In Question 7(f), Problems 41, we have an integration formula that applies in this case, and you will find that $A = \frac{16}{3}$.

Instead of using "vertical rectangles" to approximate our region, a simpler method is to use "horizontal rectangles" such as the one shown in Fig. 42-8. In this case we are subdividing an interval of the Y-axis rather than an interval of the X-axis. Hence we must express the altitude h of our typical rectangle in terms of y. It is clear that h is the X-coordinate of the point of the graph of the equation $y^2 - 4y + 2x = 0$ that corresponds to y, so we find h by solving the equation of our curve for x. We find that

$$h = x = 2y - \frac{y^2}{2},$$

and therefore the area of our typical rectangle is

$$h\,\Delta y = \left(2y - \frac{y^2}{2}\right)\Delta y.$$

A sum of such terms,

$$\sum \left(2y - \frac{y^2}{2}\right)\Delta y,$$

approximates the area of our region, and this sum suggests that the area A we seek is given by the equation

$$A = \int_0^4 \left(2y - \frac{y^2}{2}\right) dy = y^2 \Big|_0^4 - \frac{y^3}{6}\Big|_0^4 = \frac{16}{3}$$

Problems 42

1. Compute the area of the region bounded by the X-axis and the parabola whose equation is $y = 2 + x - x^2$.
2. Compute the area of the region bounded by the X-axis and the parabola whose vertex is the point $(2, -1)$ and whose directrix is the line $y = -2$.
3. Compute the area of the region between the curve $y = f(x)$ and the X-axis in the given interval.
   (a) $f(x) = \sin x$, $[0, 2\pi]$
   (b) $f(x) = \cos x$, $[0, \pi]$
   (c) $f(x) = x^3$, $[-1, 1]$
   (d) $f(x) = 3x^5 - x$, $[-2, 2]$
   (e) $f(x) = [\![x]\!]$, $[-1, 2]$
   (f) $f(x) = 1 - |x|$, $[-2, 2]$
4. Find the area of the region bounded by the given curves. Draw pictures!
   (a) $y = x^2/4$ and $y = x/2 + 2$
   (b) $y^2 = 6x$ and $x^2 = 6y$
   (c) $y^2 = 2x$ and $x - y = 4$
   (d) $\sqrt{x} + \sqrt{y} = \sqrt{a}$ and the coordinate axes
   (e) $x = y^3 - 4y$, $x = 4 - y^2$, and the X-axis
   (f) $y = x^3$, $y = (2 - x)^2$, and the X-axis.
5. Sketch the region in the first quadrant between the circles $x^2 + y^2 = a^2$ and $x^2 + y^2 = b^2$. Draw an arc of the ellipse whose equation is $x^2/a^2 + y^2/b^2 = 1$. Show that your arc divides the region between the two circles into two regions whose areas are in the ratio a/b.
6. Through opposite corners of a rectangle draw an arc of a parabola whose vertex is one of the corner points and whose axis lies along one side of your rectangle. Show that you have formed two regions such that the area of one is twice the area of the other.

7. Draw the rectangle formed by the two coordinate axes and the lines $x = a$ and $y = b$. The curve $y = bx^n/a^n$ (n a positive integer) divides the rectangle into two regions. Show that the area of one region is n times the area of the other region.

43. Volume of a Solid of Revolution

In the preceding section we used our knowledge of calculus to compute the areas of various plane regions. These regions were somewhat more complicated than the triangles, trapezoids, and other figures whose

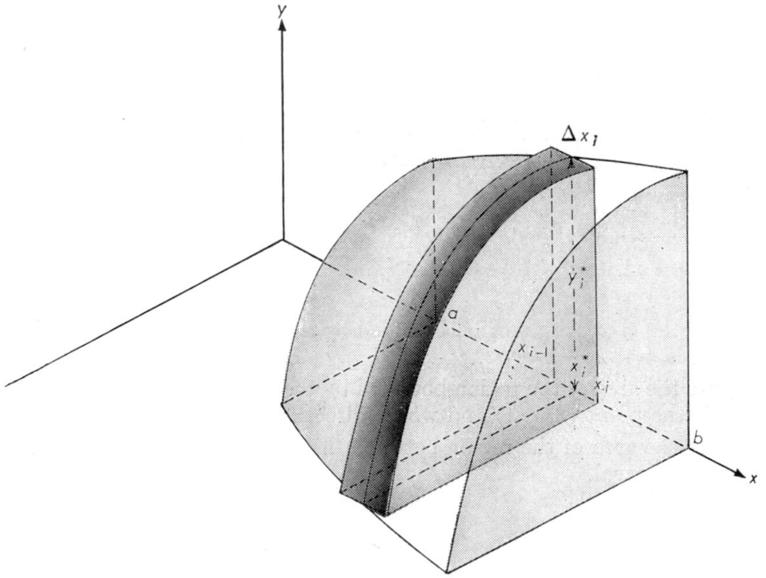

Figure 43-1

areas you learned to measure in plane geometry. In your elementary geometry course you also learned formulas that give the volume of various solid figures such as spheres, cylinders, and cones. We shall now find that calculus can help us determine the volumes of other solids as well. We shall first consider the problem of computing the volume of a solid obtained by rotating a plane region about a line. Such a solid is called a **solid of revolution.**

Let f be a function whose graph does not cross the X-axis in the interval $[a, b]$. We obtain a solid of revolution by rotating the region bounded by the graph of f, the X-axis, and the lines $x = a$ and $x = b$

about the X-axis. Figure 43-1 shows one-fourth of such a solid. To find the volume of this solid, we proceed as we did in the area problem we have just covered. We partition the interval $[a, b]$ into n subintervals, and on each subinterval with a length of Δx_i we erect a rectangle with an altitude of y_i^*, as shown in Fig. 43-1. When we rotate this "typical rectangle" about the X-axis, we obtain a circular disk with a radius of y_i^* and a thickness of Δx_i. The volume of this disk is $\pi y_i^{*2}\,\Delta x_i$, and the sum of the volumes of all these disks approximates the volume of our solid of revolution. Since $y_i^* = f(x_i^*)$, this approximating sum is

$$\sum_{i=1}^{n} \pi[f(x_i^*)]^2\,\Delta x_i.$$

Now we find the limit of this sum as the norm of the partition of the interval $[a, b]$ approaches zero (if this limit exists), and we take this limit to be the volume of our solid of revolution. If f is an integrable function, then the limit of this sum will be (as the form of its terms suggests) $\int_a^b \pi[f(x)]^2\,dx$. So we take the volume of our solid of revolution to be the number

$$V = \pi \int_a^b [f(x)]^2\,dx. \tag{43-1}$$

Instead of Equation 43-1, we frequently write the formula for the volume of the solid obtained by rotating the graph of the equation $y = f(x)$ about the X-axis as

$$V = \pi \int_a^b y^2\,dx. \tag{43-2}$$

Of course, before we evaluate the integral in Formula 43-2, we must replace y with $f(x)$.

Example 43-1. Use Equation 43-2 to compute the volume of a solid sphere whose radius is r.

Solution. The graph of the equation $y = \sqrt{r^2 - x^2}$ is a semicircle with a radius of r and with its diameter along the X-axis (Fig. 43-2). We obtain our sphere by rotating this arc about the X-axis. Now we make use of Equation 43-2 with $y = \sqrt{r^2 - x^2}$, $a = -r$, and $b = r$ to obtain

$$V = \pi \int_{-r}^{r} y^2\,dx = \pi \int_{-r}^{r} (r^2 - x^2)\,dx = \pi \left(r^2x \Big|_{-r}^{r} - \frac{x^3}{3} \Big|_{-r}^{r} \right) = \frac{4\pi r^3}{3}.$$

Rather than rely on formulas such as Equation 43-1, you should follow the steps we used in arriving at the formula:

(i) Draw a figure that includes a sketch of a "typical rectangle."

(ii) Write a formula that expresses in terms of x and Δx the volume of the disk obtained by rotating this typical rectangle. (We usually use the simplified notation x and Δx instead of x_i^* and Δx_i.)

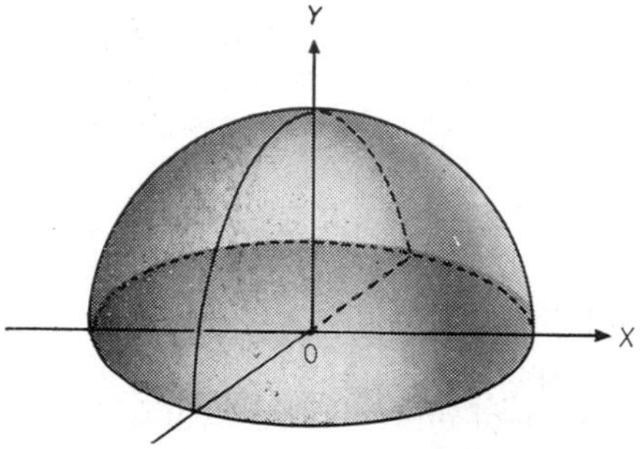

Figure 43-2

(iii) Take the volume of the solid of revolution to be the integral that is suggested by a sum of the volumes of these disks.

(iv) Evaluate the integral.

Example 43-2. Find the volume of a solid right-circular cone with an altitude of h and a base radius of r.

Solution. The surface of the cone can be obtained by rotating the line segment joining the origin and the point (h, r) about the X-axis (Fig. 43-3).

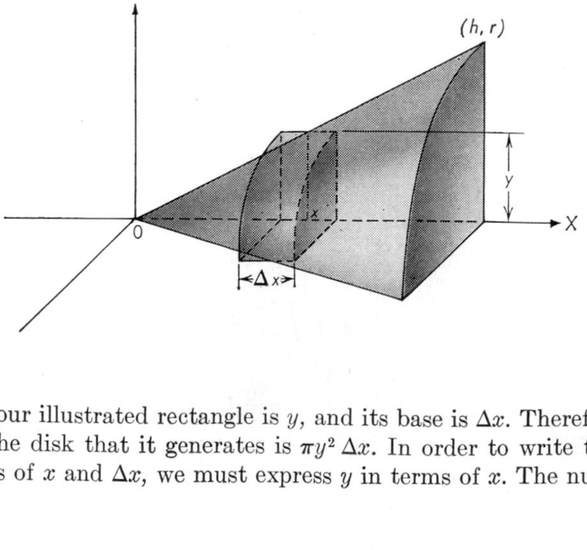

Figure 43-3

The altitude of our illustrated rectangle is y, and its base is Δx. Therefore the volume of the disk that it generates is $\pi y^2 \Delta x$. In order to write this formula in terms of x and Δx, we must express y in terms of x. The numbers x and y are related by the equation of the line that contains the point (h, r) and the origin. Thus $y = \frac{r}{h}x$, and the volume of our disk is $\pi\left(\frac{r}{h}\right)^2 x^2\,\Delta x$. The sum of these volumes has the form

$$\sum \pi\left(\frac{r}{h}\right)^2 x^2\,\Delta x,$$

and the volume of our cone is given by the integral suggested by this sum:

$$V = \pi\frac{r^2}{h^2}\int_0^h x^2\,dx = \pi\left(\frac{r^2}{h^2}\right)\left(\frac{h^3}{3}\right) = \pi\frac{r^2h}{3}.$$

No essentially new ideas are involved when we consider solids of revolution obtained by rotating plane regions about the Y-axis.

Example 43-3. The region bounded by the Y-axis, the line $y = 1$, and the graph of the equation $y = \sqrt{x}$ (Fig. 43-4) is rotated about the Y-axis. What is the volume of the solid that is generated?

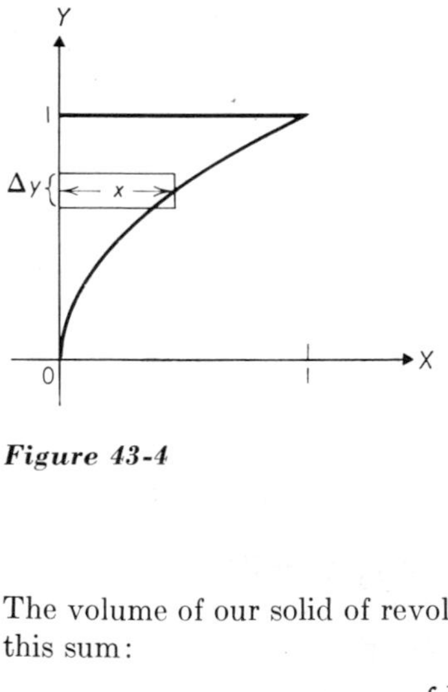

Figure 43-4

Solution. A "typical rectangle" is shown in Fig. 43-4. The volume of the disk generated by this rectangle is $\pi x^2\,\Delta y$. Here we will express this volume in terms of y and Δy, and to do so we must express x in terms of y. The numbers x and y are related by the equation of our curve; that is, $y = \sqrt{x}$. Therefore, $x^2 = y^4$, so the volume of our typical disk is $\pi y^4\,\Delta y$. A sum of such volumes has the form

$$\Sigma\pi y^4\,\Delta y.$$

The volume of our solid of revolution is given by the integral suggested by this sum:

$$V = \pi\int_0^1 y^4\,dy = \left.\frac{\pi y^5}{5}\right|_0^1 = \frac{\pi}{5}.$$

The next example is somewhat more complicated than the preceding ones, but we analyze it in much the same way.

Example 43-4. Find the volume of the solid obtained by rotating the region described in Example 43-3 about the X-axis.

Solution. When we rotate the typical rectangle shown in Fig. 43-5, it generates a solid "washer," not a disk. An end view of half this washer is shown on the right in Fig. 43-5. From this figure we see that the area of the base of the washer is $\pi \cdot 1^2 - \pi(\sqrt{x})^2 = \pi(1 - x)$. Since the washer is Δx units thick, its volume is $\pi(1 - x)\, \Delta x$. A sum of such terms, indicated

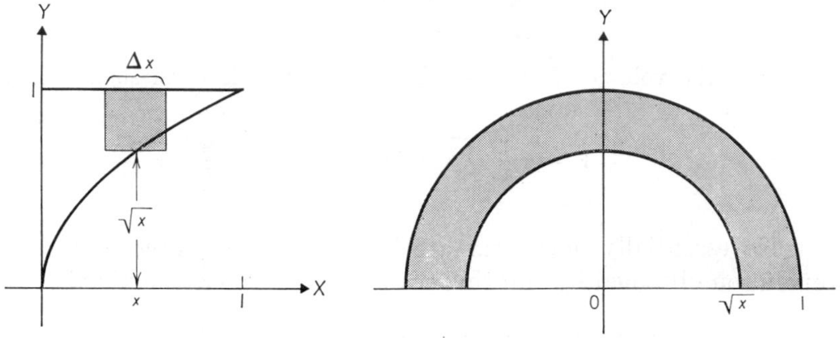

Figure 43-5

by $\Sigma\pi(1 - x)\, \Delta x$, approximates the volume of the solid under consideration. The volume is given by the integral suggested by this sum:

$$V = \pi \int_0^1 (1 - x)\, dx = \pi \left(x \Big|_0^1 - \frac{x^2}{2} \Big|_0^1 \right) = \frac{\pi}{2}.$$

Example 43-5. Find the volume obtained by rotating the region of the last two examples about the line $y = 1$.

Solution. When we rotate the typical rectangle shown in Fig. 43-5 about the line $y = 1$, it generates a disk with a radius of $(1 - \sqrt{x})$ and a thickness of Δx. Therefore, its volume is $\pi(1 - \sqrt{x})^2\, \Delta x$, and a sum of terms of the form $\Sigma\pi(1 - \sqrt{x})^2\, \Delta x$ approximates the volume of our solid. The volume of our solid is the integral suggested by this sum:

$$\begin{aligned} V &= \pi \int_0^1 (1 - \sqrt{x})^2\, dx = \pi \int_0^1 (1 - 2\sqrt{x} + x)\, dx \\ &= \pi \int_0^1 (1 - 2x^{1/2} + x)\, dx \\ &= \pi \left[x \Big|_0^1 - 2(\tfrac{2}{3})x^{3/2} \Big|_0^1 + x^2/2 \Big|_0^1 \right] = \frac{\pi}{6}. \end{aligned}$$

Problems 43

1. Find the volume of the solid ellipsoid generated by rotating the region bounded by the ellipse $b^2x^2 + a^2y^2 = a^2b^2$ about the X-axis.

2. Find the volume of the solid generated by rotating about the X-axis the region bounded by the curves given below.
   (a) $y = x^3$, $x = 2$, and the X-axis.
   (b) $y = -4x^2 + 8x - 1$, $x = 1$, and the coordinate axes.
   (c) $\sqrt{x} + \sqrt{y} = \sqrt{a}$ and the coordinate axes.
   (d) $y = x^{2/3}$, $x = -1$, $x = 1$, and the X-axis.
3. Find the volume of the solid generated by rotating about the X-axis the region in the first quadrant bounded by the Y-axis and the sine and cosine curves. (Use the identity $\cos^2 x - \sin^2 x = \cos 2x$.)
4. Find the volume of the solid obtained by rotating about the Y-axis the region bounded by the curves given.
   (a) $y = x^3$, $y = 8$, and the Y-axis.
   (b) $y = x^3$, $x = 2$, and the X-axis.
   (c) $2y^2 = x^3$ and $x = 2$.
   (d) $y = 1 + x^2$, $x = 2$, and the coordinate axes.
5. Let a be a positive number and let n be a positive integer. The curve $y = x^n$ divides the rectangle formed by the coordinate axes and the lines $x = a$ and $y = a^n$ into two regions. Two solids are obtained by rotating these regions about the X-axis. What is the ratio of their volumes? What is the ratio of the volumes of the solids obtained by rotating the two regions about the Y-axis?
6. Derive the formula for the volume of a solid truncated cone whose height is h and whose two radii are a and b.
7. Find the volume of the solid obtained by rotating about the line $x = 4$ the region bounded by the curves given below.
   (a) $y = x$, $y = 3 - x$, and $x = 4$.
   (b) $y = x^{3/2}$, $y = 0$, and $x = 4$.
   (c) $y = x^{3/2}$, $x = 0$, and $y = 8$.
   (d) $y = x$, and $y = x^2/2$.
8. Find the volume of the solid generated by rotating one arch of the sine curve about the X-axis. (Use the identity $\sin^2 x = \frac{1}{2}(1 - \cos 2x)$.)
9. Find the volume of the "torus" obtained by rotating the circle $x^2 + (y - b)^2 = a^2$ about the X-axis (assume $0 < a < b$).
10. The region common to the two ellipses $a^2x^2 + b^2y^2 = a^2b^2$ and $b^2x^2 + a^2y^2 = a^2b^2$ is rotated about the X-axis. Find the volume of the resulting solid.

44. Volumes by Slicing

We can generalize the methods of the last section so that they can be used to find volumes of solids other than solids of revolution. The integral $\pi \int_a^b [f(x)]^2\, dx$ that is the volume of the solid of revolution shown in Fig. 43-1 is the limit of sums of the form

$$\Sigma\pi[f(x)]^2\,\Delta x.$$

In each term of this sum, the number $\pi[f(x)]^2$ is the area of the base of a cylindrical disk "sliced" from our solid. If we denote this area by $A(x)$, then our sum takes the form $\Sigma A(x)\,\Delta x$. In the case of a solid of revolution, the cross-sectional area $A(x)$ is easy to calculate because the cross sections are circles. But even though the cross sections are not circles, we can still find the volume of a solid by slicing if we can calculate the cross-sectional area $A(x)$.

In Fig. 44-1 we have shown a solid whose volume we wish to determine. This solid projects onto an interval $[a, b]$ of a conveniently chosen

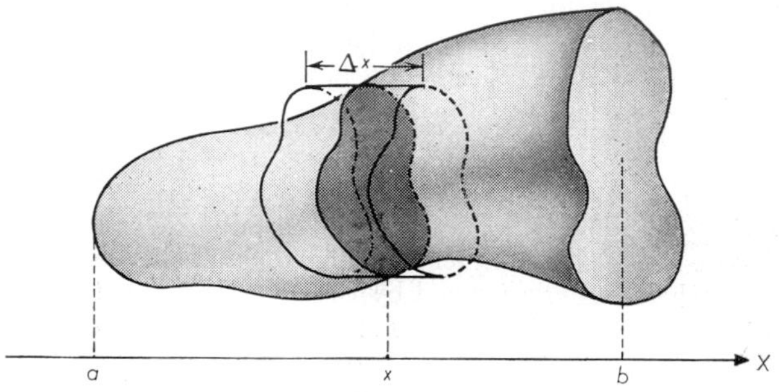

Figure 44-1

X-axis. We partition the interval into subintervals—a typical subinterval having a length of Δx. Through a point x in this sub-interval we pass a plane perpendicular to the X-axis. This plane intersects our solid in the shaded region, whose area we will denote by $A(x)$. The volume of the cylindrical "slice" whose thickness is Δx and which has the shaded region as a cross section is $A(x)\,\Delta x$. A sum of such volumes approximates the volume of our solid and is indicated by

$$\Sigma A(x)\,\Delta x.$$

We take the integral that is suggested by this sum to *be* the volume:

$$V = \int_a^b A(x)\,dx. \tag{44-1}$$

In order to apply Equation 44-1 to find the volume of a given figure, we need only find the expression $A(x)$ for the cross-sectional area and then evaluate the integral, as in the following examples.

Example 44-1. The plans for a wave guide antenna are shown in Fig. 44-2. Each cross section in a plane perpendicular to the central axis of the wave guide (here the X-axis) is an ellipse whose major diameter is twice as long as its minor diameter. The upper boundary of the widest longitudinal cross section is the graph of the equation $y = \dfrac{x^2}{3} + 1$. The entire antenna is 3 feet long. Find the volume enclosed by the wave guide.

Solution. In order to use Equation 44-1 to find the volume, we must find the area $A(x)$ of a cross section cut from the antenna by a plane perpendicular to the axis at a point x. This cross section is the ellipse shown in Fig. 44-2. In Example 42-2 we found that an ellipse with diameters of $2a$ and $2b$ has

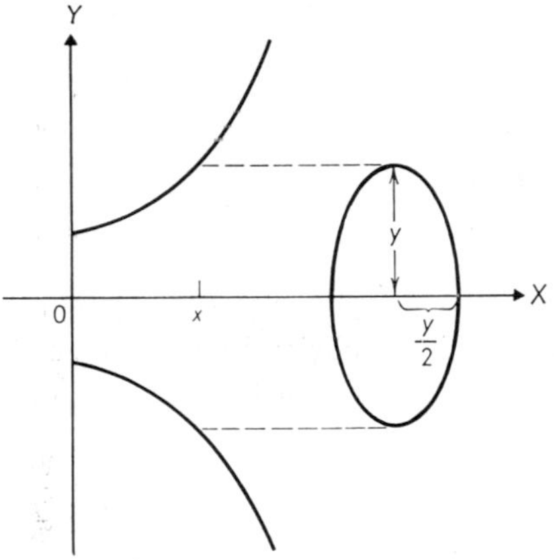

Figure 44-2

an area of πab square units. Therefore, the area of our illustrated cross section is $\frac{1}{2}\pi y^2$ square feet. Since $y = \dfrac{x^2}{3} + 1$,

$$A(x) = \left(\frac{\pi}{2}\right)\left(\frac{x^2}{3} + 1\right)^2 = \pi\left(\frac{x^4}{18} + \frac{x^2}{3} + \frac{1}{2}\right).$$

Thus Formula 44-1 gives us

$$V = \pi \int_0^3 \left(\frac{x^4}{18} + \frac{x^2}{3} + \frac{1}{2}\right) dx = \frac{36\pi}{5} \text{ cubic feet.}$$

(We leave the details of evaluating the integral to you.)

Example 44-2. A regular pyramid is 100 feet high and has a base 100 feet square. If it is made of rock weighing 100 pounds per cubic foot, how much does it weigh?

Solution. We will first find the volume, in cubic feet, of the pyramid and then multiply this result by 100 to get its weight. Figure 44-3 shows the entire pyramid and also a triangular cross section. At a height y feet above the base we have shaded a "typical slice." If we denote the area of a face of this slice by $A(y)$, then the volume of our pyramid is

$$V = \int_0^{100} A(y)\, dy.$$

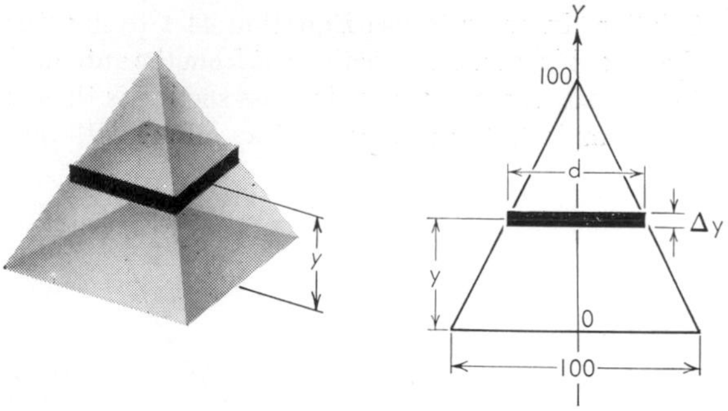

Figure 44-3

Therefore, in order to find V we must find an expression for $A(y)$. A face of our typical slice is obviously a square. Let d denote the length of a side of this square. Then from similar triangles in Fig. 44-3 we see that

$$\frac{d}{100 - y} = \frac{100}{100}.$$

Therefore, $d = 100 - y$ and $A(y) = (100 - y)^2$. Hence,

$$\begin{aligned} V &= \int_0^{100} (100 - y)^2\, dy \\ &= \int_0^{100} (100^2 - 200y + y^2)\, dy = 100^3/3. \end{aligned}$$

The weight W of the pyramid is 100 times this amount, so

$$W = 100^4/3 = 10^8/3.$$

The pyramid weighs $10^8/3$ pounds or about 16,667 tons.

The next example tests your ability to visualize three-dimensional figures.

Example 44-3. The base of a certain solid is a circle with a 2-inch radius. Cross sections perpendicular to one of the diameters of the circle are squares. Find the volume of the solid.

Solution. On the left side of Fig. 44-4 we have shown a top view of our solid with the mentioned diagonal lying along the X-axis. On the right of the figure is the view we would see if we cut the solid at the point x and looked at it down the X-axis. Our cross section is a d by d square, and we will be able to find its area $A(x)$ as soon as we find d in terms of x. From the right triangle of hypotenuse 2 and legs $d/2$ and x that we see inside

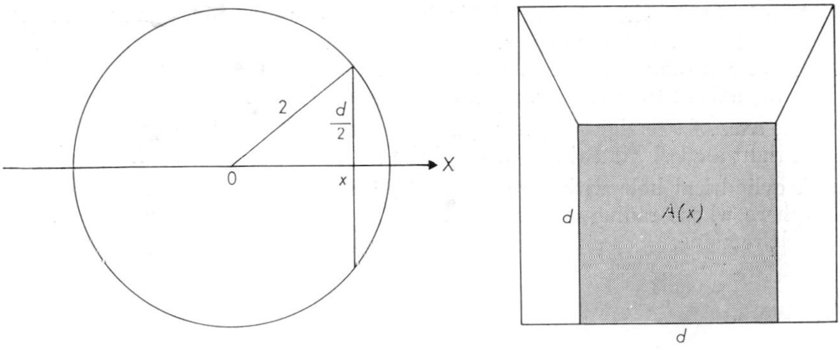

Figure 44-4

the circle, we obtain the relation $4 = (d/2)^2 + x^2$. Hence $d^2 = 16 - 4x^2$. But $A(x) = d^2$, so

$$V = \int_{-2}^{2} A(x)\,dx = \int_{-2}^{2} (16 - 4x^2)\,dx$$

$$= \left(16x - \tfrac{4}{3}x^3\right)\Big|_{-2}^{2} = \tfrac{128}{3} \text{ cubic inches.}$$

Problems 44

1. A solid is constructed with a circular base of radius 4 and such that every plane section perpendicular to a certain diameter of the base is an equilateral triangle. Find the volume of the solid.
2. A solid is constructed with a circular base of radius 2 and such that every plane section perpendicular to a certain diameter of the base is an isosceles right triangle with its hypotenuse in the base plane. Find the volume of the solid.
3. A solid is constructed with a circular base of radius 1 and such that every plane section perpendicular to a certain diameter of the base is an isosceles triangle whose altitude is 2. Find the volume of the solid.
4. A solid is constructed with a base in the form of an ellipse whose major diameter is $2a$ units long and whose minor diameter is $2b$ units long such that every cross section perpendicular to the major diameter is a square. Find the volume of the solid.
5. Use Equation 44-1 to compute the volume of a slice taken from an orange with a radius of r inches that contains k identical sections.
6. Calculate the volume of an ellipsoid; that is, a solid such that three mutually perpendicular plane sections are ellipses whose diameters are $2a$, $2b$, and $2c$ units long.
7. When two pieces of 1-inch quarter round are cut so as to fit together in the corner of a room, how much material is cut away from each piece?

8. A square hole whose sides are d inches long is cut through a long cylindrical rod with a radius of r inches. The axis of the hole intersects the axis of the cylinder at right angles, and a pair of plane faces of the hole are perpendicular to the axis of the cylinder. Find the volume of the hole.
9. The axes of two right-circular cylinders with equal radii of r inches intersect at right angles. Find the volume of the region common to both cylinders.
10. A cylindrical hole with a radius of 1 inch is drilled through a solid metal sphere whose radius is 4 inches. Find the volume of the part of the sphere that remains.

45. **Work**

The Fundamental Theorem of Calculus states that

$$\int_a^b F'(x)\,dx = F(b) - F(a). \tag{45-1}$$

Naturally we view this equation as a means of evaluating an integral by subtraction, but we could perfectly well consider it as a means of replacing a problem in subtraction with a problem in integration. Of course, if we know the numbers $F(b)$ and $F(a)$, it is foolish to find their difference by integrating. But we will now give some examples in which it is easier to find a formula for $F'(x)$ than it is to find a formula for $F(x)$ itself, and in these cases "subtraction by integration" is quite appropriate.

Suppose that one end of a spring is fixed at a point of the negative side of a number scale and that the free end is at the origin when the spring is in its natural (unstretched) position. Let us denote by $F(x)$ the work performed in pulling the free end to the point x of the number scale (as in Fig. 45-1). Thus if a and b are two points, we perform $F(a)$ units

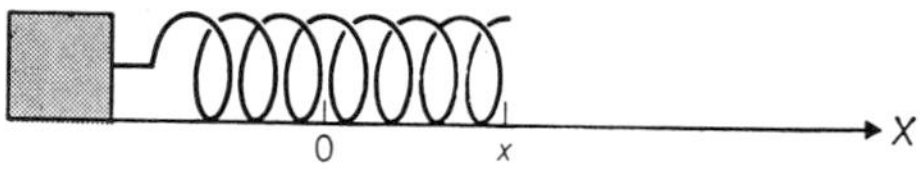

Figure 45-1

of work to pull the free end of the spring from its rest position to the point a and $F(b)$ units to pull it from its rest position to the point b. Therefore, if we denote by W the amount of work that is done in moving the free end from a to b, we see that

$$W = F(b) - F(a).$$

But we cannot find W from this equation as it stands because we don't have a formula for $F(x)$ from which to calculate $F(b)$ and $F(a)$.

Instead of finding a formula for $F(x)$, we will find a formula for $F'(x)$, and then we will find the number $F(b) - F(a)$ by evaluating the integral $\int_a^b F'(x)\,dx$. Suppose that x is a point in the interval $[a, b]$ and that h is a number such that $x + h$ is also in $[a, b]$, as shown in Fig. 45-2. We will

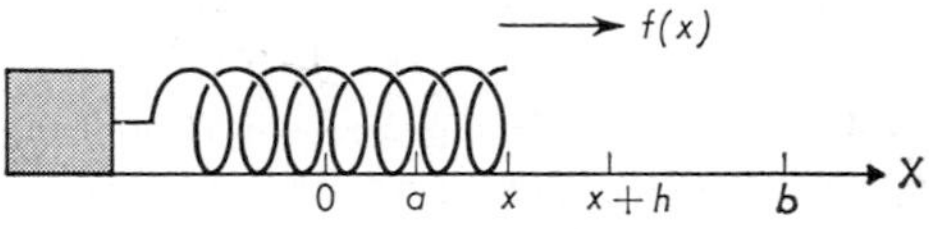

Figure 45-2

denote by $f(x)$ the force that is required to hold the free end of the spring at the point x. Then the work that is performed in pulling the free end from x to the point $x + h$ is approximately $f(x) \cdot h$ units. We say "approximately" because the force that we must apply varies as we move from x to $x + h$, so strictly speaking the elementary formula *work* = *force* × *distance* is not applicable. But if $x + h$ is close to x, the variation in the force will be slight, and we may use this formula to find an approximation to the work done. On the other hand, the work is the difference $F(x + h) - F(x)$, so we have the approximation

$$F(x + h) - F(x) \approx f(x) \cdot h;$$

that is,

$$\frac{F(x + h) - F(x)}{h} \approx f(x).$$

Since this approximation is good when h is near 0, it appears reasonable that

$$\lim_{h \to 0} \frac{F(x + h) - F(x)}{h} = f(x).$$

The left side of this equation is $F'(x)$—by the definition of the derivative—so we see that $F'(x) = f(x)$. Therefore, the work W that is performed in moving the free end of the spring from a to b is given by the equation $W = F(b) - F(a) = \int_a^b F'(x)\,dx = \int_a^b f(x)\,dx$. Thus we have the equation

$$\boldsymbol{W = \int_a^b f(x)\,dx,} \tag{45-2}$$

where $f(x)$ is the force that holds the free end of the spring x units from its rest position. Hooke's Law gives us the formula for this force,

$$f(x) = kx,$$

where k is a number, called the **spring constant,** that depends on the spring. Therefore, the work that we do when we stretch the free end of our spring from the point a to the point b is

$$W = \int_a^b kx\,dx = \frac{k}{2}(b^2 - a^2).$$

Example 45-1. If it requires a force of 10 pounds to hold a certain spring when it is stretched 2 inches, how much work is performed in pulling the free end 6 inches from its natural position?

Solution. Here $a = 0$ and $b = 6$, so $W = \int_0^6 kx\,dx = 18k$. Now we must find the spring constant k. We know that $f(2) = 10$, and therefore the equation $f(x) = kx$ tells us that $2k = 10$. Thus $k = 5$ and $W = 18 \cdot 5 = 90$ inch pounds $= 7.5$ foot pounds.

When we derived Formula 45-2, we assumed that we knew what we were talking about when we spoke of the work that is done in stretching the spring a distance of x units. We took it for granted that this work could be measured by a differentiable function F and that the elementary formula *work* = *force* $\times$ *distance* is approximately correct if the variation of the force is small. But we have not really said what work is, and so we now change our attitude toward Equation 45-2. Instead of regarding it as a formula that merely tells us how to calculate a well-defined quantity called work, we shall consider Equation 45-2 as the *definition* of the work that is done when we move the free end of the spring from a to b. In general, we define work as the integral of force. If the force function f is a constant function with value c, then the amount of work that is done as the force is applied to a point that moves from a to b is given by the formula

$$W = \int_a^b c\,dx = c(b - a).$$

This equation is our old formula *work* = *force* $\times$ *distance,* and so we see that the integral definition of work agrees with the elementary definition when both apply.

The next example is another typical work problem that we can solve with calculus.

Example 45-2. A vat has the shape of a paraboloid of revolution. It is 2 feet high, and the radius of its top is 1 foot. It is filled with water which weighs 62.5 pounds per cubic foot. How much work is required to pump the contents of the vat through a nozzle 4 feet above the top?

Solution. Figure 45-3 shows our vat and its exhaust pipe. We have drawn in a coordinate system to help us formulate our problem mathematically. Suppose that $F(y)$ foot pounds of work are required to empty the tank if it is filled to a depth of y feet. Then $F(2)$ is the number we want, and since $F(0) = 0$, we can write this number as a difference: $F(2) = F(2) - F(0)$.

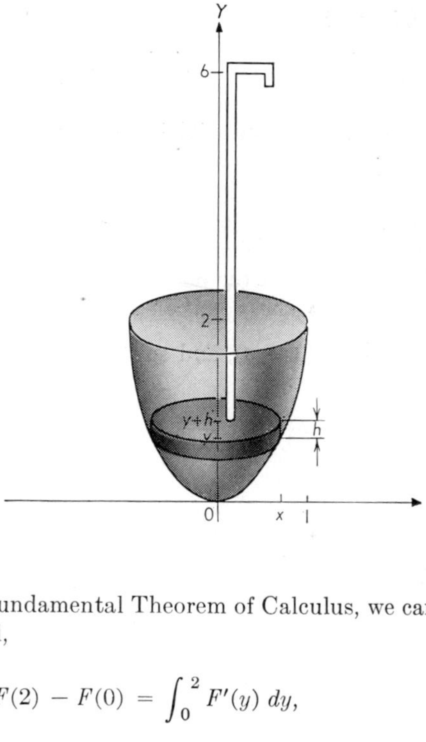

Figure 45-3

Now according to the Fundamental Theorem of Calculus, we can write this difference as an integral,

$$F(2) - F(0) = \int_0^2 F'(y)\,dy,$$

and so we may solve our given problem by finding $F'(y)$ and integrating. If h is some given number, then the number $F(y + h) - F(y)$ is the difference between the work required to pump out the tank when it is filled to a depth of $y + h$ feet and the work required when the water in the tank is y feet deep. In other words, $F(y + h) - F(y)$ is the work required to remove the part of the water in the tank that lies between the two horizontal planes that are y and $y + h$ feet above the bottom. This work is approximately the work required to remove the "disk of water" with a radius of x feet and a thickness of h feet that is shown in Fig. 45-3. The volume of this disk is $\pi x^2 h$ cubic feet, and since the density of water is 62.5 pounds per cubic foot, we see that the disk weighs $62.5\pi x^2 h$ pounds. The disk must be lifted about $6 - y$ feet, so the work required to lift the disk out through the nozzle is about $62.5\pi x^2(6 - y)h$ foot pounds. Thus

$$F(y + h) - F(y) \approx 62.5\pi x^2(6 - y)h$$

or

$$\frac{F(y + h) - F(y)}{h} \approx 62.5\pi x^2(6 - y).$$

Since the quotient $\dfrac{F(y + h) - F(y)}{h}$ also approximates the derivative $F'(y)$ when h is small, we conclude that

$$F'(y) = 62.5\pi x^2(6 - y).$$

Before we can compute its integral, we must express $F'(y)$ entirely in terms of y, so let us now replace x^2 with an expression in y. We chose the coordinate system of Fig. 45-3 so that our parabola would be in standard position, and hence its equation is $x^2 = 4cy$, where c is a number that we will now determine. Since the vat is 2 feet tall, and the radius of its top is 1 foot, we see that the point (1, 2) is on the parabola. Hence $1 = 4c \cdot 2$, so $4c = \frac{1}{2}$, and the equation of our parabola is $x^2 = \frac{1}{2}y$. Therefore, $F'(y) = \dfrac{62.5\pi}{2} y(6 - y)$, and so

$$\begin{aligned} F(2) = F(2) - F(0) &= \frac{62.5\pi}{2} \int_0^2 y(6 - y)\, dy \\ &= \frac{62.5\pi}{2} \int_0^2 (6y - y^2)\, dy \\ &= \frac{875\pi}{3} \text{ foot pounds.} \end{aligned}$$

Problems 45

1. A weight of 50 pounds stretches a spring two inches beyond its natural length. How much work is required to stretch it those 2 inches?
2. A spring is stretched 1 inch beyond its natural length by a force of 100 pounds. How much work is done in stretching it 4 inches?
3. A 1-ton elevator is lifted by means of a cable that weighs 10 pounds per foot. Find the work done in lifting the elevator 50 feet.
4. How much work is required to empty a tankful of water by pumping it over the top if the tank is a hemisphere with a radius of 2 feet?
5. A tank in the shape of a paraboloid of revolution is 6 feet deep, has a radius on the top of 3 feet, and is full of water. How much work must be done to lower the water level 2 feet by pumping the water out the top of the tank?
6. How much work is required to construct the pyramid in Example 44-2?

7. A conical cistern is 20 feet across the top, 15 feet deep, and is filled to within 5 feet of the top with water. Find the work done in pumping the water over the top to empty the tank.
8. An empty tank that is a right-circular cone with its vertex down has a base radius of 3 feet, an altitude of 8 feet, and stands on a platform 30 feet above the ground. The tank is filled by pumping water from ground level through a pipe that enters the bottom of the tank. How much work is done?
9. The weight of a body varies inversely as the square of its distance from the center of the earth. A rocket weighs 10 tons on the surface of the earth. Disregarding the loss of weight due to fuel loss, and neglecting the atmospheric resistance, compute the work done in propelling the rocket to a height of 1000 miles. (Assume the radius of the earth is 4000 miles).
10. A rocket is loaded with 1000 pounds of fuel at the surface of the earth. The fuel is burned at a steady rate with respect to distance and is entirely consumed when the rocket reaches a height of 10 miles. Neglecting the variation in the force of gravity, how much work is required just to lift the rocket's fuel?

Review Problems, Chapter Five

You can use the following problems to test yourself on the material covered in this chapter.

1. Use the area interpretation of the integral to determine which of the following numbers most closely approximates the integral $\int_0^{1/2} \frac{1}{1+x^2}\,dx$: .005, .05, .5, 5, or 50.
2. Determine the number c that makes the following integration formula correct:

$$\int \sqrt{3x+4}\,dx = c(3x+4)^{3/2}.$$

3. Use Simpson's Rule with two subintervals to compute the area of the region that is bounded by the X-axis and the curve $x^2 + y - 1 = 0$. Is your answer exact or an approximation?
4. Compute the following integrals.

(a) $\int_{-\pi}^{0} \sin x\,dx$ (b) $\int_{-1}^{8} \sqrt[3]{x}\,dx$

(c) $\int_{\pi}^{2\pi} D_t \cos^2 t\,dt$ (d) $\int_{3\pi/4}^{\pi} \left(\frac{4}{\cos x}\right)^2 dx$

(e) $\int_1^4 \frac{x^3+2}{2}\,dx$ (f) $\int_0^{3\pi/2} |\cos x|\,dx$

5. Find the area of the region that is bounded by the curves whose equations are $y = x^2$ and $y = \sqrt{8x}$.
6. Find the volume of the solid of revolution formed by rotating the region in the preceding problem about the X-axis.

7. Find the volume of the solid of revolution formed by rotating the region in Question 5 about the Y-axis.
8. A vat is 4 feet high. It has the shape of a paraboloid obtained by rotating the curve $4y = x^2$ about the Y-axis. It is filled to a depth of 1 foot with oil that weighs 60 pounds per cubic foot. How much work is required to empty the vat by pumping the oil out over the top?
9. Find the mean value of the function f in the interval $[0, 2]$ if $f(x) = x^2$.
10. A solid has one axis such that every plane section perpendicular to that axis is an ellipse whose major diameter is twice as long as its minor diameter. The major diameters of these ellipses lie in a plane, and the solid intersects this plane in a circle whose radius is a. Find the volume of the solid.

6 EXPONENTIAL, LOGARITHMIC, INVERSE TRIGONOMETRIC, AND HYPERBOLIC FUNCTIONS

In the preceding chapter we introduced the concept of the integral and gave a few examples to show how useful this concept is. In the next chapter we shall consider in some detail some further rules for calculating integrals. But before we go into this detailed study, we will use the concept of the integral to define some new and useful functions—the *exponential* and *logarithmic* functions and the associated *hyperbolic* functions.

46. Functions Defined by Integrals

We have used the fundamental process of differentiation to construct a derived function f' from a given function f. Now we are going to use the fundamental process of integration to construct a function F from a given function f. Here is an example to illustrate what we have in mind.

Example 46-1. Let F be the function defined by the equation

$$F(x) = \int_0^x |\sin t| \, dt.$$

Find $F(0)$, $F(\pi/2)$, $F(3\pi/2)$, and $F(27\pi)$.

Solution. We can interpret the functional values of F graphically as follows. In Fig. 46-1 we have drawn a graph of the equation $y = |\sin t|$. Graphically

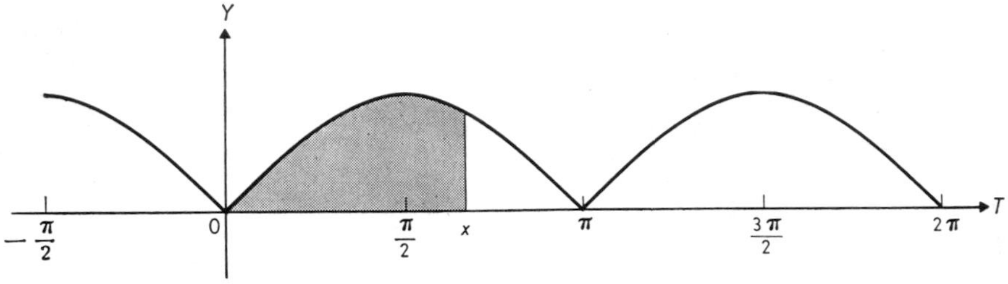

Figure 46-1

speaking, $F(x)$ is the area of the region between this curve and the interval $[0, x]$ on the T-axis. This region is shaded in the figure. We have

$$F(0) = \int_0^0 |\sin t| \, dt = 0,$$

and

$$F(\pi/2) = \int_0^{\pi/2} |\sin t| \, dt = \int_0^{\pi/2} \sin t \, dt = 1.$$

To calculate $F(3\pi/2)$ and $F(27\pi)$, we see from the graph that

$$F(3\pi/2) = 3F(\pi/2) = 3,$$

and

$$F(27\pi) = 54F(\pi/2) = 54.$$

In general, if f is a function that is integrable on an interval that contains a point c, then we can define a function F on this interval by means of the equation

$$F(x) = \int_c^x f(t) \, dt. \tag{46-1}$$

We may be forced to evaluate functional values such as $F(3)$, $F(5)$, and so on, by approximation methods such as Simpson's Rule or the Trapezoidal Rule. But Equation 46-1 does assign a number $F(x)$ corresponding to each number x in the given interval, and this correspondence defines a function even though it may be a function whose values are hard to find.

Our function F is determined by the function f and the number c. We are free to choose whatever letters we wish to indicate the variable of integration and to denote a number in the domain of F. To avoid confusion, however, the same letter should not be used to indicate both. Thus, for example, the equations

$$F(u) = \int_0^u |\sin v|\, dv,$$

$$F(t) = \int_0^t |\sin u|\, du,$$

and

$$F(t) = \int_0^t |\sin x|\, dx$$

all define the function F that we mentioned in Example 46-1.

To get an idea of the properties of functions that are defined by integrals, let us turn now to another example.

Example 46-2. Let f be the greatest integer function; that is $f(u) = [\![u]\!]$, and define the function F by the equation $F(x) = \int_0^x f(u)\, du$. Draw a graph of the function f and of the function F for the interval $[0, 2]$.

Solution. The graph of the greatest integer function for the interval $[0, 2]$ is shown on the left in Fig. 46-2. The number $F(x)$ is the area of the region

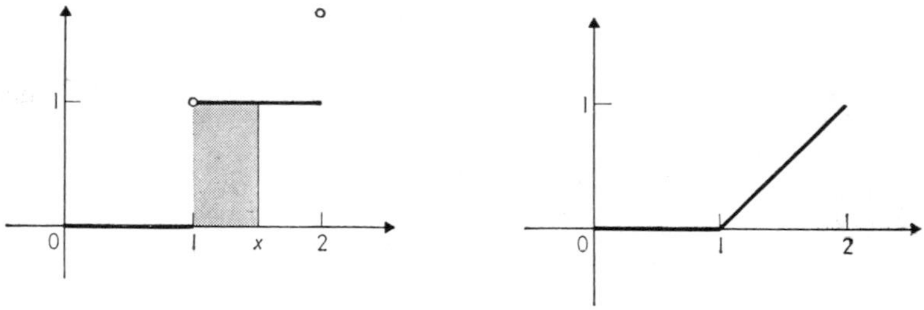

Figure 46-2

under this graph and above the interval $[0, x]$ on the horizontal axis. It is clear that if $0 \leq x \leq 1$, the area is zero, so that $F(x) = 0$ for $0 \leq x \leq 1$. If $1 < x \leq 2$, $F(x)$ is the area of the shaded rectangular region in Fig. 46-2. The area of this shaded region is $(x - 1) \cdot 1 = x - 1$ square units. Thus $F(x) = x - 1$ if $1 < x \leq 2$. The graph of F appears on the right side of Fig. 46-2.

The graphs of the functions f and F in the preceding example illustrate two important facts. First, we see that the function f is not continuous at 1 and 2. This fact is illustrated by the breaks in the graph of f at those points. On the other hand, the graph of the function F has no breaks; F is a continuous function in the interval [0, 2]. It can be shown that if f is a function that is integrable on an interval $[a, b]$, then the function F defined by the equation

$$F(x) = \int_c^x f(t)\, dt \tag{46-2}$$

is continuous in the interval $[a, b]$, but this proof belongs to advanced calculus.

Second, Fig. 46-2 reveals that the derivative $F'(x)$, the slope of the graph of F, is defined at every point in (0, 2) except the point 1. Furthermore, we see that $F'(x) = 0$ when x is between 0 and 1, and $F'(x) = 1$ when x is between 1 and 2. Thus, $F'(x) = f(x)$ in the intervals in which f is continuous. If you were given the graph on the right side of Fig. 46-2 and were asked to make a graph showing its slope, you would draw the graph on the left side of Fig. 46-2.

In the general case of a function F defined by an integral, as in Equation 46-2, we have the following theorem.

THEOREM 46-1. *If f is a continuous function and if we define the function F by means of the equation $F(x) = \int_c^x f(t)\, dt$, then $F'(x) = f(x)$.*

Proof. According to the definition of the derivative, we must show that

$$\lim_{h \to 0} \frac{F(x+h) - F(x)}{h} = f(x). \tag{46-3}$$

Now

$$\begin{aligned} F(x+h) - F(x) &= \int_c^{x+h} f(t)\, dt - \int_c^x f(t)\, dt \\ &= \int_c^{x+h} f(t)\, dt + \int_x^c f(t)\, dt \\ &= \int_x^{x+h} f(t)\, dt. \end{aligned}$$

Hence

$$\frac{F(x+h) - F(x)}{h} = \frac{1}{h} \int_x^{x+h} f(t)\, dt.$$

The Mean Value Theorem for Integrals (Theorem 37-5) states that there is a number c between x and $x + h$ such that

$$\int_x^{x+h} f(t)\, dt = f(c)\, h.$$

Therefore,

$$\frac{F(x+h)-F(x)}{h}=f(c).$$

Because c is between x and $x + h$, we see that c approaches x as h approaches 0. It then follows from the continuity of f that $f(c)$ approaches $f(x)$, and so we have Equation 46-3.

The essential content of Theorem 46-1 can be summed up in the equation

$$\text{(46-4)} \qquad D_x \int_c^x f(t)\,dt = f(x).$$

This equation shows us how differentiation "undoes" integration, just as integration "undoes" differentiation (See Section 40). Theorem 46-1 is in a sense the converse of the Fundamental Theorem of Calculus (Theorem 40-1). The Fundamental Theorem tells us that if we have an antiderivative $F(x)$ of $f(x)$, then we can evaluate integrals of f. Theorem 46-1 tells us that if we can evaluate integrals of f, then we can calculate an antiderivative $F(x)$ of $f(x)$.

Example 46-3. Find the number x for which the function F defined in the interval $[-1, 1]$ by the equation $F(x) = \int_{-1}^{x} \tan t\,dt$ takes its minimum value.

Solution. According to Theorem 46-1, $F'(x) = \tan x$. We see that $F'(x) > 0$ if $x > 0$, and $F'(x) < 0$ if $x < 0$. Therefore the point $(0, F(0))$ is a minimum point on the graph of F (see Theorem 25-1). To find the minimum *value* of F (that is, the number $F(0) = \int_{-1}^{0} \tan t\,dt$), it would be necessary for us (at the moment) to use some approximation technique such as Simpson's Rule. We would find that $F(0) \approx -.62$.

Problems 46

1. Let $F(x) = \int_0^x |t|\,dt$. Show that $F(x) = \frac{1}{2}x^2$ for $x \geq 0$, and $F(x) = -\frac{1}{2}x^2$ for $x < 0$.
2. Let $F(x) = \int_0^x \sin^3 t\,dt$.
   (a) Convince yourself, graphically, that $F(2\pi) = 0$.
   (b) For what numbers does F take maximum values? minimum values?
   (c) Convince yourself that $-\pi \leq F(x) \leq \pi$.
   (d) In what intervals is the graph of F concave up? concave down?

3. Draw graphs of the functions f and F for the interval [0, 2] if

$$F(x) = \int_0^x f(t)\,dt$$

and:
(a) $f(t) = |1 - t|$ (b) $f(t) = t^2 - 2t$
(c) $f(t) = (t - 1)|t - 1|$ (d) $f(t) = (t - 1)^3$

4. Let $F(u) = \int_0^u \sin t\,dt$. Find $F(3)$, $F'(3)$, and $F''(3)$.

5. Let $F(x) = \int_x^c f(u)\,du$. Show that $F'(x) = -f(x)$.

6. Draw a graph of the function I for the interval $[-\pi, \pi]$ if $I(x) = \int_x^0 \cos t\,dt$.

7. Find $D_x y$:
(a) $y = \int_3^x (5^t + t^5)\,dt$ (b) $y = \int_{-7}^x \sqrt[4]{|\sin u|}\,du$
(c) $y = \int_x^3 (1 + r^2)^{-1}\,dr$ (d) $y = \int_x^2 (3z + 1)^{12}\,dz$

8. If $y = \int_c^u f(t)\,dt$, where $u = g(x)$, and we incorporate Equation 46-4 into the Chain Rule, then we obtain the equation

$$\boldsymbol{D_x \int_c^u f(t)\,dt = f(u)D_x u.}$$

Use this result to find $D_x y$ if:
(a) $y = \int_2^{x^2} u^2\,du$ (b) $y = \int_0^{\sin x} 2^t\,dt$
(c) $y = \int_{-x}^0 f(t)\,dt$ (d) $y = \int_{3x+2}^{x^2} \sin t^2\,dt$

9. Let $F(x) = \int_{-x}^x f(t)\,dt$. Prove:
(a) If f is an odd function (that is, $f(-x) = -f(x)$), then $F'(x) = 0$.
(b) If f is an even function (that is, $f(-x) = f(x)$), then $F'(x) = 2f(x)$.

10. Show that

$$D_x \int_c^x f(t)\,dt = \int_c^x D_t f(t)\,dt + f(c).$$

11. For what numbers does the function F defined by the equation

$$F(x) = \int_0^x (2^t + 2^{1-t} - 3)\,dt$$

take relative maximum values? minimum values?

12. Graph the equation $y = G(x)$ for $0 \leq x \leq 5$, if

$$G(x) = \int_0^x [\![t]\!]\,dt.$$

Show that $G(n) = n(n - 1)/2$ if n is a positive integer and $G(-n) = n(n + 1)/2$. (Note: If k is a positive integer, then $1 + 2 + 3 + \cdots + k = k(k + 1)/2$.)

47. The Function *ln*

In the last section we took up the general problem of defining functions by means of integrals; now we will turn our attention to a particular example. Instead of denoting our new function by a single letter such as F, as we did in the preceding section, we will use the two lettered symbol ln and call the function, for the moment, the "ell-en" function. As we develop its properties, the function ln will look more and more familiar, and in fact it will turn out to be a logarithmic function.

DEFINITION 47-1. *The function* ln *is defined by the rule of correspondence,*

$$\ln x = \int_1^x \frac{1}{t}\, dt. \tag{47-1}$$

The domain of the function is the *set of positive numbers.* The symbol $\int_1^{-2} \frac{1}{t}\, dt$, for example, has no meaning because the function f defined by the equation $f(t) = 1/t$ is not integrable over any interval containing the number 0. The range of the function ln is the set of all real numbers.

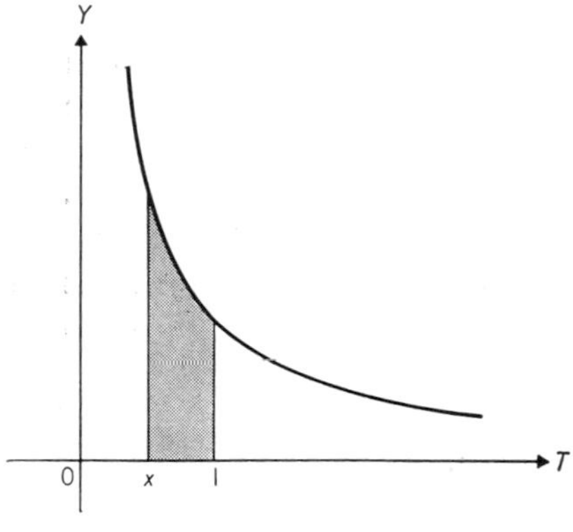

Figure 47-1

It follows directly from the definition of the function ln that

$$\ln 1 = \int_1^1 \frac{1}{t}\, dt = 0.$$

Furthermore, if $0 < x < 1$, then

$$\ln x = \int_1^x \frac{1}{t}\, dt = -\int_x^1 \frac{1}{t}\, dt.$$

This last integral is the area of the shaded region shown in Fig. 47-1. Therefore, if $0 < x < 1$, then $\ln x$ is the negative of this area. If $x > 1$, then $\ln x$ is the area of the region beneath the curve and above the interval $[1, x]$. Thus our function ln has the following properties:

$$\begin{aligned} &\ln x < 0 \quad \text{if} \quad 0 < x < 1, \\ &\ln x = 0 \quad \text{if} \quad x = 1, \\ &\ln x > 0 \quad \text{if} \quad x > 1. \end{aligned} \tag{47-2}$$

We could use Simpson's Rule, the Trapezoidal Rule, or some other method of approximate integration to calculate approximate values of the function ln. For example, we have already found in Example 39-4 that $\ln 2 \approx .6933$. The function ln is an important function, as we shall soon see, and its values have been tabulated. Table II in the back of this book is a table of values of the function ln.

The function f defined by the equation $f(t) = 1/t$ is continuous in the interval $(0, \infty)$. Therefore, according to Theorem 46-1,

$$D_x \ln x = D_x \int_1^x \frac{1}{t}\,dt = \frac{1}{x}.$$

We now have another specific differentiation formula:

$$\text{(47-3)} \qquad \boldsymbol{D_x \ln x = \frac{1}{x}}.$$

It follows from Equation 47-3 that

$$D_x^2 \ln x = D_x x^{-1} = -\frac{1}{x^2}.$$

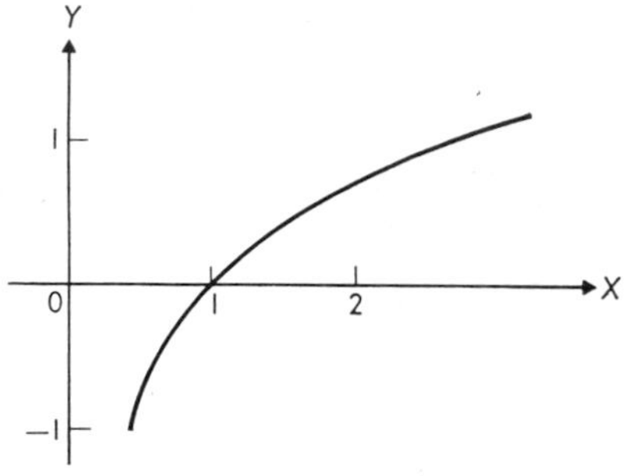

Figure 47-2

Thus $D_x \ln x > 0$ and $D_x^2 \ln x < 0$ for every number in the domain of the function ln. Therefore, ln is an *increasing* function and its graph is *concave down* in the interval $(0, \infty)$. Using this information and some values from Table II, we can plot the graph of the function ln shown in Fig. 47-2.

To make Formula 47-3 apply more generally, we incorporate it into the Chain Rule. Thus if $y = \ln u$, where $u = g(x)$, then $D_u y = 1/u$ and the Chain Rule Equation $D_x y = D_u y D_x u$ becomes

$$\text{(47-4)} \qquad \boldsymbol{D_x \ln u = \frac{1}{u} D_x u}.$$

Example 47-1. Find $D_x \ln x^4$.

Solution. We apply Formula 47-4 with $u = x^4$:

$$D_x \ln x^4 = \frac{1}{x^4} D_x x^4 = \frac{4x^3}{x^4} = \frac{4}{x}.$$

We have just found that $D_x \ln x^4 = 4/x$. We also see that

$$D_x(4 \ln x) = 4D_x \ln x = \frac{4}{x}.$$

Thus $\ln x^4$ and $4 \ln x$ have the same derivative. We shall now show that these two numbers are equal. Moreover, we may replace the number 4 with any rational number r and the resulting numbers will also be equal.

THEOREM 47-1. *If r is any rational number, then*

$$\mathbf{\ln x^r = r \ln x.} \tag{47-5}$$

Proof. First we use Equation 47-4 with $u = x^r$, and we get

$$D_x \ln x^r = \frac{1}{x^r} D_x x^r = \frac{rx^{r-1}}{x^r} = \frac{r}{x}.$$

On the other hand,

$$D_x (r \ln x) = rD_x \ln x = \frac{r}{x}.$$

Therefore,

$$D_x \ln x^r = D_x (r \ln x).$$

This equation does *not* imply that $\ln x^r$ and $r \ln x$ are equal. We can only conclude (see Theorem 21-5) that there is a number c such that the equation

$$\ln x^r = r \ln x + c \tag{47-6}$$

is valid for every positive number x. We must show that $c = 0$. Since Equation 47-6 holds for every positive number x, it must hold when $x = 1$; that is,

$$\ln 1 = r \ln 1 + c.$$

But we have already seen (Relations 47-2) that $\ln 1 = 0$. Hence it follows that $c = 0$, and so $\ln x^r = r \ln x$ for every positive number x.

Notice that Equation 47-5 is one of the basic identities of the theory of logarithms, so perhaps our choice of the symbol ln to denote the function defined by Equation 47-1 is not too far-fetched.

We will now show that our function ln possesses another of the basic properties of logarithmic functions.

THEOREM 47-2. *If a and b are two positive numbers, then*

$$\mathbf{\ln ab = \ln a + \ln b.} \tag{47-7}$$

Proof. If we set $u = ax$ in Equation 47-4, we have

$$D_x \ln ax = \frac{1}{ax} D_x(ax) = \frac{a}{ax} = \frac{1}{x}.$$

Thus $\ln ax$ and $\ln x$ have the same derivative. Therefore, (according to Theorem 21-5), there is a number c such that

$$\ln ax = \ln x + c \tag{47-8}$$

for each positive number x. Since this equation holds for each positive number x, it must hold for $x = 1$, so

$$\ln a = \ln 1 + c = 0 + c = c.$$

Therefore, $c = \ln a$, and Equation 47-8 can be written

$$\ln ax = \ln x + \ln a.$$

Now if we replace x with b, we obtain Equation 47-7, and our proof is complete.

The results in Theorems 47-1 and 47-2 enable us to compute values of the function ln outside the range of Table II.

Example 47-2. Use Table II and Theorem 47-1 and 47-2 to compute ln 45 and ln .045.

Solution. From Table II we find that $\ln 4.5 = 1.5041$, and $\ln 10 = 2.3026$. Then with the aid of Theorems 47-1 and 47-2 we can write:

$$\ln 45 = \ln (4.5)(10) = \ln 4.5 + \ln 10 = 1.5041 + 2.3026 = 3.8067;$$

$$\begin{aligned} \ln .045 &= \ln (4.5)(10)^{-2} = \ln 4.5 + \ln 10^{-2} \\ &= \ln 4.5 - 2 \ln 10 = 1.5041 - 4.6052 \\ &= -3.1011. \end{aligned}$$

Problems 47

1. From the definition of the function ln, compute ln 3 using:
   (a) the Trapezoidal Rule with $n = 4$.
   (b) Simpson's Rule with $n = 4$.
2. Let F be defined by the equation

$$F(x) = \int_2^x t^{-1}\, dt.$$

Compute $F'(x)$. How is F related to the ln function?

3. Use Theorems 47-1 and 47-2 and the values $\ln 2 = .69$ and $\ln 3 = 1.1$ to compute the following numbers.
(a) $\ln 6$ (b) $\ln \frac{1}{2}$ (c) $\ln 27$
(d) $\ln 108$ (e) $\ln \sqrt[3]{12}$ (f) $\ln \sqrt{6}$
4. Use Table II and Theorems 47-1 and 47-2 to find the following numbers. Interpolate if necessary.
(a) $\ln 54$ (b) $\ln .0054$ (c) $\ln .541$ (d) $\ln 541$
5. Use a graph to show that $\ln \frac{1}{3} = -\ln 3$.
6. Compute $D_x y$ if:
(a) $y = \ln \sqrt{x}$ (b) $y = \ln (\sin x)$
(c) $y = \ln (\sec^2 x)$ (d) $y = \ln (\ln x)$
(e) $y = \sin (\ln x)$ (f) $y = \ln x$
(g) $y = \dfrac{1}{\ln x}$ (h) $y = \sqrt{\cos \left(\dfrac{1}{\ln x}\right)}$
7. Let $G(x) = \int_1^x \ln t \, dt$, and use Fig. 47-2 to estimate $G(2)$ and $G(\frac{1}{2})$.
8. Find the mean value of the function f on the interval $[1, 2]$ if $f(x) = 1/x$.
9. Show graphically that

$$\tfrac{1}{2} + \tfrac{1}{3} + \tfrac{1}{4} + \tfrac{1}{5} < \ln 5 < 1 + \tfrac{1}{2} + \tfrac{1}{3} + \tfrac{1}{4}.$$

10. Suppose $H(x) = \int_2^x \dfrac{1}{t-1} \, dt$ for $x > 1$. Use a graphical argument to convince yourself that $H(x) = \ln (x - 1)$.
11. Use Table II to compute the area of the region bounded by the following curves: $y = \dfrac{1}{x}$, $y = 0$, $x = -10$, and $x = -7$.
12. Compute the volume of the solid obtained by rotating about the X-axis the region bounded by the curves $y = x^{-1/2}$, $x = 1$, $x = 4$, and $y = 0$.
13. Show that if $x > 0$, then

$$\frac{x}{1 + x} < \ln (1 + x) < x.$$

Use Table II to check this inequality when $x = .1$.

48. Inverse Functions

The heart of a function is its rule of correspondence between the numbers of its domain and the numbers of its range. If we choose a number x from the domain of a function, then the rule assigns a corresponding number y in the range of the function. In the cases of many important functions, we can pick the number y in the range first, apply the rule of correspondence backwards, and obtain the number x in the domain. For example, in the case of the linear function defined by the equation $y = 3x + 2$, it is clear that if we let $x = 2$, we will obtain $y = 8$.

Conversely, if we start by setting $y = 8$, we can solve the equation $8 = 3x + 2$ to obtain $x = 2$. In fact, if y is any number we can solve the equation

$$y = 3x + 2$$

for x to obtain the equation

$$x = \frac{y - 2}{3}.$$

This equation defines the *inverse* of the function defined by the equation $y = 3x + 2$. In this section we want to say a few words about the inverses of functions in general, and then in later sections we will apply our results to the inverses of specific functions, such as the function ln and the trigonometric functions.

Figure 48-1 shows the graph of a function f of the type that we want to consider here. Its domain is the interval (a, b) and its range is the interval (c, d). If we choose any number x in the interval (a, b), we will obtain the number $y = f(x)$ in the interval (c, d). Graphically we find y by drawing a line through x and parallel to the Y-axis and note where it intersects the graph of f. The line containing this point of intersection and parallel to the X-axis will intersect the Y-axis at the point $y = f(x)$. Conversely, we can start with the point y in the interval (c, d) and draw a line parallel to the X-axis. From our figure we see that this line will intersect the curve at exactly one point. A line containing this point and parallel to the Y-axis will intersect the X-axis at some point x in the interval (a, b). This number x is the single solution to the equation $y = f(x)$ that corresponds to the given number y. Thus we have a rule that assigns to each number y in the range of our function f a number x. In other words, we have a new function such that: *Its domain is the interval (c, d), and its rule of correspondence reads, "To a number y in the interval (c, d) let there correspond the number x that satisfies the equation $y = f(x)$."* This new function is called the **inverse** of the function f, and we shall denote it by the symbol f^{-1}.

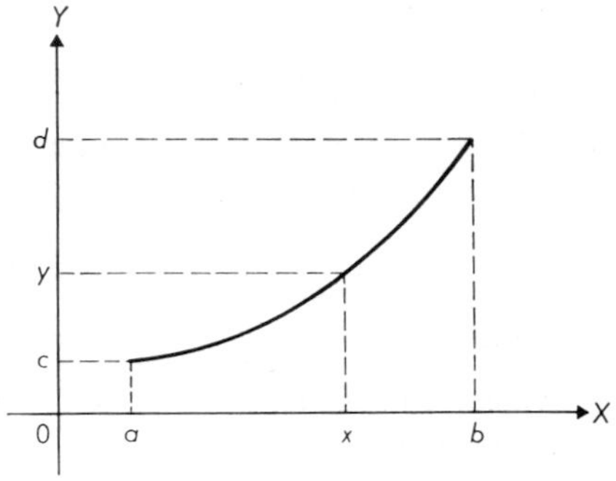

Figure 48-1

DEFINITION 48-1. *If for each number y in the range of a function f there is exactly one number x in the domain of f such that $y = f(x)$, then the function f has an* ***inverse function*** f^{-1}. *The domain of f^{-1} is the range of f, and the range of f^{-1} is the domain of f. The number that corresponds to a given number y in the range of f is the number x that satisfies the equation $y = f(x)$. Thus*

$$(48\text{-}1) \qquad \mathbf{x} = \mathbf{f}^{-1}(\mathbf{y}) \text{ if, and only if, } \mathbf{y} = \mathbf{f}(\mathbf{x}).$$

Not every function has an inverse. If a function f is to have an inverse, the equation $y = f(x)$ must have *just one* solution x for each number y in the domain of f. We can usually see whether or not a function f has an inverse by looking at the graph of f. We merely visualize a horizontal line drawn through each point on the Y-axis that is in the range of f. If each such line cuts the graph of f exactly once (as it does in Fig. 48-1), then the equation $y = f(x)$ has just one solution and the function f has an inverse. If a horizontal line through some point y cuts the graph more than once, then the equation $y = f(x)$ has more than one solution, and the function f does not have an inverse. The function f whose graph is shown in Fig. 48-1 is an increasing function in the interval (a, b); that is, if $x_1 > x_2$, then $f(x_1) > f(x_2)$. Every increasing function has an inverse (Why?). Similarly, every decreasing function has an inverse.

Example 48-1. Let f be the linear function defined by the equation $f(x) = 3x + 2$. Find the equation that defines the inverse function f^{-1}.

Solution. It is clear from the graph of the function f (a straight line with positive slope) that f is an increasing function in any interval and therefore has an inverse. To find the value of f^{-1} at a given number y, we must solve the equation $y = f(x)$ (that is, $y = 3x + 2$) for x. Thus we have $x = \frac{1}{3}y - \frac{2}{3}$; or in other words, $f^{-1}(y) = \frac{1}{3}y - \frac{2}{3}$. Of course, the letter that we use to denote a number in the domain of the inverse function is of no importance whatsoever, so this last equation can be rewritten $f^{-1}(u) = \frac{1}{3}u - \frac{2}{3}$, or $f^{-1}(s) = \frac{1}{3}s - \frac{2}{3}$, or even $f^{-1}(x) = \frac{1}{3}x - \frac{2}{3}$, and it will still define the same function f^{-1}.

Example 48-2. Does the sine function have an inverse?

Solution. No. The equation $y = \sin x$ has infinitely many solutions for each number y in the interval $[-1, 1]$. So if we pick, for example, $y = \frac{1}{2}$, then the equation $\frac{1}{2} = \sin x$ does not give us *just one* number x that corresponds to $y = \frac{1}{2}$. For example, both $\pi/6$ and $5\pi/6$ correspond to the number $y = \frac{1}{2}$. Later we will introduce a modification of the sine function so as to obtain a function that does have an inverse.

Suppose now that f is a function that has an inverse. Then the equations $y = f(x)$ and $x = f^{-1}(y)$ are equivalent (see Equations 48-1). Therefore, if the graph in Fig. 48-1 is the graph of the equation $y = f(x)$, then it is also the graph of the equation $x = f^{-1}(y)$. If we interchange the letters on the axes in Fig. 48-1, we get Fig. 48-2, in which we have the

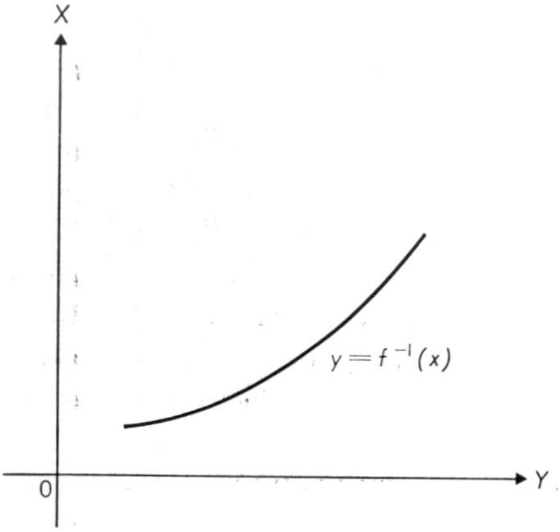

Figure 48-2

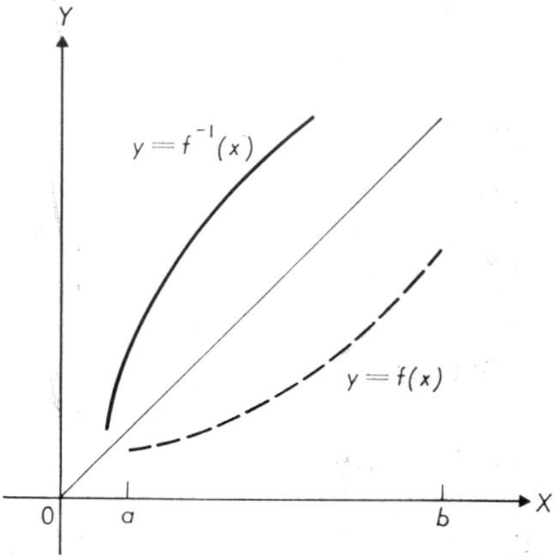

Figure 48-3

graph of the equation $x = f(y)$; that is, $y = f^{-1}(x)$. Now in order to put the X and Y-axes in their customary positions, we must turn the picture over and then rotate it to make the X-axis point to the right, and the solid curve in Fig. 48-3 results. In Fig. 48-3 we have shown the graph of f as the dashed curve. If you study the picture, you will see that *the graph of the function f^{-1} is obtained by reflecting the graph of f about the line that bisects the first and third quadrants.*

From the very definition of f^{-1}, it follows that the solution of the equation $y = f^{-1}(x)$ is $x = f(y)$. Therefore, we see that *the inverse of the function f^{-1} is the function f.*

If we return to Equations 48-1 that define an inverse function and use the equation on the right to replace y with $f(x)$ in the equation on the left, we obtain the equation

(48-2) $$\boldsymbol{x = f^{-1}[f(x)]}.$$

Similarly, if we use the equation on the left in Equations 48-1 to replace x with $f^{-1}(y)$ in the equation on the right, we obtain the equation

(48-3) $$y = f[f^{-1}(y)].$$

We can now replace the letter y in this last equation with the letter x and write

$$x = f[f^{-1}(x)]. \tag{48-4}$$

Example 48-3. Verify that Equations 48-2 and 48-4 are valid for the function defined by the equation $f(x) = 3x + 2$.

Solution. We have already seen that

$$f^{-1}(x) = \frac{x}{3} - \frac{2}{3},$$

and so

$$f^{-1}[f(x)] = \frac{f(x)}{3} - \frac{2}{3} = \frac{3x + 2}{3} - \frac{2}{3} = x.$$

On the other hand,

$$\begin{aligned} f[f^{-1}(x)] &= 3f^{-1}(x) + 2 = 3\left(\frac{x}{3} - \frac{2}{3}\right) + 2 \\ &= x - 2 + 2 = x. \end{aligned}$$

Now we shall take up the problem of finding $D_x f^{-1}(x)$. Let us consider a function f in an interval (a, b) in which $f'(x)$ exists, and let us suppose that $f'(x) \neq 0$ for every choice of x in the interval. Then it can be shown that either $f'(x) > 0$ for every point of (a, b) or else $f'(x) < 0$ for every point. In the first case, f is an increasing function, and in the second case it is a decreasing function. In either case, the inverse function f^{-1} exists, and it can be shown that f^{-1} is differentiable. Thus if $y = f^{-1}(x)$, then $D_x y$ exists. Instead of calculating $D_x y$ directly from the equation $y = f^{-1}(x)$, we use the equivalent equation $x = f(y)$. Thus we differentiate both sides of the equation $x = f(y)$ with respect to x, using the Chain Rule:

$$1 = D_x f(y) = D_y f(y) D_x y = f'(y) D_x y. \tag{48-5}$$

Then we solve for $D_x y$ and we get the following important result. *If $f'(x) \neq 0$ in some interval, and if we set $y = f^{-1}(x)$, then*

$$D_x y = \frac{1}{f'(y)}. \tag{48-6}$$

Since $f(y) = x$, we see that $f'(y) = D_y x$, so we can also write Equation 48-6 in the easily remembered form

$$D_x y = \frac{1}{D_y x}. \tag{48-7}$$

Example 48-4. Verify Equation 48-7 if $y = \frac{1}{3}x - \frac{2}{3}$.

Solution. First, we compute $D_x y = \frac{1}{3}$. On the other hand, we see that $x = 3y + 2$, so $D_y x = 3$. Hence $D_x y$ is the reciprocal of $D_y x$ and Equation 48-7 is verified.

Example 48-5. Verify Equation 48-6 if $f(x) = \sqrt{x}$.

Solution. Clearly, $f^{-1}(x) = x^2$, so if $y = f^{-1}(x)$, then $y = x^2$. Therefore, $D_x y = 2x$. On the other hand, $f'(x) = \dfrac{1}{2\sqrt{x}}$, and hence $f'(y) = \dfrac{1}{2\sqrt{y}}$ $= \dfrac{1}{2\sqrt{x^2}} = \dfrac{1}{2x}$ (Why do we assume $x > 0$?). Thus $1/f'(y) = 2x$, and we see that $D_x y = 1/f'(y)$.

Example 48-6. Let F be the function defined by the equation

$$F(x) = \int_0^x \frac{1}{1 + t^2}\, dt.$$

Show that the choice $y = F^{-1}(x)$ satisfies the differential equation $y' = 1 + y^2$.

Solution. According to Theorem 46-1, $F'(x) = 1/(1 + x^2)$. Thus we see that F is an increasing function in any interval and hence has an inverse. Now if we set $y = F^{-1}(x)$, then we see from Equation 48-6 that

$$y' = \frac{1}{F'(y)} = \frac{1}{1/(1 + y^2)} = 1 + y^2.$$

Example 48-7. Verify that if $f(x) = x^3 + x$, then f^{-1} exists, and find $D_x[f^{-1}(x)]$.

Solution. Since $f'(x) = 3x^2 + 1 > 0$ for every number x, it follows that f is an increasing function in any interval and hence has an inverse f^{-1}. To find $D_x[f^{-1}(x)]$, let us write $y = f^{-1}(x)$. Then Equation 48-6 tells us that

$$D_x y = \frac{1}{f'(y)} = \frac{1}{3y^2 + 1}.$$

To express $D_x[f^{-1}(x)]$ in terms of x we would have to solve the equation $y = f^{-1}(x)$ (that is, $x = f(y) = y^3 + y$) for y and substitute the result in our solution $D_x[f^{-1}(x)] = 1/(3y^2 = 1)$. This is easier said than done.

Problems 48

1. Each of the functions defined by the following equations has an inverse. Find the equation that defines the inverse function and verify Equations 48-2 and 48-4.

(a) $f(x) = 1 - 3x$ (b) $f(x) = x^3 - 1$
(c) $f(x) = 1/x$ (d) $f(x) = (2 - x)/(3 + x)$

2. Let $y = f^{-1}(x)$ and verify Equation 48-6 for the functions in the preceding problem.
3. Which of the functions defined by the following equations have inverses?
(a) $f(x) = 3x^2 + 2x + 1$ (b) $g(x) = |x|$
(c) $h(x) = 3x + |x|$ (d) $I(x) = \int_0^x (1 + \sin^2 t)\, dt$
4. Verify that f^{-1} exists; let $y = f^{-1}(x)$ and find $D_x y$ if:
(a) $f(x) = x^5 + x^3 + 1$ (b) $f(x) = \ln x^3$
(c) $f(x) = 2x - \sin x$ (d) $f(x) = x|x|$
5. Let

$$F(x) = \int_0^x (1 - t^2)^{-1/2}\, dt \quad \text{for } -1 < x < 1,$$

and let $y = F^{-1}(x)$. Show that $y'^2 + y^2 = 1$.
6. Let

$$F(x) = \int_2^x \frac{1}{t\sqrt{t-1}}\, dt \quad \text{for } x > 2,$$

and let $y = F^{-1}(x)$. Show that $y'^2 + y^2 = y^3$.
7. Verify Equation 48-6 if $y = f^{-1}(x)$ and $f(x) = x^4$ for $x > 0$.
8. Using the Chain Rule and Equation 48-7, we have

$$D_x^2 y = D_y(D_x y)D_x y = D_y(1/D_y x)D_x y.$$

Continue this computation and obtain the formula:

$$\mathbf{D_x^2 y = -D_y^2 x/(D_y x)^3}.$$

9. Verify the formula for $D_x^2 y$ in the preceding question if:
(a) $y = x^{1/5}$ (b) $y = x^3$
10. Use the formula for $D_x^2 y$ in Question 8 to compute $D_x^2 y$ if $y = f^{-1}(x)$ and $f(x) = x^3 + x + 2$.
11. Suppose that f^{-1} exists and that $F(x) = \int_0^x f(t)\, dt$. Show that

$$D_x(xf^{-1}(x) - F[f^{-1}(x)]) = f^{-1}(x).$$

49. The Function exp and the Number *e*

Now we will apply our knowledge of inverse functions to the function ln that we defined in Section 47 by the equation

$$\ln x = \int_1^x \frac{1}{t}\, dt \quad \text{for } x > 0.$$

Since $D_x \ln x = 1/x > 0$, we see that ln is an increasing function, and hence it has an inverse. We shall denote this inverse function by the three-lettered symbol **exp.** (The letters "exp" form an abbreviation of the word "exponent," and we will soon see why this choice is appropriate.) Thus we have

(49-1) $$\mathbf{y} = \mathbf{ln}\ \mathbf{x} \quad \textit{if, and only if,} \quad \mathbf{x} = \mathbf{exp}\ \mathbf{y}.$$

From our knowledge of inverse functions in general, we see that not only is the function exp the inverse of the function ln, but the function ln is also the inverse of the function exp.

We can find some values of the function exp by reading Table II "backwards"; that is, from right to left. For example, since ln 8 = 2.0794, exp 2.0794 = 8. The function exp is such an important function that it is tabulated directly. You will shortly see that Table III gives values of the function exp.

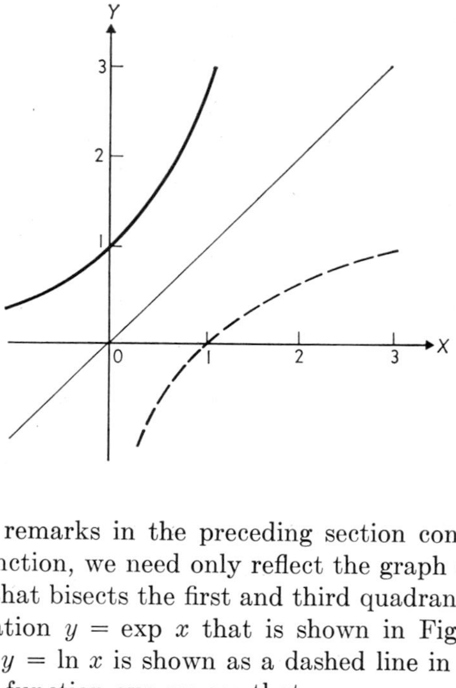

Figure 49-1

According to our remarks in the preceding section concerning the graph of an inverse function, we need only reflect the graph of the function ln about the line that bisects the first and third quadrants to obtain the graph of the equation $y = \exp x$ that is shown in Fig. 49-1. The graph of the equation $y = \ln x$ is shown as a dashed line in that figure. From the graph of the function exp we see that:

$$\begin{aligned} 0 < \exp x < 1 \quad &\text{if} \quad x < 0, \\ \exp x = 1 \quad &\text{if} \quad x = 0, \\ \exp x > 1 \quad &\text{if} \quad x > 0. \end{aligned}$$

These relations correspond to Relations 47-2 for the function ln. Just as you should know how to sketch the graphs of the trigonometric functions, so should you know what the graphs of the functions ln and exp look like.

We have already shown that the function ln has the basic logarithmic properties:

(49-2) $$\ln ab = \ln a + \ln b,$$

and

(49-3) $$\ln x^r = r \ln x.$$

Furthermore, since the functions exp and ln are inverses of each other, we have (see Equations 48-2 and 48-4)

(49-4) $$\exp(\ln u) = u$$

for any positive number u, and

(49-5) $$\ln(\exp v) = v$$

for any number v. These equations enable us to express the logarithmic properties of the function ln as exponential properties of the function exp.

THEOREM 49-1. *If x and y are any two numbers, and if r is a rational number, then*

(49-6) $$\mathbf{exp}\,(x + y) = (\mathbf{exp}\,x)(\mathbf{exp}\,y),$$

and

(49-7) $$\mathbf{exp}\,rx = (\mathbf{exp}\,x)^r.$$

Proof. We will verify Equation 49-6 and leave the verification of Equation 49-7 for the problems:

$\exp(x + y) = \exp[\ln(\exp x) + \ln(\exp y)]$ (Eq. 49-5 applied twice, once with $v = x$ and once with $v = y$)

$= \exp[\ln(\exp x \cdot \exp y)]$ (Eq. 49-2)

$= (\exp x)(\exp y)$ (Eq. 49-4 with $u = \exp x \cdot \exp y$).

Equations 49-6 and 49-7 tell us that our function exp shares certain properties with exponential functions. For instance, if r is a rational number and if the function f is defined by the equation $f(x) = 2^x$, then $f(x + y) = f(x) \cdot f(y)$ and $f(rx) = [f(x)]^r$ so that the functions f and exp both satisfy the same functional equations (Equations 49-6 and 49-7). The fact that our function exp satisfies functional equations that are also satisfied by exponential functions makes us suspect that the function exp is itself an exponential function. We shall now see that it is.

If we set $x = 1$ in Equation 49-7, we see that

$$\exp r = (\exp 1)^r. \tag{49-8}$$

Therefore, the value of the function exp for the rational number r is the rth power of the number exp 1. The number exp 1 is such an important number in mathematics that we use a particular letter for it, just as we use the letter π for the number 3.14159 .... We make the following definition.

DEFINITION 49-1.

$$\mathbf{exp\ 1} = \boldsymbol{e}.$$

From the graph in Fig. 49-1 it appears that the number e is slightly smaller than 3. It can be shown that to 5 decimal places

$$\boldsymbol{e} = \mathbf{2.71828\ldots}$$

Now that we have agreed to write e in place of exp 1, Equation 49-8 becomes

$$\exp r = e^r. \tag{49-9}$$

Thus the function exp and the exponential function with base e take the same values at the rational numbers, and we are left with the question of whether or not the numbers $\exp a$ and e^a are the same for each irrational number a. When we try to answer this question, we discover that we have never defined what we mean by the irrational power of a number. We know that $e^3 = e \cdot e \cdot e$, that $e^{-3} = \dfrac{1}{e \cdot e \cdot e}$, and that $e^{3/4} = (\sqrt[4]{e})^3$. But you probably have never seen a definition of what the symbols e^π and $e^{\sqrt{2}}$ are supposed to stand for. One good definition suggests itself now. If we want e^a to be equal to $\exp a$, we may *define* e^a *to be equal to* $\exp a$ *for each irrational number* a.

Then we see that the function exp is an exponential function whose domain is the set of all real numbers. For if x is any real number, then Equation 49-9 tells us that $\exp x = e^x$ if x is a rational number, and our definition of irrational powers of e tells us that $\exp x = e^x$ if x is irrational. Therefore, the equation

$$\mathbf{exp}\ \boldsymbol{x} = \boldsymbol{e^x} \tag{49-10}$$

is true for every real number x. Because of this equation we can write Equations 49-6 and 49-7 in the form

$$\boldsymbol{e^{x+y} = e^x e^y} \quad \text{and} \quad \boldsymbol{e^{rx} = (e^x)^r}.$$

These equations are two of the basic laws of exponents, so our definition of irrational powers of e does not violate these two fundamental laws.

According to Equation 49-10, we have $\exp y = e^y$, so we see that Equations 49-1 can be written

$$\boldsymbol{y = \ln x} \quad \textit{if, and only if,} \quad \boldsymbol{x = e^y}.$$

Let us recall that the logarithm of a positive number x to a positive base $b \neq 1$ was defined in elementary mathematics as follows:

$$y = \log_b x \quad \text{if, and only if,} \quad x = b^y.$$

This definition assumes that we know what the symbol b^y means for each real number y, irrational as well as rational. We will take up this point in Section 51. If we set $b = e$, however, we have just defined what we mean by the symbol e^y for every real number y, and so we have the statement

$$y = \log_e x \quad \text{if, and only if,} \quad x = e^y.$$

Thus we see that $\ln x$ and $\log_e x$ are the same number; namely, the solution to the equation $x = e^y$. Hence

(49-11) $$\boldsymbol{\ln x = \log_e x.}$$

From now on we will call the function **ln** the **logarithmic function (with base *e*)** and **exp** the **exponential function (with base *e*)**. We shall continue to use the notation $\ln x$, but many authors simply write $\log x$ for $\log_e x$. The number $\ln x$ is called the **natural logarithm of *x*,** and Table II is a table of natural logarithms. We will use the notation e^x more often than $\exp x$. Table III contains some values of the exponential function with base e.

In Section 47 we found that $D_x \ln x = \frac{1}{x}\cdot$ We can use this formula and the differentiation rules for inverse functions that we gave in the preceding section to find $D_x e^x$. We have

$$y = e^x \quad \text{if, and only if,} \quad x = \ln y.$$

Therefore, $D_y x = \frac{1}{y}$, and so Equation 48-7 gives us

$$D_x y = \frac{1}{D_y x} = \frac{1}{1/y} = y.$$

In other words, we have found another specific differentiation formula,

(49-12) $$\boldsymbol{D_x e^x = e^x.}$$

We might interpret Formula 49-12 by saying that e^x is "immune" to differentiation! We can incorporate this formula into our Chain Rule Equation $D_x y = D_u y D_x u$. Thus if $y = e^u$, where $u = g(x)$, then $D_u y = e^u$, and so

(49-13) $$\boldsymbol{D_x e^u = e^u D_x u.}$$

Example 49-1. Find $D_x e^{\sqrt{x}}$.

Solution. According to Equation 49-13,

$$D_x e^{\sqrt{x}} = e^{\sqrt{x}} D_x \sqrt{x} = \frac{e^{\sqrt{x}}}{2\sqrt{x}}.$$

Problems 49

1. Solve for x: $\int_1^x \frac{1}{t}\,dt = 1$.

2. Use tables to find the following:

(a) $e^{2.3}$ (b) $e^{2.35}$ (c) $\frac{1}{e^3}$

(d) e^{10} (e) $e^{\sin 1}$ (f) e^e

3. Verify Equation 49-7.

4. Let $f(x) = x^2e^{-x}$. Find the maximum and minimum points of the graph of f. Investigate the concavity of the graph of f. Sketch the graph of f.

5. Find $D_x y$.

(a) $y = e^{x+2}$ (b) $y = e^{2x}$

(c) $y = e^{x^2}$ (d) $y = \ln \sqrt{e^x}$

(e) $y = (e^x)^2$ (f) $y = \exp e^x$

(g) $y = \exp (\sin x)$ (h) $y = \exp (\ln \sqrt{x})$

6. Show that $y = e^{-x} \sin 2x$ satisfies the differential equation $y'' + 2y' + 5y = 0$.

7. Draw graphs of the equations $y = e^{-x}$ and $y = \sin x$. Use these graphs to graph the equation $y = e^{-x} \sin x$ for $x > 0$. Find the X-coordinate of the maximum point of this graph.

8. Draw a graph of the function defined by the equation $f(x) = x \ln x$. What is the minimum value of f?

9. (a) Show that $\int_1^2 \frac{1}{t}\,dt < 1$ and explain why you can conclude from this inequality that $e > 2$.

(b) Use an approximating sum based on 8 equal subintervals with the point x_i^* as the right end-point of the subinterval $[x_{i-1}, x_i]$ to conclude that $\int_1^3 \frac{1}{t}\,dt > 1$, and hence $e < 3$.

10. Let $f(x) = e^x - \ln x$. For what number x is the value of f a minimum? (Use Newton's Method to approximate the solution.)

50. Integration Formulas for Exponents and Logarithms

In the preceding sections we developed the differentiation formulas

(50-1) $$\mathbf{D_x \ln u = \frac{1}{u} D_x u}$$

and

(50-2) $$\mathbf{D_x e^u = e^u D_x u.}$$

Now we will introduce some useful integration formulas that involve exponents and logarithms.

Our first integration formula is

(50-3) $$\int \mathbf{e^{ax}\,dx = \frac{e^{ax}}{a}} \qquad (a \neq 0).$$

To show that this formula is correct, we have to show that $D_x \frac{e^{ax}}{a} = e^{ax}$. But, according to Equation 50-2 with $u = ax$,

$$D_x \frac{e^{ax}}{a} = \frac{1}{a} D_x e^{ax} = \frac{1}{a} e^{ax} D_x ax = e^{ax},$$

and so Formula 50-3 is verified.

Example 50-1. The region that is bounded by the graph of the equation $y = e^x$, the X-axis, the Y-axis, and the line $x = 1$ is rotated about the X-axis. What is the volume of the resulting solid of revolution?

Solution. Our formula for the volume of a solid of revolution tells us that

$$V = \pi \int_0^1 y^2\,dx = \pi \int_0^1 (e^x)^2\,dx = \pi \int_0^1 e^{2x}\,dx.$$

Now we use Formula 50-3 with $a = 2$:

$$V = \pi \int_0^1 e^{2x}\,dx = \tfrac{1}{2}\pi e^{2x}\Big|_0^1 = \tfrac{1}{2}\pi(e^2 - 1) \approx 10.$$

Our next integration formula is

(50-4) $$\int \mathbf{\frac{1}{x}\,dx = \ln |x|.}$$

To verify this formula, we must show that $D_x \ln |x| = \frac{1}{x}\cdot$ The equation $y = \ln |x|$ defines a function whose domain is the set of all real numbers except 0 (ln 0 is not defined). To calculate $D_x y$, we consider two cases. If $x > 0$, then $y = \ln x$ and $D_x y = \frac{1}{x}\cdot$ If $x < 0$, then $|x| = -x$, and so $y = \ln(-x)$. Now we find $D_x y$ by applying Formula 50-1 with $u = -x$:

$$D_x \ln(-x) = \frac{1}{-x} D_x(-x) = \frac{1}{-x}(-1) = \frac{1}{x}\cdot$$

Thus we have found that $D_x y = 1/x$ in both cases. Hence

$$\text{(50-5)} \qquad \boldsymbol{D_x \ln |x| = \frac{1}{x},}$$

and therefore Formula 50-4 is verified.

Example 50-2. Evaluate the integral $\int_{-8}^{-4} \frac{1}{x}\,dx$.

Solution. According to Formula 50-4,

$$\int_{-8}^{-4} \frac{1}{x}\,dx = \ln |x| \Big|_{-8}^{-4} = \ln |-4| - \ln |-8| = \ln 4 - \ln 8$$
$$= \ln \tfrac{4}{8} = \ln \tfrac{1}{2} = -\ln 2 = -.6931.$$

(Explain the geometric significance of the negative answer.)

Our final integration formula of this section is

$$\text{(50-6)} \qquad \boldsymbol{\int \ln |x|\,dx = x \ln |x| - x.}$$

To verify this formula, we must show that $D_x[x \ln |x| - x] = \ln |x|$. We have

$$D_x[x \ln |x| - x] = xD_x \ln |x| + \ln |x| D_x x - D_x x.$$

We have just seen that $D_x \ln |x| = \frac{1}{x}$, and $D_x x = 1$, so

$$D_x[x \ln |x| - x] = \frac{x}{x} + \ln |x| - 1 = \ln |x|,$$

which verifies Formula 50-6.

Often Formulas 50-4 and 50-6 are applied in intervals in which x is positive, and in that case the absolute value signs in the formulas can be deleted.

Example 50-3. Evaluate the integral $\int_1^2 \ln x^2\, dx$.

Solution. We do not have an integration formula in which the integrand is $\ln x^2$. However, $\ln x^2 = 2 \ln x$, so we can evaluate the given integral as follows:

$$\begin{aligned}\int_1^2 \ln x^2\, dx &= 2\int_1^2 \ln x\, dx = 2(x \ln x - x)\Big|_1^2 \\ &= 2[(2 \ln 2 - 2) - (1 \ln 1 - 1)] \\ &= 2[2 \ln 2 - 1] \approx .77.\end{aligned}$$

We bring this section to a close by using various differentiation formulas to calculate an important limit.

Example 50-4. Show that $\lim_{h \to 0} \ln (1 + xh)^{1/h} = x$.

Solution. Let $f(t) = \ln (1 + xt)$. Then according to our differentiation rules we have $f'(t) = x/(1 + xt)$, and so $f'(0) = x$. Now we will find another expression for $f'(0)$. The definition of the derivative states that

$$f'(0) = \lim_{h \to 0} \frac{f(h) - f(0)}{h} = \lim_{h \to 0} \frac{\ln (1 + xh)}{h}.$$

According to the rules of logarithms,

$$\frac{\ln (1 + xh)}{h} = \ln (1 + xh)^{1/h},$$

so $f'(0) = \lim_{h \to 0} \ln (1 + xh)^{1/h}$. Now we obtain the equation we seek by equating our two expressions for $f'(0)$.

The result of the preceding example can be roughly summed up in the statement, "If h is small, then $\ln (1 + xh)^{1/h}$ is approximately x." Since the exponential function is continuous, it follows that if h is small, then $e^{\ln (1+xh)^{1/h}}$ is approximately e^x; in precise language,

$$\lim_{h \to 0} e^{\ln (1+xh)^{1/h}} = e^x. \tag{50-7}$$

Now $e^{\ln (1+xh)^{1/h}} = (1 + xh)^{1/h}$, so Equation 50-7 can be written as

$$\mathbf{\lim_{h \to 0} (1 + xh)^{1/h} = e^x.} \tag{50-8}$$

If we put $x = 1$ in Equation 50-8 we see that

$$\mathbf{\lim_{h \to 0} (1 + h)^{1/h} = e.} \tag{50-9}$$

In many books you will find the number e *defined* by Equation 50-9.

Problems 50

1. Sketch the graph of the equation $y = \ln |x|$. Draw in a few tangent lines to verify graphically that $D_x y = 1/x$.
2. Develop an alternate verification of Formula 50-5 by writing

$$y = \ln |x| = \ln \sqrt{x^2} = \tfrac{1}{2} \ln x^2$$

and using Formula 50-1.
3. Compute
   (a) $D_x[e^x(x - 1)]$ (b) $D_t[-e^{-t}(2 + 2t + t^2)]$
   (c) $D_x[e^x/(1 + x)]$ (d) $D_x(\tfrac{1}{2}x^2 \ln x - \tfrac{1}{4}x^2)$
4. Write integration formulas that "correspond to" the differentiation formulas developed in the preceding problem.
5. Evaluate the following integrals.
   (a) $\int_{1/2}^{2} \ln x \, dx$ (b) $\int_{-8}^{-4} \frac{1}{|U|}$
   (c) $\int_{0}^{\ln 2} e^{3t} \, dt$ (d) $\int_{0}^{1} [(e^{2x} + 1)^2/e^x] \, dx$
   (e) $\int_{1}^{4} \frac{x^2 + 2}{x} \, dx$ (f) $\int_{1}^{2} \ln (v^2 e^{v^2}) \, dv$
   (g) $\int_{1}^{2} e^{\ln 2x} \, dx$ (h) $\int_{1}^{2} e^{-2 \ln x} \, dx$
   (i) $\int_{1/2}^{2} |\ln x| \, dx$ (j) $\int_{1}^{2} \frac{x^3 + 1}{x^2} \, dx$
6. Use the fact that $\ln ax = \ln a + \ln x$ to verify the integration formula;

$$\int \ln ax \, dx = x \ln ax - x.$$

7. Find the volume of the solid obtained by rotating about the X-axis the region bounded by: $y = e^{-x}$, $y = 0$, $x = 0$, and $x = 5$.
8. Show that $\int \ln |x| \, dx = x \ln \frac{|x|}{e}$.
9. Use Simpson's Rule with 4 subintervals to compute
   (a) $\int_{1}^{5} (\ln x)^2 \, dx$ (b) $\int_{0}^{2} e^{-x^2} \, dx$
10. Find the minimum value of the function f if $f(x) = e^{5x} - 20e^{2x}$.
11. Find the maximum value of the product xe^{-x} for $x > 0$.
12. Prove that the equation $e^x = 1 + x$ has only one real solution.
13. What is the mean value (see Section 37) of the exponential function (with base e) on the interval $[0, 1]$?

14. Show that if $y > 1$, and if n is a positive integer, then

$$n(1 - y^{-1/n}) < \ln y < n(y^{1/n} - 1).$$

(*Hint:* Consider the integrals: $\int_1^y t^{-\frac{1}{n}-1}\,dt$, $\int_1^y t^{-1}\,dt$, $\int_1^y t^{\frac{1}{n}-1}\,dt$.)

15. Suppose that $n > \ln y$. Substitute $x = \ln y$ in the inequalities in the preceding problem and use the result to obtain the inequalities:

$$\left(1 + \frac{x}{n}\right)^n < e^x < \left(1 - \frac{x}{n}\right)^{-n}.$$

16. Substitute $x = 1$ and $n = 5$ in the inequalities in the preceding problem to show that $2.4 < e < 3.2$.

51. Exponential and Logarithmic Functions (with Bases Other Than e)

In Section 49 we defined irrational powers of the number e. As a result, we know what e^x means when x is any real number. Now we will use this information to frame a definition of the power of any positive number b that applies to irrational as well as rational exponents. For example, we will give meaning to the symbol $\pi^{\sqrt{2}}$. Suppose that b is a positive number and a is any real number. Since the exponential and logarithmic functions with base e are inverses of each other, we know that

$$b = e^{\ln b}.$$

Hence, no matter how we define b^a, $b^a = (e^{\ln b})^a$. Now *if* the law of exponents $(x^m)^n = x^{mn}$ is to hold, then $(e^{\ln b})^a = e^{a \ln b}$. So, in order to preserve one of the basic rules of exponents, we must make the following definition.

DEFINITION 51-1. *If a is any real number and b is a positive number, then*

$$\boldsymbol{b^a = e^{a \ln b} = \exp (a \ln b).}$$

For example, $\pi^{\sqrt{2}} = e^{\sqrt{2} \ln \pi}$. From our table of logarithms, we find $\ln \pi \approx 1.144$, so $\sqrt{2} \ln \pi \approx 1.62$. From Table III, $e^{1.62} \approx 5.05$. Thus $\pi^{\sqrt{2}} \approx 5.05$.

Now that we have made Definition **51-1**, we must show that the usual rules of exponents and logarithms are valid. For example, we must show that $\ln x^r = r \ln x$ when r is any real number. (We already know that this equation is valid if r is *rational*.) We have

$$\begin{aligned} \ln x^r &= \ln [\exp (r \ln x)] && \text{(Definition 51-1)} \\ &= r \ln x && \text{(Eq. 49-5 with } v = r \ln x). \end{aligned}$$

Furthermore, we must show that $b^a \cdot b^c = b^{a+c}$, when a and c are any real numbers. Here we have

$$\begin{aligned} b^a \cdot b^c &= (e^{a \ln b})(e^{c \ln b}) && \text{(Definition 51-1)} \\ &= e^{a \ln b + c \ln b} && \text{(Eq. 49-6 with } x = a \ln b \text{ and } y = c \ln b) \\ &= e^{(a+c) \ln b} \\ &= b^{a+c} && \text{(Definition 51-1).} \end{aligned}$$

We will leave the proofs of the laws $(b^a)^c = b^{ac}$ and $(ab)^c = a^c b^c$ for the problems.

We have already shown that the Power Formula $D_x x^r = rx^{r-1}$ is valid for any rational number r (Section 18). Now we can extend this result to the case in which r is *any* real number, rational or irrational. According to Definition 51-1,

$$x^r = e^{r \ln x}.$$

Thus we can find the derivative of x^r by setting $u = r \ln x$ in the formula $D_x e^u = e^u D_x u$. We have

$$D_x e^{r \ln x} = e^{r \ln x} D_x(r \ln x) = x^r \cdot \frac{r}{x} = rx^{r-1}.$$

Therefore, the formula

(51-1) $$\boldsymbol{D_x x^r = r x^{r-1}}$$

is valid for any real number r.

We have just seen how to differentiate x to a real power. Now let us consider the case in which x is the exponent.

Example 51-1. Find $D_x 10^x$.

Solution. According to Definition 51-1, $10^x = e^{x \ln 10}$. Now we use the formula $D_x e^u = e^u D_x u$ with $u = x \ln 10$ and we have

$$D_x e^{x \ln 10} = e^{x \ln 10} D_x(x \ln 10) = (\ln 10)10^x.$$

Thus

$$D_x 10^x = (\ln 10)10^x \approx (2.303)10^x.$$

We can use the method of the preceding example to derive another differentiation formula. If b is any positive number,

$$D_x b^x = D_x e^{x \ln b} = e^{x \ln b} D_x(x \ln b) = e^{x \ln b} \ln b = b^x \ln b.$$

Thus

(51-2) $$\boldsymbol{D_x b^x = b^x \ln b.}$$

We incorporate this specific differentiation formula into the Chain Rule Equation in the usual way. Thus if $y = b^u$, where $u = g(x)$, then $D_u y = b^u \ln b$, and the Chain Rule Equation $D_x y = D_u y D_x u$ becomes

(51-3) $$\boldsymbol{D_x b^u = b^u \ln b\, D_x u.}$$

It follows from Equation 51-2 that if $b \neq 1$, then

$$D_x\left(\frac{b^x}{\ln b}\right) = \frac{1}{\ln b} D_x b^x = b^x,$$

so $\dfrac{b^x}{\ln b}$ is an antiderivative of b^x. Thus we have the integration formula

(51-4) $$\boldsymbol{\int b^x\, dx = \frac{b^x}{\ln b} \quad (b \neq 1).}$$

Example 51-2. The graph of the equation $y = 3^x$, the lines $x = -1$ and $x = 1$, and the X-axis enclose a region R. Find the volume of the solid obtained by rotating this region about the X-axis.

Solution. The volume we seek is given by the integral

$$V = \pi \int_{-1}^{1} y^2\, dx = \pi \int_{-1}^{1} (3^x)^2\, dx = \pi \int_{-1}^{1} 3^{2x}\, dx = \pi \int_{-1}^{1} 9^x\, dx.$$

Now Formula 51-4 (with $b = 9$) applies and we have

$$V = \frac{\pi}{\ln 9} 9^x \Big|_{-1}^{1} = \frac{\pi}{\ln 9}\left(9 - \frac{1}{9}\right) \approx 13.$$

Now let us consider logarithmic functions with bases other than e. Suppose that b is a positive number and let $y = \log_b x$. We wish to find $D_x y$. We first notice that, by definition,

$$y = \log_b x \quad \text{if, and only if,} \quad b^y = x.$$

From the equation $b^y = x$ it follows that $\ln b^y = \ln x$; that is, $y \ln b = \ln x$. Thus $y = \dfrac{\ln x}{\ln b}$, so that

(51-5) $$\log_b x = \frac{\ln x}{\ln b}.$$

From this equation we get

$$D_x \log_b x = D_x\left(\frac{\ln x}{\ln b}\right) = \frac{1}{\ln b} D_x \ln x = \frac{1}{x \ln b}.$$

Since $\dfrac{1}{\ln b} = \log_b e$ (Equation 51-5 with $x = e$), we can write our differentiation formula as

(51-6) $$\mathbf{D_x \log_b x = \frac{1}{x \ln b} = \frac{\log_b e}{x}.}$$

When we incorporate this formula into the Chain Rule Equation, we obtain the formula

(51-7) $$\mathbf{D_x \log_b u = \frac{D_x u}{u \ln b} = \frac{\log_b e}{u} D_x u.}$$

Example 51-3. Verify the following integration formula:

(51-8) $$\mathbf{\int \log_b x\, dx = x \log_b (x/e).}$$

Solution. We need only show that $\log_b x$ is the derivative of $x \log_b (x/e)$. We have

$$\begin{aligned} D_x[x \log_b (x/e)] &= D_x(x \log_b x - x \log_b e) \\ &= (D_x x) \log_b x + x D_x \log_b x - (D_x x) \log_b e \\ &= \log_b x + x(\log_b e)/x - \log_b e \\ &= \log_b x. \end{aligned}$$

Thus we see that the Integration Formula 51-8 is valid.

Example 51-4. Find $D_x y$ if $y = x^{e^x}$.

Solution. We can write

$$y = e^{e^x \ln x} = e^u, \quad \text{where } u = e^x \ln x,$$

and use the formula $D_x e^u = e^u D_x u$. You may verify that

$$D_x u = e^x \ln x + \frac{e^x}{x},$$

and so we have

$$\begin{aligned} D_x y &= e^u \left(e^x \ln x + \frac{e^x}{x}\right) \\ &= y e^x \left(\ln x + \frac{1}{x}\right) \\ &= x^{e^x} e^x \left(\ln x + \frac{1}{x}\right). \end{aligned}$$

Problems 51

1. Compute $D_x y$.
   (a) $y = 3^x$
   (b) $y = x^{\pi - 1}$
   (c) $y = 2^{2x-1}$
   (d) $y = x^\pi \pi^x$

(e) $y = 2^{5x^2}$
(f) $y = \log_2 x^3$
(g) $y = \log_{10} \dfrac{2x}{1 + x^2}$
(h) $y = \log_3 (\ln x)$
(i) $y = x^x$
(j) $y = \exp(\log_3 x)$
(k) $y = (x + 1)^x$
(l) $y = \exp(\pi^x)$
(m) $y = x^{\sqrt{x}}$
(n) $y = x^{x^2}$

2. (a) Show that $(ab)^c = a^c b^c$.
   (b) Show that $(b^a)^c = b^{ac}$.
3. Compute π^e and e^π.
4. Show that $\lim_{h \to 0} \dfrac{b^h - 1}{h} = \ln b$. (*Hint:* Let $f(x) = b^x$ and write out the definition of $f'(0)$.)
5. What is the minimum value of x^x (for $x > 0$)?
6. Evaluate the following integrals.
   (a) $\int_1^2 e^\pi \, dx$
   (b) $\int_1^2 1^x \, dx$
   (c) $\int_{-1}^1 2^t \, dt$
   (d) $\int_e^{10e} \log_{10} x \, dx$
   (e) $\int_0^1 3^{2x} \, dx$
   (f) $\int_{-1}^1 3^{-t} \, dt$
   (g) $\int_0^2 (2^x + x^2) \, dx$
   (h) $\int_1^{10} \log_{10} \sqrt{xe} \, dx$
7. Let $f(x) = 4x^\pi + x^{-\pi}$ for $x > 0$. What is the minimum value of f?
8. Let $g(x) = 4\pi^x + \pi^{-x}$. What is the minimum value of g?
9. What is the mean value of the function f if $f(x) = 2^x$ on the interval $[0, 2]$?
10. What is the mean value of the function f if $f(x) = \log_{10} x$ on the interval $[e, 10e]$?
11. Find $D_x \log_x 3$.

52. Inverse Trigonometric Functions

In Example 48-2 we pointed out that the sine function does not have an inverse. In fact, no trigonometric function has an inverse. If f is any trigonometric function and if r is a solution to the equation $y = f(x)$ for a given number y, then $r + 2\pi$ is also a solution. Thus the equation $y = f(x)$ does not have *just one* solution x for each choice of y in the range of f, and hence f does not possess an inverse. But we can construct, by "restricting the domain" of the trigonometric functions, new functions that do have inverses.

We define the **Sine function** (the capital letter S distinguishes this new function from the sine function) as the function whose domain is the interval $[-\pi/2, \pi/2]$, and whose rule of correspondence is expressed by the equation $y = \sin x$. The solid curve in Fig. 52-1 is the graph of the Sine function. We obtain this graph by removing the dashed line portion of the sine curve.

The Sine function has an inverse, and we call this inverse function the **Arcsine function.** The domain of the Arcsine function is the interval $[-1, 1]$. If y is a number in the domain of the Arcsine function, we will

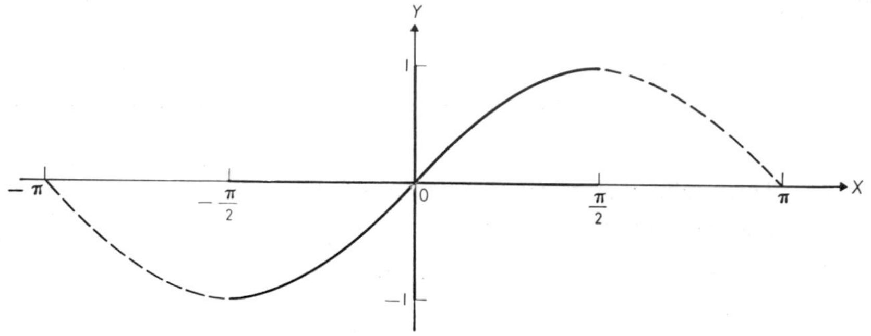

Figure 52-1

denote the associated number in the range either by Arcsin y or $\text{Sin}^{-1}\, y$. Both notations are in common use. Thus we have the following definition.

DEFINITION 52-1. *The Arcsine function is defined as follows:*

$$x = \text{Arcsin}\; y = \text{Sin}^{-1}\; y$$

if, and only if,

$$\text{(i)}\quad \sin x = y,$$

and

$$\text{(i)}\quad -\frac{\pi}{2} \leq x \leq \frac{\pi}{2}.$$

Example 52-1. Find Arcsin $\frac{1}{2}$.

Solution. We know from our study of trigonometry that $\sin \pi/6 = \frac{1}{2}$, and since $-\pi/2 \leq \pi/6 \leq \pi/2$, we see that Arcsin $\frac{1}{2} = \pi/6$.

Example 52-2. Show that $\cos(\text{Sin}^{-1} x) = \sqrt{1 - x^2}$.

Solution. If we write $t = \text{Sin}^{-1} x$, then, according to Definition 52-1, (i) $\sin t = x$ and (ii) $-\pi/2 \leq t \leq \pi/2$. We are to find $\cos t$. Now since $\cos^2 t + \sin^2 t = 1$, and since $\sin t = x$, we have $\cos^2 t = 1 - x^2$. Therefore, $\cos t = \sqrt{1 - x^2}$ or $\cos t = -\sqrt{1 - x^2}$. In view of the inequalities (ii), it follows that $\cos t \geq 0$, and so $\cos t = \sqrt{1 - x^2}$.

It follows from our discussion of the graphs of inverse functions in Section 48 that we can obtain the graph of the Arcsine function by reflecting the graph of the Sine function about the line whose equation is $y = x$. The graph of the equation $y = \mathrm{Sin}^{-1} x$ is shown in Fig. 52-2.

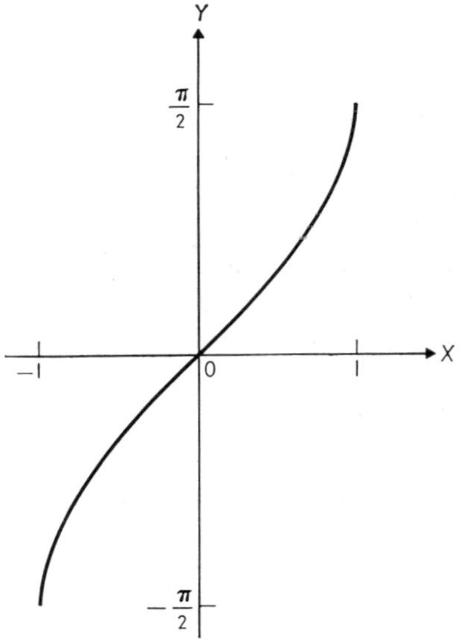

Figure 52-2

We treat the cosine function in the same way we treated the sine function. We first define the **Cosine function** (again using a capital letter to distinguish this new function from the cosine function) as the function whose domain is the interval $[0, \pi]$ and whose rule of correspondence is expressed by the equation $y = \cos x$. The graph of the Cosine function is the solid curve in Fig. 52-3. The Cosine function has an inverse called the **Arccosine function.** The domain of the Arccosine function is the interval $[-1, 1]$. The number corresponding to a given number y in the domain of the Arccosine function is denoted either by Arccos y or $\mathrm{Cos}^{-1}\, y$. We have the following definition.

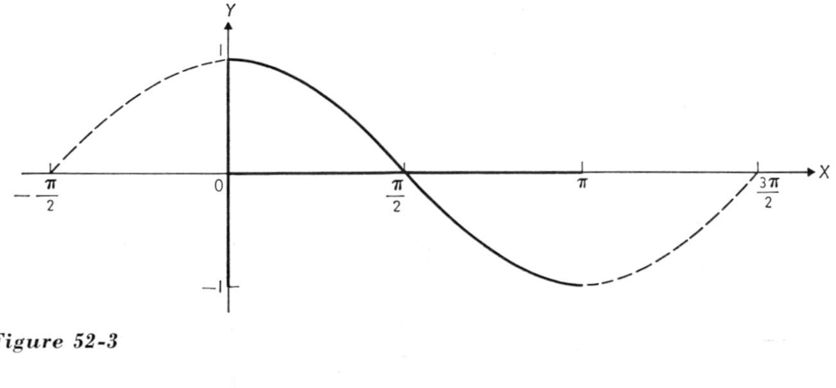

Figure 52-3

DEFINITION 52-2. *The Arccosine function is defined as follows:*

$$x = \boldsymbol{Arccos}\ y = \boldsymbol{Cos}^{-1}\ y$$

if, and only if,

$$\text{(i) } \cos x = y,$$

and

$$\text{(ii) } 0 \leq x \leq \pi.$$

The graph of the equation $y = \text{Cos}^{-1} x$ is shown in Fig. 52-4.

Now, let us turn to the tangent function. First, we define the **Tangent function** as the function whose rule of correspondence is expressed by the equation $y = \tan x$, and whose domain is the interval $(-\pi/2, \pi/2)$. The graph of the Tangent function is shown in Fig. 52-5.

The Tangent function has an inverse, called the **Arctangent function.** The domain of the Arctangent function is the set of all real numbers. The number that is associated with a given real number y is denoted by **Arctan *y*** or **Tan^{-1} *y*.** We have the following definition.

DEFINITION 52-3. *The Arctangent function is defined as follows:*

$$x = \text{Arctan } y = \text{Tan}^{-1} y$$

Figure 52-4

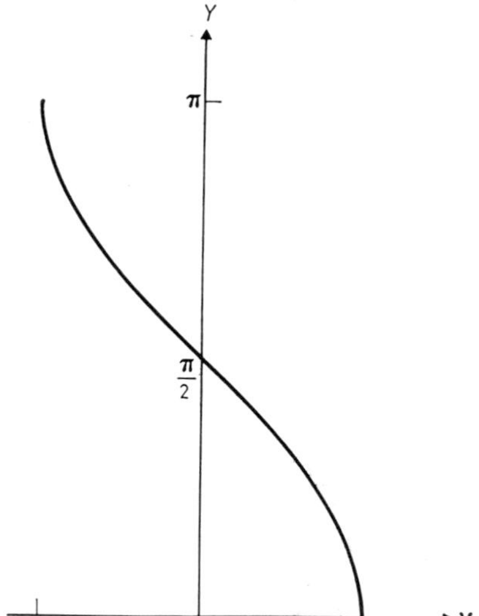

Figure 52-5

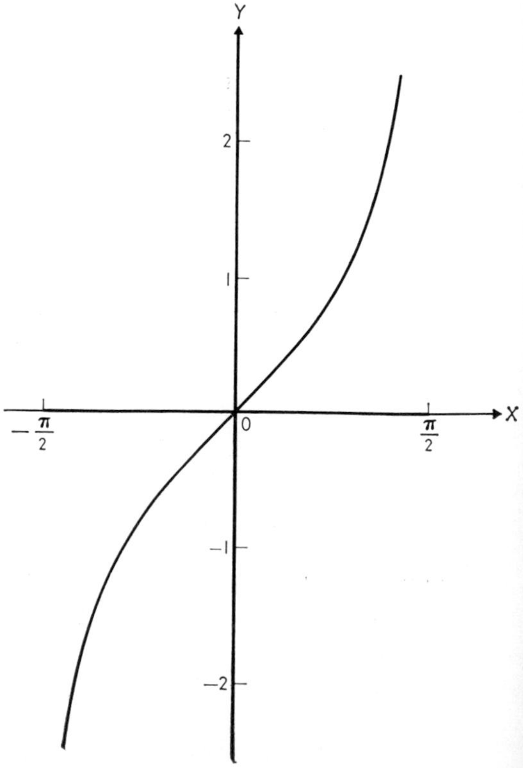

if, and only if,

$$\text{(i) } \tan x = y,$$

and

$$\text{(ii) } -\frac{\pi}{2} < x < \frac{\pi}{2}.$$

We obtain the graph of the Arctangent function (Fig. 52-6) by

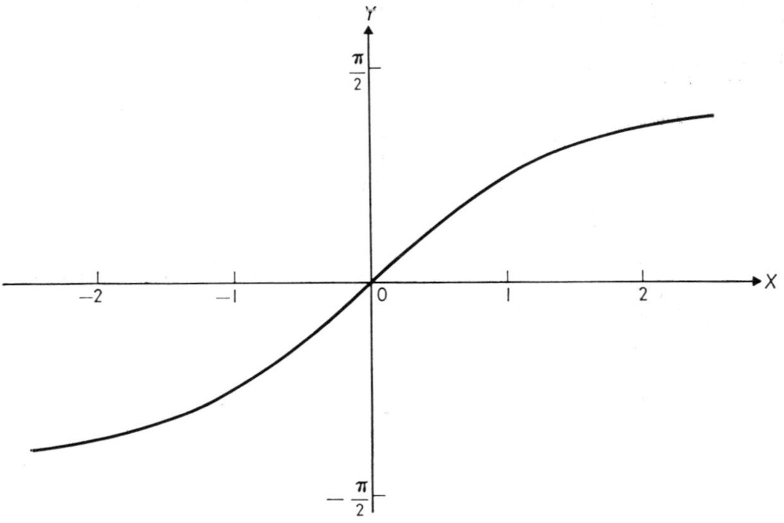

Figure 52-6

reflecting the graph of the Tangent function about the line whose equation is $y = x$.

Example 52-3. Calculate

$$\text{Tan}^{-1}\, x \Big|_{-\sqrt{3}/3}^{\sqrt{3}/3}.$$

Solution. We have

$$\begin{aligned} \text{Tan}^{-1}\, x \Big|_{-\sqrt{3}/3}^{\sqrt{3}/3} &= \text{Tan}^{-1}\,(\sqrt{3}/3) - \text{Tan}^{-1}\,(-\sqrt{3}/3) \\ &= \pi/6 - (-\pi/6) \\ &= \pi/3. \end{aligned}$$

Problems 52

1. Evaluate:
   (a) $\operatorname{Sin}^{-1} x \Big|_{1/2}^{1}$ (b) $\operatorname{Cos}^{-1} t \Big|_{1/2}^{1}$
   (c) $\operatorname{Tan}^{-1} u \Big|_{-1}^{1}$ (d) $\operatorname{Sin}^{-1} x \Big|_{-\sqrt{2}/2}^{\sqrt{3}/2}$
   (e) $\operatorname{Tan}^{-1} x \Big|_{.4228}^{.6841}$ (f) $\operatorname{Sin}^{-1} (\sin x) \Big|_{\pi/2}^{3\pi/2}$
2. Verify the following equalities. (We will need results (a) and (b) in the next section.)
   (a) $\sin (\operatorname{Cos}^{-1} x) = \sqrt{1 - x^2}$
   (b) $\sec^2 (\operatorname{Tan}^{-1} x) = 1 + x^2$
   (c) $\operatorname{Tan}^{-1} x = \operatorname{Sin}^{-1} (x/\sqrt{1 + x^2})$
   (d) $\tan (\frac{1}{2} \operatorname{Cos}^{-1} x) = \sqrt{1 - x}/\sqrt{1 + x}$
3. Use the graphs in this section to determine which number is larger.
   (a) x or $\operatorname{Sin} x$ (b) x or $\operatorname{Sin}^{-1} x$
   (c) $\operatorname{Tan}^{-1} x$ or $\operatorname{Sin}^{-1} x$
4. From the graphs in this section determine whether the following numbers are positive or negative.
   (a) $D_x \operatorname{Sin}^{-1} x$ (b) $D_x \operatorname{Cos}^{-1} x$
   (c) $D_x \operatorname{Tan}^{-1} x$ (d) $D_x(\operatorname{Cos}^{-1} x)^2$
   (e) $D_x(\operatorname{Sin}^{-1} x)^2$ for $x < 0$ (f) $D_x(\operatorname{Tan}^{-1} x)^2$ for $x < 0$.
5. Use the graphs of the inverse trigonometric functions to help you evaluate the following integrals.
   (a) $\int_0^1 \operatorname{Sin}^{-1} x \, dx$ (b) $\int_0^1 \operatorname{Cos}^{-1} t \, dt$
   (c) $\int_0^{1/2} \operatorname{Sin}^{-1} u \, du$
6. Prove that $\operatorname{Arctan} (-x) = -\operatorname{Arctan} x$.
7. Solve for t: $\operatorname{Arctan} \frac{1}{3} + \operatorname{Arctan} \frac{1}{2} = \operatorname{Arcsin} t$.
8. The **Arccotangent function** is defined as follows: $\boldsymbol{x = \operatorname{Arccot} y = \operatorname{Cot}^{-1} y}$ if, and only if, (i) $\boldsymbol{\cot x = y}$ and (ii) $\boldsymbol{0 < x < \pi}$. Show that if $x > 0$, then $\operatorname{Arctan} x = \operatorname{Arccot} (1/x)$.

53. Differentiation of the Inverse Trigonometric Functions

We can find the derivatives of $\operatorname{Sin}^{-1} x$, $\operatorname{Cos}^{-1} x$, and $\operatorname{Tan}^{-1} x$ by using the facts that we learned in Section 48. In that section we learned that if a function f has an inverse f^{-1}, then

$$y = f^{-1}(x) \quad \text{if, and only if,} \quad x = f(y);$$

and

$$D_x y = \frac{1}{D_y x}.$$

First, let us suppose that f is the Sine function. Then f^{-1} is the Arcsine function and

$$y = \operatorname{Sin}^{-1} x \quad \text{if, and only if,} \quad x = \sin y,\ -\pi/2 \leq y \leq \pi/2.$$

From this last equation we see that $D_y x = \cos y$, and hence

$$D_x y = \frac{1}{D_y x} = \frac{1}{\cos y}.$$

Therefore,

$$D_x \operatorname{Sin}^{-1} x = \frac{1}{\cos(\operatorname{Sin}^{-1} x)}.$$

But $\cos(\operatorname{Sin}^{-1} x) = \sqrt{1 - x^2}$ (see Example 52-2), so we obtain the formula

(53-1) $$\boldsymbol{D_x \operatorname{Sin}^{-1} x = \frac{1}{\sqrt{1 - x^2}}}.$$

Let us incorporate this differentiation formula for the Arcsine function into the Chain Rule Equation. Thus if $y = \operatorname{Sin}^{-1} u$, where $u = g(x)$, then $D_u y = \dfrac{1}{\sqrt{1 - u^2}}$, and the Chain Rule Equation $D_x y = D_u y D_x u$ becomes

(53-2) $$\boldsymbol{D_x \operatorname{Sin}^{-1} u = \frac{D_x u}{\sqrt{1 - u^2}}}.$$

Example 53-1. Show that if a is any positive number,

(53-3) $$D_x \operatorname{Sin}^{-1} \frac{x}{a} = \frac{1}{\sqrt{a^2 - x^2}}.$$

Solution. If we replace u with x/a in Formula 53-3, we have

$$D_x \operatorname{Sin}^{-1} \frac{x}{a} = \frac{D_x(x/a)}{\sqrt{1 - (x/a)^2}} = \frac{1}{a\sqrt{1 - (x/a)^2}} = \frac{1}{\sqrt{a^2 - x^2}}.$$

At what point did we use the assumption that a is positive?

Now let us suppose that f is the Cosine function. Then f^{-1} is the Arccosine function and

$$y = \operatorname{Cos}^{-1} x \quad \text{if, and only if,} \quad x = \cos y,\ 0 \leq y \leq \pi.$$

Thus $D_y x = -\sin y$, and so

$$D_x y = \frac{1}{D_y x} = -\frac{1}{\sin y}.$$

Therefore,

$$D_x \operatorname{Cos}^{-1} x = -\frac{1}{\sin(\operatorname{Cos}^{-1} x)}.$$

It is easy to show (see Question 2a of Problems 52) that $\sin(\operatorname{Cos}^{-1} x) = \sqrt{1 - x^2}$, so we get the formula

(53-4) $$\boldsymbol{D_x \operatorname{Cos}^{-1} x = -\frac{1}{\sqrt{1 - x^2}}}.$$

When we incorporate this formula into the Chain Rule Equation, we obtain the differentiation formula

(53-5) $$\boldsymbol{D_x \operatorname{Cos}^{-1} u = -\frac{D_x u}{\sqrt{1 - u^2}}}.$$

Example 53-2. From Equations 53-1 and 53-4 we see that $D_x \operatorname{Cos}^{-1} x = -D_x \operatorname{Sin}^{-1} x$. Does this equation imply that $\operatorname{Cos}^{-1} x$ is merely the negative of $\operatorname{Sin}^{-1} x$?

Solution. No; $\operatorname{Cos}^{-1} x$ and $-\operatorname{Sin}^{-1} x$ have the same derivative, but as we know from Theorem 21-5 this fact merely implies that there is a number c such that

$$\operatorname{Cos}^{-1} x = -\operatorname{Sin}^{-1} x + c.$$

To find c, we set $x = 0$. Thus $\operatorname{Cos}^{-1} 0 = -\operatorname{Sin}^{-1} 0 + c$. But we know (see Figs. 52-2 and 52-4, for instance) that $\operatorname{Cos}^{-1} 0 = \pi/2$ and $\operatorname{Sin}^{-1} 0 = 0$. Hence $c = \pi/2$, and we obtain the equation $\operatorname{Cos}^{-1} x = \pi/2 - \operatorname{Sin}^{-1} x$. You can also verify this equation by referring to the definitions of the Arccosine and Arcsine functions.

Finally, let us suppose that f is the Tangent function. Then f^{-1} is the Arctangent function, and

$$y = \operatorname{Tan}^{-1} x \quad \text{if, and only if,} \quad x = \tan y, \ -\pi/2 < y < \pi/2.$$

Thus $D_y x = \sec^2 y$, and so

$$D_x y = \frac{1}{D_y x} = \frac{1}{\sec^2 y} = \frac{1}{\sec^2(\operatorname{Tan}^{-1} x)}.$$

Using the fact that $\sec^2(\operatorname{Tan}^{-1} x) = 1 + x^2$ (see Question 2b of Problems 52), we obtain the formula

(53-6) $$\boldsymbol{D_x \operatorname{Tan}^{-1} x = \frac{1}{1 + x^2}}.$$

When we incorporate this formula into the Chain Rule Equation, we obtain the differentiation formula

$$(53\text{-}7) \qquad \boldsymbol{D_x \operatorname{Tan}^{-1} u = \frac{D_x u}{1 + u^2}}.$$

Example 53-3. Show that if $a \neq 0$, then

$$(53\text{-}8) \qquad D_x \operatorname{Tan}^{-1} \frac{x}{a} = \frac{a}{a^2 + x^2}.$$

Solution. When we replace u with x/a, Formula 53-7 becomes

$$D_x \operatorname{Tan}^{-1} \frac{x}{a} = \frac{1/a}{1 + (x/a)^2} = \frac{a}{a^2 + x^2}.$$

Example 53-4. Find $D_x[\operatorname{Tan}^{-1} (\cot x)]$.

Solution. If we replace u with $\cot x$, Formula 53-7 becomes

$$D_x[\operatorname{Tan}^{-1} (\cot x)] = \frac{D_x \cot x}{1 + \cot^2 x} = \frac{-\csc^2 x}{1 + \cot^2 x}.$$

Now we use the trigonometric identity $1 + \cot^2 x = \csc^2 x$, and we see that

$$D_x[\operatorname{Tan}^{-1} (\cot x)] = -1.$$

It would be a good test of your understanding of the trigonometric

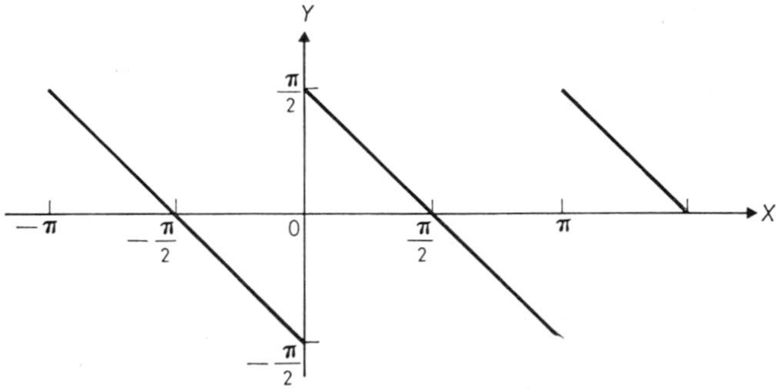

Figure 53-1

functions and the inverse trigonometric functions to verify that the graph of the equation $y = \operatorname{Tan}^{-1} (\cot x)$ is the one shown in Fig. 53-1.

Example 53-5. A searchlight 40 feet from the base of a building makes a spot 30 feet up on the side of the building. Approximately how much must the searchlight be rotated in order to raise the spot 1 foot?

Solution. Fig. 53-2 illustrates the situation; we are to find the angle α. Now

$$\tan(\theta + \alpha) = \tfrac{31}{40}$$

and

$$\tan\theta = \tfrac{3}{4},$$

so

$$\alpha = (\theta + \alpha) - \theta = \text{Tan}^{-1}\left(\tfrac{31}{40}\right) - \text{Tan}^{-1}\left(\tfrac{3}{4}\right).$$

If we let $f(x) = \text{Tan}^{-1}(x/40)$, then from Formula 53-8 with $a = 40$ we

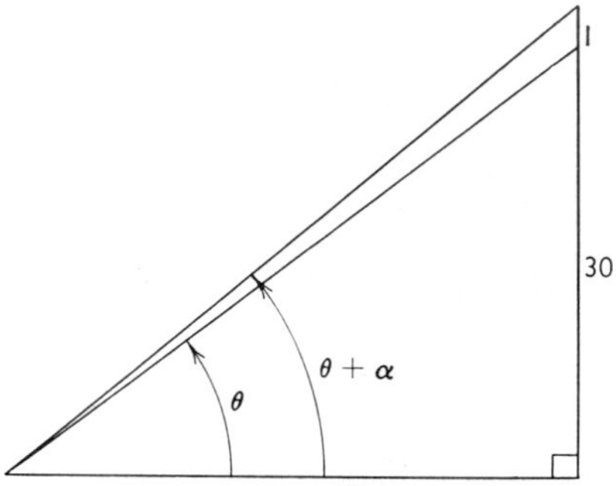

Figure 53-2

obtain $f'(x) = 40/(40^2 + x^2)$. Now we use Approximation Formula 29-2 to write

$$\alpha = f(31) - f(30) \approx 1 \cdot f'(30) = \frac{40}{40^2 + 30^2} = .016.$$

Thus the searchlight must be rotated upward approximately .016 radians, or .9°.

Problems 53

1. Find $D_x y$.
   (a) $y = \text{Arctan}\, ax^2$ (b) $y = \text{Sin}^{-1}\, x^2$
   (c) $y = \text{Arcsin}\, \sqrt{x}$ (d) $y = \text{Cos}^{-1}\, e^x$
   (e) $y = \text{Tan}^{-1}\sqrt{x - 1}$ (f) $y = \text{Arcsin}(\cos x)$
   (g) $y = \ln(\text{Cos}^{-1} x)$ (h) $y = (\text{Tan}^{-1} x^2)^3$
2. Use implicit differentiation to calculate $D_x y$ from the equation given.
   (a) $\text{Sin}^{-1} x + \text{Sin}^{-1} y = \pi/2$
   (b) $\text{Tan}^{-1} x + \text{Tan}^{-1} y = \pi/2$
   (c) $\text{Sin}^{-1} x + \text{Tan}^{-1} y = 0.$
3. Let $y = \text{Arctan}\, \dfrac{1}{x}\cdot$ Compute $D_x y$ and $D_x^2 y$, and use this information to sketch the graph of the equation.

4. Compute D_xy and sketch the graph of the equation.
(a) $y = \text{Sin}^{-1}(\sin x)$ (b) $y = \sin(\text{Sin}^{-1} x)$
(c) $y = \text{Cos}^{-1}(\cos x)$ (d) $y = \text{Tan}^{-1}(\tan x)$
5. Verify the following identities. Would they still be true if we "canceled" the symbol D_x?
(a) $D_x \text{Sin}^{-1}(-x) = -D_x \text{Sin}^{-1} x$
(b) $D_x \text{Cos}^{-1}(-x) = -D_x \text{Cos}^{-1} x$
(c) $D_x \text{Tan}^{-1}\left(\frac{2x}{1-x^2}\right) = D_x(2 \tan^{-1} x)$
(d) $D_x \text{Cos}^{-1} \frac{\sqrt{1-x^2} - x\sqrt{3}}{2} = D_x \text{Sin}^{-1} x$
6. Let $y = \text{Sin}^{-1}(\cos x) + \text{Cos}^{-1}(\sin x)$. Find D_xy and graph the equation for $0 \leq x \leq 2\pi$.
7. A statue 7 feet high is placed on a pedestal so that the base of the statue is 9 feet above your eye level. How far back should you stand from the base of the statue in order to get the "best" view?
8. Two guy wires are to be fastened at the same point P h feet above the ground on a pole so that the pole and both wires are in the same vertical plane. One wire is to be fastened to the ground x feet from the base of the pole and the other wire is to be fastened on the same side of the pole and $2x$ feet from its base. Determine x so that the angle between the wires at the point P is a maximum.
9. Find: $\lim_{h \to 0} \frac{\text{Sin}^{-1} h}{h}$. (Write out the definition of $f'(0)$ if $f(x) = \text{Sin}^{-1} x$.)
10. Use the graph of the Arcsine function to show that:

$$\int_0^x \text{Sin}^{-1} t\, dt = x \text{Sin}^{-1} x - \int_0^{\text{Sin}^{-1} x} \sin t\, dt$$
$$= x \text{Sin}^{-1} x + \cos(\text{Sin}^{-1} x) - 1$$
$$= x \text{Sin}^{-1} x + \sqrt{1-x^2} - 1.$$

Verify this equation by differentiation.
11. Graph the equation $y = \text{Arcsin}(\cos x)$ (see 1(f)).
12. Sketch the graph of the equation $y = x \text{Sin}^{-1} x$. Discuss the concavity of the graph.

54. Integration Formulas That Involve Inverse Trigonometric Functions

According to the Fundamental Theorem of Calculus, we can write an integration formula $\int f(x)\, dx = F(x)$ for each differentiation formula $D_xF(x) = f(x)$. Thus the Differentiation Formulas 53-3 and 53-8 lead to the integration formulas

$$\text{(54-1)} \quad \int \frac{1}{\sqrt{a^2 - x^2}}\, dx = \text{Sin}^{-1} \frac{x}{a} \quad (a > 0)$$

and

$$\int \frac{1}{a^2 + x^2}\,dx = \frac{1}{a}\,\mathrm{Tan}^{-1}\frac{x}{a} \qquad (a \neq 0). \tag{54-2}$$

Notice that there is a factor $\frac{1}{a}$ on the right-hand side of Equation 54-2 that is not present in Equation 54-1, and that we require a to be positive in Equation 54-1 but not in Equation 54-2.

Example 54-1. Evaluate the integral

$$\int_{-3}^{3} \frac{1}{\sqrt{12 - x^2}}\,dx.$$

Solution. We may use Equation 54-1 with $a = \sqrt{12} = 2\sqrt{3}$ to find that

$$\int_{-3}^{3} \frac{1}{\sqrt{12 - x^2}}\,dx = \mathrm{Sin}^{-1}\frac{x}{2\sqrt{3}}\Big|_{-3}^{3} = \mathrm{Sin}^{-1}\frac{\sqrt{3}}{2} - \mathrm{Sin}^{-1}\left(-\frac{\sqrt{3}}{2}\right)$$
$$= \frac{\pi}{3} - \left(-\frac{\pi}{3}\right) = \frac{2\pi}{3}.$$

Example 54-2. Use Simpson's Rule with $n = 4$ to find π from the equation

$$\frac{\pi}{4} = \int_{0}^{1} \frac{1}{1 + x^2}\,dx. \tag{54-3}$$

Solution. First, let us verify that Equation 54-3 is correct. From Formula 54-2,

$$\int_{0}^{1} \frac{1}{1 + x^2}\,dx = \mathrm{Tan}^{-1}\,x\Big|_{0}^{1} = \frac{\pi}{4} - 0 = \frac{\pi}{4}.$$

Now we will approximate the integral by Simpson's Rule. We divide the interval [0, 1] into four subintervals by the points $x_0 = 0$, $x_1 = \frac{1}{4}$, $x_2 = \frac{1}{2}$, $x_3 = \frac{3}{4}$, and $x_4 = 1$. The corresponding numbers obtained from the equation $y = 1/(1 + x^2)$ are $y_0 = 1$, $y_1 = \frac{16}{17}$, $y_2 = \frac{4}{5}$, $y_3 = \frac{16}{25}$, $y_4 = \frac{1}{2}$. In this case, $h = \frac{1}{4}$, and Simpson's Rule (Equation 39-8) gives us

$$\tfrac{1}{4}\pi \approx (\tfrac{1}{12})[1 + 4(\tfrac{16}{17}) + 2(\tfrac{4}{5}) + 4(\tfrac{16}{25}) + \tfrac{1}{2}] = .785392.$$

Hence $\pi \approx 3.14157$. Since the value of π, correct to 5 decimal places, is 3.14159, we see that our approximation is a good one.

Example 54-3. Verify the following integration formula.

$$\int \sqrt{a^2 - x^2}\,dx = \frac{1}{2}\left[x\sqrt{a^2 - x^2} + a^2\,\mathrm{Sin}^{-1}\frac{x}{a}\right] \qquad (a > 0) \tag{54-4}$$

Solution. To verify an integration formula, we must differentiate the expression on the right-hand side and obtain the integrand. We first differentiate $x\sqrt{a^2 - x^2}$:

$$\begin{aligned} D_x(x\sqrt{a^2 - x^2}) &= (D_x x)\sqrt{a^2 - x^2} + x\, D_x \sqrt{a^2 - x^2} \\ &= \sqrt{a^2 - x^2} - x^2/\sqrt{a^2 - x^2} \\ &= (a^2 - 2x^2)/\sqrt{a^2 - x^2}. \end{aligned}$$

From Formula 53-3 we see that

$$D_x[a^2 \operatorname{Sin}^{-1}(x/a)] = a^2/\sqrt{a^2 - x^2}.$$

Thus

$$\begin{aligned} D_x \frac{1}{2}\left[x\sqrt{a^2 - x^2} + a^2 \operatorname{Sin}^{-1}\frac{x}{a}\right] &= \frac{1}{2}\left(\frac{a^2 - 2x^2}{\sqrt{a^2 - x^2}} + \frac{a^2}{\sqrt{a^2 - x^2}}\right) \\ &= \sqrt{a^2 - x^2}, \end{aligned}$$

and Formula 54-4 is verified.

Example 54-4. Derive a formula for the area of the smaller region cut from a circle whose radius is r by a chord d units from the center of the circle.

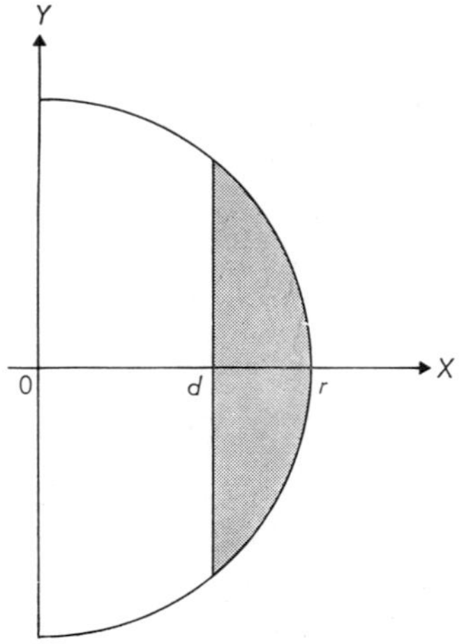

Figure 54-1

Solution. Let us choose our circle with the origin as its center so that its equation is $x^2 + y^2 = r^2$. Then we will choose our chord to lie along the line $x = d$, where $d > 0$ (see Fig. 54-1). In view of the symmetry of the circle, we see that the area we are seeking is given by the equation

$$A = 2\int_d^r \sqrt{r^2 - x^2}\,dx$$

We use Formula 54-4 to evaluate the integral:

$$\begin{aligned} A &= \left[x\sqrt{r^2 - x^2} + r^2 \operatorname{Sin}^{-1}\frac{x}{r}\right]\Bigg|_d^r \\ &= r^2 \operatorname{Sin}^{-1} 1 - d\sqrt{r^2 - d^2} - r^2 \operatorname{Sin}^{-1}\frac{d}{r} \\ &= \frac{\pi r^2}{2} - d\sqrt{r^2 - d^2} - r^2 \operatorname{Sin}^{-1}\frac{d}{r}. \end{aligned}$$

Problems 54

1. Find the area of the region that is bounded by the circle $x^2 + y^2 = 25$ and the lines $x = -3$ and $x = 4$.

2. Find the area of the region under the curve $y = 10/(9 + x^2)$ and above the interval $[-\sqrt{3}, \sqrt{3}]$.

3. Find the mean value of the function f on the indicated interval.
(a) $f(x) = 3/\sqrt{12 - x^2}$, $[-3, 3]$
(b) $f(x) = 5/\sqrt{8 - x^2}$, $[0, 2]$
(c) $f(x) = 7/(3 + x^2)$, $[-1, 1]$
(d) $f(x) = 7/(3 + x^2)$, $[0, 3]$
(e) $f(x) = 1/(4 + x^2)$, $[-1, 1]$

4. Let x be a number in the interval $(0, \pi/2)$. Compute:
(a) $\displaystyle\int_{\sin x}^{\cos x} \frac{1}{\sqrt{1 - t^2}}\,dt$ (b) $\displaystyle\int_{\cot x}^{\tan x} \frac{1}{1 + t^2}\,dt$

5. Show that for any numbers a and b the area of the region bounded by the graph of the equation $y = 1/(1 + x^2)$, the X-axis, and the lines $x = a$ and $x = b$ is less than π.

6. The region bounded by the graph of the equation $y = 1/\sqrt{1 + x^2}$, the line $x = 1$, and the coordinate axes is rotated about the X-axis. What is the volume of the resulting solid of revolution?

7. Find the area of the region interior to the ellipse $x^2/16 + y^2/9 = 1$ and to the right of the line $x = 2$.

8. The equation $f(x) = 1/\sqrt{1 - x^2}$ defines a function f such that if b is a number between 0 and 1 but "close" to 1, then $f(b)$ is a large number. Show that the mean value of f on the interval $[0, b]$ is a number close to $\pi/2$.

9. Draw the graph of the equation $y = 1/\sqrt[4]{1 - x^2}$. The region bounded by this graph, the X-axis, and the lines $x = a$ and $x = b$, where $-1 < a < b < 1$, is rotated about the X-axis. Show that the volume of the solid obtained is less than π^2.

10. The region bounded by the graph of the equation $x\sqrt{4+y^2} = 1$, the coordinate axes, and the line $y = 100$ is rotated about the Y-axis. Find, approximately, the volume of the solid thus obtained.

55. The Hyperbolic Functions

Certain combinations of e^x and e^{-x} occur so often in mathematical applications that they are used to define new functions. The **hyperbolic cosine** function and the **hyperbolic sine** function are defined by the equations

(55-1) $$\cosh x = \frac{e^x + e^{-x}}{2}$$

and

(55-2) $$\sinh x = \frac{e^x - e^{-x}}{2}.$$

These functions are called "hyperbolic" functions because their values are related to the coordinates of the points of a hyperbola in somewhat the same way that the values of the trigonometric functions are related to the coordinates of points of a circle. We won't go into the details of this relationship, but the following example will give you the essential idea.

Example 55-1. Show that for any number t

(55-3) $$\cosh^2 t - \sinh^2 t = 1.$$

Solution. According to our definitions of the hyperbolic functions,

$$\cosh^2 t - \sinh^2 t = \left(\frac{e^t + e^{-t}}{2}\right)^2 - \left(\frac{e^t - e^{-t}}{2}\right)^2.$$

It is a matter of simple algebra to expand the terms on the right side of this equation and see that the resulting number is 1. Equation 55-3 tells us that the point $(\cosh t, \sinh t)$ belongs to the hyperbola whose equation is $x^2 - y^2 = 1$, just as the point $(\cos t, \sin t)$ belongs to the circle whose equation is $x^2 + y^2 = 1$.

The remaining hyperbolic functions can be defined in terms of the hyperbolic sine and cosine functions as follows:

(55-4) $$\tanh x = \frac{\sinh x}{\cosh x} = \frac{e^x - e^{-x}}{e^x + e^{-x}},$$

(55-5) $$\coth x = \frac{1}{\tanh x} = \frac{e^x + e^{-x}}{e^x - e^{-x}}$$

(55-6) $$\operatorname{sech} x = \frac{1}{\cosh x} = \frac{2}{e^x + e^{-x}}$$

(55-7) $$\operatorname{csch} x = \frac{1}{\sinh x} = \frac{2}{e^x - e^{-x}}.$$

Figures 55-1, 55-2, and 55-3 show the graphs of the hyperbolic cosine, sine, and tangent functions. These functions are tabulated in Table III.

The values of the hyperbolic functions satisfy many identities similar to those satisfied by the trigonometric functions. In addition to Equa-

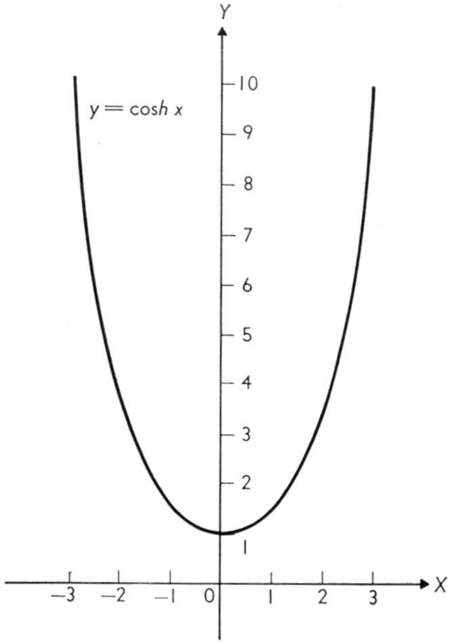

Figure 55-1

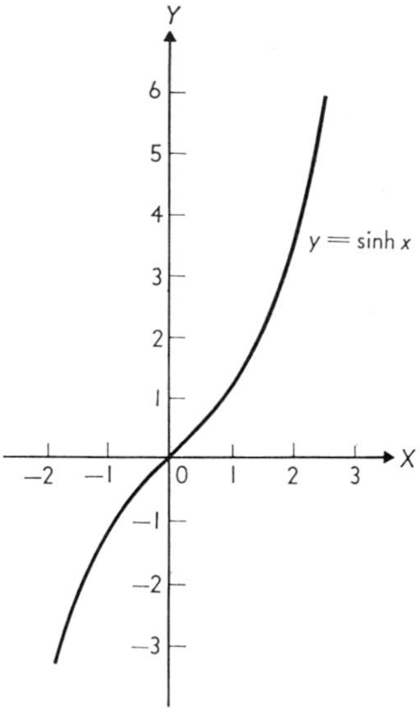

Figure 55-2

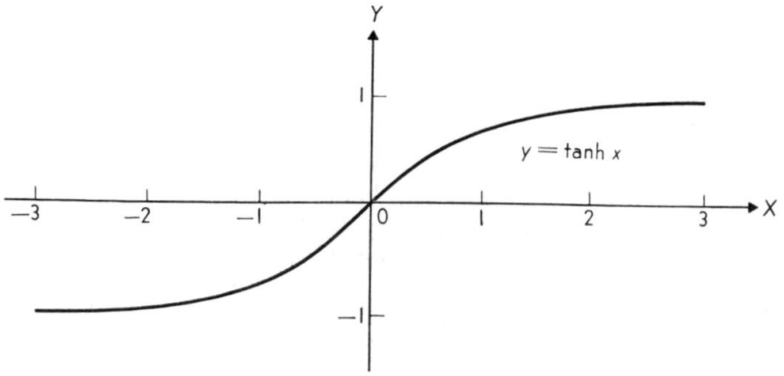

Figure 55-3

tion 55-3, which is a fundamental identity, we have:

(55-8) $$\mathbf{1 - \tanh^2 x = \operatorname{sech}^2 x,}$$

(55-9) $$\mathbf{\coth^2 x - 1 = \operatorname{csch}^2 x,}$$

(55-10) $$\mathbf{\sinh (u + v) = \sinh u \cosh v + \cosh u \sinh v,}$$

(55-11) $$\mathbf{\cosh (u + v) = \cosh u \cosh v + \sinh u \sinh v.}$$

These identities can be verified by straightforward algebraic manipulation.

Example 55-2. Find expressions for $\sinh 2x$ and $\cosh 2x$.

Solution. By setting $u = x$ and $v = x$ in Equations 55-10 and 55-11, we obtain the equations

(55-12) $$\mathbf{\sinh 2x = 2 \sinh x \cosh x}$$

and

(55-13) $$\mathbf{\cosh 2x = \cosh^2 x + \sinh^2 x.}$$

To find the derivatives of $\cosh x$, $\sinh x$, $\tanh x$, and so on, we make use of our defining equations. Thus

$$D_x \cosh x = D_x \left(\frac{e^x + e^{-x}}{2} \right) = \frac{D_x e^x + D_x e^{-x}}{2}$$
$$= \frac{e^x - e^{-x}}{2} = \sinh x.$$

Thus we find that

(55-14) $$\mathbf{D_x \cosh x = \sinh x.}$$

When we incorporate this differentiation formula into the Chain Rule Equation $D_x y = D_u y D_x u$, we obtain the formula

(55-15) $$\mathbf{D_x \cosh u = \sinh u\, D_x u.}$$

We will leave to you, in the problems at the end of this section, the verification of the following differentiation formulas:

(55-16) $$\mathbf{D_x \sinh u = \cosh u\, D_x u,}$$

(55-17) $$\mathbf{D_x \tanh u = \operatorname{sech}^2 u\, D_x u,}$$

(55-18) $$\mathbf{D_x \coth u = -\operatorname{csch}^2 u\, D_x u,}$$

(55-19) $$\mathbf{D_x \operatorname{sech} u = -\operatorname{sech} u \tanh u\, D_x u,}$$

(55-20) $$\mathbf{D_x \operatorname{csch} u = -\operatorname{csch} u \coth u\, D_x u.}$$

Example 55-3. Compute $D_x \ln(\cosh x)$.

Solution. Using Formula 55-14 and the differentiation formula for the ln function, $D_x \ln u = \frac{D_x u}{u}$ with $u = \cosh x$, we have

$$D_x \ln(\cosh x) = \frac{D_x \cosh x}{\cosh x} = \frac{\sinh x}{\cosh x}.$$

Thus we obtain the formula

$$D_x \ln(\cosh x) = \tanh x. \tag{55-21}$$

Example 55-4. Show that the function defined by the equation

$$y = A \sinh kx + B \cosh kx$$

is a solution to the differential equation $y'' - k^2 y = 0$.

Solution. From Formulas 55-15 and 55-16, with $u = kx$, we see that

$$y' = Ak \cosh kx + Bk \sinh kx$$

and

$$y'' = Ak^2 \sinh kx + Bk^2 \cosh kx.$$

Thus

$$y'' = k^2 y, \quad \text{or in other words,} \quad y'' - k^2 y = 0.$$

Example 55-5. Show that the graph of the function defined by the equation

$$y = 8 \sinh x - 17 \cosh x$$

is concave down everywhere, and find the maximum value of the function.

Solution. We have

$$y' = 8 \cosh x - 17 \sinh x$$

and

$$y'' = 8 \sinh x - 17 \cosh x.$$

To show that our graph is concave down, we will show that $y'' < 0$; that is, that $8 \sinh x < 17 \cosh x$. This last inequality is equivalent to the inequality $\tanh x < \frac{17}{8}$, which is clearly true since (see Fig. 55-3) $\tanh x \leq 1$. At the maximum point of the graph, $y' = 0$; that is,

$$8 \cosh x = 17 \sinh x.$$

This equation is equivalent to the equation $\tanh x = \frac{8}{17}$, and we see from Fig. 55-3 that its solution is a number x_0 approximately equal to .5. The maximum value of our function is therefore

$$y_0 = 8 \sinh x_0 - 17 \cosh x_0,$$

and we will now proceed to calculate this number. First of all, $\tanh x_0 = \frac{8}{17}$, and therefore it follows from Equation 55-8 that $\cosh x_0 = \frac{17}{15}$. Now we have

$$\begin{aligned} y_0 &= 8 \sinh x_0 - 17 \cosh x_0 \\ &= \cosh x_0(8 \tanh x_0 - 17) \\ &= \tfrac{17}{15}[8(\tfrac{8}{17}) - 17] = -15. \end{aligned}$$

Corresponding to each of the differentiation formulas for the hyperbolic functions is an integration formula. Thus, corresponding to Formula 55-14 is the integration formula

(55-22) $$\int \sinh x \, dx = \cosh x.$$

Similarly, corresponding to the other differentiation formulas (with $u = x$) are the following integration formulas:

(55-23) $$\int \cosh x \, dx = \sinh x,$$

(55-24) $$\int \operatorname{sech}^2 x \, dx = \tanh x,$$

(55-25) $$\int \operatorname{csch}^2 x \, dx = -\coth x,$$

(55-26) $$\int \operatorname{sech} x \tanh x \, dx = -\operatorname{sech} x,$$

(55-27) $$\int \operatorname{csch} x \coth x \, dx = -\operatorname{csch} x.$$

Example 55-6. Find the area of the region in the first quadrant that is bounded by the graph of the equation $y = \cosh x$ and the line $x = 1$.

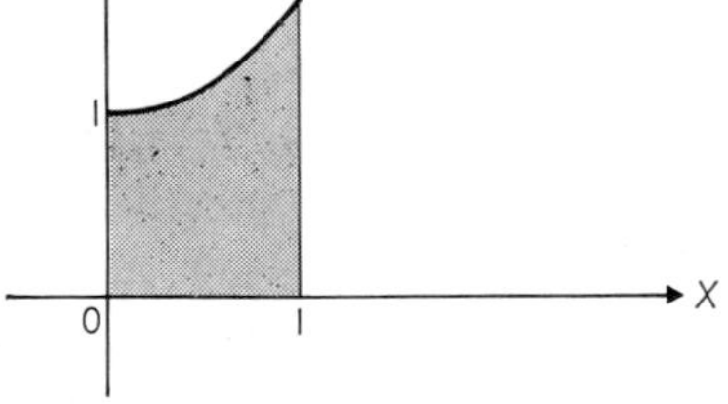

Figure 55-4

Solution. We are to find the area of the shaded region in Fig. 55-4, and therefore we must evaluate the integral $\int_0^1 \cosh x \, dx$. Using Integration Formula 55-23,

$$\begin{aligned} \int_0^1 \cosh x \, dx &= \sinh x \Big|_0^1 \\ &= \sinh 1 - \sinh 0 \\ &= \tfrac{1}{2}(e - 1/e) \approx 1.2. \end{aligned}$$

We can immediately state another integration formula from the Differentiation Formula 55-21 that we found in Example 55-3:

(55-28) $$\int \tanh x \, dx = \ln (\cosh x).$$

We will leave the verification of the following integration formula for the problems:

$$\int \coth x\,dx = \ln|\sinh x|. \tag{55-29}$$

Problems 55

1. Show that:
   (a) $\sinh(u - v) = \sinh u \cosh v - \cosh u \sinh v$.
   (b) $\cosh(u - v) = \cosh u \cosh v - \sinh u \sinh v$.
   (c) $\tanh(u + v) = (\tanh u + \tanh v)/(1 + \tanh u \tanh v)$
2. (a) Verify Formula 55-16.
   (b) Verify Formula 55-17.
   (c) Verify Formula 55-18.
   (d) Verify Formula 55-19.
   (e) Verify Formula 55-20.
3. Find $D_x y$.
   (a) $y = \cosh e^x$
   (b) $y = e^{\cosh x}$
   (c) $y = \sinh(1/x)$
   (d) $y = \sinh^2 x^2$
   (e) $y = \tanh x^2$
   (f) $y = \tanh(\tan x)$
   (g) $y = \text{sech}^2 x$
   (h) $y = \ln(\text{sech}\, x)$
   (i) $y = \ln(\text{csch}\, x)$
   (j) $y = \text{sech}(\ln x)$
   (k) $y = \text{csch}(\ln x)$
   (l) $y = \sinh(\text{csch}\, x)$
4. Suppose that $a \neq 0$. Show that:
   (a) $\int \sinh ax\,dx = \frac{1}{a}\cosh ax$
   (b) $\int \cosh ax\,dx = \frac{1}{a}\sinh ax$.
5. Use the definitions of the hyperbolic functions to show that:
   (a) $\int \cosh^2 x\,dx = \frac{\sinh 2x}{4} + \frac{x}{2}$
   (b) $\int \sinh x \cosh x\,dx = \frac{\cosh 2x}{4}$
6. Show that for each number u, $\cosh u + \sinh u = e^u$. Use this fact to verify the identity
$$(\cosh x + \sinh x)^n = \cosh nx + \sinh nx.$$
7. What is the volume of the solid that is generated by rotating the region of Example 55-6 about the X-axis?
8. Show that if $y = e^{ax}\sinh bx$, then y satisfies the differential equation $y'' - 2ay' + (a^2 - b^2)y = 0$.
9. Verify Formula 55-29.
10. Show that $\text{Tan}^{-1}(\sinh x) = \text{Sin}^{-1}(\tanh x)$.
11. Show that $D_x(2\,\text{Tan}^{-1} e^x) = D_x \text{Tan}^{-1}(\sinh x)$. Does the equality hold if the D_x symbol is "canceled"?

12. State two integration formulas with sech x as the integrand. (Use the differentiation formulas of the preceding problem.)

56. Inverse Hyperbolic Functions

You can see from Figures 55-1, 55-2, and 55-3 that the hyperbolic sine and hyperbolic tangent functions have inverses but that the hyperbolic cosine function doesn't. We may restrict the domain of the hyperbolic cosine function to obtain a new function with an inverse in much the same way that we restricted the domains of the trigonometric functions to obtain functions with inverses. Thus we define the **Hyperbolic Cosine** function as the function whose domain is the interval $[0, \infty]$ and whose rule of correspondence is $y = \cosh x$. This function has an inverse. In a similar manner we may restrict the domain of the hyperbolic secant function in order to obtain the **Hyperbolic Secant** function that has an inverse. The inverse hyperbolic functions are thus defined by the following equations.

(56-1) $\quad \boldsymbol{y = \sinh^{-1} x}$ if, and only if, $\boldsymbol{x = \sinh y}$.

(56-2) $\quad \boldsymbol{y = \mathrm{Cosh}^{-1} x}$ if, and only if, $\boldsymbol{x = \cosh y}$ and $y \geq 0$.

(56-3) $\quad \boldsymbol{y = \tanh^{-1} x}$ if, and only if, $\boldsymbol{x = \tanh y}$.

(56-4) $\quad \boldsymbol{y = \coth^{-1} x}$ if, and only if, $\boldsymbol{x = \coth y}$.

(56-5) $\quad \boldsymbol{y = \mathrm{Sech}^{-1} x}$ if, and only if, $\boldsymbol{x = \mathrm{sech}\, y}$ and $y \geq 0$.

(56-6) $\quad \boldsymbol{y = \mathrm{csch}^{-1} x}$ if, and only if, $\boldsymbol{x = \mathrm{csch}\, y}$.

Since the hyperbolic functions are defined in terms of exponentials with base e, it is not surprising that we can express the values of the inverse hyperbolic functions in terms of logarithms with base e.

Example 56-1. Show that

(56-7)
$$\boldsymbol{\tanh^{-1} x = \frac{1}{2} \ln \left(\frac{1+x}{1-x}\right), \quad |x| < 1.}$$

Solution. If we let $y = \tanh^{-1} x$, then

$$x = \tanh y = \frac{e^y - e^{-y}}{e^y + e^{-y}}.$$

Thus

$$xe^y + xe^{-y} = e^y - e^{-y},$$

and so

$$(x - 1)e^y = -(1 + x)e^{-y}.$$

When we multiply both sides of this equation by e^y, we obtain

$$(x - 1)e^{2y} = -(1 + x),$$

and thus

$$e^{2y} = (1 + x)/(1 - x).$$

Now we take the logarithm of both sides and remember that $y = \tanh^{-1} x$ to obtain Equation 56-7.

By proceeding as we did in the preceding example, you can verify that the following formulas are valid:

$$\text{(56-8)} \qquad \boldsymbol{\sinh^{-1} x = \ln (x + \sqrt{x^2 + 1}),}$$

$$\text{(56-9)} \qquad \boldsymbol{\operatorname{Cosh}^{-1} x = \ln (x + \sqrt{x^2 - 1}),}$$

$$\text{(56-10)} \qquad \boldsymbol{\coth^{-1} x = \frac{1}{2} \ln \left(\frac{x + 1}{x - 1}\right), \quad |x| > 1.}$$

To find differentiation formulas for the inverse hyperbolic functions, we may either use the rules for finding derived functions of inverse functions that we developed in Section 48, or we may differentiate the logarithmic expressions for the inverse hyperbolic functions. These two methods are illustrated in the following example.

Example 56-2. Show in two ways that

$$\text{(56-11)} \qquad \boldsymbol{D_x \sinh^{-1} x = \frac{1}{\sqrt{x^2 + 1}}.}$$

Solution. *Method 1.* By definition, $y = \sinh^{-1} x$ if, and only if, $x = \sinh y$. Thus $D_y x = \cosh y = \sqrt{\sinh^2 y + 1} = \sqrt{x^2 + 1}$ and hence

$$D_x y = 1/D_y x = 1/\sqrt{x^2 + 1}.$$

Method 2. According to Equation 56-8,

$$\begin{aligned} D_x \sinh^{-1} x &= D_x \ln (x + \sqrt{x^2 + 1}) \\ &= \frac{D_x(x + \sqrt{x^2 + 1})}{x + \sqrt{x^2 + 1}} \\ &= \frac{1 + \dfrac{x}{\sqrt{x^2 + 1}}}{x + \sqrt{x^2 + 1}} \\ &= \frac{1}{\sqrt{x^2 + 1}}, \end{aligned}$$

and so we again have Equation 56-11.

When we incorporate Equation 56-11 into the Chain Rule Equation $D_x y = D_u y D_x u$, we obtain the equation

$$(56\text{-}12) \qquad \mathbf{D_x \sinh^{-1} u = \frac{D_x u}{\sqrt{u^2+1}}.}$$

The following differentiation formulas for the other inverse hyperbolic functions may be obtained in the same way that we obtained Equation 56-12:

$$(56\text{-}13) \qquad \mathbf{D_x \operatorname{Cosh}^{-1} u = \frac{D_x u}{\sqrt{u^2-1}}} \qquad (u > 1),$$

$$(56\text{-}14) \qquad \mathbf{D_x \tanh^{-1} u = \frac{D_x u}{1-u^2}} \qquad (|u| < 1),$$

$$(56\text{-}15) \qquad \mathbf{D_x \coth^{-1} u = \frac{D_x u}{1-u^2}} \qquad (|u| > 1),$$

$$(56\text{-}16) \qquad \mathbf{D_x \operatorname{Sech}^{-1} u = \frac{-D_x u}{u\sqrt{1-u^2}}} \qquad (0 < u < 1),$$

$$(56\text{-}17) \qquad \mathbf{D_x \operatorname{csch}^{-1} u = \frac{-D_x u}{|u|\sqrt{1+u^2}}.}$$

These differentiation formulas enable us to state some integration formulas. For example, let us use Formula 56-12 to verify the integration formula

$$(56\text{-}18) \qquad \mathbf{\int \frac{1}{\sqrt{x^2+a^2}}\,dx = \sinh^{-1}\frac{x}{a} \quad (a > 0).}$$

To verify this formula, we use Formula 56-12 with $u = x/a$:

$$D_x \sinh^{-1}\frac{x}{a} = \frac{D_x(x/a)}{\sqrt{(x/a)^2+1}} = \frac{1}{a\sqrt{(x/a)^2+1}} = \frac{1}{\sqrt{x^2+a^2}}.$$

(Where did we use the fact that $a > 0$?)

In exactly the same way we can use Differentiation Formula 56-13 to verify the integration formula

$$(56\text{-}19) \qquad \mathbf{\int \frac{1}{\sqrt{x^2-a^2}}\,dx = \operatorname{Cosh}^{-1}\frac{x}{a} \quad (0 < a < x).}$$

Differentiation Formulas 56-14 and 56-15 enable us to verify the integration formulas

$$(56\text{-}20) \qquad \mathbf{\int \frac{1}{a^2-x^2}\,dx = \begin{cases} \frac{1}{a}\tanh^{-1}\frac{x}{a} & \text{if } |x| < |a|, \\ \frac{1}{a}\coth^{-1}\frac{x}{a} & \text{if } |x| > |a|. \end{cases}}$$

Equation 56-7 shows us the relation between the inverse hyperbolic tangent and the natural logarithm, and we could use such equations, together with Equations 56-20, to obtain the integration formula

$$\int \frac{1}{a^2 - x^2}\,dx = \frac{1}{2a} \ln \left| \frac{a+x}{a-x} \right|. \tag{56-21}$$

We can also verify this integration formula directly. In Section 50 we showed that $D_u \ln |u| = \frac{1}{u}$, and hence $D_x \ln |u| = \frac{D_x u}{u}$. Therefore,

$$\begin{aligned} D_x\left[\frac{1}{2a} \ln \left|\frac{a+x}{a-x}\right|\right] &= \frac{1}{2a} D_x[\ln |a+x| - \ln |a-x|] \\ &= \frac{1}{2a}\left[\frac{D_x(a+x)}{a+x} - \frac{D_x(a-x)}{a-x}\right] \\ &= \frac{1}{2a}\left[\frac{1}{a+x} + \frac{1}{a-x}\right] \\ &= \frac{1}{a^2 - x^2}, \end{aligned}$$

and this result verifies Integration Formula 56-21.

Problems 56

1. Graph the following equations.
   (a) $y = \sinh^{-1} x$ (b) $y = \text{Cosh}^{-1} x$
   (c) $y = \tanh^{-1} x$ (d) $y = \coth^{-1} x$
2. Use Tables II and III to verify that:
   (a) $\sinh^{-1} (\frac{3}{4}) = \ln 2$
   (b) $\tanh^{-1} .5 = (\frac{1}{2}) \ln [(1 + .5)/(1 - .5)]$
   (c) $\text{Cosh}^{-1} 2 = \ln (2 + \sqrt{2^2 - 1})$
   (d) $\coth^{-1} 3 = (\frac{1}{2}) \ln [(3 + 1)/(3 - 1)]$.
3. (a) Verify Formula 56-8. (b) Verify Formula 56-9.
   (c) Verify Formula 56-10. (d) Verify Formula 56-19.
4. Show that if $b > 1$, then $\sinh^{-1} \sqrt{b^2 - 1} = \text{Cosh}^{-1} b$.
5. Find $\lim_{h \to 0} \frac{\sinh^{-1} h}{h}$.
6. Compute $D_x y$.
   (a) $y = \sinh^{-1} x^{-1}$ (b) $y = \tanh^{-1} (1 - x)$
   (c) $y = \sinh^{-1} \sqrt{x - 1}$ (d) $y = \text{Cosh}^{-1} (\ln x)$
   (e) $y = \tanh^{-1} (\cos x)$ (f) $y = \text{csch}^{-1} e^x$
   (g) $y = \coth^{-1} (\cosh x)$ (h) $y = \sinh^{-1} (\tan x)$
   (i) $y = \text{Cosh}^{-1} (\cos x)$ (j) $y = \text{Cosh}^{-1} (\sec x)$

7. Evaluate the following integrals.

(a) $\int_0^2 \frac{1}{\sqrt{x^2+4}}\,dx$ (b) $\int_0^1 \frac{1}{\sqrt{1+x^2}}\,dx$

(c) $\int_2^3 \frac{1}{\sqrt{x^2-1}}\,dx$ (d) $\int_5^7 \frac{1}{\sqrt{x^2-9}}\,dx$

(e) $\int_{-1/2}^{1/2} \frac{1}{1-x^2}\,dx$ (f) $\int_{-1}^{1} \frac{1}{2-x^2}\,dx$

(g) $\int_4^5 \frac{1}{x^2-9}\,dx$ (h) $\int_{-1}^{1} \frac{1}{\sqrt{2-x^2}}\,dx$

8. Show that if $-\pi/2 < x < \pi/2$, then $\sinh^{-1}(\tan x) = \tanh^{-1}(\sin x)$.

9. Verify the following integration formulas.

(a) $\int \sqrt{x^2+a^2}\,dx = \frac{1}{2}\left(x\sqrt{x^2+a^2} + a^2 \sinh^{-1}\frac{x}{a}\right)$

(b) $\int \sqrt{x^2-a^2}\,dx = \frac{1}{2}\left(x\sqrt{x^2-a^2} - a^2 \operatorname{Cosh}^{-1}\frac{x}{a}\right)$, $(x > a)$.

10. Verify that:

(a) $D_x[x \sinh^{-1} x - \sqrt{1+x^2}] = \sinh^{-1} x$.

(b) $D_x[x \operatorname{Cosh}^{-1} x - \sqrt{x^2-1}] = \operatorname{Cosh}^{-1} x$.

(c) $D_x[x \tanh^{-1} x - \ln\sqrt{x^2-1}] = \tanh^{-1} x$

11. Let R be the region bounded by the hyperbola $y^2 - x^2 = 1$ and the line segments joining the origin to the points $(b, \sqrt{1+b^2})$ and $(-b, \sqrt{1+b^2})$ of the hyperbola. Show that the area of R is $\sinh^{-1} b$.

12. Let R be the region bounded by the hyperbola $x^2 - y^2 = 1$ and the line segments joining the origin to the points $(b, \sqrt{b^2-1})$ and $(b, -\sqrt{b^2-1})$ of the hyperbola. Show that the area of R is $\operatorname{Cosh}^{-1} b$.

Review Problems, Chapter Six

You can use the following problems to test yourself on the material covered in this chapter.

1. Compute $D_x y$.

(a) $y = x^{a^2}$ (b) $y = a^{x^2}$

(c) $y = \operatorname{Sin}^{-1}\sqrt{x}$ (d) $y = \exp(x^{e^x})$

(e) $y = \ln(\ln x) + \exp(e^x)$ (f) $y = \int_1^{x^2} e^{t^2}\,dt$

2. Verify the following integration formulas.

(a) $\int e^{ax}\cos bx\,dx = \left(\frac{a\cos bx + b\sin bx}{a^2+b^2}\right)e^{ax}$

(b) $\int e^{ax}\sin bx\,dx = \left(\frac{a\sin bx - b\cos bx}{a^2+b^2}\right)e^{ax}$

3. Find the maximum value of the product $x^2 \ln \frac{1}{x}$.

4. Sketch the graph of the equation $y = \int_1^{3^x} \frac{1}{t}\, dt$.

5. Solve for x: $\int_{x^2}^{x^3} \frac{3}{t}\, dt = 6$.

6. The region bounded by the coordinate axes, the line $x = 2$, and the graph of the equation $y = 2^{x/2}$ is rotated about the X-axis. Find the volume of the resulting solid.

7. Evaluate the following integrals.

(a) $\int_{-b}^{b} \frac{1}{\sqrt{4b^2 - x^2}}\, dx$ (b) $\int_0^4 \cosh^2 x\, dx$

(c) $\int_0^1 e^{-x} \sinh 2x\, dx$ (d) $\int_{-b}^{b} \frac{1}{4b^2 - x^2}\, dx$

8. Suppose that $0 < x < \pi/2$, $y > 0$, and $\cos x \cosh y = 1$.
(a) Show that $y = \ln(\sec x + \tan x)$.
(b) Compute $D_x y$.

9. How many solutions does the equation $e^x = ex$ have?

10. Let $f(x) = |x - 1| + |x - 2|$ and $F(x) = \int_0^x f(t)\, dt$.
(a) Sketch the graph of f.
(b) Find $F(0)$, $F(1)$, $F(2)$, and $F(3)$.
(c) Find $F'(1)$ and $F'(3)$.
(d) Sketch the graph of F.
(e) Does f have an inverse? If so, sketch the graph of f^{-1}.
(f) Does F have an inverse? If so, sketch the graph of F^{-1}.

11. Let $G(x) = \int_{-1}^{x} \mathrm{Sin}^{-1}\, t\, dt$. What is the domain of G? Discuss the concavity of the graph of G.

12. Let b be a positive number other than 1 and suppose that $u = g(x)$. Show that

$$D_x \log_b |u| = \frac{D_x u}{u \ln b}.$$

7 TECHNIQUES OF INTEGRATION

The Fundamental Theorem of Calculus tells us how the concepts of integration and differentiation are related. With each specific differentiation formula we can associate an integration formula. Although we have found many specific integration formulas in this way, we still need to develop some additional techniques to be able to fully utilize our integration formulas. This chapter will be devoted to the development of such techniques.

57. Integration Formulas

An integral $\int_a^b f(x)\,dx$ is the limit of sums of the form $\sum_{i=1}^{n} f(x_i^*)\,\Delta x_i$. In some cases we must use numerical methods such as Simpson's Rule or The Trapezoidal Rule to evaluate an integral, but often an integration formula

(57-1) $$\int f(x)\,dx = F(x)$$

applies. By Formula 57-1 we mean that the integral $\int_a^b f(x)\,dx$ is the number $F(x)\Big|_a^b = F(b) - F(a)$ for each interval $[a, b]$ in which the formula is applicable. The Fundamental Theorem of Calculus and its converse, Theorems 40-1 and 46-1, tell us that we can interpret Formula 57-1 as saying that $D_xF(x) = f(x)$; that is, that $F(x)$ is an antiderivative of $f(x)$.

We have listed a number of differentiation formulas in Table IV and integration formulas in Table V in the back of this book. The first 25 formulas from Table V are labeled as Basic Integration Formulas. They are essentially the differentiation formulas from Table IV read from right to left. You should know these formulas by heart. Notice that we have used the abbreviation $\int \frac{du}{f(u)}$ for $\int \frac{1}{f(u)}\,du$ in our tables. *To verify a specific integration formula, we differentiate the right-hand side to obtain the integrand.*

Example 57-1. Verify Integration Formulas V-20.

Solution. We must show that

$$D_u \sinh^{-1}\left(\frac{u}{a}\right) = \frac{1}{\sqrt{u^2 + a^2}},$$

and

$$D_u \ln\left[\frac{u + \sqrt{u^2 + a^2}}{a}\right] = \frac{1}{\sqrt{u^2 + a^2}}.$$

According to Formula IV-21,

$$D_u \sinh^{-1}\left(\frac{u}{a}\right) = \frac{D_u(u/a)}{\sqrt{(u/a)^2 + 1}}$$

$$= \frac{1/a}{\sqrt{(u/a)^2 + 1}} = \frac{1}{\sqrt{u^2 + a^2}}.$$

(Notice that we are assuming that $a > 0$ in these integration formulas.) We use Formula IV-9 to show that

$$D_u \ln\left[\frac{u + \sqrt{u^2 + a^2}}{a}\right] = \frac{D_u(u + \sqrt{u^2 + a^2})}{u + \sqrt{u^2 + a^2}}$$

$$= \frac{1 + u/\sqrt{u^2 + a^2}}{u + \sqrt{u^2 + a^2}} = \frac{1}{\sqrt{u^2 + a^2}}.$$

Example 57-2. Find $\int_5^{10} \frac{dt}{t}$.

Solution. According to Formula V-9,

$$\int_5^{10} \frac{dt}{t} = \ln |t| \Big|_5^{10} = \ln 10 - \ln 5$$
$$= \ln 2 \approx .69.$$

In addition to the *specific* integration formulas we have just been discussing, we can find *general* integration formulas that correspond to the general differentiation formulas

(57-2) $D_x[mf(x) + ng(x)] = mD_xf(x) + nD_xg(x)$,

(57-3) $D_x[f(x)g(x)] = f(x)D_xg(x) + g(x)D_xf(x)$ (The Product Rule),

(57-4) $D_xf(u) = D_uf(u)D_xu$ (The Chain Rule).

In Sections 58 and 60 we will develop the general integration rules that correspond to Rules 57-3 and 57-4. Now we will consider Rule 57-2. Rule 57-2 states that the derivative of the "linear combination" $mf(x) + ng(x)$ is the same linear combination of the derivatives of $f(x)$ and $g(x)$. It follows that m times an antiderivative of $f(x)$ plus n times an antiderivative of $g(x)$ is an antiderivative of $mf(x) + ng(x)$. In symbols, we write this statement as the equation

(57-5) $$\boldsymbol{\int [mf(x) + ng(x)]\, dx = m\int f(x)\, dx + n\int g(x)\, dx.}$$

Example 57-3. Find $\int (3 \cos x + 2e^x)\, dx$.

Solution. We are asked to find an antiderivative of $3 \cos x + 2e^x$. We have

$$\int (3 \cos x + 2e^x)\, dx = 3\int \cos x\, dx + 2\int e^x\, dx \qquad \text{(Eq. 57-5)}$$
$$= 3 \sin x + 2e^x.$$

It is always wise to check the solution to a problem that involves finding an antiderivative. To perform such a check, you simply differentiate your answer and see if you obtain what you started with:

$$D_x(3 \sin x + 2e^x) = 3 \cos x + 2e^x,$$

and so our result checks.

Example 57-4. Find an antiderivative of $\frac{2x^3 - 3x + 6}{x^2}$.

Solution. We have

$$\int \frac{2x^3 - 3x + 6}{x^2}\,dx = 2\int x\,dx - 3\int \frac{dx}{x} + 6\int x^{-2}\,dx$$
$$= x^2 - 3\ln|x| - 6x^{-1}.$$

Example 57-5. Verify the correctness of the equation

$$\int t^2 \tan t^3\,dt = \ln \sqrt[3]{\sec t^3}.$$

Solution. We differentiate the right side of this equation:

$$D_t \ln \sqrt[3]{\sec t^3} = D_t(\tfrac{1}{3}\ln \sec t^3) = \tfrac{1}{3}D_t \ln \sec t^3$$
$$= \frac{D_t \sec t^3}{3 \sec t^3}$$
$$= \frac{\sec t^3 \tan t^3 D_t t^3}{3 \sec t^3}$$
$$= \tfrac{1}{3}(\tan t^3)3t^2 = t^2 \tan t^3.$$

Since the derivative of the right-hand side is the integrand, we have verified the correctness of our original integration formula.

Problems 57

1. In each case determine k so that the integration formula is correct.
   (a) $\int xe^{3x^2}\,dx = ke^{3x^2}$
   (b) $\int \frac{1}{x(\ln x)^{2/3}}\,dx = k\sqrt[3]{\ln x}$
   (c) $\int \sin x \cos(\cos x)\,dx = k \sin(\cos x)$
   (d) $\int \frac{2^{1/x}}{x^2}\,dx = k2^{1/x}$
   (e) $\int \left(1 - \frac{1}{\sqrt{x}}\right)\frac{e^{\sqrt{x}}}{x}\,dx = \frac{ke^{\sqrt{x}}}{\sqrt{x}}$
   (f) $\int x[\ln(\cosh x^2)]^2 \tanh x^2\,dx = k[\ln(\cosh x^2)]^3$
2. Verify the following formulas from Table V.
   (a) V-26 (b) V-29 (c) V-30
   (d) V-33 (e) V-35 (f) V-37
3. Find:
   (a) $\int (3\sin x - 2\cos x)\,dx$
   (b) $\int (e^x + x^e)\,dx$

(c) $\int \frac{2x^3 - 1}{x} \, dx$

(d) $\int \frac{3 \, dt}{9 + t^2}$

(e) $\int \frac{\sqrt{4 + u^2} - 4 - u^2}{(4 + u^2)^{3/2}} \, du$

(f) $\int e^{z+2} \, dz$

(g) $\int \ln w^4 \, dw$

(h) $\int \ln 4t \, dt$

4. Evaluate:

(a) $\int_0^c (\sqrt{c} - \sqrt{x})^2 \, dx$

(b) $\int_{-1}^1 \operatorname{sech}^2 x \, dx$

(c) $\int_0^1 \frac{dv}{9 - v^2}$

(d) $\int_0^1 2^z \, dz$

5. The region bounded by the graph of the equation $y = 2 \sec x$, the X- and Y-axes, and the line $x = \pi/3$ is rotated about the X-axis. What is the volume of the solid that is generated?

6. Show that $\int \sec u \, du = -\ln |\sec u - \tan u|$. Does this formula agree with Formula V-33?

7. Find the maximum and minimum points of the graph of the equation $y = \operatorname{Sin}^{-1} (a \sin x)$, $0 < a < 1$. Discuss the graph if $a = 2$.

58. The Method of Substitution

We can greatly increase the generality of a specific differentiation formula

$$D_u G(u) = g(u)$$

by incorporating it into the Chain Rule Equation to obtain the equation

$$D_x G(u) = D_u G(u) D_x u = g(u) D_x u$$

(where we are assuming that $u = h(x)$ for some differentiable function h). Thus, for example, we can use the formula $D_u \sin u = \cos u$ to find $D_x \sin x^2$ as follows:

$$D_x \sin x^2 = \cos x^2 D_x x^2 = 2x \cos x^2.$$

In this section we will develop the "method of substitution" by which we introduce the Chain Rule into our specific integration formulas and thereby broaden their scope.

According to the Fundamental Theorem of Calculus, the differentiation formula $D_x G(u) = g(u) D_x u$ verifies the integration formula

$$\int g(u) D_x u \, dx = G(u),$$

and the differentiation formula $D_uG(u) = g(u)$ verifies the integration formula

$$\int g(u)\, du = G(u).$$

Thus we can write

$$\int g(u) D_x u\, dx = \int g(u)\, du, \tag{58-1}$$

and this equation is the key to our method of substitution. Suppose we are to find $\int f(x)\, dx$ and we choose a function h such that the substitution $u = h(x)$ gives us

$$f(x) = g(u) D_x u. \tag{58-2}$$

Then, according to Equations 58-1 and 58-2,

$$\int f(x)\, dx = \int g(u) D_x u\, dx = \int g(u)\, du, \tag{58-3}$$

so our problem of finding an antiderivative of $f(x)$ becomes the problem of finding an antiderivative of $g(u)$. If we make a suitable substitution $u = h(x)$, we may find that $\int g(u)\, du$ is listed in a table of integrals, even though $\int f(x)\, dx$ is not.

Example 58-1. Find $\int \sin (x + 2)\, dx$.

Solution. Here $f(x) = \sin (x + 2)$. Let us choose $u = x + 2$. Then $D_x u = 1$, and Equation 58-2 becomes $\sin (x + 2) = (\sin u) \cdot 1$, from which we obtain $g(u) = \sin u$. Therefore, according to Equation 58-3,

$$\int \sin (x + 2)\, dx = \int \sin u\, du = -\cos u = -\cos (x + 2).$$

The success or failure of the method of substitution hinges on our choice of $h(x)$. Once we set $u = h(x)$, we are committed. Then $D_x u$ is determined, and $g(u) = \dfrac{f(x)}{D_x u}$. If we now cannot find an antiderivative of $g(u)$, then we either have to start over with another substitution or admit defeat. Your success with the method of substitution will improve with experience.

Example 58-2. Find $\int xe^{-x^2}\, dx$.

Solution. Here we have $f(x) = xe^{-x^2}$, and we are to choose $u = h(x)$ and write $f(x) = g(u) D_x u$. Let us choose the substitution $u = -x^2$. Then $D_x u = -2x$, and we have

$$g(u) = \frac{f(x)}{D_x u} = \frac{xe^{-x^2}}{-2x} = -\frac{1}{2} e^{-x^2} = -\frac{1}{2} e^u.$$

Hence

$$\int xe^{-x^2}\, dx = -\tfrac{1}{2} \int e^u\, du = -\tfrac{1}{2} e^u = -\tfrac{1}{2} e^{-x^2}.$$

From the equation $\int g(u)D_xu\,dx = \int g(u)\,du$, we are tempted to conclude that

$$du = D_xu\,dx. \tag{58-4}$$

But because we have not assigned any meaning to the symbols dx and du (except as "indicators"), we really should not treat this "equation" as a true equality between numbers. Nevertheless, it is a great convenience—and it will not lead us into error here—to proceed formally as if "Equation" 58-4 were a real equation, and we shall do so. Thus our steps in using the method of substitution are:

(i) Set $u = h(x)$,

(ii) Write $du = D_xu\,dx$,

(iii) Use the equations from Steps (i) and (ii) to write $\int f(x)\,dx = \int g(u)\,du$.

Example 58-3. Find $\int \cot x\,dx$.

Solution. First we write $\int \cot x\,dx = \int \frac{\cos x}{\sin x}\,dx$. Then we set $u = \sin x$. It follows that $du = D_x \sin x\,dx = \cos x\,dx$, and hence

$$\int \cot x\,dx = \int \frac{\cos x}{\sin x}\,dx = \int \frac{du}{u} = \ln |u| = \ln |\sin x|.$$

Example 58-4. Find $\int \frac{\sec^2 \sqrt{x}}{\sqrt{x}}\,dx$.

Solution. We set $u = \sqrt{x}$. Then $du = \frac{1}{2\sqrt{x}}\,dx$; that is, $2\,du = \frac{dx}{\sqrt{x}}$. Thus

$$\int \frac{\sec^2 \sqrt{x}}{\sqrt{x}}\,dx = 2 \int \sec^2 u\,du = 2 \tan u = 2 \tan \sqrt{x}.$$

It may happen that there is more than one "natural" substitution that will lead to a solution of your problem. In such cases it makes no sense to ask which substitution is "best." The best substitution for you is the first one you find that will enable you to solve your problem correctly.

Example 58-5. Find $\int \frac{x\,dx}{\sqrt{x+1}}$.

Solution. We will indicate two different substitutions that could be used to solve this problem.

Test to Here

Method 1. Set $u = \sqrt{x+1}$. Then $du = \dfrac{1}{2\sqrt{x+1}}\,dx$, and $x = u^2 - 1$. It follows that

$$\int \frac{x\,dx}{\sqrt{x+1}} = \int 2(u^2 - 1)\,du = 2\left(\frac{u^3}{3} - u\right)$$
$$= \tfrac{2}{3}(x+1)^{3/2} - 2(x+1)^{1/2}.$$

Method 2. Set $u = x + 1$. Then $du = dx$, $x = u - 1$, and we have

$$\int \frac{x\,dx}{\sqrt{x+1}} = \int \frac{u-1}{\sqrt{u}}\,du = \int (u^{1/2} - u^{-1/2})\,du$$
$$= \tfrac{2}{3}u^{3/2} - 2u^{1/2} = \tfrac{2}{3}(x+1)^{3/2} - 2(x+1)^{1/2}.$$

Problems 58

1. Use the indicated substitution to find an antiderivative.

   (a) $\int 3x^2 e^{x^3}\,dx, \quad u = x^3$ (b) $\int 3^{x^2} x\,dx, \quad u = x^2$

   (c) $\int x^2 \sin x^3\,dx, \quad u = x^3$ (d) $\int x \ln x^2\,dx, \quad u = x^2$

   (e) $\int \dfrac{dx}{4 + 9x^2}, \quad u = 3x$ (f) $\int \dfrac{x\,dx}{3 + 4x^2}, \quad u = 3 + 4x^2$

   (g) $\int \dfrac{(\ln x)^3}{x}\,dx, \quad u = \ln x$ (h) $\int \sin^2 x \cos x\,dx, \quad u = \sin x$

   (i) $\int \tan x\,dx, \quad u = \cos x$ (j) $\int e^x \cos e^x\,dx, \quad u = e^x$

2. By making the proper substitution, each of the following can be put in the form $c \int u^p\,du$. Use such a substitution and find an antiderivative.

   (a) $\int x\sqrt{x^2+1}\,dx$ (b) $\int x^2\sqrt{x^3+1}\,dx$

   (c) $\int \dfrac{x\,dx}{\sqrt{x^2+1}}$ (d) $\int \dfrac{x^2\,dx}{\sqrt{x^3+1}}$

   (e) $\int \dfrac{t+4}{(t^2+8t+3)^2}\,dt$ (f) $\int \dfrac{v \sin v^2}{\cos v^2}\,dv$

   (g) $\int \dfrac{\sinh v}{\cosh v}\,dv$ (h) $\int \dfrac{\ln |x|}{x}\,dx$

3. Find:

   (a) $\int e^{\sin x} \cos x\,dx$ (b) $\int \cos(3x - 4)\,dx$

   (c) $\int \sec^2(2x + 3)\,dx$ (d) $\int x^{-1} \sin(\ln x)\,dx$

(e) $\int \frac{x^2}{\sqrt{x^3 - 5}}\, dx$ (f) $\int \frac{3x - 1}{3x^2 - 2x + 1}\, dx$

(g) $\int e^x \sec e^x \tan e^x \, dx$ (h) $\int \frac{e^x - e^{-x}}{e^x + e^{-x}}\, dx$

4. Find:

(a) $\int \sec^3 x \tan x \, dx$ (b) $\int \frac{dx}{x \ln x}$

(c) $\int \frac{\cos 2x}{3 + 4 \sin 2x}\, dx$ (d) $\int \frac{x^3\, dx}{\sqrt{1 - x^2}}$

(e) $\int \ln e^{3x^2}\, dx$ (f) $\int \frac{\sin (1/x)\, dx}{x^2}$

(g) $\int \frac{e^{2t}}{e^t + 1}\, dt$ (h) $\int \frac{dx}{x^2 \sqrt{x^2 + 4}}$

5. Evaluate the following integrals.

(a) $\int_0^{2\pi} \sin x \,(\cos^{13} x + 17 \cos^5 x + 23)\, dx$

(b) $\int_{\ln 2}^{\ln 7} e^x e^{e^x}\, dx$

(c) $\int_1^2 \frac{x + 2}{(x^2 + 4x + 5)^2}\, dx$

(d) $\int_0^{\pi/2} \frac{\sin t}{1 + \cos^2 t}\, dt$

6. Find an antiderivative of $\sec^6 x$ by first writing $\sec^6 x = \sec^4 x \sec^2 x = (1 + \tan^2 x)^2 \sec^2 x$ and then letting $u = \tan x$.

7. Find the area of the region enclosed by the curve whose equation is $y^2 + x^4 = 4x^2$.

8. Find an antiderivative of $\frac{1}{t\sqrt{t^2 - 4}}$ by two methods. In one case use the substitution $u = \sqrt{t^2 - 4}$, and in the other use the substitution $v = \frac{1}{t}$.

59. Change of Variable of Integration

In the preceding section we used the method of substitution to find antiderivatives. In this section we will indicate how to use the method of substitution to calculate integrals.

Example 59-1. Evaluate $\int_2^3 x \sqrt{x^2 - 2}\, dx$.

Solution. We can use the method of substitution to find an antiderivative of $x \sqrt{x^2 - 2}$ and then introduce the limits of integration. We follow our usual steps. First, we set

$$u = x^2 - 2.$$

It follows that

$$du = 2x\,dx,$$

and thus

$$\int x\sqrt{x^2-2}\,dx = \frac{1}{2}\int \sqrt{u}\,du = \frac{u^{3/2}}{3} = \frac{(x^2-2)^{3/2}}{3}.$$

Hence

$$\int_2^3 x\sqrt{x^2-2}\,dx = \frac{(x^2-2)^{3/2}}{3}\Bigg|_2^3 = \frac{7^{3/2}-2^{3/2}}{3}.$$

In the preceding example we first replaced all the x's in the integrand in terms of u. Then after we found our antiderivative in terms of u, we returned to the x's to compute the integral. This procedure is inefficient, and this last replacement of the u's with x's can be eliminated by replacing the limits of integration with the new limits that are obtained from the substitution equation. Thus since $u = x^2 - 2$, we see that $u = 7$ when $x = 3$, and $u = 2$ when $x = 2$. If, in addition to the other changes in our integral, we also change the limits to 2 and 7, the result of our substitutions is the equation

$$\int_2^3 x\sqrt{x^2-2}\,dx = \tfrac{1}{2}\int_2^7 \sqrt{u}\,du.$$

When we evaluate this last integral, we obtain the same answer as before:

$$\frac{1}{2}\int_2^7 \sqrt{u}\,du = \frac{u^{3/2}}{3}\Bigg|_2^7 = \frac{7^{3/2}-2^{3/2}}{3}.$$

Let us see why this replacement of the limits of integration gives us the correct result. We are supposing that the substitution $u = h(x)$ gives us

$$\int f(x)\,dx = \int g(u)\,du = G(u) = G[h(x)].$$

Thus

$$\int_a^b f(x)\,dx = G[h(x)]\Big|_a^b = G[h(b)] - G[h(a)].$$

But since

$$G[h(b)] - G[h(a)] = \int_{h(a)}^{h(b)} g(u)\,du,$$

it follows that

$$\int_a^b f(x)\,dx = \int_{h(a)}^{h(b)} g(u)\,du.$$

Thus we may as well use our substitution equation $u = h(x)$ to introduce limits of integration for the new variable of integration and never return to the original variable of integration at all.

Example 59-2. Evaluate $\int_1^3 \frac{dx}{4 + (x - 1)^2}$.

Solution. We let $u = x - 1$. Then $du = dx$, $u = 0$ when $x = 1$, and $u = 2$ when $x = 3$. So we have

$$\begin{aligned}\int_1^3 \frac{dx}{4 + (x - 1)^2} &= \int_0^2 \frac{du}{4 + u^2}\\ &= \frac{1}{2}\operatorname{Arctan}\left(\frac{u}{2}\right)\Big|_0^2\\ &= \tfrac{1}{2}[\operatorname{Arctan} 1 - \operatorname{Arctan} 0]\\ &= \frac{\pi}{8} - 0 = \frac{\pi}{8}.\end{aligned}$$

Example 59-3. Compute $\int_0^{\pi/6} \sin^2 x \cos x\, dx$.

Solution. We set $u = \sin x$. Then $du = \cos x\, dx$, $u = 0$ when $x = 0$, and $u = \frac{1}{2}$ when $x = \pi/6$. Thus

$$\begin{aligned}\int_0^{\pi/6} \sin^2 x \cos x\, dx &= \int_0^{1/2} u^2\, du\\ &= \frac{u^3}{3}\Big|_0^{1/2} = \frac{1}{24}.\end{aligned}$$

Example 59-4. What is the volume of the solid formed by rotating the region bounded by the graph of the equation $y = x\sqrt[3]{1 - x^3}$ and the X-axis about the X-axis?

Solution. Figure 59-1 shows the region to be rotated. The volume of the resulting solid is

$$\begin{aligned}V &= \pi \int_0^1 y^2\, dx\\ &= \pi \int_0^1 x^2(1 - x^3)^{2/3}\, dx.\end{aligned}$$

To evaluate this integral, we let $u = 1 - x^3$. Then $du = -3x^2\, dx$, $u = 1$ when $x = 0$, and $u = 0$ when $x = 1$. Hence we see that

$$\begin{aligned}V &= -\frac{\pi}{3}\int_1^0 u^{2/3}\, du = \frac{\pi}{3}\int_0^1 u^{2/3}\, du\\ &= \frac{\pi}{5} u^{5/3}\Big|_0^1 = \frac{\pi}{5}.\end{aligned}$$

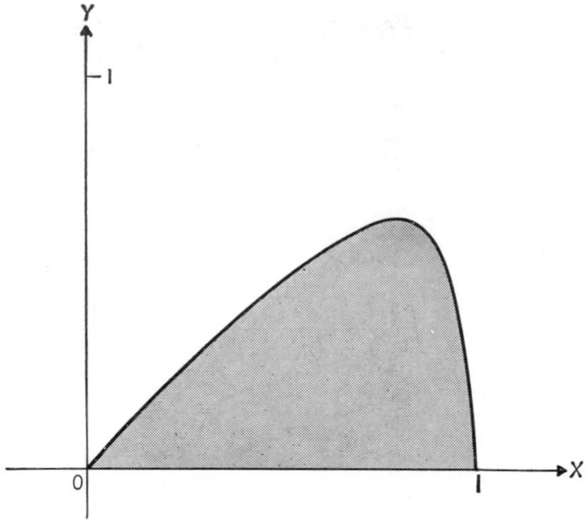

Figure 59-1

Example 59-5. Evaluate $\int_0^{2\pi} |\cos nx|\, dx$, where n is a positive integer.

Solution. Figure 59-2 shows part of the graph of the equation $y = |\cos nx|$; we must find the area of the region under this curve. After a little thought, you can see that the region is made up of $4n$ "half-humps" similar to the shaded one. Thus the area of the region under all the "humps" is $4n$ times the area of the shaded region, and so

$$\begin{aligned}\int_0^{2\pi} |\cos nx|\, dx &= 4n \int_0^{\pi/2n} |\cos nx|\, dx \\ &= 4n \int_0^{\pi/2n} \cos nx\, dx.\end{aligned}$$

To evaluate this last integral, we will make the substitution $u = nx$.

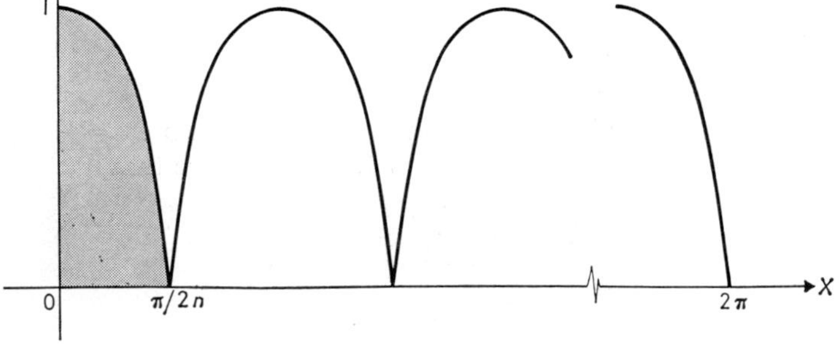

Figure 59-2

Then $du = n\,dx$, and we see that

$$4n \int_0^{\pi/2n} \cos nx\,dx = 4 \int_0^{\pi/2} \cos u\,du$$
$$= 4 \sin u \Big|_0^{\pi/2} = 4.$$

Thus the value of our integral is 4, no matter what positive integer n is chosen!

We already know that the letter we use as the variable of integration has nothing to do with the value of the integral. Thus, for example,

$$\int_a^b \sin x\,dx = \int_a^b \sin u\,du = \cos a - \cos b.$$

This equality agrees with what we said earlier in this section because we can go from the integral on the left to the one on the right by means of the substitution $u = x$. But sometimes when we deal with several integrals at once it is easy to lose sight of the basic fact that the value of an integral is independent of the letter that is used as the variable of integration. Our next example illustrates this kind of problem. To work out such a problem is a real test of your understanding of the nature of the variable of integration.

Example 59-6. Show that

$$\int_0^\pi \theta f(\sin \theta)\,d\theta = \frac{\pi}{2} \int_0^\pi f(\sin \theta)\,d\theta.$$

Solution. If we make the substitution $\phi = \pi - \theta$, we have $d\phi = -d\theta$ and $\sin \theta = \sin \phi$. Furthermore, $\phi = \pi$ when $\theta = 0$, and $\phi = 0$ when $\theta = \pi$. Thus

$$\int_0^\pi \theta f(\sin \theta)\,d\theta = -\int_\pi^0 (\pi - \phi) f(\sin \phi)\,d\phi$$
$$= \pi \int_0^\pi f(\sin \phi)\,d\phi - \int_0^\pi \phi f(\sin \phi)\,d\phi.$$

Thus

(59-1) $$\int_0^\pi \theta f(\sin \theta)\,d\theta + \int_0^\pi \phi f(\sin \phi)\,d\phi$$
$$= \pi \int_0^\pi f(\sin \phi)\,d\phi.$$

Now remember that it makes no difference which letter we use as the variable of integration. In particular, we may replace all the ϕ's, letter by letter, with θ's. If we make this replacement, Equation 59-1 can be written,

$$2 \int_0^\pi \theta f(\sin \theta)\,d\theta = \pi \int_0^\pi f(\sin \theta)\,d\theta,$$

and the desired equation follows immediately.

Problems 59

1. Evaluate the following integrals.

(a) $\int_0^{\pi/6} \cos 2x\, dx$ (b) $\int_0^2 xe^{x^2}\, dx$

(c) $\int_0^1 x\sqrt{x^2+1}\, dx$ (d) $\int_0^{\pi/2} \cos x \sin(\sin x)\, dx$

(e) $\int_1^4 \frac{e^{\sqrt{x}}}{\sqrt{x}}\, dx$ (f) $\int_0^{\pi/6} \frac{\cos x - \sin x}{\sin x + \cos x}\, dx$

(g) $\int_0^1 (2x-3)\sqrt{x^2-3x+5}\, dx$ (h) $\int_0^1 \operatorname{sech}^5 x \sinh x\, dx$

2. Show that:

(a) $\int_2^3 f(x+3)\, dx = \int_5^6 f(x)\, dx$

(b) $\int_0^1 f(x)\, g(1-x)\, dx = \int_0^1 f(1-x)g(x)\, dx$

(c) $\int_a^b f(x)\, dx = \int_a^b f(a+b-x)\, dx$

3. Evaluate the following integrals.

(a) $\int_1^2 \frac{x\, dx}{1+x^2}$ (b) $\int_0^1 \frac{x^2\, dx}{1+x^3}$

(c) $\int_1^2 \frac{x\, dx}{1+x}$ (d) $\int_{\pi/4}^{\pi/2} \cot x \ln(\sin x)\, dx$

(e) $\int_1^2 \frac{x+2}{(x+1)^2}\, dx$ (f) $\int_{-1}^1 \frac{x^3}{1+x^4}\, dx$

4. A function f is an **even function** if $f(-x) = f(x)$. Show that if f is an even function, then

$$\int_{-a}^a f(x)\, dx = 2\int_0^a f(x)\, dx.$$

5. A function f is an **odd function** if $f(-x) = -f(x)$. Show that if f is an odd function, then

$$\int_{-a}^a f(x)\, dx = 0.$$

6. The region bounded by the coordinate axes, the line $x = b$, and the catenary whose equation is $y = a \cosh(x/a)$ is revolved about the X-axis. Find the volume of the solid that is generated.

7. Sketch the graph of the equation $y = (\ln x)/\sqrt{x}$. The region bounded by this curve, the X-axis, and a vertical line through the maximum point on the curve is rotated about the X-axis. Find the volume of the solid that is generated.

8. Suppose f is an odd function. Show that $\int_0^\pi f(\cos\theta)\, d\theta = 0$.

9. Use the result of Example 59-6 to compute $\int_0^\pi \theta \sin\theta\, d\theta$.

60. Integration by Parts

In Section 57 we listed the general differentiation Formulas 57-2, 57-3, and 57-4. We have found integration formulas that correspond to Equations 57-2 and 57-4, but we have not yet discussed the integration formulas that correspond to the Product Rule 57-3:

$$D_x[f(x)g(x)] = f(x)D_xg(x) + g(x)D_xf(x)$$
$$= f(x)g'(x) + g(x)f'(x).$$

From this equation we see that the product $f(x)g(x)$ is an antiderivative of the expression $f(x)g'(x) + g(x)f'(x)$, and hence the Fundamental Theorem of Calculus tells us that

$$\int_a^b [f(x)g'(x) + g(x)f'(x)]\, dx = f(x)g(x)\Big|_a^b$$

for an arbitrary interval $[a, b]$. We may rewrite this equation in the form

(60-1) $$\int_a^b \boldsymbol{f(x)g'(x)\, dx = f(x)g(x)\Big|_a^b - \int_a^b g(x)f'(x)\, dx.}$$

In our abbreviated notation we drop the limits of integration and simply write

$$\int f(x)g'(x)\, dx = f(x)g(x) - \int g(x)f'(x)\, dx.$$

We will change the appearance, but not the content, of this last integration formula if we set $u = f(x)$ and $v = g(x)$. Then $f'(x) = D_xu$ and $g'(x) = D_xv$, and our formula is

(60-2) $$\int \boldsymbol{uD_xv\, dx = uv - \int vD_xu\, dx.}$$

Now if we replace $D_xv\, dx$ with dv and $D_xu\, dx$ with du, as we do when we use our method of substitution, this last equation takes the form

(60-3) $$\int \boldsymbol{u\, dv = uv - \int v\, du.}$$

The integration formula expressed by Equations 60-1, 60-2 or 60-3 is known as the formula for **integration by parts.** It can be used to find antiderivatives and integrals that would otherwise be difficult to obtain. Basically, the formula transforms the problem of finding $\int u\, dv$ to that of finding $\int v\, du$. For example, suppose we let $u = x$ and $v = \sin x$ in Equation 60-3. Then we have $du = dx$ and $dv = \cos x\, dx$, and our equation becomes

$$\int x \cos x\, dx = x \sin x - \int \sin x\, dx$$
$$= x \sin x + \cos x.$$

These equations show us that we transformed the problem of finding $\int x \cos x \, dx$ to the easier problem of finding $\int \sin x \, dx$. The key step in applying the integration by parts technique is to choose the u and v properly. Sometimes a little experimentation is necessary.

Example 60-1. Find $\int x \ln x \, dx$.

Solution. Here we let $u = \ln x$, and we will choose v so that $dv = x \, dx$. The simplest choice is $v = \frac{x^2}{2}$. We see that $du = \frac{1}{x} dx$, and so Equation 60-3 reads

$$\begin{aligned}\int x \ln x \, dx &= \frac{x^2}{2} \ln x - \int \frac{x^2}{2} \cdot \frac{1}{x} \, dx \\ &= \frac{x^2 \ln x}{2} - \int \frac{1}{2} x \, dx \\ &= \frac{x^2 \ln x}{2} - \frac{x^2}{4}.\end{aligned}$$

It is a simple matter to verify this result by differentiation.

When we use the integration by parts procedure, we *choose* u and dv, and then we must *compute* $du = D_x u \, dx$ and also *find* a v such that $D_x v \, dx$ is our chosen dv. There are no rules for deciding what to choose for u and what to choose for dv, but once we make our choice the rest of the calculation is straightforward.

Example 60-2. Find $\int x(x - 3)^5 \, dx$.

Solution. In this case we will choose $u = x$ and $dv = (x - 3)^5 \, dx$. It follows immediately that $du = dx$, and now we must find v such that $dv = D_x v \, dx = (x - 3)^5 \, dx$. Thus we will want $D_x v = (x - 3)^5$; in other words, v must be an antiderivative of $(x - 3)^5$. In symbols, we have

$$v = \int (x - 3)^5 \, dx,$$

from which you can find, by substitution if necessary, that $v = \frac{(x - 3)^6}{6}$ is a suitable choice for v. Now Equation 60-3 becomes

$$\begin{aligned}\int x(x - 3)^5 \, dx &= \frac{x(x - 3)^6}{6} - \frac{1}{6} \int (x - 3)^6 \, dx \\ &= \frac{x(x - 3)^6}{6} - \frac{(x - 3)^7}{42}.\end{aligned}$$

Example 60-3. Find $\int x^2 e^x\,dx$.

Solution. We let $u = x^2$ and $dv = e^x\,dx$. Then $du = 2x\,dx$, and $v = \int e^x\,dx = e^x$, so Equation 60-3 reads

$$\int x^2 e^x\,dx = x^2 e^x - 2\int x e^x\,dx. \tag{60-4}$$

To finish our problem we must find $\int xe^x\,dx$. What we have done so far is to reduce the problem of finding $\int x^2e^x\,dx$ to the simpler problem of finding $\int xe^x\,dx$. We find $\int xe^x\,dx$ by using the integration by parts procedure a second time. Here we set $u = x$, and again take $v = e^x$. Then $du = dx$ and we have

$$\int xe^x\,dx = xe^x - \int e^x\,dx = xe^x - e^x.$$

When this result is substituted in Equation 60-4 we get

$$\int x^2e^x\,dx = x^2e^x - 2xe^x + 2e^x.$$

Before we leave this problem, let us see how we could have gone wrong in our choice of u and dv. Suppose we had originally let $u = e^x$ and $dv = x^2\,dx$. Then $du = e^x\,dx$, $v = \displaystyle\int x^2\,dx = \frac{x^3}{3}$, and Equation 60-3 becomes

$$\int x^2e^x\,dx = \frac{x^3e^x}{3} - \frac{1}{3}\int x^3e^x\,dx.$$

Although this equation is correct, it leaves us with the problem of finding $\int x^3e^x\,dx$, which is at least as difficult as the original problem. It is quite common to make such a false start, and when we do we just have to go back and start over.

Example 60-4. Find $\displaystyle\int_0^1 \operatorname{Tan}^{-1} x\,dx$.

Solution. We take $f(x) = \operatorname{Tan}^{-1} x$ and $g'(x) = 1$. Then $f'(x) = \dfrac{1}{1+x^2}$, and we can take $g(x) = x$. Thus Equation 60-1 becomes

$$\begin{aligned}\int_0^1 \operatorname{Tan}^{-1} x\,dx &= x\operatorname{Tan}^{-1} x\Big|_0^1 - \int_0^1 \frac{x}{1+x^2}\,dx\\ &= x\operatorname{Tan}^{-1} x\Big|_0^1 - \tfrac{1}{2}\ln(1+x^2)\Big|_0^1\\ &= \operatorname{Tan}^{-1} 1 - \tfrac{1}{2}\ln 2 \approx .44.\end{aligned}$$

If you study mathematics further or go on in fields in which mathematics is used, you will find that integration by parts is an important tool in theoretical investigations. The following example is a simplified version of a problem that arises in the study of differential equations.

Example 60-5. Suppose that u is a function such that $u(a) = u(b) = 0$. Show that

$$\int_a^b u(x)u''(x)\,dx = -\int_a^b [u'(x)]^2\,dx.$$

Solution. We will let $f(x) = u(x)$ and $g(x) = u'(x)$ in Equation 60-1. Then

$$\begin{aligned}\int_a^b u(x)u''(x)\,dx &= u(x)u'(x)\Big|_a^b - \int_a^b u'(x)u'(x)\,dx \\ &= 0 - \int_a^b [u'(x)]^2\,dx.\end{aligned}$$

Problems 60

1. Use integration by parts to find:
   (a) $\int x \sin x\,dx$ (b) $\int x \cos 2x\,dx$
   (c) $\int xe^{2x}\,dx$ (d) $\int t \sec^2 2t\,dt$
   (e) $\int x^5 \ln x\,dx$ (f) $\int \operatorname{Tan}^{-1} 2x\,dx$
   (g) $\int \operatorname{Sin}^{-1} x\,dx$ (h) $\int \operatorname{Cosh}^{-1} x\,dx$
   (i) $\int x(x + 25)^{100}\,dx$ (j) $\int xa^x\,dx$
2. Use integration by parts to evaluate the following integrals.
   (a) $\int_0^2 x(x-2)^4\,dx$ (b) $\int_0^1 xe^{3x}\,dx$
   (c) $\int_0^{\pi/2} x \cos x\,dx$ (d) $\int_0^1 \operatorname{Cos}^{-1} x\,dx$
   (e) $\int_1^2 (\ln x)^2\,dx$ (f) $\int_0^1 x \operatorname{Tan}^{-1} x\,dx$
3. It may be necessary to apply the integration by parts procedure more than once to find the following.
   (a) $\int x^2 \cos x\,dx$ (b) $\int x^4 (\ln x)^2\,dx$
   (c) $\int x^3 \operatorname{Tan}^{-1} x\,dx$ (d) $\int_1^2 (x-1)^2(x-2)^{10}\,dx$
   (e) $\int_0^{\pi/2} x^2 \sin x\,dx$ (f) $\int_0^1 x \operatorname{Sin}^{-1} x\,dx$
4. Find $\int \ln x\,dx$ by taking $u = \ln x$ and $dv = dx$ and using integration by parts.
5. Find $\int_a^b e^{-x} \cos 2x\,dx$ by the following procedure. First, take $u = e^{-x}$ and $dv = \cos 2x\,dx$. In the new integral that results from using the integration by parts procedure take $u = e^{-x}$ and $dv = \sin 2x\,dx$ to obtain the result

$$\int_a^b e^{-x} \cos 2x\,dx = \tfrac{1}{2}e^{-x} \sin 2x\Big|_a^b - \tfrac{1}{4}e^{-x} \cos 2x\Big|_a^b - \tfrac{1}{4}\int_a^b e^{-x} \cos 2x\,dx.$$

   Find $\int_a^b e^{-x} \cos 2x\,dx$ from this equation.
6. Find: (a) $\int x^3 \cos x^2\,dx$ (b) $\int x^5 e^{x^2}\,dx$
7. Verify the formula

$$\int xf'(x)\,dx = xf(x) - \int f(x)\,dx.$$

What specific formulas do you obtain by replacing $f(x)$ with $\csc^2 x$, $\cosh x$, and e^x?

8. Find the volume of the solid obtained by rotating about the X-axis the region bounded by the X-axis and the graph of the equation $y = \sqrt[4]{x^2(1-x)}$.

9. (a) Suppose that m is a positive integer and take $u = \sin^{m-1} x$ and $dv = \sin x\, dx$ in the formula for integration by parts to obtain the equation

$$\text{(i)} \quad \int_0^{\pi/2} \sin^m x\, dx = -\cos x \sin^{m-1} x \Big|_0^{\pi/2} + (m-1)\int_0^{\pi/2} \sin^{m-2} x \cos^2 x\, dx.$$

(b) In Equation (i) replace $\cos^2 x$ by $1 - \sin^2 x$ and solve the resulting equation for $\int_0^{\pi/2} \sin^m x\, dx$.

(c) Use the formula you obtained in part (b) to evaluate the integrals $\int_0^{\pi/2} \sin^5 x\, dx$ and $\int_0^{\pi/2} \sin^6 x\, dx$.

10. Use integration by parts to obtain the following formulas.

(a) $\int_0^a x^2 f'''(x)\, dx = a^2 f''(a) - 2af'(a) + 2f(a) - 2f(0)$.

(b) $\int_a^b f(x)g''(x)\, dx = [f(x)g'(x) - f'(x)g(x)]\Big|_a^b + \int_a^b f''(x)g(x)\, dx$.

11. What is wrong with the following argument? We start with the identity

$$\int_{\pi/6}^{\pi/3} \cot x\, dx = \int_{\pi/6}^{\pi/3} \cos x \csc x\, dx.$$

Now we use the integration by parts procedure with $u = \csc x$ and $dv = \cos x\, dx$ to evaluate the integral on the right. We have $du = -\csc x \cot x\, dx$ and $v = \sin x$. Since $uv = 1$, we have

$$\int_{\pi/6}^{\pi/3} \cot x\, dx = 1 + \int_{\pi/6}^{\pi/3} \sin x \csc x \cot x\, dx;$$

that is,

$$\int_{\pi/6}^{\pi/3} \cot x\, dx = 1 + \int_{\pi/6}^{\pi/3} \cot x\, dx,$$

from which it follows that

$$0 = 1.$$

61. Use of Integration Formulas

The most practical way to find an antiderivative is to look it up in a table. In addition to the Basic Integration Formulas in Table V, we have listed a number of Additional Integration Formulas. There are reference books in your school library that contain still more formulas. Any standard set of "mathematical tables" will contain a "table of integrals." You should learn how to use such tables.

Example 61-1. Find $\int \frac{dx}{x(3+4x)}$.

Solution. In this case we simply set $a = 3$, $b = 4$, and $u = x$ in Formula V-28 to obtain the equation

$$\int \frac{dx}{x(3 + 4x)} = \frac{1}{3} \ln \left| \frac{x}{3 + 4x} \right|.$$

Example 61-2. Evaluate $\int_0^{\pi/2} e^{-x} \sin 2x \, dx$.

Solution. Here we apply Formula V-35 with $a = -1$ and $b = 2$ to obtain

$$\begin{aligned} \int_0^{\pi/2} e^{-x} \sin 2x \, dx &= \left. \frac{e^{-x}[-\sin 2x - 2 \cos 2x]}{5} \right|_0^{\pi/2} \\ &= \tfrac{2}{5}[e^{-\pi/2} + 1]. \end{aligned}$$

Of course, we may have to use the method of substitution described in Section 58 in order to apply the formula listed in the table.

Example 61-3. Find $\int e^x \sec e^x \, dx$.

Solution. Here we let $u = e^x$. Then $du = e^x \, dx$, and so $\int e^x \sec e^x \, dx = \int \sec u \, du$. Now we may use Formula V-33. It tells us that $\int \sec u \, du = \ln |\sec u + \tan u|$, and hence we have $\int e^x \sec e^x \, dx = \ln |\sec e^x + \tan e^x|$.

Some of the formulas in Table V are *reduction formulas*. They may not give us the answer we seek directly, but they help us proceed one step in the right direction.

Example 61-4. Find $\int u^3 e^u \, du$.

Solution. If we apply Formula V-41 with $n = 3$ and $a = 1$, we have

(61-1) $$\int u^3 e^u \, du = u^3 e^u - 3 \int u^2 e^u \, du.$$

We have "reduced the exponent" of u from 3 to 2. Now we apply Formula V-41 again, this time with $n = 2$:

$$\int u^2 e^u \, du = u^2 e^u - 2 \int u e^u \, du.$$

Then Equation 61-1 becomes

(61-2) $$\int u^3 e^u \, du = u^3 e^u - 3u^2 e^u + 6 \int u e^u \, du.$$

Now the exponent of u is reduced to 1, and we apply Formula V-41 with $n = 1$:

$$\int u e^u \, du = u e^u - \int e^u \, du = u e^u - e^u.$$

When we substitute this result in Equation 61-2, we get the final answer:

$$\begin{aligned} \int u^3 e^u \, du &= u^3 e^u - 3u^2 e^u + 6u e^u - 6e^u \\ &= (u^3 - 3u^2 + 6u - 6)e^u \end{aligned}$$

Example 61-5. Evaluate $\int_0^{\pi/2} x^2 \sin x \, dx$.

Solution. We first apply Formula V-42 with $n = 2$ and $a = 1$:

$$(61\text{-}3) \qquad \int_0^{\pi/2} x^2 \sin x \, dx = -x^2 \cos x \Big|_0^{\pi/2} + 2 \int_0^{\pi/2} x \cos x \, dx$$
$$= 2 \int_0^{\pi/2} x \cos x \, dx.$$

Now we use Formula V-43 with $n = 1$:

$$\int_0^{\pi/2} x \cos x \, dx = x \sin x \Big|_0^{\pi/2} - \int_0^{\pi/2} \sin x \, dx$$
$$= \frac{\pi}{2} + \cos x \Big|_0^{\pi/2} = \frac{\pi}{2} - 1.$$

We substitute this result in Equation 61-3 to get our final answer:

$$\int_0^{\pi/2} x^2 \sin x \, dx = \pi - 2.$$

In the next section we shall have to find

$$\int \frac{(Bx + C) \, dx}{(x^2 + bx + c)^r},$$

where B, C, b, and c are given real numbers, with $b^2 - 4c < 0$, and r is a positive integer. Obviously the problem amounts to finding the antiderivatives

$$\int \frac{x \, dx}{(x^2 + bx + c)^r} \quad \text{and} \quad \int \frac{dx}{(x^2 + bx + c)^r}.$$

To solve this problem we simply use Formulas V-44 and V-45, if $r = 1$. If $r > 1$, we apply Formulas V-46 and V-47 as often as may be necessary till we reduce the problem to finding

$$\int \frac{dx}{x^2 + bx + c}.$$

Then Formula V-44 will apply since $b^2 - 4c < 0$.

Example 61-6. Find $\int \frac{(3x + 4) \, dx}{(x^2 - 2x + 2)^2}$.

Solution. Clearly,

$$(61\text{-}4) \qquad \int \frac{(3x + 4) \, dx}{(x^2 - 2x + 2)^2} = 3 \int \frac{x \, dx}{(x^2 - 2x + 2)^2} + 4 \int \frac{dx}{(x^2 - 2x + 2)^2}.$$

According to Formula V-47,

$$(61\text{-}5)\quad \int \frac{x\,dx}{(x^2-2x+2)^2} = \frac{-(4-2x)}{4(x^2-2x+2)} - \left(-\frac{2}{4}\right)\int \frac{dx}{(x^2-2x+2)}$$

$$= \frac{x-2}{2(x^2-2x+2)} + \frac{1}{2}\int \frac{dx}{x^2-2x+2}.$$

Now we use Formula V-44 to see that

$$(61\text{-}6)\quad \int \frac{dx}{x^2-2x+2} = \frac{2}{\sqrt{4}}\,\mathrm{Tan}^{-1}\left[\frac{2x-2}{\sqrt{4}}\right]$$

$$= \mathrm{Tan}^{-1}(x-1).$$

Therefore, Equation 61-5 becomes

$$(61\text{-}7)\quad \int \frac{x\,dx}{(x^2-2x+2)^2} = \frac{x-2}{2(x^2-2x+2)} + \frac{1}{2}\,\mathrm{Tan}^{-1}(x-1).$$

Now we turn to the second term on the right side of Equation 61-4. According to Formula V-46,

$$(61\text{-}8)\quad \int \frac{dx}{(x^2-2x+2)^2} = \frac{2x-2}{4(x^2-2x+2)} + \frac{2}{4}\int \frac{dx}{x^2-2x+2}$$

$$= \frac{x-1}{2(x^2-2x+2)} + \frac{1}{2}\int \frac{dx}{x^2-2x+2}$$

$$= \frac{x-1}{2(x^2-2x+2)} + \frac{1}{2}\,\mathrm{Tan}^{-1}(x-1).$$

(See Eq. 61-6.)

When we substitute Formulas 61-7 and 61-8 in Equation 61-4 we see that

$$\int \frac{(3x+4)\,dx}{(x^2-2x+2)} = \frac{3(x-2)+4(x-1)}{2(x^2-2x+2)} + \left(\frac{3}{2}+\frac{4}{2}\right)\mathrm{Tan}^{-1}(x-1)$$

$$= \frac{7x-10}{2(x^2-2x+2)} + \frac{7}{2}\,\mathrm{Tan}^{-1}(x-1).$$

Problems 61

Same as 340

1. With the aid of Table V and the method of substitution, find:

(a) $\int x^3 \ln x\,dx$

(b) $\int \frac{dt}{t(3t+4)^2}$

(c) $\int \frac{u\,du}{u^2+1}$

(d) $\int \frac{x\,dx}{(x+1)^2}$

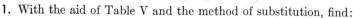

(e) $\int \frac{du}{u^2 + 4}$ (f) $\int e^{-2v} \cos 3v \, dv$

(g) $\int xe^{x^2} \sin 2x^2 \, dx$ (h) $\int \sqrt{4x^2 - 1} \, dx$

2. Use integration formulas to find:

(a) $\int \frac{\sec \sqrt{x}}{\sqrt{x}} \, dx$ (b) $\int \frac{e^x \, dx}{2e^{2x} + 3e^x + 4}$

(c) $\int \frac{\cot x \, dx}{2 \sin x + 3}$ (d) $\int \frac{\sqrt{4 - (\ln x)^2}}{x} \, dx$

(e) $\int \frac{\sinh x \, dx}{2 \cosh x + 4}$ (f) $\int \frac{dx}{x^2(2 + x)}$

3. Use appropriate reduction formulas to find:

(a) $\int x^3 e^{3x} \, dx$ (b) $\int \tan^8 x \, dx$

(c) $\int \tan^7 x \, dx$ (d) $\int \frac{dx}{(x^2 + 4)^3}$

(e) $\int xe^{2x} \, dx$ (f) $\int \frac{(2x + 1) \, dx}{(x^2 - 4x + 5)^2}$

4. Evaluate the following integrals:

(a) $\int_0^{\pi/2} \sin^8 x \, dx$ (b) $\int_0^{\pi/2} \sin^9 x \, dx$

(c) $\int_0^{\pi/3} \sin^5 3t \, dt$ (d) $\int_0^1 x^4 e^x \, dx$

(e) $\int_0^1 \frac{x \, dx}{x^2 - 4x + 5}$ (f) $\int_1^2 x^3 \ln x \, dx$

5. Find the area of the region bounded by the X-axis, the lines $x = 1$ and $x = 2$, and the graph of the equation $x^2 y + xy = 1$.

6. The region in the first quadrant bounded by the Y-axis, the lines $y = 1$ and $y = 4$, and the graph of the equation $yx^2(y + 1)^2 = 1$ is rotated about the Y-axis. Find the volume of the resulting solid.

7. Use the integration by parts procedure to "derive" the following integration formulas:
(a) V-35 (b) V-36 (c) V-38 (d) V-39

62. Antiderivatives of Rational Expressions

If n is a positive integer or 0 and if $a_0, a_1, \ldots, a_n$ are $n + 1$ real numbers, where $a_n \neq 0$, then the expression

$$P(x) = a_n x^n + a^{n-1} x^{n-1} + \cdots + a_0$$

is called a **polynomial of degree *n* in *x*** with real **coefficients** $a_0, a_1, \ldots, a_n$. A *ratio* of two polynomials is termed a **rational expression.** For example $\frac{3x^2 + 2x - 1}{x - 2}$ and $\frac{1}{x^2 + 1}$ are rational expressions. In general, a rational expression has the form

$$\text{(62-1)} \qquad F(x) = \frac{a_n x^n + a_{n-1}x^{n-1} + \cdots + a_0}{b_m x^m + b_{m-1}x^{m-1} + \cdots + b_0} = \frac{P(x)}{D(x)}.$$

You have studied polynomials in your earlier mathematics courses. You know how to add, subtract, and multiply two polynomials, and you know that there are theorems about factoring polynomials, and so on. We will now discuss a method of finding antiderivatives of rational expressions that is based on this algebraic theory.

The basic algebraic fact that we use here is that every rational expression $F(x)$ can be written as a sum of terms of the forms

$$\text{(62-2)} \qquad q_r x^r + q_{r-1}x^{r-1} + \cdots + q_0, \quad \frac{A}{(x-a)^r},$$

and

$$\frac{Bx + C}{(x^2 + bx + c)^r}, \quad \text{where} \quad b^2 - 4c < 0.$$

For example,

(62-3)

$$\frac{x^9 - 6x^8 + 19x^7 - 35x^6 + 34x^5 - 5x^4 - 30x^3 + 48x^2 - 39x + 12}{x^7 - 6x^6 + 17x^5 - 28x^4 + 28x^3 - 16x^2 + 4x}$$
$$= x^2 + 2 + \frac{3}{x} + \frac{2}{x-1} - \frac{1}{(x-1)^2} + \frac{1}{x^2 - 2x + 2} + \frac{-8x + 11}{(x^2 - 2x + 2)^2}.$$

Once we have "decomposed" $F(x)$ into such a sum, we can proceed to find an antiderivative of each term, and the sum of these antiderivatives will be an antiderivative of $F(x)$.

Before we go into the details of how to decompose a rational expression $F(x)$, let us point out that we already know how to find antiderivatives of the resulting Expressions 62-2. We treated expressions of the third type in the last section, and of course it is a simple matter to handle a polynomial $q_r x^r + \cdots + q_0$. To find $\int \frac{A\,dx}{(x-a)^r}$, we simply make the substitution $u = x - a$. Then

$$\int \frac{A\,dx}{(x-a)^r} = A \int \frac{du}{u^r} = A \int u^{-r}\,du,$$

and Formula V-1 applies if the positive integer r is greater than 1, and Formula V-9 applies if $r = 1$.

Example 62-1. Find $\int \frac{5\,dx}{(x+3)^3}$.

Solution. We let $u = x + 3$ and so

$$\int \frac{5\,dx}{(x+3)^3} = 5 \int u^{-3}\,du$$
$$= \frac{5u^{-2}}{-2} = \frac{-5}{2(x+3)^2}.$$

Now that we see how to find antiderivatives of the individual terms of the decomposition of a rational expression, let us turn to the matter of obtaining the decomposition. Suppose we have a rational expression such as $F(x)$ of Equation 62-1. If the degree of the numerator is as large as or larger than the degree of the denominator; that is, $n \geq m$, then we can use the process of long division to write

$$F(x) = Q(x) + \frac{R(x)}{D(x)}, \tag{62-4}$$

where $Q(x)$ is a polynomial, $q_r x^r + \cdots + q_0$, and $R(x)$ is a polynomial whose degree is actually less than the degree of $D(x)$. The first step in finding the decomposition of a rational expression $F(x)$ is to write it in the form indicated in Equation 62-4.

Example 62-2. Perform the first step in the decomposition of $\frac{x^3+1}{x-2}$ and find $\int \frac{(x^3+1)\,dx}{x-2}$.

Solution. We use long division

$$\begin{array}{r|l} & x^2 + 2x + 4 \\ \hline x - 2 & x^3 + 1 \\ & x^3 - 2x^2 \\ \hline & \quad 2x^2 \\ & \quad 2x^2 - 4x \\ \hline & \qquad 4x + 1 \\ & \qquad 4x - 8 \\ \hline & \qquad\qquad 9 \end{array}$$

to find the quotient $Q(x) = x^2 + 2x + 4$ and the remainder 9 that enable us to write

$$\frac{x^3+1}{x-2} = x^2 + 2x + 4 + \frac{9}{x-2}.$$

Notice that the degree of the remainder is 0, a number less than the degree (1) of the denominator $x - 2$. From this last equation we find that

$$\int \frac{x^3 + 1}{x - 2}\,dx = \int (x^2 + 2x + 4)\,dx + 9\int \frac{dx}{x - 2}$$

$$= \frac{x^3}{3} + x^2 + 4x + 9 \ln |x - 2|.$$

After we have performed any necessary long division we are left with the rational expression $\frac{R(x)}{D(x)}$ to decompose. The degree of $R(x)$ is less than the degree of $D(x)$. Now we factor the denominator $D(x)$ into the product of real factors. These factors can all be reduced to one of two forms, either $x - a$ or $x^2 + bx + c$, where $b^2 - 4c < 0$. (If $b^2 - 4c \geq 0$, we can factor $x^2 + bx + c$ into two real linear factors.) Some of the factors may be repeated, so our denominator will be a product of powers of such factors. [The so-called Fundamental Theorem of Algebra guarantees that such a factorization is (theoretically) possible.] For example, the denominator of the rational Expression 62-3 is the product $x(x - 1)^2(x^2 - 2x + 2)^2$.

Each factor $(x - a)^r$ *in the denominator leads to a sum of the form*

$$\frac{A_1}{x - a} + \frac{A_2}{(x - a)^2} + \cdots + \frac{A_r}{(x - a)^r}$$

in the decomposition of $F(x)$. For example, the factor $(x - 1)^2$ in the denominator of Expression 62-3 led to the sum $\frac{2}{x - 1} - \frac{1}{(x - 1)^2}$ in its decomposition. An example will show us how we proceed.

Example 62-3. Decompose the rational expression

$$\frac{x^2 - 7x + 8}{(x - 2)(x - 3)^2}.$$

Solution. We notice first that the degree of the numerator (2) is less than the degree of the denominator (3), so we can omit the step of long division. The factor $x - 2$ in the denominator leads to a term $\frac{A}{x - 2}$ and the factor $(x - 3)^2$ leads to a sum $\frac{B}{x - 3} + \frac{C}{(x - 3)^2}$ in the decomposition. In other words,

$$\text{(62-5)} \qquad \frac{x^2 - 7x + 8}{(x - 2)(x - 3)^2} = \frac{A}{x - 2} + \frac{B}{x - 3} + \frac{C}{(x - 3)^2},$$

and now we have to determine the numbers A, B, and C. To do so we multiply both sides of Equation 62-5 by $(x-2)(x-3)^2$ and obtain the equation

$$x^2 - 7x + 8 = A(x-3)^2 + B(x-2)(x-3) + C(x-2). \tag{62-6}$$

There are now two ways to proceed. We could multiply out the terms on the right in Equation 62-6 and obtain the equation

$$x^2 - 7x + 8 = (A+B)x^2 + (-6A - 5B + C)x + 9A + 6B - 2C.$$

Now when we equate the coefficients of corresponding powers of x, we obtain the following system of equations

$$\begin{aligned} A + B &= 1 \\ -6A - 5B + C &= -7 \\ 9A + 6B - 2C &= 8. \end{aligned}$$

We find that the solution to this system of algebraic equations is $A = -2$, $B = 3$, and $C = -4$.

We can arrive at the same numbers by means of a somewhat simpler calculation. Equation 62-6 is to be valid for each real number x. If we set, in turn, $x = 2$, 3, and 0, we get the three equations

$$\begin{aligned} A &= -2 \\ C &= -4 \\ 9A + 6B - 2C &= 8. \end{aligned}$$

The first two equations give us A and C, and then the third equation tells us that $B = 3$. Thus both methods give us the decomposition

$$\frac{x^2 - 7x + 8}{(x-2)(x-3)^2} = \frac{-2}{x-2} + \frac{3}{x-3} - \frac{4}{(x-3)^2}.$$

If a factor of the form $(x^2 + bx + c)^r$ appears in the denominator of our rational expression, then in its decomposition we will have a sum of terms of the form

$$\frac{B_1x + C_1}{(x^2 + bx + c)} + \frac{B_2x + C_2}{(x^2 + bx + c)^2} + \cdots + \frac{B_rx + C_r}{(x^2 + bx + c)^r}.$$

For example, the decomposition shown in Equation 62-3 contains the sum

$$\frac{1}{(x^2 - 2x + 2)} + \frac{-8x + 11}{(x^2 - 2x + 2)^2}.$$

Again, an example will show us how we proceed.

Example 62-4. Decompose the rational expression

$$\frac{2x^2 + 1}{(x^2 - x + 1)^2}.$$

Solution. We must find numbers A, B, C, and D such that

$$\frac{2x^2 + 1}{(x^2 - x + 1)^2} = \frac{Ax + B}{(x^2 - x + 1)} + \frac{Cx + D}{(x^2 - x + 1)^2}.$$

We multiply both sides of this equation by $(x^2 - x + 1)^2$ and obtain the equation

$$\begin{aligned} 2x^2 + 1 &= (Ax + B)(x^2 - x + 1) + Cx + D, \\ &= Ax^3 + (-A + B)x^2 + (A - B + C)x + (B + D). \end{aligned}$$

Now we equate the coefficients of corresponding powers of x:

$$\begin{aligned} A &= 0, \\ -A + B &= 2, \\ A - B + C &= 0, \\ B + D &= 1. \end{aligned}$$

When we solve this system of equations, we find $B = 2$, $C = 2$, and $D = -1$, and we have

$$\frac{2x^2 + 1}{(x^2 - x + 1)^2} = \frac{2}{x^2 - x + 1} + \frac{2x - 1}{(x^2 - x + 1)^2}.$$

Example 62-5. Find

$$\int \frac{6x^3 + 5x^2 + 21x + 12}{x(x + 1)(x^2 + 4)}\, dx.$$

Solution. We first write

$$\frac{6x^3 + 5x^2 + 21x + 12}{x(x + 1)(x^2 + 4)} = \frac{A}{x} + \frac{B}{x + 1} + \frac{Cx + D}{x^2 + 4}.$$

When we clear of fractions, we obtain the equation

$$\begin{aligned} 6x^3 + 5x^2 + 21x + 12 &= A(x + 1)(x^2 + 4) + Bx(x^2 + 4) \\ &\qquad + (Cx + D)x(x + 1) \\ &= (A + B + C)x^3 + (A + D + C)x^2 \\ &\qquad + (4A + 4B + D)x + 4A. \end{aligned}$$

Therefore,

$$\begin{aligned} A + B + C &= 6, \\ A + C + D &= 5, \\ 4A + 4B + D &= 21, \\ 4A &= 12. \end{aligned}$$

Now we solve this system of equations and find $A = 3$, $B = 2$, $C = 1$, $D = 1$, and so

$$\int \frac{6x^3 + 5x^2 + 21x + 12}{x(x+1)(x^2+4)}\, dx = \int \frac{3}{x}\, dx + \int \frac{2}{x+1}\, dx + \int \frac{x+1}{x^2+4}\, dx.$$

We will leave it to you to show that we can use our integration formulas to write

$$\int \frac{6x^3 + 5x^2 + 21x + 12}{x(x+1)(x^2+4)}\, dx = 3 \ln |x| + 2 \ln |x+1| + \frac{1}{2} \ln (x^2+4)$$
$$+ \frac{1}{2} \operatorname{Arctan} \frac{x}{2} = \ln |x^3(x+1)^2 \sqrt{x^2+4}| + \frac{1}{2} \operatorname{Arctan} \frac{x}{2}.$$

Problems 62

1. Decompose the following rational expressions.
   (a) $\dfrac{x^3}{x+1}$ (b) $\dfrac{x}{x^2+x}$
   (c) $\dfrac{5x+2}{x^2-4}$ (d) $\dfrac{x^2}{x^2-x}$
   (e) $\dfrac{5x+2}{x^2+4}$ (f) $\dfrac{1}{x^2(x+1)}$
2. Find an antiderivative of each of the expressions in the preceding problem.
3. Use the method of this section to find:
   (a) $\displaystyle\int \frac{3x^2+4x+4}{x(x+1)(x+2)}\, dx$ (b) $\displaystyle\int \frac{5x^2-3}{x^3-x}\, dx$
   (c) $\displaystyle\int \frac{x^3}{(x+1)^2}\, dx$ (d) $\displaystyle\int \frac{dx}{x^3+4x}$
   (e) $\displaystyle\int \frac{(x+1)^2}{x^3}\, dx$ (f) $\displaystyle\int \frac{x^3+1}{x(x-1)^3}\, dx$
   (g) $\displaystyle\int \frac{t^4-8}{t^3+2t^2}\, dt$ (h) $\displaystyle\int \frac{x^3+3x}{x^4+2x^2+1}\, dx$
4. Use the method of this section to "derive" the following formulas.
   (a) V-27 (b) V-29

5. Use the method of this section to "derive" the formula

$$\int \frac{du}{u^2 - a^2} = \frac{1}{2a} \ln \left| \frac{u - a}{u + a} \right|.$$

(See Formulas V-22 and V-23.)

6. Find:

(a) $\int \frac{3x^2 + 2x + 1}{(x + 1)(x^2 + x + 1)} dx$ (b) $\int \frac{(x + 1)^2 \, dx}{(x^2 + 1)^2}$

(c) $\int \frac{(x^2 + x) \, dx}{(x - 1)(x^2 + 1)}$ (d) $\int \frac{dt}{t^4 + t^2}$

(e) $\int \frac{2 \, dz}{z^4 - 1}$ (f) $\int \frac{x^5 \, dx}{(x^2 + 4)^2}$

7. Evaluate:

(a) $\int_1^2 \frac{(x - 3) \, dx}{x^3 + x^2}$ (b) $\int_1^3 \frac{(2 - t^2) \, dt}{t^3 + 3t^2 + 2t}$

(c) $\int_0^1 \frac{dx}{x^3 + 1}$ (d) $\int_0^1 \frac{z \, dz}{(z + 2)(z^2 + 1)}$

(e) $\int_3^4 \frac{5x^3 - 4x}{x^4 - 16} dx$ (f) $\int_0^1 \frac{x \, dx}{x^3 + 1}$

8. One method of "deriving" the formula for $\int \csc u \, du$ is to proceed as follows. Let $u = 2v$ so that

$$\int \csc u \, du = \int \frac{du}{\sin u} = \int \frac{dv}{\sin v \cos v} = \int \frac{\cos v \, dv}{\sin v \cos^2 v}$$

$$= \int \frac{\cos v \, dv}{\sin v(1 - \sin^2 v)}.$$

Now make the substitution $x = \sin v$, and use the method of this section to obtain Formula V-34.

63. Integrands That Contain Values of the Trigonometric Functions

If an integrand contains values of the trigonometric functions, the use of appropriate trigonometric identities can often lead to a simplifying substitution. Some of the most useful trigonometric identities for this purpose are

$$\cos^2 x + \sin^2 x = 1$$
$$\tan^2 x = \sec^2 x - 1 \tag{63-1}$$
$$\cot^2 x = \csc^2 x - 1,$$

and

$$\sin^2 x = \frac{1 - \cos 2x}{2}$$
$$\cos^2 x = \frac{1 + \cos 2x}{2}. \tag{63-2}$$

Example 63-1. Find $\int \tan^2 x\, dx$.

Solution. Using the second of Equations 63-1, we have

$$\begin{aligned}\int \tan^2 x\, dx &= \int (\sec^2 x - 1)\, dx = \int \sec^2 x\, dx - \int dx \\ &= \tan x - x.\end{aligned}$$

Example 63-2. One arch of the sine curve is rotated about the X-axis. What is the volume of the resulting solid?

Solution. Let us consider that part of the graph of the equation $y = \sin x$ for which $0 \leq x \leq \pi$, so the volume of our solid of revolution is

$$V = \pi \int_0^\pi y^2\, dx = \pi \int_0^\pi \sin^2 x\, dx.$$

Now we replace $\sin^2 x$ with $\dfrac{1 - \cos 2x}{2}$ to get

$$\begin{aligned}V &= \frac{\pi}{2} \int_0^\pi (1 - \cos 2x)\, dx \\ &= \frac{\pi}{2}\left[x - \frac{\sin 2x}{2}\right]\Bigg|_0^\pi = \frac{\pi^2}{2}.\end{aligned}$$

Often we can reduce a problem to finding either

$$\int f(\cos x) \sin x\, dx \text{ or } \int f(\sin x) \cos x\, dx.$$

In the first case, we let $u = \cos x$. Then $du = -\sin x\, dx$ and we have

$$\int f(\cos x) \sin x\, dx = -\int f(u)\, du.$$

Similarly, the substitution $u = \sin x$ gives us

$$\int f(\sin x) \cos x\, dx = \int f(u)\, du$$

in the second case.

Example 63-3. Find $\displaystyle\int \frac{\cos x}{\sqrt{9 - \sin^2 x}}\, dx$.

Solution. Notice that the integrand is of the form $f(\sin x) \cos x$. If we let $u = \sin x$, then $du = \cos x\, dx$, and we have

$$\begin{aligned}\int \frac{\cos x}{\sqrt{9 - \sin^2 x}}\, dx &= \int \frac{1}{\sqrt{9 - u^2}}\, du \\ &= \operatorname{Sin}^{-1}\left(\frac{u}{3}\right) \\ &= \operatorname{Sin}^{-1}\left(\frac{\sin x}{3}\right).\end{aligned}$$

Example 63-4. Evaluate the integral

$$\int_0^{\pi/2} \sin^4 x \cos^5 x \, dx.$$

Solution. In order to write $\sin^4 x \cos^5 x$ in the form $f(\sin x) \cos x$, we first express $\cos^4 x$ in terms of $\sin x$. Since $\cos^2 x = 1 - \sin^2 x$, we see that $\cos^4 x = (1 - \sin^2 x)^2$. Therefore,

$$\int_0^{\pi/2} \sin^4 x \cos^5 x \, dx = \int_0^{\pi/2} \sin^4 x (1 - \sin^2 x)^2 \cdot \cos x \, dx.$$

Now we let $u = \sin x$. Then $du = \cos x \, dx$, and $u = 0$ when $x = 0$ and $u = 1$ when $x = \pi/2$. Therefore, our integral becomes

$$\int_0^1 u^4(1 - u^2)^2 \, du = \int_0^1 (u^4 - 2u^6 + u^8) \, du$$
$$= \tfrac{8}{315}.$$

We can use the method illustrated in the preceding example to find an antiderivative of the form

$$\int \sin^n x \cos^m x \, dx$$

if at least one of the exponents m or n is an odd positive integer. If $m = 2k + 1$, then we write

$$\sin^n x \cos^m x = \sin^n x \cos^{2k} x \cos x = \sin^n x \, (1 - \sin^2 x)^k \cos x.$$

Then the integrand is of the form

$$f(\sin x) \cos x,$$

and we use the substitution $u = \sin x$. If $n = 2k + 1$, the integrand can be written as

$$\sin^n x \cos^m x = (1 - \cos^2 x)^k \cos^m x \sin x = f(\cos x) \sin x,$$

and we use the substitution $u = \cos x$.

Example 63-5. Find $\int \sin^3 x \, dx$.

Solution. The integrand is of the form $\sin^n x \cos^m x$, with $n = 3$ and $m = 0$. We have

$$\int \sin^3 x \, dx = \int (1 - \cos^2 x) \sin x \, dx.$$

If we set $u = \cos x$, then $du = -\sin x \, dx$, and we have

$$\int \sin^3 x \, dx = -\int (1 - u^2) \, du = -u + \frac{u^3}{3}$$
$$= -\cos x + \frac{\cos^3 x}{3}.$$

Although we have hardly begun to list the many trigonometric substitution tricks that have been developed, we shall not proceed much farther in this direction. We bring this section to a close with just one more example. This example shows how we can use the trigonometric identities

$$\begin{aligned} 2 \sin A \cos B &= \sin (A + B) + \sin (A - B), \\ 2 \sin A \sin B &= \cos (A - B) - \cos (A + B), \\ 2 \cos A \cos B &= \cos (A - B) + \cos (A + B). \end{aligned} \tag{63-3}$$

Example 63-6. In certain applications of mathematics we meet the expression

$$B(m, n) = \int_{-\pi}^{\pi} \sin mx \sin nx \, dx,$$

where m and n are positive integers. Evaluate $B(5, 3)$ and $B(5, 5)$.

Solution. From the second of Formulas 63-3 we have

$$\sin mx \sin nx = \frac{\cos (m - n)x - \cos (m + n)x}{2},$$

and so

$$B(m, n) = \tfrac{1}{2} \int_{-\pi}^{\pi} [\cos (m - n)x - \cos (m + n)x] \, dx. \tag{63-4}$$

Therefore,

$$\begin{aligned} B(5, 3) &= \tfrac{1}{2} \int_{-\pi}^{\pi} (\cos 2x - \cos 8x) \, dx \\ &= \frac{1}{2} \left[\frac{\sin 2x}{2} - \frac{\sin 8x}{8} \right] \Bigg|_{-\pi}^{\pi} \\ &= \frac{\sin 2\pi}{4} - \frac{\sin 8\pi}{16} + \frac{\sin 2\pi}{4} - \frac{\sin 8\pi}{16} = 0. \end{aligned}$$

From Equation 63-4 we have

$$\begin{aligned} B(5, 5) &= \tfrac{1}{2} \int_{-\pi}^{\pi} (1 - \cos 10x) \, dx \\ &= \frac{1}{2} \left[x - \frac{\sin 10x}{10} \right] \Bigg|_{-\pi}^{\pi} = \pi. \end{aligned}$$

You should be able to show that $B(m, n) = 0$ if m and n are unequal positive integers, while $B(m, m) = \pi$ for every positive integer m.

Problems 63

1. Find:
   (a) $\int \cot^2 x\, dx$
   (b) $\int \sin x \cos^2 x\, dx$
   (c) $\int \cos^3 x \sin^2 x\, dx$
   (d) $\int \tan^2 x \sec^2 x\, dx$
   (e) $\int \sin x \sqrt{\cos x}\, dx$
   (f) $\int \sqrt[3]{\cos^2 x} \sin^5 x\, dx$
2. Make substitutions using Equation 63-2 to find:
   (a) $\int \cos^2 3x\, dx$
   (b) $\int \sin^2 \left(\frac{x}{2}\right) dx$
   (c) $\int \sin^4 x\, dx$
   (d) $\int \sin^2 t \cos^2 t\, dt$
3. Apply Formula V-38 to find $\int \sin^3 x\, dx$. Compare your result with Example 63-5.
4. Find:
   (a) $\int \sec^5 x \sin x\, dx$
   (b) $\int \ln (\sin x) \cot x\, dx$
   (c) $\int \tan^2 x \cos x\, dx$
   (d) $\int \tan^4 x\, dx$
5. Let m and n be integers. Show that

$$\int_{-\pi}^{\pi} \cos mx \sin nx\, dx = 0.$$

6. Let m and n be positive integers and let

$$A(m, n) = \int_{-\pi}^{\pi} \cos mx \cos nx\, dx.$$

   Show that $A(m, n) = 0$ if $m \neq n$ and that $A(m, m) = \pi$.
7. Find:
   (a) $\int \cos 4x \cos 3x\, dx$
   (b) $\int \cos 4x \sin 3x\, dx$
   (c) $\int \sin 4x \sin 3x\, dx$
   (d) $\int \sin 4x \cos 3x\, dx$
8. Use the substitution $t = \text{Tan}^{-1} u$ and Formula V-20 to find $\int \sec t\, dt$. Compare your result with Formula V-33.
9. The region bounded by the X-axis and the graphs of the equations $y = \text{Sin}^{-1} x$ and $y = \text{Cos}^{-1} x$ is rotated about the Y-axis. Find the volume of the resulting solid.
10. Evaluate:
    (a) $\int_0^{\pi} |\cos^3 t|\, dt$
    (b) $\int_{-\pi}^{\pi} |\sin^5 t|\, dt$

64. The Differential Equation $D_xF(x) = f(x)$

By definition, $F(x)$ is an antiderivative of $f(x)$ if it satisfies the differential equation

$$D_xF(x) = f(x). \tag{64-1}$$

Thus, for example, $\sin x$ is an antiderivative of $\cos x$, since $D_x \sin x = \cos x$; $x^3 + 4$ is an antiderivative of $3x^2$, since $D_x(x^3 + 4) = 3x^2$, and so on. Therefore, finding an antiderivative of $f(x)$ is equivalent to finding $F(x)$ so that $y = F(x)$ satisfies the differential equation

$$D_x y = f(x). \tag{64-2}$$

Up to now we have been interested in solving differential equations such as Equation 64-1 or 64-2 so that we could evaluate an integral $\int_a^b f(x)\,dx$ by means of the formula

$$\int_a^b f(x)\,dx = F(x)\Big|_a^b = F(b) - F(a).$$

For this purpose, *any* solution of Equation 64-1 will do. For example, suppose we wish to find

$$\int_1^2 3x^2\,dx.$$

We first solve the differential equation

$$D_xF(x) = 3x^2 \tag{64-3}$$

For $F(x)$, and then

$$\int_1^2 3x^2\,dx = F(2) - F(1).$$

Equation 64-3 has infinitely many solutions, two of which are given by the equations $F(x) = x^3 + 4$ and $F(x) = x^3 - 13$. Any solution can be used to evaluate our integral; thus

$$\int_1^2 3x^2\,dx = (x^3 + 4)\Big|_1^2 = (2^3 + 4) - (1^3 + 4) = 2^3 - 1^3 = 7,$$

and

$$\int_1^2 3x^2\,dx = (x^3 - 13)\Big|_1^2 = (2^3 - 13) - (1^3 - 13) = 2^3 - 1^3 = 7.$$

There are times, however, when just any solution of Equation 64-1 is not satisfactory; only one solution will do. In this section we will consider some examples of such problems.

We will treat the problem of finding solutions of differential equations having the form of Equation 64-1 in the following way. We first find the general form that all solutions of our given differential equation must have, and then we select the specific solution we want. In Section 21 we pointed out that if $F(x)$ satisfies Equation 64-1, then so does $F(x) + C$ for every number C, and conversely (see Theorem 21-5) that every antiderivative of $f(x)$ must be of the form $F(x) + C$ for some number C. Therefore, if y satisfies the equation $D_x y = f(x)$, then $y = F(x) + C$. If we have additional information about y, then we can determine C.

Example 64-1. Solve the differential equation $D_x y = e^x$.

Solution. By inspection, we see that one antiderivative of e^x is e^x itself. Therefore, every solution of our differential equation is given by an equation of the form $y = e^x + C$.

Example 64-2. At each point (x, y) of a certain graph, the slope is given by the formula $m = \sec^2 x$. Furthermore, the graph contains the point $(\pi/4, 3)$. What is the equation of the graph?

Solution. Since the slope of the graph is $D_x y$, we see that y must satisfy the differential equation $D_x y = \sec^2 x$. One antiderivative of $\sec^2 x$ is $\tan x$, so we must have $y = \tan x + C$, where C is chosen so that the graph contains the point $(\pi/4, 3)$. Thus we must have $3 = \tan \pi/4 + C$, and hence $C = 2$. The equation of our curve is therefore $y = \tan x + 2$.

Example 64-3. Find y if $y' = \dfrac{x}{\sqrt{x^2 - 16}}$ and $y = 5$ when $x = 5$.

Solution. We first find an antiderivative $\displaystyle\int \frac{x\,dx}{\sqrt{x^2 - 16}}$ of $\dfrac{x}{\sqrt{x^2 - 16}}$. We set $u = x^2 - 16$, so $du = 2x\,dx$, and

$$\int \frac{x\,dx}{\sqrt{x^2 - 16}} = \frac{1}{2}\int \frac{du}{\sqrt{u}} = u^{1/2} = \sqrt{x^2 - 16}.$$

Therefore, $y = \sqrt{x^2 - 16} + C$, where the number C is to be chosen so that $y = 5$ when $x = 5$. Thus $5 = \sqrt{25 - 16} + C$; that is, $C = 2$. Finally, then, we have

$$y = \sqrt{x^2 - 16} + 2.$$

Let us recall that if a body is displaced s feet from some initial position t seconds after some initial instant, then the numbers $D_t s = v$ and $D_t^2 s = D_t v = a$ represent its velocity and acceleration. The acceleration of an unsupported body in a vacuum at the surface of the earth is approximately -32 feet per second per second. (The minus sign simply indicates that we will measure distance by means of a number scale pointing upwards.) Let us take the origin of the number scale on the surface of the earth. Then the differential equation governing the motion of a falling body is

$$D_t^2 s = -32 \quad \text{or} \quad D_t v = -32.$$

Now we will solve this differential equation under the assumption that our body has a velocity of v_0 feet per second when $t = 0$ and is s_0 feet above the surface of the earth at that instant. Since $D_t v = -32$, it follows that $v = -32t + C$ for some suitably chosen number C. We must have $v = v_0$ when $t = 0$, so we see that C must be v_0; that is,

$$v = -32t + v_0.$$

This last equation can be written as the differential equation

$$D_t s = -32t + v_0,$$

and so

$$s = -16t^2 + v_0 t + K,$$

where K is a number to be determined. Since $s = s_0$ when $t = 0$, we have $K = s_0$ and our final equation for s is

(64-4) $$s = -16t^2 + v_0 t + s_0.$$

Example 64-4. You are in a hotel window 100 feet up with a paper bag full of water. A man is walking toward the spot directly under your window at the rate of 10 feet per second. If you throw the bag straight down when he is 20 feet from the spot, how fast should you throw it?

Solution. We may use Equation 64-4 to find the initial velocity v_0. We are told that the initial height is $s_0 = 100$. Furthermore, since the target will be in position when $t = 2$, we see that we want $s = 0$ at that time. Therefore, Equation 64-4 becomes

$$0 = -16 \cdot 2^2 + 2v_0 + 100.$$

From this equation we find that $v_0 = -18$. We must throw the bag with a speed of 18 feet per second (the minus sign indicates that we are to throw the bag downward).

We pointed out in Section 46 (see Theorem 46-1) that if f is a continuous function on the interval $[a, b]$, and if $F(x) = \int_{x_0}^{x} f(t)\,dt$, where x_0 is any number in $[a, b]$, then $F'(x) = f(x)$. Therefore, every solution of the differential equation

(64-5) $$y' = f(x)$$

is given by an equation of the form

(64-6) $$y = \int_{x_0}^{x} f(t)\,dt + C,$$

for some number C. It may be necessary to use graphical techniques or other approximation methods to calculate the values of the function defined by Equation 64-6, but they can be calculated. In fact, by using modern computing machines, it usually isn't a great deal of trouble to calculate these values. Therefore, we can really solve "all" differential equations of the type of Equation 64-5.

Example 64-5. The graph of a function f is shown in Fig. 64-1. Let y satisfy the differential equation $y' = f(x)$ and be such that $y = 3$ when $x = 0$. Find y when $x = 2$, 3, and 6.

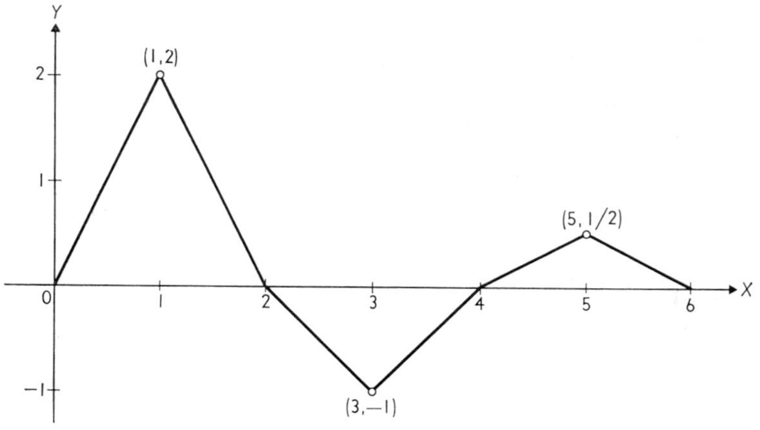

Figure 64-1

Solution. According to Equation 64-6 with $x_0 = 0$,

$$y = \int_0^x f(t)\,dt + C,$$

where C is a number to be determined. Since $y = 3$ when $x = 0$,

$$3 = \int_0^0 f(t)\,dt + C = 0 + C.$$

Hence $C = 3$, and so

$$y = \int_0^x f(t)\,dt + 3. \tag{64-7}$$

Thus when $x = 2$, $y = \int_0^2 f(t)\,dt + 3$.

To evaluate the integral $\int_0^2 f(t)\,dt$, we notice that it is simply the area of the triangle based on the interval [0, 2] and with vertex (1, 2). The base of this triangle is 2 units long, and its altitude is 2, so its area is 2 square units. Thus

$$\int_0^2 f(t)\,dt = 2, \text{ and } y = 2 + 3 = 5 \text{ when } x = 2.$$

When $x = 3$,

$$y = \int_0^3 f(t)\,dt + 3 = \int_0^2 f(t)\,dt + \int_2^3 f(t)\,dt + 3$$

$$= 2 + \int_2^3 f(t)\,dt + 3 = 5 + \int_2^3 f(t)\,dt.$$

To evaluate the integral $\int_2^3 f(t)\,dt$, we see from Fig. 64-1 that it is simply the negative of the area of a triangle whose base is 1 and altitude is 1. Therefore,

$$\int_2^3 f(t)\,dt = -\tfrac{1}{2},$$

so

$$y = 5 - \tfrac{1}{2} = \tfrac{9}{2} \text{ when } x = 3.$$

When $x = 6$,

$$y = \int_0^6 f(t)\,dt + 3 = \int_0^2 f(t)\,dt + \int_2^4 f(t)\,dt + \int_4^6 f(t)\,dt + 3.$$

We again evaluate our integrals by interpreting them as areas, and we get

$$y = 2 - 1 + \tfrac{1}{2} + 3 = \tfrac{9}{2}.$$

The following table lists the answers to our problem

x	y
2	5
3	$\frac{9}{2}$
6	$\frac{9}{2}$

Problems 64

1. Find the equations of the graphs that contain the given points and whose slopes are expressed by the given equations.
   (a) $m = 3$, $(1, -1)$ (b) $m = (x + 1)/x$, $(1, 3)$
   (c) $m = x \sin x^2$, $(\sqrt{\pi}, 2)$ (d) $m = e^{2x}$, $(\ln 2, 5)$
2. Find the formula for $f(x)$ if:
   (a) $f'(x) = \sqrt{2x}$ and $f(2) = 2$
   (b) $f'(x) = e^{2x}$ and $f(0) = 0$
   (c) $f'(x) = \dfrac{\cos(\ln x)}{x}$ and $f(1) = 2$
   (d) $f'(x) = \dfrac{3}{2 + x}$ and $f(5) = \ln 7$.

3. Find $f(x)$ if you know that $f''(x) = 3 \sin x + 2 \cos x$, $f(0) = 1$, and $f'(0) = -1$.
4. Find $f(2)$ if you know that $f''(x) = 6x^2 - 2$, $f(0) = 1$, and $f'(0) = 5$.
5. Use an integral to express the solution of the differential equation $y' = f(x)$ subject to the condition $y = 2$ when $x = 1$ if:
(a) $f(x) = |x|$ (b) $f(x) = e^{-x^2}$
6. Show that you cannot choose a number x_0 such that the equation $f(x) = \int_{x_0}^{x} \cos t \, dt$ supplies the solution to the differential equation $f'(x) = \cos x$ for which $f(0) = 2$. (This example shows that it is necessary to include the number C in Equation 64-6.)
7. Compute $f(2)$ if $f'(x) = \sqrt{1 + x^3}$ and $f(0) = 0$. Use four subintervals and
(a) The Trapezoidal Rule (b) Simpson's Rule
8. Find the equation of the curve that contains the points (2, 1) and (4, −2) if the slope of the curve at every point is proportional to the X-coordinate of the point.
9. A particle moves along a line so that its acceleration is given by the equation $a = \sin t^2$, $(t \geq 0)$. At what times is the velocity a maximum?
10. A ball is thrown directly upward with an initial velocity of v_0. One second later a second ball is thrown directly upward along the path of the first ball and with an initial velocity of $2v_0$. The second ball collides with the first ball just as the first ball reaches the top of its upward flight. Find v_0. (Neglect the radii of the balls.)
11. A ball is thrown directly upward with an initial velocity of v_0, and t_0 seconds later a second ball is thrown directly upward along the path of the first ball and with an initial velocity of kv_0. Is it possible to choose t_0 and k in such a way that the two balls collide just as both of them reach the top of their upward flight? (Neglect the radii of the balls.)

65. The Differential Notation

We have said that the only role played by the symbol dx in the integral $\int_a^b f(x)\, dx$ is to identify the variable of integration. Thus

$$\int_0^2 6tx^2 \, dx = 2tx^3 \Big|_{x=0}^{x=2} = 16t$$

and

$$\int_0^2 6tx^2 \, dt = 3t^2 x^2 \Big|_{t=0}^{t=2} = 12x^2.$$

When we make the substitution that replaces the variable of integration x with the variable of integration u, we find it convenient to assume that the "indicators" dx and du are related by the equation

$$du = D_x u \, dx. \tag{65-1}$$

Since we have not interpreted dx and du as numbers, perhaps we should not think of this equation in the usual way—as a relation among numbers. For us, Equation 65-1 means that when making a substitution under an integral sign we get the correct result if we replace $D_x u\,dx$ with du. But as we have already indicated, however, we won't go wrong if we do treat this equation as if du and dx were numbers.

There are many instances in mathematics in which we find it convenient to perform such purely formal manipulations with dx and du. For example, suppose we divide both sides of Equation 65-1 by dx. Then we obtain the equation

$$\frac{du}{dx} = D_x u. \tag{65-2}$$

We take this equation as the *definition* of the symbol $\frac{du}{dx}$. Notice that since $D_x u$ is a well-defined number, we have a perfectly good definition of the "quotient" $\frac{du}{dx}$ even though we haven't defined the numerator and denominator individually. This **differential notation** for the derivative is due to Leibnitz; you will find it widely used in mathematics. For example, if $y = \sin x$, then we write $\frac{dy}{dx} = \cos x$, or even $\frac{d(\sin x)}{dx} = \cos x$. We have used various notations for the derivative, $f'(x)$, $D_x y$, y', and $D_x f(x)$ throughout this book so that you would get experience using the different notations. From now on, we will also use the differential notation $\frac{dy}{dx}$. In the differential notation, second and third derivatives are written as $\frac{d^2y}{dx^2}$ and $\frac{d^3y}{dx^3}$, and higher derivatives are treated in a similar manner. Thus $\frac{d^4y}{dx^4}$ represents the fourth derivative of y whereas $\left(\frac{dy}{dx}\right)^4$ is the fourth power of the first derivative. Of course, these numbers are *not* always equal as you can see by setting $y = e^x$, for example. It might help you to remember this new symbolism for higher derivatives if you think of the symbol $\frac{d}{dx}$ as replacing the symbol D_x. Then $D_x^2 y = \left(\frac{d}{dx}\right)^2 y = \frac{d^2y}{dx^2}$, and so on.

The differential notation makes a number of formulas easy to remember. But it is misleading, too, for it makes certain basic theorems of calculus look like trivial algebraic identities, which they are not. For example, if we replace $D_x y$, $D_u y$, and $D_x u$ with $\frac{dy}{dx}$, $\frac{dy}{du}$, and $\frac{du}{dx}$ in the Chain Rule Equation $D_x y = D_u y D_x u$, we obtain the equation

$$\frac{dy}{dx} = \frac{dy}{du}\frac{du}{dx}. \tag{65-3}$$

In like manner, the equation connecting derivatives of inverse functions, $D_y x = 1/D_x y$, becomes

$$\frac{dx}{dy} = 1/\frac{dy}{dx}. \tag{65-4}$$

Written this way, these formulas are very attractive; anyone who can perform the simplest arithmetic with fractions can "see" that they are true. The only drawback is that the symbols dx, dy, and du alone don't have any meaning for us; only *quotients* of these symbols have been defined (Equation 65-2). Nevertheless, Equations 65-3, and 65-4 are correct, as we have shown earlier.

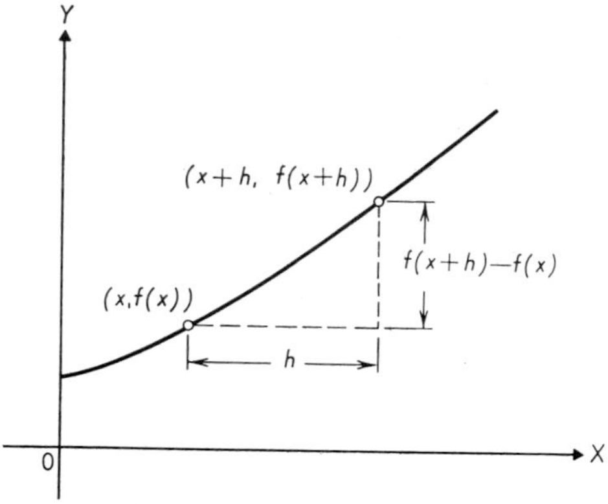

Figure 65-1

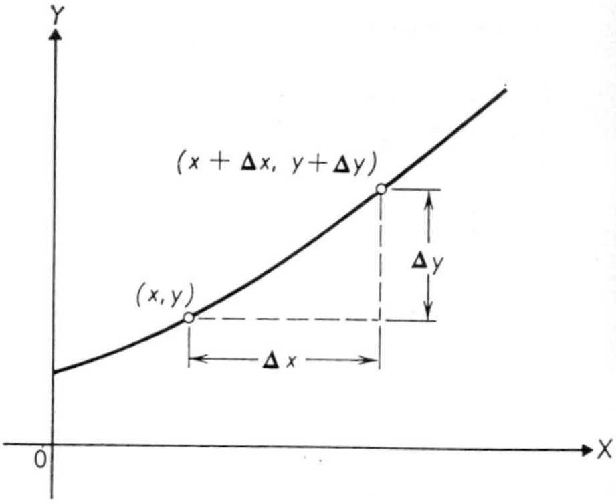

Figure 65-2

Authors who use the differential notation for the derivative may also use a somewhat different notation for a difference quotient from the one we have been using. Let us recall the definition of the derivative of $f(x)$. If f is a given function and x is a point in its domain, then we choose a number h and form the difference quotient

$$\frac{f(x + h) - f(x)}{h} \tag{65-5}$$

Fig. 65-1 shows the geometrical significance of the Difference Quotient 65-5. This quotient is the slope of the chord joining the points $(x, f(x))$ and $(x + h, f(x + h))$ of the graph of the equation $y = f(x)$. The numerator of the difference quotient is the difference of the Y-coordinates of the two points, and the denominator is the difference of the X-coordinates. Another common notation used in labeling the same picture is illustrated in Fig. 65-2. Here the difference between the X-coordinates is denoted by Δx, and the difference between the Y-coordinates is Δy. Thus in this notation, $\Delta x = h$ and $\Delta y = f(x + h) - f(x)$. Then the Difference Quotient 65-5 becomes

$$\frac{\Delta y}{\Delta x}.$$

The derivative is the limit of the difference quotient as h approaches zero; that is, as Δx approaches 0. So in the differential notation we have

$$\frac{dy}{dx} = \lim_{\Delta x \to 0} \frac{\Delta y}{\Delta x}.$$

Example 65-1. If $y = x^3$, express $\frac{\Delta y}{\Delta x}$ in terms of Δx and compute $\lim_{\Delta x \to 0} \frac{\Delta y}{\Delta x}$ to find $\frac{dy}{dx}$.

Solution. By definition,

$$y + \Delta y = (x + \Delta x)^3,$$

$$\Delta y = (x + \Delta x)^3 - x^3,$$

and so

$$\frac{\Delta y}{\Delta x} = \frac{(x + \Delta x)^3 - x^3}{\Delta x} = 3x^2 + 3x\,\Delta x + (\Delta x)^2.$$

Since $\frac{dy}{dx} = \lim_{\Delta x \to 0} \frac{\Delta y}{\Delta x}$, we see that $\frac{dy}{dx} = 3x^2$.

Example 65-2. Compute $\frac{dy}{dx}$ if $y = e^{\sin x}$.

Solution. We write $y = e^u$ with $u = \sin x$. Then $\frac{dy}{du} = e^u$, $\frac{du}{dx} = \cos x$, and the Chain Rule Equation

$$\frac{dy}{dx} = \frac{dy}{du}\frac{du}{dx}$$

becomes

$$\frac{dy}{dx} = e^u \cos x = e^{\sin x} \cos x.$$

Example 65-3. Find y such that y satisfies the differential equation $x\frac{dy}{dx} = 1$ and $y = 1$ when $x = 2$.

Solution. We can write $\frac{dy}{dx} = \frac{1}{x}\cdot$ One solution of this differential equation is provided by the formula $\int \frac{dx}{x} = \ln |x|$, and so

$$y = \ln |x| + C.$$

To determine C we set $x = 2$ and $y = 1$. Thus

$$1 = \ln |2| + C, \text{ and so } C = 1 - \ln 2.$$

Therefore,

$$y = \ln |x| + 1 - \ln 2;$$

that is,

$$y = \ln \left| \frac{ex}{2} \right|.$$

Problems 65

1. Find $\frac{dy}{dx}$:

   (a) $y = 2x^{-3} - 3x^{-2}$ (b) $y = x \sin x^2$
   (c) $y = (\ln x)/x$ (d) $y = e^{e^x}$

2. Find $\frac{d^3y}{dx^3}$ if $y = \int_0^x e^{-t^2}\, dt$.

3. Show that if $y = \ln\left(\frac{1}{x}\right)$, then $\frac{d^2y}{dx^2} = \left[\frac{dy}{dx}\right]^2$.

4. Express $\frac{\Delta y}{\Delta x}$ in terms of Δx. Use your knowledge of derivatives to find what $\lim_{\Delta x \to 0} \frac{\Delta y}{\Delta x}$ is equal to.

   (a) $y = (x + 1)^2$ (b) $y = \sin x^2$
   (c) $y = \ln x$ (d) $y = \cosh x$

5. Find $\frac{dx}{dy}$ if y is given by the equations in the preceding problem.

6. Use implicit differentiation to find $\frac{d^2y}{dx^2}$ if:

   (a) $x^2 + y^2 = 4$ (b) $xy - y^2 = 1$
   (c) $xy + \sin y = 1$ (d) $\sin x + \cos y = 1$

7. Let $y = e^{-x} \int_1^x t^{-1}e^t\, dt$ and compute $\frac{dy}{dx} + y - \frac{1}{x}\cdot$

8. Suppose $t = e^{-x}$. Compare $\frac{d^2x}{dt^2}$ and $\left(\frac{dx}{dt}\right)^2$.

Review Problems, Chapter Seven

You can use the following problems to test yourself on the material covered in this chapter.

1. Find (a) $\int x^2 e^{x^3}\,dx$ and (b) $\int x^3 e^{x^2}\,dx$.
2. Find (a) $\displaystyle\int \frac{x^3 - 8}{2x - 1}\,dx$ and (b) $\displaystyle\int \frac{2x - 1}{x^3 - 8}\,dx$.
3. Find (a) $\int x^2 \sqrt{x^3 + 1}\,dx$ and (b) $\int x^3 \sqrt{x^2 + 1}\,dx$.
4. Find (a) $\int x \cos^2 x^2\,dx$ and (b) $\int x^2 \cos x\,dx$.
5. Let $u = 2x + 1 + 2\sqrt{x^2 + x + 1}$ and evaluate the integral
$$\int_0^1 \frac{dx}{\sqrt{x^2 + x + 1}}.$$
6. Evaluate the following integrals.
(a) $\displaystyle\int_0^{2\pi} \sin x \cos x \cos 2x\,dx$ (b) $\displaystyle\int_0^{2\pi} \sin x \cos x \sin 2x\,dx$
(c) $\displaystyle\int_0^{\frac{\pi}{2}} \cos^4 x\,dx$
7. Suppose that f is a continuous function in the interval $[a, b]$ and that x_0 is a point in $[a, b]$. Let y_0 be a given number. Show that if $\dfrac{dy}{dx} = f(x)$, and $y = y_0$ when $x = x_0$, then $y = \displaystyle\int_{x_0}^{x} f(t)\,dt + y_0$.
8. Show that $\displaystyle\int_a^{a+2\pi} f(\cos x)\,dx = \int_0^{2\pi} f(\cos x)\,dx$ for every choice of a.

8 POLAR COORDINATES. VECTORS IN THE PLANE

We will now return to the subject of analytic geometry. This chapter has a twofold purpose. First of all, we will get a new look at the problem of representing points in the plane by means of pairs of numbers. Later it will turn out that some of the tools that we use in taking this new look—vector methods—are also useful in the study of three-dimensional space. So a second objective of this chapter is to lay the groundwork for the study of analytic geometry of three-dimensional space that we will take up in Chapter Nine.

66. Polar Coordinates

By introducing a pair of perpendicular lines and a unit of distance, we are able to assign to each point in the plane a pair of real numbers called the rectangular **cartesian coordinates** of the point. There are other ways to associate pairs of numbers with points, and now we are going to study one of the most important of these other ways. Let P be a point in a plane in which we have a system of cartesian coordinates (Fig. 66-1) and let r be the length of the segment OP. Suppose that θ is the measure of an angle whose initial side is the positive X-axis and whose terminal side contains the segment OP. Then we can associate the numbers r and θ with the point P. We say that P has **polar coordinates (r, θ).** If we write just a number in place of the angular measure θ (for example $\theta = \pi/4$), we shall suppose that our angle is measured in radians. To indicate degree measure we use the symbol °—for example $\theta = 45°$. We refer to the point O (the origin in Fig. 66-1) as the **pole** of our polar coordinate system, and the initial side of the polar angle (here the positive X-axis) is called the **polar axis** of the system. Clearly, it is possible to introduce a polar coordinate system without reference to a cartesian coordinate system. We simply choose a point in the plane to be the pole of our system and choose any half-line emanating from the pole to be the polar axis.

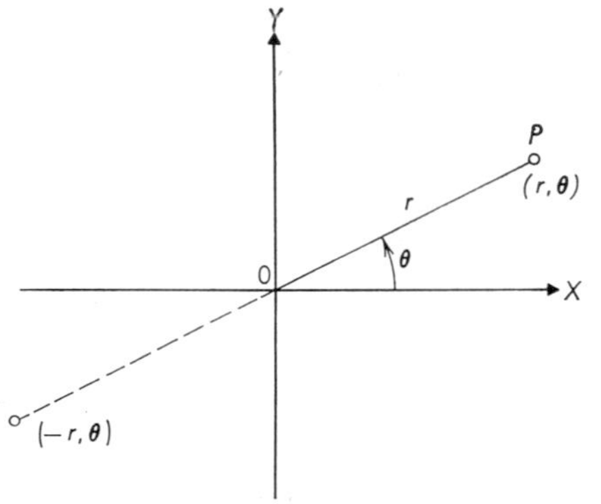

Figure 66-1

We will allow the use of angles greater than one revolution, and we will also allow negative angles, those angles formed by rotating the initial side in a clockwise direction. We therefore see that a given point P always has infinitely many pairs of polar coordinates. For example, the pairs (2, 30°), (2, 390°), and (2, −330°) all represent the same point. We also occasionally find it convenient to use a negative number for the radial polar coordinate of a point. To plot the point (r, θ) with $r > 0$, we proceed r units from the point O along the terminal side of the polar angle. To plot the point $(-r, \theta)$, we proceed r units from the pole along the extension of the terminal side through the origin (Fig. 66-1). Thus (r, θ) and $(-r, \theta + \pi)$ are polar coordinates of the same point. The coordinates $(0, \theta)$ represent the pole for every θ.

Example 66-1. Plot the points $(2, \pi/2)$, $(3, -225°)$, $(-3, 225°)$ and $(0, 17°)$.

Solution. The listed points are shown in Fig. 66-2.

When a polar coordinate system is superimposed on a given cartesian coordinate system, each point in the plane can be represented either by its cartesian coordinates (x, y) or by polar coordinates (r, θ) (Fig. 66-3). If $r > 0$, the basic Equations 10-2 concerning trigonometric functions of

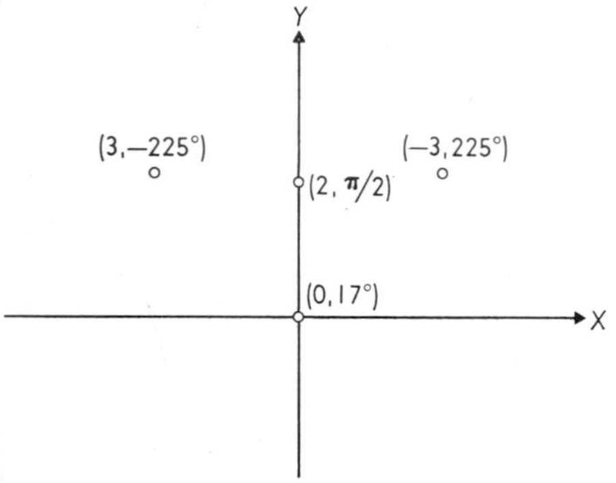

Figure 66-2

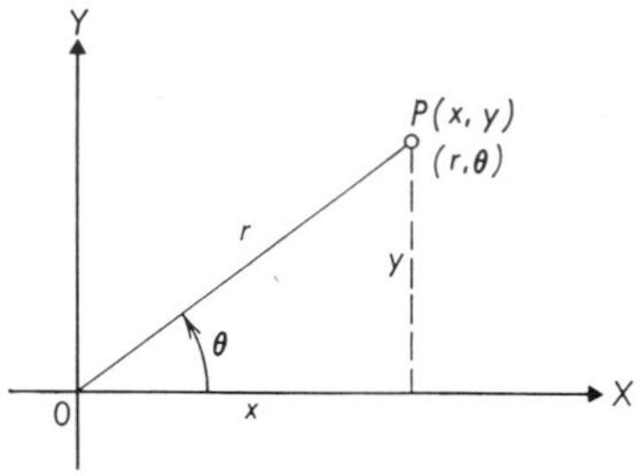

Figure 66-3

angles tell us the fundamental relations between the cartesian and polar coordinates of a point:

$$\mathbf{x = r \cos \theta} \qquad (66\text{-}1)$$
$$\mathbf{y = r \sin \theta.}$$

We will leave it to you to verify that these equations are also valid if the polar coordinates of the point are such that $r < 0$. We can easily see how to use Equations 66-1 to find the XY-coordinates of a point if we know its polar coordinates (r, θ). We will use an example to illustrate how we use Equations 66-1 to calculate a pair of polar coordinates of a point when we are given its cartesian coordinates.

Example 66-2. Find a pair of polar coordinates of the point whose cartesian coordinates are $(-1, \sqrt{3})$.

Solution. Figure 66-4 shows the point $(-1, \sqrt{3})$, and we have labeled the distance r and the angle of θ that we are to determine. According to Equations 66-1, we must pick r and θ so that

$$-1 = r \cos \theta \qquad (66\text{-}2)$$
$$\sqrt{3} = r \sin \theta.$$

If we square both of these equations and add, we see that

$$4 = r^2(\cos^2 \theta + \sin^2 \theta) = r^2.$$

Thus we can choose either $r = 2$ or $r = -2$. Let us take $r = 2$. Then Equations 66-2 tell us that we must choose θ so that $\cos\theta = -\frac{1}{2}$ and $\sin\theta = \sqrt{3}/2$. From trigonometry we know that the reference angle (see θ_1 in Fig. 66-4) is the acute angle whose cosine is $\frac{1}{2}$. Therefore, $\theta_1 = \pi/3$, and we may take $\theta = \pi - \theta_1 = 2\pi/3$. Thus a pair of polar coordinates of our point is $(2, 2\pi/3)$. Examples of other pairs of polar coordinates of

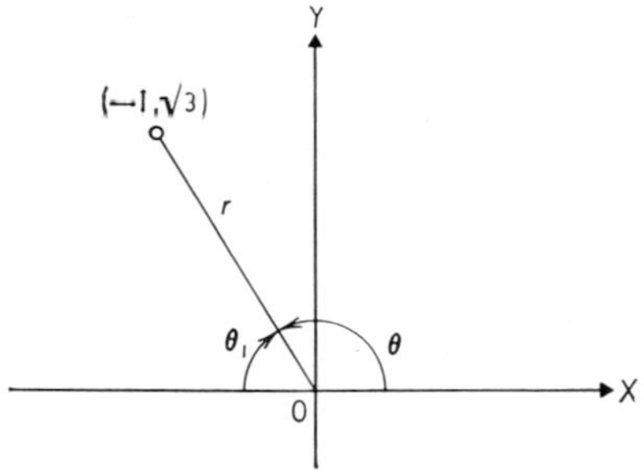

Figure 66-4

our point are $(2, 8\pi/3)$, $(2, -4\pi/3)$, and $(-2, -\pi/3)$. You might check to see that each of these pairs satisfies Equations 66-2.

In the preceding example we found it convenient to square both sides of Equations 66-2 and add the resulting equations. If we square both sides of Equations 66-1 and add, we obtain the following useful formula that relates the XY-coordinates of a point and its radial polar coordinate r:

$$x^2 + y^2 = r^2. \tag{66-3}$$

The graph of an equation in x and y is the set of points whose XY-coordinates satisfy the equation. Similarly, the graph of an equation in the polar coordinates r and θ is the set of those points that have polar coordinates that satisfy the equation. Thus, for example, the graph of the equation $2x - 3y + 5 = 0$ is a straight line. If we replace x with $r\cos\theta$ and y with $r\sin\theta$, we obtain the equation of the same line in polar coordinates:

$$2r\cos\theta - 3r\sin\theta + 5 = 0.$$

The straightforward way to plot the graph of any equation is to begin with a table of values, plot the points whose coordinates are contained in the table, and fill in the curve suggested by the plotted points. We use the following example to illustrate this procedure in the case of polar coordinates.

Example 66-3. Sketch the graph of the equation

$$r = 2(1 - \cos \theta).$$

Solution. In this example we can lighten our labor by noting that, since $\cos(-\theta) = \cos \theta$, the point $(r, -\theta)$ belongs to the graph if the point (r, θ) does. Therefore, our graph is symmetric about the line lying along the polar axis. We can sketch the graph by plotting points whose angular coordinates lie between 0° and 180° and then reflect this portion about the line of symmetry. The table accompanying Fig. 66-5 lists the coordinates we used to sketch the curve. This heart-shaped curve is called a **cardioid.**

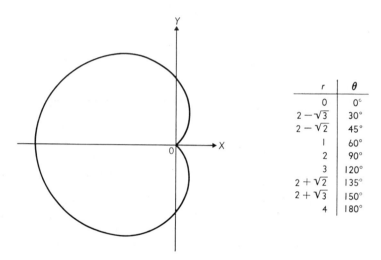

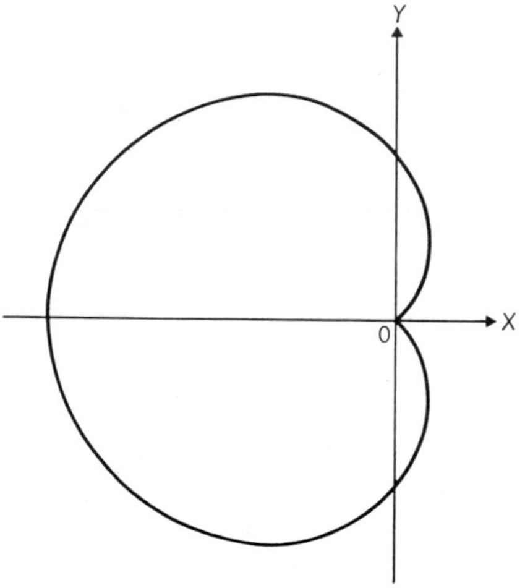

r	θ
0	0°
$2-\sqrt{3}$	30°
$2-\sqrt{2}$	45°
1	60°
2	90°
3	120°
$2+\sqrt{2}$	135°
$2+\sqrt{3}$	150°
4	180°

Figure 66-5

Frequently our knowledge of cartesian equations of curves helps us when we deal with polar equations.

Example 66-4. Discuss the graph of the equation

$$r = 4 \cos \theta - 2 \sin \theta.$$

Solution. We could plot the graph of this equation as we did in the preceding example, but instead we will transform the equation to an equation involving cartesian coordinates x and y. First, we multiply both sides of the given equation by r to obtain the equation

$$r^2 = 4r \cos \theta - 2r \sin \theta.$$

Now we use Equations 66-1 and 66-3 to obtain our equation in cartesian coordinates:

$$x^2 + y^2 = 4x - 2y.$$

We then complete the square to obtain

$$(x^2 - 4x + 4) + (y^2 + 2y + 1) = 4 + 1,$$
$$(x - 2)^2 + (y + 1)^2 = 5,$$

and we find that our equation represents the circle whose center is the point $(2, -1)$ and whose radius is $\sqrt{5}$.

We have said that a point belongs to the graph of an equation in r and θ if it has a pair of polar coordinates that satisfy the equation. Since each point has infinitely many pairs of polar coordinates, it may be true that some of these pairs satisfy the equation while others don't. For example, the pair of coordinates $(1, 0)$ satisfies the equation $r = e^{2\theta}$, so the point whose polar coordinates are $(1, 0)$ belongs to the graph of the equation. But the same point has polar coordinates $(-1, \pi)$ and $(1, 2\pi)$, and neither of these pairs satisfies the equation. Similarly, the graph of the equation $r = -6 \cos \theta$ contains the pole since the coordinates $(0, \pi/2)$ satisfy the equation, but other coordinates of the pole (for example, $(0, \pi/7)$) do not satisfy the equation.

It is also true that different polar equations may have the same graph. For example, you can easily see that the graphs of the equations $r = 5$, $r = -5$, and $r^2 = 25$ are all the same circle. You can also verify that the graph of the equation $r = -2(1 + \cos \theta)$ is the cardioid of Example 66-3 (see question 5 of Problems 66). We make these remarks to warn you that you must keep your eyes open when using polar coordinates. In the following example we will illustrate one type of pitfall that you should avoid.

Example 66-4. Find the points of intersection of the cardioid $r = 2(1 - \cos \theta)$ and the circle whose equation is $r = -6 \cos \theta$.

Solution. Figure 66-6 shows our two curves. We will attempt to find their points of intersection by finding simultaneous solutions to their equations. We equate the two expressions for r and get the trigonometric equation

$$2(1 - \cos \theta) = -6 \cos \theta,$$

from which we see that $\cos \theta = -\frac{1}{2}$. Two choices of θ that satisfy this last equation are $\theta = 2\pi/3$ and $\theta = 4\pi/3$. We see that $r = 3$, no matter which solution for θ is chosen, so we have found two points of intersection, $(3, 2\pi/3)$ and $(3, 4\pi/3)$. However, when we examine our graphs in Fig. 66-6, we see that there are actually three points of intersection. The pole is a point of intersection that we cannot find by solving the equations simultaneously. No pair of coordinates of the pole satisfies both equations. For example, the coordinates $(0, \pi/2)$ satisfy the equation of the circle but not of the cardioid; and the coordinates $(0, 0)$ satisfy the equation of the

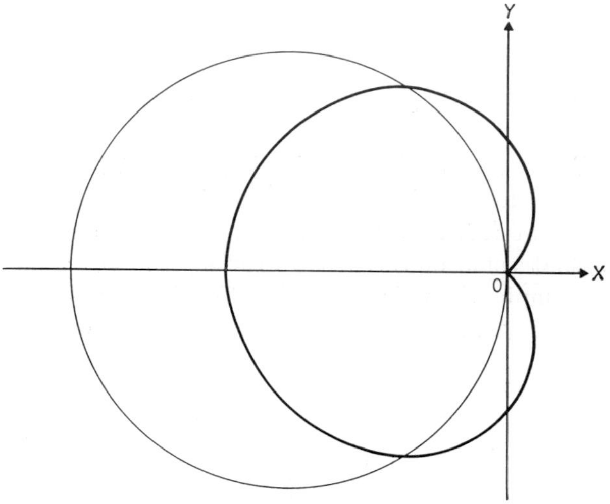

Figure 66-6

cardioid, but not of the circle. Nevertheless, the pole certainly does belong to both curves and is therefore a point of intersection.

Problems 66

1. Find the cartesian coordinates of the points with polar coordinates:
(a) $(4, 30°)$ (b) $(8, -420°)$
(c) $(-6, 3\pi/4)$ (d) (π, π)
(e) $(90, 90°)$ (f) $(-1, 13\pi/6)$
2. Find a set of polar coordinates of the points whose cartesian coordinates are:
(a) $(-4, 0)$ (b) $(-3\sqrt{3}, -3)$
(c) $(-6, 6\sqrt{3})$ (d) (π, π)
(e) $(0, -270)$ (f) $(-4, 3)$
3. Does it follow from Equations 66-1 that $r = \sqrt{x^2 + y^2}$ and $\theta = \text{Tan}^{-1}(y/x)$? (Consider the point whose cartesian coordinates are $(-1, 1)$.)
4. Transform the following equations to cartesian coordinates and graph.
(a) $r = 2 \cos \theta$ (b) $r = 3 \sec \theta$ (c) $\tan \theta = 5$ (d) $r \sin \theta \tan \theta = 1$
5. Show that the equations $r = 2(1 - \cos \theta)$ and $r = -2(1 + \cos \theta)$ represent the same curve.

6. Sketch the graphs of the following equations.
   (a) $r = 4 \cos 2\theta$ (b) $r = 3 \cos 3\theta$
   (c) $r = 2 - \cos \theta$ (d) $r = 1 - 2 \cos \theta$
7. Sketch the graph of the equation $r = 2\sqrt{\cos \theta}$. Is the graph a circle?
8. Find a polar equation of the line that contains the points whose polar coordinates are $(1, \pi)$ and $(2, \pi/2)$. (*Hint:* You can write the cartesian coordinate equation first and then change to polar coordinates.)
9. Discuss the symmetry of the graph of a polar coordinate equation if it can be written in the form:
   (a) $r^2 = f(\theta)$ (b) $r = f(\cos \theta)$
   (c) $r = f(\sin \theta)$ (d) $r = f(\theta)$, f an odd function
   (e) $r = f(\theta)$, f an even function (f) $r^2 = f(\theta)$, f an even function
10. Sketch the graph of the equation $r\theta = 1$. Show that as θ approaches zero the Y-coordinate of a point (r, θ) of this graph approaches 1.
11. Find the points of intersection of the graphs of the following pairs of equations (draw a sketch).
   (a) $r = 4 \cos 2\theta$, $r = 2$ (b) $r = 4 \cos 2\theta$, $r = 4 \cos \theta$
   (c) $r^2 = \sin^2 2\theta$, $\tan \theta = 1$ (d) $r = 1 - \cos \theta$, $r = \sin \dfrac{\theta}{2}$.
12. Let f be a periodic function of period 2π. If s and t are interpreted as cartesian coordinates, then the graph of the equation $s = f(t)$ in the interval $[0, 2\pi]$ consists of straight-line segments successively joining the points $(0, 1)$, $(\pi/2, 0)$, $(\pi, 2)$, $(3\pi/2, 0)$, and $(2\pi, 1)$. Sketch the graph of the equation $s = f(t)$ if (s, t) is interpreted as a pair of polar coordinates of a point. (Remark: Sometimes it is useful to draw an auxiliary graph of $r = f(\theta)$ interpreting r and θ as cartesian coordinates before plotting the polar coordinate graph.)

67. Lines, Circles, and Conics in Polar Coordinates

In earlier sections we discussed the cartesian equations of certain common curves—lines, circles, and conics. Now we will consider the representation of these particular curves in polar coordinates. In this section we will suppose that we have superimposed a polar coordinate system on a cartesian system as we did in the preceding section.

If α is a given number, then it is clear that every point that has polar coordinates (r, θ) such that

$$\theta = \alpha \tag{67-1}$$

belongs to the line that contains the pole and makes an angle of α with the polar axis, and conversely. Thus Equation 67-1 represents a line that contains the pole.

Now let us consider a line that does not contain the pole O (Fig. 67-1). Suppose that P is the point of this line such that OP is perpendicular to the line, and let $p = \overline{OP}$. Let Q be any point of the line, let $r = \overline{OQ}$, and suppose that OQ makes an angle of θ with the polar axis. Then (r, θ) are polar coordinates of the point Q. If the line OP makes an angle of β with the polar axis, we see that

(67-2) $\quad \boldsymbol{r \cos(\theta - \beta) = p}.$

This equation is the polar equation of a line not containing the pole. We may write Equation 67-2 as

$$r \cos\theta \cos\beta + r \sin\theta \sin\beta = p;$$

that is, since $x = r\cos\theta$ and $y = r\sin\theta$,

(67-3) $\quad \boldsymbol{x \cos\beta + y \sin\beta = p}.$

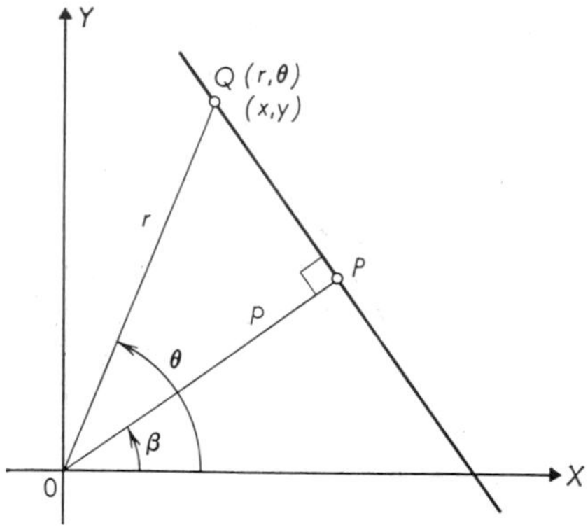

Figure 67-1

We see immediately that Equation 67-3 is a linear equation in x and y, as it should be since it has a line as its graph. Any linear equation in x and y that is written in the form

(67-4) $$Ax + By = C \quad (C > 0),$$

can be put in the form of Equation 67-3. We simply divide both sides of Equation 67-4 by $\sqrt{A^2 + B^2}$. Then

$$\cos\beta = \frac{A}{\sqrt{A^2 + B^2}},$$

$$\sin\beta = \frac{B}{\sqrt{A^2 + B^2}},$$

and

$$p = \frac{C}{\sqrt{A^2 + B^2}}.$$

Example 67-1. Find the distance between the origin and the line $2x - 3y + 7 = 0$.

Solution. We write

$$-2x + 3y = 7$$

and divide both sides of this equation by

$$\sqrt{(-2)^2 + 3^2} = \sqrt{13}$$

to obtain

$$-\frac{2}{\sqrt{13}}x + \frac{3}{\sqrt{13}}y = \frac{7}{\sqrt{13}}.$$

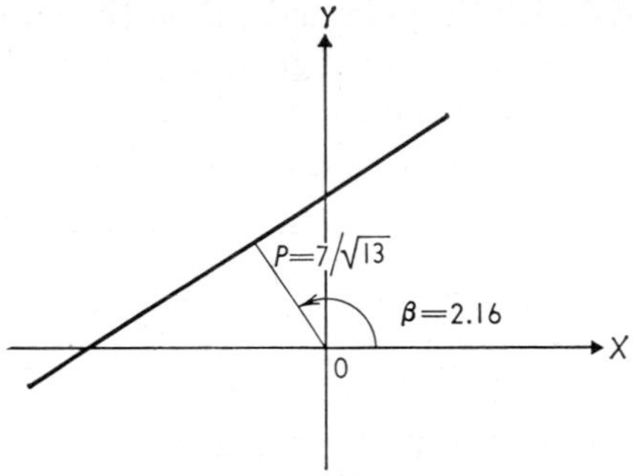

Figure 67-2

Thus $p = 7/\sqrt{13}$ is the distance between the origin and the line. If β is such that $\cos \beta = -2/\sqrt{13}$, and $\sin \beta = 3/\sqrt{13}$, then the equation of our line can be written in polar form as

$$r \cos (\theta - \beta) = 7/\sqrt{13}.$$

One possible choice for β is (approximately) $\beta = 2.16$. The graph of our line is shown in Fig. 67-2.

It is clear that the equation

$$r = a \tag{67-5}$$

represents the circle whose center is the pole and whose radius is $|a|$ units long. Now let us consider the circle shown in Fig. 67-3. This circle contains the pole, and its diameter OD makes an angle of α with the polar axis. The radius of the circle is a units long, so we see that $\overline{OD} = 2a$. Now let P be a point of the circle. If $\overline{OP} = r$ and the segment OP makes

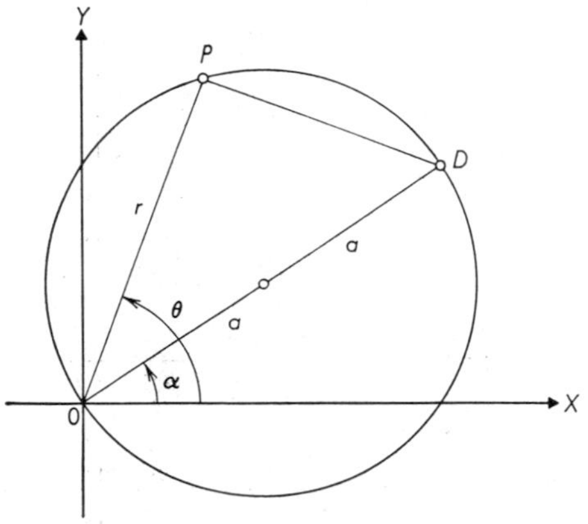

Figure 67-3

an angle of θ with the polar axis, then the numbers (r, θ) are polar coordinates of P. It is a theorem of geometry that triangle OPD is a right triangle and therefore (since the cosine of an angle in a right triangle is the ratio of the adjacent leg to the hypotenuse) we see that

(67-6) $$r = 2a \cos (\theta - \alpha).$$

This equation is the polar equation of a circle that contains the origin. The polar equation of a circle that does not contain the origin is, in general, more complicated than the cartesian equation, and we shall leave its discussion to the problems. Two special cases of Equation 67-6 are particularly important. If $\alpha = 0$, then the center of the circle is a point of the X-axis and we have

(67-7) $$r = 2a \cos \theta,$$

and if $\alpha = \pi/2$, then the center of our circle is a point of the Y-axis,

(67-8) $$r = 2a \sin \theta.$$

Polar coordinates are particularly well suited for representing conics. Definition 35-1 tells us how a conic is determined by a point called a *focus*, a line called a *directrix*, and a positive number called the *eccentricity* of the conic. A conic contains a point if, and only if, the ratio of the distance between the point and the focus to the distance between the point and the directrix is the eccentricity. Suppose we know the focus F, the corresponding directrix d, located p units from F, and the eccentricity e of a certain conic. Let us introduce polar coordinates so that the pole is the focus F and so that the directrix is perpendicular to the polar axis at the point with polar coordinates (p, π), where $p > 0$. We have sketched an arc of our conic in Fig. 67-4. If our conic is a hyperbola ($e > 1$), it will also have a branch lying to the left of d, but in the case of an ellipse ($e < 1$) or a parabola ($e = 1$), the entire conic lies to the right of the directrix. Suppose that P is a point of our conic. Let (r, θ) be any pair of polar coordinates of P for which $r > 0$; so $\overline{FP} = r$. If the point P lies to the right of the directrix d, then the distance between P and d is $p + r \cos \theta$. On the other hand, if P lies to the left of d (as it might in the case of a hyperbola), then the distance between P and d is $-(p + r \cos \theta)$. Thus the definition of a conic tells us that either

(67-9) $$\frac{r}{p + r \cos \theta} = e \quad \text{or} \quad \frac{r}{-(p + r \cos \theta)} = e$$

depending on whether the point (r, θ) lies to the right or to the left of the directrix d. Now it is easy to show (see Problem 4 at the end of this section) that if the coordinates (r, θ) of a certain point satisfy one of

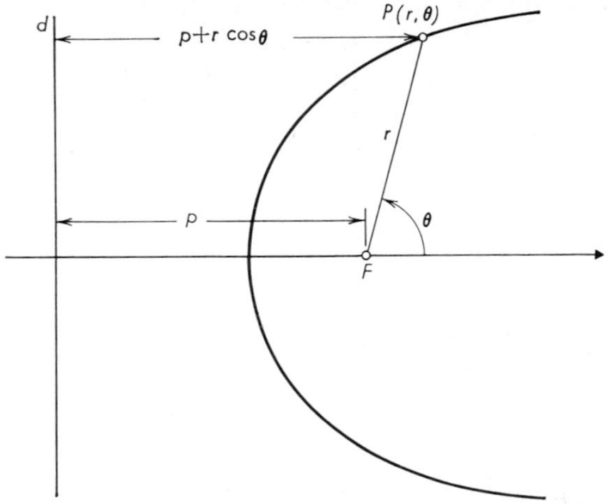

Figure 67-4

Equations 67-9, then the coordinates $(-r, \theta + \pi)$ *of the same point* satisfy the other equation. It follows that we do not need both of Equations 67-9 to describe our conic; either one will do. We will take the equation that is obtained by solving the first of Equations 67-9 for r to be the standard form of the polar equation of our conic:

$$r = \frac{ep}{1 - e\cos\theta}. \tag{67-10}$$

By reasoning as we did above, you can find that if the focus is the pole, and if the directrix is to the right of the pole (See Fig. 67-5), then

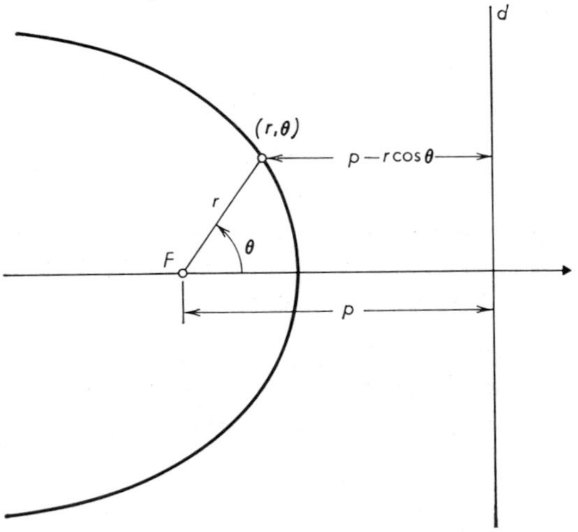

Figure 67-5

we can take the standard form of the equation of our conic to be

(67-11) $$r = \frac{ep}{1 + e\cos\theta}.$$

If the directrix is parallel to the polar axis, we take the standard polar equation of the conic to be

(67-12) $$r = \frac{ep}{1 + e\sin\theta}$$

if the directrix is above the focus, and

(67-13) $$r = \frac{ep}{1 - e\sin\theta}$$

if the directrix is below the focus (see Fig. 67-6).

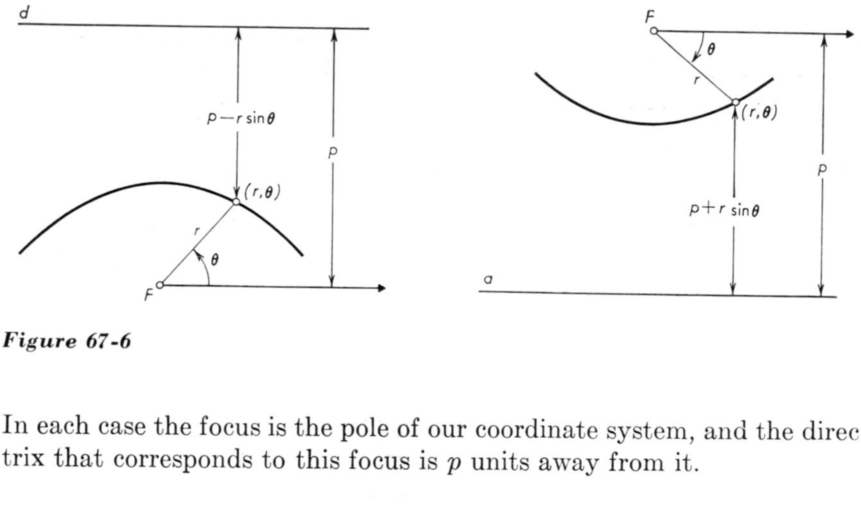

Figure 67-6

In each case the focus is the pole of our coordinate system, and the directrix that corresponds to this focus is p units away from it.

Example 67-2. Write a polar equation of the parabola whose focus is the pole, whose axis lies along the polar axis, which opens to the right, and whose graph contains the point $(2, \pi/3)$.

Solution. Since our parabola opens to the right, its directrix lies to the left of the focus (the pole), and hence Equation 67-10 is the equation we want. We are dealing with a parabola, so $e = 1$, and our equation is

$$r = \frac{p}{1 - \cos\theta}.$$

We determine p by setting $r = 2$ and $\theta = \pi/3$, since the point $(2, \pi/3)$ belongs to the parabola. Thus

$$2 = \frac{p}{1 - \cos \pi/3} = \frac{p}{1 - \frac{1}{2}} = 2p,$$

and hence $p = 1$. Therefore, the equation of our parabola is

$$r = \frac{1}{1 - \cos \theta}.$$

Example 67-3. Discuss the graph of the equation

$$r = \frac{16}{5 + 3 \sin \theta}. \tag{67-14}$$

Solution. If we divide the numerator and the denominator of our fraction by 5, we can write Equation 67-14 in the form of Equation 67-12:

$$r = \frac{\frac{16}{5}}{1 + \frac{3}{5} \sin \theta} = \frac{\frac{3}{5} \cdot \frac{16}{3}}{1 + \frac{3}{5} \sin \theta}.$$

Here $e = \frac{3}{5}$ and $p = \frac{16}{3}$. Our curve is an ellipse, since $e < 1$, and its major diameter contains the pole and is perpendicular to the polar axis. Thus

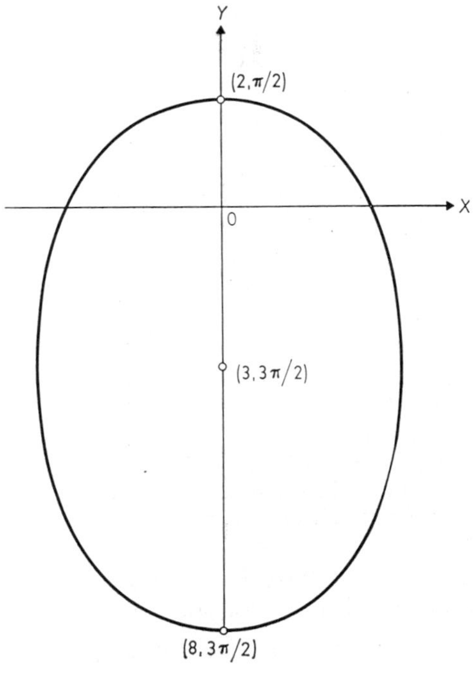

Figure 67-7

we find the vertices of the ellipse by setting $\theta = \pi/2$ and $\theta = 3\pi/2$ in Equation 67-14. We obtain

$$r = \frac{16}{5 + 3 \cdot 1} = 2 \quad \text{when} \quad \theta = \frac{\pi}{2},$$

and

$$r = \frac{16}{5 + 3 \cdot (-1)} = 8 \quad \text{when} \quad \theta = \frac{3\pi}{2}$$

So the vertices are the points with polar coordinates $(2, \pi/2)$ and $(8, 3\pi/2)$. The major diameter is $8 + 2 = 10$ units long. In Section 35 we saw that the eccentricity of an ellipse is the ratio of the distance between its foci to the length of its major diameter. The major diameter of our present ellipse is $2b = 10$ units long, and if its foci are $2c$ units apart, we have the equation $e = 2c/10$; that is $\frac{3}{5} = 2c/10$. It follows that $2c = 6$, and hence $c = 3$. Finally, if the minor diameter of our ellipse is $2a$ units long, then $a = \sqrt{b^2 - c^2} = \sqrt{25 - 9} = 4$. Our ellipse is shown in Fig. 67-7. You may readily verify that its cartesian equation is

$$\frac{x^2}{16} + \frac{(y + 3)^2}{25} = 1.$$

Problems 67

1. Find the distance between the line $3x + 4y = 30$ and the origin.
2. Find the polar equation of the line of which the point $(3, 27°)$ is the point nearest to the origin.
3. Find the polar equation of the circle whose center has rectangular coordinates $(-1, 1)$ and which contains the pole.
4. Show that if the coordinates (r, θ) of a certain point satisfy one of the Equations 67-9, then the coordinates $(-r, \theta + \pi)$ of the same point satisfy the other equation.
5. Sketch the graphs of the following polar equations. In each case label the vertices (or vertex) and the foci (or focus) of the conic.

   (a) $r = \dfrac{16}{3 + 5 \sin \theta}$ (b) $r = \dfrac{16}{5 - 3 \cos \theta}$

   (c) $r = \dfrac{4}{1 + \sin \theta}$ (d) $r = \dfrac{16}{5 + 3 \cos \theta}$

   (e) $r \sin \theta = 1 - r$ (f) $3r \sin \theta = 5r - 16$
6. A conic has the origin of a cartesian coordinate system as a focus and a corresponding directrix whose equation is $x = -4$. Identify the conic and find its polar equation if the conic contains the point whose cartesian coordinates are:

   (a) $(5, 12)$ (b) $(5, 2\sqrt{14})$ (c) $(5, 5)$
7. Show that the equation

$$r \sin (\theta - \alpha) = q \sin (\beta - \alpha)$$

represents the line that contains the point with polar coordinates (q, β) that has a slope of $m = \tan \alpha$.

8. Express Equation 67-10 in cartesian coordinates.

9. Describe the conic for which $p = 5{,}000{,}000$ and $e = 1/1{,}000{,}000$.

10. Show that the standard form of the polar equation of a parabola can be written as

$$r = \frac{p}{2} \csc^2 \frac{\theta}{2}.$$

11. A chord that contains a focus of a conic is divided into two segments by the focus. Prove that the sum of the reciprocals of the lengths of these two segments is the same no matter what chord is chosen.

12. Suppose $e < 1$ in Equation 67-10 and let $2a$ denote the length of the major diameter of the ellipse represented by that equation. Show that

$$a = \frac{ep}{1 - e^2}.$$

13. Suppose $e < 1$ in Equation 67-10 and let $2c$ denote the distance between the foci of the ellipse represented by that equation. Show that $c = e^2p/(1 - e^2)$.

68. Tangents to Polar Curves

In the preceding two sections we have considered the elementary notion of the graph of a polar equation, and now we are ready to apply some of our knowledge of calculus to find out more about such graphs. In this section we will discuss tangent lines, and in the next section we will take up the area problem for curves whose equations are given in polar coordinates.

Suppose that the tangent line to the graph of the equation $r = f(\theta)$ at the point (r, θ) makes an angle of α with the polar axis. If we introduce XY-coordinates in the usual way, so that the positive X-axis is the polar axis, and transform our polar equation into an equation in x and y, then we know that

$$\tan \alpha = \frac{dy}{dx}. \tag{68-1}$$

Since we wish to compute $\tan \alpha$ directly from our polar equation $r = f(\theta)$, we will express the derivative $\frac{dy}{dx}$ in terms of polar coordinates. We combine the Chain Rule Equation (Equation 65-3)

$$\frac{dy}{dx} = \frac{dy}{d\theta}\frac{d\theta}{dx}$$

and the formula for the derivative of an inverse (Equation 65-4)

$$\frac{d\theta}{dx} = \frac{1}{\dfrac{dx}{d\theta}}$$

to obtain the equation

(68-2)
$$\frac{dy}{dx} = \frac{\dfrac{dy}{d\theta}}{\dfrac{dx}{d\theta}}.$$

Now let us calculate $\frac{dy}{d\theta}$ and $\frac{dx}{d\theta}$. Since $y = r \sin \theta$, and for our curve $r = f(\theta)$, we have $y = f(\theta) \sin \theta$. Thus

$$\frac{dy}{d\theta} = f'(\theta) \sin \theta + f(\theta) \cos \theta.$$

Similarly, $x = r \cos \theta = f(\theta) \cos \theta$, and hence

$$\frac{dx}{d\theta} = f'(\theta) \cos \theta - f(\theta) \sin \theta.$$

When we substitute these values in Equation 68-2 to find $\frac{dy}{dx}$, Equation 68-1 becomes

(68-3)
$$\boldsymbol{\tan \alpha = \frac{f'(\theta) \sin \theta + f(\theta) \cos \theta}{f'(\theta) \cos \theta - f(\theta) \sin \theta}}.$$

Notice that the slope of the tangent line to the graph of a polar equation $r = f(\theta)$ at a point is *not* $D_\theta r$.

Example 68-1. Find the angle that the tangent line to the cardioid $r = 2(1 - \cos \theta)$ at the point $(2, \pi/2)$ makes with the polar axis.

Solution. Here we have $f(\theta) = 2(1 - \cos \theta)$, so $f'(\theta) = 2 \sin \theta$. Hence Equation 68-3 gives us

$$\tan \alpha = \frac{(2 \sin \theta) \sin \theta + 2(1 - \cos \theta) \cos \theta}{(2 \sin \theta) \cos \theta - 2(1 - \cos \theta) \sin \theta}$$
$$= \frac{\cos \theta - \cos 2\theta}{\sin 2\theta - \sin \theta}.$$

Thus at the point $(2, \pi/2)$ we find that $\tan \alpha = -1$. It follows that α is an angle of $\frac{3\pi}{4}$ radians or 135°. You should check this result with Fig. 66-5.

If $f(\theta_1) = 0$ but $f'(\theta_1) \neq 0$, and we set $\theta = \theta_1$ in Equation 68-3, then we have

$$\tan \alpha = \tan \theta_1. \tag{68-4}$$

The equation $f(\theta_1) = 0$ means that the pole (which has coordinates $(0, \theta_1)$) belongs to the graph of the equation $r = f(\theta)$. Hence, Equation 68-4 tells us that the polar equation $\theta = \theta_1$ represents the line tangent to the curve at the pole. Thus we obtain the tangents to the graph of the equation $r = f(\theta)$ at the pole by solving the equation $f(\theta) = 0$.

Example 68-2. Find the equations of the tangents to the graph of the equation $r = 2 \cos 3\theta$ at the pole.

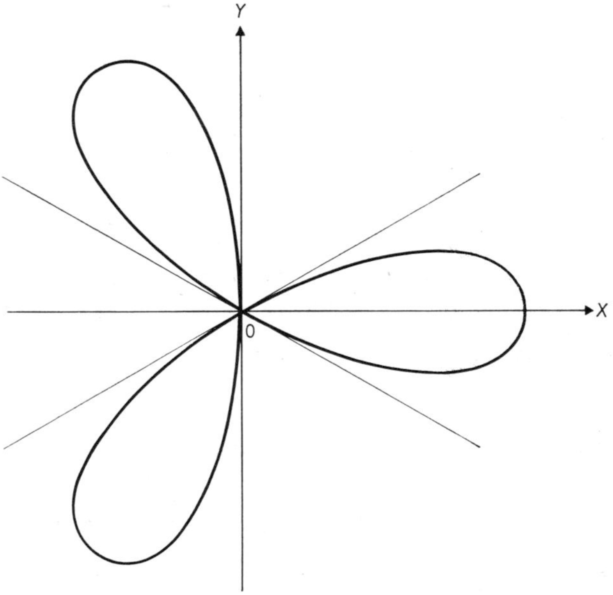

Figure 68-1

Solution. Here $f(\theta) = 2 \cos 3\theta$, so we must solve the equation $2 \cos 3\theta = 0$. From this equation it follows that $3\theta = \frac{\pi}{2} + n\pi$; that is, $\theta = \frac{\pi}{6} + \frac{n\pi}{3}\cdot$ There are three tangents at the pole, and equations of these tangents are $\theta = \pi/6$, $\theta = \pi/2$, and $\theta = 5\pi/6$. The graph of our equation, showing the tangent lines at the pole, appears in Fig. 68-1.

Equation 68-3 enables us to find the tangent of the angle that the tangent line to the graph of the equation $r = f(\theta)$ at the point (r, θ)

makes with the polar axis. In many cases we are interested in the angle of ψ, whose vertex is the point (r, θ), whose initial side is the radial line that contains this point, whose terminal side is the tangent line, and which is such that $0 \leq \psi < \pi$ (Fig. 68-2). The angles of ψ, α, and θ are

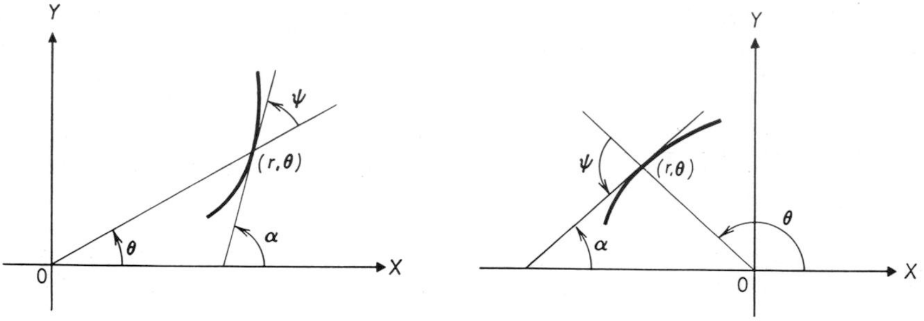

Figure 68-2

not independent of each other. At each point of the graph there is an integer n such that ψ is related to α and θ by the equation

$$\psi = \alpha - \theta + n\pi.$$

For example, in the configuration on the left in Fig. 68-2 we have $\psi = \alpha - \theta$, and in the configuration on the right we have $\psi = \alpha - \theta + \pi$. But in any case,

$$\tan \psi = \tan [(\alpha - \theta) + n\pi] = \tan (\alpha - \theta).$$

From trigonometry we have the formula

$$\tan (\alpha - \theta) = \frac{\tan \alpha - \tan \theta}{1 + \tan \alpha \tan \theta},$$

and if we replace $\tan \alpha$ in this quotient with the right-hand side of Equation 68-3, we will have an expression for $\tan (\alpha - \theta) = \tan \psi$ in terms of θ. We leave it to the problems for you to make the substitution and show that

$$\text{(68-5)} \qquad \boldsymbol{\tan \psi = \frac{f(\theta)}{f'(\theta)} = \frac{r}{D_\theta r}}.$$

Example 68-3. Find the points of the graph of the equation $r = 2 \cos 3\theta$ at which the tangent line is perpendicular to the radial line.

Solution. The tangent line is perpendicular to the radial line at points where $\psi = \pi/2$; that is, at points where $\tan \psi$ is not defined. From Equation 68-5 we see that $\tan \psi$ is not defined at those points for which $D_\theta r = 0$. Since $D_\theta r = -6 \sin 3\theta$, we must solve the equation

$$-6 \sin 3\theta = 0.$$

From this equation we find that $3\theta = n\pi$; that is, $\theta = \frac{n\pi}{3}\cdot$ With the aid of the graph in Fig. 68-1, we see that we need only take the solutions $\theta = 0, \pi/3$, and $2\pi/3$ to obtain the three points at which the tangent lines are perpendicular to the radial lines.

Example 68-4. Find the tangent of the angle that the tangent line to a parabola at a point P makes with the line that contains P and the focus.

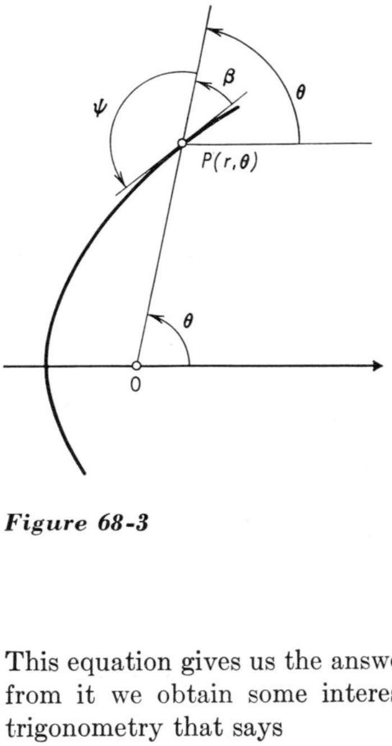

Figure 68-3

Solution. In Fig. 68-3 we have shown a parabola whose polar equation is (Equation 67-10 with $e = 1$)

$$r = \frac{p}{1 - \cos \theta}. \tag{68-6}$$

We are looking for $\tan \beta$. From Fig. 68-3 and Equation 68-5 we see that

$$\tan \beta = -\tan \psi = -\frac{r}{D_\theta r}\cdot$$

From Equation 68-6 we have

$$D_\theta r = D_\theta\left(\frac{p}{1 - \cos \theta}\right) = \frac{-p \sin \theta}{(1 - \cos \theta)^2},$$

and hence

$$\tan \beta = \frac{1 - \cos \theta}{\sin \theta}\cdot$$

This equation gives us the answer to the question we originally asked, and from it we obtain some interesting information. There is a formula in trigonometry that says

$$\frac{1 - \cos \theta}{\sin \theta} = \tan \frac{\theta}{2}\cdot$$

Thus

$$\tan \beta = \tan \frac{\theta}{2}\cdot$$

This equation tells us that the horizontal line through P in Fig. 68-3 makes the same angle with the tangent line that the radial line through O and P does. Therefore, we have another demonstration of the focusing property of the parabola that we discussed in Section 35.

Problems 68

1. Find ψ at the point $(4\pi, 2\pi)$ of the graph of the equation $r = 2\theta$.
2. Find the slope of the tangent to the graph of the equation $r = 2 \cos 3\theta$ at the point at which:
(a) $\theta = 0$ (b) $\theta = 2\pi/3$ (c) $\theta = 4\pi/3$ (d) $\theta = -\pi/4$
3. Find the polar equations of the lines tangent at the origin to the graphs of the following equations.
(a) $r = 4 \cos 2\theta$ (b) $r = \sin 3\theta$
(c) $r^2 = \cos 2\theta$ (d) $r = 1 - 3 \cos \theta$
4. Find the slope of the tangent to the graph of the given equation at the point with indicated angular coordinate.
(a) $r = 1 - 2 \cos \theta$, $\theta = \pi/2$ (b) $r = \sec^2 \theta$, $\theta = \pi/3$
(c) $r = 1 + 2\sqrt{\theta}$, $\theta = \pi$ (d) $r = (1 + 2 \cos \theta)^{-1}$, $\theta = 0$
5. Show that the angular coordinate of a point of the graph of the equation $r = 2 \cos 3\theta$ at which the tangent line is parallel to the polar axis satisfies the equation $3 \tan^4 \theta - 12 \tan^2 \theta + 1 = 0$.
6. Find the points of the cardioid $r = 2(1 - \cos \theta)$ at which the tangent line is perpendicular to the polar axis.
7. Find the polar coordinates of the "highest" point of the cardioid $r = 2(1 - \cos \theta)$.
8. What can you say about the angle between the radial line and the tangent line at a point of the graph of the equation $r = f(\theta)$ that is a maximum distance from the pole?
9. Sketch the curve $r = e^{\theta}$, and show that at any point of this curve the tangent line makes an angle of 45° with the radial line.
10. Are there any points of the spiral curve $r\theta = 1$ at which $\psi = \pi/2$? Examine ψ for very large θ.
11. Show that $\tan \psi = \tan \frac{1}{2}\theta$ at points of the cardioid $r = 2(1 - \cos \theta)$.
12. Derive Equation 68-5 by making the substitution suggested in the paragraph preceding that equation.
13. Use the formula for $\tan (\psi_2 - \psi_1)$ to find the angle between the tangents at the points of intersection of the graphs of the given equations.
(a) $r = 2(1 - \cos \theta)$, $r = -6 \cos \theta$ (b) $r = \sin \theta$, $r = \cos 2\theta$
14. Show that the curves whose equations are $r = 3\theta$ and $r\theta = 3$ intersect at right angles.
15. Let P be a point of the ellipse whose polar equation is

$$r = \frac{ep}{1 - e \cos \theta}$$

(a) Show that

$$\tan \psi = \frac{-p}{r \sin \theta} = \frac{-p}{y}.$$

(b) Let F be the focus of the ellipse not the pole of the coordinate system chosen for part (a). Choose a new polar coordinate system whose pole is F so that if P has coordinates $(\bar{r}, \bar{\theta})$ in this new system, then

$$\bar{r} = \frac{ep}{1 + e \cos \bar{\theta}}.$$

Show that

$$\tan \bar{\psi} = \frac{p}{y} = -\tan \psi, \text{ and conclude that } \bar{\psi} = \pi - \psi.$$

(c) Draw a figure to help you deduce that the equation $\bar{\psi} = \pi - \psi$ means that the tangent line to the ellipse at a point P bisects the angle between the two lines that join P to the foci of the ellipse. (The focusing property of the ellipse is a result of this property of an ellipse.)

69. Areas in Polar Coordinates

In this section we consider the problem of finding the area A of the region that is bounded by the graph of a polar equation $r = f(\theta)$ and radial lines $\theta = \alpha$ and $\theta = \beta$, as shown in Fig. 69-1. Let us suppose that $\alpha < \beta$ and that we use radian measure for our angles. It will be easier to solve this area problem if we word it as follows. Let θ be a number such that $\alpha \leq \theta \leq \beta$ and denote by $S(\theta)$ the area of the part of our given region that lies between the radial lines making angles of α and θ with the polar axis. Then we are to find the number $A = S(\beta)$.

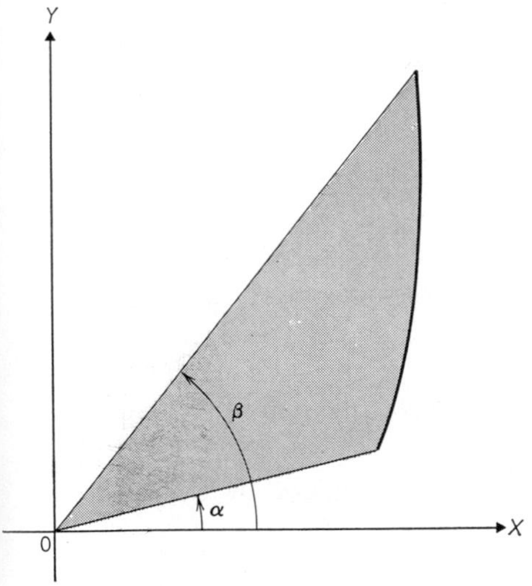

Figure 69-1

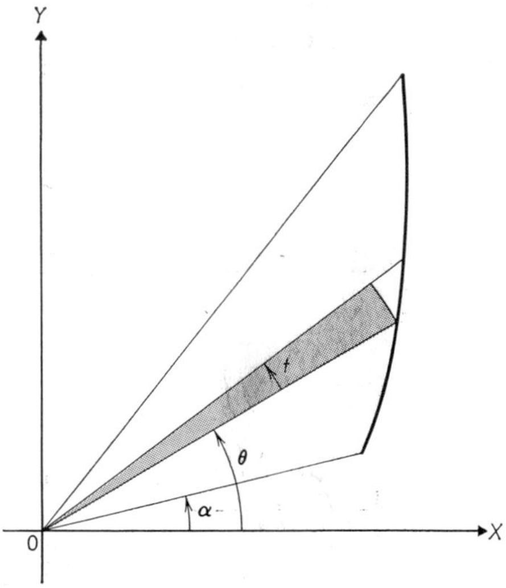

Figure 69-2

A simple formula for $S(\theta)$ is not immediately apparent, but with the aid of a figure we can easily find $S'(\theta)$. Suppose that θ and t are as shown in Fig. 69-2, and let $r = f(\theta)$. The number $S(\theta + t)$ is the area of the part of our region that lies between the radial lines that make angles of α and $\theta + t$ with the polar axis, and the number $S(\theta)$ is the area of the part that lies between the radial lines that make angles of α and θ with the polar axis. Thus the difference $S(\theta + t) - S(\theta)$ is the area of the part of the region that lies between the lines that make angles of θ and $\theta + t$ with the polar axis. From Fig. 69-2 we see that this area is approximately the same as the area of the shaded circular sector with a radius of r and a central angle of t. The area of this sector (See Appendix A) is $\frac{1}{2}r^2t$, and so we have

$$S(\theta + t) - S(\theta) \approx \tfrac{1}{2}r^2t;$$

that is,

$$\frac{S(\theta + t) - S(\theta)}{t} \approx \frac{1}{2}r^2.$$

(In our argument, based on Fig. 69-2, we have assumed that t is positive, but we would arrive at the same formula if we took t to be negative.) From the figure it appears that the closer t is to 0 the better this approximation is, and hence we conclude that

$$\lim_{t \to 0} \frac{S(\theta + t) - S(\theta)}{t} = \frac{1}{2}r^2.$$

The limit of the difference quotient $\dfrac{S(\theta + t) - S(\theta)}{t}$ is the number $S'(\theta)$, and therefore our geometrical argument shows that $S'(\theta) = \frac{1}{2}r^2$. Now according to the Fundamental Theorem of Calculus,

$$\text{(69-1)} \qquad \int_\alpha^\beta S'(\theta)\, d\theta = S(\beta) - S(\alpha).$$

From the definition of $S(\alpha)$ it follows that $S(\alpha) = 0$, and since $S'(\theta) = \frac{1}{2}r^2 = \frac{1}{2}[f(\theta)]^2$ and $S(\beta)$ is the area A of our given region, Equation 69-1 yields the desired area formula:

$$\text{(69-2)} \qquad \boldsymbol{A = \tfrac{1}{2}\int_\alpha^\beta r^2\, d\theta = \tfrac{1}{2}\int_\alpha^\beta [f(\theta)]^2\, d\theta.}$$

Example 69-1. Find the area of the region bounded by the cardioid $r = 2(1 - \cos\theta)$.

Solution. Because of the symmetry of the cardioid (see Fig. 66-5) we see that we may calculate the area of the part of the region for which $0 \leq \theta \leq \pi$, and multiply it by 2. Thus our desired area A is

$$A = 2(\tfrac{1}{2})\int_0^{\pi} r^2\,d\theta = 4\int_0^{\pi}(1-\cos\theta)^2\,d\theta$$
$$= 4\int_0^{\pi}(1-2\cos\theta+\cos^2\theta)\,d\theta$$
$$= 6\pi.$$

The area represented by the integral in Equation 69-2 should be thought of as the area of the region "swept out" by the radial line segment joining the pole to the point (r, θ) as this point moves along the

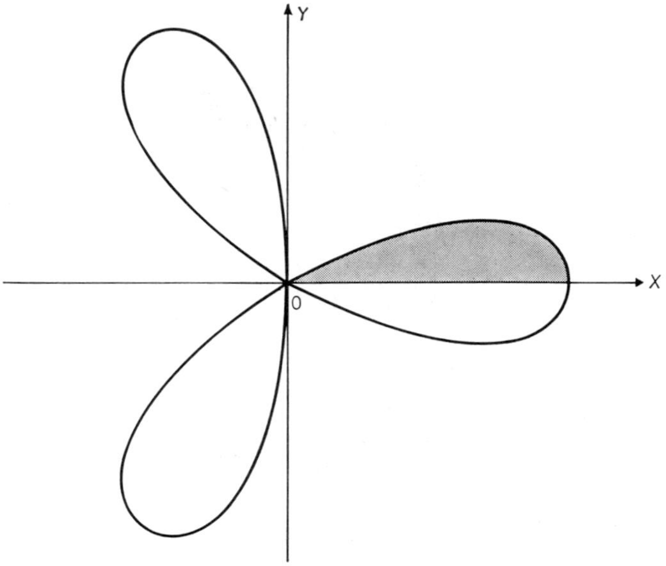

Figure 69-3

curve for $\alpha \leq \theta \leq \beta$. Thus, for example, if we consider the circle $r = 5$, and let $\alpha = 0$, $\beta = 3\pi$, then the area

$$A = \tfrac{1}{2}\int_0^{3\pi} 25\,d\theta = 75\pi/2$$

is one and one-half times the area of the circle. You should make a sketch showing the region whose area you intend to find and carefully determine α and β so that this region is swept out once, and only once, by the radial line segment to the point (r, θ) for $\alpha \leq \theta \leq \beta$. If you study the following example carefully, it will help you avoid a common error in determining α and β.

Example 69-2. Find the area of the region that is cut out of the first quadrant by the curve $r = 2 \cos 3\theta$.

Solution. We are interested in the shaded region shown in Fig. 69-3. The proper numbers α and β are *not 0 and $\pi/2$*. You can easily convince yourself that the portion of the curve in the first quadrant is traced out as θ goes from 0 to $\pi/6$. Thus the area we want is

$$A = \tfrac{1}{2} \int_0^{\pi/6} 4 \cos^2 3\theta = 2 \int_0^{\pi/6} \cos^2 3\theta \, d\theta = \pi/6.$$

Formula 69-2 can be used to find areas of regions bounded by two polar curves. An example will show us how.

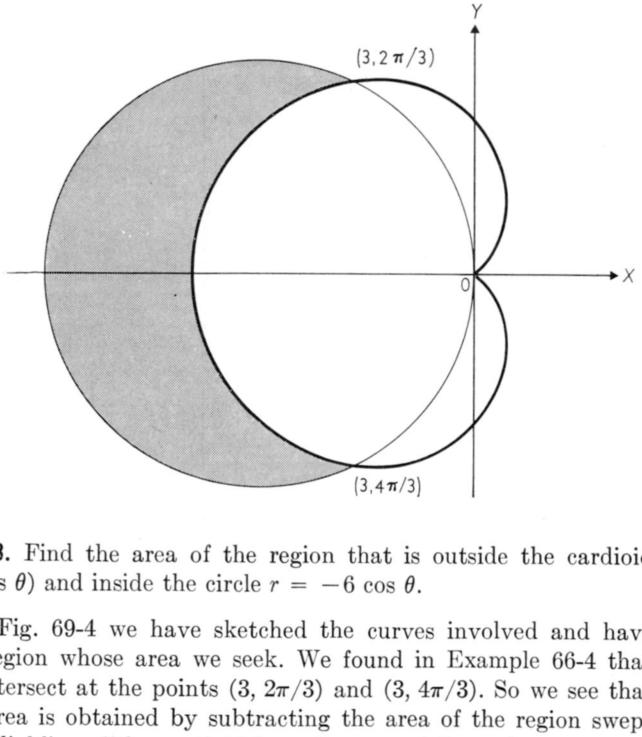

Figure 69-4

Example 69-3. Find the area of the region that is outside the cardioid $r = 2(1 - \cos \theta)$ and inside the circle $r = -6 \cos \theta$.

Solution. In Fig. 69-4 we have sketched the curves involved and have shaded the region whose area we seek. We found in Example 66-4 that our curves intersect at the points $(3, 2\pi/3)$ and $(3, 4\pi/3)$. So we see that the desired area is obtained by subtracting the area of the region swept out by the radial line of the cardioid from the area of the region swept out by the radial line of the circle as θ goes from $2\pi/3$ to $4\pi/3$. Making use of the symmetry of our region,

$$\begin{aligned} A &= 2\left[(\tfrac{1}{2}) \int_{2\pi/3}^{\pi} 36 \cos^2 \theta \, d\theta - (\tfrac{1}{2}) \int_{2\pi/3}^{\pi} 4(1 - \cos \theta)^2 \, d\theta \right] \\ &= \int_{2\pi/3}^{\pi} [36 \cos^2 \theta - 4(1 - 2 \cos \theta + \cos^2 \theta)] \, d\theta \\ &= 4 \int_{2\pi/3}^{\pi} (4 \cos 2\theta + 2 \cos \theta + 3) \, d\theta = 4\pi. \end{aligned}$$

Problems 69

1. Find the area of the region bounded by one loop of the graph of the equation $r = 2 \cos 2\theta$.
2. Find the area of the region bounded by the "first" turn of a spiral $(0 \leq \theta \leq 2\pi)$ and the polar axis if the equation of the spiral is:
(a) $r = \theta$ (b) $r = e^{\theta}$ (c) $r = \cosh \theta$
3. Find the area of the region bounded by the circle whose polar equation is $r = 6 \cos \theta + 8 \sin \theta$.
4. Find the area of the region enclosed by the graph of the polar equation $r = \sin \theta \cos^2 \theta$.
5. Show that the area of the region bounded by two radial lines and the spiral $r\theta = k$ is directly proportional to the difference of the lengths of the two radial segments.
6. Find the area of the region bounded by the inside loop of the graph of the equation $r = 1 - 2 \cos \theta$.
7. Find the area of the region bounded by the curve $r = 3 + 2 \cos \theta$.
8. How much material is needed to cover the face of a bow tie whose outline is the curve $r^2 = 8 \cos 2\theta$?
9. Find the area of the region outside the circle $r = -6 \cos \theta$ and inside the cardioid $r = 2(1 - \cos \theta)$ (see Fig. 69-4).
10. Show that the area of the region enclosed by the rose curve $r = a \cos n\theta$ is one-half the area of the region bounded by the circle in which the rose is inscribed if n is an even positive integer and one-fourth the area of the region bounded by the circle if n is an odd positive integer.
11. Find the area of the region that is enclosed by the graph of the equation $r^2 \cos^4 \theta - 5 \cos^2 \theta + 1 = 0$.
12. Interpret the following integral as the area of a region enclosed by a certain ellipse in order to find the value of the integral: $\int_0^{2\pi} \frac{2\, d\theta}{(2 - \cos \theta)^2}$.

70. Rotation of Axes

We now return to the problem of changing from one cartesian coordinate system to another. In Section 31 we found that we can often simplify the form of certain equations by translating the axes. For example, we saw that by a proper translation the equation of any circle can be put in the form $\bar{x}^2 + \bar{y}^2 = r^2$. At that time we only considered new coordinate systems whose axes were parallel to the original axes. Now we are ready to take up more complicated transformations of axes.

In Fig. 70-1 we show two cartesian coordinate systems—an XY-system and an $\overline{XY}$-system, with the same origin, but such that the $\bar{X}$ axis makes an angle of α with the X-axis. We say that the $\overline{XY}$-system is obtained from the XY-system by a **rotation** through α. Each point P

will have two sets of coordinates, (x, y) and $(\bar{x}, \bar{y})$, and we will now find the equations that relate these coordinates.

We will introduce two polar coordinate systems, both systems having the origin O as the pole. In one system the positive X-axis is the polar axis, and in the other system the positive $\bar{X}$-axis is the polar axis. Then our point P will have polar coordinates (r, θ) and $(\bar{r}, \bar{\theta})$ in addition to its two pairs of cartesian coordinates. It is easy to find the relations

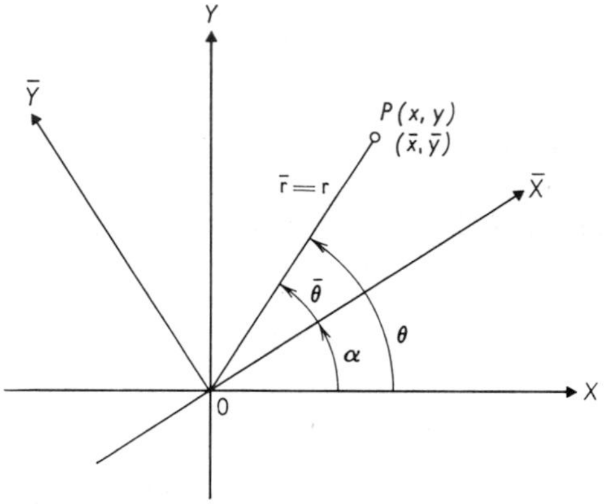

Figure 70-1

between the two sets of polar coordinates of P, and because we know how the polar and cartesian coordinates of a point are related, we can then find the equations that connect the two sets of cartesian coordinates of P. Thus we see that

$$\bar{r} = r, \quad \text{and} \quad \bar{\theta} = \theta - \alpha.$$

Therefore, the equations

$$\bar{x} = \bar{r} \cos \bar{\theta} \quad \text{and} \quad \bar{y} = \bar{r} \sin \bar{\theta}$$

that express the "barred" cartesian coordinates in terms of the "barred" polar coordinates give us

(70-1) $$\bar{x} = r \cos (\theta - \alpha) \quad \text{and} \quad \bar{y} = r \sin (\theta - \alpha).$$

Using the trigonometric identities

$$\cos (\theta - \alpha) = \cos \theta \cos \alpha + \sin \theta \sin \alpha$$

and

$$\sin (\theta - \alpha) = \sin \theta \cos \alpha - \cos \theta \sin \alpha,$$

we can write Equations 70-1 as

$$\text{(70-2)} \qquad \begin{aligned} \bar{x} &= r\cos\theta\cos\alpha + r\sin\theta\sin\alpha \\ \bar{y} &= r\sin\theta\cos\alpha - r\cos\theta\sin\alpha. \end{aligned}$$

Now we return to the "unbarred" cartesian coordinates (x, y) by means of the equations

$$\text{(70-3)} \qquad x = r\cos\theta \quad \text{and} \quad y = r\sin\theta.$$

We replace $r\cos\theta$ with x and $r\sin\theta$ with y in Equations 70-2, and we obtain our transformation equations

$$\text{(70-4)} \qquad \begin{aligned} \bar{x} &= x\cos\alpha + y\sin\alpha \\ \bar{y} &= -x\sin\alpha + y\cos\alpha. \end{aligned}$$

If we know the XY-coordinates of a point, then Equations 70-4 tell us how to find the $\bar{X}\bar{Y}$-coordinates of the point. We can solve these equations for x and y, and when we do we obtain the equations (see Question 1 of Problems 70)

$$\text{(70-5)} \qquad \begin{aligned} x &= \bar{x}\cos\alpha - y\sin\alpha, \\ y &= \bar{x}\sin\alpha + \bar{y}\cos\alpha. \end{aligned}$$

Example 70-1. Suppose the $\bar{X}\bar{Y}$-axes are obtained by rotating the XY-axes through an angle of 45°. To what does the equation $xy = 1$ transform?

Solution. Here $\alpha = 45°$, so Equations 70-5 become

$$x = \frac{\bar{x}}{\sqrt{2}} - \frac{\bar{y}}{\sqrt{2}},$$

$$y = \frac{\bar{x}}{\sqrt{2}} + \frac{\bar{y}}{\sqrt{2}}.$$

Hence $$xy = \frac{(\bar{x} - \bar{y})(\bar{x} + \bar{y})}{2} = \frac{(\bar{x}^2 - \bar{y}^2)}{2}.$$

Thus the equation $xy = 1$ is transformed into the equation

$$\frac{\bar{x}^2}{2} - \frac{\bar{y}^2}{2} = 1.$$

This equation is the standard form for an equilateral hyperbola whose asymptotes bisect the quadrants in the $\bar{X}\bar{Y}$-coordinate system. Thus the equation $xy = 1$ represents an equilateral hyperbola whose asymptotes are the X- and Y-axes (see Fig. 70-2).

Example 70-2. Find the distance between the point $P(1, 4)$ and the line $2y - x = 2$.

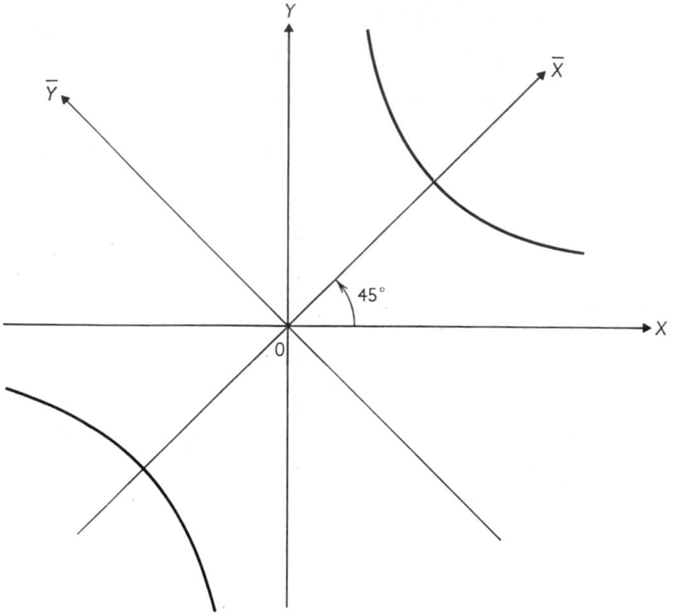

Figure 70-2

Solution. Figure 70-3 shows the given point and line. The slope of the line is $\tan \alpha = \frac{1}{2}$, where α is the measure of the angle of inclination. Now let us introduce an $\overline{XY}$-coordinate system in such a way that the $\bar{X}$-axis is parallel to our given line. We can obtain such an $\overline{XY}$-system by a rotation of axes through α. Since $\tan \alpha = \frac{1}{2}$, we see that $\sin \alpha = 1/\sqrt{5}$ and $\cos \alpha = 2/\sqrt{5}$. Thus the Transformation Equations 70-4 and 70-5 become

$$\bar{x} = \frac{2x}{\sqrt{5}} + \frac{y}{\sqrt{5}}, \quad \bar{y} = \frac{-x}{\sqrt{5}} + \frac{2y}{\sqrt{5}}$$

$$x = \frac{2\bar{x}}{\sqrt{5}} - \frac{\bar{y}}{\sqrt{5}}, \quad y = \frac{\bar{x}}{\sqrt{5}} + \frac{2\bar{y}}{\sqrt{5}}.$$

When we substitute these expressions for x and y in the equation of our line, we find that the equation of the line becomes $\bar{y} = \dfrac{2}{\sqrt{5}}\cdot$ Furthermore, these transformation equations tell us that the $\bar{Y}$-coordinate of the point P is $\dfrac{7}{\sqrt{5}}\cdot$ Since the line is parallel to the $\bar{X}$-axis, we find the distance d be-

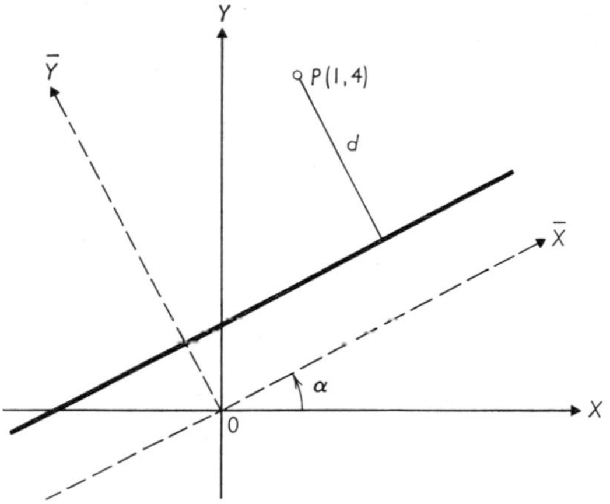

Figure 70-3

tween it and P by subtraction:

$$d = \frac{7}{\sqrt{5}} - \frac{2}{\sqrt{5}} = \frac{5}{\sqrt{5}} = \sqrt{5}.$$

The **general rigid transformation** equations

$$\text{(70-6)} \quad \begin{aligned} \bar{x} &= x \cos \alpha + y \sin \alpha - h \\ \bar{y} &= -x \sin \alpha + y \cos \alpha - k \end{aligned}$$

are the transformation equations that result from a rotation through α *followed* by a translation.

Example 70-3. Sketch the two cartesian coordinate systems that are related by the equations

$$\text{(70-7)} \quad \begin{aligned} \bar{x} &= \tfrac{3}{5}x + \tfrac{4}{5}y - 3 \\ \bar{y} &= -\tfrac{4}{5}x + \tfrac{3}{5}y - 1. \end{aligned}$$

Draw the XY-system in the "usual" position.

Solution. The points whose $\overline{X}\overline{Y}$-coordinates are (0, 0) and (1, 0) determine the $\bar{X}$-axis, and the points whose $\overline{X}\overline{Y}$-coordinates are (0, 0) and (0, 1) determine the $\bar{Y}$-axis. We will locate these points by finding their XY-coordinates from Equations 70-7 and then plotting them in the XY-coordinate system of Fig. 70-4. The XY-coordinates of the point whose $\overline{X}\overline{Y}$-coordinates are (0, 0) are given by the equations

$$0 = \tfrac{3}{5}x + \tfrac{4}{5}y - 3$$

and

$$0 = -\tfrac{4}{5}x + \tfrac{3}{5}y - 1.$$

When we solve these equations, we obtain $x = 1$ and $y = 3$. Similarly, we find that the point whose $\bar{X}\bar{Y}$-coordinates are (1, 0) has XY-coordinates $(\frac{8}{5}, \frac{19}{5})$. The point whose $\bar{X}\bar{Y}$-coordinates are (0, 1) has XY-coordinates $(\frac{1}{5}, \frac{18}{5})$. Now we plot these points and draw in the $\bar{X}\bar{Y}$-axes (Fig. 70-4). We see that the $\bar{X}\bar{Y}$-axes are obtained by first rotating the axes through

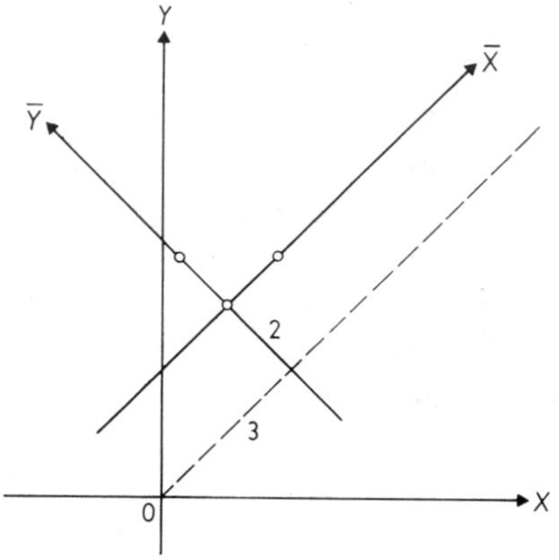

Figure 70-4

an angle of α, where $\cos\alpha = \frac{3}{5}$ and $\sin\alpha = \frac{4}{5}$, and then translating the origin 3 units in the "new X direction" and 2 units in the "new Y direction."

Problems 70

1. Solve Equations 70-4 to obtain Equations 70-5.
2. Find the $\bar{X}\bar{Y}$-coordinates of the point $(-2, 4)$ after a rotation through:
   (a) 30° (b) 135° (c) 240° (d) −180°
   (e) π (f) $-\pi/2$ (g) 2π (h) $-\pi/4$
3. Suppose the $\bar{X}\bar{Y}$-coordinate system is obtained by a rotation through 60°. Find the XY-coordinates of the point whose $\bar{X}\bar{Y}$-coordinates are:
   (a) (1, 0) (b) (0, 1)
   (c) (1, 1) (d) $(-2, \sqrt{3})$
4. Given the transformation equations

$$\bar{x} = 0.8x + 0.6y$$
$$\bar{y} = -0.6x + 0.8y.$$

   What angle does the $\bar{X}$-axis make with the X-axis? Sketch the XY- and the $\bar{X}\bar{Y}$-coordinate axes.
5. Suppose that we rotate our axes through an angle of α, where $0 \leq \alpha < \pi/2$. Let the slope of the $\bar{X}$-axis relative to the X-axis be m. What is the slope of

the X-axis relative to the $\bar{X}$-axis? Show that the transformation equations can be written

$$\bar{x} = \frac{x + my}{\sqrt{1 + m^2}}, \quad \bar{y} = \frac{-mx + y}{\sqrt{1 + m^2}}$$

6. To what equation does the equation $x^{1/2} + y^{1/2} = 1$ transform under a rotation through 45°? Describe the graph of the equation.

7. Find the distance between the given point and the given line.
(a) $(6, -2)$ and $3x - 4y + 4 = 0$ (b) $(-1, 7)$ and $x + 3y - 6 = 0$
(c) $(4, 3)$ and $x + y + 1 = 0$ (d) $(-2, -3)$ and $2x - y - 4 = 0$

8. Find the distance between the parallel lines $x + y - 2 = 0$ and $2x + 2y - 1 = 0$.

9. What are the transformation equations that relate the XY-coordinates and the $\bar{X}\bar{Y}$-coordinates if we first translate the origin to the point (h, k) and then rotate through an angle of α?

10. Plot the graph of the equation

$$2x^3 - 6x^2y + 6xy^2 - 2y^3 - x - y = 0$$

by first performing a rotation through $-45°$.

71. The General Quadratic Equation

For certain choices of the numbers A, B, C, D, E, and F we already know that the quadratic equation

$$Ax^2 + Bxy + Cy^2 + Dx + Ey + F = 0 \tag{71-1}$$

represents a circle, a conic, or a straight line. For example, if we choose $A = 1$, $B = 0$, $C = -1$, $D = 0$, $E = 0$, and $F = -1$, then Equation 71-1 becomes

$$x^2 - y^2 = 1,$$

which we recognize as the equation of an equilateral hyperbola. But other choices of A, B, C, D, E, and F lead to equations that we have not yet studied—for example, the equation

$$6x^2 + 24xy - y^2 - 12x + 26y + 11 = 0. \tag{71-2}$$

In this section we shall see that the graph of a quadratic equation is always a familiar figure. In particular, it will turn out that the graph of Equation 71-2 is a hyperbola.

To find the graph of a quadratic equation we will first make a transformation of axes that reduces the equation to one of the standard forms that we have already studied. Thus in Example 70-1 we saw that a rotation of axes through 45° transformed the equation $xy = 1$ into the standard equation of an equilateral hyperbola

$$\frac{\bar{x}^2}{2} - \frac{\bar{y}^2}{2} = 1.$$

The question that naturally comes to mind is, "How did we decide to rotate through 45°?" The following example shows how we pick our angle of rotation.

Example 71-1. By a suitable rotation of axes, reduce the equation

$$8x^2 - 4xy + 5y^2 = 36 \tag{71-3}$$

to a standard form.

Solution. When we make the rotation given by Equations 70-5, our equation becomes

$$8(\bar{x}\cos\alpha - \bar{y}\sin\alpha)^2 - 4(\bar{x}\cos\alpha - \bar{y}\sin\alpha)\cdot(\bar{x}\sin\alpha + \bar{y}\cos\alpha) + 5(\bar{x}\sin\alpha + \bar{y}\cos\alpha)^2 = 36.$$

Then we expand and collect terms and have

$$\begin{aligned}(8\cos^2\alpha - 4\sin\alpha\cos\alpha + 5\sin^2\alpha)\bar{x}^2 &\\ + (4\sin^2\alpha - 6\sin\alpha\cos\alpha - 4\cos^2\alpha)\bar{x}\bar{y} &\\ + (8\sin^2\alpha + 4\sin\alpha\cos\alpha + 5\cos^2\alpha)\bar{y}^2 &= 36.\end{aligned} \tag{71-4}$$

This last equation is of the form

$$\bar{A}\bar{x}^2 + \bar{B}\bar{x}\bar{y} + \bar{C}\bar{y}^2 = 36, \tag{71-5}$$

where the numbers $\bar{A}$, $\bar{B}$, and $\bar{C}$ depend on α. Now we want to choose α so that Equation 71-5 is of a familiar form. Therefore, we will choose α so that $\bar{B} = 0$; that is, so that

$$4\sin^2\alpha - 6\sin\alpha\cos\alpha - 4\cos^2\alpha = 0.$$

Since $\cos^2\alpha - \sin^2\alpha = \cos 2\alpha$ and $\sin\alpha\cos\alpha = \frac{1}{2}\sin 2\alpha$, this equation can be written as

$$-3\sin 2\alpha - 4\cos 2\alpha = 0,$$

from which we see that

$$\cot 2\alpha = -\tfrac{3}{4}.$$

We can select an angle of 2α in the range $0 < 2\alpha < 180°$ that satisfies this equation, and thus $0 < \alpha < 90°$. To find the coefficients of $\bar{x}^2$ and $\bar{y}^2$ we find the numbers $\cos\alpha$ and $\sin\alpha$ from the trigonometric identities

$$\cos\alpha = \sqrt{\frac{1+\cos 2\alpha}{2}} \quad\text{and}\quad \sin\alpha = \sqrt{\frac{1-\cos 2\alpha}{2}}.$$

Since $\cot 2\alpha = -\frac{3}{4}$, it follows that the radial line through the point

$(-3, 4)$ makes an angle of 2α with the positive X-axis. Hence $\cos 2\alpha = -\frac{3}{5}$, and we have

$$\cos \alpha = \sqrt{\frac{1 - \frac{3}{5}}{2}} = \sqrt{\frac{1}{5}} \quad \text{and} \quad \sin \alpha = \sqrt{\frac{1 + \frac{3}{5}}{2}} = \sqrt{\frac{4}{5}}.$$

When we substitute these numbers in Equation 71-4, the equation becomes

$$4\bar{x}^2 + 9\bar{y}^2 = 36.$$

In other words,

$$\frac{\bar{x}^2}{9} + \frac{\bar{y}^2}{4} = 1.$$

So we see that the graph of Equation 71-3 is an ellipse whose major diameter is 6 units long and whose minor diameter is 4 units long. We have shown our ellipse together with the rotated axes in Fig. 71-1.

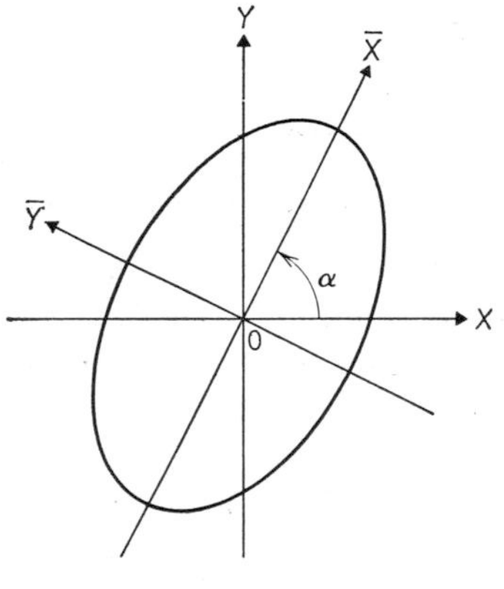

Figure 71-1

We can employ the procedure used in the preceding example to reduce any quadratic expression

$$(71\text{-}6) \qquad Ax^2 + Bxy + Cy^2$$

in which $B \neq 0$ to the form

$$(71\text{-}7) \qquad \bar{A}\bar{x}^2 + \bar{C}\bar{y}^2.$$

We simply replace x and y in terms of $\bar{x}$ and $\bar{y}$ according to the rotation Equations 70-5 and obtain the expression $A(\bar{x} \cos \alpha - \bar{y} \sin \alpha)^2 + B(\bar{x} \cos \alpha - \bar{y} \sin \alpha)(\bar{x} \sin \alpha + \bar{y} \cos \alpha) + C(\bar{x} \sin \alpha + \bar{y} \cos \alpha)^2$. When we multiply out and collect the coefficients of $\bar{x}^2$, $\bar{x}\bar{y}$, and $\bar{y}^2$, we find that

$$Ax^2 + Bxy + Cy^2 = \bar{A}\bar{x}^2 + \bar{B}\bar{x}\bar{y} + \bar{C}\bar{y}^2,$$

where

$$\bar{A} = A\cos^2\alpha + B\sin\alpha\cos\alpha + C\sin^2\alpha,$$
$$(71\text{-}8)\qquad \bar{B} = (C - A)\sin 2\alpha + B\cos 2\alpha,$$
$$\bar{C} = A\sin^2\alpha - B\sin\alpha\cos\alpha + C\cos^2\alpha.$$

We see from the second of Equations 71-8 that $\bar{B}$ will be 0 if we choose α so that

$$(71\text{-}9)\qquad \cot 2\alpha = \frac{A - C}{B}.$$

Clearly, we can always choose α to be an angle such that $0° < 2\alpha < 180°$. We sum up our results as a theorem.

THEOREM 71-1. *Every quadratic expression* $Ax^2 + Bxy + Cy^2$ *in which* $B \neq 0$ *can be reduced to the form* $\bar{A}\bar{x}^2 + \bar{C}\bar{y}^2$ *by rotating axes through an angle of* α, *where* $0 < \alpha < 90°$, *and* $\cot 2\alpha = (A - C)/B$.

By rotating axes through the angle of α, as described in Theorem 71-1, we can reduce any quadratic equation of the form of Equation 71-1 in which $B \neq 0$ to a quadratic equation of the form

$$\bar{A}\bar{x}^2 + \bar{C}\bar{y}^2 + \bar{D}\bar{x} + \bar{E}\bar{y} + \bar{F} = 0.$$

If we don't recognize the graph of this equation, a suitable translation will bring it to a form that we do recognize. We will illustrate the entire procedure by an example. It will pay you to review our work on translation in Chapter 4.

Example 71-2. Describe the graph of Equation 71-2.

Solution. Here $A = 6$, $B = 24$, and $C = -1$. So we first rotate the axes through the acute angle of α such that

$$\cot 2\alpha = \tfrac{7}{24}.$$

It is easy to see that $\cos 2\alpha = \frac{7}{25}$, and hence

$$(71\text{-}10)\qquad \cos\alpha = \sqrt{\frac{1 + \cos 2\alpha}{2}} = \frac{4}{5}$$

and

$$(71\text{-}11)\qquad \sin\alpha = \sqrt{\frac{1 - \cos 2\alpha}{2}} = \frac{3}{5}.$$

Therefore, our rotation equations are

$$x = \frac{4\bar{x}}{5} - \frac{3\bar{y}}{5} \quad\text{and}\quad y = \frac{3\bar{x}}{5} + \frac{4\bar{y}}{5}.$$

When we substitute these quantities in Equation 71-2 we obtain the equation

(71-12) $$15\bar{x}^2 - 10\bar{y}^2 + 6\bar{x} + 28\bar{y} + 11 = 0.$$

Now we will translate the axes by means of the equations (see Section 31),

(71-13) $$\bar{x} = \bar{\bar{x}} + h \quad \text{and} \quad \bar{y} = \bar{\bar{y}} + k,$$

where h and k are to be determined so as to make our resulting equation "simpler" than Equation 71-12. In terms of $\bar{\bar{x}}$ and $\bar{\bar{y}}$, Equation 71-12 reads

(71-14) $$15\bar{\bar{x}}^2 - 10\bar{\bar{y}}^2 + (30h + 6)\bar{\bar{x}} + (-20k + 28)\bar{\bar{y}} + 15h^2 - 10k^2 + 6h + 28k + 11 = 0.$$

Now we select h and k so that $30h + 6 = 0$ and $-20k + 28 = 0$; that is, $h = -\frac{1}{5}$ and $k = \frac{7}{5}$. Then Equation 71-14 becomes

$$15\bar{\bar{x}}^2 - 10\bar{\bar{y}}^2 + 30 = 0.$$

Finally, we write this equation in the standard form

(71-15) $$\frac{\bar{\bar{y}}^2}{3} - \frac{\bar{\bar{x}}^2}{2} = 1,$$

and we see that our graph is a hyperbola. The "specifications"—diameter, length of latus rectum, focal length, and so on—of our hyperbola can be read from Equation 71-15. The graph of our equation is shown in Fig. 71-2 together with the three different coordinate axes involved.

In the preceding example we began with a quadratic equation

(71-16) $$Ax^2 + Bxy + Cy^2 + Dx + Ey + F = 0,$$

and rotated axes to obtain an equation of the form

(71-17) $$\bar{A}\bar{x}^2 + \bar{C}\bar{y}^2 + \bar{D}\bar{x} + \bar{E}\bar{y} + \bar{F} = 0.$$

You can easily verify, by using the proper translation, that if $\bar{A}\bar{C} < 0$ (as it was in the preceding example) then the graph of Equation 71-17 is a hyperbola (or a "degenerate" hyperbola). If $\bar{A}\bar{C} > 0$, the graph of Equation 71-17 is an ellipse, and if $\bar{A}\bar{C} = 0$, the graph is a parabola (again allowing for "degeneracies"). Now you can use Equations 71-8 to verify (see exercise 4 of Problems 71) that

$$\bar{B}^2 - 4\bar{A}\bar{C} = B^2 - 4AC$$

regardless of the angle of rotation. In particular, if we choose α so that $\bar{B} = 0$, then we find that

$$-4\bar{A}\bar{C} = B^2 - 4AC.$$

Therefore, the sign of $\bar{A}\bar{C}$ is determined by the sign of $B^2 - 4AC$. Thus from our remarks concerning the graph of Equation 71-17, we can conclude that *the graph of Equation 71-16 is*

(i) *a parabola if* $B^2 - 4AC = 0$,
(ii) *an ellipse if* $B^2 - 4AC < 0$,
(iii) *a hyperbola if* $B^2 - 4AC > 0$,

with the understanding that degenerate cases may occur.

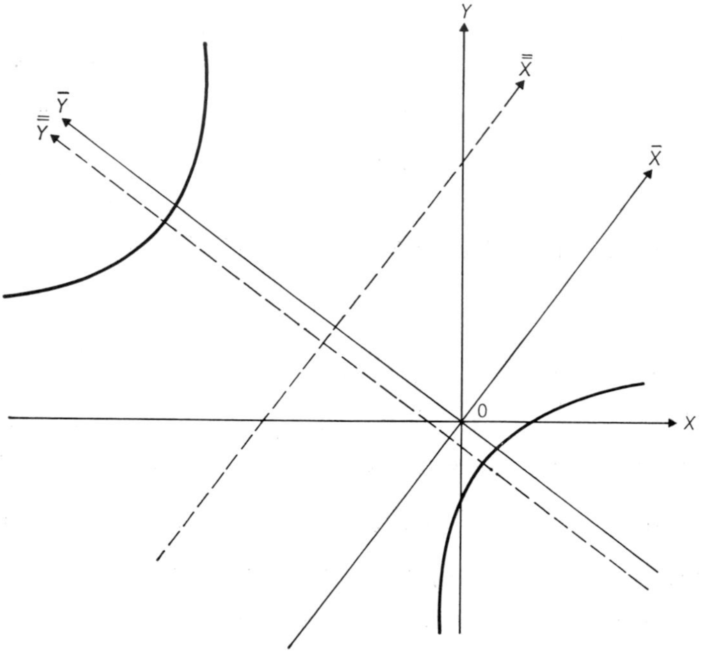

Figure 71-2

The number $B^2 - 4AC$ is called the *discriminant* of the quadratic Equation 71-16. Notice that the discriminant of Equation 71-2 is $(24)^2 - 4 \cdot 6 \cdot (-1) = 600$, and we found that the graph of this equation is a hyperbola. The discriminant of Equation 71-3 is $(-4)^2 - 4 \cdot 8 \cdot 5 = -144$, and we found that the graph of this equation is an ellipse.

Problems 71

1. Reduce the following quadratic expressions to the form $\bar{A}\bar{x}^2 + \bar{C}\bar{y}^2$:
   (a) $x^2 + 4xy + y^2$ (b) $4x^2 + 15xy - 4y^2$
   (c) $x^2 + 4xy + 4y^2$ (d) $x^2 - 9xy + y^2$

2. Rotate the axes so that the following equations take the form $\bar{A}\bar{x}^2 + \bar{C}\bar{y}^2 = \bar{F}$. Sketch the graphs of these equations. Find the algebraic sign of the discriminant of each equation and use the result to check the form of your graph.
(a) $11x^2 + 24xy + 4y^2 = 20$
(b) $25x^2 + 14xy + 25y^2 = 288$
(c) $3x^2 + 4xy = 4$
(d) $9x^2 - 24xy + 16y^2 - 400x - 300y = 0$

3. Use translations and rotations to help you sketch the graphs of the following equations. Find the algebraic sign of the discriminant of each equation and use the result to check the form of your graph.
(a) $5x^2 + 6xy + 5y^2 - 32x - 32y + 32 = 0$
(b) $x^2 - 4xy + 4y^2 + 5y - 9 = 0$
(c) $9x^2 - 24xy + 16y^2 - 56x - 92y + 688 = 0$
(d) $x^2 + 2xy + y^2 - 2x - 2y - 3 = 0$

4. Use Equations 71-8 to show that $\bar{A} + \bar{C} = A + C$, and $\bar{B}^2 - 4\bar{A}\bar{C} = B^2 - 4AC$.

5. Find the XY-coordinate equation of the set of points the sum of whose distances from the points $(1, 1)$ and $(-1, -1)$ is 4 by first writing the equation in a rotated system, and then using the rotation Equations 70-4 to obtain the equation in x and y.

6. A parabola has the origin as its vertex, and its directrix is the line $y + x + 1 = 0$. What is the equation of the parabola in a coordinate system whose $\bar{X}$-axis is obtained by rotating the X-axis through 45°. Find the equation of the parabola in XY-coordinates.

7. Solve the equation $2x^2 + 2xy + y^2 = 9$ for y to obtain $y = -x + \sqrt{9 - x^2}$ or $y = -x - \sqrt{9 - x^2}$. Sketch the graphs of the equations $y = -x$ and $y = \sqrt{9 - x^2}$, and use these graphs to sketch the graph of the given equation by addition or subtraction of Y-coordinates. Use the algebraic sign of the discriminant of the equation to check the form of your graph.

8. Use the method of the preceding question to sketch the graph of the equation $y^2 - 2xy + 2x - 2y + 2 = 0$.

9. Identify the conic that contains the following points:
(a) $(-3, -2)$, $(2, -2)$, $(2, 1)$, $(0, -5)$, $(3, 0)$
(b) $(1, 2)$, $(1, 8)$, $(-1, 6)$, $(-1, 0)$, $(-5, 0)$
(c) $(3, 4)$, $(-3, -2)$, $(-3, 0)$, $(-2, 0)$, $(2, 4)$.

10. How must A, B, and C be related algebraically for the graph of the equation $Ax^2 + Bxy + Cy^2 + Dx + Ey + F = 0$ to be a circle (or a degenerate circle).

11. Use the discriminant to identify the "conic" whose equation is $2x^2 + xy - y^2 + 6y - 8 = 0$. Notice that the equation can be written in factored form as $(x + y - 2)(2x - y + 4) = 0$, and describe the graph of this "conic."

72. Vectors in the Plane

Physicists and engineers talk and think a great deal in terms of **vectors.** These scientists describe a vector quantity as one that has both magnitude and direction, and they use vectors to represent such things as velocity, force, and the like. Geometrically, a vector is represented as an arrow in space, the length of the arrow being the magnitude of the vector and the direction of the arrow being the assigned direction of the vector. For the present we shall confine ourselves to vectors that lie in a plane, but in the next chapter we shall take up the question of vectors in three-dimensional space.

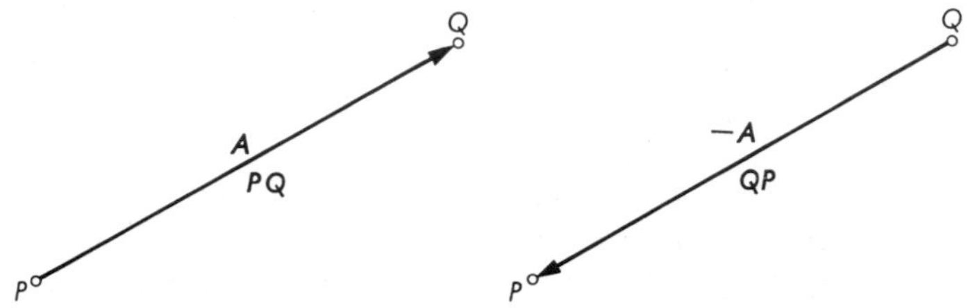

Figure 72-1

A vector is determined by an ordered pair of points in the plane—the **initial point** and the **terminal point** of the vector (Fig. 72-1). We use bold face type to denote vectors. For instance, we have labeled the vector on the left in Fig. 72-1 as ***A***, and we might also call it ***PQ*** if we want to emphasize that it is the vector from P to Q. We denote the magnitude of the vector ***A*** by the symbol $|\boldsymbol{A}|$. We often refer to this number as

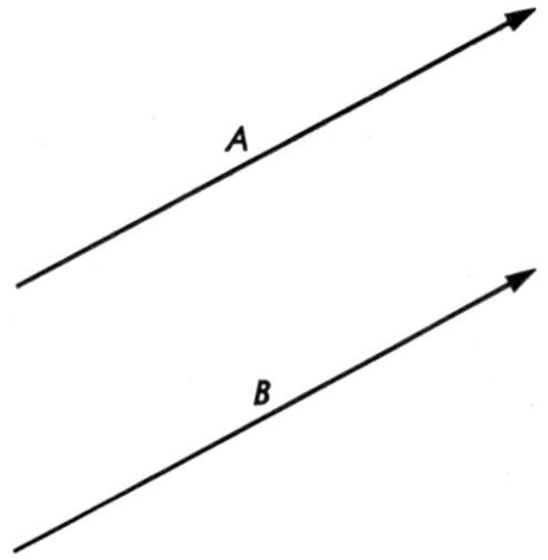

Figure 72-2

the **absolute value** of ***A***. If ***A*** is the vector ***PQ***, then the vector ***QP*** is denoted by $-\boldsymbol{A}$ (see Fig. 72-1).

Two vectors are considered equal if, and only if, they have the same magnitude and the same direction. Thus for the vectors ***A*** and ***B*** in Fig. 72-2 we have $\boldsymbol{A} = \boldsymbol{B}$. Notice that we do not require that equal vectors coincide, but they must be parallel, have the same length, and point in the same direction.

If we have two vectors ***A*** and ***B*** as shown on the left in Fig. 72-3,

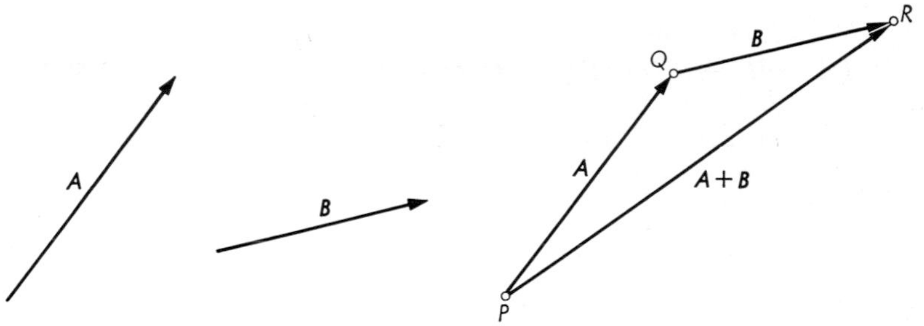

Figure 72-3

then we obtain the vector sum $\boldsymbol{A} + \boldsymbol{B}$ by placing the initial point of $\boldsymbol{B}$ on the terminal point of $\boldsymbol{A}$ and joining the initial point of $\boldsymbol{A}$ to the terminal point of $\boldsymbol{B}$ as shown on the right in Fig. 72-3. Thus, if P, Q, and R are points such that $\boldsymbol{A} = \boldsymbol{PQ}$ and $\boldsymbol{B} = \boldsymbol{QR}$, then $\boldsymbol{A} + \boldsymbol{B} = \boldsymbol{PR}$; that is,

$$\boldsymbol{PQ} + \boldsymbol{QR} = \boldsymbol{PR}.$$

We get the sum $\boldsymbol{B} + \boldsymbol{A}$ by placing the initial point of $\boldsymbol{A}$ on the terminal point of $\boldsymbol{B}$ and joining the initial point of $\boldsymbol{B}$ to the terminal point

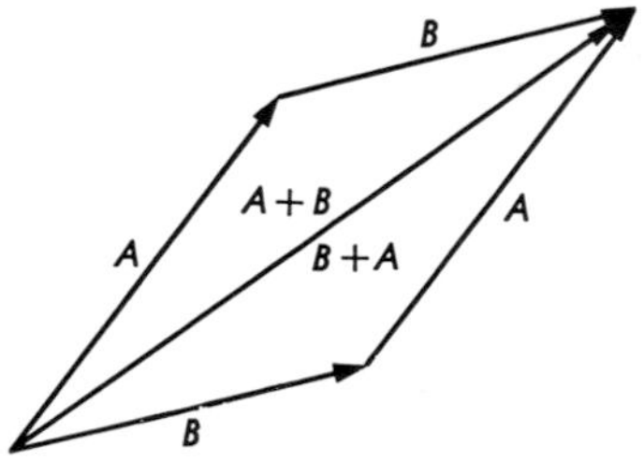

Figure 72-4

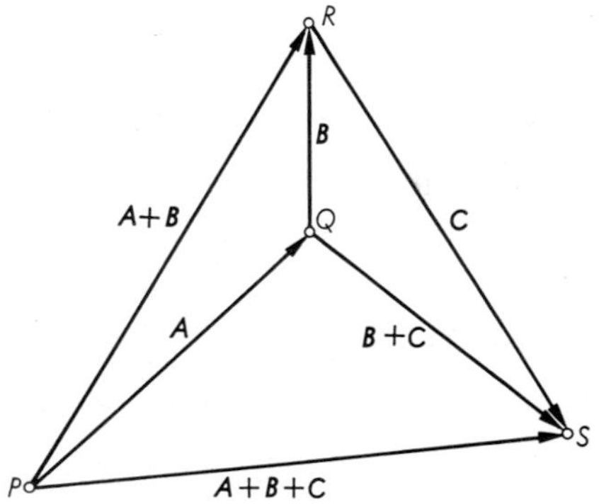

Figure 72-5

of $\boldsymbol{A}$. Figure 72-4 shows how we construct $\boldsymbol{A} + \boldsymbol{B}$ and $\boldsymbol{B} + \boldsymbol{A}$, and from this figure it is apparent that the **commutative law** of addition,

$$\boldsymbol{A} + \boldsymbol{B} = \boldsymbol{B} + \boldsymbol{A}, \tag{72-1}$$

holds for vector addition. Figure 72-4 suggests the name *parallelogram rule* that is often used to describe the method of adding vectors.

If $\boldsymbol{A} = \boldsymbol{PQ}$, $\boldsymbol{B} = \boldsymbol{QR}$, and $\boldsymbol{C} = \boldsymbol{RS}$ (see Fig. 72-5),

then

$$(\boldsymbol{A} + \boldsymbol{B}) + \boldsymbol{C} = (\boldsymbol{PQ} + \boldsymbol{QR}) + \boldsymbol{RS} = \boldsymbol{PR} + \boldsymbol{RS} = \boldsymbol{PS},$$

and

$$\boldsymbol{A} + (\boldsymbol{B} + \boldsymbol{C}) = \boldsymbol{PQ} + (\boldsymbol{QR} + \boldsymbol{RS}) = \boldsymbol{PQ} + \boldsymbol{QS} = \boldsymbol{PS}.$$

Thus the **associative law** of addition,

(72-2) $$(\boldsymbol{A} + \boldsymbol{B}) + \boldsymbol{C} = \boldsymbol{A} + (\boldsymbol{B} + \boldsymbol{C}),$$

is valid for vectors, and we write $\boldsymbol{A} + \boldsymbol{B} + \boldsymbol{C}$ for this sum.

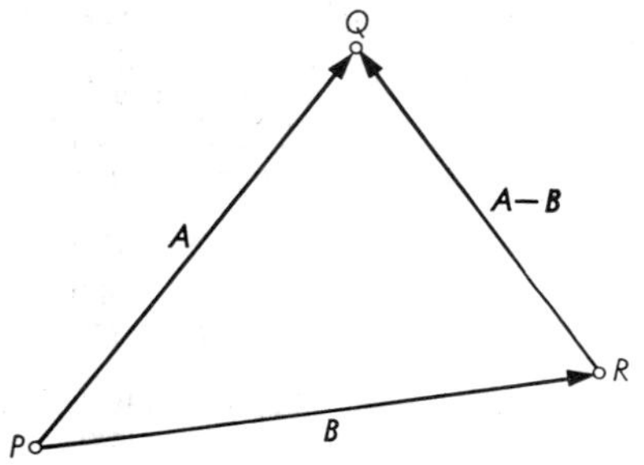

Figure 72-6

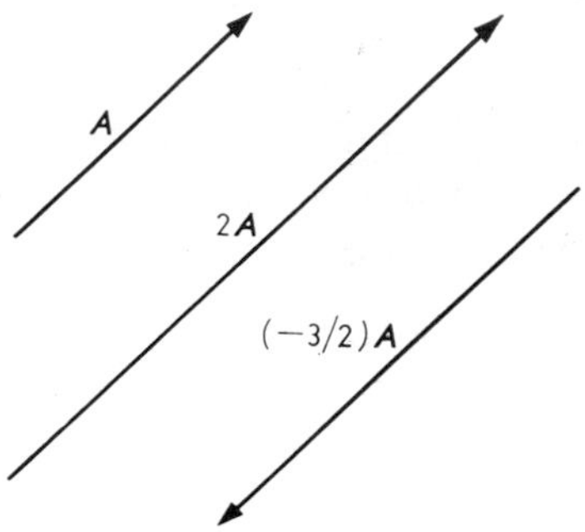

Figure 72-7

We find it convenient to introduce the **zero vector 0,** which can be represented as $\boldsymbol{PP}$, where P is any point. The magnitude of $\boldsymbol{0}$ is 0, and its direction is unspecified. If $\boldsymbol{A}$ is any vector, then

(72-3) $$\boldsymbol{A} + \boldsymbol{0} = \boldsymbol{0} + \boldsymbol{A} = \boldsymbol{A}.$$

Furthermore, our rules of vector addition tell us that

(72-4) $$\boldsymbol{A} + (-\boldsymbol{A}) = (-\boldsymbol{A}) + \boldsymbol{A} = \boldsymbol{0}.$$

We define the difference $\boldsymbol{A} - \boldsymbol{B}$ by means of the equation

(72-5) $$\boldsymbol{A} - \boldsymbol{B} = \boldsymbol{A} + (-\boldsymbol{B}).$$

Then it follows that

$$(\boldsymbol{A} - \boldsymbol{B}) + \boldsymbol{B} = \boldsymbol{A} + [(-\boldsymbol{B}) + \boldsymbol{B}] = \boldsymbol{A} + \boldsymbol{0} = \boldsymbol{A};$$

that is, the difference $\boldsymbol{A} - \boldsymbol{B}$ is the vector that must be added to $\boldsymbol{B}$ to obtain $\boldsymbol{A}$. If $\boldsymbol{A} = \boldsymbol{PQ}$ and $\boldsymbol{B} = \boldsymbol{PR}$, then

$$\boldsymbol{A} - \boldsymbol{B} = \boldsymbol{PQ} - \boldsymbol{PR} = \boldsymbol{PQ} + \boldsymbol{RP} = \boldsymbol{RP} + \boldsymbol{PQ} = \boldsymbol{RQ}.$$

Figure 72-6 shows the graphical relation among the vectors $\boldsymbol{A}$, $\boldsymbol{B}$, and $\boldsymbol{A} - \boldsymbol{B}$.

Some physical quantities, such as temperature and density, are not described by vectors, but rather by numbers. Because he can measure these quantities by means of a number scale, the scientist calls them **scalar quantities** and the numbers that measure them, **scalars.** So, in the context of our vector analysis, the word *scalar* simply means *real number*. Notice that the absolute value $|\boldsymbol{A}|$ of the vector $\boldsymbol{A}$ is a scalar.

If a is a scalar (real number) and $\boldsymbol{A}$ is a vector, then we denote by $a\boldsymbol{A}$ or by $\boldsymbol{A}a$ *the vector that is* $|a|$ *times as long as* $\boldsymbol{A}$ *and in the direction of* $\boldsymbol{A}$ *if* a *is positive and in the opposite direction if* a *is negative* (see Fig. 72-7). You can convince yourself that the following "natural" rules of arithmetic are valid.

$$\begin{aligned} 1\boldsymbol{A} &= \boldsymbol{A} \\ (a+b)\boldsymbol{A} &= a\boldsymbol{A} + b\boldsymbol{A} \\ a(\boldsymbol{A}+\boldsymbol{B}) &= a\boldsymbol{A} + a\boldsymbol{B} \\ (ab)\boldsymbol{A} &= a(b\boldsymbol{A}). \end{aligned} \tag{72-6}$$

Notice that our rules for operating with vectors, Equations 72-1 to 72-6, are like the usual rules of arithmetic, so you should have no trouble performing the various operations we have introduced.

With the help of vectors we can furnish elegant proofs of certain theorems of geometry. The following example provides a vector proof for a well-known plane geometry theorem.

Example 72-1. Show that the diagonals of a parallelogram bisect each other.

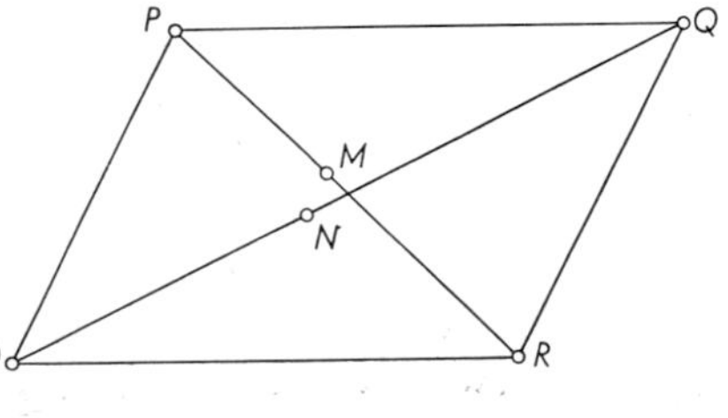

Figure 72-8

Solution. Figure 72-8 shows a parallelogram $OPQR$. We have labeled the midpoint of PR as M and the midpoint of OQ as N, and we are to show that M and N are the same point. To prove that these points coincide, we will show that $\boldsymbol{ON} = \boldsymbol{OM}$. Since N is the midpoint of OQ, we see that $\boldsymbol{ON} = \frac{1}{2}\boldsymbol{OQ}$. But $\boldsymbol{OQ} = \boldsymbol{OR} + \boldsymbol{RQ}$, so we have

$$\boldsymbol{ON} = \tfrac{1}{2}\boldsymbol{OQ} = \tfrac{1}{2}(\boldsymbol{OR} + \boldsymbol{RQ}). \tag{72-7}$$

On the other hand, $\boldsymbol{OM} = \boldsymbol{OP} + \boldsymbol{PM}$. Since M is the midpoint of PR, $\boldsymbol{PM} = \frac{1}{2}\boldsymbol{PR}$. But $\boldsymbol{PR} = \boldsymbol{OR} - \boldsymbol{OP}$, so $\boldsymbol{PM} = \frac{1}{2}(\boldsymbol{OR} - \boldsymbol{OP})$, and hence

(72-8) $$\boldsymbol{OM} = \boldsymbol{OP} + \tfrac{1}{2}(\boldsymbol{OR} - \boldsymbol{OP}) = \tfrac{1}{2}(\boldsymbol{OR} + \boldsymbol{OP}) = \tfrac{1}{2}(\boldsymbol{OR} + \boldsymbol{RQ}).$$

When we compare Equations 72-7 and 72-8, we see that $\boldsymbol{OM} = \boldsymbol{ON}$, and our assertion is proved.

If two vectors $\boldsymbol{A}$ and $\boldsymbol{B}$ have the same or opposite directions, then they are parallel. For convenience, we say that the zero vector $\boldsymbol{0}$ is parallel to every vector. If $\boldsymbol{A}$ and $\boldsymbol{B}$ are parallel vectors, then one is a scalar multiple of the other. On the other hand, if $\boldsymbol{A}$ and $\boldsymbol{B}$ are not parallel, then one cannot be represented as a scalar multiple of the other and it follows that the *single* vector equation

$$x\boldsymbol{A} + y\boldsymbol{B} = \boldsymbol{0}$$

is equivalent to the *two* equations

$$x = 0 \quad \text{and} \quad y = 0.$$

Example 72-2. Show that two medians of a triangle intersect at the point on each median that is $\frac{2}{3}$ of the way from the vertex that lies on the median.

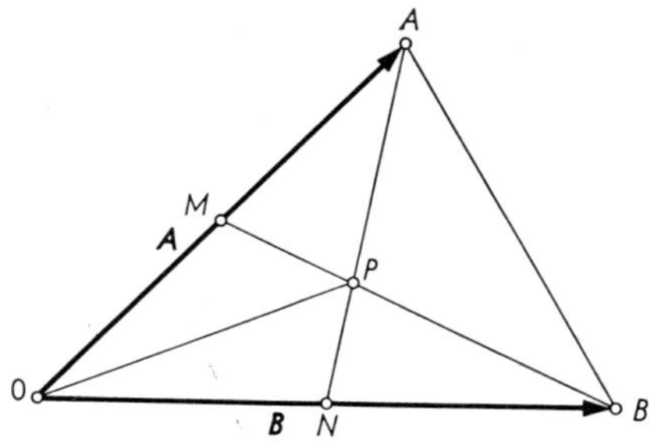

Figure 72-9

Solution. A triangle OAB is determined by two non-parallel vectors $\boldsymbol{A}$ and $\boldsymbol{B}$ as shown in Fig. 72-9. We will denote by M and N the midpoints of sides OA and OB and let P denote the intersection of the medians drawn to these midpoints. You can readily see that the medians terminating at M and N can be expressed as the vectors $\frac{1}{2}\boldsymbol{A} - \boldsymbol{B}$ and $\frac{1}{2}\boldsymbol{B} - \boldsymbol{A}$. Now the vector $\boldsymbol{OP}$ can be thought of either as the sum of $\boldsymbol{A}$ and a multiple $x(\frac{1}{2}\boldsymbol{B} - \boldsymbol{A})$ of the median terminating at N or as the sum of $\boldsymbol{B}$ and a multiple $y(\frac{1}{2}\boldsymbol{A} - \boldsymbol{B})$ of the median terminating at M. Therefore we have the equation

(72-10) $$\boldsymbol{A} + x(\tfrac{1}{2}\boldsymbol{B} - \boldsymbol{A}) = \boldsymbol{B} + y(\tfrac{1}{2}\boldsymbol{A} - \boldsymbol{B}),$$

and we are to show that $x = y = \frac{2}{3}$. Simple algebraic manipulation of Equation 72-10 gives us the vector equation

$$(1 - x - \tfrac{1}{2}y)\boldsymbol{A} + (\tfrac{1}{2}x + y - 1)\boldsymbol{B} = \boldsymbol{0}.$$

Since $\boldsymbol{A}$ and $\boldsymbol{B}$ are not parallel, their coefficients must both be zero, so we have the two equations

$$x + \tfrac{1}{2}y = 1 \quad \text{and} \quad \tfrac{1}{2}x + y = 1.$$

When we solve these equations, we find that $x = y = \frac{2}{3}$, which we were to prove.

Problems 72

1. Let $\boldsymbol{OP} = \boldsymbol{OA} + \boldsymbol{OB}$. Find the coordinates of P if O is the origin and A and B are the points whose coordinates are:
   (a) (1, 0) and (0, 2) (b) (1, 1) and (0, 3)
   (c) (−1, 0) and (2, 3) (d) (−1, 2) and (3, −1)
2. Compute $|\boldsymbol{OP} + \boldsymbol{OQ}|$ and $|\boldsymbol{OP} - \boldsymbol{OQ}|$ if O is the origin and the coordinates of P and Q are:
   (a) (−2, −1) and (2, 1) (b) (1, 1) and (−1, 3)
3. Suppose that the vectors $\boldsymbol{A}$ and $\boldsymbol{B}$ are perpendicular. Express the following quantities in terms of the lengths $|\boldsymbol{A}|$ and $|\boldsymbol{B}|$.
   (a) $|\boldsymbol{A} + \boldsymbol{B}|$ (b) $|\boldsymbol{A} - \boldsymbol{B}|$
   (c) $|3\boldsymbol{A} + 4\boldsymbol{B}|$ (d) $|\,\boldsymbol{A}/|\boldsymbol{A}|\,|$
   (e) $|\,|\boldsymbol{A}|\boldsymbol{B} + |\boldsymbol{B}|\boldsymbol{A}\,|$ (f) $|\,|\boldsymbol{A}|\boldsymbol{B} - |\boldsymbol{B}|\boldsymbol{A}\,|$
4. Let A, B, and C be three points in the plane. Find:
   (a) $2\boldsymbol{AB} + 2\boldsymbol{BC} + \boldsymbol{CA}$ (b) $3\boldsymbol{AB} - 3\boldsymbol{CB}$
   (c) $-\boldsymbol{AC} - \boldsymbol{CB}$ (d) $6\boldsymbol{AB} + 4\boldsymbol{CA} + 6\boldsymbol{BC}$
5. One diagonal of the parallelogram with sides $\boldsymbol{A}$ and $\boldsymbol{B}$ is $\boldsymbol{A} + \boldsymbol{B}$ (see Fig. 72-4). What is the other diagonal?
6. Suppose that the three points P, Q, and R of the circle of unit radius whose center is the origin O divide the circumference into three equal parts. Find $\boldsymbol{OP} + \boldsymbol{OQ} + \boldsymbol{OR}$.
7. Suppose that $\boldsymbol{A}$ and $\boldsymbol{B}$ are nonparallel vectors. Solve the following equations for t (if possible).
   (a) $(t^2 - 4)\boldsymbol{A} + (2t - 4)\boldsymbol{B} = \boldsymbol{0}$.
   (b) $\cos t\,\boldsymbol{A} + \sin t\,\boldsymbol{B} = \boldsymbol{0}$.
8. Suppose that $\boldsymbol{A}$ and $\boldsymbol{B}$ are non-parallel vectors. Is there a number t such that the vector $(1 - t)\boldsymbol{A} + t\boldsymbol{B}$ is parallel to the vector $\boldsymbol{A} + \boldsymbol{B}$?, $\boldsymbol{A} - \boldsymbol{B}$?
9. Draw a sketch and interpret geometrically the inequalities:
   (a) $|\boldsymbol{A} + \boldsymbol{B}| \leq |\boldsymbol{A}| + |\boldsymbol{B}|$.
   (b) $|\boldsymbol{A} - \boldsymbol{B}| \geq |\boldsymbol{A}| - |\boldsymbol{B}|$.
10. The initial point of a unit vector $\boldsymbol{N}$ (a "unit vector" is a vector that is 1 unit long) is the point (1, 1) of the curve $y = x^2$ and $\boldsymbol{N}$ is perpendicular to the tangent line to this curve at the point (1, 1). Find the coordinates of the possible terminal points of $\boldsymbol{N}$.

73. Basis Vectors and the Dot Product

Let us introduce a cartesian coordinate system into our plane. If we place a given vector $\boldsymbol{R}$ so that its initial point is the origin O of this coordinate system (Fig. 73-1), then its terminal point P will determine a pair of numbers (x, y). Conversely, any point P with coordinates (x, y) determines the vector $\boldsymbol{R} = \boldsymbol{OP}$. We shall refer to a vector whose initial

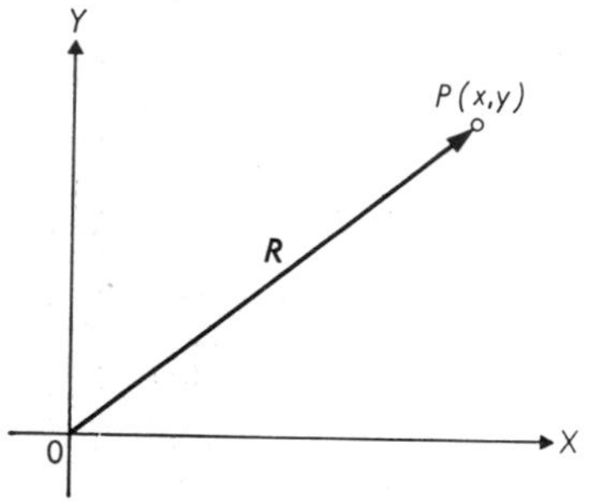

Figure 73-1

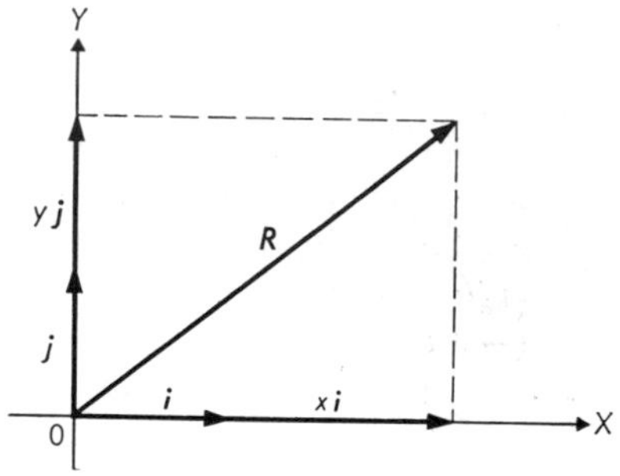

Figure 73-2

point is the origin as a **radius vector,** or **position vector.** Thus we see that, with reference to a particular coordinate system, a pair of numbers determines a position vector and a position vector determines a pair of numbers. The numbers (x, y) are called the **components** of the vector $\boldsymbol{R}$ in that coordinate system.

If we let $\boldsymbol{i}$ and $\boldsymbol{j}$ be vectors in the directions of the positive X- and Y-axis and if both vectors are 1 unit long, then (see Fig. 73-2)

$$\boldsymbol{R} = x\boldsymbol{i} + y\boldsymbol{j}. \tag{73-1}$$

The vectors $x\boldsymbol{i}$ and $y\boldsymbol{j}$ are called the **projections** of $\boldsymbol{R}$ along $\boldsymbol{i}$ and $\boldsymbol{j}$. The unit vectors $\boldsymbol{i}$ and $\boldsymbol{j}$ form a **basis** for our system of vectors in the plane. Every vector in the plane can be written as a *linear combination* of $\boldsymbol{i}$ and $\boldsymbol{j}$, as in Equation 73-1. The coefficients of $\boldsymbol{i}$ and $\boldsymbol{j}$ are the components of the vector.

If $\boldsymbol{A} = \boldsymbol{P_1P_2}$, where P_1 is the point (x_1, y_1) and P_2 is the point (x_2, y_2), as shown in Fig. 73-3, we can determine the components of $\boldsymbol{A}$ as follows. We simply note that $\boldsymbol{A} = \boldsymbol{R}_2 - \boldsymbol{R}_1$, where $\boldsymbol{R}_1$ and $\boldsymbol{R}_2$ are the position vectors determined by the points P_1 and P_2. Then since $\boldsymbol{R}_1 = x_1\boldsymbol{i} + y_1\boldsymbol{j}$ and $\boldsymbol{R}_2 = x_2\boldsymbol{i} + y_2\boldsymbol{j}$, we see that

$$\boldsymbol{A} = (x_2\boldsymbol{i} + y_2\boldsymbol{j}) - (x_1\boldsymbol{i} + y_1\boldsymbol{j});$$

in other words,

(73-2) $$A = (x_2 - x_1)i + (y_2 - y_1)j.$$

We will denote the components of the vector A by A_x and A_y. Thus we see from Equation 73-2 that

$$A_x = x_2 - x_1,$$
$$A_y = y_2 - y_1.$$

The distance between the points P_1 and P_2 is the magnitude of A, so we have the formula

(73-3) $$|A| = \sqrt{(x_2 - x_1)^2 + (y_2 - y_1)^2} = \sqrt{A_x^2 + A_y^2}.$$

Our rules of addition and multiplication by scalars that we listed in the preceding section tell us that to add vectors we add components;

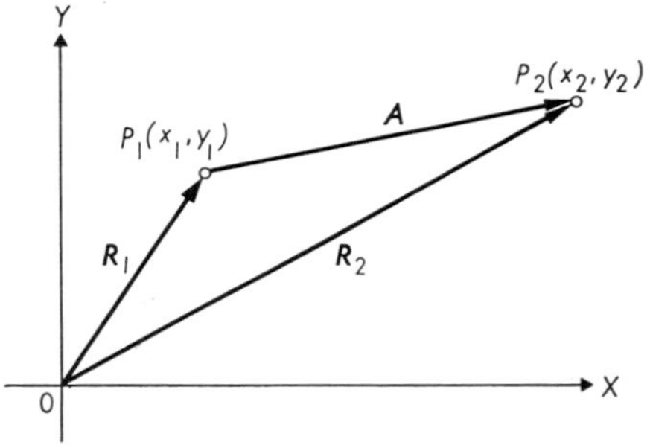

Figure 73-3

that is, if $A = A_x i + A_y j$ and $B = B_x i + B_y j$, then $A + B = (A_x + B_x)i + (A_y + B_y)j$.

Example 73-1. What are the coordinates of the point P that is $\frac{2}{3}$ of the way from the point Q with coordinates $(4, -2)$ to the point R with coordinates $(7, 10)$.

Solution. Our problem is illustrated in Fig. 73-4. The coordinates of the point P are the components of the position vector OP, so we shall express OP in terms of its components. First of all, $OP = OQ + QP = OQ + \frac{2}{3}QR$. Now $QR = 3i + 12j$ (Equation 73-2), and $OQ = 4i - 2j$ (Equation 73-1). Hence

$$OP = 4i - 2j + \tfrac{2}{3}(3i + 12j) = 4i - 2j + 2i + 8j$$
$$= 6i + 6j.$$

Thus we see that the coordinates of P are $(6, 6)$.

We know how to associate with two given vectors a third *vector* called their sum. Now we are going to associate with a pair of vectors a *number*. Two vectors $\boldsymbol{A}$ and $\boldsymbol{B}$ determine an angle of θ, where $0 \leq \theta \leq$

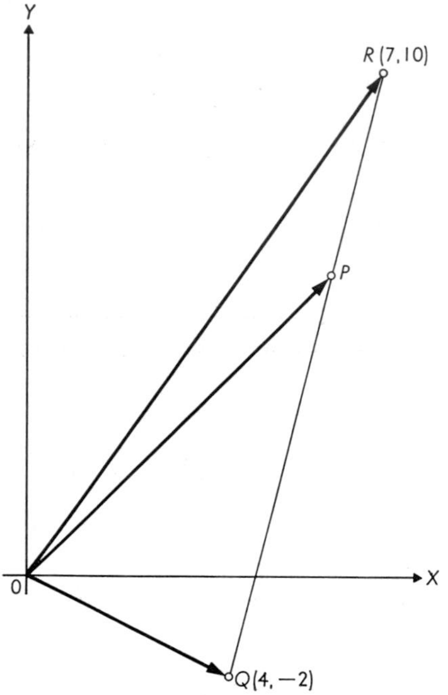

Figure 73-4

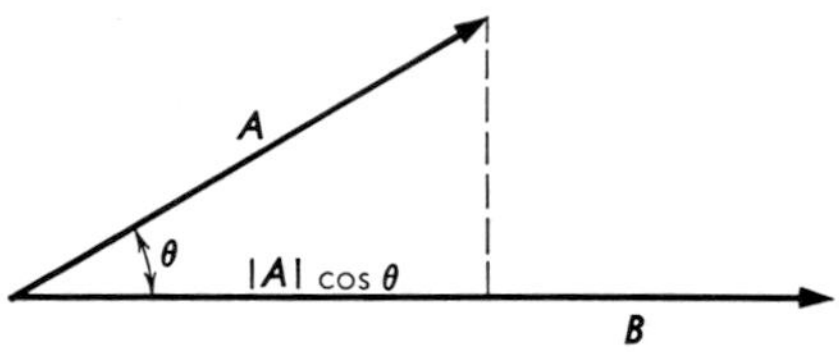

Figure 73-5

180°, as shown in Fig. 73-5. We define the **dot product** of $\boldsymbol{A}$ and $\boldsymbol{B}$ by the equation

$$\boldsymbol{A} \cdot \boldsymbol{B} = |\boldsymbol{A}|\,|\boldsymbol{B}| \cos \theta. \tag{73-4}$$

Since the dot product is a scalar, it is sometimes called the **scalar product** of the two vectors.

The following "rules of arithmetic" are valid:

$$\begin{aligned} \boldsymbol{A} \cdot \boldsymbol{B} &= \boldsymbol{B} \cdot \boldsymbol{A} && \text{(The Commutative Law),} \\ (\boldsymbol{A} + \boldsymbol{B}) \cdot \boldsymbol{C} &= \boldsymbol{A} \cdot \boldsymbol{C} + \boldsymbol{B} \cdot \boldsymbol{C} && \text{(The Distributive Law),} \\ (a\boldsymbol{A}) \cdot \boldsymbol{B} &= a(\boldsymbol{A} \cdot \boldsymbol{B}) \end{aligned} \tag{73-5}$$

You can easily verify the validity of the commutative law by examining Equation 73-4, which defines the dot product. It is not too hard to verify the other two laws, but we will omit the verification in the interests of brevity. The number $|\boldsymbol{A}| \cos \theta$ (see Fig. 73-5) is called the *component of* $\boldsymbol{A}$ *along* $\boldsymbol{B}$ (and, similarly, the number $|\boldsymbol{B}| \cos \theta$ is called the component of $\boldsymbol{B}$ along $\boldsymbol{A}$). Thus the dot product is the product of the length of $\boldsymbol{B}$ and the component of $\boldsymbol{A}$ along $\boldsymbol{B}$. Hence we see that

$$\text{(73-6)} \qquad \textit{The component of } \boldsymbol{A} \textit{ along } \boldsymbol{B} = \frac{\boldsymbol{A} \cdot \boldsymbol{B}}{|\boldsymbol{B}|}.$$

In particular, if $\boldsymbol{B}$ is a basis vector in the direction of one of our coordinate axes, Equation 73-6 gives us the component of $\boldsymbol{A}$ in the direction of that axis. Thus (since $|\boldsymbol{i}| = |\boldsymbol{j}| = 1$),

$$\text{(73-7)} \qquad \begin{aligned} A_x &= \boldsymbol{A} \cdot \boldsymbol{i} \\ A_y &= \boldsymbol{A} \cdot \boldsymbol{j} \end{aligned}$$

From the definition of the dot product, we see that the dot product of a vector $\boldsymbol{A}$ with itself is given by the formula

$$\text{(73-8)} \qquad \boldsymbol{A} \cdot \boldsymbol{A} = |\boldsymbol{A}|^2 \cos 0 = |\boldsymbol{A}|^2;$$

that is, the *dot product of a vector with itself is the square of its magnitude* Some authors use the abbreviation $\boldsymbol{A}^2 = \boldsymbol{A} \cdot \boldsymbol{A}$.

It also follows directly from the definition of the dot product that $\boldsymbol{A} \cdot \boldsymbol{B} = 0$ if, and only if, at least one of the following equations holds; $|\boldsymbol{A}| = 0$, $|\boldsymbol{B}| = 0$, or $\theta = \pi/2$. Two vectors $\boldsymbol{A}$ and $\boldsymbol{B}$ are perpendicular, $\boldsymbol{A} \perp \boldsymbol{B}$, if $\theta = \pi/2$; and if we agree that the zero vector is perpendicular to every vector, we see that

$$\text{(73-9)} \qquad \boldsymbol{A} \perp \boldsymbol{B} \quad \textit{if, and only if,} \quad \boldsymbol{A} \cdot \boldsymbol{B} = 0.$$

As particular examples of Equations 73-8 and 73-9, notice that the dot products of the basis vectors are

$$\text{(73-10)} \qquad \boldsymbol{i} \cdot \boldsymbol{i} = \boldsymbol{j} \cdot \boldsymbol{j} = 1 \quad \textit{and} \quad \boldsymbol{i} \cdot \boldsymbol{j} = \boldsymbol{j} \cdot \boldsymbol{i} = 0.$$

If $\boldsymbol{A} = A_x\boldsymbol{i} + A_y\boldsymbol{j}$, and $\boldsymbol{B} = B_x\boldsymbol{i} + B_y\boldsymbol{j}$, then we can use Equations 73-5 and 73-10 to express the dot product $\boldsymbol{A} \cdot \boldsymbol{B}$ in terms of the components of its factors. According to Rules 73-5,

$$\begin{aligned} \boldsymbol{A} \cdot \boldsymbol{B} &= (A_x\boldsymbol{i} + A_y\boldsymbol{j}) \cdot (B_x\boldsymbol{i} + B_y\boldsymbol{j}) \\ &= A_xB_x\boldsymbol{i} \cdot \boldsymbol{i} + A_yB_x\boldsymbol{j} \cdot \boldsymbol{i} + A_xB_y\boldsymbol{i} \cdot \boldsymbol{j} + A_yB_y\boldsymbol{j} \cdot \boldsymbol{j}. \end{aligned}$$

We now use Equations 73-10 to simplify this expression, and we see that

$$\text{(73-11)} \qquad \boldsymbol{A} \cdot \boldsymbol{B} = A_xB_x + A_yB_y.$$

Example 73-2. Find the measure of the angle between the position vectors to the points $(-1, 2)$ and $(3, 4)$.

Solution. Our two position vectors can be written as

$$\boldsymbol{R}_1 = -\boldsymbol{i} + 2\boldsymbol{j}$$
$$\boldsymbol{R}_2 = 3\boldsymbol{i} + 4\boldsymbol{j}.$$

Let θ be the measure of the angle between $\boldsymbol{R}_1$ and $\boldsymbol{R}_2$. From the definition of the dot product (Equation 73-4), we have

$$\cos\theta = \frac{\boldsymbol{R}_1 \cdot \boldsymbol{R}_2}{|\boldsymbol{R}_1|\,|\boldsymbol{R}_2|}.$$

We may use Equation 73-11 to see that

$$\boldsymbol{R}_1 \cdot \boldsymbol{R}_2 = -3 + 8 = 5,$$

and we readily find that $|\boldsymbol{R}_1| = \sqrt{5}$ and $|\boldsymbol{R}_2| = 5$. Hence

$$\cos\theta = 5/5\sqrt{5} = \sqrt{5}/5,$$

and so

$$\theta = \operatorname{Arccos}(\sqrt{5}/5) \approx 63°.$$

Example 73-3. Use the concept of the dot product to obtain the Law of Cosines.

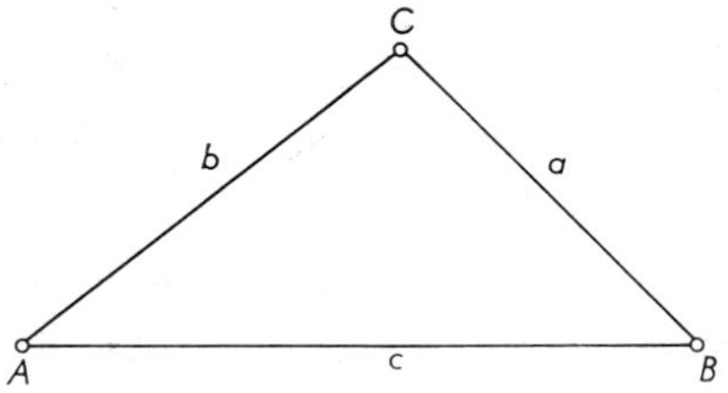

Figure 73-6

Solution. Figure 73-6 shows a general triangle ABC with sides whose lengths are a, b, and c. We see that $a = |\boldsymbol{BC}|$, $b = |\boldsymbol{AC}|$, and $c = |\boldsymbol{AB}|$. Therefore,

$$a^2 = |\boldsymbol{BC}|^2 = \boldsymbol{BC} \cdot \boldsymbol{BC}.$$

But $\boldsymbol{BC} = \boldsymbol{AC} - \boldsymbol{AB}$, so

$$\begin{aligned} a^2 &= (\boldsymbol{AC} - \boldsymbol{AB}) \cdot (\boldsymbol{AC} - \boldsymbol{AB}) \\ &= \boldsymbol{AC} \cdot \boldsymbol{AC} - \boldsymbol{AB} \cdot \boldsymbol{AC} - \boldsymbol{AC} \cdot \boldsymbol{AB} + \boldsymbol{AB} \cdot \boldsymbol{AB} \\ &= \boldsymbol{AC}^2 + \boldsymbol{AB}^2 - 2\boldsymbol{AC} \cdot \boldsymbol{AB} \\ &= |\boldsymbol{AC}|^2 + |\boldsymbol{AB}|^2 - 2|\boldsymbol{AC}|\,|\boldsymbol{AB}| \cos\theta \\ &= b^2 + c^2 - 2bc\cos\theta. \end{aligned}$$

The equation $a^2 = b^2 + c^2 - 2bc\cos\theta$ is the Law of Cosines.

Problems 73

1. Write $\boldsymbol{A}$ in the form $\boldsymbol{A} = A_x\boldsymbol{i} + A_y\boldsymbol{j}$ and find $|\boldsymbol{A}|$ if $\boldsymbol{A}$ is the vector whose initial point is the first and whose terminal point is the second of the following points.
   (a) $(-1, 3)$, $(2, 7)$ (b) $(3, 5)$, $(-3, -3)$
   (c) $(0, 3)$, $(0, -2)$ (d) $(2, -1)$, $(-1, -2)$
2. Let $\boldsymbol{A} = 2\boldsymbol{i} - 3\boldsymbol{j}$ and $\boldsymbol{B} = 4\boldsymbol{i} + \boldsymbol{j}$. Find the components of the following vectors.
   (a) $2\boldsymbol{A}$ (b) $-3\boldsymbol{B}$ (c) $\boldsymbol{A} + \boldsymbol{B}$
   (d) $\boldsymbol{A} - \boldsymbol{B}$ (e) $2\boldsymbol{A} + 3\boldsymbol{B}$ (f) $\boldsymbol{A} - 2\boldsymbol{B}$
3. Find the midpoint of the segment joining the terminal points of the position vectors $\boldsymbol{R}_1 = x_1\boldsymbol{i} + y_1\boldsymbol{j}$ and $\boldsymbol{R}_2 = x_2\boldsymbol{i} + y_2\boldsymbol{j}$.
4. Let P be the point $(-5, -9)$ and Q be the point $(7, 7)$.
   (a) Find the point that is $\frac{3}{4}$ of the way from P to Q.
   (b) Find the point that is 5 units from P along the line from P to Q.
   (c) Find the point that is as far beyond Q as Q is from P.
5. Find the angles of the triangle whose vertices are the points $(-2, -1)$, $(2, 2)$, and $(-1, 6)$.
6. (a) Show that $|\boldsymbol{A} + \boldsymbol{B}|^2 + |\boldsymbol{A} - \boldsymbol{B}|^2 = 2|\boldsymbol{A}|^2 + 2|\boldsymbol{B}|^2$.
   (b) Prove that the sum of the squares of the lengths of the diagonals of a parallelogram is equal to the sum of the squares of the lengths of its four sides.
7. Find the equation that must be satisfied by the coordinates (x, y) of a point P such that $\boldsymbol{OP}$ is perpendicular to $2\boldsymbol{i} + 3\boldsymbol{j}$. Find a unit vector perpendicular to $2\boldsymbol{i} + 3\boldsymbol{j}$. Illustrate this problem with a sketch.
8. Let $\boldsymbol{A}$ and $\boldsymbol{B}$ be unit position vectors that make angles of α and β with $\boldsymbol{i}$. Write $\boldsymbol{A}$ and $\boldsymbol{B}$ in component form. Compute $\boldsymbol{A} \cdot \boldsymbol{B}$ to obtain a formula for $\cos(\alpha - \beta)$.
9. Let $\boldsymbol{R}_1$ and $\boldsymbol{R}_2$ be unit position vectors and let θ be the measure of the angle between them, $0 \leq \theta \leq \pi$. Show that
$$\sin\frac{\theta}{2} = \frac{1}{2}|\boldsymbol{R}_2 - \boldsymbol{R}_1|.$$
10. Let $\boldsymbol{A} = 3\boldsymbol{i} + \boldsymbol{j}$. Let $\boldsymbol{B}$ be the unit vector that is perpendicular to $\boldsymbol{A}$ and has a positive component along $\boldsymbol{i}$. Let $\boldsymbol{C} = -\boldsymbol{i} + 2\boldsymbol{j}$. Find a and b such that $\boldsymbol{C} = a\boldsymbol{A} + b\boldsymbol{B}$.

74. Vector Equations of Curves. Parametric Equations

Up to this point we have dealt primarily with functions whose ranges are sets of numbers. To each number in the domain of such a function there corresponds a *number*. Now we wish to consider **vector-valued functions**; to each number in the domain there will correspond a *vector*. We will denote a vector-valued function by a boldface letter. An example of such a function is the function $\boldsymbol{F}$ whose domain is the interval $[0, 2\pi]$ and whose rule of correspondence is

$$\boldsymbol{F}(t) = \cos t\,\boldsymbol{i} + \sin t\,\boldsymbol{j}.$$

Here we see that corresponding to the *number* $t = 0$ is the *vector* $\boldsymbol{F}(0) = \cos 0\,\boldsymbol{i} + \sin 0\,\boldsymbol{j} = \boldsymbol{i}$; corresponding to the *number* $t = \pi/4$ is the *vector* $\boldsymbol{F}\left(\frac{\pi}{4}\right) = \left(\frac{\sqrt{2}}{2}\right)\boldsymbol{i} + \left(\frac{\sqrt{2}}{2}\right)\boldsymbol{j}$, and so on.

We will graph a vector-valued function $\boldsymbol{F}$ as follows. For each number t in the domain of $\boldsymbol{F}$ we plot the *terminal point of the position vector*

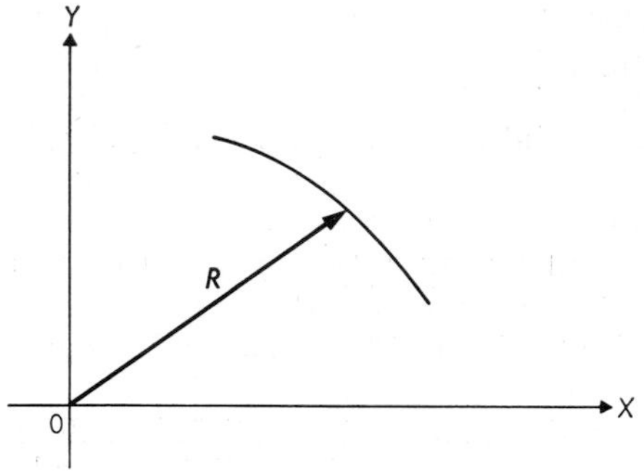

Figure 74-1

$\boldsymbol{R} = \boldsymbol{F}(t)$ (Fig. 74-1). The set of all such points in the plane is the **graph** of $\boldsymbol{F}$. The graph of one of our vector-valued functions will appear as a curve in the plane.

Example 74-1. Graph the vector-valued function defined by the equation $\boldsymbol{R} = \cos t\,\boldsymbol{i} + \sin t\,\boldsymbol{j}$ for $0 \leq t \leq 2\pi$.

Solution. We have tabulated some of our vectors and their terminal points and plotted these points in Fig. 74-2. If we plot enough points, they will form a good outline of the graph of our vector equation. But even without plotting many points we can see what our curve is. For each number t,

$$|\boldsymbol{R}| = \sqrt{\cos^2 t + \sin^2 t} = \sqrt{1} = 1.$$

Thus each of our vectors is 1 unit long, and hence its terminal point will be 1 unit from the origin. It is easy to see that since $0 \leq t \leq 2\pi$, the graph of the vector equation $\boldsymbol{R} = \cos t\,\boldsymbol{i} + \sin t\,\boldsymbol{j}$ is the circle whose radius is 1 and whose center is the origin. Notice that if, for example, we had re-

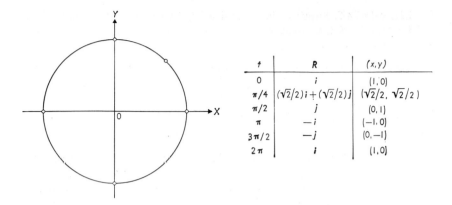

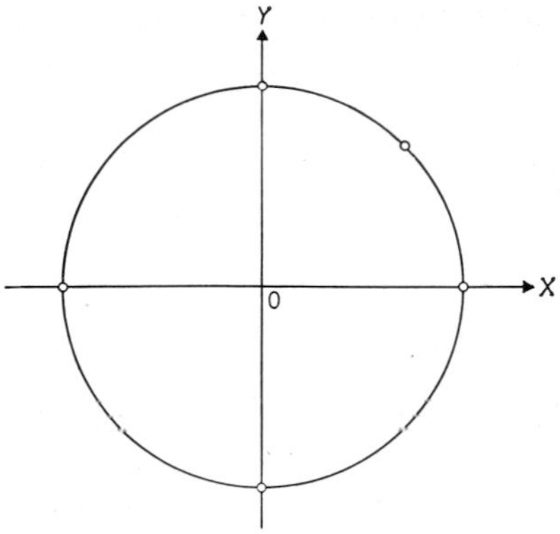

t	R	(x, y)
0	i	$(1, 0)$
$\pi/4$	$(\sqrt{2}/2)i + (\sqrt{2}/2)j$	$(\sqrt{2}/2, \sqrt{2}/2)$
$\pi/2$	j	$(0, 1)$
π	$-i$	$(-1, 0)$
$3\pi/2$	$-j$	$(0, -1)$
2π	i	$(1, 0)$

Figure 74-2

stricted t to lie in the interval $[0, \pi]$, our graph would have formed only the upper semicircle in Fig. 74-2.

If we write the vector equation

$$\text{(74-1)} \qquad \boldsymbol{R} = \boldsymbol{F}(t)$$

in terms of the components of the vectors $\boldsymbol{R} = x\boldsymbol{i} + y\boldsymbol{j}$ and $\boldsymbol{F}(t) = F_x(t)\boldsymbol{i} + F_y(t)\boldsymbol{j}$, we have

$$x\boldsymbol{i} + y\boldsymbol{j} = F_x(t)\boldsymbol{i} + F_y(t)\boldsymbol{j}.$$

Thus the Vector Equation 74-1 is equivalent to the *two* scalar equations:

$$\text{(74-2)} \qquad x = F_x(t) \quad \text{and} \quad y = F_y(t).$$

These equations assign a point (x, y) to each number t in the domain of $\boldsymbol{F}$. The set of these points is the graph of $\boldsymbol{F}$. Equations 74-2 are referred to as **parametric equations** of this graph, and t is called a **parameter.** Thus the equations

$$x = \cos t \quad \text{and} \quad y = \sin t, \quad \text{where } t \text{ is in the interval } [0, 2\pi],$$

are parametric equations of the circle whose "non-parametric" equation is $x^2 + y^2 = 1$.

We frequently want to change parametric equations to non-parametric form in order to use our knowledge of the graphs of equations in x and y.

Example 74-2. Suppose that a and b are two positive numbers. What is the graph of the equation $\boldsymbol{R} = a \cosh t\,\boldsymbol{i} + b \sinh t\,\boldsymbol{j}$, where t is in the interval $(-\infty, \infty)$?

Solution. Parametric equations of our curve are

$$x = a \cosh t \quad \text{and} \quad y = b \sinh t.$$

We must eliminate t from these equations to find a relation between x and y. A direct way to eliminate t would be to solve the second equation for t and substitute in the first. Thus $t = \sinh^{-1}\left(\frac{y}{b}\right)$, and so we have $x = a \cosh\left[\sinh^{-1}\left(\frac{y}{b}\right)\right]$. This form of the equation tells us no more about the graph than the original vector equation did. However, if we write the parametric equations as $\frac{x}{a} = \cosh t$ and $\frac{y}{b} = \sinh t$, and substitute in the identity $\cosh^2 t - \sinh^2 t = 1$, we see that

$$\frac{x^2}{a^2} - \frac{y^2}{b^2} = 1.$$

Thus the graph of our equation is a part of a hyperbola. Since $\frac{x}{a} = \cosh t > 0$, you can convince yourself that our graph consists of only one branch of the hyperbola.

Sometimes we wish to transform a non-parametric equation in x and y to a pair of parametric equations that have the same graph. The non-parametric equation

$$y = f(x), \tag{74-3}$$

for example, can always be replaced by the parametric equations

$$x = t \quad \text{and} \quad y = f(t). \tag{74-4}$$

A given curve can be represented by many different pairs of parametric equations. The choice of which pair to use is dictated by convenience more than anything else.

Example 74-3. Find a system of parametric equations whose graph is the graph of the equation $x^{2/3} + y^{2/3} = a^{2/3}$.

Solution. We might set $x = t$ and then solve the equation $t^{2/3} + y^{2/3} = a^{2/3}$ for y to obtain the pair of parametric equations

$$x = t \quad \text{and} \quad y = (a^{2/3} - t^{2/3})^{3/2}.$$

These equations represent (for t in the interval $[-a, a]$) the portion of the graph of our given equation that lies above the X-axis. Because the given curve is symmetric about the X-axis, we can obtain the remainder of the graph by reflecting the upper half about the X-axis. But we can find a more "symmetric" pair of parametric equations for the graph of the given equation as follows. Suppose we divide both sides of this equation by $a^{2/3}$ to obtain the equation

$$\left(\frac{x^{1/3}}{a^{1/3}}\right)^2 + \left(\frac{y^{1/3}}{a^{1/3}}\right)^2 = 1.$$

Here we have a sum of two squares that equals 1, and this equation suggests that we set

$$\frac{x^{1/3}}{a^{1/3}} = \sin t \quad \text{and} \quad \frac{y^{1/3}}{a^{1/3}} = \cos t.$$

Hence we see that another pair of parametric equations of our curve is the pair

$$x = a \sin^3 t \quad \text{and} \quad y = a \cos^3 t.$$

This pair gives us (for t in the interval $[0, 2\pi]$) our entire curve.

Let us now consider the problem of finding a **vector equation of a line.** A scalar equation of a line takes the form $y = mx + b$, where the

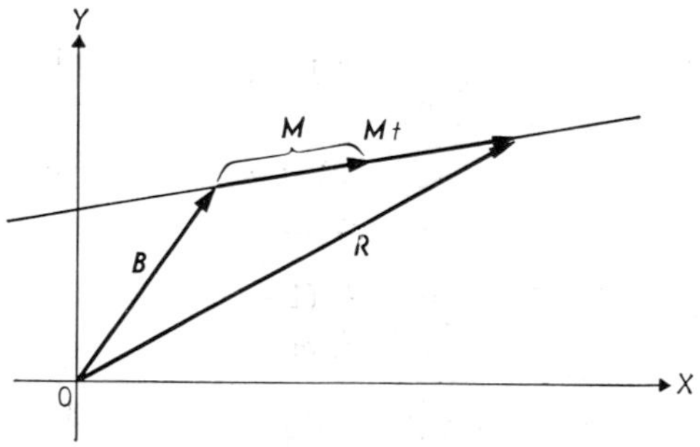

Figure 74-3

number m determines the direction (slope) of the line, and the number b determines a point (the Y-intercept) of the line. Now we will show that the vector equation

(74-5) $\qquad \mathbf{R} = \mathbf{M}t + \mathbf{B}, \quad t$ in the interval $(-\infty, \infty)$,

is the equation of a line. Furthermore, the vector $\mathbf{M}$ determines the direction of the line and the position vector $\mathbf{B}$ determines a point of the line. Equation 74-5 states that the position vector $\mathbf{R}$ is obtained by adding the multiple $\mathbf{M}t$ of the vector $\mathbf{M}$ to the vector $\mathbf{B}$. Figure 74-3 shows how this statement implies that our line is the line containing the terminal point of $\boldsymbol{B}$ and in the direction of $\boldsymbol{M}$. Thus Equation 74-5 gives us the vector equation of a line. We see that if $\boldsymbol{M} = M_x\boldsymbol{i} + M_y\boldsymbol{j}$ and $\boldsymbol{B} = B_x\boldsymbol{i} + B_y\boldsymbol{j}$, then parametric equations of the line are

(74-6) $x = M_xt + B_x$ and $y = M_yt + B_y$, where t is the interval $(-\infty, \infty)$.

Now let us write vector and parametric equations of the line containing points $P_1(x_1, y_1)$ and $P_2(x_2, y_2)$. If we take for $\boldsymbol{B}$ the position vector $\boldsymbol{OP_1}$ and for $\boldsymbol{M}$ the vector $\boldsymbol{P_1P_2}$, then a vector equation of our line is

(74-7) $$\boldsymbol{R} = \boldsymbol{P_1P_2}t + \boldsymbol{OP_1}.$$

We equate the components of the vectors in this equation and obtain the two scalar equations

$$x = (x_2 - x_1)t + x_1 \quad \text{and} \quad y = (y_2 - y_1)t + y_2.$$

We can write these parametric equations of our line as

(74-8) $$x = tx_2 + (1 - t)x_1 \quad \text{and} \quad y = ty_2 + (1 - t)y_1,$$

t in the interval $(-\infty, \infty)$. From the vector Equation 74-7, you can see that if we restrict t to the interval $(0, 1)$, then we obtain the line segment *between* the points (x_1, y_1) and (x_2, y_2).

Example 74-4. Find parametric equations of the line that contains the points $(-1, 2)$ and $(2, 3)$.

Solution. If we take as P_1 the point $(-1, 2)$ and as P_2 the point $(2, 3)$ and use Equations 74-8, we obtain the parametric equations

$$x = 2t + (1 - t)(-1) = 3t - 1,$$
$$y = 3t + (1 - t)(2) = t + 2.$$

Many times a curve that is defined in terms of a physical motion is most naturally described by means of parametric equations. We conclude this section with an example of a famous curve of this type.

Example 74-5. A circular hoop with a radius of a rolls along a straight line. Find the parametric equations of the curve that is traced out by a given point on the hoop.

Solution. Let us suppose that our given point P originally is the origin of a cartesian coordinate system, and that the hoop rolls along the X-axis. In Fig. 74-4 we have pictured the hoop after it has rolled through an angle whose radian measure is t. We must find an expression for the position

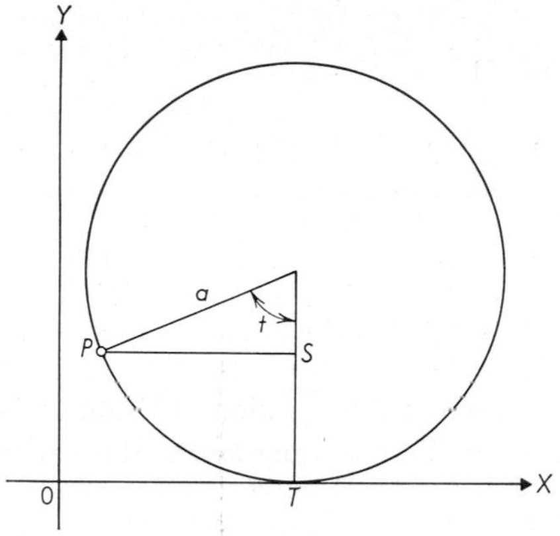

Figure 74-4

vector $\boldsymbol{OP}$ in terms of t. From Fig. 74-4 we see that

$$\boldsymbol{OP} = \boldsymbol{OT} + \boldsymbol{TS} + \boldsymbol{SP}.$$

Because $|\boldsymbol{OT}| = \text{arc } TP = at$, it follows that $\boldsymbol{OT} = at\boldsymbol{i}$. Furthermore, simple trigonometry shows us that

$$\boldsymbol{TS} = (a - a\cos t)\boldsymbol{j} = a(1 - \cos t)\boldsymbol{j}$$

and

$$\boldsymbol{SP} = -\boldsymbol{PS} = -a\sin t\,\boldsymbol{i}.$$

Hence

$$\begin{aligned}\boldsymbol{OP} &= at\boldsymbol{i} + a(1 - \cos t)\boldsymbol{j} - a\sin t\,\boldsymbol{i}\\ &= a(t - \sin t)\boldsymbol{i} + a(1 - \cos t)\boldsymbol{j}.\end{aligned}$$

From this vector equation we obtain the following pair of parametric equations for the coordinates (x, y) of the point P of our curve:

$$x = a(t - \sin t) \quad \text{and} \quad y = a(1 - \cos t),$$

t in the interval $[0, \infty]$. This curve is called a **cycloid,** and we have sketched part of its graph in Fig. 74-5.

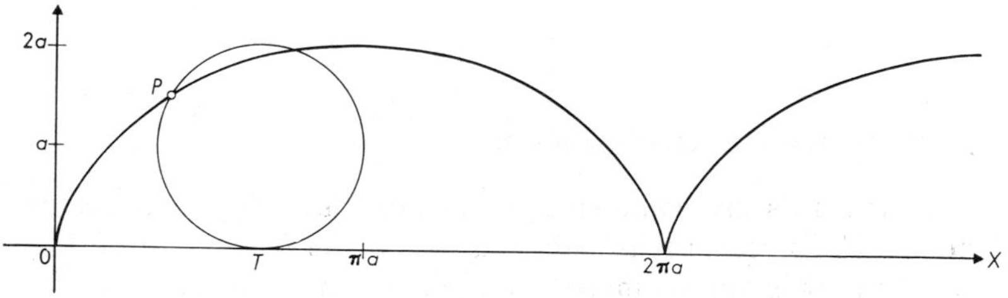

Figure 74-5

Problems 74

1. Describe the graphs of the following vector equations.
   (a) $\boldsymbol{R} = 3\cos 2t\,\boldsymbol{i} + 3\sin 2t\,\boldsymbol{j}$, t in the interval $[0, \pi/2]$.
   (b) $\boldsymbol{R} = t\boldsymbol{i} + t^2\boldsymbol{j}$, t in the interval $[-1, 1]$.
   (c) $\boldsymbol{R} = \sin t\,\boldsymbol{i} + \sin t\,\boldsymbol{j}$, t in the interval $[0, \pi/2]$.
   (d) $\boldsymbol{R} = t\boldsymbol{i} + 2t\boldsymbol{j}$, t in the interval $[0, 1]$.
   (e) $\boldsymbol{R} = e^t\boldsymbol{i} + e^{-t}\boldsymbol{j}$, t in the interval $(-\infty, \infty)$.
   (f) $\boldsymbol{R} = 5\sin t\,\boldsymbol{i} + \cos t\,\boldsymbol{j}$, t in the interval $[-\pi, \pi]$.
2. Sketch the graph of the equation in Example 74-3.
3. Show that the following scalar and vector equations have the same graph.
   (a) $2x - 3y + 4 = 0$, $\boldsymbol{R} = (3t + 4)\boldsymbol{i} + (2t + 4)\boldsymbol{j}$
   (b) $y = 2\cosh x$, $\boldsymbol{R} = \ln t\,\boldsymbol{i} + (t + 1/t)\boldsymbol{j}$
   (c) $y^2 = x^3$, $\boldsymbol{R} = t^2\boldsymbol{i} + t^3\boldsymbol{j}$.
4. Explain why both vector equations have the same graph. (In each case t is in the interval $(-\infty, \infty)$).
   (a) $\boldsymbol{R} = \pi^t\boldsymbol{i} + \pi^{-t}\boldsymbol{j}$ and $\boldsymbol{R} = e^t\boldsymbol{i} + e^{-t}\boldsymbol{j}$
   (b) $\boldsymbol{R} = \cos 2t\,\boldsymbol{i} + \sin 2t\,\boldsymbol{j}$ and $\boldsymbol{R} = \sin t\,\boldsymbol{i} + \cos t\,\boldsymbol{j}$.
   (c) $\boldsymbol{R} = (t^3 + 2t + 3)\boldsymbol{i} + (t^6 + 4t^4 + 6t^3 + 4t^2 + 12t + 9)\boldsymbol{j}$ and $\boldsymbol{R} = t\boldsymbol{i} + t^2\boldsymbol{j}$.
5. Find parametric equations for each of the following lines.
   (a) $y = 3x + 7$ (b) $2x - 4y + 5 = 0$
   (c) $x = 5$ (d) $y = -1$
6. Find two pairs of parametric equations corresponding to each of the following cartesian equations.
   (a) $y^2 = x^3$ (b) $x^2/4 + y^2 = 1$
   (c) $y^2 + 1 = x^2$ (d) $y = 2x^2 - 1$
7. Find vector equations of the following lines.
   (a) The line containing the points $(2, 3)$ and $(-1, 4)$.
   (b) The line whose equation is $3x + 2y + 6 = 0$.
   (c) The line of slope 3 that contains the point $(-1, 1)$.
   (d) The line of slope 0 that contains the point $(1, 3)$.
8. Find the slope and Y-intercept of the line whose vector equation is $\boldsymbol{R} = (3t - 1)\boldsymbol{i} + (1 - 5t)\boldsymbol{j}$.
9. Show that the spiral whose polar equation is $r\theta = 1$ is the graph of the vector equation

$$\boldsymbol{R} = \frac{\cos t}{t}\boldsymbol{i} + \frac{\sin t}{t}\boldsymbol{j}.$$

75. Derivatives of Vectors. Arclength

Now let us use some calculus in our discussion of a vector-valued function $\boldsymbol{F}$. It seems reasonable to define the derivative of $\boldsymbol{F}(t)$ as the quantity that is approximated by the difference quotient

$$\frac{\boldsymbol{F}(t + h) - \boldsymbol{F}(t)}{h} \tag{75-1}$$

when h is close to 0. Since this difference quotient is a vector, the derivative will be a vector that we denote by $\boldsymbol{F}'(t)$. In precise terms, we define the derivative $\boldsymbol{F}'(t)$ of $\boldsymbol{F}(t)$ by the equation

$$\boldsymbol{F}'(t) = \lim_{h \to 0} \frac{\boldsymbol{F}(t+h) - \boldsymbol{F}(t)}{h}, \tag{75-2}$$

where this vector equation means the same thing as the scalar equation

$$\lim_{h \to 0} \left| \frac{\boldsymbol{F}(t+h) - \boldsymbol{F}(t)}{h} - \boldsymbol{F}'(t) \right| = 0.$$

We can use a geometric argument to show that the derivative $\boldsymbol{F}'(t)$ lies along the tangent to the graph of $\boldsymbol{F}$. In Fig. 75-1 we have drawn the

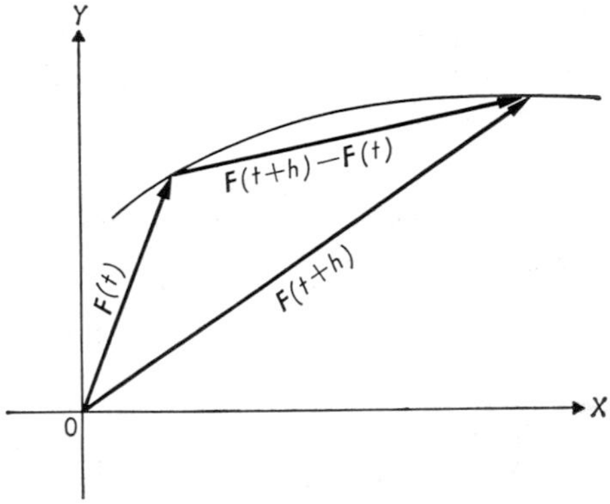

Figure 75-1

vectors $\boldsymbol{F}(t)$, $\boldsymbol{F}(t+h)$ and $\boldsymbol{F}(t+h) - \boldsymbol{F}(t)$. The vector $\boldsymbol{F}(t+h) - \boldsymbol{F}(t)$ lies along a chord of the curve, and when h is close to zero, this chord approximates the tangent to the graph of the equation $\boldsymbol{R} = \boldsymbol{F}(t)$. Since we obtain the Difference Quotient 75-1 by multiplying this vector by the number $\frac{1}{h}$ (which doesn't change the line along which the vector lies), we see that the difference quotient vector is a vector that is approximately tangent to the curve when h is near 0. Therefore, since the limit of the difference quotient vector as h approaches 0 is the vector $\boldsymbol{F}'(t)$, it appears that *the vector $\boldsymbol{F}'(t)$ is tangent to the graph of the equation $\boldsymbol{R} = \boldsymbol{F}(t)$ at the terminal point of $\boldsymbol{F}(t)$.*

We follow the "natural" rules of differentiation when we compute vector derivatives. Thus if

$$\boldsymbol{F}(t) = F_x(t)\boldsymbol{i} + F_y(t)\boldsymbol{j},$$

where F_x and F_y are ordinary numerical-valued differentiable functions, then

(75-3) $$\boldsymbol{F}'(t) = F_x'(t)\boldsymbol{i} + F_y'(t)\boldsymbol{j}.$$

We also use our other notations for the derivative. Thus, if $\boldsymbol{R} = \boldsymbol{F}(t)$, then we write $\boldsymbol{R}'$, $D_t\boldsymbol{R}$ and $\dfrac{d\boldsymbol{R}}{dt}$ for the derivative $\boldsymbol{F}'(t)$. Also, since $\boldsymbol{R} = x\boldsymbol{i} + y\boldsymbol{j}$, where $x = F_x(t)$ and $y = F_y(t)$, we can write Equation 75-3 as

$$\boldsymbol{R}' = x'\boldsymbol{i} + y'\boldsymbol{j},$$

or

$$\frac{d\boldsymbol{R}}{dt} = \frac{dx}{dt}\boldsymbol{i} + \frac{dy}{dt}\boldsymbol{j},$$

and so on.

Example 75-1. A stone is being whirled in a counter-clockwise direction around the circle whose vector equation is $\boldsymbol{R} = \cos t\boldsymbol{i} + \sin t\boldsymbol{j}$. When $t = \pi/6$, the stone is released and flies off on a tangent. Does it hit an innocent spectator standing at the point $(-1, \sqrt{3})$?

Solution. We first find a vector tangent to the circle at the point given by $t = \pi/6$. According to Equation 75-3, $\boldsymbol{R}' = -\sin t\boldsymbol{i} + \cos t\boldsymbol{j}$. Thus, if $t = \pi/6$,

$$\boldsymbol{R} = \frac{\sqrt{3}}{2}\boldsymbol{i} + \frac{1}{2}\boldsymbol{j},$$

and

$$\boldsymbol{R}' = -\frac{1}{2}\boldsymbol{i} + \frac{\sqrt{3}}{2}\boldsymbol{j}.$$

Therefore, the stone is at the point $(\sqrt{3}/2, \frac{1}{2})$ of the circle when it is released, and it flies along a line parallel to the vector $-\frac{1}{2}\boldsymbol{i} + \frac{\sqrt{3}}{2}\boldsymbol{j}$. We leave it to you to show that the vector joining the point $(\sqrt{3}/2, \frac{1}{2})$ of the circle to the point in question $(-1, \sqrt{3})$ is not parallel to the tangent vector $-\frac{1}{2}\boldsymbol{i} + \frac{\sqrt{3}}{2}\boldsymbol{j}$, and so the innocent bystander is spared. You should draw a sketch illustrating this problem, and you might try to solve it graphically.

It is not hard to show, using Equation 75-3 (Question 6 of Problems 75), that the usual product rule is valid when we compute the derivative of a scalar times a vector; that is,

(75-4) $$D_t[f(t)\boldsymbol{F}(t)] = f(t)\boldsymbol{F}'(t) + f'(t)\boldsymbol{F}(t).$$

The product rule also applies to the dot product. Thus

(75-5) $$D_t[\boldsymbol{F}(t) \cdot \boldsymbol{G}(t)] = \boldsymbol{F}(t) \cdot \boldsymbol{G}'(t) + \boldsymbol{F}'(t) \cdot \boldsymbol{G}(t).$$

As a final rule of differentiation, let us write the Chain Rule as it applies to vector-valued functions. If $\boldsymbol{R} = \boldsymbol{F}(t)$, where $t = g(s)$, then

(75-6) $$\frac{d\boldsymbol{R}}{ds} = \frac{d\boldsymbol{R}}{dt}\frac{dt}{ds}.$$

Example 75-2. Let $\boldsymbol{F}$ be a vector-valued function such that $|\boldsymbol{F}(t)| = c$, where c is a number that is independent of t in an interval $[a, b]$. Show that $\boldsymbol{F}'(t)$ and $\boldsymbol{F}(t)$ are perpendicular vectors for each t in $[a, b]$.

Solution. Since $|\boldsymbol{F}(t)| = c$,

$$\boldsymbol{F}(t) \cdot \boldsymbol{F}(t) = c^2.$$

Then we use Equation 75-5 and we find that

$$\boldsymbol{F}(t) \cdot \boldsymbol{F}'(t) + \boldsymbol{F}'(t) \cdot \boldsymbol{F}(t) = 0,$$

and so

$$\boldsymbol{F}(t) \cdot \boldsymbol{F}'(t) = 0.$$

This equation is equivalent to saying that $\boldsymbol{F}(t)$ and $\boldsymbol{F}'(t)$ are perpendicular.

The graph of a vector equation $\boldsymbol{R} = \boldsymbol{F}(t)$, for t in an interval $[a, b]$ in which $|\boldsymbol{F}'(t)| > 0$, is a curve in the plane. We will now find a formula for the length of such a curve, and in later sections we will discuss its "curvature" and the area of the surface that is generated when the curve is rotated about one of the coordinate axes. In these discussions we shall suppose that $\boldsymbol{F}''(t)$ exists for each t in $[a, b]$. The graph of such a function $\boldsymbol{F}$ is called a **smooth arc.**

Before we take up the question of how we measure the length of an arc, we should say a word or two about what we mean by arclength. Of course, if our arc is a line segment, there is no question about what we mean by its length. Also, we have derived all our formulas for the trigonometric functions on the supposition that we understand the concept of arclength along a circle. But the idea of the length of a general smooth arc needs defining, just as the area under a general curve must be defined. We could start our discussion of arclength by giving a formal definition of arclength and then finding a formula for it. Instead, we will proceed as we did when we treated areas earlier. We will assume that we know what arclength is and what properties it possesses. On the basis of these assumed properties, we will develop a formula for arclength, a formula which we may then use to *define* what we mean by the length of a smooth arc.

So let us first suppose that there is a differentiable function f such that for each choice of t in the interval $[a, b]$ the number $s = f(t)$ is the length of the part of our smooth arc that joins the terminal points of $\boldsymbol{F}(a)$ and $\boldsymbol{F}(t)$ as shown in Fig. 75-2. If h is a number such that $t + h$ is also a point in $[a, b]$, then the number $f(t + h)$ is the distance along the arc from the terminal point of $\boldsymbol{F}(a)$ to the terminal point of $\boldsymbol{F}(t + h)$. If $h > 0$,

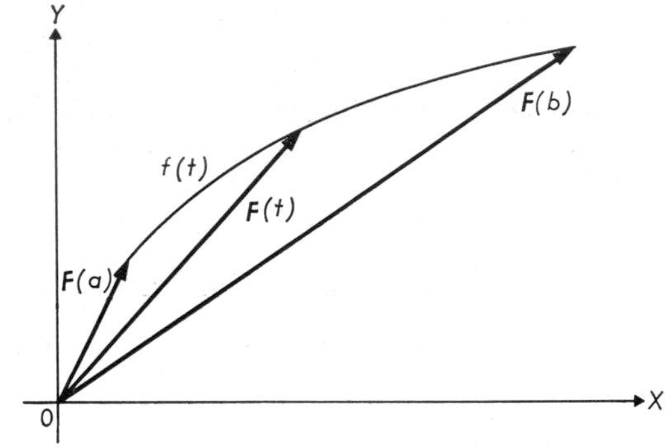

Figure 75-2

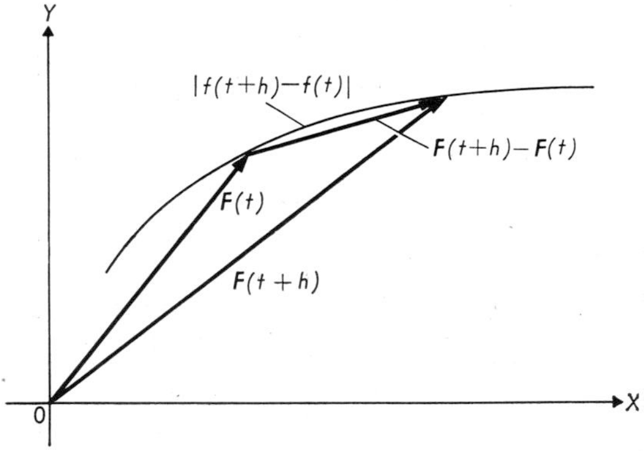

Figure 75-3

then the terminal point of $\boldsymbol{F}(t + h)$ is "beyond" the terminal point of $\boldsymbol{F}(t)$, and $f(t + h) > f(t)$, whereas if $h < 0$, then $f(t + h) < f(t)$. In either case, the distance, measured along the arc, between the terminal points of $\boldsymbol{F}(t)$ and $\boldsymbol{F}(t + h)$ is $|f(t + h) - f(t)|$ (see Fig. 75-3). It seems natural to require that the ratio of the length of the arc joining any two points of our curve to the length of the straight line segment, or chord, that joins these points should approach 1 as one point approaches the other. The chord that joins the terminal points of the vectors $\boldsymbol{F}(t + h)$ and

$\boldsymbol{F}(t)$ is $|\boldsymbol{F}(t+h) - \boldsymbol{F}(t)|$ units long, so we will suppose that

$$\lim_{h \to 0} \frac{|f(t+h) - f(t)|}{|\boldsymbol{F}(t+h) - \boldsymbol{F}(t)|} = 1.$$

With the aid of this equation, we can determine what the distance function f must be.

We see that the difference quotient $\dfrac{f(t+h) - f(t)}{h}$ is always positive (why?), and so we can write

$$\begin{aligned} \frac{f(t+h) - f(t)}{h} &= \left| \frac{f(t+h) - f(t)}{h} \right| \\ &= \frac{|f(t+h) - f(t)|}{|\boldsymbol{F}(t+h) - \boldsymbol{F}(t)|} \cdot \left| \frac{\boldsymbol{F}(t+h) - \boldsymbol{F}(t)}{h} \right|. \end{aligned}$$

Hence

$$\begin{aligned} f'(t) = \lim_{h \to 0} \frac{f(t+h) - f(t)}{h} &= \lim_{h \to 0} \frac{|f(t+h) - f(t)|}{|\boldsymbol{F}(t+h) - \boldsymbol{F}(t)|} \lim_{h \to 0} \left| \frac{\boldsymbol{F}(t+h) - \boldsymbol{F}(t)}{h} \right| \\ &= 1 \cdot |\boldsymbol{F}'(t)|. \end{aligned}$$

Therefore, the distance function f must be a function such that $f'(t) = |\boldsymbol{F}'(t)|$. Furthermore, it must be true that $f(a) = 0$ (because $f(a)$ measures the "distance" between the terminal point of $\boldsymbol{F}(a)$ and the terminal point of $\boldsymbol{F}(a)$). Therefore, the equation $s = f(t)$ must furnish the solution to the differential problem consisting of the differential equation $\dfrac{ds}{dt} = |\boldsymbol{F}'(t)|$ and the condition that $s = 0$ when $t = a$. In Section 64 we saw that the solution to this differential problem is

(75-7) $$s = \int_a^t |\boldsymbol{F}'(u)|\, du,$$

so our arclength function f must be the function that is defined by the equation $f(t) = \int_a^t |\boldsymbol{F}'(u)|\, du$.

We developed Formula 75-7 on the assumption that there is an arclength function f that possesses certain properties that we would naturally expect such a function to have. Now that we have this "natural" formula for arclength, we needn't attempt to justify any assumptions that we made to find it. We will simply start with the formula and *define* the length of the arc that joins the terminal points of the vectors $\boldsymbol{F}(a)$ and $\boldsymbol{F}(t)$ on our smooth arc as the number s that is given by the formula.

Example 75-3. Show that Formula 75-7 gives the correct arclength along the circle whose radius is 5 and that is described by the vector equation $\boldsymbol{R} = 5 \cos t\boldsymbol{i} + 5 \sin t\boldsymbol{j}$.

Solution. Here we have $\boldsymbol{F}(u) = 5 \cos u\boldsymbol{i} + 5 \sin u\boldsymbol{j}$, and hence $\boldsymbol{F}'(u) = -5 \sin u\boldsymbol{i} + 5 \cos u\boldsymbol{j}$. Therefore, $|\boldsymbol{F}'(u)| = 5$, and if we choose to measure the arclength from the point where $t = 0$, then Formula 75-7 gives us

$$s = \int_0^t 5\, du = 5t$$

as the length of the arc of our circle that joins the points that correspond to the parameter values 0 and t. When $t = 2\pi$, s is the circumference of our circle; $s = 5 \cdot 2\pi = 10\pi$. If we take $t = 4\pi$, then $s = 20\pi$, which is the length of arc traversed when we go around the circle twice. In this example t is the radian measure of the angle formed by the positive X-axis and the ray from the origin containing the point of the circle corresponding to t. In general, the parameter need not have such a direct geometric interpretation.

Formula 75-7 gives us the length s of arc that is traversed in moving along the curve from the terminal point of $\boldsymbol{F}(a)$ to the terminal point of $\boldsymbol{F}(t)$. From this equation we see that the length L of arc traversed in moving along the curve from the terminal point of $\boldsymbol{F}(a)$ to the terminal point of $\boldsymbol{F}(b)$ is

$$L = \int_a^b |\boldsymbol{F}'(t)|\, dt. \tag{75-8}$$

(In this last formula we have used the variable of integration t, rather than u, but, of course, the choice of letter for the variable of integration does not affect the value of the integral.) If we set $\boldsymbol{R}' = \boldsymbol{F}'(t) = x'\boldsymbol{i} + y'\boldsymbol{j}$, then $|\boldsymbol{F}'(t)| = \sqrt{x'^2 + y'^2}$, and our expression for arclength takes the form

$$L = \int_a^b \sqrt{x'^2 + y'^2}\, dt. \tag{75-9}$$

Example 75-4. Show that the length of the graph of the equation $y = f(x)$ for $a \leq x \leq b$ is given by the formula

$$L = \int_a^b \sqrt{1 + [f'(x)]^2}\, dx. \tag{75-10}$$

Solution. We have already noticed that parametric equations that furnish the graph of the equation $y = f(x)$ are

$$x = t \quad \text{and} \quad y = f(t).$$

Then

$$x' = 1 \quad \text{and} \quad y' = f'(t),$$

so Equation 75-10 follows immediately from Equation **75-9.**

Example 75-5. Find the length of the arc of the curve whose equation is $y = \cosh x$ that joins the points (0, 1) and (1, cosh 1). (This curve is called a **catenary.**)

Solution. We use Equation 75-10, with $a = 0$, $b = 1$, and $f(x) = \cosh x$. Then $f'(x) = \sinh x$, and $1 + [f'(x)]^2 = 1 + \sinh^2 x = \cosh^2 x$. Thus

$$L = \int_0^1 \cosh x\, dx = \sinh x \Big|_0^1 = \sinh 1 = 1.175.$$

From Equation 75-7 we see that $\dfrac{ds}{dt} = |\boldsymbol{F}'(t)|$, and for a smooth arc, $|\boldsymbol{F}'(t)| > 0$. Therefore, Equation 75-7 defines an increasing function, and hence one that has an inverse. In other words, we can solve (theoretically) Equation 75-7 for t in terms of s. Thus we can express the radius vector $\boldsymbol{R}$ to a point of the graph of $\boldsymbol{F}$ in terms of s. According to the Chain Rule,

$$\frac{d\boldsymbol{R}}{ds} = \frac{d\boldsymbol{R}}{dt}\frac{dt}{ds}.$$

Now

$$\frac{d\boldsymbol{R}}{dt} = \boldsymbol{F}'(t) \quad \text{and} \quad \frac{dt}{ds} = \frac{1}{\dfrac{ds}{dt}}, \quad \text{so} \quad \frac{d\boldsymbol{R}}{ds} = \boldsymbol{F}'(t) \Big/ \frac{ds}{dt}.$$

We have just pointed out that Equation 75-7 yields

(75-11) $$\frac{ds}{dt} = |\boldsymbol{F}'(t)|,$$

and hence the derivative $\dfrac{d\boldsymbol{R}}{ds}$ can be written as

$$\frac{d\boldsymbol{R}}{ds} = \frac{\boldsymbol{F}'(t)}{|\boldsymbol{F}'(t)|}.$$

The vector $\boldsymbol{F}'(t)$ is tangent to our graph, and when we divide this vector by its length, we obtain a unit tangent vector, which we shall call $\boldsymbol{T}$. Thus

(75-12) $$\boldsymbol{T} = \frac{d\boldsymbol{R}}{ds} = \frac{\boldsymbol{F}'(t)}{|\boldsymbol{F}'(t)|}.$$

Problems 75

1. Find $\boldsymbol{F}'(1)$ if $\boldsymbol{F}(t) = F_x(t)\boldsymbol{i} + F_y(t)\boldsymbol{j}$ and
   (a) $F_x(t) = \ln t$, $F_y(t) = t$ (b) $F_x(t) = e^t$, $F_y(t) = t^2 - 1$
   (c) $F_x(t) = \cos^2 t$, $F_y(t) = \sin^2 t$
   (d) $F_x(t) = \cosh t$, $F_y(t) = \sinh(1 - t^2)$
2. Find a tangent vector to the curve whose vector equation is $\boldsymbol{R} = e^t \sin t\, \boldsymbol{i} + e^{-t} \cos t\, \boldsymbol{j}$ at the point corresponding to $t = 0$. What is the slope of the tangent line to the curve at the point corresponding to $t = 1$?

3. Find unit vectors tangent to the graphs of the following curves at the point corresponding to the given parameter value.
   (a) $\boldsymbol{R} = t^3\boldsymbol{i} + t^4\boldsymbol{j}$, $t = 1$
   (b) $\boldsymbol{R} = 3\cos 2t\,\boldsymbol{i} + 3\sin 2t\,\boldsymbol{j}$, $t = 5$
   (c) $\boldsymbol{R} = e^t\boldsymbol{i} + \ln t\,\boldsymbol{j}$, $t = 1$
   (d) $\boldsymbol{R} = \boldsymbol{M}t + \boldsymbol{B}$, $t = \theta$
   (e) $\boldsymbol{R} = t\sin t\,\boldsymbol{i} + \cos t\,\boldsymbol{j}$, $t = \pi/2$
4. The equation $\boldsymbol{R} = \cos t\,\boldsymbol{i} + \sin t\,\boldsymbol{j}$, with t in the interval $[0, 2\pi]$, and the equation $\boldsymbol{R} = \cos t^2\,\boldsymbol{i} + \sin t^2\boldsymbol{j}$, with t in the interval $[\sqrt{2\pi}, \sqrt{4\pi}]$, both represent the unit circle. Show that Equation 75-9 yields the circumference of this circle when we use either of these vector representations.
5. Find the vector equation of the line that is tangent to the graph of the equation $\boldsymbol{R} = e^t\boldsymbol{i} + \ln t\,\boldsymbol{j}$ at the point at which $t = 1$.
6. With the aid of Equation 75-3:
   (a) Prove that Equation 75-4 is valid.
   (b) Prove that Equation 75-5 is valid.
7. Find the length of one arch of the cycloid that we discussed in Example 74-5.
8. Let s denote the length of the arc of the parabola $y = x^2$ from the origin to the point where $x = c$. Express s in terms of c. Find the length of the arc from the origin to the point $(1, 1)$.
9. Find the total length of the curve represented by the parametric equations $x = \cos^3 t$, $y = \sin^3 t$, t in the interval $[0, 2\pi]$.
10. Find the "circumference" of the *hypocycloid* whose equation is $x^{2/3} + y^{2/3} = a^{2/3}$.
11. Find the length of the arc whose parametric equations are $x = t^3$, $y = 2t^2$, t in the interval $[0, 1]$.
12. Find the length of the part of the graph of the equation $y = x^{3/2}$ for x in the interval $[0, \frac{4}{3}]$.
13. Find the length of the arc whose equation is $y = \dfrac{x^3}{6} + \dfrac{1}{2x}$ for x in the interval $[1, 2]$.

76. Curvature, Velocity, and Acceleration

In this section we will use calculus to go more deeply into the geometry of plane curves and then apply our knowledge to describe the path of a particle moving in the plane. As in the preceding section, we will assume that we are dealing with a vector-valued function $\boldsymbol{F}$ such that the graph of the equation $\boldsymbol{R} = \boldsymbol{F}(t)$ for t in an interval $[a, b]$ is a smooth curve.

Let $\boldsymbol{T} = \dfrac{\boldsymbol{R}'}{|\boldsymbol{R}'|}$ be a unit tangent vector to this curve. Suppose that the angle whose initial side is the vector $\boldsymbol{i}$ and whose terminal side is the vector $\boldsymbol{T}$ is an angle of α (Fig. 76-1). Because $\boldsymbol{T}$ is a unit vector, its components are cos α and sin α, so

$$\boldsymbol{T} = \cos \alpha\, \boldsymbol{i} + \sin \alpha\, \boldsymbol{j}.$$

Therefore,

$$\frac{d\boldsymbol{T}}{ds} = (-\sin \alpha\, \boldsymbol{i} + \cos \alpha\, \boldsymbol{j}) \frac{d\alpha}{ds}. \tag{76-1}$$

For short, let us write $\boldsymbol{U} = -\sin \alpha\, \boldsymbol{i} + \cos \alpha\, \boldsymbol{j}$. This vector $\boldsymbol{U}$ is a unit vector. Furthermore $\boldsymbol{T} \cdot \boldsymbol{U} = 0$; that is, $\boldsymbol{U}$ is perpendicular to the tangent vector $\boldsymbol{T}$. Thus $\frac{d\boldsymbol{T}}{ds}$ is a vector that is perpendicular to the tangent vector $\boldsymbol{T}$, and $\left|\frac{d\boldsymbol{T}}{ds}\right| = \left|\frac{d\alpha}{ds}\right|$.

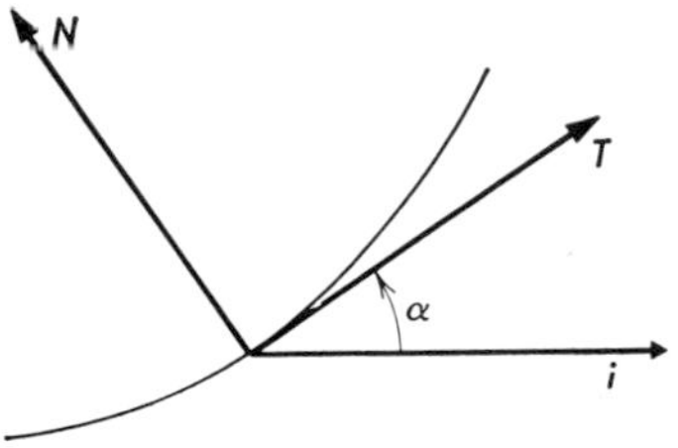

Figure 76-1

We will denote the number $\left|\frac{d\alpha}{ds}\right|$ by the Greek letter κ; thus

$$\kappa = \left|\frac{d\alpha}{ds}\right|. \tag{76-2}$$

We see that the number κ measures the absolute value of the rate of change of α with respect to s. Since it is the tangent vector $\boldsymbol{T}$ that makes the angle of α with $\boldsymbol{i}$, we often say that κ measures the absolute value of the "arc rate at which the tangent vector turns." We call κ the **curvature** of our curve at a point. From Equation 76-1 we see that the vector $\frac{d\boldsymbol{T}}{ds}$ can be written as the product of the curvature κ and a vector $\boldsymbol{N}$ that is perpendicular to the tangent vector:

$$\frac{d\boldsymbol{T}}{ds} = \kappa \boldsymbol{N}. \tag{76-3}$$

This unit normal vector $\boldsymbol{N}$ is either the vector $\boldsymbol{U}$ or the vector $-\boldsymbol{U}$, depending on the sign of $\frac{d\alpha}{ds}$. You might try to convince yourself, by means of examples, that the vector $\frac{d\boldsymbol{T}}{ds}$ (and hence $\boldsymbol{N}$) is always directed, as shown in Fig. 76-1, into the convex region between an arc of the curve and its chord.

According to Equation 76-2, if we want to determine the curvature κ of a curve, we should express α in terms of s and then differentiate. That is easier said than done, so we will find a formula for κ that looks more complicated than Equation 76-2 but which is considerably easier to apply. Since $\boldsymbol{N}$ is a unit vector, Equation 76-3 tells us that $\kappa = \left|\frac{d\boldsymbol{T}}{ds}\right|$. Thus we can find κ by differentiating the tangent vector $\boldsymbol{T}$ with respect to s and calculating the length of the resulting vector. To find the derivative of $\boldsymbol{T}$ we will use the Chain Rule,

$$\frac{d\boldsymbol{T}}{ds} = \frac{d\boldsymbol{T}}{dt}\frac{dt}{ds} = \boldsymbol{T}'\frac{dt}{ds}.$$

In the preceding section (see Equation 75-11) we found that $\frac{dt}{ds} = \frac{1}{|\boldsymbol{R}'|}$, so

$$\frac{d\boldsymbol{T}}{ds} = \frac{\boldsymbol{T}'}{|\boldsymbol{R}'|}.$$

Now $\boldsymbol{T} = \frac{\boldsymbol{R}'}{|\boldsymbol{R}'|}$, and therefore

$$\boldsymbol{T}' = \frac{|\boldsymbol{R}'|\boldsymbol{R}'' - |\boldsymbol{R}'|'\boldsymbol{R}'}{|\boldsymbol{R}'|^2}.$$

Hence

$$\text{(76-4)} \qquad \frac{d\boldsymbol{T}}{ds} = \frac{|\boldsymbol{R}'|\boldsymbol{R}'' - |\boldsymbol{R}'|'\boldsymbol{R}'}{|\boldsymbol{R}|'^3}.$$

Since $\kappa = \left|\frac{d\boldsymbol{T}}{ds}\right|$, our task is now to find the length of the vector $|\boldsymbol{R}'|\boldsymbol{R}'' - |\boldsymbol{R}'|'\boldsymbol{R}'$ and then divide that number by $|\boldsymbol{R}'|^3$. We can simplify this computation as follows. Equation 76-4 tells us that the vector $|\boldsymbol{R}'|\boldsymbol{R}'' - |\boldsymbol{R}'|'\boldsymbol{R}'$ is parallel to the vector $\frac{d\boldsymbol{T}}{ds}$ and hence to the normal vector $\boldsymbol{N}$. Therefore, it is perpendicular to the tangent vector $\boldsymbol{R}' = x'\boldsymbol{i} + y'\boldsymbol{j}$, and so we can find its length by computing its dot product with a unit vector that is perpendicular to $\boldsymbol{R}'$. Such a unit vector, as you can easily check, is $\boldsymbol{V} = \frac{-y'\boldsymbol{i} + x'\boldsymbol{j}}{|\boldsymbol{R}'|}$. When we take into account the fact that $\boldsymbol{V} \cdot \boldsymbol{R}' = 0$, we find that

$$\boldsymbol{V} \cdot (|\boldsymbol{R}'|\boldsymbol{R}'' - |\boldsymbol{R}'|'\boldsymbol{R}') = x'y'' - y'x''.$$

Therefore, the length of the vector $|\boldsymbol{R}'|\boldsymbol{R}'' - |\boldsymbol{R}'|'\boldsymbol{R}'$ is

$$|x'y'' - y'x''|.$$

Since $|\boldsymbol{R}'| = (x'^2 + y'^2)^{1/2}$, we have $|\boldsymbol{R}'|^3 = (x'^2 + y'^2)^{3/2}$, and so

$$\text{(76-5)} \qquad \kappa = \frac{|x'y'' - y'x''|}{(x'^2 + y'^2)^{3/2}}.$$

Example 76-1. Find the curvature of the circle whose radius is a and whose parametric equations are $x = a \cos t$ and $y = a \sin t$, where t is in the interval $[0, 2\pi]$.

Solution. When we substitute in Equation 76-5, we find that

$$\kappa = \frac{|(-a \sin t)(-a \sin t) - (a \cos t)(-a \cos t)|}{[(-a \sin t)^2 + (a \cos t)^2]^{3/2}}$$

$$= \frac{a^2}{a^3} = \frac{1}{a}.$$

In the preceding example we found that the reciprocal of the curvature of a circle is the radius of the circle. In general, we define the number

$$r = 1/\kappa \tag{76-6}$$

to be the **radius of curvature** of the graph of the equation $\boldsymbol{R} = \boldsymbol{F}(t)$ at the terminal point of $\boldsymbol{R}$. If you construct a circle whose radius is r and whose center is r units from the terminal point of $\boldsymbol{R}$ along the normal vector $\boldsymbol{N}$, then you obtain what is called the **circle of curvature** at the point. This circle is the circle that "best fits" the curve in the neighborhood of the given point.

Example 76-2. Find the formula for the curvature of the curve whose equation in non-parametric form is $y = f(x)$.

Solution. One pair of parametric equations for our curve is

$$x = t \quad \text{and} \quad y = f(t).$$

Then $x' = 1$ and $x'' = 0$, and Equation 76-5 becomes

$$\kappa = \frac{|y''|}{(1 + y'^2)^{3/2}}. \tag{76-7}$$

Example 76-3. Find the curvature of the parabola whose equation is $y = x^2$ at the point (1, 1). Show that this parabola is nearly a straight line at points far distant from the origin.

Solution. Using Equation 76-7 with $y' = 2x$ and $y'' = 2$, we have

$$\kappa = \frac{2}{(1 + 4x^2)^{3/2}}. \tag{76-8}$$

Thus the curvature of our parabola at the point (1, 1) is

$$\kappa = \frac{2}{5^{3/2}} \approx .18.$$

If a point is very far from the origin, then the square of its X-coordinate is very large. And if x^2 is a large number, then the number κ given by Equation 76-8 is nearly zero. Thus at points far from the origin, the curvature of the parabola is nearly zero; that is, the parabola is almost a straight line.

We often apply our theory of curves to describe the path of a particle moving in a plane. Usually in such cases the parameter t measures time. Thus if the graph of the equation $\boldsymbol{R} = \boldsymbol{F}(t)$ represents the path

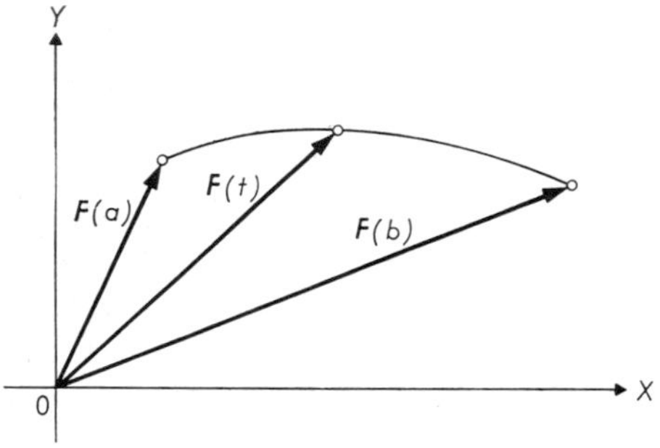

Figure 76-2

of some particle moving on a smooth arc in the plane, then t time units (seconds, for example) after we start to measure time, the particle is at the terminal point of $\boldsymbol{F}(t)$ (Fig. 76-2).

The length s of the arc joining the terminal points of the vectors $\boldsymbol{F}(a)$ and $\boldsymbol{F}(t)$ is (see Equation 75-7)

(76-9) $$s = \int_a^t |\boldsymbol{F}'(u)|\, du.$$

This number measures the distance that the particle has moved in the time interval $[a, t]$. When $t = a$, $s = 0$, for example. The derivative of s with respect to t—that is, the number ds/dt (or $D_t s$)—measures the rate of change of distance along our smooth arc with respect to time. It is natural to call this number ds/dt the **speed** of our moving particle. The vector $\boldsymbol{F}'(t)$ is called the **velocity** $\boldsymbol{V}$ of the particle, thus

(76-10) $$\boldsymbol{V} = \boldsymbol{F}'(t).$$

Furthermore, since $\dfrac{ds}{dt} = |\boldsymbol{F}'(t)|$, we see that

(76-11) $$|\boldsymbol{V}| = |\boldsymbol{F}'(t)| = ds/dt.$$

Thus the velocity of our particle is given by a *vector*, and the length of the velocity vector is the *scalar* called the speed of the particle. We can also express the velocity vector $\boldsymbol{V}$ by the equation

(76-12) $$\boldsymbol{V} = \frac{d\boldsymbol{R}}{ds}\frac{ds}{dt} = \boldsymbol{T}\frac{ds}{dt},$$

where $\boldsymbol{T} = d\boldsymbol{R}/ds$ is the unit tangent vector.

The derivative of $\boldsymbol{V}$ with respect to t measures the rate of change of velocity; we call it the **acceleration** $\boldsymbol{A}$ of the moving particle. Thus

(76-13) $$\boldsymbol{A} = \frac{d\boldsymbol{V}}{dt} = \frac{d^2\boldsymbol{R}}{dt^2}.$$

Notice that acceleration is measured by a *vector*. The length of the velocity vector $\boldsymbol{V}$ is the speed of our moving particle, but you should keep clearly in mind (see Question 8 of Problems 76) that the length of the acceleration vector is not, in general, the rate of change of the speed of the particle.

Example 76-4. A projectile is fired at an angle of 30° with the horizontal at a speed of 1000 feet per second. Describe the path of the projectile.

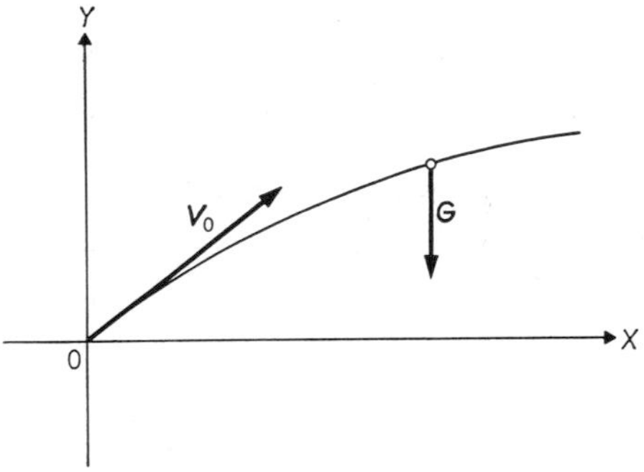

Figure 76-3

Solution. In Fig. 76-3 we have introduced a coordinate system and have drawn in our initial velocity vector $\boldsymbol{V}_0$. We know that $|\boldsymbol{V}_0| = 1000$, and that $\boldsymbol{V}_0$ makes an angle of 30° with the positive X-axis, so

$$\begin{aligned}\boldsymbol{V}_0 &= 1000(\cos 30°\,\boldsymbol{i} + \sin 30°\,\boldsymbol{j})\\ &= 500\sqrt{3}\,\boldsymbol{i} + 500\boldsymbol{j}.\end{aligned}$$

We will assume that the only force acting on the projectile in flight is the force of gravity and that this force is constant. Thus if we measure distance in feet and time in seconds, then the gravitational acceleration is $\boldsymbol{G} = -32\boldsymbol{j}$. Since acceleration is the derivative of velocity,

$$D_t\boldsymbol{V} = \boldsymbol{G}.$$

From this equation we see (as in Section 64) that

$$\boldsymbol{V} = \boldsymbol{G}t + \boldsymbol{C}_0,$$

where the vector $\boldsymbol{C}_0$ is independent of t. We determine $\boldsymbol{C}_0$ as follows. Since $\boldsymbol{V} = \boldsymbol{V}_0$ when $t = 0$, we can replace t with 0 and $\boldsymbol{V}$ with $\boldsymbol{V}_0$ in the equation above, and we will have

$$\boldsymbol{V}_0 = \boldsymbol{C}_0.$$

Therefore, our expression for $\boldsymbol{V}$ becomes

$$\boldsymbol{V} = \boldsymbol{G}t + \boldsymbol{V}_0.$$

But $\boldsymbol{V}$ is the derivative of $\boldsymbol{R}$, so

$$D_t\boldsymbol{R} = \boldsymbol{G}t + \boldsymbol{V}_0.$$

From this equation we find that

$$\boldsymbol{R} = \tfrac{1}{2}\boldsymbol{G}t^2 + \boldsymbol{V}_0t + \boldsymbol{C}_1,$$

where the vector $\boldsymbol{C}_1$ is independent of t. We determine $\boldsymbol{C}_1$ as follows. Since $\boldsymbol{R} = \boldsymbol{0}$ when $t = 0$ (see Fig. 76-3), we can replace t with 0 and $\boldsymbol{R}$ with $\boldsymbol{0}$ in our equation for $\boldsymbol{R}$, and then we see that $\boldsymbol{C}_1 = \boldsymbol{0}$. Thus we have finally found that the path of our projectile is the graph of the vector equation

$$\boldsymbol{R} = \tfrac{1}{2}\boldsymbol{G}t^2 + \boldsymbol{V}_0t = 500\sqrt{3}\,t\boldsymbol{i} + (500t - 16t^2)\boldsymbol{j}.$$

Parametric equations of the projectile's path are

$$x = 500\sqrt{3}\,t \quad \text{and} \quad y = 500t - 16t^2.$$

To obtain a non-parametric equation of the path, we can solve the first equation for t in terms of x and substitute the result in the second, thus giving us

$$y = \frac{x}{\sqrt{3}} - \frac{16x^2}{3(500)^2}.$$

You should recognize this equation as the equation of a parabola.

Let us denote the speed of a moving particle by v; that is, $v = ds/dt$. Then Equation 76-12 becomes

$$\boldsymbol{V} = v\boldsymbol{T},$$

and we can find the acceleration of the particle from this equation. Thus

$$\boldsymbol{A} = \frac{d(v\boldsymbol{T})}{dt} = \frac{dv}{dt}\boldsymbol{T} + v\frac{d\boldsymbol{T}}{dt}.$$

We use the Chain Rule to write

$$\frac{d\boldsymbol{T}}{dt} = \frac{d\boldsymbol{T}}{ds}\frac{ds}{dt} = v\frac{d\boldsymbol{T}}{ds},$$

and hence our formula for the acceleration becomes

$$A = \frac{dv}{dt}T + v^2\frac{dT}{ds}.$$

Finally, since $dT/ds = \kappa N$ (Equation 76-3), we see that

$$A = \frac{dv}{dt}T + \kappa v^2 N. \tag{76-14}$$

Thus the acceleration can be considered as the sum of the tangential acceleration $(dv/dt)T$ and the normal acceleration $\kappa v^2 N$. The normal acceleration is also called the **centripetal acceleration.**

Example 76-5. A rocket plane makes a circular turn at a constant speed of 2400 miles per hour. If the radius of the turn is 10 miles, determine the magnitude of the centripetal acceleration. How many "G's" is the pilot subjected to?

Solution. The centripetal acceleration has a magnitude of κv^2. If we convert our units to feet and seconds and utilize the fact that the curvature of our circle is the reciprocal of its radius (see Example 76-1), then we find that the magnitude of the centripetal acceleration is

$$\kappa v^2 = \frac{1}{52{,}800}\left(\frac{2400 \cdot 5280}{60 \cdot 60}\right)^2 \approx 235 \text{ feet per second per second.}$$

Since 1 "G" is about 32 feet per second per second, we see that the pilot is subjected to slightly more than 7 G's as he makes his turn.

Problems 76

1. Show that the curvature of a straight line is zero at every point. Can you show the converse?
2. Find κ at the point corresponding to the given t.
   (a) $R = \sin t\, i + 2\cos t\, j$, $t = 0$
   (b) $R = (t^2 - 2t)i + 3tj$, $t = 1$
   (c) $R = e^t i + e^{-t} j$, $t = 0$
   (d) $R = 2(t - \sin t)i + 2(1 - \cos t)j$, $t = \pi/3$
3. Find κ at the point indicated.
   (a) $y = x^2 - 2x + 3$, $(1, 2)$.
   (b) $y = e^{3x/4}$, $(0, 1)$
   (c) $y = \cos x$, $(\pi/2, 0)$
   (d) $y^2 = x + 3$, $(6, 3)$
4. At what points of the graph of the equation $y = x^3$ is the radius of curvature a minimum? At what points is the curvature a minimum?

5. Draw the parabola whose equation is $y^2 = 6x$, and also draw its circle of curvature at the point at which $y = 4$.

6. If the tangent to the graph of the equation $y = f(x)$ is nearly parallel to the X-axis, engineers regard the number $|y''|$ as an approximation of κ. Why?

7. Let a and b be positive numbers with $a > b$. A point moves in an elliptical path whose vector equation is $\boldsymbol{R} = a \cos t\, \boldsymbol{i} + b \sin t\boldsymbol{j}$. Sketch the path.
(a) What is the velocity of the point when $t = 0$?
(b) What is its maximum speed? Its minimum speed?
(c) Find the acceleration vector $\boldsymbol{A}$. Describe its direction.

8. Show that the length of the acceleration vector is not in general equal to the rate of change of speed of a moving particle. When is it equal?

9. Find the magnitudes of the centripetal acceleration and tangential acceleration at the indicated point.
(a) $\boldsymbol{R} = 3t\boldsymbol{i} + 3 \ln t\boldsymbol{j}$, $t = 3$
(b) $\boldsymbol{R} = 2 \tan t\, \boldsymbol{i} + 2 \cot t\boldsymbol{j}$, $t = \pi/4$.

10. A bug sits on a hoop of radius 2 feet that rolls along a straight line and makes 1 revolution per second. Find the velocity and acceleration of the bug: (a) at the instant the bug is at the top of the hoop (b) at the instant the bug is at the bottom of the hoop (see Example 74-5).

77. The Area of a Surface of Revolution

Suppose we are given a vector valued function $\boldsymbol{F}$ such that the graph of the equation $\boldsymbol{R} = \boldsymbol{F}(t)$ for t in the interval $[a, b]$ is a smooth arc that

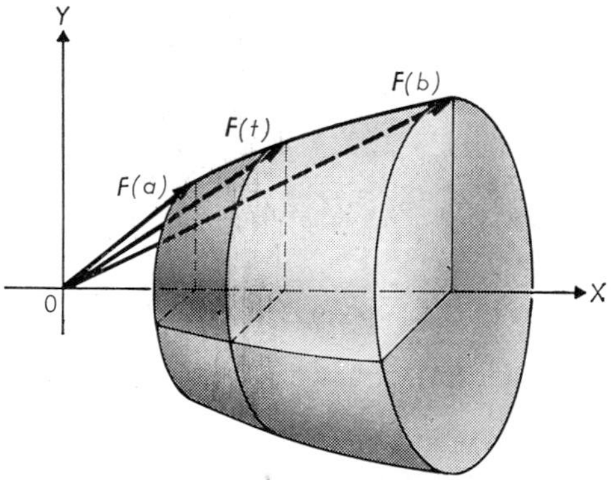

Figure 77-1

lies entirely above the X-axis as shown in Fig. 77-1. Thus if $\boldsymbol{F}(t) = F_x(t)\boldsymbol{i} + F_y(t)\boldsymbol{j}$, we are supposing that $F_y(t) > 0$ for t in the interval $[a, b]$. If our arc is rotated about the X-axis, we will obtain a surface of revolution, and we will now find a formula for the area of this surface.

We will proceed here somewhat as we did when we found our formula for arclength. Thus, instead of starting with a discussion of what we mean by the area of a curved surface, we will simply assume that there is a differentiable function f such that the number $s = f(t)$ is the area of the surface that is obtained by rotating about the X-axis the arc that joins the terminal point of $\boldsymbol{F}(a)$ to the terminal point of $\boldsymbol{F}(t)$. Then, assuming that this function has certain properties that we would expect an area function to have, we will derive a formula that defines the function. This formula will be the formula for the area of our surface of revolution.

So suppose that we have an area function f. Then if h is a number such that $t + h$ is a point in $[a, b]$, the area of the surface that is obtained

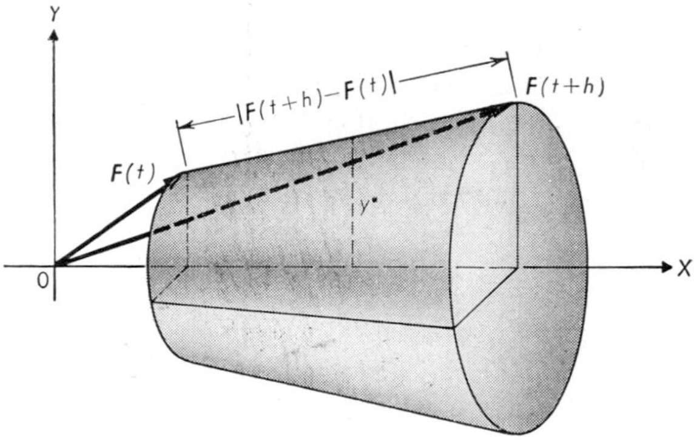

Figure 77-2

by rotating about the X-axis the arc that joins the terminal points of the vectors $\boldsymbol{F}(a)$ and $\boldsymbol{F}(t + h)$ is the number $f(t + h)$. If we rotate only the part of the arc that joins the terminal points of $\boldsymbol{F}(t)$ and $\boldsymbol{F}(t + h)$ about the X-axis, we obtain a surface whose area is $|f(t + h) - f(t)|$. If the chord that joins these points is rotated about the X-axis, we obtain the frustum of a cone (see Fig. 77-2). The slant height of this frustum is $|\boldsymbol{F}(t + h) - \boldsymbol{F}(t)|$ and its mean radius is $y^* = \frac{1}{2}[F_y(t) + F_y(t + h)]$. Therefore (see Question 2 of Problems 77), the area of the frustum is $2\pi y^*|\boldsymbol{F}(t + h) - \boldsymbol{F}(t)|$. When h is small this area should closely approximate the area of the surface generated by the arc joining the terminal points of $\boldsymbol{F}(t)$ and $\boldsymbol{F}(t + h)$. So we will assume our area function f has the property that

$$\lim_{h \to 0} \frac{|f(t + h) - f(t)|}{2\pi y^*|\boldsymbol{F}(t + h) - \boldsymbol{F}(t)|} = 1.$$

Since $\lim_{h \to 0} y^* = y = F_y(t)$, it follows from this equation that

(77-1) $$\lim_{h \to 0} \left| \frac{f(t + h) - f(t)}{\boldsymbol{F}(t + h) - \boldsymbol{F}(t)} \right| = 2\pi y.$$

Now $\dfrac{f(t+h)-f(t)}{h}$ is positive whether h is positive or negative, and so we can write

$$\frac{f(t+h)-f(t)}{h} = \left|\frac{f(t+h)-f(t)}{h}\right|$$
$$= \left|\frac{f(t+h)-f(t)}{\boldsymbol{F}(t+h)-\boldsymbol{F}(t)}\right| \cdot \left|\frac{\boldsymbol{F}(t+h)-\boldsymbol{F}(t)}{h}\right|.$$

If we now take limits as h approaches 0, and use the definition of a derivative and Equation 77-1, we find that

(77-2) $$f'(t) = 2\pi y\,|\boldsymbol{F}'(t)|.$$

Thus our area function f must be a solution of Equation 77-2. Furthermore, the "area" of the "surface" that is generated by rotating the "arc" that joins the terminal point of $\boldsymbol{F}(a)$ to itself is clearly 0, so we shall suppose that $f(a) = 0$. In Section 64 we saw that the solution to Differential Equation 77-2 that is 0 when $t = a$ is given by the equation

(77-3) $$S = 2\pi \int_a^t y|\boldsymbol{F}'(u)|\,du,$$

and we shall take Equation 77-3 as our formula for surface area. In particular, the area A of the surface that is obtained by rotating about the X-axis the arc that joins the endpoints of $\boldsymbol{F}(a)$ and $\boldsymbol{F}(b)$ is given by the equation

(77-4) $$A = 2\pi \int_a^b y|\boldsymbol{F}'(t)|\,dt.$$

Since $\boldsymbol{F}'(t) = \boldsymbol{R}' = x'\boldsymbol{i} + y'\boldsymbol{j}$, then $|\boldsymbol{F}'(t)| = \sqrt{x'^2 + y'^2}$, and so we often write Formula 77-4 as

(77-5) $$A = 2\pi \int_a^b y\sqrt{x'^2 + y'^2}\,dt.$$

In particular, if our arc is the graph of the equation $y = f(x)$, we can regard $x = t$ and $y = f(t)$ as parametric equations of the arc, and then Equation 77-5 becomes

(77-6) $$A = 2\pi \int_a^b y\sqrt{1 + (D_xy)^2}\,dx.$$

Example 77-1. Use Equation 77-5 to find the area of the surface of a sphere whose radius is a.

Solution. A sphere with a radius of a is obtained by rotating about the X-axis the arc with parametric equations

$$x = a\cos t, \quad y = a\sin t,$$

where t is in the interval $[0, \pi]$. Therefore, $x' = -a \sin t$ and $y' = a \cos t$. When we substitute these numbers in Equation 77-5 we get

$$A = 2\pi \int_0^\pi a \sin t \sqrt{(-a \sin t)^2 + (a \cos t)^2}\, dt$$

$$= 2\pi a^2 \int_0^\pi \sin t\, dt = 4\pi a^2.$$

If we rotate an arc about the Y-axis instead of the X-axis, the area of the resulting surface can be found by interchanging x and y in the above formulas.

Example 77-2. Find the area of the surface obtained by rotating the arc of the parabola with parametric equations $x = t$, $y = t^2$, where t is in the interval $[0, 1]$, about the Y-axis.

Solution. We use the formula

$$A = 2\pi \int_0^1 x \sqrt{x'^2 + y'^2}\, dt$$

$$= 2\pi \int_0^1 t \sqrt{1 + 4t^2}\, dt.$$

Now we change the variable of integration by the substitution $u = 1 + 4t^2$ to obtain

$$A = \frac{2\pi}{8} \int_1^5 \sqrt{u}\, du = \frac{\pi}{4} \frac{2}{3} u^{3/2} \Big|_1^5$$

$$= \frac{\pi}{6} (5^{3/2} - 1) \approx 5.33.$$

Example 77-3. The upper half of the cardioid that is the graph of the polar equation $r = 2(1 - \cos \theta)$ (see Fig. 66-5) is rotated about the X-axis. Find the area of this surface of revolution.

Solution. We recall that the cartesian coordinates (x, y) of a point are related to polar coordinates (r, θ) of the same point by the equations

$$x = r \cos \theta$$

$$y = r \sin \theta.$$

If we replace r with $2(1 - \cos \theta)$ in these equations, we obtain parametric equations for our cardioid;

$$x = 2(1 - \cos \theta) \cos \theta = 2(\cos \theta - \cos^2 \theta),$$

$$y = 2(1 - \cos \theta) \sin \theta = 2(\sin \theta - \cos \theta \sin \theta),$$

where θ is the parameter and the parameter interval for the upper half of our cardioid is $[0, \pi]$. If we use primes to denote differentiation with respect to the parameter θ, we have

$$x' = 2(-\sin\theta + 2\cos\theta\sin\theta) = 2(-\sin\theta + \sin 2\theta),$$
$$y' = 2(\cos\theta - \cos^2\theta + \sin^2\theta) = 2(\cos\theta - \cos 2\theta).$$

We then find that

$$\begin{aligned} x'^2 + y'^2 &= 4(2 - 2\sin\theta\sin 2\theta - 2\cos\theta\cos 2\theta) \\ &= 8[1 - (\cos 2\theta\cos\theta + \sin 2\theta\sin\theta)] \\ &= 8(1 - \cos\theta). \end{aligned}$$

Thus Formula 77-5 becomes

$$\begin{aligned} A &= 2\pi \int_0^\pi 2(1 - \cos\theta)\sin\theta\sqrt{8(1 - \cos\theta)}\,d\theta \\ &= 8\sqrt{2}\,\pi \int_0^\pi (1 - \cos\theta)^{3/2}\sin\theta\,d\theta. \end{aligned}$$

To evaluate this integral, we change the variable of integration, letting $u = 1 - \cos\theta$. Then $du = \sin\theta\,d\theta$ and

$$A = 8\sqrt{2}\,\pi \int_0^2 u^{3/2}\,du = \frac{128\pi}{5}.$$

Problems 77

1. If a right circular cone with a base radius of r and a slant height of k is "slit" down the side and laid flat, it will form a sector of a circle. Show that the area of this sector, and hence the surface area of the cone, is πrk.
2. The frustum of a cone is obtained by removing a cone with a base radius of r_2, a slant height of k_2, and an area of A_2 from the top of a cone whose base radius is r_1, slant height is k_1, and area is A_1. The slant height of the frustum is $k = k_1 - k_2$, and its mean radius $\bar{r} = \frac{1}{2}(r_1 + r_2)$. The area of the frustum is $A = A_1 - A_2 = \pi(r_1k_1 - r_2k_2)$ (see Question 1). From similar triangles deduce that $r_2/k_2 = r_1/k_1$, so that $r_2k_1 - r_1k_2 = 0$. Thus $A = \pi(r_1k_1 - r_2k_2 + r_2k_1 - r_1k_2)$. Conclude that $A = 2\pi\bar{r}k$.
3. Use Equation 77-6 to compute the area of the surface of the cone that is generated by rotating the line segment joining the origin to the point (h, r) about the X-axis.
4. Find the areas of the surfaces that are obtained by rotating the graphs of the following equations about the X-axis.
   (a) $\mathbf{R} = (2t^2 + 1)\mathbf{i} + 3t\mathbf{j}$, t in the interval $[0, 1]$
   (b) $\mathbf{R} = 3e^t\mathbf{i} + 4e^t\mathbf{j}$, t in the interval $[0, \ln 3]$
5. Find the area of the surface of the ellipsoid that is generated by rotating about the X-axis the curve with parametric equations $x = 5\cos t$ and $y = 3\sin t$.
6. Find the area of the surface that is generated by rotating about the X-axis the arc whose parametric equations are $x = e^{-t}\cos t$ and $y = e^{-t}\sin t$, t in the interval $[0, \pi/2]$.

7. Find the areas of the surfaces that are obtained by rotating the graphs of the following equations about the X-axis.
   (a) $y = 2\sqrt{x}$, x in the interval $[0, 8]$
   (b) $y = \frac{x^3}{3}$, x in the interval $[0, 2]$
   (c) $y = \cosh x$, x in the interval $[0, 1]$
   (d) $y = \frac{x^3}{6} + \frac{1}{2x}$, x in the interval $[1, 3]$.
8. Find the area of the surface that is generated by rotating about the Y-axis the arc whose parametric equations are $x = t^2$, and $y = t^3$, t in the interval $[0, 2]$.
9. Find the area of the surface that is generated by rotating the arc of the parabola $y = x^2$ that joins the point $(\sqrt{2}, 2)$ to the origin about the Y-axis.
10. One arch of the cycloid (Example 74-5) with parametric equations $x = a(t - \sin t)$, $y = a(1 - \cos t)$ is rotated about the X-axis. Find the area of the surface that is generated.
11. If the arc of the circle whose equation is $x^2 + y^2 = a^2$ that lies above the interval $[x_1, x_1 + h]$ is rotated about the X-axis, a surface called a **spherical zone of altitude h** is generated. Show that the area of such a surface is $2\pi ah$.
12. Find the area of the surface that is generated by rotating about the X-axis the curve whose polar equation is $r^2 = a^2 \cos 2\theta$.

Review Problems, Chapter Eight

You may use these questions to test yourself on the material covered in this chapter.

1. Suppose that P, Q, R, and S are points in the plane such that P and Q are symmetric with respect to the Y-axis, P and R are symmetric with respect to the origin, and P and S are symmetric with respect to the X-axis. If (r, θ) are polar coordinates of P, find polar coordinates of Q, R, and S.
2. Find a polar equation of the parabola whose focus is the origin and whose vertex is the point $\left(-2, \frac{\pi}{4}\right)$.
3. At a maximum or minimum point of the graph of an equation $y = f(x)$ in cartesian coordinates, $D_x y = 0$. At what points of the graph of an equation $r = f(\theta)$ in polar coordinates is $D_\theta r = 0$?
4. The area of the region that is bounded by the polar axis, a radial line making a positive acute angle of θ with the polar axis, and the graph of a certain equation is given by the formula $A(\theta) = 2e^{2\theta}$. What is this "certain curve"?
5. If we rotate our cartesian axes through any angle θ, the equation $x^2 + y^2 = 1$ is transformed into the equation $\bar{x}^2 + \bar{y}^2 = 1$. Through what angles of rotation of the axes is the equation $x^4 + y^4 = 1$ transformed into $\bar{x}^4 + \bar{y}^4 = 1$?
6. Find the equations of the asymptotes to the hyperbola whose equation is $x^2 - 24xy - 6y^2 - 26x + 12y - 11 = 0$.

7. Let $\boldsymbol{A}$ and $\boldsymbol{B}$ be two vectors, with $\boldsymbol{B} \neq \boldsymbol{0}$. For what number x is the number $|\boldsymbol{A} - x\boldsymbol{B}|$ a minimum?
8. Show that two vectors $\boldsymbol{A}$ and $\boldsymbol{B}$ are parallel if, and only if, $|\boldsymbol{A}|^2|\boldsymbol{B}|^2 - (\boldsymbol{A} \cdot \boldsymbol{B})^2 = 0$.
9. What is the equation of the tangent line to the graph of the equation $\boldsymbol{R} = \boldsymbol{F}(t)$ at the point at which $t = a$?
10. Suppose that $\boldsymbol{A}$ and $\boldsymbol{B}$ are mutually perpendicular unit vectors. Find the length of the arc of the curve $\boldsymbol{R} = t\boldsymbol{A} + t^2\boldsymbol{B}$ that joins the origin to the terminal point of the vector $\boldsymbol{A} + \boldsymbol{B}$.
11. What is the curvature of the curve in Question 10?
12. What is the area of the surface that is generated when the arc in Question 10 is rotated about a line that contains the origin and is parallel to the vector $\boldsymbol{B}$?

9 ANALYTIC GEOMETRY IN THREE-DIMENSIONAL SPACE

Because we live in a three-dimensional world, many practical problems that we want to solve mathematically must be stated in terms of solid, rather than plane, geometry. Thus we need to know the language of solid analytic geometry—the subject of this chapter. In later chapters we will see how calculus applies to certain problems in three-dimensional space.

78. Coordinates and Vectors in Three Dimensions

A **cartesian coordinate system** in three-dimensional space is formed by three mutually perpendicular number scales that have a common unit of length and a common origin, as shown in Fig. 78-1. These number scales are customarily labeled as the X-, Y-, and Z-axes as shown. The illustrated system is known as a **right-handed system.** A right-handed screw pointed along the Z-axis would advance if the positive X-axis were rotated 90° into the position of the positive Y-axis. If we were to interchange the labels on any two axes—for example, the X- and Y-axes—then we would obtain a **left-handed system.** Most books on applied mathematics use right-handed systems, and we shall use only such systems in this book.

The three planes that contain the various pairs of axes are known as the **coordinate planes.** They are called the **XY-plane,** the **YZ-plane,** and the **XZ-plane.** To each point P we assign coordinates (x, y, z) as follows. The plane containing the point P that is parallel to the YZ-plane intersects the X-axis in a point. But since the X-axis is a number scale, this point represents a number, and we call this number the X-coordinate of P. The Y- and Z-coordinates of P are assigned in a similar manner. Figure 78-1 shows the point whose coordinates are (3, 4, 4). You should draw similar figures for other points, including points with one or more negative coordinates, in order to familiarize yourself with the coordinate system in three-dimensional space.

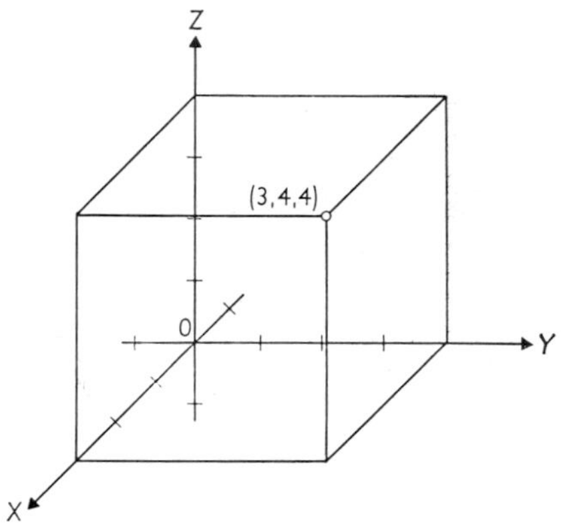

Figure 78-1

In Section 72 we introduced the vector concept to help us in our study of the geometry of the plane. Vectors are also very convenient tools to use in dealing with geometry in space. As before, we consider a vector to be an arrow. The concept of equality, the definitions of addition and subtraction of vectors and of multiplication of vectors by scalars, as discussed in Section 72, carry over without change to the three-dimensional situation. In particular, the rules governing vector algebra in three-space are exactly the same as before; that is, Equations 72-1 to 72-6 remain valid.

Example 78-1. Let $ABCD$ be a quadrilateral in space (notice that the points A, B, C, D need not lie in the same plane), and denote by P, Q, R, and S the midpoints of the sides AB, BC, CD, and AD. Show that $PQRS$ is a parallelogram.

Solution. Figure 78-2 shows the original quadrilateral as well as the quadrilateral whose vertices are the midpoints P, Q, R, and S. To show that this latter quadrilateral is a parallelogram, we need only show that the sides PS and QR are parallel and of equal length, which will be true if $\mathbf{PS} = \mathbf{QR}$. So we will show that $\mathbf{PS} = \mathbf{QR}$; in other words, that $\mathbf{PS} - \mathbf{QR} = \mathbf{PS} + \mathbf{RQ} = \mathbf{0}$. Now $\mathbf{PS} = \mathbf{AS} - \mathbf{AP} = \frac{1}{2}\mathbf{AD} - \frac{1}{2}\mathbf{AB}$ and also $\mathbf{RQ} = (\mathbf{AB} + \mathbf{BQ}) - (\mathbf{AD} + \mathbf{DR}) = \mathbf{AB} + \frac{1}{2}\mathbf{BC} - \mathbf{AD} - \frac{1}{2}\mathbf{DC}$.
Hence

$$\begin{aligned}\mathbf{PS} + \mathbf{RQ} &= \tfrac{1}{2}\mathbf{AD} - \tfrac{1}{2}\mathbf{AB} + \mathbf{AB} + \tfrac{1}{2}\mathbf{BC} - \mathbf{AD} - \tfrac{1}{2}\mathbf{DC} \\ &= \tfrac{1}{2}\mathbf{AB} + \tfrac{1}{2}\mathbf{BC} - \tfrac{1}{2}\mathbf{DC} - \tfrac{1}{2}\mathbf{AD} \\ &= \tfrac{1}{2}(\mathbf{AB} + \mathbf{BC} + \mathbf{CD} + \mathbf{DA}) = \mathbf{0},\end{aligned}$$

as was to be shown.

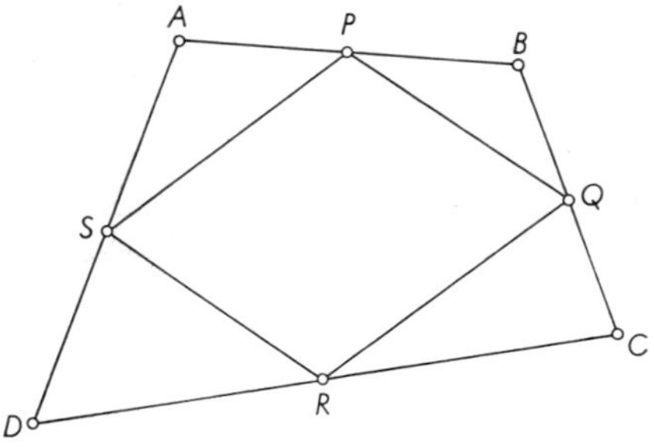

Figure 78-2

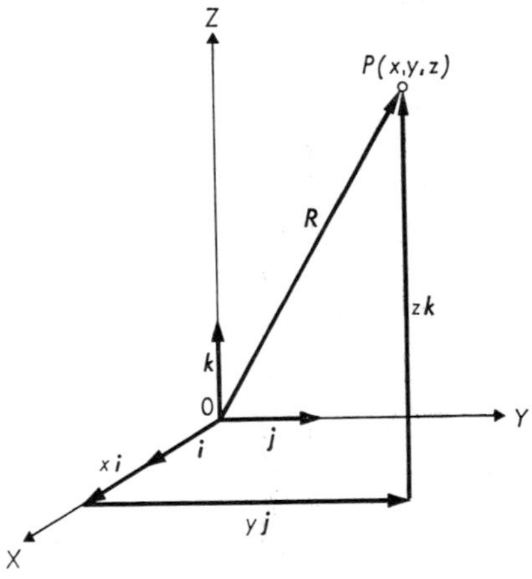

Figure 78-3

As in the plane, we introduce unit vectors parallel to the coordinate axes. The vectors $\mathbf{i}$, $\mathbf{j}$, and $\mathbf{k}$ are parallel to the X-, Y-, and Z-axes respectively, and are 1 unit long. Every point P with coordinates (x, y, z) determines (see Fig. 78-3) the **position vector** $\mathbf{R} = \mathbf{OP}$ with components x, y, and z. Thus

$$\mathbf{R} = x\mathbf{i} + y\mathbf{j} + z\mathbf{k}. \tag{78-1}$$

If $\mathbf{A}$ is a vector with initial point P_1 and terminal point P_2, where the coordinates of these points are (x_1, y_1, z_1) and (x_2, y_2, z_2), then

$$\begin{aligned} \boldsymbol{A} = \boldsymbol{OP}_2 - \boldsymbol{OP}_1 &= x_2\boldsymbol{i} + y_2\boldsymbol{j} + z_2\boldsymbol{k} - (x_1\boldsymbol{i} + y_1\boldsymbol{j} + z_1\boldsymbol{k}) \\ &= (x_2 - x_1)\boldsymbol{i} + (y_2 - y_1)\boldsymbol{j} + (z_2 - z_1)\boldsymbol{k}. \end{aligned}$$

Thus if

(78-2) $$\boldsymbol{A} = A_x\boldsymbol{i} + A_y\boldsymbol{j} + A_z\boldsymbol{k},$$

then the components of $\boldsymbol{A}$ are given by the equations

(78-3) $$A_x = x_2 - x_1, \quad A_y = y_2 - y_1, \quad \text{and} \quad A_z = z_2 - z_1.$$

Example 78-2. Find the coordinates of the midpoint of the segment PQ, where P is the point $(-1, 2, 5)$ and Q is the point $(3, 0, -1)$.

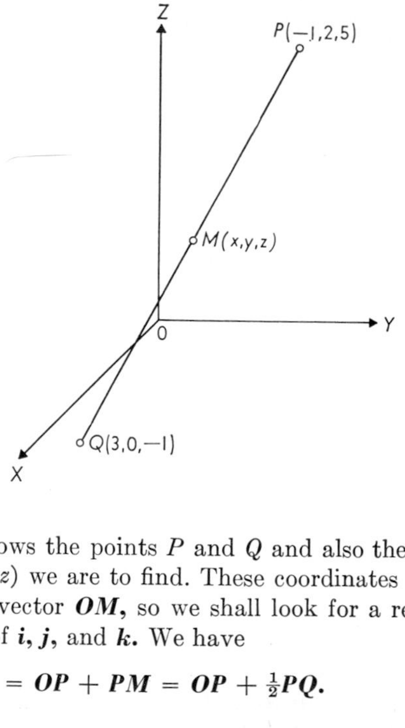

Figure 78-4

Solution. Figure 78-4 shows the points P and Q and also the midpoint M whose coordinates (x, y, z) we are to find. These coordinates are the components of the position vector $\boldsymbol{OM}$, so we shall look for a representation of that vector in terms of $\boldsymbol{i}$, $\boldsymbol{j}$, and $\boldsymbol{k}$. We have

$$\boldsymbol{OM} = \boldsymbol{OP} + \boldsymbol{PM} = \boldsymbol{OP} + \tfrac{1}{2}\boldsymbol{PQ}.$$

Now

$$\boldsymbol{OP} = -\boldsymbol{i} + 2\boldsymbol{j} + 5\boldsymbol{k} \quad \text{and} \quad \boldsymbol{PQ} = 4\boldsymbol{i} - 2\boldsymbol{j} - 6\boldsymbol{k},$$

and hence

$$\begin{aligned} \boldsymbol{OM} &= (-\boldsymbol{i} + 2\boldsymbol{j} + 5\boldsymbol{k}) + \tfrac{1}{2}(4\boldsymbol{i} - 2\boldsymbol{j} - 6\boldsymbol{k}) \\ &= (-\boldsymbol{i} + 2\boldsymbol{j} + 5\boldsymbol{k}) + (2\boldsymbol{i} - \boldsymbol{j} - 3\boldsymbol{k}) \\ &= \boldsymbol{i} + \boldsymbol{j} + 2\boldsymbol{k}. \end{aligned}$$

Thus the coordinates of the midpoint M are $(1, 1, 2)$.

To help us find a formula for the length $|\boldsymbol{A}|$ of a vector $\boldsymbol{A} = A_x\boldsymbol{i} + A_y\boldsymbol{j} + A_z\boldsymbol{k}$, we first draw it as a position vector (Fig. 78-5). The three planes containing the terminal point (A_x, A_y, A_z) that are parallel to the coordinate planes and the coordinate planes themselves form a rectangular parallelopiped (box). We have labeled three vertices of the box P, Q,

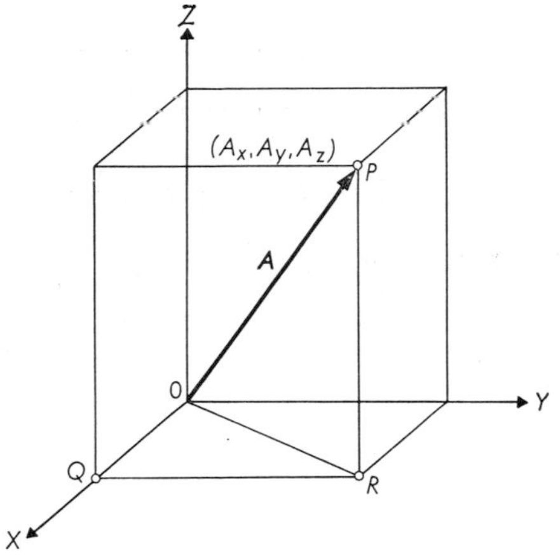

Figure 78-5

and R. Since ORP is a right triangle, the length of $\boldsymbol{A}$ is given by the equation

$$|\boldsymbol{A}|^2 = \overline{OP}^2 = \overline{OR}^2 + \overline{RP}^2.$$

We see that OQR is a right triangle and hence $\overline{OR}^2 = \overline{OQ}^2 + \overline{QR}^2$. Thus

$$\overline{OP}^2 = \overline{OQ}^2 + \overline{QR}^2 + \overline{RP}^2.$$

Since $\overline{OP}^2 = |\boldsymbol{A}|^2$, $\overline{OQ}^2 = A_x^2$, $\overline{QR}^2 = A_y^2$, and $\overline{RP}^2 = A_z^2$, we can write this last equation as

$$|\boldsymbol{A}|^2 = A_x^2 + A_y^2 + A_z^2;$$

in other words, *the length of the vector* $|\boldsymbol{A}|$ *is given by the equation*

$$\text{(78-4)} \qquad |\boldsymbol{A}| = \sqrt{A_x^2 + A_y^2 + A_z^2}.$$

Now suppose that $\boldsymbol{A}$ is the vector $\boldsymbol{P_1P_2}$, where P_1 and P_2 are two given points in space. Since the components of $\boldsymbol{A}$ are given in terms of its end points by Equations 78-3, we can word our formula for the length of $\boldsymbol{A}$ as follows. *If* P_1 *and* P_2 *are two points in three dimensional space with coordinates* (x_1, y_1, z_1) *and* (x_2, y_2, z_2), *then the distance* $\overline{P_1P_2}$ *is given by the formula*

$$\text{(78-5)} \qquad \overline{P_1P_2} = \sqrt{(x_2 - x_1)^2 + (y_2 - y_1)^2 + (z_2 - z_1)^2}.$$

Example 78-3. Show that the three points $P(-2, 2, 1)$, $Q(-1, 0, 1)$, and $R(0, 3, 2)$ form the vertices of a right triangle.

Solution. We will calculate the squares of the sides of the triangle, $\overline{PQ}^2$, $\overline{QR}^2$, and $\overline{RP}^2$, and show that one of these numbers is the sum of the other two. Thus

$$\overline{PQ}^2 = 1^2 + (-2)^2 + 0^2 = 5,$$

$$\overline{QR}^2 = 1^2 + 3^2 + 1^2 = 11,$$

and

$$\overline{RP}^2 = (-2)^2 + (-1)^2 + (-1)^2 = 6.$$

Since $11 = 5 + 6$, our assertion is true.

Problems 78

1. Plot the following points in a three-dimensional cartesian coordinate system.
   (a) $(-3, 4, 5)$ (b) $(3, -4, 5)$
   (c) $(3, -4, -5)$ (d) $(4, 0, -1)$
   (e) $(0, 3, 0)$
2. Let $\boldsymbol{A}$, $\boldsymbol{B}$, $\boldsymbol{C}$, $\boldsymbol{D}$, and $\boldsymbol{E}$ be position vectors to the points (a), (b), (c), (d), and (e) of the preceding problem. Write each of the following vectors in terms of the unit vectors $\boldsymbol{i}$, $\boldsymbol{j}$, and $\boldsymbol{k}$.
   (a) $\boldsymbol{A} + \boldsymbol{B}$ (b) $2\boldsymbol{C} - \boldsymbol{D}$
   (c) $\boldsymbol{B} - \boldsymbol{C} + \boldsymbol{E}$ (d) $\frac{1}{2}(\boldsymbol{A} + \boldsymbol{B} + \boldsymbol{C})$
3. Let P and Q have coordinates $(-1, 2, -3)$ and $(11, 11, 3)$ respectively.
   (a) Express the vector $\boldsymbol{PQ}$ in terms of the unit vectors $\boldsymbol{i}$, $\boldsymbol{j}$, and $\boldsymbol{k}$.
   (b) Find the point that is one-third of the way from P to Q.
   (c) What is the distance between P and Q?
   (d) Find the point R such that $\boldsymbol{PR} = 2\boldsymbol{PQ}$.
   (e) Find a point R such that angle PRQ is a right angle.
4. Let $\boldsymbol{A} = \boldsymbol{i} + 3\boldsymbol{j} - \boldsymbol{k}$, $\boldsymbol{B} = 2\boldsymbol{i} + 4\boldsymbol{j} - 2\boldsymbol{k}$, and $\boldsymbol{C} = -\boldsymbol{i} + 2\boldsymbol{j} + 4\boldsymbol{k}$. Determine c so that $\boldsymbol{A} + \boldsymbol{B} + c\boldsymbol{C}$ is parallel to the YZ-plane.
5. Suppose that P, Q, R, and S are points in space such that $\boldsymbol{OP} - \boldsymbol{OQ} = \boldsymbol{OS} - \boldsymbol{OR}$. Show that $PQRS$ is a parallelogram.
6. Let P, Q, R, and S be the points $(1, 1, 1)$, $(2, 3, 0)$, $(3, 5, -2)$, and $(0, -1, 1)$, respectively. Show that the segments PQ and RS are parallel and find the ratio of their lengths.
7. Two position vectors $\boldsymbol{A}$ and $\boldsymbol{B}$ are non-parallel sides of a parallelogram. Find the position vectors whose terminal points are the vertex opposite the origin and the center of the parallelogram.
8. Prove that the line segment joining the midpoints of two sides of a triangle in space is parallel to the third side and is half as long as the third side.

9. Suppose we have a vector $\boldsymbol{A}$ and a number x. Describe $\boldsymbol{X}$ if $|\boldsymbol{X}| = x$ and $|\boldsymbol{A} + \boldsymbol{X}|$ is a maximum. A minimum. What is the maximum value of $|\boldsymbol{A} + \boldsymbol{X}|$? (Express your answer in the form of an inequality.)

10. Let $\boldsymbol{A}$, $\boldsymbol{B}$, and $\boldsymbol{C}$ be position vectors. Show that $\boldsymbol{A}$, $\boldsymbol{B}$, and $\boldsymbol{C}$ are in the same plane if, and only if, there exist numbers x, y, and z (not all zero) such that $x\boldsymbol{A} + y\boldsymbol{B} + z\boldsymbol{C} = \boldsymbol{0}$.

79. Products of Vectors

The dot, or scalar, product of two vectors $\boldsymbol{A}$ and $\boldsymbol{B}$ in three dimensions is defined just as it is in the plane. Thus, if the vectors form an angle of θ, where $0° \leq \theta \leq 180°$, when they are placed so as to have a common initial point (see Fig. 79-1), then

$$\boldsymbol{A} \cdot \boldsymbol{B} = |\boldsymbol{A}|\,|\boldsymbol{B}| \cos \theta. \tag{79-1}$$

The dot product in three dimensions obeys the "natural" rules of arithmetic. Thus if $\boldsymbol{A}$, $\boldsymbol{B}$, and $\boldsymbol{C}$ are any vectors, and if a is any scalar, then

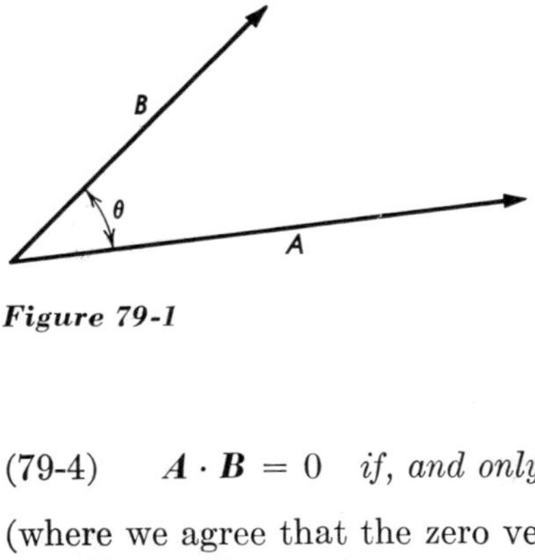

Figure 79-1

$$\begin{aligned} \boldsymbol{A} \cdot \boldsymbol{B} &= \boldsymbol{B} \cdot \boldsymbol{A}, \\ \boldsymbol{A} \cdot (\boldsymbol{B} + \boldsymbol{C}) &= \boldsymbol{A} \cdot \boldsymbol{B} + \boldsymbol{A} \cdot \boldsymbol{C}, \\ (a\boldsymbol{A}) \cdot \boldsymbol{B} &= a(\boldsymbol{A} \cdot \boldsymbol{B}). \end{aligned} \tag{79-2}$$

As in two dimensions, we see that

$$\boldsymbol{A} \cdot \boldsymbol{A} = |\boldsymbol{A}|^2. \tag{79-3}$$

Again we have the theorem which states that

(79-4) $\boldsymbol{A} \cdot \boldsymbol{B} = 0$ *if, and only if,* $\boldsymbol{A}$ *and* $\boldsymbol{B}$ *are perpendicular*

(where we agree that the zero vector is perpendicular to every vector).

We readily see that

$$\begin{aligned} \boldsymbol{i} \cdot \boldsymbol{i} = \boldsymbol{j} \cdot \boldsymbol{j} &= \boldsymbol{k} \cdot \boldsymbol{k} = 1, \\ \boldsymbol{i} \cdot \boldsymbol{j} = \boldsymbol{j} \cdot \boldsymbol{k} &= \boldsymbol{k} \cdot \boldsymbol{i} = 0. \end{aligned} \tag{79-5}$$

You can use these equations and Equations 79-2 to verify (see Equation 73-11) that we can express the dot product of two vectors $\boldsymbol{A} = A_x\boldsymbol{i} + A_y\boldsymbol{j} + A_z\boldsymbol{k}$ and $\boldsymbol{B} = B_x\boldsymbol{i} + B_y\boldsymbol{j} + B_z\boldsymbol{k}$ in terms of their components as follows:

$$\boldsymbol{A} \cdot \boldsymbol{B} = A_xB_x + A_yB_y + A_zB_z. \tag{79-6}$$

Example 79-1. Find the angle between the two vectors $\boldsymbol{A} = 2\boldsymbol{i} - \boldsymbol{j} + \boldsymbol{k}$ and $\boldsymbol{B} = \boldsymbol{i} + \boldsymbol{j} + 2\boldsymbol{k}$.

Solution. Since $\boldsymbol{A} \cdot \boldsymbol{B} = |\boldsymbol{A}|\,|\boldsymbol{B}| \cos \theta$,

$$\cos \theta = \boldsymbol{A} \cdot \boldsymbol{B}/|\boldsymbol{A}|\,|\boldsymbol{B}|.$$

According to Equation 79-6, $\boldsymbol{A} \cdot \boldsymbol{B} = 2 \cdot 1 + (-1) \cdot 1 + 1 \cdot 2 = 3$, and we readily see that $|\boldsymbol{A}| = |\boldsymbol{B}| = \sqrt{6}$. Hence

$$\cos \theta = 3/\sqrt{6}\,\sqrt{6} = \tfrac{1}{2}.$$

It follows that $\theta = \pi/3$.

As in the two-dimensional case, the number $|\boldsymbol{A}| \cos \theta$ is called the *component of* $\boldsymbol{A}$ *along* $\boldsymbol{B}$ (and, similarly, the number $|\boldsymbol{B}| \cos \theta$ is the component of $\boldsymbol{B}$ along $\boldsymbol{A}$). Thus

(79-7) *The component of* $\boldsymbol{A}$ *along* $\boldsymbol{B} = \boldsymbol{A} \cdot \boldsymbol{B}/|\boldsymbol{B}|$.

If $\boldsymbol{B}$ is a unit vector, then the length of $\boldsymbol{B}$ is 1, and the component of $\boldsymbol{A}$ along $\boldsymbol{B}$ is simply the dot product $\boldsymbol{A} \cdot \boldsymbol{B}$. So, in particular,

(79-8) $$A_x = \boldsymbol{A} \cdot \boldsymbol{i}, \quad A_y = \boldsymbol{A} \cdot \boldsymbol{j}, \quad A_z = \boldsymbol{A} \cdot \boldsymbol{k}.$$

The dot product of two vectors is a scalar (a number). Now we are going to introduce a product of two vectors that is a vector. This vector

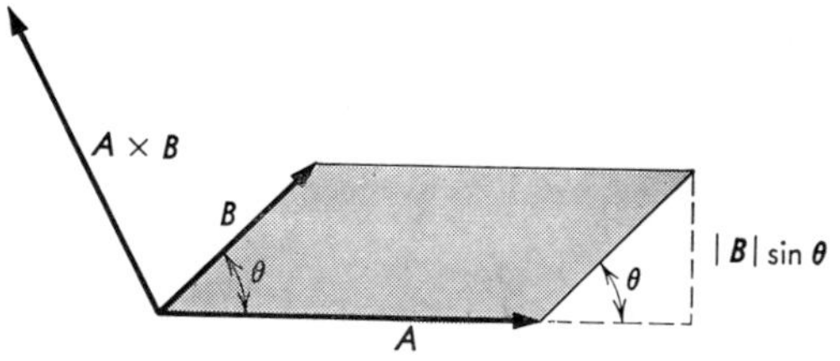

Figure 79-2

is written $\boldsymbol{A} \times \boldsymbol{B}$ and is called the **cross product,** or **vector product, of** $\boldsymbol{A}$ **by** $\boldsymbol{B}$. It is defined in the following way. Since $\boldsymbol{A} \times \boldsymbol{B}$ is to be a vector, we must prescribe both its length and its direction. The length of $\boldsymbol{A} \times \boldsymbol{B}$ is given by the equation

$$|\boldsymbol{A} \times \boldsymbol{B}| = |\boldsymbol{A}|\,|\boldsymbol{B}| \sin \theta,$$

where we are supposing, as usual, that if the vectors $\boldsymbol{A}$ and $\boldsymbol{B}$ have a common initial point they make an angle of θ, with $0° \leq \theta \leq 180°$ (see Fig. 79-2). We see that if $\boldsymbol{A}$ and $\boldsymbol{B}$ are parallel, then $\theta = 0°$ or $\theta = 180°$, and hence $\sin\theta = 0$. Thus $\boldsymbol{A} \times \boldsymbol{B} = \boldsymbol{0}$. If $\boldsymbol{A}$ and $\boldsymbol{B}$ are not parallel, then they determine a plane. We shall choose the direction of $\boldsymbol{A} \times \boldsymbol{B}$ so that *$\boldsymbol{A} \times \boldsymbol{B}$ is perpendicular to this plane and points in the direction that a right-handed screw would advance if $\boldsymbol{A}$ is rotated into $\boldsymbol{B}$ through the angle of θ.*

From Fig. 79-2 you can see that $|\boldsymbol{B}| \sin\theta$ is the altitude of the parallelogram that is determined by the vectors $\boldsymbol{A}$ and $\boldsymbol{B}$. Hence $|\boldsymbol{A}|\,|\boldsymbol{B}| \sin\theta$ is the area of this parallelogram. In other words, we can interpret the number $|\boldsymbol{A} \times \boldsymbol{B}|$ as the area of the parallelogram determined by $\boldsymbol{A}$ and $\boldsymbol{B}$.

We have already seen that if $\boldsymbol{A}$ and $\boldsymbol{B}$ are parallel, then $\boldsymbol{A} \times \boldsymbol{B} = \boldsymbol{0}$. Conversely, if $\boldsymbol{A} \times \boldsymbol{B} = \boldsymbol{0}$, then either $\sin\theta = 0$ or one of the vectors $\boldsymbol{A}$ or $\boldsymbol{B}$ is the vector $\boldsymbol{0}$. If $\sin\theta = 0$, then $\theta = 0°$ or $\theta = 180°$. In either case the vectors are parallel. Let us agree that the vector $\boldsymbol{0}$ is parallel to every vector. Then we can make the following statement: *The vectors $\boldsymbol{A}$ and $\boldsymbol{B}$ are parallel if, and only if, $\boldsymbol{A} \times \boldsymbol{B} = \boldsymbol{0}$.*

You can use the definition of the cross product to verify the following products of the unit basis vectors:

$$\begin{aligned} &\boldsymbol{i} \times \boldsymbol{j} = \boldsymbol{k}, && \boldsymbol{j} \times \boldsymbol{k} = \boldsymbol{i}, && \boldsymbol{k} \times \boldsymbol{i} = \boldsymbol{j}, \\ &\boldsymbol{j} \times \boldsymbol{i} = -\boldsymbol{k}, && \boldsymbol{k} \times \boldsymbol{j} = -\boldsymbol{i}, && \boldsymbol{i} \times \boldsymbol{k} = -\boldsymbol{j}, \\ &\boldsymbol{i} \times \boldsymbol{i} = \boldsymbol{0}, && \boldsymbol{j} \times \boldsymbol{j} = \boldsymbol{0}, && \boldsymbol{k} \times \boldsymbol{k} = \boldsymbol{0}. \end{aligned} \tag{79-9}$$

When we dealt with the dot product, we found that we could use our "usual" rules of arithmetic. Some of these rules do not apply to the cross product. For example, in Equations 79-9 we see that $\boldsymbol{i} \times \boldsymbol{j} = \boldsymbol{k}$, whereas $\boldsymbol{j} \times \boldsymbol{i} = -\boldsymbol{k}$. Therefore, the product $\boldsymbol{i} \times \boldsymbol{j}$ is not the same as the product $\boldsymbol{j} \times \boldsymbol{i}$, and so the commutative law is not valid in the case of the cross product. You can easily see that for each pair of vectors $\boldsymbol{A}$ and $\boldsymbol{B}$, we have, in fact, the "anti-commutative" rule

$$\boldsymbol{B} \times \boldsymbol{A} = -(\boldsymbol{A} \times \boldsymbol{B}). \tag{79-10}$$

The associative law of multiplication does not hold either; that is, the products $(\boldsymbol{A} \times \boldsymbol{B}) \times \boldsymbol{C}$ and $\boldsymbol{A} \times (\boldsymbol{B} \times \boldsymbol{C})$ are not necessarily the same vector (see Problem 1 at the end of this section).

The following laws of arithmetic, however, are valid for the cross product. If $\boldsymbol{A}$, $\boldsymbol{B}$, and $\boldsymbol{C}$ are any vectors, and if a is a scalar, then

$$\boldsymbol{A} \times (\boldsymbol{B} + \boldsymbol{C}) = \boldsymbol{A} \times \boldsymbol{B} + \boldsymbol{A} \times \boldsymbol{C}, \tag{79-11}$$

and,

$$(a\boldsymbol{A}) \times \boldsymbol{B} = \boldsymbol{A} \times (a\boldsymbol{B}) = a(\boldsymbol{A} \times \boldsymbol{B}). \tag{79-12}$$

Now suppose we have two vectors

$$\boldsymbol{A} = A_x\boldsymbol{i} + A_y\boldsymbol{j} + A_z\boldsymbol{k}$$

and

$$\boldsymbol{B} = B_x\boldsymbol{i} + B_y\boldsymbol{j} + B_z\boldsymbol{k}.$$

If we use the general Equations 79-11 and 79-12 and the specific multiplication Formulas 79-9 to expand the product

$$\boldsymbol{A} \times \boldsymbol{B} = (A_x\boldsymbol{i} + A_y\boldsymbol{j} + A_z\boldsymbol{k}) \times (B_x\boldsymbol{i} + B_y\boldsymbol{j} + B_z\boldsymbol{k}),$$

we will obtain the formula

(79-13) $$\boldsymbol{A} \times \boldsymbol{B} = (A_yB_z - A_zB_y)\boldsymbol{i} - (A_xB_z - A_zB_x)\boldsymbol{j} + (A_xB_y - A_yB_x)\boldsymbol{k}.$$

A determinant of the second order is defined by the equation

$$\begin{vmatrix} m & n \\ p & q \end{vmatrix} = mq - np.$$

In this notation

$$(A_yB_z - A_zB_y) = \begin{vmatrix} A_y & A_z \\ B_y & B_z \end{vmatrix},$$

and so on, and hence we can write our cross product in the form

(79-14) $$\boldsymbol{A} \times \boldsymbol{B} = \begin{vmatrix} A_y & A_z \\ B_y & B_z \end{vmatrix} \boldsymbol{i} - \begin{vmatrix} A_x & A_z \\ B_x & B_z \end{vmatrix} \boldsymbol{j} + \begin{vmatrix} A_x & A_y \\ B_x & B_y \end{vmatrix} \boldsymbol{k}.$$

This last equation is sometimes symbolically expressed as

(79-15) $$\boldsymbol{A} \times \boldsymbol{B} = \begin{vmatrix} \boldsymbol{i} & \boldsymbol{j} & \boldsymbol{k} \\ A_x & A_y & A_z \\ B_x & B_y & B_z \end{vmatrix}.$$

Example 79-2. Find the area of the triangle whose vertices are the points $A(a, 0, 0)$, $B(0, b, 0)$, and $C(0, 0, c)$.

Solution. The length of the vector $\boldsymbol{CA} \times \boldsymbol{CB}$ is the area of the parallelogram with $\boldsymbol{CA}$ and $\boldsymbol{CB}$ as two sides. The area of our triangle is one-half of this area (see Fig. 79-3). We see that

$$\boldsymbol{CA} = a\boldsymbol{i} - c\boldsymbol{k} \quad \text{and} \quad \boldsymbol{CB} = b\boldsymbol{j} - c\boldsymbol{k}.$$

Thus

$$\boldsymbol{CA} \times \boldsymbol{CB} = \begin{vmatrix} 0 & -c \\ b & -c \end{vmatrix} \boldsymbol{i} - \begin{vmatrix} a & -c \\ 0 & -c \end{vmatrix} \boldsymbol{j} + \begin{vmatrix} a & 0 \\ 0 & b \end{vmatrix} \boldsymbol{k}$$

$$= bc\boldsymbol{i} + ac\boldsymbol{j} + ab\boldsymbol{k}.$$

Therefore, $|\boldsymbol{CA} \times \boldsymbol{CB}|^2 = b^2c^2 + a^2c^2 + a^2b^2$, and hence the area of our triangle is

$$\tfrac{1}{2}|\boldsymbol{CA} \times \boldsymbol{CB}| = \tfrac{1}{2}\sqrt{b^2c^2 + a^2c^2 + a^2b^2}.$$

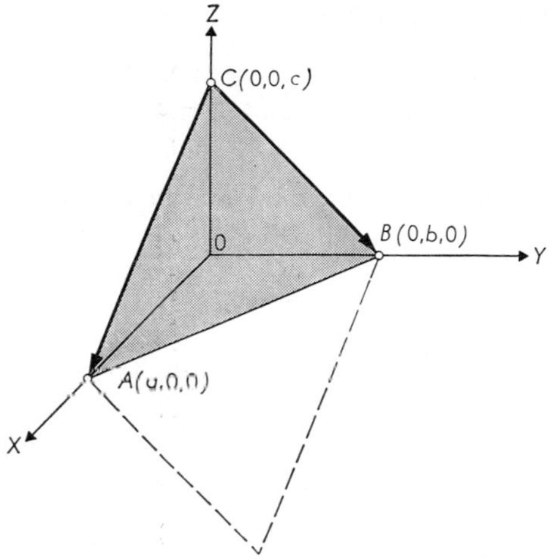

Figure 79-3

We can consider quantities that are obtained by "mixing" our vector and scalar products. Although many combinations are possible (and are discussed in courses in vector analysis), we shall consider only the combination $\boldsymbol{A} \cdot (\boldsymbol{B} \times \boldsymbol{C})$. This product is called the **scalar triple product** of $\boldsymbol{A}$, $\boldsymbol{B}$, and $\boldsymbol{C}$. If $\boldsymbol{A} = A_x\boldsymbol{i} + A_y\boldsymbol{j} + A_z\boldsymbol{k}$, $\boldsymbol{B} = B_x\boldsymbol{i} + B_y\boldsymbol{j} + B_z\boldsymbol{k}$, and $\boldsymbol{C} = C_x\boldsymbol{i} + C_y\boldsymbol{j} + C_z\boldsymbol{k}$, then we can express their scalar triple product as follows:

$$\boldsymbol{A} \cdot (\boldsymbol{B} \times \boldsymbol{C}) = (A_x\boldsymbol{i} + A_y\boldsymbol{j} + A_z\boldsymbol{k}) \cdot \left\{ \begin{vmatrix} B_y & B_z \\ C_y & C_z \end{vmatrix} \boldsymbol{i} - \begin{vmatrix} B_x & B_z \\ C_x & C_z \end{vmatrix} \boldsymbol{j} + \begin{vmatrix} B_x & B_y \\ C_x & C_y \end{vmatrix} \boldsymbol{k} \right\};$$

that is,

$$\text{(79-16)} \quad \boldsymbol{A} \cdot (\boldsymbol{B} \times \boldsymbol{C}) = A_x \begin{vmatrix} B_y & B_z \\ C_y & C_z \end{vmatrix} - A_y \begin{vmatrix} B_x & B_z \\ C_x & C_z \end{vmatrix} + A_z \begin{vmatrix} B_x & B_y \\ C_x & C_y \end{vmatrix}.$$

If you are familiar with determinants of the third order (we will discuss them in Section 90), you will realize that we can write this result as

$$\text{(79-17)} \qquad \boldsymbol{A} \cdot (\boldsymbol{B} \times \boldsymbol{C}) = \begin{vmatrix} A_x & A_y & A_z \\ B_x & B_y & B_z \\ C_x & C_y & C_z \end{vmatrix}.$$

Example 79-3. Show that the area of the triangle in the plane whose vertices are the points (x_1, y_1), (x_2, y_2), and (x_3, y_3) is given by the absolute value of the number

$$(79\text{-}18)\quad \frac{1}{2}\begin{vmatrix} 1 & 1 & 1 \\ x_1 & x_2 & x_3 \\ y_1 & y_2 & y_3 \end{vmatrix} = \tfrac{1}{2}[(x_2y_3 - x_3y_2) - (x_1y_3 - x_3y_1) + (x_1y_2 - x_2y_1)].$$

Solution. Let us consider the plane in which our given triangle lies to be the XY-plane of a three-dimensional space so that the vertices of the triangle are the points $A(x_1, y_1, 0)$, $B(x_2, y_2, 0)$, and $C(x_3, y_3, 0)$. The area of our triangle is (see Example 79-2) $\frac{1}{2}|\boldsymbol{CA} \times \boldsymbol{CB}|$. Since the vectors $\boldsymbol{CA}$ and $\boldsymbol{CB}$ lie in the XY-plane, we see that the vector $\boldsymbol{CA} \times \boldsymbol{CB}$ is parallel to the Z-axis. Therefore, the absolute value of the dot product of the vector $\boldsymbol{CA} \times \boldsymbol{CB}$ and the unit vector $\boldsymbol{k}$ is the product of the lengths $|\boldsymbol{CA} \times \boldsymbol{CB}|$ and $|\boldsymbol{k}| = 1$. Thus our desired area is simply the absolute value of the number $\frac{1}{2}\boldsymbol{k} \cdot (\boldsymbol{CA} \times \boldsymbol{CB})$. Now

$$\boldsymbol{CA} = (x_1 - x_3)\boldsymbol{i} + (y_1 - y_3)\boldsymbol{j}$$

and

$$\boldsymbol{CB} = (x_2 - x_3)\boldsymbol{i} + (y_2 - y_3)\boldsymbol{j},$$

so when we substitute in Equation 79-16, we get

$$\tfrac{1}{2}\boldsymbol{k} \cdot (\boldsymbol{CA} \times \boldsymbol{CB}) = \tfrac{1}{2} \cdot 1 \cdot \begin{vmatrix} x_1 - x_3 & y_1 - y_3 \\ x_2 - x_3 & y_2 - y_3 \end{vmatrix}.$$

We now expand this second order determinant and simplify, and we obtain the expression on the right of Equation 79-18.

Problems 79

1. Consider the products $(\boldsymbol{i} \times \boldsymbol{i}) \times \boldsymbol{j}$ and $\boldsymbol{i} \times (\boldsymbol{i} \times \boldsymbol{j})$ to show that the associative law does not hold for cross products.
2. Let $\boldsymbol{A} = 2\boldsymbol{i} - 4\boldsymbol{j} + \boldsymbol{k}$, $\boldsymbol{B} = \boldsymbol{i} + \boldsymbol{j} - 3\boldsymbol{k}$, and $\boldsymbol{C} = -\boldsymbol{i} + 2\boldsymbol{j} + 2\boldsymbol{k}$. Compute the following quantities
   (a) $\boldsymbol{A} \cdot \boldsymbol{B}$ (b) $(\boldsymbol{A} + \boldsymbol{B}) \cdot \boldsymbol{C}$
   (c) $\boldsymbol{A} \times \boldsymbol{B}$ (d) $(\boldsymbol{A} \times \boldsymbol{B}) \cdot \boldsymbol{C}$
   (e) $(\boldsymbol{A} \times \boldsymbol{B}) \cdot (\boldsymbol{C} \times \boldsymbol{A})$ (f) $\boldsymbol{A} \cdot (\boldsymbol{B} \times \boldsymbol{C}) - (\boldsymbol{A} \times \boldsymbol{B}) \cdot \boldsymbol{C}$
3. Find the cosine of the angle between the vectors $\boldsymbol{A} = 2\boldsymbol{i} + 2\boldsymbol{j} - \boldsymbol{k}$ and $\boldsymbol{B} = \boldsymbol{i} - 2\boldsymbol{j} + 2\boldsymbol{k}$.
4. Show that the vectors $\boldsymbol{A} = \boldsymbol{i} + 4\boldsymbol{j} + 3\boldsymbol{k}$ and $\boldsymbol{B} = 4\boldsymbol{i} + 2\boldsymbol{j} - 4\boldsymbol{k}$ are perpendicular.
5. Show that the vector $(\boldsymbol{B} \cdot \boldsymbol{B})\boldsymbol{A} - (\boldsymbol{A} \cdot \boldsymbol{B})\boldsymbol{B}$ is perpendicular to $\boldsymbol{B}$.
6. Let $\boldsymbol{A} = 2\boldsymbol{i} - \boldsymbol{j} + \boldsymbol{k}$, $\boldsymbol{B} = \boldsymbol{i} + 2\boldsymbol{j} - \boldsymbol{k}$, and $\boldsymbol{C} = \boldsymbol{i} + \boldsymbol{j} - 2\boldsymbol{k}$. Find a vector that is parallel to the plane of $\boldsymbol{B}$ and $\boldsymbol{C}$ and perpendicular to $\boldsymbol{A}$.
7. Find a vector that is perpendicular to the vectors $\boldsymbol{A} = 2\boldsymbol{i} - \boldsymbol{j} + \boldsymbol{k}$, and $\boldsymbol{B} = 2\boldsymbol{i} + 2\boldsymbol{j} - \boldsymbol{k}$.
8. Find the component of $\boldsymbol{A} = 3\boldsymbol{i} - \boldsymbol{j} + 2\boldsymbol{k}$ along the vector $\boldsymbol{B} = \boldsymbol{i} + 2\boldsymbol{j} - \boldsymbol{k}$.

9. Find the area of the triangle whose vertices in an XY-plane are (1, 1), (5, 4) and (−1, 5).

10. Show that

$$(\boldsymbol{A} \times \boldsymbol{B}) \cdot (\boldsymbol{A} \times \boldsymbol{B}) = \begin{vmatrix} \boldsymbol{A} \cdot \boldsymbol{A} & \boldsymbol{A} \cdot \boldsymbol{B} \\ \boldsymbol{A} \cdot \boldsymbol{B} & \boldsymbol{B} \cdot \boldsymbol{B} \end{vmatrix}$$

11. Convince yourself that the absolute value of the scalar triple product $\boldsymbol{A} \cdot (\boldsymbol{B} \times \boldsymbol{C})$ equals the volume of the parallelopiped (prism) determined by the vectors $\boldsymbol{A}$, $\boldsymbol{B}$, and $\boldsymbol{C}$.

12. Let $\boldsymbol{P}$, $\boldsymbol{Q}$, and $\boldsymbol{R}$ be position vectors to points P, Q, and R. Show that the vector $(\boldsymbol{P} \times \boldsymbol{Q}) + (\boldsymbol{Q} \times \boldsymbol{R}) + (\boldsymbol{R} \times \boldsymbol{P})$ is perpendicular to the plane PQR.

80. Planes

Just as the set of points in the plane whose coordinates satisfy an equation in x and y usually forms a *curve*, so do the points in space whose

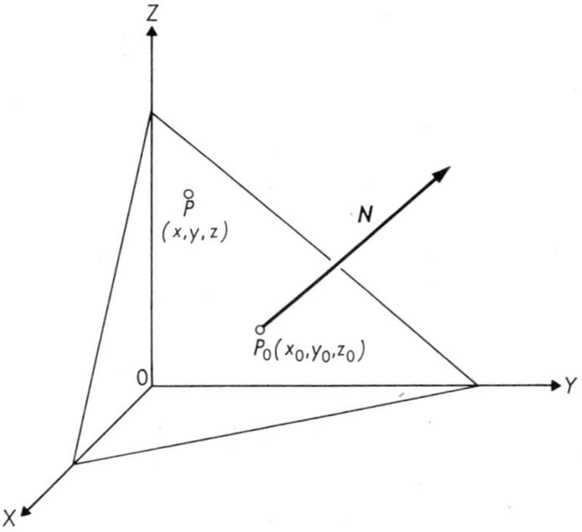

Figure 80-1

coordinates satisfy an equation in x, y, and z usually form a *surface*. For example, we will see that the equation $3x - 2y + 4z = 7$ represents a plane and the equation $x^2 + y^2 + z^2 = 16$ represents the surface of a sphere. In this section we will take up the simplest kind of surfaces—namely, planes.

In plane geometry we determine a line by assigning its direction and specifying one of its points. Similarly, in solid analytic geometry we determine a plane by giving its orientation and specifying one of its points. Thus in Fig. 80-1 we have shown a point P_0 and a vector $\boldsymbol{N}$. These quantities determine the plane consisting of those points P for which the vector $\boldsymbol{P_0P}$ is perpendicular to $\boldsymbol{N}$. The vector $\boldsymbol{N}$ is called a **normal** to the plane. (Note that $\boldsymbol{N}$ need not be a unit vector.) For two vectors to be perpendicular, their dot product must be 0, so

(80-1) $$\boldsymbol{N} \cdot \boldsymbol{P_0P} = 0.$$

This equation is one equation of the plane. Now suppose that the coordinates of P_0 are (x_0, y_0, z_0), the coordinates of P are (x, y, z), and $\boldsymbol{N} = a\boldsymbol{i} + b\boldsymbol{j} + c\boldsymbol{k}$. Then

$$\boldsymbol{P_0P} = (x - x_0)\boldsymbol{i} + (y - y_0)\boldsymbol{j} + (z - z_0)\boldsymbol{k},$$

and Equation 80-1 becomes

(80-2) $$a(x - x_0) + b(y - y_0) + c(z - z_0) = 0.$$

This form of the equation of our plane corresponds to the point-slope form of the equation of a line.

Example 80-1. Find the equation of the plane that contains the point (1, 2, 3) and has the vector $\boldsymbol{N} = 2\boldsymbol{i} - \boldsymbol{j} + 3\boldsymbol{k}$ as a normal.

Solution. Here we have $x_0 = 1$, $y_0 = 2$, $z_0 = 3$, $a = 2$, $b = -1$, and $c = 3$. Hence Equation 80-2 becomes

$$2(x - 1) - (y - 2) + 3(z - 3) = 0.$$

We can rewrite this equation of our plane as

$$2x - y + 3z - 9 = 0.$$

We can expand Equation 80-2 and write it in the form

(80-3) $$ax + by + cz + d = 0,$$

where $d = -ax_0 - by_0 - cz_0$. Notice the similarity between Equation 80-3 and the equation $ax + by + c = 0$ of a line in plane analytic geometry (see Section 9). We can easily determine the slope of such a line from the coefficients of x and y. Similarly, the coefficients of x, y, and z are the components of a vector normal to the plane; that is, the vector $\boldsymbol{N} = a\boldsymbol{i} + b\boldsymbol{j} + c\boldsymbol{k}$ is normal to the plane whose equation is Equation 80-3.

Example 80-2. Discuss the plane whose equation is $2x + y + 3z = 6$.

Solution. A plane is determined by 3 points, and we can find points of a surface by choosing 2 coordinates and solving for the third. Thus if we let $x = 0$ and $y = 0$, we find $z = 2$, and hence the point (0, 0, 2) is one of the points of our plane. We find that two other points are (3, 0, 0) and

(0, 6, 0). These points are the points at which the plane intercepts the axes and Fig. 80-2 shows how they determine the plane. The coefficients of x, y, and z give us a vector that is normal to the plane: $\mathbf{N} = 2\mathbf{i} + \mathbf{j} + 3\mathbf{k}$.

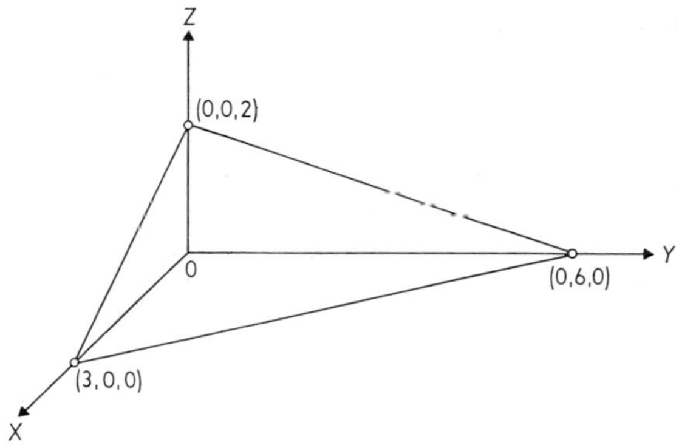

Figure 80-2

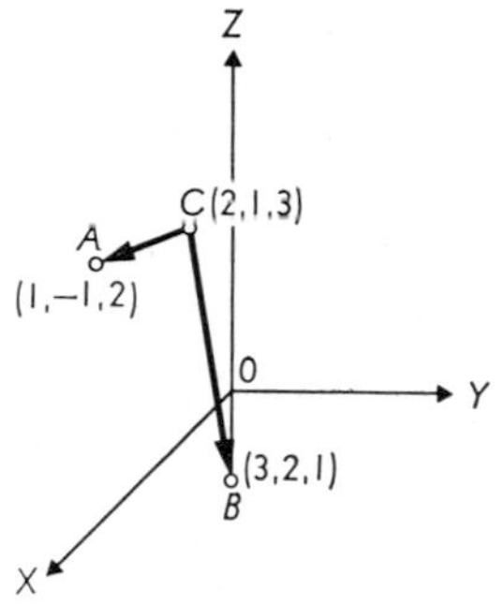

Figure 80-3

Example 80-3. Find the equation of the plane that contains the points $A(1, -1, 2)$, $B(3, 2, 1)$, and $C(2, 1, 3)$.

Solution. Figure 80-3 shows our three points A, B, and C, and we have also drawn the vectors $\mathbf{CA}$ and $\mathbf{CB}$. The vector $\mathbf{CA} \times \mathbf{CB}$ is a vector that is normal to our plane. Since

$$\mathbf{CA} = -\mathbf{i} - 2\mathbf{j} - \mathbf{k},$$

and

$$\mathbf{CB} = \mathbf{i} + \mathbf{j} - 2\mathbf{k},$$

we readily find (with the aid of Equation 79-13) that

$$\mathbf{CA} \times \mathbf{CB} = 5\mathbf{i} - 3\mathbf{j} + \mathbf{k}.$$

If we let the point $A(1, -1, 2)$ play the role of P_0 in Equation 80-1 (either of the points B or C would do as well), and let $\mathbf{N} = \mathbf{CA} \times \mathbf{CB}$, then we obtain the equation of our plane in the form of Equation 80-2:

$$5(x - 1) - 3(y + 1) + (z - 2) = 0.$$

We can rewrite this equation in the form of Equation 80-3 as

$$5x - 3y + z = 10.$$

Example 80-4. Find the distance d between the point (2, 3, 4) and the plane $2x + y + 2z = 2$.

Solution. Our point and plane are shown in Fig. 80-4. We sketched the plane by finding its intercepts (1, 0, 0), (0, 2, 0), and (0, 0, 1). We know that the vector $\boldsymbol{N} = 2\boldsymbol{i} + \boldsymbol{j} + 2\boldsymbol{k}$ is perpendicular to this plane. Therefore, so is $-\boldsymbol{N}$, and if we regard the point (2, 3, 4) as the initial point of the vector $-\boldsymbol{N}$, as shown in Fig. 80-4, we determine a line that intersects the plane at right angles. Now let $\boldsymbol{A}$ denote the vector from our given

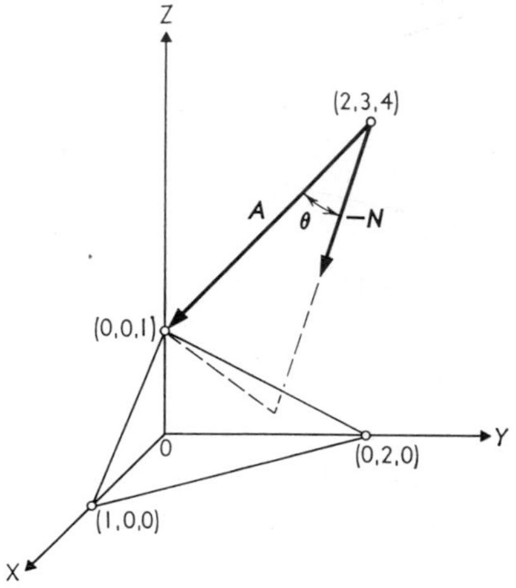

Figure 80-4

point (2, 3, 4) to the point (0, 0, 1) (any other point in the plane would also do). If θ is the angle between $\boldsymbol{A}$ and $-\boldsymbol{N}$, it is clear from our figure that the distance d we want is the absolute value of the number $|\boldsymbol{A}| \cos \theta$; that is, the component of $\boldsymbol{A}$ along $-\boldsymbol{N}$. Hence

$$d = \frac{\boldsymbol{A} \cdot (-\boldsymbol{N})}{|\boldsymbol{N}|} = \frac{(-2\boldsymbol{i} - 3\boldsymbol{j} - 3\boldsymbol{k}) \cdot (-2\boldsymbol{i} - \boldsymbol{j} - 2\boldsymbol{k})}{\sqrt{4 + 1 + 4}}$$

$$= \tfrac{13}{3}.$$

Problems 80

1. Find unit vectors normal to the following planes. Sketch the graphs of the planes.
   (a) $2x + y - 2z = 5$ (b) $3x - 4y = 12$
   (c) $x + y + z = 0$ (d) $y - z - 4x - 7 = 0$

2. Find an equation of the plane for which the given vector is a normal vector and which contains the given point.
   (a) $\boldsymbol{N} = 2\boldsymbol{i} - 3\boldsymbol{j} + \boldsymbol{k}$, (1, 2, 3)
   (b) $\boldsymbol{N} = 3\boldsymbol{i} - \boldsymbol{k}$, (−1, −2, −3)
   (c) $\boldsymbol{N} = \boldsymbol{i}$, (0, 0, 0)
   (d) $\boldsymbol{N} = \boldsymbol{j} + \boldsymbol{k}$, (0, 1, 0)
3. Describe the set of planes such that each plane in the set can be represented by the equation $2x - 3y + 4z + d = 0$ for some number d.
4. Find an equation of the plane that contains the points (1, 0, −1), (2, 3, 1), and (−2, 1, 1).
5. Find an equation of the plane that contains the points (1, 2, 3) and (−2, 1, 1) and which does not intersect the Y-axis.
6. Find a vector that is parallel to the line of intersection of the planes represented by the equations $2x - y + 3z + 12 = 0$ and $x + 2y - z - 17 = 0$.
7. Find an equation of the plane that contains the point (−1, 7, 9) and is parallel to the plane $3x + 4y - z + 6 = 0$.
8. Find the cosine of the angle between the (normals to the) planes represented by the equations $x - 2y + z + 4 = 0$ and $2x - 3y - z + 1 = 0$.
9. Find the distance between the two parallel planes $2x - y + 2z + 3 = 0$ and $2x - y + 2z - 6 = 0$.
10. Find the coordinates of the point P of the plane $2x + y + 2z + 10 = 0$ such that the position vector $\boldsymbol{OP}$ is parallel to the vector $\boldsymbol{i} + \boldsymbol{j} + \boldsymbol{k}$.
11. Find an equation of the plane that is perpendicular to the plane $14x + 2y + 7 = 0$, that contains the origin, and whose normal makes a 45° angle with the Z-axis.
12. Find an equation of the plane that is the set of all points equidistant from the two points (2, 5, −1) and (5, −2, −4).

81. Cylinders. Surfaces of Revolution

The **cylinders** are among the simpler types of surfaces. You can think of a cylinder as being "generated" by the parallel movement of a line perpendicular to a given plane along a curve in that plane. Thus, for example, an ordinary right-circular cylinder (tin can) is generated by moving a line that is perpendicular to the plane of a circle around the circle; a parabolic cylinder is generated by moving a line that is perpendicular to the plane of a parabola along the parabola; and so on. The straight lines are the **generators** of the cylinder.

When the generators are parallel to one of the coordinate axes, the equation of the surface does not involve the corresponding coordinate. For example, the equation $x^2 + z^2 = 4$ represents in space the right circular cylinder whose generators are parallel to the Y-axis (Fig. 81-1). We see, for instance, that every point with coordinates $(\sqrt{2}, y, \sqrt{2})$ (whatever the number y may be) lies in the surface. The collection of all such points forms one generator, the line that is parallel to the Y-axis and contains the point $(\sqrt{2}, 0, \sqrt{2})$.

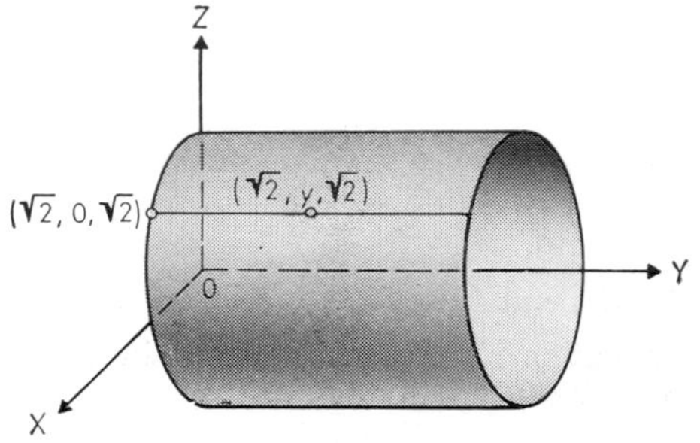

Figure 81-1

To graph a cylindrical surface whose equation is "missing a coordinate" we simply plot the base curve in the appropriate coordinate plane and then "slide" the curve in the direction of the axis of the missing coordinate.

Example 81-1. Plot the surface whose equation is $y^2 = x$.

Solution. Our equation does not involve z, so its graph is a cylinder whose generators are parallel to the Z-axis. We plot the base curve—the parabola whose equation is $y^2 = x$—in the XY-plane (Fig. 81-2). Then we obtain the desired cylinder by sliding the parabola parallel to the Z-axis.

Another simple type of surface consists of the surfaces formed by rotating plane curves about a line. The equation of such a surface of revolution is easy to recognize if the axis of rotation is one of the coordinate axes. For example, let us look at the surface in Fig. 81-3. This surface is obtained by rotating a plane curve about the Z-axis. From the figure we see that planes parallel to the XY-plane intersect the surface in circles. If we let r denote the radius of the circle that is cut by the plane that is z units from the XY-plane, then we have a rule that assigns a number r to each choice of z. Thus we have a function (we can call it f) in which a number $r = f(z)$ corresponds to each number z. To find the number r that corresponds to a given z, we must find the distance of a point (x, y, z) of our surface from the point $(0, 0, z)$ of the Z-axis. Clearly, that distance is

$$r = \sqrt{x^2 + y^2},$$

so the equation $r = f(z)$ becomes

$$\sqrt{x^2 + y^2} = f(z).$$

Thus it appears that the equation of the surface illustrated in Fig. 81-3 contains x and y only in the combination $x^2 + y^2$. In general it is true that if an equation in x, y, and z contains x and y only in the combination

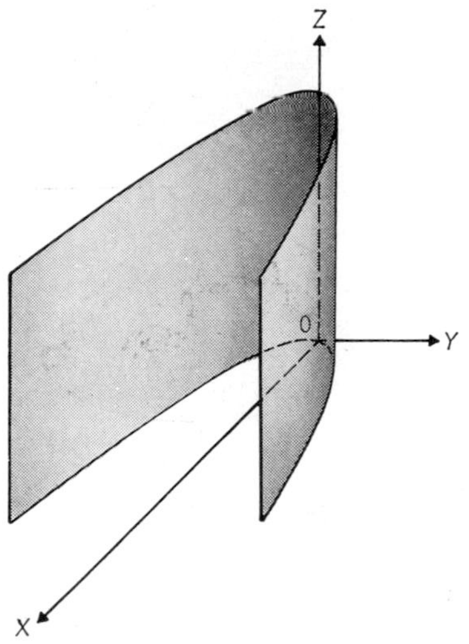

Figure 81-2

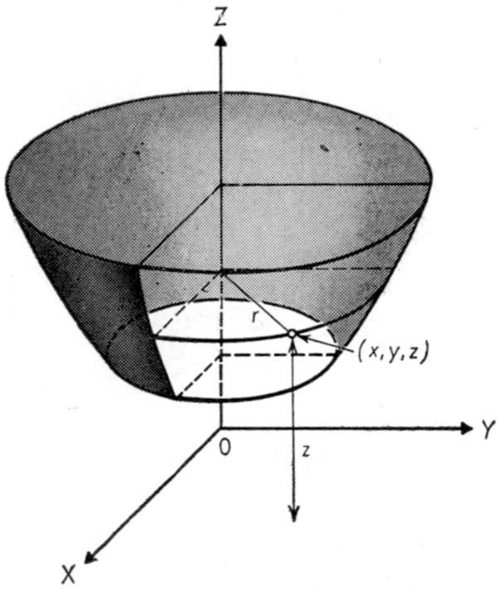

Figure 81-3

$x^2 + y^2$, then the graph of the equation is a surface that may be obtained by revolving a plane curve about the Z-axis. An equation that contains x and z only in the combination $x^2 + z^2$ represents a surface of revolution about the Y-axis, and an equation that contains y and z only in the combination $y^2 + z^2$ represents a surface of revolution about the X-axis.

Example 81-2. Describe the surface whose equation is $y = x^2 + z^2$.

Solution. Since our equation contains x and z only in the combination $x^2 + z^2$, we know that we can obtain its graph by rotating some plane curve about the Y-axis. We can obtain such a plane curve by finding the intersection of our surface with any plane that contains the Y-axis; for example, the YZ-plane. The X-coordinate of every point in the YZ-plane is 0, so the coordinates of a point in that plane have the form $(0, y, z)$. A point whose coordinates are $(0, y, z)$ lies in the surface whose equation is $y = x^2 + z^2$ if, and only if, $y = z^2$. Thus the equation of the plane curve of intersection of our surface with the YZ-plane is $y = z^2$. This curve, as we know, is a parabola. After we plot this parabola in the YZ-plane, we rotate it about the Y-axis to obtain the surface shown in Fig. 81-4.

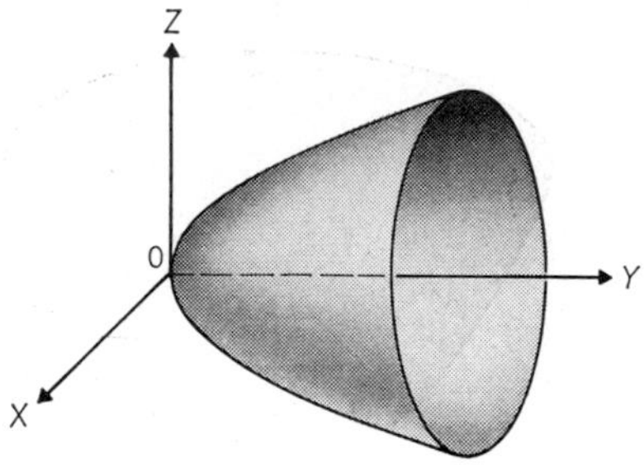

Figure 81-4

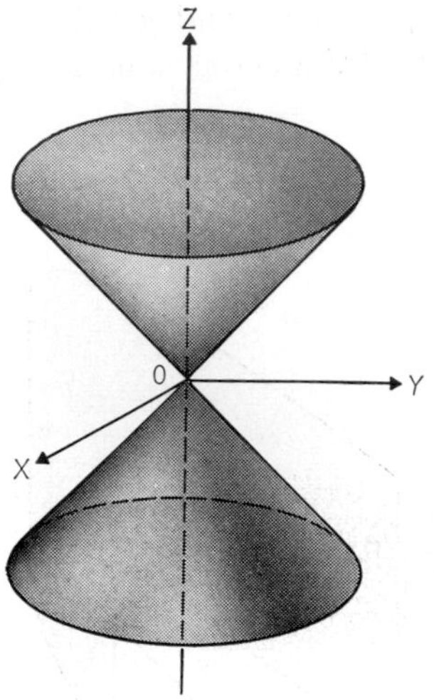

Figure 81-5

Example 81-3. Describe the surface represented by the equation $z^2 = x^2 + y^2$.

Solution. This equation represents a surface of revolution whose axis is the Z-axis. If we set $x = 0$, we obtain the equation of the intersection of the surface of the YZ-plane. Thus the surface intersects the YZ-plane in the curve whose equation is $z^2 = y^2$. Now $z^2 = y^2$ if, and only if, $z = y$ or $z = -y$, and hence the graph of the equation $z^2 = y^2$ consists of two lines in the YZ-plane—one bisecting the first quadrant and one bisecting the second quadrant. When we rotate these lines about the Z-axis, we get the cone shown in Fig. 81-5.

From Examples 81-2 and 81-3 we see how to find the equation of a plane curve that generates a given surface of revolution. We simply replace $x^2 + y^2$ with x^2 or y^2 (or $y^2 + z^2$ with y^2 or z^2, and so on). Conversely, if we wish to find the equation of the surface of revolution that results when we rotate a given plane curve about an axis, then we replace x^2 with $x^2 + y^2$, and so on.

Example 81-4. Find the equation of the surface that is generated by rotating the circle $(y - 2)^2 + z^2 = 1$ about the Y-axis.

Solution. Here we simply replace z^2 with $x^2 + z^2$ to obtain the equation $(y - 2)^2 + x^2 + z^2 = 1$. This surface is shown in Fig. 81-6.

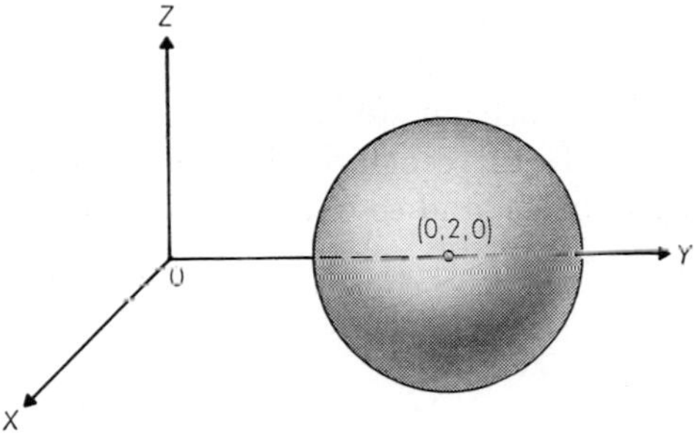

Figure 81-6

Problems 81

1. Sketch the following cylinders.
   (a) $3y + 2z = 6$ (b) $(x - 2)^2 + y^2 = 4$
   (c) $z = 4 - y^2$ (d) $z = x^3$
   (e) $z = |y|$ (f) $z = \cos \pi y$

2. Find the equation of the surface that results when we rotate the plane graph of the given equation about the indicated axis.
   (a) $z = x^2$, Z-axis (b) $y = x$, X-axis
   (c) $y^2/4 + z^2/9 = 1$, Y-axis (d) $y^2/4 - z^2/9 = 1$, Z-axis
   (e) $z = x^2$, X-axis (f) $y = mx + b$, X-axis

3. Sketch the graphs of the following equations.
   (a) $4x^2 - y^2 - z^2 = 4$ (b) $3 - z = 2(x^2 + y^2)$
   (c) $4z^2 = x^2 + y^2$ (d) $9x^2 + 4y^2 + 9z^2 = 36$
   (e) $x^2 + z^2 = \sin^2 y$ (f) $(x^2 + y^2)^2 = 1 - z^2$

4. Describe the surface whose equation is $9(x - 1)^2 + 9(y + 1)^2 + 4(z - 3)^2 = 36$.

5. Let $b > r > 0$. Then the graph of the equation $y^2 + (z - b)^2 = r^2$ is a circle in the YZ-plane. If we rotate this circle about the Y-axis, we get a doughnut-shaped figure called a **torus.** Find the equation of our torus and make a sketch showing the surface.

6. The cardioid in the XY-plane whose polar coordinate equation in the XY-plane is $r = 2(1 - \cos \theta)$ is rotated about the X-axis. Find the equation of the resulting surface.

7. Describe the surface that is the set of all points that are equidistant from the Y-axis and the plane whose equation is $x = 4$.

8. Use the methods we discussed in Section 77 to find the area of the surface whose equation is $9x^2 + 9y^2 + 25z^2 = 225$.

82. Quadric Surfaces

In our study of plane analytic geometry we considered the graphs of quadratic equations; that is, equations of the form $Ax^2 + Bxy + Cy^2 + Dx + Ey + F = 0$. We found that by suitably translating and rotating axes we could reduce our study to equations in certain "standard" forms, and we are able to recognize the standard forms of the equations of ellipses, hyperbolas, and so on. In this section we will briefly discuss the

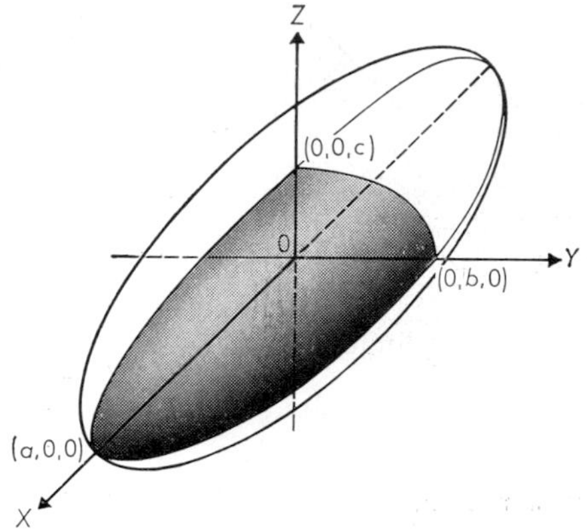

Figure 82-1

standard forms for analogous figures in space. These figures, whose equations are quadratic equations in x, y, and z, are called **quadric surfaces.**

A surface whose equation has the form

$$\frac{x^2}{a^2} + \frac{y^2}{b^2} + \frac{z^2}{c^2} = 1 \tag{82-1}$$

is called an **ellipsoid.** We obtain the curves of intersection of this figure with the coordinate planes by setting x, y, and z equal to 0, one at a time. These curves of intersection are ellipses. In fact, it is not hard to see that every plane that is parallel to one of the coordinate planes, and that intersects our ellipsoid, intersects it in an ellipse. Figure 82-1 shows the graph of Equation 82-1. You will notice that if $a = b = c$, then Equation 82-1 represents the sphere of radius a whose center is the origin.

The surface represented by Equation 82-1 intersects all three coordinate planes in ellipses. A surface whose equation has the form

$$\frac{x^2}{a^2} + \frac{y^2}{b^2} - \frac{z^2}{c^2} = 1 \tag{82-2}$$

intersects the XY-plane in an ellipse, but it intersects the other two coordinate planes in hyperbolas. Such a surface is called a **hyperboloid of one sheet,** and it is shown in Fig. 82-2. If x and z (or y and z) are interchanged in Equation 82-2, we still obtain a hyperboloid of one sheet but its axis is then the X-axis (or the Y-axis).

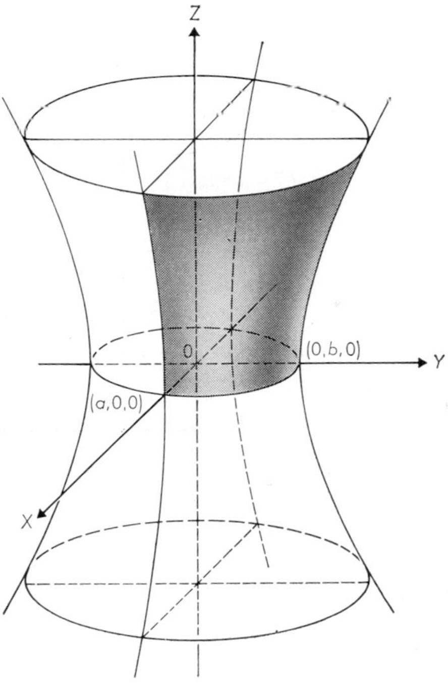

Figure 82-2

A surface whose equation has the form

$$\frac{x^2}{a^2} - \frac{y^2}{b^2} - \frac{z^2}{c^2} = 1 \tag{82-3}$$

intersects the XY- and XZ-planes in hyperbolas, but it doesn't intersect the YZ-plane at all (for no point with coordinates $(0, y, z)$ can satisfy Equation 82-3). However, a plane $x = k$, where $k^2 > a^2$, intersects the surface in an ellipse. For if (k, y, z) is a point of such a plane, then y and z satisfy the equation

$$\frac{k^2}{a^2} - \frac{y^2}{b^2} - \frac{z^2}{c^2} = 1,$$

which can be written in the standard form of the equation of an ellipse:

$$\frac{y^2}{b^2(k^2 - a^2)/a^2} + \frac{z^2}{c^2(k^2 - a^2)/a^2} = 1.$$

The surface represented by Equation 82-3 is called a **hyperboloid of two sheets,** and Fig. 82-3 shows what such a surface looks like.

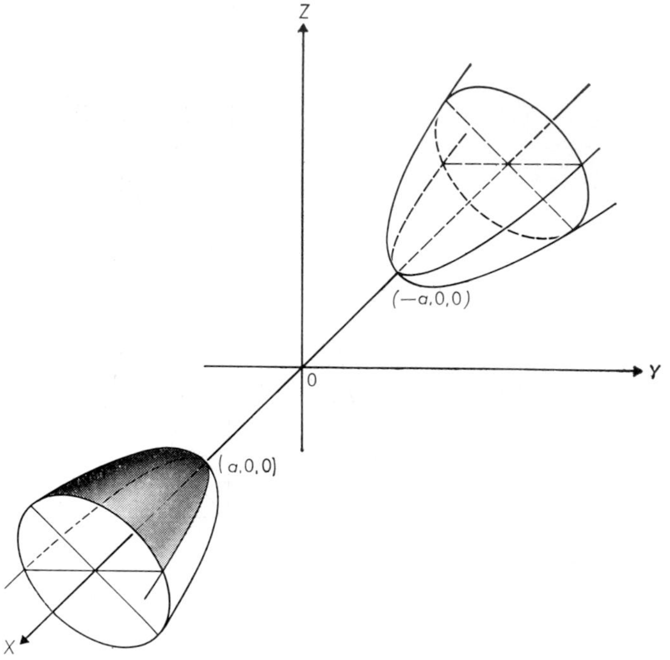

Figure 82-3

Corresponding to the parabola in two dimensions we have the **elliptic paraboloid** in three dimensions. The equation

(82-4) $$\boldsymbol{z = \frac{x^2}{a^2} + \frac{y^2}{b^2}}$$

represents such a surface. We notice that the XZ-plane cuts the surface in the parabola whose equation is $z = x^2/a^2$, and the YZ-plane cuts it in the parabola whose equation is $z = y^2/b^2$. Each plane $z = k$, where $k > 0$, cuts the surface in an ellipse. In Fig. 82-4 we have drawn the graph of Equation 82-4.

If the elliptical cross sections of an ellipsoid, hyperboloid, or elliptical paraboloid are circles, then the surface is merely a surface of revolution. Our next surface does not resemble a surface of revolution in any way.

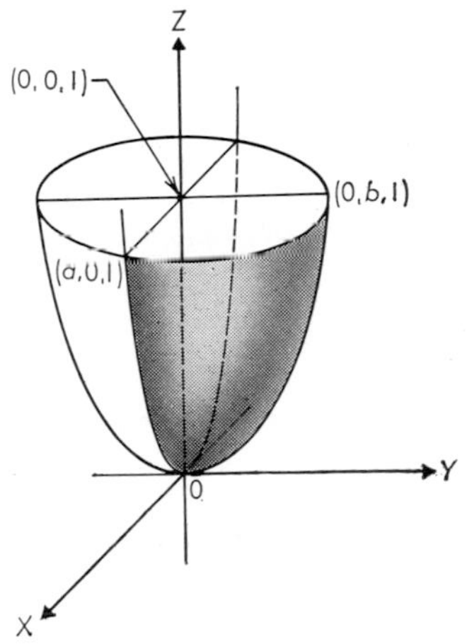

Figure 82-4

The equation

$$(82\text{-}5) \qquad \boldsymbol{z + \frac{x^2}{a^2} - \frac{y^2}{b^2} = 0}$$

represents a **hyperbolic paraboloid.** This surface intersects the YZ-plane in the parabola $z = y^2/b^2$ and the XZ-plane in the parabola $z = -x^2/a^2$. It intersects planes parallel to the XY-plane in hyperbolas, as shown in Fig. 82-5.

As a final quadric surface, we consider the **elliptical cone** whose equation is

$$(82\text{-}6) \qquad \boldsymbol{\frac{x^2}{a^2} + \frac{y^2}{b^2} = \frac{z^2}{c^2}}.$$

If $x = 0$, we see that either $z = cy/b$ or $z = -cy/b$. Thus the surface intersects the YZ-plane in the two lines represented by these last equations. Similarly, the surface intersects the XZ-plane in the lines with equations $z = cx/a$ and $z = -cx/a$. Planes parallel to the XY-plane cut the surface in ellipses.

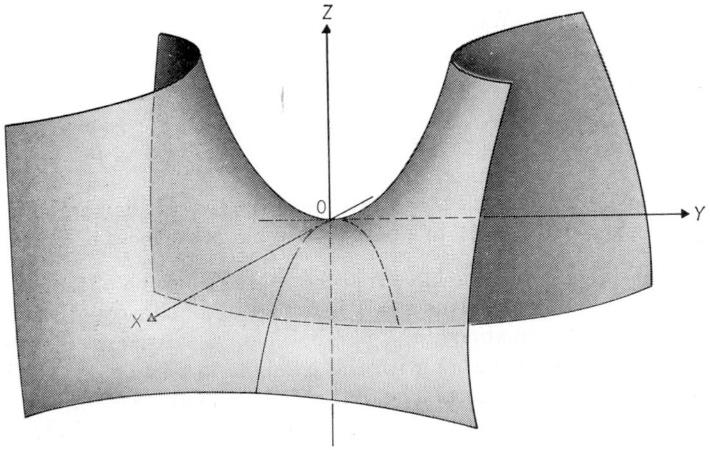

Figure 82-5

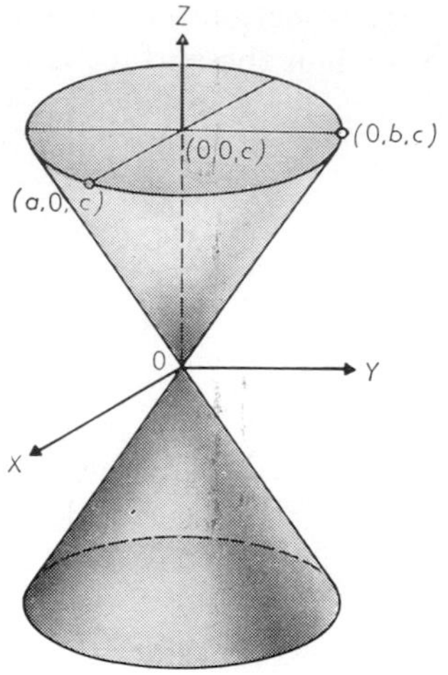

Figure 82-6

Figure 82-6 shows the surface represented by Equation 82-6. If $a = b$, the surface is a **right circular cone.**

Example 82-1. The dimensions of the smallest rectangular box that will hold a certain ellipsoidal cheese are $10'' \times 8'' \times 6''$. What is the equation of the surface of the cheese? (Assume the diameters of the ellipsoid are parallel to the edges of the box.)

Solution. Since our cheese is an ellipsoid, its equation will have the form of Equation 82-1. We are to find the numbers a, b, and c. These numbers are the semi-diameters of the ellipses that are cut from our surface by the coordinate planes. We can set up a coordinate system such that $a = 5$, $b = 4$, and $c = 3$, and in this coordinate system our surface has the equation

$$\frac{x^2}{25} + \frac{y^2}{16} + \frac{z^2}{9} = 1.$$

Example 82-2. The plane $z = 1$ intersects the hyperbolic paraboloid whose equation is $x = 6y^2 - 4z^2$ in a parabola. What is the focus of this parabola?

Solution. When $z = 1$, we have $x = 6y^2 - 4$. The graph of the intersection of the surface and the plane $z = 1$ is the graph of this equation, as shown in Fig. 82-7. The equation of this parabola can be written as $x + 4 = 4 \cdot \frac{3}{2}y^2$, so we know from our work with the parabola in Section 34 that its focus is $\frac{3}{2}$ units from the vertex. The vertex is the point $(-4, 0)$, and thus the X-coordinate of the focus is $-4 + \frac{3}{2} = -\frac{5}{2}$. The Y-coordinate is 0, and of course the Z-coordinate is 1. Therefore, the point we were asked to find is the point $(-\frac{5}{2}, 0, 1)$.

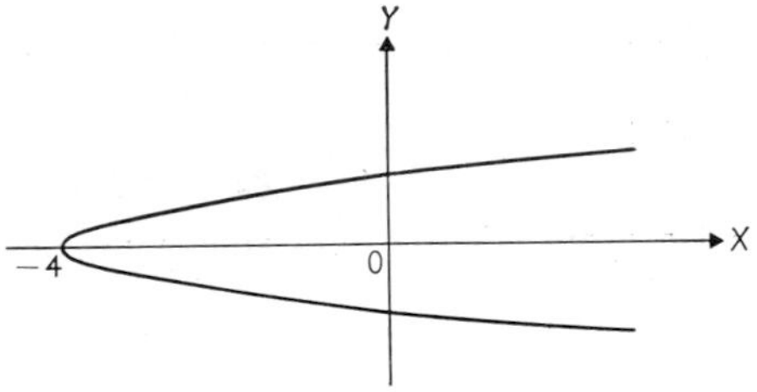

Figure 82-7

Example 82-3. Find the equation of the surface of the sphere whose radius is r and whose center is the point (h, k, l).

Solution. A point (x, y, z) is in the desired surface if, and only if, the distance between (x, y, z) and (h, k, l) is r units; that is,

$$\sqrt{(x-h)^2 + (y-k)^2 + (z-l)^2} = r.$$

We usually write this equation in the form

$$(x-h)^2 + (y-k)^2 + (z-l)^2 = r^2. \tag{82-7}$$

Problems 82

1. Describe the graphs of the following equations, and sketch that part of each surface that lies in the first octant.
(a) $x^2 + 2y^2 + 3z^2 = 6$
(b) $9y^2 - 36z^2 = 36 + 4x^2$
(c) $\dfrac{x^2}{9} + \dfrac{z^2}{16} = 1 + \dfrac{y^2}{25}$
(d) $4x = 4y^2 + z^2$
(e) $4y^2 = x^2 + 4z^2$
(f) $x + z^2 = y^2$

2. When the hyperbolic paraboloid represented by the equation $z = \dfrac{x^2}{4} - \dfrac{y^2}{9}$ is intersected by the following planes, we obtain familiar plane curves. Name these curves, find the coordinates of their vertices, and use the resulting information to sketch the hyperbolic paraboloid.
(a) the YZ-plane
(b) the XY-plane
(c) the plane parallel to the XZ-plane and 3 units to its right
(d) the plane parallel to the XY-plane and 1 unit below it
(e) the plane parallel to the YZ-plane and 4 units in front of it

3. Find numbers A, B, C, and D such that the quadric surface whose equation is $Ax^2 + By^2 + Cz^2 + D = 0$ contains the following points. Name the surface.
(a) $(1, 1, -1)$, $(2, 1, 0)$, $(5, -5, 3)$
(b) $(2, -1, 1)$, $(-3, 0, 0)$, $(1, -1, -2)$
(c) $(1, 2, -1)$, $(0, 1, 0)$, $(3, 1, -2)$

4. Find the center and radius of the sphere represented by the equation:
(a) $x^2 + y^2 + z^2 - 2x + 2y - 2 = 0$
(b) $x^2 + y^2 + z^2 - x - 2y - 4z + 3 = 0$

5. Find the equation of the plane that is tangent to the given sphere at the given point.
   (a) $x^2 + y^2 + z^2 = 9$, $(1, 2, 2)$
   (b) $x^2 + y^2 + z^2 - 10x + 4y - 6z - 187 = 0$, $(-9, 3, 1)$
6. Discuss the graphs of the following equations. (*Hint:* First complete the square.)
   (a) $x^2 + 4y^2 - 9z^2 - 2x - 16y - 19 = 0$
   (b) $x^2 + z^2 + 2x - 4y - 2z + 6 = 0$
   (c) $x^2 - y^2 - z^2 - 2x - 2y + 2z - 2 = 0$
7. Let the point (x, y, z) be at a distance d_1 from the point $(0, 2, 0)$ and at a distance d_2 from the plane $y = -2$. Find the equation of the surface that contains the point (x, y, z) in the following cases. Describe the surface.
   (a) $d_1 = d_2$ (b) $d_1 = 2d_2$ (c) $d_2 = 2d_1$
8. Find the equation of the surface that contains the point (x, y, z) and describe the surface if:
   (a) the square of the distance from the point to the Y-axis is $\frac{2}{5}$ the distance from the point to the XZ-plane.
   (b) the distance from the point to the origin is $\frac{3}{2}$ its distance from the Z-axis.
9. Prove that a point the sum of whose distances from two fixed points is a given number belongs to an ellipsoid of revolution.
10. Prove that a point the difference of whose distances from two fixed points is a given number belongs to a hyperboloid of revolution.

83. Space Curves

The graph of a function $\boldsymbol{F}$ whose values are vectors in three-dimensional space is obtained in exactly the same way that we found the graphs of vector-valued functions in two dimensions in Section 74. Thus for each number t in the domain of $\boldsymbol{F}$ we plot the terminal point of the position vector $\boldsymbol{R} = \boldsymbol{F}(t)$. The set of all such points is the graph of $\boldsymbol{F}$, and in general we will find that these points form a curve in space. As in Section 74, if we write the vector equation

$$\boldsymbol{R} = \boldsymbol{F}(t) \tag{83-1}$$

in terms of the components of the vectors involved, then

$$x\boldsymbol{i} + y\boldsymbol{j} + z\boldsymbol{k} = F_x(t)\boldsymbol{i} + F_y(t)\boldsymbol{j} + F_z(t)\boldsymbol{k}.$$

Thus the vector Equation 83-1 yields three scalar equations, called **parametric equations** of the graph;

$$x = F_x(t) \quad y = F_y(t) \quad z = F_z(t). \tag{83-2}$$

Example 83-1. Graph the vector equation $\boldsymbol{R} = a \cos t\,\boldsymbol{i} + b \sin t\,\boldsymbol{j} + t\boldsymbol{k}$.

Solution. We construct the table of values shown in Fig. 83-1, plot the terminal points of these vectors, and join the plotted points to form the curve shown in the figure. This curve is called a **helix.** Parametric equations of our helix are

$$x = a \cos t,$$
$$y = b \sin t,$$
$$z = t.$$

If (x, y, z) is any point of our helix, we see that $\dfrac{x^2}{a^2} + \dfrac{y^2}{b^2} = 1$, and so our

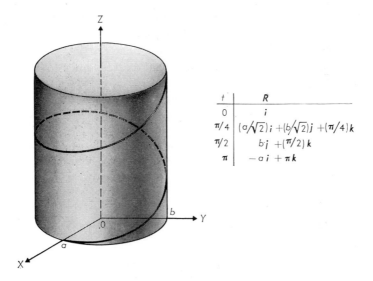

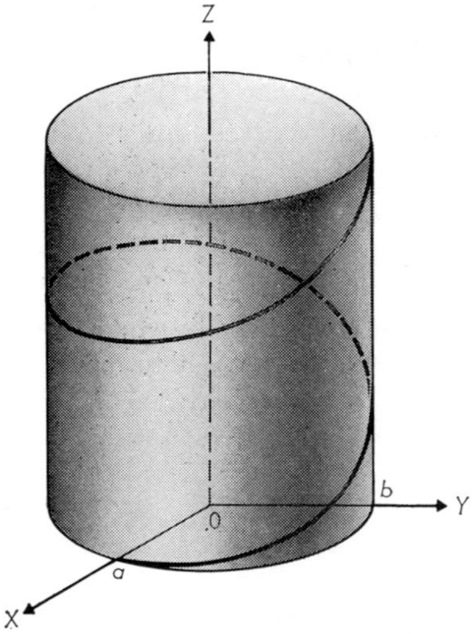

t	R
0	i
$\pi/4$	$(a/\sqrt{2})i + (b/\sqrt{2})j + (\pi/4)k$
$\pi/2$	$bj + (\pi/2)k$
π	$-ai + \pi k$

Figure 83-1

helix lies in an elliptical cylinder whose generators are parallel to the Z-axis. The helix forms a "barber's pole stripe" in this cylinder. In particular, if $b = a$ the helix is called a *circular helix*, and it lies in the right-circular cylinder whose equation is $x^2 + y^2 = a^2$.

As in the case of vectors in the plane, we define the derivative $\boldsymbol{F}'(t)$ by means of the equation (see Equation 75-2)

(83-3) $$\boldsymbol{F}'(t) = \lim_{h\to 0} \frac{\boldsymbol{F}(t + h) - \boldsymbol{F}(t)}{h}.$$

It can be shown that

(83-4) $$\boldsymbol{F}'(t) = F_x'(t)\boldsymbol{i} + F_y'(t)\boldsymbol{j} + F_z'(t)\boldsymbol{k}.$$

Again we find that the usual rules concerning sums and products, and the chain rule are valid (see Equations 75-4, 75-5, and 75-6). In particular, the usual product rules apply when we differentiate the cross product and the scalar triple product:

(83-5) $$D_t(\boldsymbol{F}(t) \times \boldsymbol{G}(t)) = \boldsymbol{F}(t) \times \boldsymbol{G}'(t) + \boldsymbol{F}'(t) \times \boldsymbol{G}(t),$$

(83-6) $$D_t[\boldsymbol{F}(t) \cdot (\boldsymbol{G}(t) \times \boldsymbol{H}(t))] = \boldsymbol{F}'(t) \cdot (\boldsymbol{G}(t) \times \boldsymbol{H}(t)) + \boldsymbol{F}(t) \cdot (\boldsymbol{G}'(t) \times \boldsymbol{H}(t)) + \boldsymbol{F}(t) \cdot (\boldsymbol{G}(t) \times \boldsymbol{H}'(t)).$$

The vector $\boldsymbol{F}'(t)$ plays the same role relative to space curves that it does relative to plane curves. Thus *$\boldsymbol{F}'(t)$ is a vector tangent to the graph of $\boldsymbol{F}$.* If the parameter t measures time and we consider our space curve to be the path of a moving particle, then the number $|\boldsymbol{F}'(t)|$ is the *speed* of the particle. The vector $\boldsymbol{V} = \boldsymbol{F}'(t)$ is the *velocity* of the particle and the vector $\boldsymbol{A} = \boldsymbol{F}''(t)$ is the *acceleration* of the particle.

If L is the length of the arc that corresponds to the parameter interval $[a, b]$, then

(83-7) $$L = \int_a^b |\boldsymbol{F}'(t)|\, dt = \int_a^b \sqrt{x'^2 + y'^2 + z'^2}\, dt.$$

Example 83-2. The portion of the circular helix whose equation is $\boldsymbol{R} = \cos t\,\boldsymbol{i} + \sin t\,\boldsymbol{j} + t\boldsymbol{k}$ that corresponds to the T-interval $[0, 2\pi]$ makes one complete circuit about the Z-axis. How long is this arc?

Solution. Here $\boldsymbol{F}'(t) = -\sin t\,\boldsymbol{i} + \cos t\,\boldsymbol{j} + \boldsymbol{k}$. Hence

$$|\boldsymbol{F}'(t)| = \sqrt{\sin^2 t + \cos^2 t + 1} = \sqrt{2},$$

and Equation 83-7 gives us

$$L = \int_0^{2\pi} \sqrt{2}\, dt = \sqrt{2}\, 2\pi \approx 8.9.$$

Example 83-3. Interpret the circular helix of the preceding example as the path of a moving particle (with t measuring time). Show that the particle moves with a constant speed, and find its acceleration.

Solution. We found in the preceding example that $|\boldsymbol{F}'(t)| = \sqrt{2}$, and that number is the speed of the particle. Thus if we measure distance in feet and time in seconds, then the particle is moving at the rate of $\sqrt{2}$ feet per second. The acceleration of the particle is given by the equation

$$\boldsymbol{A} = -\cos t\,\boldsymbol{i} - \sin t\,\boldsymbol{j}.$$

If we let s denote the length of the arc joining the endpoints of the vectors $\boldsymbol{F}(a)$ and $\boldsymbol{F}(t)$ (see Equation 75-7), then

$$s = \int_a^t |\boldsymbol{F}'(u)|\, du,$$

and

$$ds/dt = |\boldsymbol{F}'(t)| = \sqrt{x'^2 + y'^2 + z'^2}.$$

The vector $\boldsymbol{T}$ defined by the equation

(83-8) $$\boldsymbol{T} = \frac{\boldsymbol{F}'(t)}{|\boldsymbol{F}'(t)|} = \frac{d\boldsymbol{R}}{ds}$$

is called the **unit tangent** to the graph of the equation $\boldsymbol{R} = \boldsymbol{F}(t)$.

As in the two-dimensional case, if a vector has the same length at each point of an interval, then it is perpendicular to its derivative. In particular, since the length of the vector $\boldsymbol{T}$ is always 1, $\frac{d\boldsymbol{T}}{ds}$ is perpendicular to $\boldsymbol{T}$. If we use the two-dimensional case (Section 76) as a model, we can define the **unit normal** $\boldsymbol{N}$ and the **curvature** κ of a space curve so that they satisfy the equation

(83-9) $$\frac{d\boldsymbol{T}}{ds} = \kappa \boldsymbol{N}.$$

In order to completely determine the direction of $\boldsymbol{N}$, we arbitrarily specify that the curvature κ shall be non-negative; that is, $\kappa \geq 0$. Then

(83-10) $$\kappa = \left|\frac{d\boldsymbol{T}}{ds}\right| = \left|\frac{d\boldsymbol{T}}{dt}\frac{dt}{ds}\right| = \left|\frac{d\boldsymbol{T}}{dt}\right| \Big/ \left|\frac{d\boldsymbol{R}}{dt}\right|.$$

Since $\boldsymbol{N}$ is perpendicular to $\boldsymbol{T}$, we see that $|\boldsymbol{T} \times \boldsymbol{N}| = |\boldsymbol{T}|\,|\boldsymbol{N}| \sin 90° = 1 \cdot 1 \cdot 1 = 1$. The unit vector $\boldsymbol{B}$ defined by the equation

(83-11) $$\boldsymbol{B} = \boldsymbol{T} \times \boldsymbol{N}$$

is called the **unit binormal** to the curve. The three unit vectors $\boldsymbol{T}$, $\boldsymbol{N}$, and $\boldsymbol{B}$ are basic vectors that are used to study space curves. In addition to Equation 83-11, it is easy to see that $\boldsymbol{N} = \boldsymbol{B} \times \boldsymbol{T}$ and $\boldsymbol{T} = \boldsymbol{N} \times \boldsymbol{B}$.

Example 83-4. Find the three basic vectors $\boldsymbol{T}$, $\boldsymbol{N}$, and $\boldsymbol{B}$ associated with the circular helix of Example 83-2 and find the curvature of that helix.

Solution. Again let us use primes to denote differentiation with respect to our parameter t. Then

$$\boldsymbol{R}' = -\sin t\,\boldsymbol{i} + \cos t\,\boldsymbol{j} + \boldsymbol{k}, \quad \text{and} \quad |\boldsymbol{R}'| = \sqrt{2}.$$

Thus

$$\boldsymbol{T} = \frac{\boldsymbol{R}'}{|\boldsymbol{R}'|} = \frac{1}{\sqrt{2}}(-\sin t\,\boldsymbol{i} + \cos t\,\boldsymbol{j} + \boldsymbol{k}).$$

Hence

$$\boldsymbol{T}' = \frac{1}{\sqrt{2}}(-\cos t\,\boldsymbol{i} - \sin t\,\boldsymbol{j}),$$

and so

$$|\boldsymbol{T}'| = \frac{1}{\sqrt{2}}.$$

We see from Equation 83-10 that

$$\kappa = \frac{|\boldsymbol{T}'|}{|\boldsymbol{R}'|} = \frac{1/\sqrt{2}}{\sqrt{2}} = \tfrac{1}{2}.$$

Now

$$\frac{\boldsymbol{T}'}{|\boldsymbol{R}'|} = (\tfrac{1}{2})(-\cos t\,\boldsymbol{i} - \sin t\,\boldsymbol{j}) = \kappa \boldsymbol{N},$$

so

$$\boldsymbol{N} = -\cos t\,\boldsymbol{i} - \sin t\,\boldsymbol{j}.$$

It then follows that

$$\boldsymbol{B} = \boldsymbol{T} \times \boldsymbol{N} = \begin{vmatrix} \frac{\cos t}{\sqrt{2}} & \frac{1}{\sqrt{2}} \\ -\sin t & 0 \end{vmatrix} \boldsymbol{i} - \begin{vmatrix} -\frac{\sin t}{\sqrt{2}} & \frac{1}{\sqrt{2}} \\ -\cos t & 0 \end{vmatrix} \boldsymbol{j} + \begin{vmatrix} -\frac{\sin t}{\sqrt{2}} & \frac{\cos t}{\sqrt{2}} \\ -\cos t & -\sin t \end{vmatrix} \boldsymbol{k}$$

$$= \frac{1}{\sqrt{2}}(\sin t\,\boldsymbol{i} - \cos t\,\boldsymbol{j} + \boldsymbol{k}).$$

Example 83-5. We know that $d\boldsymbol{T}/ds = \kappa\boldsymbol{N}$. Find expressions for $d\boldsymbol{N}/ds$ and $d\boldsymbol{B}/ds$.

Solution. Since $\boldsymbol{B}$ is 1 unit long, we know that $d\boldsymbol{B}/ds$ is perpendicular to $\boldsymbol{B}$. Also, $\boldsymbol{T} \cdot \boldsymbol{B} = 0$, and when we differentiate this equation, we obtain the equation $\boldsymbol{T} \cdot d\boldsymbol{B}/ds + \kappa\boldsymbol{N} \cdot \boldsymbol{B} = 0$. Thus, since $\boldsymbol{N} \cdot \boldsymbol{B} = 0$, we have $\boldsymbol{T} \cdot d\boldsymbol{B}/ds = 0$. So we see that $d\boldsymbol{B}/ds$ is perpendicular to both $\boldsymbol{B}$ and $\boldsymbol{T}$, and it must therefore lie along the line determined by the vector $\boldsymbol{N}$. Thus $d\boldsymbol{B}/ds$ is a scalar multiple of $\boldsymbol{N}$. The negative of the scalar by which we multiply $\boldsymbol{N}$ to obtain $d\boldsymbol{B}/ds$ is termed the **torsion** of the curve, and it is denoted by the Greek letter τ. Thus we write

$$\text{(83-12)} \qquad \frac{d\boldsymbol{B}}{ds} = -\tau\boldsymbol{N}.$$

Then

$$\frac{dN}{ds} = \frac{d}{ds}(\boldsymbol{B} \times \boldsymbol{T}) = \boldsymbol{B} \times \kappa\boldsymbol{N} + (-\tau\boldsymbol{N}) \times \boldsymbol{T}$$

$$= \tau\boldsymbol{B} - \kappa\boldsymbol{T}.$$

The three formulas

(83-13) $$\frac{d\boldsymbol{T}}{ds} = \kappa\boldsymbol{N}, \quad \frac{d\boldsymbol{N}}{ds} = \tau\boldsymbol{B} - \kappa\boldsymbol{T}, \quad \text{and} \quad \frac{d\boldsymbol{B}}{ds} = -\tau\boldsymbol{N}$$

are called the *Frenet Formulas*. They are of fundamental importance in the study of curves in space.

Problems 83

1. Find the unit tangent vector $\boldsymbol{T}$ at the point corresponding to $t = \pi/2$. Also find the length of the arc corresponding to the T-interval $[0, \pi]$.
   (a) $\boldsymbol{R} = e^t \cos t\,\boldsymbol{i} + e^t \sin t\,\boldsymbol{j} + e^t\boldsymbol{k}$
   (b) $\boldsymbol{R} = \cos 2t\,\boldsymbol{i} + \sin 2t\,\boldsymbol{j} + 3t\boldsymbol{k}$
   (c) $\boldsymbol{R} = 3t \cos t\,\boldsymbol{i} + 3t \sin t\,\boldsymbol{j} + 4t\boldsymbol{k}$
   (d) $\boldsymbol{R} = \cos t/4\,\boldsymbol{i} + \sin t/4\,\boldsymbol{j} + \ln(\cos t/4)\boldsymbol{k}$
2. The helix $\boldsymbol{R} = \cos t\,\boldsymbol{i} + \sin t\,\boldsymbol{j} + t\boldsymbol{k}$ intersects the graph of the equation $\boldsymbol{R} = (1 - 2t)\boldsymbol{i} - (t^2 - 2t)\boldsymbol{j} + (t^3 + t)\boldsymbol{k}$ at the point $(1, 0, 0)$. What is the angle between the tangents at this point?
3. Find a unit vector that is tangent to the graph of the equation $\boldsymbol{R} = (t - 1)\boldsymbol{i} + (t^2 + t)\boldsymbol{j} + t^4\boldsymbol{k}$ at the point where the curve intersects the YZ-plane.
4. The three-dimensional graphs of the equations $y = \sin x$ and $z = \cos x$ are cylinders. Write a vector equation of the curve of intersection of these two cylinders.
5. Find the length of the graph of the equation $\boldsymbol{R} = t\boldsymbol{i} + \frac{t^2}{\sqrt{2}}\boldsymbol{j} + \frac{t^3}{3}\boldsymbol{k}$ for t in the interval $[0, 2]$.
6. The position vector of a point moving in space is $\boldsymbol{R} = \cos t\,\boldsymbol{i} + \sin t\,\boldsymbol{j} + t\boldsymbol{k}$, where we measure time in seconds and distance in feet. When $t = \pi/4$, we release the particle and it flies off on a tangent. Where is it when $t = \pi/2$?
7. Let $\boldsymbol{C}$ be a given vector, independent of t; for example, $\boldsymbol{C} = 3\boldsymbol{i} + 4\boldsymbol{j} + \boldsymbol{k}$. Describe the relation between the graphs of the equations $\boldsymbol{R} = \boldsymbol{F}(t)$ and $\boldsymbol{R} = \boldsymbol{F}(t) + \boldsymbol{C}$.
8. Show that the curvature is equal to the torsion at all points of the graph of the equation $\boldsymbol{R} = (3t - t^3)\boldsymbol{i} + 3t^2\boldsymbol{j} + (3t + t^3)\boldsymbol{k}$. What is the curvature at the origin?
9. Find the 3 basic vectors $\boldsymbol{T}$, $\boldsymbol{N}$, and $\boldsymbol{B}$, associated with the graph of the equation $\boldsymbol{R} = \cosh t\,\boldsymbol{i} + \sinh t\,\boldsymbol{j} + t\boldsymbol{k}$.
10. Find:
    (a) $D_t(\boldsymbol{F}(t) \times \boldsymbol{F}'(t))$
    (b) $D_t[\boldsymbol{F}(t) \cdot (\boldsymbol{F}'(t) \times \boldsymbol{F}''(t))]$
    (c) $D_t|\boldsymbol{F}(t)|$
    (d) $D_t[(\boldsymbol{F}(t) \times \boldsymbol{F}'(t)) \cdot \boldsymbol{F}'(t)]$

11. The number $|dN/ds|$ is called the **screw curvature.** Express the screw curvature in terms of the curvature and torsion.
12. Express d^3R/ds^3 in terms of T, N, and B.
13. Compute the following numbers if primes denote differentiation with respect to s.
(a) $T' \cdot B'$ (b) $R' \cdot R''$ (c) $R' \cdot R'''$
(d) $R'' \cdot R'''$ (e) $(R' \times R'') \cdot R'''$

84. Lines in Space

In Section 74 we found that a line in the plane could be represented by a vector equation

(84-1) $$R = Mt + B, \quad t \text{ in the interval } (-\infty, \infty).$$

When the vectors R, M, and B are chosen from three-dimensional vector space, this equation represents a line in space. If the initial point of B

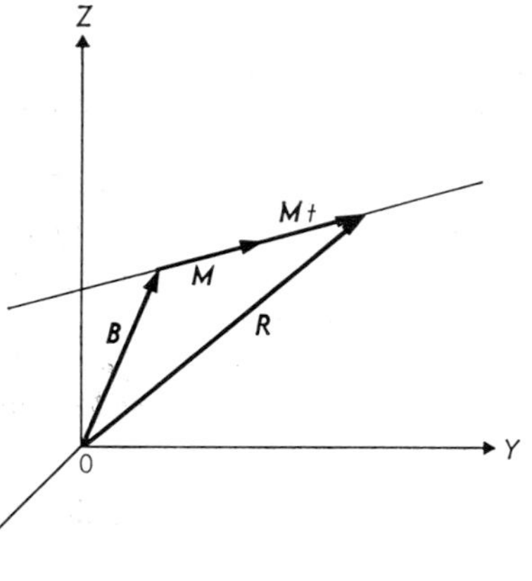

Figure 84-1

is the origin, then the terminal point of B is a point of the line. The vector M gives the direction of the line (see Fig. 84-1).

Example 84-1. Find an equation of the line that contains the points $P(-1, 2, 3)$ and $Q(2, 1, -3)$.

Solution. Our answer will be an equation of the form $R = Mt + B$. For the direction vector M we can take the vector $M = PQ = 3i - j - 6k$. Since the point P belongs to the line, we can take the position vector B to be $B = OP = -i + 2j + 3k$. Thus an equation of our line is

$$\begin{aligned} R &= (3i - j - 6k)t + (-i + 2j + 3k) \\ &= (3t - 1)i - (t - 2)j - (6t - 3)k. \end{aligned}$$

We could also have chosen the position vector $\boldsymbol{B}$ to be the vector $\boldsymbol{B} = \boldsymbol{OQ} = 2\boldsymbol{i} + \boldsymbol{j} - 3\boldsymbol{k}$, which would have given us the equation

$$\boldsymbol{R} = (3t + 2)\boldsymbol{i} - (t - 1)\boldsymbol{j} - (6t + 3)\boldsymbol{k}.$$

Although our two vector equations are different, you can readily check to see that both represent the line that contains the points P and Q, and hence either equation will serve as a solution to our problem.

Example 84-2. Find the equation of the line that contains the point $(2, -1, 3)$ and meets the plane $x + 2y - 4z + 12 = 0$ at right angles.

Solution. Our line will be represented by an equation of the form $\boldsymbol{R} = \boldsymbol{M}t + \boldsymbol{B}$, where $\boldsymbol{B}$ is the position vector to a point of the line and $\boldsymbol{M}$ determines the direction of the line. The point $(2, -1, 3)$ belongs to our line, so we can take $\boldsymbol{B} = 2\boldsymbol{i} - \boldsymbol{j} + 3\boldsymbol{k}$. The direction of our line is that of a normal to the given plane. The vector $\boldsymbol{i} + 2\boldsymbol{j} - 4\boldsymbol{k}$ is normal to the plane, and so we can take this vector to be our vector $\boldsymbol{M}$. Hence an equation of our line is

$$\begin{aligned} \boldsymbol{R} &= (\boldsymbol{i} + 2\boldsymbol{j} - 4\boldsymbol{k})t + (2\boldsymbol{i} - \boldsymbol{j} + 3\boldsymbol{k}) \\ &= (t + 2)\boldsymbol{i} + (2t - 1)\boldsymbol{j} + (-4t + 3)\boldsymbol{k}. \end{aligned}$$

Example 84-3. Find an equation of the line that contains the point $(-1, 2, 0)$ and is parallel to the line that joins the points $P(-1, -2, -3)$ and $Q(1, 2, 3)$.

Solution. We can take $\boldsymbol{B} = -\boldsymbol{i} + 2\boldsymbol{j} + 0\boldsymbol{k} = -\boldsymbol{i} + 2\boldsymbol{j}$, and $\boldsymbol{M} = \boldsymbol{PQ} = 2\boldsymbol{i} + 4\boldsymbol{j} + 6\boldsymbol{k}$, and an equation of our line will be

$$\begin{aligned} \boldsymbol{R} &= (2\boldsymbol{i} + 4\boldsymbol{j} + 6\boldsymbol{k})t + (-\boldsymbol{i} + 2\boldsymbol{j}). \\ &= (2t - 1)\boldsymbol{i} + (4t + 2)\boldsymbol{j} + 6t\boldsymbol{k}. \end{aligned}$$

If the direction vector of a line is $\boldsymbol{M} = l\boldsymbol{i} + m\boldsymbol{j} + n\boldsymbol{k}$ and the position vector is $\boldsymbol{B} = a\boldsymbol{i} + b\boldsymbol{j} + c\boldsymbol{k}$, then the vector equation $\boldsymbol{R} = \boldsymbol{M}t + \boldsymbol{B}$ becomes

$$x\boldsymbol{i} + y\boldsymbol{j} + z\boldsymbol{k} = (lt + a)\boldsymbol{i} + (mt + b)\boldsymbol{j} + (nt + c)\boldsymbol{k}.$$

Thus parametric equations of our line are

$$(84\text{-}2) \qquad x = lt + a, \quad y = mt + b, \quad \text{and} \quad z = nt + c.$$

If the numbers l, m, and n are not 0, then

$$t = \frac{x - a}{l}, \quad t = \frac{y - b}{m}, \quad \text{and} \quad t = \frac{z - c}{n}.$$

You will frequently see the equations of the line with direction numbers l, m, and n that contains the point (a, b, c) written as

$$(84\text{-}3) \qquad \frac{x-a}{l} = \frac{y-b}{m} = \frac{z-c}{n}.$$

Example 84-4. Show that a line in the direction of the vector $\boldsymbol{M} = l\boldsymbol{i} + m\boldsymbol{j} + n\boldsymbol{k}$ is parallel to the planes

$$(84\text{-}4) \qquad \frac{x-a}{l} = \frac{y-b}{m}, \quad \frac{y-b}{m} = \frac{z-c}{n}, \quad \text{and} \quad \frac{x-a}{l} = \frac{z-c}{n}.$$

Solution. We must show that $\boldsymbol{M}$ is perpendicular to each of the normals to these planes. The first plane can be written in the form

$$mx - ly + lb - ma = 0.$$

A normal to this plane is $\boldsymbol{N} = m\boldsymbol{i} - l\boldsymbol{j} + 0\boldsymbol{k}$, and we see that

$$\begin{aligned} \boldsymbol{M} \cdot \boldsymbol{N} &= (l\boldsymbol{i} + m\boldsymbol{j} + n\boldsymbol{k}) \cdot (m\boldsymbol{i} - l\boldsymbol{j} + 0\boldsymbol{k}) \\ &= lm - ml = 0. \end{aligned}$$

The fact that $\boldsymbol{M}$ is perpendicular to the other normals is proved in the same way.

If the vector $\boldsymbol{M}$ in Equation 84-1 is a unit vector, then the com-

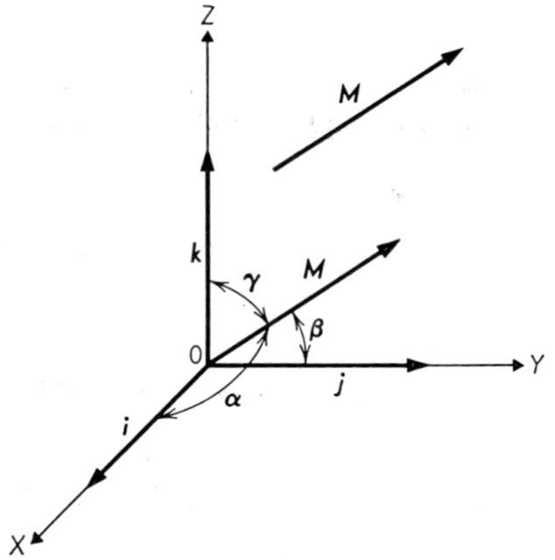

Figure 84-2

ponents M_x, M_y, and M_z of $\boldsymbol{M}$ are given by the equations

$$M_x = \boldsymbol{M} \cdot \boldsymbol{i} = \cos\alpha, \ M_y = \boldsymbol{M} \cdot \boldsymbol{j} = \cos\beta, \ M_z = \boldsymbol{M} \cdot \boldsymbol{k} = \cos\gamma,$$

where α, β, and γ measure the angles between $\boldsymbol{M}$ and the basis vectors (see Fig. 84-2). The numbers $\cos\alpha$, $\cos\beta$, and $\cos\gamma$ are called **direction cosines** of the line represented by Equation 84-1. Since we are assuming that $\boldsymbol{M}$ is a unit vector, then $M_x^2 + M_y^2 + M_z^2 = 1$, and the direction cosines of a line satisfy the equation

$$\cos^2 \alpha + \cos^2 \beta + \cos^2 \gamma = 1. \tag{84-5}$$

Example 84-5. Find direction cosines of the line that is the intersection of the two planes $2x - 3y + z = 4$ and $x + 4y - 2z = 6$.

Solution. The vector $\boldsymbol{N}_1 = 2\boldsymbol{i} - 3\boldsymbol{j} + \boldsymbol{k}$ is a normal vector to the plane $2x - 3y + z = 4$, and the vector $\boldsymbol{N}_2 = \boldsymbol{i} + 4\boldsymbol{j} - 2\boldsymbol{k}$ is a normal vector to the plane $x + 4y - 2z = 6$. The vector $(\boldsymbol{N}_1 \times \boldsymbol{N}_2)/|\boldsymbol{N}_1 \times \boldsymbol{N}_2|$ is a unit vector along the line of intersection of the two planes (why?). We find that

$$\boldsymbol{N}_1 \times \boldsymbol{N}_2 = \begin{vmatrix} -3 & 1 \\ 4 & -2 \end{vmatrix} \boldsymbol{i} - \begin{vmatrix} 2 & 1 \\ 1 & -2 \end{vmatrix} \boldsymbol{j} + \begin{vmatrix} 2 & -3 \\ 1 & 4 \end{vmatrix} \boldsymbol{k}$$

$$= 2\boldsymbol{i} + 5\boldsymbol{j} + 11\boldsymbol{k}.$$

Thus

$$|\boldsymbol{N}_1 \times \boldsymbol{N}_2| = \sqrt{150} = 5\sqrt{6},$$

and so the vector

$$\frac{2}{(5\sqrt{6})}\boldsymbol{i} + \frac{1}{\sqrt{6}}\boldsymbol{j} + \frac{11}{(5\sqrt{6})}\boldsymbol{k}$$

is a unit vector along our line. Therefore, its components are direction cosines of the line. Using four-place decimal approximations, we find

$$\cos \alpha = .1633, \quad \cos \beta = .4082, \quad \cos \gamma = .8981,$$

and so

$$\alpha \approx 81°, \quad \beta \approx 66°, \quad \gamma \approx 26°.$$

Problems 84

1. Find vector equations of the lines that contain the following points.
   (a) $(-1, 2, -4)$, $(2, 0, 3)$
   (b) $(0, 0, 0)$, $(0, 1, 0)$
   (c) $(1, 2, 3)$, $(-1, -3, 2)$
2. Show that the following vector equations all represent the same line.

$$\boldsymbol{R} = (3t - 1)\boldsymbol{i} + (1 - 2t)\boldsymbol{j} + 4t\boldsymbol{k}$$
$$\boldsymbol{R} = (3t + 2)\boldsymbol{i} - (2t + 1)\boldsymbol{j} + (4t + 4)\boldsymbol{k}$$
$$\boldsymbol{R} = (6t - 10)\boldsymbol{i} + (7 - 4t)\boldsymbol{j} + (8t - 12)\boldsymbol{k}$$

3. Find an equation of the line that contains the point $(2, -1, 3)$ and is parallel to the line $\boldsymbol{R} = (3t - 2)\boldsymbol{i} + 2t\boldsymbol{j} + (4 - t)\boldsymbol{k}$.
4. Find vector equations of the following lines:

   (a) $\dfrac{x + 2}{2} = \dfrac{y - 1}{1} = \dfrac{z - 2}{2}$

   (b) $\dfrac{x - 2}{3} = \dfrac{y}{2} = \dfrac{z - 4}{1}$

5. Find the cosine of the angle between the two lines of the preceding problem.
6. Find a vector equation for the line of intersection of the planes $2x - 3y + z = 5$ and $x + 2z = 7$.
7. Find the point of intersection of the lines:

$$\boldsymbol{R} = (3t - 1)\boldsymbol{i} + (2t + 2)\boldsymbol{j} + (1 - t)\boldsymbol{k},$$

and

$$\boldsymbol{R} = (t - 3)\boldsymbol{i} + (8 - 3t)\boldsymbol{j} + (2t - 3)\boldsymbol{k}.$$

8. Find the equation of the plane that contains the two lines of the preceding problem.
9. Does the line that is tangent to the graph of the equation $\boldsymbol{R} = t\boldsymbol{i} + t^2\boldsymbol{j} + t^3\boldsymbol{k}$ at the point at which $t = 2$ contain the point $(1, 0, -4)$?
10. Determine whether or not the following lines intersect:

$$\frac{x-2}{-1} = \frac{y+1}{3} = z \quad \text{and} \quad \frac{x+1}{7} = \frac{y-8}{-3} = z - 3.$$

11. Find the direction cosines of the lines in the preceding problem.
12. Find the angle between the normal to the plane $2x + y + z = 7$ and the line

$$x - 3 = \frac{y+1}{2} = \frac{z-4}{-1}.$$

85. Cylindrical Coordinates. Spherical Coordinates

Cartesian coordinates do not provide the only method of associating numbers with points in space. Other coordinate systems are also useful. In this section we discuss two other coordinate systems that are often used in applied mathematics—cylindrical coordinates and spherical coordinates.

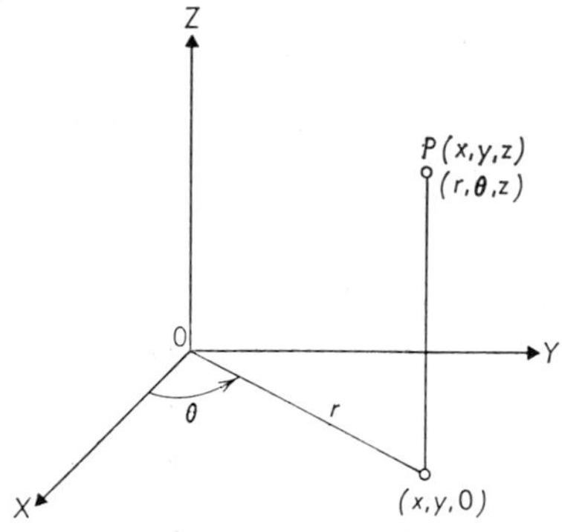

Figure 85-1

Let P be a point in space and suppose that its cartesian coordinates are (x, y, z). Let r and θ be polar coordinates of the point $(x, y, 0)$ in the XY-plane (see Fig. 85-1). Then we say that (r, θ, z) are **cylindrical coordinates** of P. From our knowledge of polar coordinates (Section 66), we know that $x = r \cos \theta$ and $y = r \sin \theta$. Thus the cartesian coordinates of P are related to the cylindrical coordinates of P by the equations

$$
\begin{aligned}
x &= r \cos \theta \\
y &= r \sin \theta \\
z &= z
\end{aligned}
\tag{85-1}
$$

A **coordinate surface** in a given coordinate system is a surface whose equation is obtained by "fixing" one of the coordinates. For example, in a cartesian coordinate system the equation $y = 2$ defines the coordinate surface that consists of the set of points with coordinates $(x, 2, z)$. This coordinate surface is a plane, and in fact, you can readily see that any coordinate surface in a cartesian coordinate system is a plane. When we examine the coordinate surfaces in a cylindrical coordinate system, we find that they are of two kinds. The coordinate surface whose equation is $z = a$ is a plane parallel to the XY-plane, and the coordinate surface whose equation is $\theta = b$ is a plane that contains the Z-axis. The coordinate surface whose equation is $r = c$ is a right-circular cylinder, and it is from this fact that the name cylindrical coordinates is derived.

Example 85-1. Plot the points $(2, \pi/2, 3)$, $(3, -45°, 1)$ and $(-2, 225°, -1)$.

Solution. The listed points are plotted in Fig. 85-2.

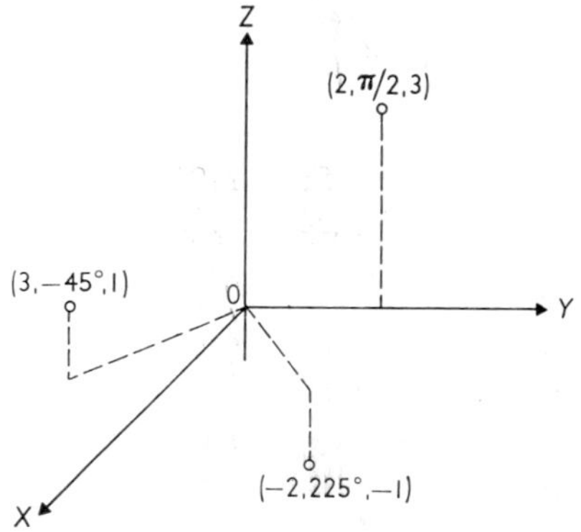

Figure 85-2

Example 85-2. Describe the surface whose equation is $\theta = z$.

Solution. Let us find some points of our surface. If we let $\theta = 0$, then $z = 0$. Since r is missing from our equation, we see that any point $(r, 0, 0)$ lies in our surface, no matter what number r is. The set of all these points forms the X-axis. Similarly, the set of all points whose coordinates are $(r, \pi/4, \pi/4)$ lies in our surface. This set of points is a line that is parallel to the XY-plane and $\pi/4$ units above it, and it is directed so that it bisects the angle between the XZ-plane and the YZ-plane. Our surface might be thought of as being generated by a line that is kept parallel to the XY-plane while it is simultaneously moved along the Z-axis and twisted about it. A surface that is generated by a moving line is called a **ruled surface,** and our surface here is a particular ruled surface called a **helicoid.** (The

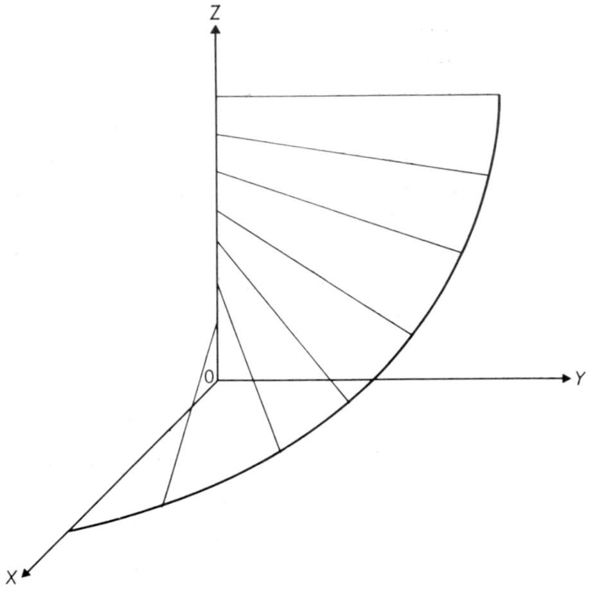

Figure 85-3

cylinders discussed in Section 81 are also ruled surfaces.) In Fig. 85-3 we have shown part of our helicoid.

Just as a curve in space can be represented by three parametric equations for the cartesian coordinates x, y, and z (see Equations 83-2), so we can also represent the equation of a space curve by giving three parametric equations for the cylindrical coordinates r, θ, and z. For example, the curve represented by the parametric equations

$$r = 1, \quad \theta = t, \quad z = t$$

is the circular helix of Example 83-2.

Equations 83-7 state the following formula for the length of a curve in space:

$$\mathbf{L} = \int_a^b \sqrt{x'^2 + y'^2 + z'^2}\, dt. \tag{85-2}$$

In order to use this formula to find the length of the curve with parametric equations

$$r = f(t), \quad \theta = g(t), \quad z = h(t) \quad \text{for } t \text{ in the interval } [a, b],$$

we must express the derivatives x' and y' in terms of r' and θ'. We therefore differentiate both sides of the first two of Equations 85-1 to obtain

$$x' = r'\cos\theta - r\theta'\sin\theta,$$
$$y' = r'\sin\theta + r\theta'\cos\theta.$$

Then you can easily check to see that

$$x'^2 + y'^2 + z'^2 = r'^2 + r^2\theta'^2 + z'^2,$$

and therefore Equation 85-2 becomes

$$\text{(85-3)} \qquad \boldsymbol{L = \int_a^b \sqrt{r'^2 + r^2\theta'^2 + z'^2}\, dt.}$$

Example 85-3. Find the length of the curve with parametric equations $r = ae^t$, $\theta = t$, $z = e^t$ for $0 \leq t \leq 1$.

Solution. Here we have

$$r'^2 = a^2e^{2t}, \quad r^2 = a^2e^{2t}, \quad \theta'^2 = 1, \quad \text{and} \quad z'^2 = e^{2t}.$$

Thus Formula 85-3 tells us that the length of our curve is

$$L = \int_0^1 \sqrt{a^2e^{2t} + a^2e^{2t} + e^{2t}}\, dt$$
$$= \int_0^1 e^t\sqrt{2a^2+1}\, dt = \sqrt{2a^2+1}\,(e-1).$$

Again let (x, y, z) be the cartesian coordinates of a point P and let r and θ, $r \geq 0$, be polar coordinates of the point $(x, y, 0)$ in the XY-plane. Let ϕ be the measure of the angle between the position vector $\boldsymbol{OP}$ and $\boldsymbol{k}$, $0 \leq \phi \leq \pi$, and let $|\boldsymbol{OP}| = \rho$ (see Fig. 85-4). Then the numbers (ρ, θ, ϕ) are called **spherical coordinates** of P. You can see that $z = \rho\cos\phi$ and $r = \rho\sin\phi$. Since we also know that $x = r\cos\theta$ and $y =$

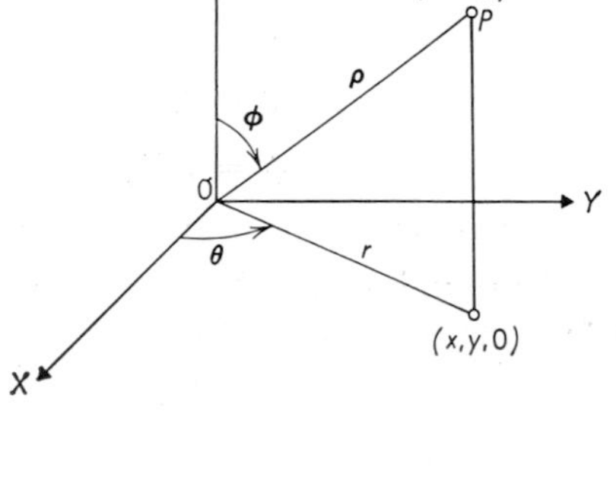

Figure 85-4

$r \sin \theta$, we obtain the relations

$$\begin{aligned} x &= \rho \cos \theta \sin \phi \\ y &= \rho \sin \theta \sin \phi \\ z &= \rho \cos \phi. \end{aligned} \tag{85-4}$$

In the spherical coordinate system the coordinate surface that is represented by the equation $\theta = a$ is a plane that contains the Z-axis. The coordinate surface represented by the equation $\phi = b$ is a cone with vertex at 0 (unless $b = 0$, $b = \pi$, or $b = \pi/2$, in which case the cone "degenerates"). The coordinate surface $\rho = c$ is a sphere.

Example 85-4. Plot the points $(1, \pi/4, \pi/3)$, $(2, -\pi/4, \pi/2)$, and $(2, \pi/6, 3\pi/4)$.

Solution. The listed points are shown in Fig. 85-5.

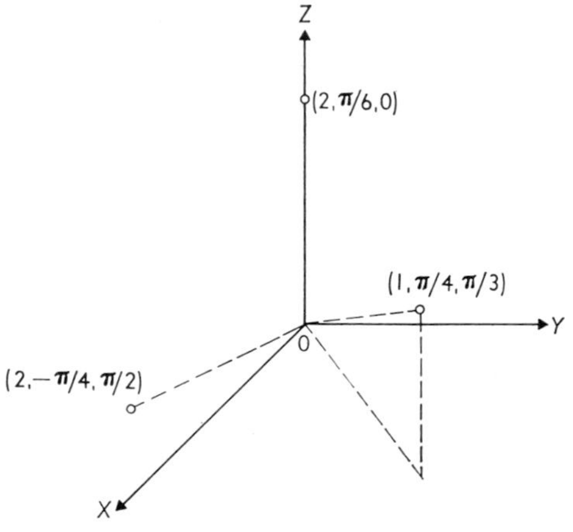

Figure 85-5

A space curve may be represented by parametric equations involving spherical coordinates. We leave it to you to show that the parametric equations

$$\begin{aligned} \rho &= t, \\ \theta &= t, \\ \phi &= \pi/4, \end{aligned} \tag{85-5}$$

represent a curve that winds around a cone in much the same manner that a helix winds around a cylinder (see Example 83-1).

To find a formula for the length of the curve with parametric equations $\rho = f(t)$, $\theta = g(t)$, $\phi = h(t)$, where t is in the interval $[a, b]$, we must express x', y', and z' in terms of ρ', θ', and ϕ' and then substitute these expressions in Equation 85-2. When we differentiate both sides of each of Equations 85-4, we obtain

$$\begin{aligned} x' &= \rho' \cos\theta \sin\phi - \rho\theta' \sin\theta \sin\phi + \rho\phi' \cos\theta \cos\phi, \\ y' &= \rho' \sin\theta \sin\phi + \rho\theta' \cos\theta \sin\phi + \rho\phi' \sin\theta \cos\phi, \\ z' &= \rho' \cos\phi - \rho\phi' \sin\phi. \end{aligned}$$

It is now a simple matter of elementary trigonometry and algebra to show that

$$x'^2 + y'^2 + z'^2 = \rho'^2 + (\rho^2 \sin^2\phi)\,\theta'^2 + \rho^2\phi'^2.$$

We substitute this result in Equation 85-2 to obtain the arclength formula

$$\text{(85-6)} \qquad \boldsymbol{L = \int_a^b \sqrt{\rho'^2 + (\rho^2 \sin^2\phi)\,\theta'^2 + \rho^2\phi'^2}\, dt.}$$

Example 85-5. Find the length of the first winding of the conical helix given by Equations 85-5; that is, find the length of the arc that corresponds to the parameter interval $[0, 2\pi]$.

Solution. Here we have

$$\phi' = 0, \quad \rho' = \theta' = 1, \quad \sin^2\phi = \tfrac{1}{2}, \quad \text{and} \quad \rho = t.$$

Therefore, Formula 85-6 becomes

$$\begin{aligned} L &= \int_0^{2\pi} \sqrt{1 + \tfrac{1}{2}t^2}\, dt \\ &= \frac{1}{\sqrt{2}} \int_0^{2\pi} \sqrt{t^2 + 2}\, dt. \end{aligned}$$

We use Integration Formula V-31 to evaluate this integral, and we find that

$$\begin{aligned} L &= \pi\sqrt{2\pi^2 + 1} + \frac{1}{\sqrt{2}} \ln\left(\pi\sqrt{2} + \sqrt{2\pi^2 + 1}\right) \\ &\approx 16. \end{aligned}$$

Problems 85

1. Plot the points whose cylindrical coordinates are given and find their cartesian coordinates.
   (a) $(2, 30°, -1)$ (b) $(0, 90°, 5)$ (c) $(2, 45°, 1)$
   (d) (π, π, π) (e) $(1, -90°, -1)$ (f) $(1, 1, 1)$

2. Plot the points whose spherical coordinates are given and find their cartesian coordinates.
(a) $(2, 30°, 60°)$ (b) $(2, 45°, 45°)$
(c) $(5, 90°, 90°)$ (d) (π, π, π)
(e) $(1, -90°, 0)$ (f) $(1, 1, 1)$
3. Find the cartesian-coordinate equation corresponding to each of the following equations in cylindrical coordinates and describe the surface it represents.
(a) $z = 2r^2$
(b) $(r^2/4) + (z^2/9) = 1$
(c) $3r \cos \theta + r \sin \theta + z = 2$
(d) $\theta = \pi/4$.
4. Find the cartesian-coordinate equation corresponding to each of the following equations in spherical coordinates and describe the surface it represents.
(a) $\rho = 3$ (b) $\rho - 2 \cos \phi = 0$
(c) $\rho \sin \phi = 5$ (d) $\rho \cos \phi = -3$
5. Find the cylindrical-coordinate equation corresponding to each of the following equations.
(a) $x^2 + y^2 = z$ (b) $x^2 + y^2 = z^2$
(c) $y = 5$ (d) $x^2 + y^2 + 2y = 0$
6. Find the spherical-coordinate equation corresponding to each of the following equations.
(a) $y = \sqrt{3}\, x$ (b) $z^2 = x^2 + y^2$
(c) $x^2 + y^2 + z^2 - 4z = 0$ (d) $x^2 + y^2 = 4$
7. Find the lengths of the curves with parametric equations in cylindrical coordinates as given for the listed interval.
(a) $r = 5 \cos t,\ \theta = \sec t,\ z = 5 \sin t,\ [0, \pi/6]$
(b) $r = \cos t,\ \theta = \sqrt{2} \sec t,\ z = \sec t,\ [0, \pi/4]$
8. Verify the equation $x'^2 + y'^2 + z'^2 = r'^2 + r^2\theta'^2 + z'^2$ used in the derivation of Equation 85-3.
9. Verify the equation $x'^2 + y'^2 + z'^2 = \rho'^2 + (\rho^2 \sin^2\phi)\, \theta'^2 + \rho^2\phi'^2$.
10. Find parametric equations involving spherical coordinates that represent the curve that is the intersection of the surfaces $\rho = 2$ and $\rho \sin^2 \phi = 3 \cos \phi$. What is the length of this curve?
11. Find the length of the curve with parametric equations in spherical coordinates of $\rho = 1$, $\theta = k \ln (\sec t + \tan t)$, $\phi = \dfrac{\pi}{2} - t$ for t in the interval $[0, \pi/2]$. Describe the curve.

Review Problems, Chapter Nine

You can use these questions to test yourself on the material covered in this chapter.

1. Suppose that the coordinates of point P are $(3, 4, 5)$. What are the coordinates of the points Q, R, S, and T, where Q is symmetric to P with respect to the plane $z = 1$, R is symmetric to P with respect to the plane $x = -2$, S is symmetric to P with respect to the point $(1, 2, 3)$, and T is symmetric to P with respect to the plane $x + y = 0$?

2. Let $P(-1, -2, -3)$, $Q(-3, 2, 4)$, and $R(2, -1, 0)$ be three points in space. Find the point S such that $PQRS$ is the parallelogram in which Q and S are opposite vertices.
3. Suppose that $\boldsymbol{A}$ and $\boldsymbol{B}$ are non-parallel vectors. Find a number t such that the vectors $(1 - t)\boldsymbol{A} + t\boldsymbol{B}$ and $3\boldsymbol{A} + 4\boldsymbol{B}$ are parallel.
4. Convince yourself that the equation $(\boldsymbol{A} \times \boldsymbol{B}) \times (\boldsymbol{C} \times \boldsymbol{D}) = \boldsymbol{0}$ means that the vectors $\boldsymbol{A}$, $\boldsymbol{B}$, $\boldsymbol{C}$, and $\boldsymbol{D}$ are parallel to the same plane.
5. What is the equation of the plane that intercepts the coordinate axes at the points $(a, 0, 0)$, $(0, b, 0)$, and $(0, 0, c)$?
6. Suppose that along the line $x + y = 1$ in the XY-plane we move a line that is parallel to the vector $\boldsymbol{i} + \boldsymbol{j} + \boldsymbol{k}$. What is the equation of the plane that the moving line generates?
7. Show that if a certain surface is a surface of revolution about *both* the X-axis and the Y-axis, then it must be a sphere whose center is the origin.
8. At what point of the graph of the vector equation

$$\boldsymbol{R} = (3t + 1)\boldsymbol{i} + 2t^2\boldsymbol{j} + (6t - 1)\boldsymbol{k}$$

is the tangent vector parallel to the vector $\boldsymbol{i} + 4\boldsymbol{j} + 2\boldsymbol{k}$?
9. Find a vector equation of the line that is tangent to the space curve whose equation is $\boldsymbol{R} = \boldsymbol{F}(t)$ at the point at which $t = a$.
10. Let $P(a, \theta, \phi)$ be a point of the sphere $\rho = a$, and extend the segment OP until it intersects the cylinder $r = a$. What are the cylindrical coordinates of the point of intersection?

10 LINEAR SYSTEMS AND MATRICES

Problems in which we have a number of unknown quantities that satisfy a system of linear equations occur frequently in mathematical applications. As we study systems of linear equations, we are led naturally to the concept of a **matrix** and associated numbers called **determinants.** We have already encountered systems of linear equations (in Sections 9 and 62, for example) and determinants (in Section 79) in this book. Now we are going to offer a brief, systematic discussion of these topics.

Matrices and matrix notation are useful not only to solve systems of linear equations but in other areas of mathematics as well. In the second part of the chapter we shall use matrices in connection with coordinate transformations in space.

86. Systems of Linear Equations. Triangular Form

A **linear equation** in n unknowns $x_1, \ldots, x_n$ has the form

$$a_1x_1 + \cdots + a_nx_n = b$$

where $a_1, \ldots, a_n$ and b are given numbers. For example,

$$3x - 4y = 5,$$

$$5s - 46t + 7u = 9,$$

and

$$43x_1 - 57x_2 + 4x_3 - x_4 = 29$$

are linear equations in two, three, and four unknowns, respectively. In this section we will be concerned with methods by which we can solve a system of n linear equations in n unknowns. A **solution** of a system of equations in n unknowns consists of a set of n numbers that satisfy all the equations of the system. For example, you can readily verify by substitution that the three numbers $x_1 = 1$, $x_2 = 0$, and $x_3 = 2$ satisfy each of the equations of the system

$$\begin{aligned} 3x_1 - 4x_2 + x_3 &= 5 \\ 6x_1 - 8x_2 - 2x_3 &= 2 \\ x_1 + 3x_2 - x_3 &= -1. \end{aligned} \tag{86-1}$$

We shall often write our solution as $(x_1, x_2, x_3) = (1, 0, 2)$.

DEFINITION 86-1. *Two systems of linear equations are* ***equivalent*** *if every solution of one system is also a solution of the other.*

The systems

$$\begin{aligned} 7x + 3y &= 4 \\ x + y &= 0, \end{aligned}$$

and

$$\begin{aligned} x &= 1 \\ x + y &= 0, \end{aligned}$$

for example, are equivalent, since the only solution of each system is the number pair $(x, y) = (1, -1)$.

When confronted with a system of linear equations, we shall try to replace it with an equivalent system that is easier to solve. Any time we perform one of the following operations on a system of linear equations to obtain a new system of equations we obtain a system that is equivalent to the original system.

Operation 86-1. Interchange the position of two equations.

Operation 86-2. Replace an equation with a non-zero multiple of itself. (A multiple of an equation is the equation that results when we multiply both sides of the equation by the same number.)

Operation 86-3. Replace an equation with the sum of a non-zero multiple of itself and a multiple of another equation of the system. (Adding two equations means, of course, adding the corresponding sides of the equations.)

Let us illustrate these three operations by applying each to System 86-1. As an example of Operation 86-1 we will interchange the positions of the first and third equations of System 86-1 to obtain the system

$$\begin{aligned} x_1 + 3x_2 - x_3 &= -1 \\ 6x_1 - 8x_2 - 2x_3 &= 2 \\ 3x_1 - 4x_2 + x_3 &= 5. \end{aligned} \tag{86-2}$$

As an example of Operation 86-2, let us replace the second equation of System 86-1 with the equation that results from multiplying the second equation by $\frac{1}{2}$ to obtain the system

$$\begin{aligned} 3x_1 - 4x_2 + x_3 &= 5 \\ 3x_1 - 4x_2 - x_3 &= 1 \\ x_1 + 3x_2 - x_3 &= -1. \end{aligned} \tag{86-3}$$

As an example of Operation 86-3 let us replace the second equation of System 86-1 with the sum of three times the second equation and eight times the third equation to obtain the system

$$\begin{aligned} 3x_1 - 4x_2 + \quad x_3 &= 5 \\ 26x_1 \qquad\quad - 14x_3 &= -2 \\ x_1 + 3x_2 - \quad x_3 &= -1. \end{aligned} \tag{86-4}$$

Each of the Systems 86-2, 86-3, and 86-4 is equivalent to System 86-1.

In elementary algebra we solved two linear equations in two unknowns by first eliminating one of the unknowns. This method is basically a scheme for replacing one system of two linear equations with an equivalent system of equations that is easier to solve. To illustrate this fact, let us consider an example.

Example 86-1. Solve the system of equations

$$\begin{aligned} 2x + 3y &= 4 \\ 3x - \ y &= -5. \end{aligned} \tag{86-5}$$

Solution. If we multiply the second equation by 3 and add it to the first, we obtain an equation that involves x alone. We can replace the first equation of our system with this equation in x alone and obtain the equivalent system

$$\begin{aligned} 11x \quad &= -11 \\ 3x - y &= -5. \end{aligned} \tag{86-6}$$

System 86-6 is easy to solve; we find $x = -1$ from the first equation and then substitute $x = -1$ in the second equation to find $y = 2$. Since System 86-6 is equivalent to System 86-5, we conclude that the solution of System 86-5 is $(x, y) = (-1, 2)$.

System 86-6 is in what is called *triangular* form. A system of n linear equations in n unknowns is said to be in **triangular form** if the first equation involves only x_1; the second equation involves x_2 and perhaps x_1, but not $x_3, x_4, \ldots,$ and x_n; the third equation involves x_3 and perhaps x_1 and x_2, but not $x_4, \ldots, x_n$; and so on. The following system, for example, is in triangular form:

$$\begin{aligned} 2x \qquad\qquad &= 4 \\ 3x - 2y \qquad &= 8 \\ x + y - 4z &= 1. \end{aligned} \tag{86-7}$$

From the first equation of this system it is apparent that $x = 2$. Once we know that $x = 2$, it is clear from the second equation that $y = -1$, and then we can solve the third equation to find $z = 0$. Thus the solution of System 86-7 is $(x, y, z) = (2, -1, 0)$.

It is easy to solve a system of equations that is in triangular form, so we adopt the following method of solving a system of linear equations. *By using Operations 86-1, 86-2, and 86-3, we try to replace a given system of linear equations with an equivalent system that is in triangular form.* "Most" systems can be reduced to triangular form in this way, and, as we shall see in the next section, our efforts will not be wasted if we attempt the reduction on a system that is not equivalent to a system in triangular form. We can best describe the procedure by applying it to some typical examples.

Example 86-2. Solve the system of equations

$$\begin{aligned} \tfrac{1}{2}x - \tfrac{2}{3}y + z &= \tfrac{8}{3} \\ 2x - y + z &= 6 \\ 3x + 2y \quad &= 4. \end{aligned} \tag{86-8}$$

Solution. To simplify things, we multiply the first equation by 6 and interchange the order of the equations to obtain

$$\begin{aligned} 3x + 2y \qquad &= 4 \\ 3x - 4y + 6z &= 16 \\ 2x - y \;\; + z &= 6. \end{aligned}$$

Now we multiply the third equation by 6 and subtract it from the second to obtain the system

$$\begin{aligned} 3x + 2y \qquad &= 4 \\ -9x + 2y \qquad &= -20 \\ 2x - y + z &= 6. \end{aligned} \tag{86-9}$$

Next we get an equivalent system in triangular form by subtracting the second of Equations 86-9 from the first:

$$\begin{aligned} 12x \qquad\qquad &= 24 \\ -9x + 2y \qquad &= -20 \\ 2x - y + z &= 6. \end{aligned} \tag{86-10}$$

System 86-10 easily yields the solution $(x, y, z) = (2, -1, 1)$.

Example 86-3. Solve the system

$$\begin{aligned} x - 6y + 2z &= 5 \\ 2x - 3y + z &= 4 \\ 3x + 4y - z &= -2. \end{aligned}$$

Solution. When we add the third equation to the second, and twice the third equation to the first, we get the equivalent system

$$\begin{aligned} 7x + 2y \qquad &= 1 \\ 5x + y \qquad &= 2 \\ 3x + 4y - z &= -2. \end{aligned} \tag{86-11}$$

Next we subtract twice the second of Equations 86-11 from the first to obtain the equivalent system in triangular form

$$\begin{aligned} -3x \qquad\qquad &= -3 \\ 5x + y \qquad &= 2 \\ 3x + 4y - z &= -2. \end{aligned} \tag{86-12}$$

We can then easily find that the solution of this system is $(x, y, z) = (1, -3, -7)$.

Notice that the last equation was used to eliminate one of the unknowns from all the other equations; then the next to the last equation was used to eliminate another unknown from the equation above it. Although this procedure stops after two steps in our example, it is clear that it is a direct method that can be used to reduce a system consisting of more linear equations in more unknowns to triangular form.

All the operations used in solving a system of linear equations are the simplest possible—multiplication, division, addition, and subtraction. But there are a lot of operations involved. In the next section we will introduce some notation that simplifies writing out the method of solution that we have introduced here.

Problems 86

1. Solve the following systems of equations.

(a) $\begin{aligned} 2x + 4y &= 0 \\ 3x - 2y &= 8 \end{aligned}$ (b) $\begin{aligned} 2x + 4y &= 6 \\ 3x - 2y &= -7 \end{aligned}$

(c) $\begin{aligned} x - 5y &= -5 \\ 2x + y &= 1 \end{aligned}$ (d) $\begin{aligned} x - 5y &= 2 \\ 2x + y &= 4 \end{aligned}$

(e) $\begin{aligned} \frac{x}{3} + y &= 1 \\ x - \frac{y}{4} &= \frac{2}{5} \end{aligned}$ (f) $\begin{aligned} \frac{x}{3} + y &= \frac{4}{3} \\ x - \frac{y}{4} &= \frac{3}{4} \end{aligned}$

2. Solve the following systems of equations.

(a) $\begin{aligned} x + 2y &= 5 \\ x - 2y &= -3 \\ 2x + 4y - 2z &= 12 \end{aligned}$ (b) $\begin{aligned} x + 2y &= 4 \\ x - 2y &= 0 \\ 2x + 4y - 2z &= 6 \end{aligned}$

(c) $\begin{aligned} x + 3y - 4z &= -2 \\ 2x - y + 2z &= 6 \\ 4x - 6y + z &= 9 \end{aligned}$ (d) $\begin{aligned} x + 3y - 4z &= 2 \\ 2x - y + 2z &= 1 \\ 4x - 6y + z &= 9 \end{aligned}$

(e) $\begin{aligned} 3x - 4y + 2w &= 11 \\ 2x - y + w &= 5 \\ x + 5y - z &= -4 \\ y - 3z + w &= 1 \end{aligned}$ (f) $\begin{aligned} 3x - 4y + 2w &= -7 \\ 2x - y + w &= -1 \\ x + 5y - z &= 13 \\ y - 3z + w &= 7 \end{aligned}$

3. Express x and y in terms of a, b, c, d, u, and v if

$$\begin{aligned} ax + by &= u \\ cx + dy &= v. \end{aligned}$$

4. Solve the following "homogeneous" systems.

(a) $\begin{aligned} x + 3y - 4z &= 0 \\ 2x - y + 2z &= 0 \\ 4x - 6y + z &= 0 \end{aligned}$ (b) $\begin{aligned} x + 2y - 2z &= 0 \\ 2x - y + z &= 0 \\ 4x + y - 3z &= 0 \end{aligned}$

5. Show that both (1, 2, −1) and (6, 5, −8) are solutions of the following system:

$$\begin{aligned} 2x - y + z &= -1 \\ x + 3y + 2z &= 5 \\ x - 4y - z &= -6 \end{aligned}$$

6. Show that $(1 + 5t, 2 + 3t, -1 - 7t)$ is a solution of the system in the preceding problem for each number t.
7. Let A, B, and C denote the degree measure of the angles of a triangle. One angle is 20° less than the sum of the other two, and 10° more than the positive difference of the other two. Find the measures of the angles.
8. Show that the three lines that are defined by the equations $x - 2y - 3 = 0$, $2x + y + 1 = 0$, and $3x + 4y + 5 = 0$ intersect in a point.

87. Matrices. Determinative Systems

The process of solving a system of linear equations by reducing it to triangular form requires us to write a number of equivalent systems. We can cut down the amount of labor involved in this process by using a notation in which the symbols for the unknowns need not be copied down every time we write out a new equivalent system.

To illustrate this notation, consider the system

(87-1)
$$\begin{aligned} \tfrac{1}{2}x - 3y + z \quad &= 5 \\ x + 4y - \quad 3z &= 2 \\ 2x \qquad + \tfrac{1}{4}z &= -1. \end{aligned}$$

The coefficients of the unknowns can be exhibited as an array of numbers:

(87-2)
$$\begin{bmatrix} \frac{1}{2} & -3 & 1 \\ 1 & 4 & -3 \\ 2 & 0 & \frac{1}{4} \end{bmatrix}.$$

An array of numbers such as this one is called a **matrix.** In particular, if there are the same number of rows and columns in the array, the matrix is called a **square matrix.** The square Matrix 87-2 is the **coefficient matrix** of System 87-1. The numbers on the right-hand sides of the equations in System 87-1 can be displayed as the matrix

(87-3)
$$\begin{bmatrix} 5 \\ 2 \\ -1 \end{bmatrix}.$$

A matrix such as this one, with only one column, is called a **column matrix.** We combine the coefficient matrix with the column matrix of the numbers on the right-hand sides of the equations to get the **aug-**

mented matrix of a system. The matrix

$$\left[\begin{array}{ccc|c} \frac{1}{2} & -3 & 1 & 5 \\ 1 & 4 & -3 & 2 \\ 2 & 0 & \frac{1}{4} & -1 \end{array}\right]$$

is the augmented matrix of System 87-1.

We can translate the operations that we used to obtain equivalent systems of equations from a given system into operations to be performed on the rows of numbers in the augmented matrix of the system. These operations always produce a matrix of an equivalent system of equations. They can be summarized as follows.

Operation 87-1. Interchange two rows in a matrix.

Operation 87-2. Multiply all the elements of some row by the same non-zero number. (We say that we *multiply the row* by the number.)

Operation 87-3. Replace a row with the sum of a non-zero multiple of itself and a multiple of another row. (Adding two rows means, of course, adding corresponding elements.)

Example 87-1. Use matrix notation to solve the system in Example 86-3.

Solution. The augmented matrix that corresponds to the system in Example 86-3 is

$$\left[\begin{array}{ccc|c} 1 & -6 & 2 & 5 \\ 2 & -3 & 1 & 4 \\ 3 & 4 & -1 & -2 \end{array}\right].$$

If we add the last row to the second row, and add twice the last row to the first, we obtain the matrix (corresponding to System 86-11)

$$\left[\begin{array}{ccc|c} 7 & 2 & 0 & 1 \\ 5 & 1 & 0 & 2 \\ 3 & 4 & -1 & -2 \end{array}\right].$$

Now subtracting twice the second row from the first produces the matrix

$$\left[\begin{array}{ccc|c} -3 & 0 & 0 & -3 \\ 5 & 1 & 0 & 2 \\ 3 & 4 & -1 & -2 \end{array}\right].$$

This matrix corresponds to the triangular System 86-12, from which we easily obtained the solution of the original system.

Example 87-2. Solve the system of equations that corresponds to the matrix

$$\left[\begin{array}{cccc|c} 2 & -1 & 1 & -1 & -1 \\ 1 & 3 & -2 & 0 & -5 \\ 3 & -2 & 0 & 4 & 1 \\ -1 & 1 & -3 & -1 & -6 \end{array}\right]. \tag{87-4}$$

Solution. First, we multiply the last row by 4 and add to the third; then we subtract the last row from the first to produce the matrix

$$\left[\begin{array}{rrrr|r} 3 & -2 & 4 & 0 & 5 \\ 1 & 3 & -2 & 0 & -5 \\ -1 & 2 & -12 & 0 & -23 \\ -1 & 1 & -3 & -1 & -6 \end{array}\right].$$

The fourth column is now in satisfactory form, so we concentrate on the first three rows and work to obtain zeros in the third column in the first two rows. We multiply the second row by 6. Then we subtract the third row from this new second row. Now we multiply the first row by 3 and add the third row. These operations yield the matrix

$$\left[\begin{array}{rrrr|r} 8 & -4 & 0 & 0 & -8 \\ 7 & 16 & 0 & 0 & -7 \\ -1 & 2 & -12 & 0 & -23 \\ -1 & 1 & -3 & -1 & -6 \end{array}\right].$$

Now we add the second row to 4 times the first and obtain the matrix

$$\left[\begin{array}{rrrr|r} 39 & 0 & 0 & 0 & -39 \\ 7 & 16 & 0 & 0 & -7 \\ -1 & 2 & -12 & 0 & -23 \\ -1 & 1 & -3 & -1 & -6 \end{array}\right].$$

This matrix is the matrix of the system of equations in triangular form

$$\begin{aligned} 39x_1 & & & &= -39 \\ 7x_1 + 16x_2 & & & &= -7 \\ -x_1 + 2x_2 &- 12x_3 & & &= -23 \\ -x_1 + x_2 &- 3x_3 &- x_4 & &= -6. \end{aligned} \tag{87-5}$$

From System 87-5 we readily find that the solution is $(x_1, x_2, x_3, x_4) = (-1, 0, 2, 1)$.

For most systems of linear equations that we have seen thus far, there has been exactly one set of numbers that satisfies all the equations—that is, the system has just one solution. We will call a system of linear equations with exactly one solution a **determinative system.** Not all systems are determinative. A system may have no solution, in which case we say that the system is **inconsistent.** On the other hand, a system of n linear equations in n unknowns may have more than one solution, in which case the system is called **dependent.** The method of solving systems of linear equations by trying to reduce them to triangular form is still applicable to inconsistent and dependent systems. In fact, this method will enable us to tell when these conditions occur. The following two examples illustrate how we can detect these situations.

Example 87-3. Solve the system of equations

$$\begin{aligned} 2x - y + z &= 1 \\ x + 2y - z &= 3 \\ x + 7y - 4z &= 2. \end{aligned} \tag{87-6}$$

Solution. In matrix notation the steps used to reduce the system to triangular form appear as

$$\left[\begin{array}{rrr|r} 2 & -1 & 1 & 1 \\ 1 & 2 & -1 & 3 \\ 1 & 7 & -4 & 2 \end{array}\right] \to \left[\begin{array}{rrr|r} 9 & 3 & 0 & 6 \\ 3 & 1 & 0 & 10 \\ 1 & 7 & -4 & 2 \end{array}\right] \to \left[\begin{array}{rrr|r} 0 & 0 & 0 & -24 \\ 3 & 1 & 0 & 10 \\ 1 & 7 & -4 & 2 \end{array}\right].$$

The third matrix results from subtracting 3 times the second row from the first row of the second matrix. This operation removes the 3 in the first row, but it also removes the 9. The final matrix can be considered as the matrix of the system

$$\begin{aligned} 0 &= 24 \\ 3x + y &= 10 \\ x + 7y - 4z &= 2. \end{aligned}$$

We must now interpret the presence of the false statement $0 = 24$. Logically, our argument runs as follows. *If* there is a solution to System 87-6, *then* $0 = 24$. Since $0 \neq 24$, we conclude that there simply cannot be a solution of System 87-6. The system is therefore *inconsistent.*

Example 87-4. Solve the system of equations

$$\begin{aligned} 2x - y + z &= 1 \\ x + 2y - z &= 3 \\ x + 7y - 4z &= 8. \end{aligned} \tag{87-7}$$

Solution. In this case the matrix reduction is as follows:

$$\left[\begin{array}{rrr|r} 2 & -1 & 1 & 1 \\ 1 & 2 & -1 & 3 \\ 1 & 7 & -4 & 8 \end{array}\right] \to \left[\begin{array}{rrr|r} 9 & 3 & 0 & 12 \\ 3 & 1 & 0 & 4 \\ 1 & 7 & -4 & 8 \end{array}\right] \to \left[\begin{array}{rrr|r} 0 & 0 & 0 & 0 \\ 3 & 1 & 0 & 4 \\ 1 & 7 & -4 & 8 \end{array}\right].$$

This last matrix is the matrix of the system

$$\begin{aligned} 0 &= 0 \\ 3x + y &= 4 \\ x + 7y - 4z &= 8. \end{aligned} \tag{87-8}$$

Unlike Example 87-3 (which yielded $0 = 24$), the first equation here is of absolutely no help. There is nothing false about the statement that $0 = 0$, but it doesn't tell us anything we didn't already know. Now there are many solutions to System 87-8, and hence to System 87-7. For instance, we could take $x = 1$; then $y = 1$ and $z = 0$. Or if $x = 0$, then $y = 4$ and $z = 5$. Indeed, if t is any number, then a solution to System 87-7 is $x = t$, $y = 4 - 3t$, and $z = 5 - 5t$. System 87-7 is dependent.

If a system consists of two linear equations in two unknowns, or three linear equations in three unknowns, and if all the given numbers are real, then there is a simple way of interpreting geometrically what it means for the system to be determinative. Since a linear equation $ax + by = c$, where a, b, and c are real numbers, is the equation of a line in a plane, the *pair* of equations

$$\begin{aligned} ax + by &= c \\ dx + ey &= f \end{aligned} \tag{87-9}$$

represents *two* lines in a plane. A solution of System 87-9 is a pair of real numbers, and we can interpret these numbers as the coordinates of a point that belongs to both the lines represented by System 87-9. Thus *System 87-9 is determinative if, and only if, the lines represented by that system are distinct and non-parallel and hence intersect in one point.*

A linear equation $ax + by + cz = d$, where a, b, c, and d are real numbers, is the equation of a plane in space. Thus a system of three linear equations in three unknowns represents three planes in space. The solution of such a system is a triple of real numbers, and we can interpret these numbers as the coordinates of a point in space that lies in all three of the planes represented by the system. Thus *a system of three linear equations in three unknowns is determinative if, and only if, the planes represented by that system are distinct and have exactly one point in common.*

Problems 87

1. Use matrix notation to solve the following systems of equations.

(a) $\begin{aligned} 2x + 3y &= 7 \\ 3x - y &= 5 \end{aligned}$ (b) $\begin{aligned} 2x + 3y &= 1 \\ 3x - y &= -4 \end{aligned}$

(c) $\begin{aligned} 2x + 3y &= 1 \\ x + 2y &= 1 \end{aligned}$ (d) $\begin{aligned} 2x + 3y &= -1 \\ x + 2y &= -1 \end{aligned}$

(e) $\begin{aligned} 2y &= 6 \\ x - y &= 1 \end{aligned}$ (f) $\begin{aligned} 2y &= 2 \\ x - y &= 3 \end{aligned}$

2. Use matrix notation to solve the following systems of equations.

(a) $\begin{aligned} 2x + 3y - z &= -2 \\ x - y + 2z &= 4 \\ x + 2y + z &= 0 \end{aligned}$ (b) $\begin{aligned} 2x + 3y - z &= 0 \\ x - y + 2z &= 0 \\ x + 2y + z &= 0 \end{aligned}$

(c) $\begin{aligned} x + 4y - 2z &= 0 \\ -2x + y &= 0 \\ x - y + z &= 0 \end{aligned}$ (d) $\begin{aligned} x + 4y - 2z &= -1 \\ -2x + y &= 3 \\ x - y + z &= 0 \end{aligned}$

(e) $\begin{aligned} x + y &= 2 \\ y + z &= -1 \\ z + w &= 0 \\ x - y + z - w &= 0 \end{aligned}$ (f) $\begin{aligned} x + y &= 3 \\ y + z &= 5 \\ z + w &= 7 \\ x - y + z - w &= -2 \end{aligned}$

3. Use matrix notation to solve the following "homogeneous" systems.

(a) $\begin{aligned} 2x - y + z &= 0 \\ x + 3y + 2z &= 0 \\ x - 4y - z &= 0 \end{aligned}$ (b) $\begin{aligned} 2x - y + z &= 0 \\ x + 3y + 2z &= 0 \\ 3x + 2y + 3z &= 0 \end{aligned}$

4. The augmented matrix of a system of equations is

$$\left[\begin{array}{ccc|c} 24 & 0 & 0 & 0 \\ 1 & 2 & 0 & 2 \\ 3 & 4 & 1 & 5 \end{array}\right].$$

Is the system determinative?

5. Solve, if possible, the following systems.

(a) $\begin{aligned} 2x - 3y + z &= -4 \\ x - 4y - z &= -3 \\ x - 9y - 4z &= -5 \end{aligned}$ (b) $\begin{aligned} 2x - 3y + z &= 4 \\ x - 4y - z &= 3 \\ x - 9y - 4z &= 5 \end{aligned}$

(c) $\begin{aligned} 2x - 3y + z &= 3 \\ x - 4y - z &= 4 \\ x - 9y - 4z &= 5 \end{aligned}$ (d) $\begin{aligned} 2x - 3y + z &= 0 \\ x - 4y - z &= 0 \\ x - 9y - 4z &= 0 \end{aligned}$

6. The sum of the digits of a three-digit number is 14 and the middle digit is the sum of the other two digits. If the last two digits are interchanged, the number obtained is 27 less than the original number. Find the number.

7. Can you solve the preceding problem if all the information is the same except that the number obtained when the last two digits are interchanged is 72 less than the original number?

8. Consider how three planes in space can intersect (or fail to intersect). From these geometric considerations, what can you conclude about the possible solutions of a system of three linear equations in three unknowns?

88. Vectors and Matrices

We have already considered vectors in the plane and in three-dimensional space. Once we choose a cartesian coordinate system in the plane, a vector $\boldsymbol{a}$ can be expressed in terms of the basis vectors $\boldsymbol{i}$ and $\boldsymbol{j}$:

$$\boldsymbol{a} = a_1\boldsymbol{i} + a_2\boldsymbol{j}.$$

Similarly, a vector $\boldsymbol{b}$ in space may be written as

$$\boldsymbol{b} = b_1\boldsymbol{i} + b_2\boldsymbol{j} + b_3\boldsymbol{k}$$

relative to a particular coordinate system. The pair of numbers (a_1, a_2) and the triple (b_1, b_2, b_3) determine, and are determined by, the vectors, if a cartesian coordinate system has already been introduced in the plane or in space. Thus we can identify (consider as the same) a plane vector and the pair of numbers consisting of its components or a space vector and the triple of numbers consisting of its components relative to a given coordinate system.

In this section we are going to think of pairs or triples of numbers themselves as being vectors. Thus we will write, for example, $\boldsymbol{a} = (a_1, a_2)$, and $\boldsymbol{b} = (b_1, b_2, b_3)$.

The numbers a_1 and a_2 and b_1, b_2, and b_3 are called the **components** of $\boldsymbol{a}$ and $\boldsymbol{b}$. Mathematical operations with these vectors—addition, dot product, and so on—will be defined in terms of their components. We now define these operations, and as you can see, our definitions are suggested by our previous work with vectors.

DEFINITION 88-1. *If* $\boldsymbol{a} = (a_1, a_2, a_3)$, $\boldsymbol{b} = (b_1, b_2, b_3)$, *and* c *is a number, then*

$$\boldsymbol{a} = \boldsymbol{b} \quad \textit{if, and only if,} \quad a_1 = b_1,\ a_2 = b_2,\ a_3 = b_3,$$

$$\boldsymbol{a} + \boldsymbol{b} = (a_1 + b_1, a_2 + b_2, a_3 + b_3),$$

$$c\boldsymbol{a} = (ca_1, ca_2, ca_3),$$

$$\boldsymbol{a} \cdot \boldsymbol{b} = a_1b_1 + a_2b_2 + a_3b_3.$$

On the basis of these definitions, it is a simple matter to verify the "natural" rules of arithmetic. Thus $\boldsymbol{a} + \boldsymbol{b} = \boldsymbol{b} + \boldsymbol{a}$, $\boldsymbol{a} \cdot (\boldsymbol{b} + \boldsymbol{c}) = \boldsymbol{a} \cdot \boldsymbol{b} + \boldsymbol{a} \cdot \boldsymbol{c}$, and so forth. The vector $\boldsymbol{0} = (0, 0, 0)$ acts like the number zero, and the vector $(-1)\boldsymbol{a}$ plays the role of $-\boldsymbol{a}$. Thus $\boldsymbol{a} + (-1)\boldsymbol{a} = \boldsymbol{0}$. If the dot product $\boldsymbol{a} \cdot \boldsymbol{b}$ is 0, then the vectors $\boldsymbol{a}$ and $\boldsymbol{b}$ are said to be **perpendicular** or **orthogonal.** We speak of the number $\sqrt{\boldsymbol{a} \cdot \boldsymbol{a}}$ as the **length** of the vector $\boldsymbol{a}$.

Example 88-1. Find $(3, 0, 5) - (1, 4, 3)$.

Solution. Of course, we define $\boldsymbol{a} - \boldsymbol{b}$ as $\boldsymbol{a} + (-\boldsymbol{b})$, so

$$(3, 0, 5) - (1, 4, 3) = (3 - 1, 0 - 4, 5 - 3) = (2, -4, 2).$$

We have stated Definition 88-1 for vectors with three components, that is, vectors that are in a three-dimensional space. The way to modify this definition to make it apply to the two-dimensional case is clear. But the interesting modification is not to lower, but to higher, dimensions. Nothing in Definition 88-1 depends on the fact that our vectors have three components. The same rules could be set down to apply to sequences consisting of 5 numbers, or 25, or 125. We would then obtain vector spaces of dimensions 5, 25, or 125. We cannot identify these vectors in higher dimensions with geometric arrows, but such an identification is not necessary for the various operations on vectors that we are now going to carry out.

In this chapter we are going to write our formulas in terms of vectors in two or three dimensions because we are mainly interested in the applications of our theory to problems in the geometry of two- or three-dimensional space. In addition, formulas that involve only two or three components are easier to write out explicitly than those which contain a larger number of components. But all our work can also be carried out in higher dimensions.

We adopt the following notation. A capital letter, such as A, will denote a square matrix. Because we will be dealing only with vectors in two and three dimensions, we need only consider square matrices that are either 2 by 2 or 3 by 3; that is, of *order* 2 or *order* 3. The number in row i and column j of the matrix A will be denoted by a_{ij}. Thus, for example, we write

$$A = \begin{bmatrix} a_{11} & a_{12} & a_{13} \\ a_{21} & a_{22} & a_{23} \\ a_{31} & a_{32} & a_{33} \end{bmatrix}. \tag{88-1}$$

The rows and columns of a matrix can be regarded as vectors. Thus we can write the matrix A of Equation 88-1 as

$$A = \begin{bmatrix} \boldsymbol{r}_1 \\ \boldsymbol{r}_2 \\ \boldsymbol{r}_3 \end{bmatrix} = [\boldsymbol{c}_1, \boldsymbol{c}_2, \boldsymbol{c}_3] \tag{88-2}$$

where

$$\begin{aligned} \boldsymbol{r}_1 &= (a_{11}, a_{12}, a_{13}) & \boldsymbol{c}_1 &= (a_{11}, a_{21}, a_{31}) \\ \boldsymbol{r}_2 &= (a_{21}, a_{22}, a_{23}) & \boldsymbol{c}_2 &= (a_{12}, a_{22}, a_{32}) \\ \boldsymbol{r}_3 &= (a_{31}, a_{32}, a_{33}) & \boldsymbol{c}_3 &= (a_{13}, a_{23}, a_{33}). \end{aligned}$$

Example 88-2. Find the dot product of the first row vector and the second column vector of the matrix $\begin{bmatrix} 2 & -1 \\ 3 & 2 \end{bmatrix}$.

Solution. Here $\boldsymbol{r}_1 = (2, -1)$ and $\boldsymbol{c}_2 = (-1, 2)$. So

$$\boldsymbol{r}_1 \cdot \boldsymbol{c}_2 = (2, -1) \cdot (-1, 2) = -2 - 2 = -4.$$

Example 88-3. Show that the column vectors of the matrix

$$\begin{bmatrix} 1 & 1 & 2 \\ -1 & 1 & 2 \\ 0 & 4 & -1 \end{bmatrix}$$

are mutually orthogonal.

Solution. The column vectors are $\boldsymbol{c}_1 = (1, -1, 0)$, $\boldsymbol{c}_2 = (1, 1, 4)$, and $\boldsymbol{c}_3 = (2, 2, -1)$. You can readily verify that $\boldsymbol{c}_1 \cdot \boldsymbol{c}_2 = \boldsymbol{c}_1 \cdot \boldsymbol{c}_3 = \boldsymbol{c}_2 \cdot \boldsymbol{c}_3 = 0$, so each column vector is orthogonal to the other two.

We will now define the product of a vector in three dimensions by a square matrix of order 3. It will be clear how to modify our definition to apply to vectors in two dimensions and matrices of order 2. Let $\boldsymbol{x} = (x_1, x_2, x_3)$, and let $\boldsymbol{r}_1$, $\boldsymbol{r}_2$, and $\boldsymbol{r}_3$ be the row vectors of a matrix A (See Equation 88-2). Then $A\boldsymbol{x}$ is the *vector* defined by the equation

$$A\boldsymbol{x} = (\boldsymbol{r}_1 \cdot \boldsymbol{x}, \boldsymbol{r}_2 \cdot \boldsymbol{x}, \boldsymbol{r}_3 \cdot \boldsymbol{x}). \tag{88-3}$$

Example 88-4. Let $\boldsymbol{x} = (2, 3, 4)$ and let A be the matrix of Example 88-3. Find the vector $A\boldsymbol{x}$.

Solution. We have $\boldsymbol{r}_1 \cdot \boldsymbol{x} = (1, 1, 2) \cdot (2, 3, 4) = 13$. Similarly, $\boldsymbol{r}_2 \cdot \boldsymbol{x} = (-1, 1, 2) \cdot (2, 3, 4) = 9$ and $\boldsymbol{r}_3 \cdot \boldsymbol{x} = (0, 4, -1) \cdot (2, 3, 4) = 8$. Thus $A\boldsymbol{x} = (13, 9, 8)$.

If k is any number, and if $\boldsymbol{u}$ and $\boldsymbol{v}$ are any vectors, it is not hard to show that

$$\begin{aligned} A(\boldsymbol{u} + \boldsymbol{v}) &= A\boldsymbol{u} + A\boldsymbol{v} \\ A(k\boldsymbol{u}) &= kA\boldsymbol{u}. \end{aligned} \tag{88-4}$$

Notice that we have not defined (and we will not define) the symbol $\boldsymbol{x}A$.

The concept of the product of a vector by a matrix provides us with an especially simple and useful notation for a system of equations. Thus suppose that

$$A = \begin{bmatrix} 1 & -6 & 2 \\ 2 & -3 & 1 \\ 3 & 4 & -1 \end{bmatrix}$$

and that $\boldsymbol{x} = (x_1, x_2, x_3)$. Then $A\boldsymbol{x}$ is the vector

$$A\boldsymbol{x} = (x_1 - 6x_2 + 2x_3, 2x_1 - 3x_2 + x_3, 3x_1 + 4x_2 - x_3). \tag{88-5}$$

Now suppose, for example, that $\boldsymbol{b} = (10, 8, 1)$. Then the single equation

$$A\boldsymbol{x} = \boldsymbol{b} \tag{88-6}$$

states that each component of the vector in Equation 88-5 must be equal to the corresponding component of the vector (10, 8, 1). Thus the matrix-vector Equation 88-6 is equivalent to the system of three linear equations

$$\begin{aligned} x_1 - 6x_2 + 2x_3 &= 10 \\ 2x_1 - 3x_2 + x_3 &= 8 \\ 3x_1 + 4x_2 - x_3 &= 1. \end{aligned} \tag{88-7}$$

Of course, we could start with a system of equations such as System 88-7 and find the matrix A and the vector $\boldsymbol{b}$ of the equivalent matrix-vector equation. Using matrices of order n and vectors with n components, we could represent any system of n linear equations in n unknowns as a single matrix-vector equation.

In the next section we shall have more to say about matrix-vector equations, but first we will take up the algebra of square matrices. The definitions of equality of matrices, of addition of matrices, and of the multiplication of matrices by numbers (scalars) are natural extensions of the definitions of these concepts as applied to vectors.

DEFINITION 88-2. *If*

$$A = \begin{bmatrix} a_{11} & a_{12} & a_{13} \\ a_{21} & a_{22} & a_{23} \\ a_{31} & a_{32} & a_{33} \end{bmatrix}, \qquad B = \begin{bmatrix} b_{11} & b_{12} & b_{13} \\ b_{21} & b_{22} & b_{23} \\ b_{31} & b_{32} & b_{33} \end{bmatrix},$$

and k is a number, then $A = B$ if, and only if, $a_{ij} = b_{ij}$ for all i and j;

$$A + B = \begin{bmatrix} a_{11} + b_{11} & a_{12} + b_{12} & a_{13} + b_{13} \\ a_{21} + b_{21} & a_{22} + b_{22} & a_{23} + b_{23} \\ a_{31} + b_{31} & a_{32} + b_{32} & a_{33} + b_{33} \end{bmatrix}$$

and

$$kA = \begin{bmatrix} ka_{11} & ka_{12} & ka_{13} \\ ka_{21} & ka_{22} & ka_{23} \\ ka_{31} & ka_{32} & ka_{33} \end{bmatrix}.$$

The matrix 0, called the **zero matrix** and defined by the equation

$$0 = \begin{bmatrix} 0 & 0 & 0 \\ 0 & 0 & 0 \\ 0 & 0 & 0 \end{bmatrix},$$

plays the role of zero in our algebra. Thus $0 + A = A + 0 = A$. If we define $-A = (-1)A$, and $A - B = A + (-B)$, then $A - A = 0$. It is not hard to show that the "natural" rules of arithmetic hold, so that, for example,

$$A + B = B + A, \quad A + (B + C) = (A + B) + C,$$
$$k(A + B) = kA + kB, \text{ and } (k + m)A = kA + mA.$$

Multiplication of matrices is more complicated. We define the product AB as follows. First, we consider the matrix B to be expressed in terms of its column vectors (See Equation 88-2)

$$B = [\mathbf{c}_1, \mathbf{c}_2, \mathbf{c}_3].$$

Then we define the product AB as the matrix whose column vectors we obtain by multiplying the column vectors of B by A; that is

(88-8) $$AB = [A\mathbf{c}_1, A\mathbf{c}_2, A\mathbf{c}_3].$$

Now let us recall how we compute these column vectors $A\mathbf{c}_1$, $A\mathbf{c}_2$, and $A\mathbf{c}_3$. If $\mathbf{r}_1$, $\mathbf{r}_2$, and $\mathbf{r}_3$ are the row vectors of A; that is, if

(88-9) $$A = \begin{bmatrix} \mathbf{r}_1 \\ \mathbf{r}_2 \\ \mathbf{r}_3 \end{bmatrix},$$

then $A\mathbf{c}_1 = (\mathbf{r}_1 \cdot \mathbf{c}_1, \mathbf{r}_2 \cdot \mathbf{c}_1, \mathbf{r}_3 \cdot \mathbf{c}_1)$, and so on. It then follows that we can write our product AB as

(88-10) $$AB = \begin{bmatrix} \mathbf{r}_1 \cdot \mathbf{c}_1 & \mathbf{r}_1 \cdot \mathbf{c}_2 & \mathbf{r}_1 \cdot \mathbf{c}_3 \\ \mathbf{r}_2 \cdot \mathbf{c}_1 & \mathbf{r}_2 \cdot \mathbf{c}_2 & \mathbf{r}_2 \cdot \mathbf{c}_3 \\ \mathbf{r}_3 \cdot \mathbf{c}_1 & \mathbf{r}_3 \cdot \mathbf{c}_2 & \mathbf{r}_3 \cdot \mathbf{c}_3 \end{bmatrix}.$$

Thus the rule for forming the product AB is the following. *The number in row i and column j of the matrix AB is the dot product of the ith row vector of A and the jth column vector of B.*

Example 88-5. Compute both AB and BA if

$$A = \begin{bmatrix} 0 & 1 \\ 2 & -1 \end{bmatrix} \text{ and } B = \begin{bmatrix} 1 & 2 \\ 0 & 0 \end{bmatrix}.$$

Solution. By definition,

$$AB = \begin{bmatrix} (0, 1) \cdot (1, 0) & (0, 1) \cdot (2, 0) \\ (2, -1) \cdot (1, 0) & (2, -1) \cdot (2, 0) \end{bmatrix} = \begin{bmatrix} 0 & 0 \\ 2 & 4 \end{bmatrix}$$

and

$$BA = \begin{bmatrix} (1, 2) \cdot (0, 2) & (1, 2) \cdot (1, -1) \\ (0, 0) \cdot (0, 2) & (0, 0) \cdot (1, -1) \end{bmatrix} = \begin{bmatrix} 4 & -1 \\ 0 & 0 \end{bmatrix}.$$

The preceding example shows that *it is not always true that AB and BA are equal.* Most of the other rules of arithmetic are valid for matrices, however. Thus, for example,

$$A(BC) = (AB)C \quad \text{and} \quad A(B + C) = AB + AC.$$

Furthermore,

$$(AB)\boldsymbol{x} = A(B\boldsymbol{x}) \quad \text{and} \quad (A + B)\boldsymbol{x} = A\boldsymbol{x} + B\boldsymbol{x}.$$

The matrix I defined by the equation

$$I = \begin{bmatrix} 1 & 0 & 0 \\ 0 & 1 & 0 \\ 0 & 0 & 1 \end{bmatrix}$$

acts like the number 1 of our real number system. Thus

$$IA = AI = A \quad \text{and} \quad I\boldsymbol{x} = \boldsymbol{x}.$$

The matrix I is called the **identity matrix.**

Problems 88

1. If $\boldsymbol{a} = (2, 1, -3)$ and $\boldsymbol{b} = (3, 0, 2)$, calculate
   (a) $3\boldsymbol{a} + 2\boldsymbol{b}$ (b) $3(\boldsymbol{a} \cdot \boldsymbol{b})$ (c) $\boldsymbol{a} \cdot \boldsymbol{a}$ (d) $\boldsymbol{a} \cdot (\boldsymbol{a} + \boldsymbol{b})$
2. Let $A = \begin{bmatrix} 1 & -2 \\ 3 & 4 \end{bmatrix}$, $\boldsymbol{x} = (2, 1)$, $\boldsymbol{y} = (1, 1)$. Calculate
   (a) $A\boldsymbol{x} \cdot \boldsymbol{y}$ (b) $A\boldsymbol{y} \cdot \boldsymbol{x}$ (c) $A\boldsymbol{y} \cdot A\boldsymbol{x}$.
3. (a) Find a vector that is orthogonal to the vector $\boldsymbol{x} = (2, 1)$.
   (b) Find a unit vector (a vector that is 1 unit long) that is orthogonal to the vector $\boldsymbol{x} = (2, 1)$.
4. Show that any two row vectors or any two column vectors of the following matrix are orthogonal.
$$\begin{bmatrix} 0 & 1 & 0 & 0 \\ 0 & 0 & 0 & 1 \\ 1 & 0 & 0 & 0 \\ 0 & 0 & 1 & 0 \end{bmatrix}$$
5. Find A^2 if A is the matrix of the preceding problem.
6. Find A^3 if A is the following matrix: $\begin{bmatrix} 0 & 1 & 2 \\ 0 & 0 & 3 \\ 0 & 0 & 0 \end{bmatrix}$.
7. Compute the following products.
   (a) $\begin{bmatrix} 1 & 2 \\ -1 & 3 \end{bmatrix} (2, 0)$ (b) $\begin{bmatrix} 1 & 7 \\ 6 & 4 \end{bmatrix} \begin{bmatrix} -1 & 0 \\ 2 & 0 \end{bmatrix}$
   (c) $\begin{bmatrix} 2 & 5 & -1 \\ 6 & 0 & 2 \\ 1 & 3 & 4 \end{bmatrix} (1, -1, 2)$ (d) $\begin{bmatrix} -1 & 0 & 1 \\ 2 & 5 & -3 \\ 4 & 1 & -1 \end{bmatrix} \begin{bmatrix} 0 & 2 & 6 \\ 4 & -1 & 0 \\ 2 & 2 & 1 \end{bmatrix}$

8. Let $A = \begin{bmatrix} 1 & 2 \\ -1 & 3 \end{bmatrix}$ and $B = \begin{bmatrix} 2 & 0 \\ 1 & 1 \end{bmatrix}$. Compute the following matrices.
(a) $2A + 3B$ (b) $AB - BA$ (c) ABA

9. Let $J = \begin{bmatrix} 0 & 1 \\ -1 & 0 \end{bmatrix}$. Show that $J^2 = -I$.

10. Suppose that each of the vectors $\boldsymbol{u}$ and $\boldsymbol{v}$ satisfies the equation $A\boldsymbol{x} = \boldsymbol{b}$. Show that the vector $\boldsymbol{u} - \boldsymbol{v}$ satisfies the equation $A\boldsymbol{x} = \boldsymbol{0}$. If $\boldsymbol{w}$ satisfies the equation $A\boldsymbol{x} = \boldsymbol{0}$, show that $t\boldsymbol{w}$ satisfies the same equation for any number t. Illustrate these remarks by considering the system of equations of Number 5 of Problems 86.

11. Find S^{10} when $S = \begin{bmatrix} 1 & 1 & 1 \\ 1 & 1 & 1 \\ 1 & 1 & 1 \end{bmatrix}$.

12. Let S be the matrix of the preceding problem. Let $\boldsymbol{x} = (1, 1, 1)$, $\boldsymbol{y} = (2, -1, -1)$, and $\boldsymbol{z} = (0, 1, -1)$. Show that $S\boldsymbol{x} = 3\boldsymbol{x}$, $S\boldsymbol{y} = 0\boldsymbol{y}$, and $S\boldsymbol{z} = 0\boldsymbol{z}$. Show also that $\boldsymbol{x} \cdot \boldsymbol{y} = 0$, $\boldsymbol{x} \cdot \boldsymbol{z} = 0$, and $\boldsymbol{y} \cdot \boldsymbol{z} = 0$.

13. To see one reason why matrix multiplication is defined as it is, consider the two-dimensional case. Let A and B be square matrices of order 2, and let $\boldsymbol{x}$ be a vector with two components. Show that the Associative Law $A(B\boldsymbol{x}) = (AB)\boldsymbol{x}$ holds. Now, conversely, show that if C is a matrix such that $A(B\boldsymbol{x}) = C\boldsymbol{x}$ for every $\boldsymbol{x}$, then $C = AB$.

89. The Inverse of a Matrix

In the preceding section we saw how to express a system of three linear equations in three unknowns in matrix-vector form

$$A\boldsymbol{x} = \boldsymbol{b}. \tag{89-1}$$

We are supposing that the coefficient matrix A and the vector $\boldsymbol{b}$ are given and the unknowns of our system are the components of $\boldsymbol{x}$. The natural way to solve Equation 89-1 for $\boldsymbol{x}$ is to "divide" both sides by the matrix A; that is, to multiply both sides by the "reciprocal of A." So we shall use this problem to introduce the idea of the *reciprocal*, or *inverse*, of a matrix. We start with the following definition.

DEFINITION 89-1. *The matrix A^{-1} is the* ***inverse*** *of the matrix A if*

$$AA^{-1} = A^{-1}A = I. \tag{89-2}$$

(From the symmetry of this definition we see that A is also the inverse of A^{-1}, that is $(A^{-1})^{-1} = A$.)

Example 89-1. If $A = \begin{bmatrix} 2 & 1 \\ 1 & 1 \end{bmatrix}$, show that $A^{-1} = \begin{bmatrix} 1 & -1 \\ -1 & 2 \end{bmatrix}$.

Solution. We need only verify that

$$\begin{bmatrix} 2 & 1 \\ 1 & 1 \end{bmatrix}\begin{bmatrix} 1 & -1 \\ -1 & 2 \end{bmatrix} = \begin{bmatrix} 1 & -1 \\ -1 & 2 \end{bmatrix}\begin{bmatrix} 2 & 1 \\ 1 & 1 \end{bmatrix} = \begin{bmatrix} 1 & 0 \\ 0 & 1 \end{bmatrix}.$$

Example 89-2. Show that the matrix $A = \begin{bmatrix} 1 & 1 \\ 1 & 1 \end{bmatrix}$ does not have an inverse.

Solution. Let us take an arbitrary matrix $X = \begin{bmatrix} a & b \\ c & d \end{bmatrix}$ and consider the product AX. We have

$$AX = \begin{bmatrix} 1 & 1 \\ 1 & 1 \end{bmatrix}\begin{bmatrix} a & b \\ c & d \end{bmatrix} = \begin{bmatrix} a + c & b + d \\ a + c & b + d \end{bmatrix}.$$

It is clear that no choice of a, b, c, and d will make this product the identity matrix I. We simply cannot, for example, choose a and c so that $a + c = 1$ *and* $a + c = 0$. Therefore, we cannot solve the equation $AX = I$, and so we cannot hope to satisfy Equations 89-2.

If the matrix A has an inverse, then the solution of Equation 89-1 can be expressed in terms of the inverse matrix and the given vector $\boldsymbol{b}$. We simply multiply both sides of Equation 89-1 by A^{-1} to obtain

$$\begin{aligned} A^{-1}A\boldsymbol{x} &= A^{-1}\boldsymbol{b}, \\ I\boldsymbol{x} &= A^{-1}\boldsymbol{b}, \\ \boldsymbol{x} &= A^{-1}\boldsymbol{b}. \end{aligned}$$

Example 89-3. Solve the system of equations

$$\begin{aligned} 2x + y &= 3 \\ x + y &= -4. \end{aligned}$$

Solution. If we express this system in the form of the matrix-vector Equation 89-1, we will have

$$A = \begin{bmatrix} 2 & 1 \\ 1 & 1 \end{bmatrix}, \quad \boldsymbol{b} = (3, -4), \quad \text{and } \boldsymbol{x} = (x, y).$$

We are given A^{-1} in Example 89-1, and therefore

$$\boldsymbol{x} = A^{-1}\boldsymbol{b} = \begin{bmatrix} 1 & -1 \\ -1 & 2 \end{bmatrix}(3, -4) = (7, -11).$$

You may verify this solution by substituting $(x, y) = (7, -11)$ in the original system of equations.

Let us put aside the question of the existence of the inverse of a given matrix for the moment and turn to the question of calculating the inverse, supposing that there is one. If a matrix A has an inverse A^{-1}, then $X = A^{-1}$ is a solution of the equation

$$AX = I. \tag{89-3}$$

Suppose we denote the column vectors of the matrix X by $\boldsymbol{x}_1$, $\boldsymbol{x}_2$, and $\boldsymbol{x}_3$. Then the matrix equation $AX = I$ is equivalent to the three matrix-vector equations

$$A\boldsymbol{x}_1 = (1, 0, 0),\ A\boldsymbol{x}_2 = (0, 1, 0),\ A\boldsymbol{x}_3 = (0, 0, 1), \tag{89-4}$$

where the vectors $(1, 0, 0)$, $(0, 1, 0)$, and $(0, 0, 1)$ are, of course, the three column vectors of the identity matrix. Each of the three matrix-vector Equations 89-4 is, in turn, equivalent to a system of three linear equations in three unknowns, and we can solve such systems by the methods we discussed in Section 87. In this way we can find the solution $X = A^{-1}$ of Equation 89-3.

Let us use an example to show how we actually proceed. Suppose that A is the matrix

$$A = \begin{bmatrix} 2 & 1 & 2 \\ 2 & -4 & 1 \\ 1 & 1 & 1 \end{bmatrix}.$$

Then to solve Equations 89-4 by the methods of Section 87 we "manipulate" the augmented matrices

$$\left[\begin{array}{ccc|c} 2 & 1 & 2 & 1 \\ 2 & -4 & 1 & 0 \\ 1 & 1 & 1 & 0 \end{array}\right], \left[\begin{array}{ccc|c} 2 & 1 & 2 & 0 \\ 2 & -4 & 1 & 1 \\ 1 & 1 & 1 & 0 \end{array}\right], \text{ and } \left[\begin{array}{ccc|c} 2 & 1 & 2 & 0 \\ 2 & -4 & 1 & 0 \\ 1 & 1 & 1 & 1 \end{array}\right].$$

The operations we perform on these augmented matrices are determined by the square matrix on the left of the vertical line. Since this square matrix is the same in each of the three cases, we won't treat them separately but will lump them together in the single augmented matrix

$$\left[\begin{array}{ccc|ccc} 2 & 1 & 2 & 1 & 0 & 0 \\ 2 & -4 & 1 & 0 & 1 & 0 \\ 1 & 1 & 1 & 0 & 0 & 1 \end{array}\right].$$

We treat this matrix just as we treated the augmented matrices of Section 87. By various row operations we try to reduce the matrix on the left of the vertical line to triangular form. The matrix on the right will be changed in the process, but we pay no attention to that. Thus we have

$$(89\text{-}5)\quad \left[\begin{array}{rrr|rrr} 2 & 1 & 2 & 1 & 0 & 0 \\ 2 & -4 & 1 & 0 & 1 & 0 \\ 1 & 1 & 1 & 0 & 0 & 1 \end{array}\right] \to \left[\begin{array}{rrr|rrr} 0 & -1 & 0 & 1 & 0 & -2 \\ 1 & -5 & 0 & 0 & 1 & -1 \\ 1 & 1 & 1 & 0 & 0 & 1 \end{array}\right]$$

$$\to \left[\begin{array}{rrr|rrr} 0 & -5 & 0 & 5 & 0 & -10 \\ 1 & -5 & 0 & 0 & 1 & -1 \\ 1 & 1 & 1 & 0 & 0 & 1 \end{array}\right] \to \left[\begin{array}{rrr|rrr} -1 & 0 & 0 & 5 & -1 & -9 \\ 1 & -5 & 0 & 0 & 1 & -1 \\ 1 & 1 & 1 & 0 & 0 & 1 \end{array}\right].$$

Now we can stop and solve for the vectors $\boldsymbol{x}_1$, $\boldsymbol{x}_2$, and $\boldsymbol{x}_3$. For example, if $\boldsymbol{x}_1 = (u, v, w)$, then the components u, v, and w satisfy the system of equations

$$\begin{aligned} -u \qquad\qquad &= 5 \\ u - 5v \qquad &= 0 \\ u + v + w &= 0, \end{aligned}$$

and so $\boldsymbol{x}_1 = (-5, -1, 6)$. Similar calculations show that $\boldsymbol{x}_2 = (1, 0, -1)$ and $\boldsymbol{x}_3 = (9, 2, -10)$. It follows that the matrix

$$X = [\boldsymbol{x}_1, \boldsymbol{x}_2, \boldsymbol{x}_3] = \begin{bmatrix} -5 & 1 & 9 \\ -1 & 0 & 2 \\ 6 & -1 & -10 \end{bmatrix}$$

satisfies the equation $AX = I$. You can also verify that $XA = I$, so our matrix X really is A^{-1}.

A more elegant way to proceed is to continue Chain 89-5 until the matrix on the left of the vertical line becomes the identity matrix. To accomplish this result, we apply row operations to make the elements in the lower left corner zero, and then we multiply as necessary to make the elements that remain in the diagonal 1:

$$\left[\begin{array}{rrr|rrr} -1 & 0 & 0 & 5 & -1 & -9 \\ 1 & -5 & 0 & 0 & 1 & -1 \\ 1 & 1 & 1 & 0 & 0 & 1 \end{array}\right] \to \left[\begin{array}{rrr|rrr} -1 & 0 & 0 & 5 & -1 & -9 \\ 0 & -5 & 0 & 5 & 0 & -10 \\ 0 & 1 & 1 & 5 & -1 & -8 \end{array}\right]$$

$$\to \left[\begin{array}{rrr|rrr} -1 & 0 & 0 & 5 & -1 & -9 \\ 0 & -1 & 0 & 1 & 0 & -2 \\ 0 & 1 & 1 & 5 & -1 & -8 \end{array}\right] \to \left[\begin{array}{rrr|rrr} -1 & 0 & 0 & 5 & -1 & -9 \\ 0 & -1 & 0 & 1 & 0 & -2 \\ 0 & 0 & 1 & 6 & -1 & -10 \end{array}\right]$$

$$\to \left[\begin{array}{rrr|rrr} 1 & 0 & 0 & -5 & 1 & 9 \\ 0 & 1 & 0 & -1 & 0 & 2 \\ 0 & 0 & 1 & 6 & -1 & -10 \end{array}\right].$$

Now we see that the matrix to the right of the vertical line is A^{-1}.

We can sum up the procedure for finding the inverse of a matrix A as follows. First, form the augmented matrix

$$[\ A \mid I\ ].$$

Then apply Operations 87-1, 87-2, and 87-3 until this augmented matrix takes the form

$$[\ I \mid A^{-1}\ ].$$

As we indicated in our example, a systematic way to proceed is to first reduce the matrix on the left of the vertical line to triangular form. At that point our augmented matrix will look like this

$$\left[\begin{array}{ccc|ccc} d_1 & 0 & 0 & * & * & * \\ * & d_2 & 0 & * & * & * \\ * & * & d_3 & * & * & * \end{array}\right].$$

Now whether or not we can continue to reduce the matrix on the left to the identity depends on the diagonal numbers d_1, d_2, and d_3. If none of these numbers is zero, then we can reduce the matrix on the left to the identity matrix; otherwise not. Thus the question of solving the equation $AX = I$ is reduced to the question of whether or not the three numbers d_1, d_2, and d_3 are all different from zero.

Let us now put this criterion into different words. If we were to attempt to solve the homogeneous (we use the word "homogeneous" when the vector on the right side of the equation is the vector $\mathbf{0}$) matrix-vector equation

$$A\boldsymbol{x} = \mathbf{0}$$

by the methods we used in Section 87, we would set up the augmented matrix

$$[A \mid \mathbf{0}]$$

and reduce to triangular form

$$\left[\begin{array}{ccc|c} d_1 & 0 & 0 & 0 \\ * & d_2 & 0 & 0 \\ * & * & d_3 & 0 \end{array}\right].$$

If all the numbers d_1, d_2, and d_3 are different from zero, then the equation $A\boldsymbol{x} = \mathbf{0}$ has only the solution $\boldsymbol{x} = \mathbf{0}$; otherwise it also has non-zero solutions. Since the numbers d_1, d_2, and d_3 are the same as those in the preceding paragraph, it follows that the matrix equation $AX = I$ has a solution if, and only if, the homogeneous matrix-vector equation $A\boldsymbol{x} = \mathbf{0}$ has only the "trivial" solution $\boldsymbol{x} = \mathbf{0}$. Then it can be shown that the solution of the equation $AX = I$ is the inverse of A, so we can state the following theorem.

THEOREM 89-1. *The matrix A has an inverse if, and only if, the homogeneous matrix-vector equation $A\boldsymbol{x} = \mathbf{0}$ has only the "trivial" solution $\boldsymbol{x} = \mathbf{0}$. The matrix A^{-1} is the solution of the matrix equation $AX = I$.*

Example 89-4. Show that the homogeneous system

$$\begin{aligned} 2x - y + z &= 0 \\ x - 2y + 3z &= 0 \\ 3x \qquad - z &= 0 \end{aligned}$$

has non-trivial solutions. What can you conclude about the existence of the inverse of the coefficient matrix?

Solution. Using matrix notation to reduce to triangular form, we have

$$\left[\begin{array}{ccc|c} 2 & -1 & 1 & 0 \\ 1 & -2 & 3 & 0 \\ 3 & 0 & -1 & 0 \end{array}\right] \to \left[\begin{array}{ccc|c} 5 & -1 & 0 & 0 \\ 10 & -2 & 0 & 0 \\ 3 & 0 & -1 & 0 \end{array}\right] \to \left[\begin{array}{ccc|c} 0 & 0 & 0 & 0 \\ 10 & -2 & 0 & 0 \\ 3 & 0 & -1 & 0 \end{array}\right].$$

Thus we obtain the equivalent system

$$\begin{aligned} 10x - 2y &= 0 \\ 3x - z &= 0. \end{aligned}$$

It follows that $y = 5x$ and $z = 3x$. Hence we may choose x to be any number t we please and we will obtain the solution $(t, 5t, 3t)$. For example, $(1, 5, 3)$ is a non-trivial solution to our system. It follows from Theorem 89-1 that the matrix

$$\begin{bmatrix} 2 & -1 & 1 \\ 1 & -2 & 3 \\ 3 & 0 & -1 \end{bmatrix}$$

does not have an inverse.

Problems 89

1. Verify that the members of the following pairs of matrices are inverses of each other.
   (a) $\begin{bmatrix} 2 & 1 \\ 5 & 3 \end{bmatrix}, \begin{bmatrix} 3 & -1 \\ -5 & 2 \end{bmatrix}$
   (b) $\begin{bmatrix} 1 & 0 & 0 \\ 0 & -2 & 0 \\ 0 & 0 & 3 \end{bmatrix}, \begin{bmatrix} 1 & 0 & 0 \\ 0 & -\frac{1}{2} & 0 \\ 0 & 0 & \frac{1}{3} \end{bmatrix}$
   (c) $\begin{bmatrix} 0 & 0 & 1 \\ 0 & 1 & 0 \\ 1 & 0 & 0 \end{bmatrix}, \begin{bmatrix} 0 & 0 & 1 \\ 0 & 1 & 0 \\ 1 & 0 & 0 \end{bmatrix}$
   (d) $\begin{bmatrix} 1 & 0 & 0 \\ 2 & 1 & 0 \\ 3 & 2 & 1 \end{bmatrix}, \begin{bmatrix} 1 & 0 & 0 \\ -2 & 1 & 0 \\ 1 & -2 & 1 \end{bmatrix}$
2. Find the inverses of each of the following matrices.
   (a) $\begin{bmatrix} 0 & 1 \\ -1 & 0 \end{bmatrix}$
   (b) $\begin{bmatrix} \frac{2}{3} & 0 & 0 \\ 0 & -1 & 0 \\ 0 & 0 & \frac{3}{5} \end{bmatrix}$
   (c) $\begin{bmatrix} 0 & 1 & 0 \\ 1 & 0 & 0 \\ 0 & 0 & 1 \end{bmatrix}$
   (d) $\begin{bmatrix} 1 & 0 & 0 \\ 1 & 1 & 0 \\ 1 & 1 & 1 \end{bmatrix}$
   (e) $\begin{bmatrix} 1 & 0 & 0 \\ 0 & 2 & 1 \\ 0 & 5 & 3 \end{bmatrix}$
   (f) $\begin{bmatrix} 0 & 0 & 1 \\ 0 & 2 & 0 \\ 3 & 0 & 0 \end{bmatrix}$

3. Use the result of Problem 1(a) to express x and y in terms of u and v if

$$\begin{aligned} 2x + y &= u \\ 5x + 3y &= v. \end{aligned}$$

4. Find the inverses of each of the following matrices.

(a) $\begin{bmatrix} 4 & 1 \\ 7 & 2 \end{bmatrix}$ (b) $\begin{bmatrix} 5 & 9 \\ 1 & 2 \end{bmatrix}$ (c) $\begin{bmatrix} 2 & 2 & 1 \\ 1 & -4 & 1 \\ 2 & 1 & 1 \end{bmatrix}$ (d) $\begin{bmatrix} 1 & 2 & 2 \\ 1 & 1 & 2 \\ 1 & -4 & 1 \end{bmatrix}$

(e) $\begin{bmatrix} 1 & 2 & 0 & 0 \\ 4 & 9 & 0 & 0 \\ 0 & 0 & -3 & 1 \\ 0 & 0 & -8 & 3 \end{bmatrix}$ (f) $\begin{bmatrix} 13 & 4 & 0 & 0 \\ 3 & 1 & 0 & 0 \\ 0 & 0 & -2 & 3 \\ 0 & 0 & -1 & 2 \end{bmatrix}$

5. Use the result of Problem 4(c) to solve the system

$$\begin{aligned} 2x + 2y + z &= 2 \\ x - 4y + z &= 1 \\ 2x + y \;\; + z &= 0 \end{aligned}$$

by computing $A^{-1}\boldsymbol{b}$, where A is the coefficient matrix and $\boldsymbol{b} = (2, 1, 0)$.

6. Find the inverses of the following matrices.

(a) $\begin{bmatrix} 1 & 2 \\ 3 & 4 \end{bmatrix}$ (b) $\begin{bmatrix} 1 & 3 \\ 2 & 4 \end{bmatrix}$ (c) $\begin{bmatrix} 2 & 3 & -1 \\ 1 & -1 & 2 \\ 1 & 2 & 1 \end{bmatrix}$ (d) $\begin{bmatrix} -1 & 2 & 1 \\ 3 & -1 & 2 \\ 2 & 1 & 1 \end{bmatrix}$

(e) $\begin{bmatrix} 1 & 2 & -1 \\ 3 & 0 & 2 \\ 1 & 1 & 1 \end{bmatrix}$ (f) $\begin{bmatrix} 1 & 3 & 1 \\ 1 & 0 & 2 \\ 1 & 2 & -1 \end{bmatrix}$

7. Let $A = \begin{bmatrix} a_{11} & a_{12} \\ a_{21} & a_{22} \end{bmatrix}$.
Solve the system of four equations obtained from the matrix equation $AX = I$ to find the formula for A^{-1}.

90. The Determinant of a Matrix

To find the inverse of the 2 by 2 matrix

$$A = \begin{bmatrix} a_{11} & a_{12} \\ a_{21} & a_{22} \end{bmatrix}$$

we must solve the matrix equation $AX = I$. The solution

$$X = \begin{bmatrix} x_{11} & x_{12} \\ x_{21} & x_{22} \end{bmatrix}$$

will be our inverse. The single matrix equation $AX = I$ is equivalent to 4 linear equations in x_{11}, x_{12}, x_{21} and x_{22}. These equations are easily solved (Number 7 of Problems 89), and yield

$$x_{11} = \frac{a_{22}}{|A|}, \; x_{12} = -\frac{a_{12}}{|A|}, \; x_{21} = -\frac{a_{21}}{|A|}, \text{ and } x_{22} = \frac{a_{11}}{|A|},$$

where we have introduced the abbreviation

$$|A| = a_{11}a_{22} - a_{12}a_{21}.$$

Thus we can write the matrix $X = A^{-1}$ in the form

$$A^{-1} = \frac{1}{|A|}\,\mathcal{A},$$

where $\mathcal{A}$ is the matrix

$$\mathcal{A} = \begin{bmatrix} a_{22} & -a_{12} \\ -a_{21} & a_{11} \end{bmatrix}.$$

Of course, our formula for A^{-1} makes sense only if $|A| \neq 0$. However, if we multiply A by $\mathcal{A}$ we find that

(90-1) $$A\mathcal{A} = \mathcal{A}A = |A|I$$

whether $|A| = 0$ or not.

The number $|A|$ is called the **determinant** of the matrix A. We denote the determinant of a matrix by vertical bars. Thus the symbols $|A|$ and $\begin{vmatrix} a_{11} & a_{12} \\ a_{21} & a_{22} \end{vmatrix}$ stand for the determinant of the matrix

$$A = \begin{bmatrix} a_{11} & a_{12} \\ a_{21} & a_{22} \end{bmatrix}.$$

In this notation

(90-2) $$|A| = \begin{vmatrix} a_{11} & a_{12} \\ a_{21} & a_{22} \end{vmatrix} = a_{11}a_{22} - a_{12}a_{21}.$$

Example 90-1. Find $\begin{vmatrix} 7 & 2 \\ 1 & -3 \end{vmatrix}$.

Solution. According to Equation 90-2,

$$\begin{vmatrix} 7 & 2 \\ 1 & -3 \end{vmatrix} = 7(-3) - 2 \cdot 1 = -21 - 2 = -23.$$

With each square matrix A, of any order, we can associate a matrix $\mathcal{A}$ and a number $|A|$ such that Equation 90-1 is valid. The details of this association are somewhat complicated, however, and we shall restrict our attention to the case of a 3 by 3 matrix

$$A = \begin{bmatrix} a_{11} & a_{12} & a_{13} \\ a_{21} & a_{22} & a_{23} \\ a_{31} & a_{32} & a_{33} \end{bmatrix}.$$

We first construct nine 2 by 2 submatrices of A as follows. *We define* A_{ij}

as the 2 by 2 matrix that is obtained by striking out the ith row and the jth column of the matrix A. Thus, for example, we obtain the submatrix A_{21} by striking out the second row and the first column of A:

$$A_{21} = \begin{bmatrix} a_{12} & a_{13} \\ a_{32} & a_{33} \end{bmatrix}.$$

Now we compute the determinants of these submatrices and use these nine numbers to form our matrix $\mathcal{A}$. This matrix is defined by the equation

$$\mathcal{A} = \begin{bmatrix} |A_{11}| & -|A_{21}| & |A_{31}| \\ -|A_{12}| & |A_{22}| & -|A_{32}| \\ |A_{13}| & -|A_{23}| & |A_{33}| \end{bmatrix}.$$

This definition of $\mathcal{A}$ is completely analogous to the definition of $\mathcal{A}$ in the 2 by 2 case. By striking out rows and columns of our 2 by 2 matrix, we obtain the four submatrices $A_{11} = [a_{22}]$, $A_{12} = [a_{21}]$, $A_{21} = [a_{12}]$, and $A_{22} = [a_{11}]$. Then we define

$$\mathcal{A} = \begin{bmatrix} |A_{11}| & -|A_{21}| \\ -|A_{12}| & |A_{22}| \end{bmatrix},$$

where by the determinant of a matrix consisting of just one number we mean the number itself. Thus $|A_{11}| = a_{22}$, $|A_{12}| = a_{21}$, and so on, and we see that this formula for $\mathcal{A}$ coincides with our previous formula.

Now we return to the formula for $\mathcal{A}$ in the 3 by 3 case. If we replace $|A_{11}|$ with

$$\begin{vmatrix} a_{22} & a_{23} \\ a_{32} & a_{33} \end{vmatrix} = a_{22}a_{33} - a_{23}a_{32},$$

$|A_{12}|$ with

$$\begin{vmatrix} a_{21} & a_{23} \\ a_{31} & a_{33} \end{vmatrix} = a_{21}a_{33} - a_{23}a_{31},$$

and so on, in our expression for $\mathcal{A}$ and then multiply by the matrix A, we will obtain Equation 90-1 with

$$|A| = a_{11}a_{22}a_{33} + a_{12}a_{23}a_{31} + a_{13}a_{21}a_{32} - a_{13}a_{22}a_{31} - a_{11}a_{23}a_{32} - a_{12}a_{21}a_{33}.$$

Thus the determinant of a 3 by 3 matrix is given by the equation

$$\text{(90-3)} \quad \begin{vmatrix} a_{11} & a_{12} & a_{13} \\ a_{21} & a_{22} & a_{23} \\ a_{31} & a_{32} & a_{33} \end{vmatrix} = a_{11}a_{22}a_{33} + a_{12}a_{23}a_{31} + a_{13}a_{21}a_{32} - a_{13}a_{22}a_{31} - a_{11}a_{23}a_{32} - a_{12}a_{21}a_{33}.$$

Example 90-2. Show that, in the case of our 3 by 3 matrix,

$$\text{(90-4)} \qquad |A| = a_{11}|A_{11}| - a_{12}|A_{12}| + a_{13}|A_{13}|.$$

Solution. According to Equation 90-1, the number $|A|$ appears in the first row and first column of the product $A\mathcal{A}$. But the definition of matrix multiplication tells us that this number is the dot product of the first row of A and the first column of $\mathcal{A}$ and you will notice that this dot product is simply the right side of Equation 90-4.

Example 90-3. Evaluate the determinant $\begin{vmatrix} 1 & 2 & 0 \\ 3 & -2 & 1 \\ -4 & 3 & 2 \end{vmatrix}$.

Solution. We use Equations 90-4 and 90-2:

$$\begin{vmatrix} 1 & 2 & 0 \\ 3 & -2 & 1 \\ -4 & 3 & 2 \end{vmatrix} = 1\begin{vmatrix} -2 & 1 \\ 3 & 2 \end{vmatrix} - 2\begin{vmatrix} 3 & 1 \\ -4 & 2 \end{vmatrix} + 0\begin{vmatrix} 3 & -2 \\ -4 & 3 \end{vmatrix}$$
$$= 1(-4-3) - 2(6+4) + 0 = -27.$$

You might use Equation 90-3 to check this result.

If A and B are square matrices of the same order, then

$$|AB| = |A|\,|B|. \tag{90-5}$$

Thus if we multiply the matrices A and B and then calculate the determinant of the product matrix, we get the same number that we would obtain by first calculating the determinants of A and B individually and then multiplying these numbers. In Number 3 of Problems 90 we ask you to verify Equation 90-5 for 2 by 2 matrices. The verification for matrices of higher order is also perfectly straightforward but quite tedious.

From Equation 90-1 we see that if $|A| \neq 0$, then

$$A\left(\frac{1}{|A|}\mathcal{A}\right) = \frac{1}{|A|}\mathcal{A}A = I.$$

Hence A^{-1} exists and equals $(1/|A|)\mathcal{A}$. So *if* the determinant of a matrix is not 0, *then* the matrix has an inverse. Conversely, suppose that A^{-1} exists. Then $AA^{-1} = I$. According to Equation 90-5, $|A|\,|A^{-1}| = |I|$. Since it is clear that $|I| = 1$, we have $|A|\,|A^{-1}| = 1$. Therefore, $|A| \neq 0$, and $|A^{-1}| = |A|^{-1}$. We have the following theorem.

THEOREM 90-1. *The matrix A has an inverse if, and only if, $|A| \neq 0$.*

This theorem enables us to prove the following theorem which is basic to the study of systems of linear equations.

THEOREM 90-2. *The homogeneous matrix-vector equation $A\mathbf{x} = \mathbf{0}$ has a non-trivial solution if, and only if, $|A| = 0$.*

Proof. According to Theorem 89-1, the equation $A\boldsymbol{x} = 0$ has a non-trivial solution if, and only if, the matrix A *does not* have an inverse. But now Theorem 90-1 tells us that this condition is equivalent to the equation $|A| = 0$. Hence the equation $A\boldsymbol{x} = \mathbf{0}$ has a non-trivial solution if, and only if, $|A| = 0$.

Problems 90

1. Evaluate the following determinants.
(a) $\begin{vmatrix} 2 & 3 \\ 4 & 5 \end{vmatrix}$ (b) $\begin{vmatrix} \mathrm{a} & 0 \\ \mathrm{b} & \mathrm{c} \end{vmatrix}$ (c) $\begin{vmatrix} 2 & 4 \\ -4 & -8 \end{vmatrix}$ (d) $\begin{vmatrix} \cos\theta & \sin\theta \\ -\sin\theta & \cos\theta \end{vmatrix}$
2. Verify the following equations.
(a) $\begin{vmatrix} a & b \\ c & d \end{vmatrix} = \begin{vmatrix} a & c \\ b & d \end{vmatrix}$ (b) $\begin{vmatrix} ka & kb \\ kc & kd \end{vmatrix} = k^2 \begin{vmatrix} a & b \\ c & d \end{vmatrix}$
(c) $\begin{vmatrix} a & b \\ c & d \end{vmatrix} = -\begin{vmatrix} c & d \\ a & b \end{vmatrix}$ (d) $\begin{vmatrix} ka & b \\ kc & d \end{vmatrix} = k \begin{vmatrix} a & b \\ c & d \end{vmatrix}$
(e) $\begin{vmatrix} a + tc & b + td \\ c & d \end{vmatrix} = \begin{vmatrix} a & b \\ c & d \end{vmatrix}$
3. Let $A = \begin{bmatrix} a_{11} & a_{12} \\ a_{21} & a_{22} \end{bmatrix}$ and $B = \begin{bmatrix} b_{11} & b_{12} \\ b_{21} & b_{22} \end{bmatrix}$. Show that $|AB| = |A|\,|B|$.
4. Evaluate the following determinants.
(a) $\begin{vmatrix} 1 & 2 & -1 \\ 3 & 0 & 2 \\ 1 & 1 & 1 \end{vmatrix}$ (b) $\begin{vmatrix} 2 & 0 & 0 \\ 5 & 3 & 0 \\ -2 & 1 & 7 \end{vmatrix}$ (c) $\begin{vmatrix} 1 & 1 & 1 \\ 1 & 1 & 1 \\ 1 & 1 & 1 \end{vmatrix}$
(d) $\begin{vmatrix} 1 & 0 & 0 \\ 0 & 1 & 0 \\ 0 & 0 & 1 \end{vmatrix}$ (e) $\begin{vmatrix} 2 & 1 & 0 \\ -1 & 1 & 2 \\ 3 & 6 & -2 \end{vmatrix}$ (f) $\begin{vmatrix} 1 & 2 & 0 \\ 3 & 0 & 0 \\ -1 & 5 & 2 \end{vmatrix}$
5. Show that (if A is a 3 by 3 matrix):
(a) $|A| = a_{11}|A_{11}| - a_{21}|A_{21}| + a_{31}|A_{31}|$
(b) $|A| = -a_{12}|A_{12}| + a_{22}|A_{22}| - a_{32}|A_{32}|$
(c) $0 = -a_{11}|A_{21}| + a_{12}|A_{22}| - a_{13}|A_{23}|$
6. Let $A = \begin{bmatrix} 2 & -1 & 1 \\ 1 & 3 & 2 \\ 1 & -4 & -1 \end{bmatrix}$. Does the equation $A\boldsymbol{x} = \mathbf{0}$ have a non-trivial solution?
7. Solve for x: $\begin{vmatrix} 2 - x & 1 \\ 4 & 5 - x \end{vmatrix} = 0.$
8. For what values of k does the following system have non-trivial solutions?
$$(6 - k)x - 2y = 0$$
$$-2x + (3 - k)y = 0.$$
9. From a 3 by 3 matrix A form the matrix A^* whose rows are the columns of A (in the same order). Show that then the columns of A^* are the rows of A and that $|A^*| = |A|$.

10. Compare Equation 90-4 with Equation 79-16 for the scalar triple product $A \cdot (B \times C)$.

91. The Transpose of a Matrix

Suppose we have a matrix

$$A = \begin{bmatrix} a_{11} & a_{12} & a_{13} \\ a_{21} & a_{22} & a_{23} \\ a_{31} & a_{32} & a_{33} \end{bmatrix}$$

and two vectors

$$\mathbf{x} = (x_1, x_2, x_3), \ \mathbf{y} = (y_1, y_2, y_3).$$

Since the product $A\mathbf{x}$ is a vector, we can compute its dot product with the vector $\mathbf{y}$. You can easily verify the following expression of the number $A\mathbf{x} \cdot \mathbf{y}$ in terms of the elements of A, $\mathbf{x}$, and $\mathbf{y}$:

$$\begin{aligned} A\mathbf{x} \cdot \mathbf{y} = {} & (a_{11}x_1 + a_{12}x_2 + a_{13}x_3)y_1 \\ & + (a_{21}x_1 + a_{22}x_2 + a_{23}x_3)y_2 \\ & + (a_{31}x_1 + a_{32}x_2 + a_{33}x_3)y_3. \end{aligned}$$

Now let us regroup the terms in this sum, factoring out the numbers x_1, x_2, and x_3. Thus

$$\begin{aligned} A\mathbf{x} \cdot \mathbf{y} = {} & (a_{11}y_1 + a_{21}y_2 + a_{31}y_3)x_1 \\ & + (a_{12}y_1 + a_{22}y_2 + a_{32}y_3)x_2 \\ & + (a_{13}y_1 + a_{23}y_2 + a_{33}y_3)x_3. \end{aligned} \tag{91-1}$$

From this last equation we see that we can obtain the dot product $A\mathbf{x} \cdot \mathbf{y}$ by first multiplying $\mathbf{y}$ by a suitable matrix and then dotting the resulting vector with $\mathbf{x}$. We denote the "suitable" matrix by A^* and call it the **transpose** of A. Thus the basic relation between a matrix A and its transpose A^* is the following equation, valid for every pair of vectors $\mathbf{x}$ and $\mathbf{y}$,

$$A\mathbf{x} \cdot \mathbf{y} = \mathbf{x} \cdot A^*\mathbf{y}. \tag{91-2}$$

It is clear from Equation 91-1 that

$$A^* = \begin{bmatrix} a_{11} & a_{21} & a_{31} \\ a_{12} & a_{22} & a_{32} \\ a_{13} & a_{23} & a_{33} \end{bmatrix}; \tag{91-3}$$

that is, the rows of A become the columns of A^*, and the columns of A become the rows of A^*. Thus we also have $(A^*)^* = A$.

Example 91-1. Let $A = \begin{bmatrix} 1 & 2 \\ 3 & 4 \end{bmatrix}$, $\boldsymbol{x} = (1, 1)$, and $\boldsymbol{y} = (1, -1)$; verify Equation 91-2.

Solution. We have $A\boldsymbol{x} = (3, 7)$, and so $A\boldsymbol{x} \cdot \boldsymbol{y} = -4$. To get A^* we replace the rows of A with its columns. Thus

$$A^* = \begin{bmatrix} 1 & 3 \\ 2 & 4 \end{bmatrix}.$$

Now $A^*\boldsymbol{y} = (-2, -2)$, and hence $\boldsymbol{x} \cdot A^*\boldsymbol{y} = -4$, the same number we had formerly found for $A\boldsymbol{x} \cdot \boldsymbol{y}$. Equation 91-2 tells us that "when we transfer A across the dot, it becomes A^*."

Example 91-2. Show that $\boldsymbol{x} \cdot A^*A\boldsymbol{x} \geq 0$ regardless of the vector $\boldsymbol{x}$ or matrix A.

Solution. When we transfer A across the dot in the product $A\boldsymbol{x} \cdot A\boldsymbol{x}$, we obtain the equation

$$A\boldsymbol{x} \cdot A\boldsymbol{x} = \boldsymbol{x} \cdot A^*A\boldsymbol{x}.$$

The right side of this equation is the number we are considering. The left side is the dot product of a vector by itself (the square of its length) and hence is greater than or equal to zero.

Suppose we express a matrix A in terms of its row and column vectors:

$$A = \begin{bmatrix} \boldsymbol{r}_1 \\ \boldsymbol{r}_2 \\ \boldsymbol{r}_3 \end{bmatrix} = [\boldsymbol{c}_1, \boldsymbol{c}_2, \boldsymbol{c}_3].$$

The rows of the transpose A^* are the columns of A, and the columns of A^* are the rows of A, so

$$A^* = \begin{bmatrix} \boldsymbol{c}_1 \\ \boldsymbol{c}_2 \\ \boldsymbol{c}_3 \end{bmatrix} = [\boldsymbol{r}_1, \boldsymbol{r}_2, \boldsymbol{r}_3].$$

Now let us recall that the elements of the product of two matrices are the dot products of the rows of the first factor and the columns of the second. Therefore,

$$\text{(91-4)} \qquad AA^* = \begin{bmatrix} \boldsymbol{r}_1 \cdot \boldsymbol{r}_1 & \boldsymbol{r}_1 \cdot \boldsymbol{r}_2 & \boldsymbol{r}_1 \cdot \boldsymbol{r}_3 \\ \boldsymbol{r}_2 \cdot \boldsymbol{r}_1 & \boldsymbol{r}_2 \cdot \boldsymbol{r}_2 & \boldsymbol{r}_2 \cdot \boldsymbol{r}_3 \\ \boldsymbol{r}_3 \cdot \boldsymbol{r}_1 & \boldsymbol{r}_3 \cdot \boldsymbol{r}_2 & \boldsymbol{r}_3 \cdot \boldsymbol{r}_3 \end{bmatrix}$$

and

$$\text{(91-5)} \qquad A^*A = \begin{bmatrix} \boldsymbol{c}_1 \cdot \boldsymbol{c}_1 & \boldsymbol{c}_1 \cdot \boldsymbol{c}_2 & \boldsymbol{c}_1 \cdot \boldsymbol{c}_3 \\ \boldsymbol{c}_2 \cdot \boldsymbol{c}_1 & \boldsymbol{c}_2 \cdot \boldsymbol{c}_2 & \boldsymbol{c}_2 \cdot \boldsymbol{c}_3 \\ \boldsymbol{c}_3 \cdot \boldsymbol{c}_1 & \boldsymbol{c}_3 \cdot \boldsymbol{c}_2 & \boldsymbol{c}_3 \cdot \boldsymbol{c}_3 \end{bmatrix}.$$

We introduced Equations 91-4 and 91-5 so that we could use them now as we study orthogonal matrices. A matrix R is said to be **orthogonal** if $R^* = R^{-1}$. Therefore, an orthogonal matrix R satisfies the equations

$$RR^* = R^*R = I.$$

From Equation 91-4 we see that if R is orthogonal, then the dot product of each row with itself is 1 and with each other row is 0. Thus each row vector is a "unit vector," and is orthogonal to the other row vectors. The converse is also true. That is, if each row vector of a matrix R is 1 unit long and is orthogonal to the other row vectors, then Equation 91-4 shows that $RR^* = I$. Hence $R^* = R^{-1}$, and so R is orthogonal. Equation 91-5 tells us that the same remarks apply to the column vectors of an orthogonal matrix.

Example 91-3. Show that the matrix

$$R = \begin{bmatrix} \cos\theta & \sin\theta \\ -\sin\theta & \cos\theta \end{bmatrix}$$

is orthogonal, regardless of the choice of θ.

Solution. We must show that $R^* = R^{-1}$; that is, that $RR^* = I$:

$$\begin{bmatrix} \cos\theta & \sin\theta \\ -\sin\theta & \cos\theta \end{bmatrix} \begin{bmatrix} \cos\theta & -\sin\theta \\ \sin\theta & \cos\theta \end{bmatrix} = \begin{bmatrix} 1 & 0 \\ 0 & 1 \end{bmatrix}.$$

Example 91-4. Solve the system of equations

$$\bar{x} = x\cos\theta + y\sin\theta$$
$$\bar{y} = -x\sin\theta + y\cos\theta$$

for x and y in terms of $\bar{x}$ and $\bar{y}$.

Solution. If we set $\boldsymbol{v} = (x, y)$ and $\bar{\boldsymbol{v}} = (\bar{x}, \bar{y})$, then we can write this system of equations in matrix-vector form

$$\bar{\boldsymbol{v}} = R\boldsymbol{v},$$

where R is the matrix of the preceding example. Now we multiply both sides of this equation by R^* and use the fact that $R^*R = I$ to see that

$$\boldsymbol{v} = R^*\bar{\boldsymbol{v}}.$$

This matrix-vector equation is equivalent to the system

$$x = \bar{x}\cos\theta - \bar{y}\sin\theta$$
$$y = \bar{x}\sin\theta + \bar{y}\cos\theta.$$

You can easily verify that for any 2 by 2 or 3 by 3 matrix A, we have $|A^*| = |A|$ (see Numbers 2(a) and 9 of Problems 90). Also $|A|\,|A^{-1}| = |AA^{-1}| = |I| = 1$. Thus if R is an orthogonal matrix,

$$1 = |R|\,|R^{-1}| = |R|\,|R^*| = |R|\,|R| = |R|^2;$$

that is, the square of the determinant of an orthogonal matrix is 1. Hence $|R| = 1$ or $|R| = -1$; that is, *the determinant of an orthogonal matrix is either 1 or* -1.

Problems 91

1. Verify the equation $A\boldsymbol{x} \cdot \boldsymbol{y} = \boldsymbol{x} \cdot A^*\boldsymbol{y}$ in the following cases.

(a) $A = \begin{bmatrix} 2 & -1 \\ -3 & 5 \end{bmatrix}$, $\quad \boldsymbol{x} = (3, 2),\ \boldsymbol{y} = (-1, 4)$

(b) $A = \begin{bmatrix} 2 & 1 \\ 1 & 0 \end{bmatrix}$, $\quad \boldsymbol{x} = (1, 3),\ \boldsymbol{y} = (-2, 2)$

(c) $A = \begin{bmatrix} 2 & -1 & 1 \\ 3 & 0 & 2 \\ 1 & 2 & -1 \end{bmatrix}$, $\quad \boldsymbol{x} = (2, -1, 1),\ \boldsymbol{y} = (1, 0, 2)$

(d) $A = \begin{bmatrix} 2 & -1 & 3 \\ -1 & 0 & 1 \\ 3 & 1 & 2 \end{bmatrix}$, $\quad \boldsymbol{x} = (2, 1, 0),\ \boldsymbol{y} = (0, 1, 2)$

2. The following equations are true for any matrices. Verify their validity for the choices

$$A = \begin{bmatrix} 2 & 1 \\ 1 & 1 \end{bmatrix} \quad \text{and} \quad B = \begin{bmatrix} 1 & 2 \\ -1 & 0 \end{bmatrix}.$$

(a) $(A^*)^* = A$, (b) $|B^*| = |B|$, (c) $(A + B)^* = A^* + B^*$, (d) $(A^{-1})^* = (A^*)^{-1}$, (e) $(AB)^* = B^*A^*$

3. Show that $(A + B)^* = A^* + B^*$.

4. Show that $\boldsymbol{x} \cdot A^*B\boldsymbol{y} = B^*A\boldsymbol{x} \cdot \boldsymbol{y}$.

5. Show that $A\boldsymbol{x} \cdot \boldsymbol{x} = A^*\boldsymbol{x} \cdot \boldsymbol{x}$.

6. Verify that the following matrices are orthogonal.

(a) $\begin{bmatrix} 0 & 1 & 0 \\ 1 & 0 & 0 \\ 0 & 0 & 1 \end{bmatrix}$ (b) $\begin{bmatrix} 1 & 0 & 0 \\ 0 & -1 & 0 \\ 0 & 0 & -1 \end{bmatrix}$ (c) $\begin{bmatrix} \cos\theta & 0 & \sin\theta \\ 0 & 1 & 0 \\ -\sin\theta & 0 & \cos\theta \end{bmatrix}$

(d) $\begin{bmatrix} \frac{2}{3} & \frac{1}{3} & -\frac{2}{3} \\ \frac{1}{3} & \frac{2}{3} & \frac{2}{3} \\ \frac{2}{3} & -\frac{2}{3} & \frac{1}{3} \end{bmatrix}$ (e) $\begin{bmatrix} \frac{1}{\sqrt{3}} & \frac{2}{\sqrt{6}} & 0 \\ \frac{1}{\sqrt{3}} & \frac{-1}{\sqrt{6}} & \frac{1}{\sqrt{2}} \\ \frac{1}{\sqrt{3}} & \frac{-1}{\sqrt{6}} & \frac{-1}{\sqrt{2}} \end{bmatrix}$ (f) $\begin{bmatrix} \frac{3}{5} & \frac{4}{5} \\ \frac{4}{5} & -\frac{3}{5} \end{bmatrix}$

7. If R is an orthogonal matrix, show that $R\boldsymbol{x} \cdot R\boldsymbol{y} = \boldsymbol{x} \cdot \boldsymbol{y}$ for every pair of vectors $\boldsymbol{x}$ and $\boldsymbol{y}$.

8. Is there a number t such that $\begin{bmatrix} 1 & 0 \\ 4 & t \end{bmatrix}$ is an orthogonal matrix?

9. Determine numbers u, v, w, x, y, and z so that the matrix $\begin{bmatrix} u & 0 & 0 \\ v & w & 0 \\ x & y & z \end{bmatrix}$ is an orthogonal matrix.

10. Regardless of the numbers θ and ϕ, the matrices

$$A = \begin{bmatrix} \cos\theta & \sin\theta \\ -\sin\theta & \cos\theta \end{bmatrix} \quad \text{and} \quad B = \begin{bmatrix} \cos\phi & \sin\phi \\ -\sin\phi & \cos\phi \end{bmatrix}$$

are orthogonal. Show that AB is also orthogonal.

11. Prove that $(AB)^* = B^*A^*$ for 2 by 2 matrices. (The result is true for matrices of any order.)

12. Suppose that A and B are orthogonal matrices. Show that AB is also orthogonal. (Use $(AB)^* = B^*A^*$.)

92. Characteristic Values and the Diagonalization of a Matrix

A matrix A transforms a vector $\boldsymbol{x}$ into another vector $A\boldsymbol{x}$. A question that frequently arises is the following. Under what circumstances is the transformed vector simply a scalar multiple of the original vector? Thus, when is $A\boldsymbol{x} = 5\boldsymbol{x}$, or $A\boldsymbol{x} = \pi\boldsymbol{x}$, or $A\boldsymbol{x} = 0\boldsymbol{x}$? In general, we ask, "Is there a scalar multiplier λ such that the equation

$$A\boldsymbol{x} = \lambda\boldsymbol{x} \tag{92-1}$$

holds for some vector $\boldsymbol{x}$." If A is any matrix and λ is any number, then the vector $\boldsymbol{x} = \boldsymbol{0}$ will satisfy Equation 92-1. This solution is called the **trivial solution,** and we hereby rule out the trivial solution as an answer to our question.

We can write Equation 92-1 as $A\boldsymbol{x} = \lambda I\boldsymbol{x}$, and so we have

$$(A - \lambda I)\boldsymbol{x} = \boldsymbol{0}. \tag{92-2}$$

Now we can apply the results of Section 90. Theorem 90-2 says that a homogeneous matrix-vector equation possesses a non-trivial solution if, and only if, the determinant of the coefficient matrix is 0. Therefore, Equation 92-1 has a solution $\boldsymbol{x} \neq \boldsymbol{0}$ if, and only if, λ is a number that satisfies the **characteristic equation**

$$|A - \lambda I| = 0. \tag{92-3}$$

Example 92-1. Solve Equation 92-1 if A is replaced by the matrix

$$S = \begin{bmatrix} 3 & 2 \\ 2 & 0 \end{bmatrix}.$$

Solution. In this case our characteristic Equation 92-3 is

$$\begin{vmatrix} 3 - \lambda & 2 \\ 2 & -\lambda \end{vmatrix} = (3 - \lambda)(-\lambda) - 4 = (\lambda - 4)(\lambda + 1) = 0.$$

Its solutions are the numbers $\lambda = 4$ and $\lambda = -1$. Corresponding to each of these numbers is a solution $\boldsymbol{x} = (x_1, x_2) \neq (0, 0)$ of Equation 92-1 (or the equivalent Equation 92-2). Let us choose $\lambda = 4$. Then the coefficient matrix of Equation 92-2 becomes

$$S - 4I = \begin{bmatrix} 3 - 4 & 2 \\ 2 & -4 \end{bmatrix} = \begin{bmatrix} -1 & 2 \\ 2 & -4 \end{bmatrix}.$$

Thus to find a vector $\boldsymbol{x}$ that corresponds to the number 4, we must find a solution of the homogeneous system

$$-x_1 + 2x_2 = 0$$

$$2x_1 - 4x_2 = 0.$$

We see that the vector $\boldsymbol{x} = (2, 1)$ is one solution of this system. Therefore, for this vector $\boldsymbol{x}$,

$$S\boldsymbol{x} = 4\boldsymbol{x}.$$

If we set $\lambda = -1$, we can take $\boldsymbol{x} = (1, -2)$, and then $S\boldsymbol{x} = (-1)\boldsymbol{x}$, as you can easily verify.

The preceding example illustrates the following facts about Equation 92-1. The characteristic equation is an algebraic equation whose degree is the order of the matrix A. Thus the matrix of our example was a 2 by 2 matrix, and λ satisfied a quadratic equation. Therefore, the number of different possible choices for λ is at most the order of A. These numbers λ are called the **characteristic values** of the matrix A. Corresponding to each characteristic value there is a **characteristic vector $\boldsymbol{x}$,** that is, a vector $\boldsymbol{x} \neq \mathbf{0}$ that satisfies Equation 92-1. If $\boldsymbol{x}$ is a characteristic vector, then so is any non-zero multiple of $\boldsymbol{x}$, for example $3\boldsymbol{x}$, $5\boldsymbol{x}$, and so on. Frequently we multiply a characteristic vector by the reciprocal of its length to get a **unit characteristic vector.** For example, the vector $\boldsymbol{x} = (2/\sqrt{5}, 1/\sqrt{5})$ is a characteristic vector of the matrix S of Example 92-1, and it is 1 unit long. The vector $\boldsymbol{x} = (-2/\sqrt{5}, -1/\sqrt{5})$ is another unit characteristic vector that corresponds to the characteristic value 4.

The matrix of Example 92-1 is of a special form that appears often in mathematical applications. A matrix S is said to be **symmetric** if $S^* = S$, and you will notice that our matrix S of Example 92-1 is a symmetric matrix. The characteristic vectors (2, 1) and (1, −2) of the symmetric matrix of Example 92-1 are orthogonal, and the next theorem shows that this fact is no accident.

THEOREM 92-1. *If $\boldsymbol{x}$ and $\boldsymbol{y}$ are characteristic vectors of a symmetric matrix S that correspond to different characteristic values λ and μ, then $\boldsymbol{x} \cdot \boldsymbol{y} = 0$.*

Proof. We are supposing that

$$S\boldsymbol{x} = \lambda\boldsymbol{x} \quad \text{and} \quad S\boldsymbol{y} = \mu\boldsymbol{y}.$$

If we dot the first of these equations with $\boldsymbol{y}$ and the second with $\boldsymbol{x}$ and subtract, then we obtain the equation

$$\boldsymbol{y} \cdot S\boldsymbol{x} - \boldsymbol{x} \cdot S\boldsymbol{y} = (\lambda - \mu)\boldsymbol{x} \cdot \boldsymbol{y}.$$

Because S is symmetric, $\boldsymbol{y} \cdot S\boldsymbol{x} = S^*\boldsymbol{y} \cdot \boldsymbol{x} = S\boldsymbol{y} \cdot \boldsymbol{x} = \boldsymbol{x} \cdot S\boldsymbol{y}$, and so the left side of this equation is 0. Furthermore, we are assuming that $\lambda - \mu \neq 0$, and hence we see that $\boldsymbol{x} \cdot \boldsymbol{y} = 0$.

Although we shall not prove it, even if the characteristic values of a real symmetric n by n matrix are not all different, we can find n mutually orthogonal characteristic vectors.

To see the implications of the fact that we can choose the characteristic vectors of a symmetric matrix to be pairwise orthogonal, let us return to our matrix of Example 92-1. The vectors $\boldsymbol{x}_1 = (2/\sqrt{5}, 1/\sqrt{5})$ and $\boldsymbol{x}_2 = (1/\sqrt{5}, -2/\sqrt{5})$ are characteristic vectors of the matrix S. Each is 1 unit long, and their dot product is 0. Now we form the matrix whose column vectors are these vectors:

$$P = \begin{bmatrix} 2/\sqrt{5} & 1/\sqrt{5} \\ 1/\sqrt{5} & -2/\sqrt{5} \end{bmatrix}.$$

Because its columns are orthogonal and each is 1 unit long, this matrix is an orthogonal matrix. Furthermore, as you can easily check,

$$P^*SP = \begin{bmatrix} 4 & 0 \\ 0 & -1 \end{bmatrix}.$$

Thus we have "transformed" S into a diagonal matrix by means of the orthogonal matrix P. The diagonal elements of the resulting matrix are the characteristic values of S.

Here is the general situation. Suppose that S is a symmetric matrix with characteristic values λ_1, λ_2, and λ_3 and corresponding characteristic vectors $\boldsymbol{x}_1$, $\boldsymbol{x}_2$, and $\boldsymbol{x}_3$, each of which is 1 unit long and orthogonal to the other two. Now we form the matrix

$$P = [\boldsymbol{x}_1, \boldsymbol{x}_2, \boldsymbol{x}_3].$$

Because the vectors $\boldsymbol{x}_1$, $\boldsymbol{x}_2$, and $\boldsymbol{x}_3$ are pairwise orthogonal and of unit length, this matrix P is an orthogonal matrix. Now

$$SP = [S\boldsymbol{x}_1, S\boldsymbol{x}_2, S\boldsymbol{x}_3] = [\lambda_1\boldsymbol{x}_1, \lambda_2\boldsymbol{x}_2, \lambda_3\boldsymbol{x}_3],$$

and you may readily verify that this product may be written as PD, where

(92-4) $$D = \begin{bmatrix} \lambda_1 & 0 & 0 \\ 0 & \lambda_2 & 0 \\ 0 & 0 & \lambda_3 \end{bmatrix}.$$

Thus $SP = PD$, and since $P^*P = I$, then

$$P^*SP = D.$$

In this way we can transform any symmetric matrix to diagonal form by means of an orthogonal matrix, as stated in the following theorem.

THEOREM 92-2. *If S is a symmetric matrix with characteristic values λ_1, λ_2, and λ_3, then there exists an orthogonal matrix P such that $P^*SP = D$, where the matrix D is given by Equation* 92-4.

Example 92-2. Diagonalize the symmetric matrix

$$S = \begin{bmatrix} 1 & 1 & 1 \\ 1 & 1 & 1 \\ 1 & 1 & 1 \end{bmatrix}.$$

Solution. In Number 12 of Problems 88 you were asked to verify that the characteristic values of S are the numbers 3, 0, 0 and that corresponding mutually orthogonal characteristic vectors are (1, 1, 1), (2, −1, −1), and (0, 1, −1). Now we divide each of these vectors by its length and use the resulting unit vectors as the columns of an orthogonal matrix P:

$$P = \begin{bmatrix} 1/\sqrt{3} & 2/\sqrt{6} & 0 \\ 1/\sqrt{3} & -1/\sqrt{6} & 1/\sqrt{2} \\ 1/\sqrt{3} & -1/\sqrt{6} & -1/\sqrt{2} \end{bmatrix}.$$

Our theory says, and you may confirm, that

$$P^*SP = \begin{bmatrix} 3 & 0 & 0 \\ 0 & 0 & 0 \\ 0 & 0 & 0 \end{bmatrix}.$$

Problems 92

1. Let S be the matrix $S = \begin{bmatrix} 2 & 1 \\ 1 & 2 \end{bmatrix}$.
   (a) What is the characteristic equation of S?
   (b) What are the characteristic values of S?

(c) Find characteristic vectors that correspond to the characteristic values.
(d) Construct an orthogonal matrix P whose column vectors are characteristic vectors of S.
(e) Show that $P^*SP = D$, where D is a diagonal matrix.

2. Answer the questions in Number 1 if $S = \begin{bmatrix} 1 & -2 \\ -2 & 1 \end{bmatrix}$.

3. For each of the following symmetric matrices S we can find an orthogonal matrix P such that $P^*SP = D$, a diagonal matrix. Find D in each case.

(a) $\begin{bmatrix} 4 & 1 \\ 1 & 4 \end{bmatrix}$ (b) $\begin{bmatrix} 4 & 2 \\ 2 & 1 \end{bmatrix}$ (c) $\begin{bmatrix} 0 & 1 \\ 1 & 0 \end{bmatrix}$

(d) $\begin{bmatrix} 1 & 2 \\ 2 & 3 \end{bmatrix}$ (e) $\begin{bmatrix} 2 & 3 \\ 3 & -2 \end{bmatrix}$

4. If a, b, and c are real numbers, show that the characteristic values of the matrix $\begin{bmatrix} a & b \\ b & c \end{bmatrix}$ are real numbers. (It can be shown that the characteristic numbers of any real symmetric matrix are real).

5. Let S be the matrix $S = \begin{bmatrix} 1 & 1 & 1 \\ 1 & 2 & 0 \\ 1 & 0 & 2 \end{bmatrix}$.

(a) What is the characteristic equation of S?
(b) What are the characteristic values of S?
(c) Find characteristic vectors that correspond to the characteristic values.
(d) Construct an orthogonal matrix P whose column vectors are characteristic vectors of S.
(e) Show that $P^*SP = D$, a diagonal matrix.

6. Answer the questions in Number 5 if $S = \begin{bmatrix} 2 & -2 & -2 \\ -2 & 1 & -1 \\ -2 & -1 & 1 \end{bmatrix}$.

7. For each of the following symmetric matrices S we can find an orthogonal matrix P such that $P^*SP = D$ is a diagonal matrix. Find D in each case.

(a) $\begin{bmatrix} 0 & 0 & 2 \\ 0 & 1 & 0 \\ 2 & 0 & 0 \end{bmatrix}$ (b) $\begin{bmatrix} 4 & 1 & 0 \\ 1 & 4 & 0 \\ 0 & 0 & 2 \end{bmatrix}$ (c) $\begin{bmatrix} 2 & 0 & 1 \\ 0 & 1 & 0 \\ 1 & 0 & 2 \end{bmatrix}$

(d) $\begin{bmatrix} 0 & 1 & 0 \\ 1 & 0 & 1 \\ 0 & 1 & 0 \end{bmatrix}$ (e) $\begin{bmatrix} 5 & -1 & -1 \\ -1 & 3 & 1 \\ -1 & 1 & 3 \end{bmatrix}$

93. Rotation of Axes

We have used the word "vector" in two different senses in this book. In Chapters 8 and 9 we thought of a vector as being an "arrow" in the plane or in space. We might call these arrows "geometric vectors." In this chapter we have considered a vector as a triple of numbers. We have already pointed out that if we have a cartesian coordinate system in space, then there is a natural correspondence between geometric vectors and vectors that consist of triples of numbers. We simply identify a geometric vector with the triple of numbers that are its components relative to the given coordinate system. For this reason we might call the triple of numbers a "component vector." Thus the introduction of a cartesian coordinate system in space sets up a correspondence between geometric vectors and component vectors.

In this section we wish to take up the question of rotation of axes in three-dimensional space. For this purpose we will have to distinguish carefully between a geometric vector and a component vector. We will be dealing with two coordinate systems, and each geometric vector will have two component vectors corresponding to it, one for each coordinate system.

A cartesian coordinate system is determined by choosing an origin and three mutually perpendicular unit basis vectors $\boldsymbol{i}$, $\boldsymbol{j}$, and $\boldsymbol{k}$. Then a geometric vector $\boldsymbol{V}$ can be expressed as a sum

$$\boldsymbol{V} = x\boldsymbol{i} + y\boldsymbol{j} + z\boldsymbol{k}. \tag{93-1}$$

The components of $\boldsymbol{V}$ relative to this coordinate system are the numbers x, y, and z. Therefore, corresponding to the geometric vector $\boldsymbol{V}$ is the component vector $\boldsymbol{v} = (x, y, z)$.

Now we are going to introduce a new cartesian coordinate system determined by an orthogonal matrix

$$R = \begin{bmatrix} r_{11} & r_{12} & r_{13} \\ r_{21} & r_{22} & r_{23} \\ r_{31} & r_{32} & r_{33} \end{bmatrix}.$$

We shall take the origin of this new system to be the origin of the original system and its unit basis vectors to be the vectors $\bar{\boldsymbol{\imath}}$, $\bar{\boldsymbol{\jmath}}$, and $\bar{\boldsymbol{k}}$ defined by the following equations:

$$\begin{aligned} \bar{\boldsymbol{\imath}} &= r_{11}\boldsymbol{i} + r_{12}\boldsymbol{j} + r_{13}\boldsymbol{k} \\ \bar{\boldsymbol{\jmath}} &= r_{21}\boldsymbol{i} + r_{22}\boldsymbol{j} + r_{23}\boldsymbol{k} \\ \bar{\boldsymbol{k}} &= r_{31}\boldsymbol{i} + r_{32}\boldsymbol{j} + r_{33}\boldsymbol{k}. \end{aligned} \tag{93-2}$$

Our first task is to verify that these vectors really do form a basis for a cartesian system; that is, that each is 1 unit long and perpendicular to the other two. This fact follows from the orthogonality of R. Each of the row vectors of R is a unit vector and is orthogonal to the other two row vectors. Therefore,

$$\begin{aligned} \bar{\boldsymbol{\imath}} \cdot \bar{\boldsymbol{\imath}} &= (r_{11}\boldsymbol{i} + r_{12}\boldsymbol{j} + r_{13}\boldsymbol{k}) \cdot (r_{11}\boldsymbol{i} + r_{12}\boldsymbol{j} + r_{13}\boldsymbol{k}) \\ &= r_{11}^2 + r_{12}^2 + r_{13}^2 = 1 \end{aligned}$$

and

$$\bar{\imath} \cdot \bar{\jmath} = (r_{11}\boldsymbol{i} + r_{12}\boldsymbol{j} + r_{13}\boldsymbol{k}) \cdot (r_{21}\boldsymbol{i} + r_{22}\boldsymbol{j} + r_{23}\boldsymbol{k})$$
$$= r_{11}r_{21} + r_{12}r_{22} + r_{13}r_{23} = 0,$$

and so on.

Thus an orthogonal matrix determines a set of three mutually perpendicular vectors, each 1 unit long, which will serve as a basis for a new cartesian coordinate system. Conversely, if we have a second cartesian coordinate system based on 3 mutually perpendicular unit vectors $\bar{\imath}$, $\bar{\jmath}$, and $\bar{k}$, then an orthogonal matrix is determined. For the vectors $\bar{\imath}$, $\bar{\jmath}$, and $\bar{k}$ can be expressed in terms of the original basis vectors $\boldsymbol{i}$, $\boldsymbol{j}$, and $\boldsymbol{k}$. Therefore, we will have a system of equations, System 93-2, in which the coefficients $r_{11}, r_{12}, \ldots, r_{33}$ are the components of $\bar{\imath}$, $\bar{\jmath}$, and $\bar{k}$ relative to the original coordinate system. Since we are assuming that $\bar{\imath} \cdot \bar{\imath} = 1$ and $\bar{\imath} \cdot \bar{\jmath} = 0$, we find that

$$r_{11}^2 + r_{12}^2 + r_{13}^2 = 1 \text{ and } r_{11} \cdot r_{21} + r_{12} \cdot r_{22} + r_{13} \cdot r_{23} = 0,$$

and so on. Therefore, the matrix of coefficients of System 93-2 is an orthogonal matrix.

We can express a given geometric vector $\boldsymbol{V}$ either in terms of the basis vectors $\boldsymbol{i}$, $\boldsymbol{j}$, and $\boldsymbol{k}$, as in Equation 93-1, or in terms of the basis vectors $\bar{\imath}$, $\bar{\jmath}$, and $\bar{k}$:

$$\boldsymbol{V} = \bar{x}\bar{\imath} + \bar{y}\bar{\jmath} + \bar{z}\bar{k}. \tag{93-3}$$

Therefore, relative to our second coordinate system, we see that the geometric vector $\boldsymbol{V}$ corresponds to the component vector $\bar{\boldsymbol{v}} = (\bar{x}, \bar{y}, \bar{z})$. Let us find the relation between the component vectors $\boldsymbol{v}$ and $\bar{\boldsymbol{v}}$. From Equations 93-1 and 93-3 we see that

$$x\boldsymbol{i} + y\boldsymbol{j} + z\boldsymbol{k} = \bar{x}\bar{\imath} + \bar{y}\bar{\jmath} + \bar{z}\bar{k}.$$

In this equation we may replace $\bar{\imath}$, $\bar{\jmath}$, and $\bar{k}$ in terms of $\boldsymbol{i}$, $\boldsymbol{j}$, and $\boldsymbol{k}$ according to Equations 93-2:

$$\begin{aligned} x\boldsymbol{i} + y\boldsymbol{j} + z\boldsymbol{k} = \bar{x}(&r_{11}\boldsymbol{i} + r_{12}\boldsymbol{j} + r_{13}\boldsymbol{k}) \\ + \bar{y}(&r_{21}\boldsymbol{i} + r_{22}\boldsymbol{j} + r_{23}\boldsymbol{k}) \\ + \bar{z}(&r_{31}\boldsymbol{i} + r_{32}\boldsymbol{j} + r_{33}\boldsymbol{k}). \end{aligned}$$

Now we collect terms and equate the coefficients of $\boldsymbol{i}$, $\boldsymbol{j}$, and $\boldsymbol{k}$ to obtain the system of equations

$$\begin{aligned} x &= r_{11}\bar{x} + r_{21}\bar{y} + r_{31}\bar{z} \\ y &= r_{12}\bar{x} + r_{22}\bar{y} + r_{32}\bar{z} \\ z &= r_{13}\bar{x} + r_{23}\bar{y} + r_{33}\bar{z}. \end{aligned} \tag{93-4}$$

In matrix-vector form, this system of equations is simply

$$\boldsymbol{v} = R^*\bar{\boldsymbol{v}}. \tag{93-5}$$

If we multiply both sides of Equation 93-5 by R and take into account the fact that $RR^* = I$, we see that

$$\bar{\boldsymbol{v}} = R\boldsymbol{v}. \tag{93-6}$$

If we think of our geometric vector $\boldsymbol{V}$ as the position vector of a point P, then the component vectors $\boldsymbol{v} = (x, y, z)$ and $\bar{\boldsymbol{v}} = (\bar{x}, \bar{y}, \bar{z})$ give us the coordinates of P relative to our two coordinate systems. Equations 93-5 and 93-6 are therefore the transformation of coordinates equations for the two cartesian systems.

Example 93-1. Discuss the transformation of coordinates that is determined by the orthogonal matrix

$$R = \begin{bmatrix} \cos\theta & \sin\theta \\ -\sin\theta & \cos\theta \end{bmatrix}.$$

Solution. In this case the matrix-vector Equation 93-6 is equivalent to the system of equations

$$\bar{x} = x\cos\theta + y\sin\theta$$

$$\bar{y} = -x\sin\theta + y\cos\theta.$$

We recognize (See Section 70) these equations as the transformation equations for a rotation of axes through an angle of θ. In this case our orthogonal matrix determines a rotation.

It is "almost" true that the transformation determined by every orthogonal matrix is a rotation. The facts are these. In Section 91 we learned that the determinant of an orthogonal matrix R is either $+1$ or -1. We can show, by using Equations 93-2 to compute $\bar{\boldsymbol{\imath}} \times \bar{\boldsymbol{\jmath}}$ and taking into account the fact that R is orthogonal, that $\bar{\boldsymbol{\imath}} \times \bar{\boldsymbol{\jmath}} = |R|\bar{\boldsymbol{k}}$. If $|R| = 1$, the basis vectors $\bar{\boldsymbol{\imath}}$, $\bar{\boldsymbol{\jmath}}$, and $\bar{\boldsymbol{k}}$ have the same orientation (right-handed or left-handed) as the vectors $\boldsymbol{i}, \boldsymbol{j}$, and $\boldsymbol{k}$. In that case, the two sets of coordinate axes can be brought into coincidence by ordinary Euclidean rotations. If $|R| = -1$, then $\bar{\boldsymbol{\imath}} \times \bar{\boldsymbol{\jmath}} = -\bar{\boldsymbol{k}}$, and to bring the two axis systems into coincidence we must perform Euclidean rotations *and* reflect along one of the coordinate axes.

Example 93-2. Discuss the transformation determined by the orthogonal matrix

$$R = \begin{bmatrix} \frac{2}{3} & \frac{1}{3} & -\frac{2}{3} \\ \frac{1}{3} & \frac{2}{3} & \frac{2}{3} \\ \frac{2}{3} & -\frac{2}{3} & \frac{1}{3} \end{bmatrix}.$$

Solution. You can easily verify that $|R| = 1$, so the transformation determined by this matrix is a rotation. To locate the $\bar{X}$-, $\bar{Y}$-, and $\bar{Z}$-axes relative to the X-, Y-, and Z-axes, we recall that the rows of R are the components of the basis vectors $\bar{\imath}$, $\bar{\jmath}$, and $\bar{k}$ relative to the XYZ-axes. Therefore, the points $(\frac{2}{3}, \frac{1}{3}, -\frac{2}{3})$, $(\frac{1}{3}, \frac{2}{3}, \frac{2}{3})$, and $(\frac{2}{3}, -\frac{2}{3}, \frac{1}{3})$ determine the $\bar{X}$-, $\bar{Y}$-, and $\bar{Z}$-axes, as shown in Fig. 93-1.

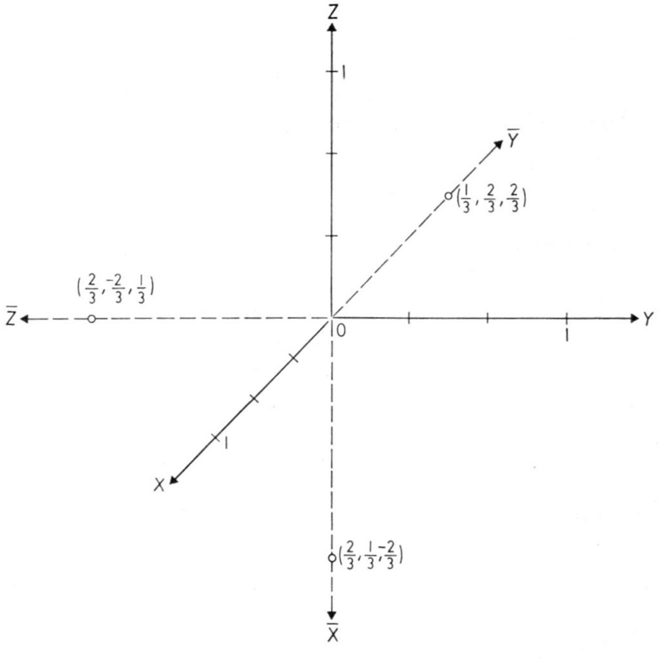

Figure 93-1

Example 93-3. Discuss the transformation determined by the orthogonal matrix

$$R = \begin{bmatrix} 0 & 0 & 1 \\ 0 & 1 & 0 \\ 1 & 0 & 0 \end{bmatrix}.$$

Solution. The terminal points of the vectors $\bar{\imath}$, $\bar{\jmath}$, and $\bar{k}$ are the points (0, 0, 1), (0, 1, 0), and (1, 0, 0). Hence the $\bar{X}$-axis is the Z-axis, the $\bar{Y}$-axis is the Y-axis, and the $\bar{Z}$-axis is the X-axis. Notice that $R = -1$ and that no rotation will bring the $\overline{X}\overline{Y}\overline{Z}$- and XYZ-axes into coincidence (see Fig. 93-2).

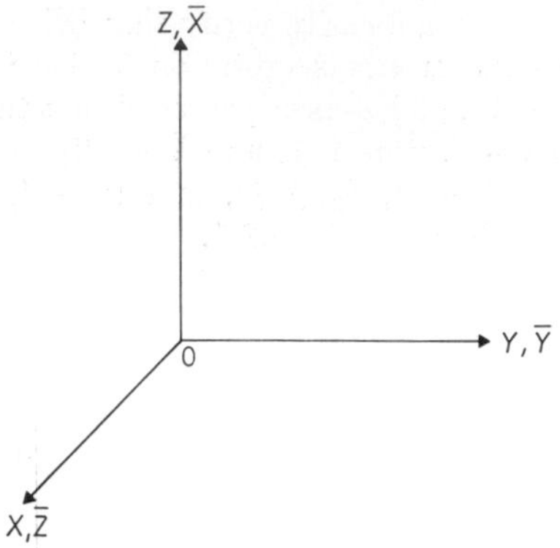

Figure 93-2

Problems 93

1. Let $\boldsymbol{v} = (x, y)$ and $\bar{\boldsymbol{v}} = (\bar{x}, \bar{y})$, the coordinates of a point relative to an XY- and an $\bar{X}\bar{Y}$-coordinate system, be related by the equation $\bar{\boldsymbol{v}} = R\boldsymbol{v}$. Draw the XY-axes in "standard position" and sketch the $\bar{X}\bar{Y}$-axes for the following choices of R.

(a) $\begin{bmatrix} \frac{3}{5} & \frac{4}{5} \\ -\frac{4}{5} & \frac{3}{5} \end{bmatrix}$ (b) $\begin{bmatrix} 0 & 1 \\ 1 & 0 \end{bmatrix}$ (c) $\begin{bmatrix} 1 & 0 \\ 0 & -1 \end{bmatrix}$ (d) $\begin{bmatrix} 0 & 1 \\ -1 & 0 \end{bmatrix}$

(e) $\begin{bmatrix} 1/\sqrt{2} & 1/\sqrt{2} \\ -1/\sqrt{2} & 1/\sqrt{2} \end{bmatrix}$

2. Let $\begin{bmatrix} a & b \\ c & d \end{bmatrix}$ be an orthogonal matrix. Show that there is an angle θ such that $a = \cos\theta$ and $b = \sin\theta$. Then show that either $c = -\sin\theta$ and $d = \cos\theta$, or $c = \sin\theta$ and $d = -\cos\theta$. It follows that every 2 by 2 orthogonal matrix must either be a rotation matrix $\begin{bmatrix} \cos\theta & \sin\theta \\ -\sin\theta & \cos\theta \end{bmatrix}$ or a matrix $\begin{bmatrix} \cos\theta & \sin\theta \\ \sin\theta & -\cos\theta \end{bmatrix}$ that represents a rotation and a reflection.

3. The matrix $\begin{bmatrix} \frac{1}{2}\sqrt{3} & \frac{1}{2} \\ -\frac{1}{2} & \frac{1}{2}\sqrt{3} \end{bmatrix}$ represents a rotation of axes through an acute angle θ. Find θ.

4. Let the coordinates $\boldsymbol{v} = (x, y, z)$ and $\bar{\boldsymbol{v}} = (\bar{x}, \bar{y}, \bar{z})$ of a point relative to an XYZ- and an $\bar{X}\bar{Y}\bar{Z}$-coordinate system be related by the equation $\bar{\boldsymbol{v}} = R\boldsymbol{v}$. Draw the XYZ-axes in "standard position" and sketch the $\bar{X}\bar{Y}\bar{Z}$-axes for the following choices of R.

(a) $\begin{bmatrix} 0 & 1 & 0 \\ 1 & 0 & 0 \\ 0 & 0 & 1 \end{bmatrix}$ (b) $\begin{bmatrix} 1 & 0 & 0 \\ 0 & -1 & 0 \\ 0 & 0 & -1 \end{bmatrix}$ (c) $\begin{bmatrix} \frac{1}{3} & -\frac{2}{3} & \frac{2}{3} \\ \frac{2}{3} & \frac{2}{3} & \frac{1}{3} \\ -\frac{2}{3} & \frac{1}{3} & \frac{2}{3} \end{bmatrix}$

(d) $\begin{bmatrix} \frac{3}{5} & 0 & \frac{4}{5} \\ 0 & 1 & 0 \\ -\frac{4}{5} & 0 & \frac{3}{5} \end{bmatrix}$ (e) $\begin{bmatrix} 1/\sqrt{3} & 2/\sqrt{6} & 0 \\ 1/\sqrt{3} & -1/\sqrt{6} & 1/\sqrt{2} \\ 1/\sqrt{3} & -1/\sqrt{6} & -1/\sqrt{2} \end{bmatrix}$

5. Let the coordinates $\boldsymbol{v} = (x, y, z)$ and $\bar{\boldsymbol{v}} = (\bar{x}, \bar{y}, \bar{z})$ of a point relative to an XYZ- and an $\overline{X}\overline{Y}\overline{Z}$-coordinate system be related by the equation $\bar{\boldsymbol{v}} = R\boldsymbol{v}$,

where $$R = \begin{bmatrix} \frac{2}{3} & \frac{1}{3} & -\frac{2}{3} \\ \frac{1}{3} & \frac{2}{3} & \frac{2}{3} \\ \frac{2}{3} & -\frac{2}{3} & \frac{1}{3} \end{bmatrix}.$$

(a) Find the $\overline{X}\overline{Y}\overline{Z}$-coordinates of the point whose XYZ-coordinates are (3, −6, 9).
(b) Find the XYZ-coordinates of the point whose $\overline{X}\overline{Y}\overline{Z}$-coordinates are (3, −6, 9).
(c) The plane whose XYZ-coordinate equation is $6x - 9y + 3z + 1 = 0$ has a similar equation in terms of $\bar{x}$, $\bar{y}$, and $\bar{z}$. What is it?
(d) What is the equation of the XY-plane in terms of $\bar{x}$, $\bar{y}$, and $\bar{z}$?
(e) Show that $\bar{x}^2 + \bar{y}^2 + \bar{z}^2 = x^2 + y^2 + z^2$.

94. Graphs of Quadratic Equations

The graph of a quadratic equation (in the plane) is a conic, as we know. To find out more about the conic, we may want to rotate axes to reduce the given equation to "standard form." Similarly, we shall now show that a rotation of axes in three dimensions will reduce a general quadratic equation such as

(94-1) $$5x^2 + 2y^2 + 11z^2 + 20xy - 16xz + 4yz = 9$$

to the standard form of the equation of a quadric surface.

We shall use vector-matrix notation. Let us introduce the symmetric matrix

(94-2) $$S = \begin{bmatrix} a & d & e \\ d & b & f \\ e & f & c \end{bmatrix}$$

and the vector $\boldsymbol{v} = (x, y, z)$. You may readily verify the equation

(94-3) $$S\boldsymbol{v} \cdot \boldsymbol{v} = ax^2 + by^2 + cz^2 + 2dxy + 2exz + 2fyz.$$

If we compare the right side of Equation 94-3 with the left side of Equation 94-1, we see that Equation 94-1 can be written as

(94-4) $$S\boldsymbol{v} \cdot \boldsymbol{v} = 9,$$

where

$$S = \begin{bmatrix} 5 & 10 & -8 \\ 10 & 2 & 2 \\ -8 & 2 & 11 \end{bmatrix}.$$

Let us first sketch our line of attack on Equation 94-4, and then we will come back later and fill in the details. According to Theorem 92-2, there is an orthogonal matrix P such that $P^*SP = D$, where D is a diagonal matrix,

(94-5) $$D = \begin{bmatrix} \lambda_1 & 0 & 0 \\ 0 & \lambda_2 & 0 \\ 0 & 0 & \lambda_3 \end{bmatrix}.$$

Now we set $R = P^*$ and introduce new coordinates $\bar{\boldsymbol{v}} = (\bar{x}, \bar{y}, \bar{z})$ by means of the equation $\bar{\boldsymbol{v}} = R\boldsymbol{v}$ (see Equation 93-6). Therefore, $\boldsymbol{v} = R^*\bar{\boldsymbol{v}} = P\bar{\boldsymbol{v}}$, and Equation 94-4 becomes $SP\bar{\boldsymbol{v}} \cdot P\bar{\boldsymbol{v}} = 9$. When we transfer P across the dot, it becomes P^*, and hence this last equation is

$$P^*SP\bar{\boldsymbol{v}} \cdot \bar{\boldsymbol{v}} = D\bar{\boldsymbol{v}} \cdot \bar{\boldsymbol{v}} = 9.$$

Now if we calculate the product $D\bar{\boldsymbol{v}} \cdot \bar{\boldsymbol{v}}$, we obtain the sum $\lambda_1\bar{x}^2 + \lambda_2\bar{y}^2 + \lambda_3\bar{z}^2$, and so, in terms of $\bar{x}$, $\bar{y}$, and $\bar{z}$, our original Equation 94-1 reads

(94-6) $$\lambda_1\bar{x}^2 + \lambda_2\bar{y}^2 + \lambda_3\bar{z}^2 = 9.$$

This equation is the standard form of the equation of a quadric surface, and we studied such standard forms in Section 82.

Now we turn to the task of finding the numbers λ_1, λ_2, and λ_3, and the matrix R. The numbers λ_1, λ_2, and λ_3 are the characteristic values of the matrix S, and hence we find them by solving the characteristic equation

$$\begin{vmatrix} 5-\lambda & 10 & -8 \\ 10 & 2-\lambda & 2 \\ -8 & 2 & 11-\lambda \end{vmatrix} = 0.$$

When we expand the determinant, this equation becomes

$$\lambda^3 - 18\lambda^2 - 81\lambda + 1458 = 0.$$

The solutions of this equation are $\lambda_1 = 18$, $\lambda_2 = 9$, and $\lambda_3 = -9$. Therefore, Equation 94-6 is

$$2\bar{x}^2 + \bar{y}^2 - \bar{z}^2 = 1.$$

We recognize this equation as the equation of a hyperboloid of one sheet in standard form relative to the $\bar{X}\bar{Y}\bar{Z}$-coordinate system. Thus the graph of Equation 94-1 is a hyperboloid. If we were merely interested in the form of the graph, we could stop now. However, if we actually want to sketch the graph, we must find how the $\bar{X}$-, $\bar{Y}$-, and $\bar{Z}$-axes are related to the X-, Y-, and Z-axes. To this end, we must find the transformation matrix R.

The columns of $P = R^*$ are unit characteristic vectors of S, so they are solutions of the equations obtained from the equation

$$(S - \lambda I)\boldsymbol{x} = \mathbf{0}$$

by setting $\lambda = 18$, 9, and -9. The first such equation is

$$\begin{bmatrix} -13 & 10 & -8 \\ 10 & -16 & 2 \\ -8 & 2 & -7 \end{bmatrix} \boldsymbol{x} = \mathbf{0}.$$

We leave it to you to show that $\boldsymbol{x} = (2, 1, -2)$ is a solution, and when we divide this vector by its length, 3, we obtain the unit characteristic vector $\boldsymbol{x}_1 = (\frac{2}{3}, \frac{1}{3}, -\frac{2}{3})$ that corresponds to the characteristic value $\lambda_1 = 18$. Unit characteristic vectors that correspond to the characteristic values $\lambda_2 = 9$ and $\lambda_3 = -9$ are $\boldsymbol{x}_2 = (\frac{1}{3}, \frac{2}{3}, \frac{2}{3})$ and $\boldsymbol{x}_3 = (\frac{2}{3}, -\frac{2}{3}, \frac{1}{3})$. These vectors form the columns of our matrix P and therefore the rows of the transformation matrix $R = P^*$. Thus

$$R = \begin{bmatrix} \frac{2}{3} & \frac{1}{3} & -\frac{2}{3} \\ \frac{1}{3} & \frac{2}{3} & \frac{2}{3} \\ \frac{2}{3} & -\frac{2}{3} & \frac{1}{3} \end{bmatrix}.$$

This matrix is the transformation matrix we studied in Example 93-2, and the relation of the $\bar{X}$-, $\bar{Y}$-, and $\bar{Z}$-axes to the X-, Y-, and Z-axes is shown in Fig. 93-1. Our study of the graph of Equation 94-1 is therefore complete.

We proceed in the same way with any quadratic equation of the form

$$(94\text{-}7) \qquad ax^2 + by^2 + cz^2 + 2dxy + 2exz + 2fyz = g.$$

According to Equation 94-3, this equation is equivalent to the equation

$$(94\text{-}8) \qquad S\boldsymbol{v} \cdot \boldsymbol{v} = g,$$

where S is the symmetric matrix defined by Equation 94-2, and $\boldsymbol{v}$ is the vector $\boldsymbol{v} = (x, y, z)$. We know that there is an orthogonal matrix P such that $P^*SP = D$, where D is the diagonal matrix of Equation 94-5. So we set $R = P^*$ and introduce new coordinates $\bar{\boldsymbol{v}} = (\bar{x}, \bar{y}, \bar{z})$ by means of the equation $\bar{\boldsymbol{v}} = R\boldsymbol{v}$. Thus $\boldsymbol{v} = R^*\bar{\boldsymbol{v}} = P\bar{\boldsymbol{v}}$, and therefore Equation 94-8 becomes

$$S\boldsymbol{v} \cdot \boldsymbol{v} = SP\bar{\boldsymbol{v}} \cdot P\bar{\boldsymbol{v}} = P^*SP\bar{\boldsymbol{v}} \cdot \bar{\boldsymbol{v}} = D\bar{\boldsymbol{v}} \cdot \bar{\boldsymbol{v}} = g.$$

But $D\bar{\boldsymbol{v}} \cdot \bar{\boldsymbol{v}} = \lambda_1\bar{x}^2 + \lambda_2\bar{y}^2 + \lambda_3\bar{z}^2$, so we see that there is an orthogonal transformation of axes (actually it can always be chosen to be a rotation) under which Equation 94-7 is reduced to the form

$$\lambda_1\bar{x}^2 + \lambda_2\bar{y}^2 + \lambda_3\bar{z}^2 = g. \tag{94-9}$$

This equation tells us the form of the graph of Equation 94-7. If we want to sketch the graph, we must go on to calculate the transformation matrix R.

Example 94-1. Discuss the graph of the quadratic equation

$$2x^2 + 5y^2 + 3z^2 + 4xy = 3.$$

Solution. The symmetric matrix S associated with this equation is

$$S = \begin{bmatrix} 2 & 2 & 0 \\ 2 & 5 & 0 \\ 0 & 0 & 3 \end{bmatrix}.$$

Its characteristic values are solutions of the equation

$$\begin{vmatrix} 2-\lambda & 2 & 0 \\ 2 & 5-\lambda & 0 \\ 0 & 0 & 3-\lambda \end{vmatrix} = (3-\lambda)[(2-\lambda)(5-\lambda) - 4]$$

$$= (3-\lambda)(\lambda-6)(\lambda-1) = 0.$$

Hence $\lambda_1 = 6$, $\lambda_2 = 3$, and $\lambda_3 = 1$. There is a coordinate system, a rotation of the XYZ-system, in which our surface is the graph of the equation $6\bar{x}^2 + 3\bar{y}^2 + \bar{z}^2 = 3$. The graph of this equation is an ellipsoid.

Example 94-2. What is the plane graph of the equation $x^2 - 4xy - 2y^2 = 3$?

Solution. In this case our matrix S is a 2 by 2 matrix. It is

$$S = \begin{bmatrix} 1 & -2 \\ -2 & -2 \end{bmatrix}.$$

Its characteristic values are the solutions of the equation

$$\begin{vmatrix} 1-\lambda & -2 \\ -2 & -2-\lambda \end{vmatrix} = \lambda^2 + \lambda - 6 = (\lambda+3)(\lambda-2) = 0.$$

Therefore, $\lambda_1 = 2$ and $\lambda_2 = -3$. There is a rotation of axes under which our equation becomes

$$2\bar{x}^2 - 3\bar{y}^2 = 3,$$

and we recognize this equation as the equation of a hyperbola.

In Section 71 we found that the graph of the quadratic equation

$$ax^2 + bxy + cy^2 + dx + ey + f = 0 \tag{94-10}$$

is a conic, and we can tell which conic by examining the *discriminant* $b^2 - 4ac$. In accordance with the ideas we have been developing in this chapter, we would treat Equation 94-10 as follows. The matrix associated with the quadratic form $ax^2 + bxy + cy^2$ is

$$S = \begin{bmatrix} a & \frac{1}{2}b \\ \frac{1}{2}b & c \end{bmatrix},$$

and we find the characteristic values λ_1 and λ_2 of this matrix by solving the characteristic equation

$$\text{(94-11)} \qquad \begin{vmatrix} a - \lambda & \dfrac{b}{2} \\ \dfrac{b}{2} & c - \lambda \end{vmatrix} = \lambda^2 - (a + c)\lambda + \frac{4ac - b^2}{4} = 0.$$

After a suitable translation and rotation of axes, our equation reduces to the form

$$\lambda_1\bar{\bar{x}}^2 + \lambda_2\bar{\bar{y}}^2 = k$$

(or $\bar{\bar{x}}^2 = k\bar{\bar{y}}$ if one of the characteristic values is 0). Thus, except for "degenerate cases," Equation 94-10 represents an ellipse if λ_1 and λ_2 have the same sign, a hyperbola if they have opposite signs, and a parabola if one of them is 0. Now the term $\dfrac{4ac - b^2}{4}$ in the quadratic Equation 94-11 is the product of the roots λ_1 and λ_2. Thus we see that λ_1 and λ_2 have the same sign if $4ac - b^2$ is positive, have opposite signs if $4ac - b^2$ is negative, and that one of the characteristic values is 0 if $4ac - b^2$ is 0. Therefore, as before, we find that the graph of Equation 94-10 is

(i) an ellipse if $4ac - b^2 > 0$,
(ii) a hyperbola if $4ac - b^2 < 0$,
(iii) a parabola if $4ac - b^2 = 0$.

Problems 94

1. Consider the quadratic equation $2x^2 + 2xy + 2y^2 = 1$. (See Number 1 of Problems 92.)
   (a) Under a suitable rotation of axes, the equation is reduced to what standard form?
   (b) Find a rotation matrix that produces this transformation.
   (c) Through what angle are the axes rotated?
2. Answer the questions in Problem 1 for the quadratic equation $x^2 - 4xy + y^2 = 1$.

3. Express the following quadratic equations in standard form.
   (a) $4x^2 + 2xy + 4y^2 = 3$ (b) $2x^2 + 6xy - 2y^2 = 13$
   (c) $2xy = 1$ (d) $x^2 + 4xy + 3y^2 = 1$
   (e) $4x^2 + 4xy + y^2 = 5$ (f) $x^2 + 2xy + y^2 + x - y = 0$
4. Consider the equation $x^2 + 2y^2 + 2z^2 + 2xy + 2xz = 1$. (See Number 4 of Problems 92.)
   (a) Under a suitable rotation of axes, this equation is reduced to what standard form?
   (b) Find a rotation matrix that produces this transformation.
   (c) Sketch the graph of our equation.
5. Answer the questions in Problem 4 for the equation $2x^2 + y^2 + z^2 - 4xy - 4xz - 2yz = 1$.
6. Express the following quadratic equations in standard form.
   (a) $4x^2 + 4y^2 + 2z^2 + 2xy = 2$ (b) $2x^2 + y^2 + 2z^2 + 2xz = 5$
   (c) $2xy + 2yz = 2$ (d) $y^2 + 4xz = 3$
   (e) $5x^2 + 3y^2 + 3z^2 - 2xy - 2xz + 2yz = 6$
   (f) $-x^2 - y^2 - 7z^2 + 16xy + 8xz + 8yz = 9$

Review Problems, Chapter Ten

You can use the following problems to test yourself on the material covered in this chapter.

1. Suppose you have a combination of ten coins consisting of nickels, dimes, and quarters whose total value is \$1.25. How many of each coin do you have?
2. Show that the following system is inconsistent unless $2r - s - 3t = 0$:

$$\begin{aligned} x + 3y \phantom{{}-3z} &= r \\ 2x \phantom{{}+3y} - 3z &= s \\ 2y + z &= t. \end{aligned}$$

3. Show that $\begin{vmatrix} x & y & 1 \\ x_1 & y_1 & 1 \\ x_2 & y_2 & 1 \end{vmatrix} = 0$ is the equation of the line that is determined by the points (x_1, y_1) and (x_2, y_2).
4. Let $S = \begin{bmatrix} \cos^2 x & \sin x \cos x \\ \sin x \cos x & \sin^2 x \end{bmatrix}$, and let S' be the matrix whose elements are the derivatives of the elements of S. Show that (a) $S^2 = S$ and (b) $SS'S = 0$.
5. Suppose that $A = \begin{bmatrix} a & b \\ c & d \end{bmatrix}$. What are the relations among the numbers a, b, c, and d if $AA^* = A^*A$?
6. Which of the following statements are true and which false? (To test whether a matrix X is the inverse of a matrix Y, we simply multiply them and see if we get the identity matrix I.)
   (a) $(A^{-1})^{-1} = A$, (b) $(AB)^{-1} = A^{-1}B^{-1}$,
   (c) $(AB)^{-1} = B^{-1}A^{-1}$, (d) $(A + B)^{-1} = A^{-1} + B^{-1}$,
   (e) $(3A)^{-1} = 3A^{-1}$.
7. Suppose that A is a matrix such that $A^4 = 0$. Show that $(I - A)^{-1} = I + A + A^2 + A^3$.

8. Let $\boldsymbol{a} = (2, 1, -2)$, $\boldsymbol{b} = (3, 3, 0)$, and $\boldsymbol{c} = (-1, -2, 7)$. First find a number k such that the vector $\boldsymbol{d} = \boldsymbol{b} + k\boldsymbol{a}$ is orthogonal to $\boldsymbol{a}$. Then find numbers m and n such that the vector $\boldsymbol{e} = \boldsymbol{c} + m\boldsymbol{a} + n\boldsymbol{d}$ is orthogonal to both $\boldsymbol{a}$ and $\boldsymbol{d}$.
9. Find the characteristic values and corresponding characteristic vectors for the matrix $S = \begin{bmatrix} 0 & 1 & 1 \\ 1 & 0 & 1 \\ 1 & 1 & 0 \end{bmatrix}$. Now find an orthogonal matrix P such that P^*SP is a diagonal matrix.
10. Discuss the graph of the equation $xy + yz + zx = 1$ (see Problem 9).

11 PARTIAL DERIVATIVES

The law of a falling body, $s = 16t^2$, defines a simple function. With each number t there is associated a number s. Many physical situations cannot be described by such simple functions, however. For example, to compute the pressure of a certain quantity of gas in a cylinder we must prescribe not one but two numbers—namely, numbers that measure the volume and temperature. In this chapter we will extend our notion of function to cover such cases and extend our knowledge of calculus to deal with such functions.

95. Functions of Several Variables

When we introduced the concept of a function in Section 3, we considered functions in which to each number of a given set there corresponded just one number of another set. The domain and range of such a function are sets of numbers. Later, when we took up vector-valued functions, we considered functions in which to each number of a given set there corresponded a *vector* (represented by an ordered *pair* or ordered *triple* of numbers). The domain of such a function is a set of numbers, but the range is a set of vectors. Now we will consider functions whose domains consist of vectors and whose ranges are sets of numbers.

The domain of a **function of two variables** is a set of ordered pairs of numbers, the domain of a **function of three variables** is a set of ordered triples of numbers, and so on. The range of such a function is a set of numbers. If f is a function of two variables, then the number associated with the pair (x, y) by the function f is denoted by $f(x, y)$; if f is a function of three variables, then the symbol $f(x, y, z)$ is used to denote a function value, and so on. We will now sometimes speak of a function whose domain is simply a set of numbers as a **function of one variable.**

Example 95-1. Suppose that the set of all ordered triples of numbers is the domain of a function f and let its rule of correspondence be expressed by the statement, "To each triple (x, y, z) there corresponds the number xy^2z^3." Find $f(1, 2, 3)$, $f(2, 1, 3)$, $f(-1, 2, 3)$, $f(a, b, c)$, $f(a, -b, c)$, $f(x^2, y^2, z^2)$, $f(z, y, x)$, and $f(y, -z, x)$.

Solution. The rule of correspondence of our function f can be written as the equation $f(x, y, z) = xy^2z^3$. This equation simply means that we should multiply the number appearing in the first space in the symbol

$$f(\quad,\quad,\quad)$$

by the product of the square of the number in the second space and the cube of the number in the third. Hence we have

$$\begin{aligned}
f(1, 2, 3) &= 1 \cdot 2^2 \cdot 3^3 = 108,\\
f(2, 1, 3) &= 2 \cdot 1^2 \cdot 3^3 = 54,\\
f(-1, 2, 3) &= (-1) \cdot 2^2 \cdot 3^3 = -108,\\
f(a, b, c) &= ab^2c^3,\\
f(a, -b, c) &= a(-b)^2c^3 = ab^2c^3,\\
f(x^2, y^2, z^2) &= x^2(y^2)^2(z^2)^3 = x^2y^4z^6,\\
f(z, y, x) &= zy^2x^3 = x^3y^2z,\\
f(y, -z, x) &= y(-z)^2x^3 = x^3yz^2.
\end{aligned}$$

Because we can identify numbers with points of a line, we often speak of the domain of a function f of one variable as a set of points of the line; for example, the domain of a function may be a certain interval.

Similarly, since pairs of numbers represent points in the plane and triples of numbers represent points in space, we often consider the domains of functions of several variables as collections of points in the plane or in space, and we make free use of geometric language in describing such functions.

Example 95-2. Let g be the function that makes correspond to each point (x, y, z) its distance from the point $(1, 2, 3)$. What is the formula for $g(x, y, z)$?

Solution. According to the distance formula, we have

$$g(x, y, z) = \sqrt{(x - 1)^2 + (y - 2)^2 + (z - 3)^2}.$$

Because we live in a three-dimensional world and write on two-dimensional paper, we encounter technical problems when we try to graph a function of several variables. We can draw pictures only in the case of functions of two variables, and in that case we proceed just as we do with functions of one variable. The graph of a function f of two variables consists of those points (x, y, z) in three-dimensional space for which the pair (x, y) is in the domain of f and $z = f(x, y)$. Thus the graph of a function f is simply the graph of the equation $z = f(x, y)$, and we have discussed such graphs in Chapter 9.

Example 95-3. Sketch the graph of the function that is defined by the equation $f(x, y) = 2\sqrt{4 - x^2 - 4y^2}$.

Solution. As in the case of functions of one variable, when we use a formula to define a function we suppose that the domain of the function is (unless otherwise specified) the entire set of points for which the formula makes sense. The domain of our function f is therefore the set of all points such that $4 - x^2 - 4y^2 \geq 0$, which is the set D that consists of the points of and interior to the ellipse $\frac{x^2}{4} + y^2 = 1$. The graph of our function is the graph of the equation $z = 2\sqrt{4 - x^2 - 4y^2}$, and so the resulting surface is the upper half of the ellipsoid

$$\frac{x^2}{4} + y^2 + \frac{z^2}{16} = 1$$

that is shown in Fig. 95-1.

A function f (of one variable) is continuous at a point x if

$$\lim_{h \to 0} f(x + h) = f(x).$$

In rough terms this equation says that the number $f(x + h)$ approximates the number $f(x)$ if h is close to zero. Similarly, a function f of two variables is **continuous** at a point (x, y) if

$$\lim_{(h,k)\to(0,0)} f(x+h, y+k) = f(x, y). \tag{95-1}$$

In rough terms this equation says that the number $f(x + h, y + k)$ approximates the number $f(x, y)$ if both h and k are close to zero. A more precise definition of what Equation 95-1 says is the following. Let I be a plane region consisting of all points but the center of a circular disk about the origin, and denote by $J(I)$ the smallest closed interval that contains every number $f(x + h, y + k)$, when (h, k) is in I. Then Equation 95-1 means that the number $f(x, y)$ is in $J(I)$ for each choice of I and is, in fact, the *only* number that is in *each* interval $J(I)$. Similar remarks apply to functions of more than two variables. Just as it is helpful to think of the graph of a continuous function of one variable as a "curve with no breaks," so it is convenient to regard the graph of a continous function of two variables as a "surface with no tears."

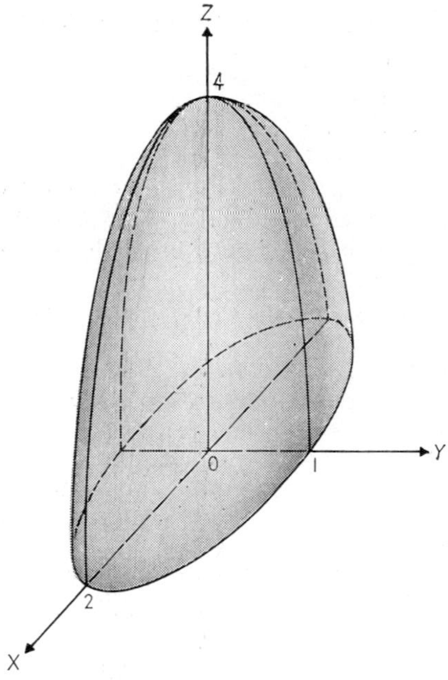

Figure 95-1

Problems 95

1. Find $f(1, 2, 3)$ in each case.
   (a) $f(x, y, z) = x^3y^2z$ (b) $f(u, v, w) = vw \ln u$
   (c) $f(x, y, z) = xz \sin \pi y$ (d) $f(r, s, t) = r^2 + s^2 + t^2$
2. Find $f(z, y, x^2)$ if:
   (a) $f(x, y, z) = e^z \sin xy$ (b) $f(x, y, z) = y^2 + z$
   (c) $f(u, v, w) = wvu^2$ (d) $f(r, s, t) = rt - s^2$
3. Find and simplify the quotient $\dfrac{f(2 + h, 3) - f(2, 3)}{h}$ if:
   (a) $f(x, y) = x^2 \ln y$ (b) $f(x, y) = y^2 \ln x$ (c) $f(x, y) = x^y$

4. Sketch the graph of f if:
(a) $f(x, y) = x^2 + y^2$ (b) $f(x, y) = \sin x$
(c) $f(x, y) = 4x^2 - y^2$ (d) $f(x, y) = x - y^2$

5. Find $f(u + v, u - v)$ if:
(a) $f(u, v) = e^u \sin v$ (b) $f(x, y) = e^{x+y} \sin (x - y)$

6. What are the domains of the functions defined by the following equations?
(a) $f(x, y) = \dfrac{x + y}{x - y}$ (b) $f(x, y, z) = \sqrt{x - y} \ln z$
(c) $f(x, y) = \text{Arcsin } (x + y)$ (d) $f(x, y) = \ln \dfrac{x + y}{xy}$

7. Let f be the function that makes correspond to a point (x, y) in the plane the slope (if any) of the line joining (x, y) and the origin. What is the formula that defines f? Graph the function. Is it a continuous function in the entire plane?

8. Let f be the function whose domain is the entire plane and whose rule of correspondence is the following:
$f(x, y) = 1$ if (x, y) is a point closer to the Y-axis than to the X-axis,
$f(x, y) = -1$ if (x, y) is a point closer to the X-axis than to the Y-axis,
$f(x, y) = 0$ if (x, y) is a point equidistant from the X- and Y-axes.
Describe the graph of the function. Is it a continuous function?

9. The resistance of a piece of wire is directly proportional to its length and inversely proportional to the square of its radius. If a wire 10 centimeters long with a radius of 2 millimeters has a resistance of .1 ohms, what is the formula expressing the resistance in terms of the length and radius? In what units should the various quantities in your formula be expressed?

10. Let

$$f(x, y, z) = \begin{vmatrix} 1 & 1 & 1 \\ x & y & z \\ x^2 & y^2 & z^2 \end{vmatrix}.$$

Describe the set of points in space for which $f(x, y, z) = 0$.

11. Let f be the function such that $f(x, y, z)$ is the dot product of the position vector from the origin to (x, y, z) with the vector $2\mathbf{i} - 3\mathbf{j} + 4\mathbf{k}$. Describe the set of points in space for which $f(x, y, z) = 7$.

12. Show that if $f(x, y) \geq f(y, x)$ for every pair of numbers (x, y), then $f(x, y) = f(y, x)$.

96. Partial Differentiation

If f is a given function of two variables, then we define two **derived functions** f_1 and f_2 by means of the equations

$$f_1(x, y) = \lim_{h \to 0} \frac{f(x + h, y) - f(x, y)}{h} \tag{96-1}$$

and

$$f_2(x, y) = \lim_{h \to 0} \frac{f(x, y + h) - f(x, y)}{h}. \tag{96-2}$$

The numbers $\boldsymbol{f_1(x, y)}$ and $\boldsymbol{f_2(x, y)}$ are called the **(first) partial derivatives** of $f(x, y)$ with respect to the first and second variables, respectively. The derivatives $f_1(x, y)$ and $f_2(x, y)$ are analogous to the derivative $g'(x)$ of a function g of one variable. If $z = g(x)$, then the notation $\dfrac{dz}{dx} = g'(x)$ can also be used for this derivative. In the case of partial derivatives, the "straight" d is replaced by the "curved d" ∂. Thus if $z = f(x, y)$, then we often write

$$\frac{\partial z}{\partial x} = f_1(x, y) \quad \text{and} \quad \frac{\partial z}{\partial y} = f_2(x, y).$$

To calculate the partial derivatives of $f(x, y)$, we need only compute some ordinary derivatives. We will illustrate this fact by an example.

Example 96-1. Find $f_1(2, 3)$ if $f(x, y) = 2y^3 \sin x$.

Solution. According to Equation 96-1,

$$\text{(96-3)} \qquad f_1(2, 3) = \lim_{h \to 0} \frac{f(2 + h, 3) - f(2, 3)}{h}$$

$$= \lim_{h \to 0} \frac{2 \cdot 3^3 \sin (2 + h) - 2 \cdot 3^3 \sin 2}{h}$$

$$= \lim_{h \to 0} \frac{54 \sin (2 + h) - 54 \sin 2}{h}.$$

Now let us define the function g (of one variable) by means of the equation $g(x) = f(x, 3) = 2 \cdot 3^3 \sin x = 54 \sin x$. Then Equation 96-3 can be written as

$$f_1(2, 3) = \lim_{h \to 0} \frac{g(2 + h) - g(2)}{h}.$$

But this last limit is, by definition, the number $g'(2)$, so we see that $f_1(2, 3) = g'(2)$. Now $g'(x) = D_x 54 \sin x = 54 \cos x$. Hence $g'(2) = 54 \cos 2$, and therefore $f_1(2, 3) = 54 \cos 2$.

In practice we do not formally introduce the substitution $g(x) = 54 \sin x$. We find $f_1(x, y)$ by differentiating $2y^3 \sin x$ with respect to x, treating the factor y^3 exactly as we treat the factor 2. Thus $f_1(x, y) = 2y^3 \cos x$, and hence $f_1(2, 3) = 54 \cos 2$.

The lesson we are to learn from Example 96-1 is that we can find $f_1(x, y)$ by differentiating $f(x, y)$ with respect to x, treating y just as we treat all the numbers in the formula except x. We sometimes say that we "keep y fixed"; that is, we proceed as if y were a "fixed" number such as 2. It is often convenient to carry out this differentiation by applying the "operator" $\frac{\partial}{\partial x}$ to $f(x, y)$. This operator is just like the operator $D_x \left(\text{or } \frac{d}{dx}\right)$ of ordinary differentiation. Similarly, we find $f_2(x, y)$ by differentiating $f(x, y)$ with respect to y, holding x "fixed." In this case we apply the operator $\frac{\partial}{\partial y}$. Since the computation of a partial derivative really just amounts to computing an ordinary derivative, all the familiar rules for differentiation apply to partial differentiation.

Example 96-2. Find $f_1(x, y)$ and $f_2(x, y)$ if $f(x, y) = y^2e^{xy}$.

Solution. First, we keep y fixed, and we have

$$\begin{aligned} f_1(x, y) &= \frac{\partial(y^2e^{xy})}{\partial x} = y^2\frac{\partial e^{xy}}{\partial x} = y^2e^{xy}\frac{\partial(xy)}{\partial x} \\ &= y^2ye^{xy} = y^3e^{xy}. \end{aligned}$$

Similarly,

$$\begin{aligned} f_2(x, y) &= \frac{\partial(y^2e^{xy})}{\partial y} = y^2\frac{\partial(e^{xy})}{\partial y} + e^{xy}\frac{\partial(y^2)}{\partial y} \\ &= y^2xe^{xy} + e^{xy}2y = (xy^2 + 2y)e^{xy}. \end{aligned}$$

The derivative of $f_1(x, y)$ with respect to the first variable is the **second derivative** of $f(x, y)$ with respect to the first variable, which we denote by the symbol $f_{11}(x, y)$. The derivative of $f_1(x, y)$ with respect to the second variable is the **"mixed derivative"** $f_{12}(x, y)$, and so on. Other symbols for these numbers, if $z = f(x, y)$, are

$$\frac{\partial^2 z}{\partial x^2} = f_{11}(x, y),$$

$$\frac{\partial^2 z}{\partial y\,\partial x} = f_{12}(x, y),$$

$$\frac{\partial^2 z}{\partial x\,\partial y} = f_{21}(x, y),$$

and

$$\frac{\partial^2 z}{\partial y^2} = f_{22}(x, y).$$

Of course, we also talk about derivatives of order higher than the second; and we apply these ideas to functions of more than two variables, too.

Example 96-3. Find all the second derivatives of z if $z = (x + y) \sin x$.

Solution. The first derivatives of z are

$$\frac{\partial z}{\partial x} = \sin x + (x + y) \cos x \text{ and } \frac{\partial z}{\partial y} = \sin x.$$

Therefore,

$$\frac{\partial^2 z}{\partial x^2} = \frac{\partial}{\partial x}\left(\frac{\partial z}{\partial x}\right) = \frac{\partial}{\partial x}[\sin x + (x + y) \cos x] = 2 \cos x - (x + y) \sin x,$$

$$\frac{\partial^2 z}{\partial y^2} = \frac{\partial}{\partial y}\left(\frac{\partial z}{\partial y}\right) = \frac{\partial}{\partial y}(\sin x) = 0,$$

$$\frac{\partial^2 z}{\partial y\, \partial x} = \frac{\partial}{\partial y}\left(\frac{\partial z}{\partial x}\right) = \frac{\partial}{\partial y}[\sin x + (x + y) \cos x] = \cos x,$$

and

$$\frac{\partial^2 z}{\partial x\, \partial y} = \frac{\partial}{\partial x}\left(\frac{\partial z}{\partial y}\right) = \frac{\partial}{\partial x} \sin x = \cos x.$$

You may have difficulty in remembering that $f_{12}(x, y)$ means $\frac{\partial}{\partial y}\left(\frac{\partial z}{\partial x}\right)$ instead of $\frac{\partial}{\partial x}\left(\frac{\partial z}{\partial y}\right)$ (where $z = f(x, y)$). In Example 96-3 we see that it does not matter, the two numbers are the same, anyway. In fact, the two numbers $f_{12}(x, y)$ and $f_{21}(x, y)$ are equal for almost every function f that you are likely to encounter in mathematical applications. The following theorem is proved in advanced calculus.

THEOREM 96-1. *Let (x, y) be a point in the domain of a function f, at which the derived functions f_{12} and f_{21} are continuous. Then $f_{12}(x, y) = f_{21}(x, y)$.*

Theorem 96-1 tells us that the mixed derivatives of the second order are equal (under suitable conditions of continuity). In fact, this theorem can be used to show that mixed derivatives of higher order with the same subscripts are also equal (under suitable hypotheses of continuity). And, as before, our results can be easily extended to functions of more than two variables.

Example 96-4. If $f(x, y) = e^{xy}$, show that $f_{112}(x, y) = f_{121}(x, y) = f_{211}(x, y)$.

Solution. We have

$$f_1(x, y) = ye^{xy} \quad \text{and} \quad f_2(x, y) = xe^{xy}.$$

Hence

$$f_{11}(x, y) = y^2e^{xy}, f_{12}(x, y) = f_{21}(x, y) = (1 + xy)e^{xy}.$$

Thus

$$f_{112}(x, y) = (2y + xy^2)e^{xy},$$

and

$$f_{121}(x, y) = f_{211}(x, y) = ye^{xy} + (1 + xy)ye^{xy} = (2y + xy^2)e^{xy}.$$

We recall that $f'(x)$ is interpreted geometrically as the slope of the line tangent to the graph of f at the point $(x, f(x))$. Now we shall take up the geometric meaning of partial derivatives. The graph of a function

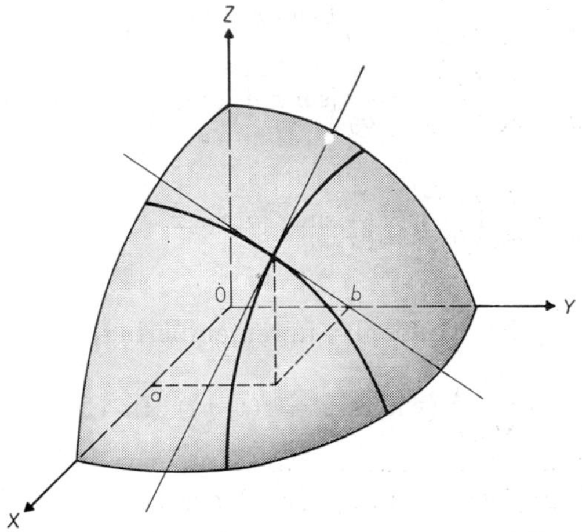

Figure 96-1

f of two variables is a surface. The intersection of this surface with the plane $y = b$ is a curve. If we define the function g of a single variable by the equation $g(x) = f(x, b)$, then a sketch of the graph of the equation $z = g(x)$ is a picture of this curve of intersection. Furthermore, $f_1(x, b) = g'(x)$. Thus the number $f_1(a, b) = g'(a)$ is the slope of the graph of g at the point where $x = a$ (see Fig. 96-1). Similarly, the intersection of the graph of f with the plane $x = a$ is a curve, and if we define $h(y) = f(a, y)$, then a sketch of the graph of the equation $z = h(y)$ is a picture of this curve of intersection. Now $f_2(a, y) = h'(y)$, so the number $f_2(a, b) = h'(b)$ is the slope of the graph of h at the point where $y = b$. Thus we may interpret $f_1(a, b)$ and $f_2(a, b)$ as the slopes of the "profile" curves obtained by cutting the graph of f with planes that contain the point $(a, b, f(a, b))$ and are parallel to the XZ-plane and the YZ-plane.

One of the most-used theorems in the calculus of functions of one variable is the Chain Rule. Let us see how this rule applies in a situation that involves functions of more than one variable. You will recall that if

$w = f(u)$, where $u = g(x)$ (f and g being differentiable functions), then the Chain Rule Equation reads

$$D_x w = f'(u) D_x u. \tag{96-5}$$

Now suppose that our function g is a function of two variables; thus $u = g(x, y)$. Then $w = f(g(x, y))$, and we seek the partial derivatives $\frac{\partial w}{\partial x}$ and $\frac{\partial w}{\partial y}$ rather than the "total" derivative $D_x w$. To find $\frac{\partial w}{\partial x}$, we keep y "fixed"; that is, we treat g as if it were a function of one variable. Then we may utilize the usual Chain Rule, which tells us that the derivative of w with respect to x is the product of $f'(u)$ and the derivative of u with respect to x. The derivatives of w and u are partial derivatives with y "fixed," so Equation 96-5 must be replaced by the equation

$$\frac{\partial w}{\partial x} = f'(u) \frac{\partial u}{\partial x}. \tag{96-6}$$

Similarly,

$$\frac{\partial w}{\partial y} = f'(u) \frac{\partial u}{\partial y}. \tag{96-7}$$

Example 96-5. Show that if f is any differentiable function of one variable, then the equation $w = f(3x + 4y)$ determines a solution of the partial differential equation

$$4 \frac{\partial w}{\partial x} - 3 \frac{\partial w}{\partial y} = 0.$$

Solution. Here we have $w = f(u)$, where $u = 3x + 4y$. Since $\frac{\partial u}{\partial x} = 3$ and $\frac{\partial u}{\partial y} = 4$, Equations 96-6 and 96-7 give us

$$\frac{\partial w}{\partial x} = 3f'(u) = 3f'(3x + 4y), \quad \text{and} \quad \frac{\partial w}{\partial y} = 4f'(u) = 4f'(3x + 4y).$$

Therefore,

$$4 \frac{\partial w}{\partial x} - 3 \frac{\partial w}{\partial y} = 12f'(3x + 4y) - 12f'(3x + 4y) = 0.$$

Just as in the case of ordinary derivatives, there are many notations for partial derivatives. Some books use the notation $f_x(x, y)$, z_x, and $\frac{\partial f(x, y)}{\partial x}$, where we have used $f_1(x, y)$ and $\frac{\partial z}{\partial x}$. Analogous notations are then used for other partial derivatives. For example, the symbols z_{yx} and $f_{yx}(x, y)$ are used to denote $f_{21}(x, y)$.

Problems 96

1. Find $f_1(3, -2)$ if:

(a) $f(x, y) = x^2e^y$
(b) $f(x, y) = e^x y^2$
(c) $f(x, y) = \sin xy$
(d) $f(x, y) = \sin \dfrac{x}{y}$
(e) $f(x, y) = x^y$
(f) $f(x, y) = y^x$
(g) $f(x, y) = \ln (2x - y)$
(h) $f(x, y) = (\ln x)^y$
(i) $f(x, y) = \int_y^x g(t)\, dt$
(j) $f(x, y) = \int_x^y g(t)\, dt$

2. Calculate $f_{12}(x, y)$ and $f_{21}(x, y)$ and show that they are equal for each function f defined in the preceding question.

3. Find $f_2(x, y)$ if:

(a) $f(x, y) = e^x \sin y^2$
(b) $f(x, y) = e^x \sinh y^2$
(c) $f(x, y) = \exp (x^2 + y^2)$
(d) $f(x, y) = \ln (x^2 + y^2)$
(e) $f(x, y) = \ln xy$
(f) $f(x, y) = \sinh xy$
(g) $f(x, y) = \sin xy$
(h) $f(x, y) = \mathrm{Tan}^{-1}\, xy$

4. Determine from Fig. 96-1 whether the numbers $f_1(a, b)$ and $f_2(a, b)$ are positive or negative. What about the numbers $f_{11}(a, b)$ and $f_{22}(a, b)$?

5. Show that the following formulas define solutions of the differential equation

$$\frac{\partial^2 z}{\partial x^2} + \frac{\partial^2 z}{\partial y^2} = 0.$$

(a) $z = 2x + 3y - 1$ (b) $z = e^x \cos y$ (c) $z = x^2 - y^2$

6. The point (1, 2, 3) is on a mountain whose equation is $z = 17 - 2x^2 - 3y^2$. Is the path down from the point steeper in the positive X-direction or in the positive Y-direction?

7. Let $w = \cos (3x - 4y + 5z)$ and form the vector $\boldsymbol{V} = \dfrac{\partial w}{\partial x}\boldsymbol{i} + \dfrac{\partial w}{\partial y}\boldsymbol{j} + \dfrac{\partial w}{\partial z}\boldsymbol{k}$.

Show that $\boldsymbol{V}$ is perpendicular to the vector $8\boldsymbol{i} + \boldsymbol{j} - 4\boldsymbol{k}$.

8. Let $u = x \cos y$ and $v = x \sin y$ and evaluate the determinant $\begin{vmatrix} \dfrac{\partial u}{\partial x} & \dfrac{\partial u}{\partial y} \\ \dfrac{\partial v}{\partial x} & \dfrac{\partial v}{\partial y} \end{vmatrix}$.

9. If $z = \int_3^{x^2-2y} e^{-t^2}\, dt$, find $\dfrac{\partial^2 z}{\partial x\, \partial y}$.

10. Let $z = 3x^2 + 4xy + 5y^2$ and evaluate the determinant

$$\begin{vmatrix} \dfrac{\partial^2 z}{\partial x^2} & \dfrac{\partial^2 z}{\partial x\, \partial y} \\ \dfrac{\partial^2 z}{\partial x\, \partial y} & \dfrac{\partial^2 z}{\partial y^2} \end{vmatrix}.$$

11. Suppose that f is a given function, and let $w = f(x^2, y^2)$. Does it necessarily follow that $f_1(x^2, y^2) = \dfrac{\partial w}{\partial x}$?

12. The gas in a certain cylinder is at a pressure of P pounds when its volume is V cubic centimeters and its temperature is $T°$. P is related to T and V by the equation $P = \frac{10T}{V}$. Suppose $V = 200$. How much does the pressure change if we change T from 100 to 101? Approximately what change in volume would produce the same pressure change if the temperature is kept at 100?

97. A Chain Rule for Functions of Two Variables

If a function g of one variable satisfies certain conditions of continuity and differentiability on an interval $[a, c]$, then the Theorem of

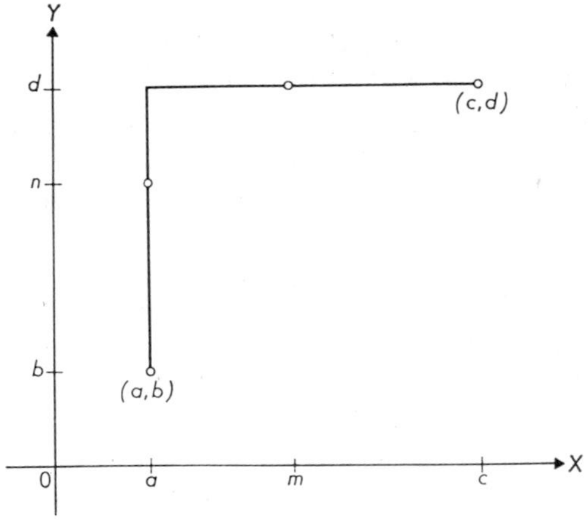

Figure 97-1

the Mean (Theorem 21-2) states that there is a number m between a and c such that

$$g(c) - g(a) = g'(m)(c - a). \tag{97-1}$$

We will now develop an extension of this formula that applies to functions of two variables.

Suppose that a function f of two variables has the partial derivatives $f_1(x, y)$ and $f_2(x, y)$ at each point of the "right-angle" path that joins the points (a, b) and (c, d), as shown in Fig. 97-1. We will use the Theorem of the Mean to show that there are numbers m and n, where m is *between* a and c, and n is *between* b and d, such that

$$\boldsymbol{f(c, d) - f(a, b) = f_1(m, d)(c - a) + f_2(a, n)(d - b).} \tag{97-2}$$

To establish this equation we write

$$f(c, d) - f(a, b) = f(c, d) - f(a, d) + f(a, d) - f(a, b) \tag{97-3}$$

and look at the differences $f(c, d) - f(a, d)$ and $f(a, d) - f(a, b)$ separately. Let us set $g(x) = f(x, d)$. Then $f(c, d) - f(a, d) = g(c) - g(a)$. The Theorem of the Mean states that there is a number m between a and c for which Equation 97-1 holds. In our present case, $g'(m) = f_1(m, d)$, so we see that Equation 97-1 becomes

$$f(c, d) - f(a, d) = f_1(m, d)(c - a). \tag{97-4}$$

In exactly the same way we can show that there is a number n between b and d for which

$$f(a, d) - f(a, b) = f_2(a, n)(d - b). \tag{97-5}$$

Equation 97-2 now follows from Equations 97-3, 97-4, and 97-5.

Example 97-1. Show that if $f_1(x, y) = 0$ and $f_2(x, y) = 0$ at every point (x, y), then f is a constant function.

Solution. We must show that the value of f at any point (a, b) is the same as its value at any other point (c, d). Since the first partial derivatives are 0, Equation 97-2 reduces to the equation $f(c, d) - f(a, b) = 0$; that is, $f(c, d) = f(a, b)$.

If f and g are functions of one variable, then the equation $w = f(g(x))$ defines a new function of one variable, the composition of g by f. Now that we have functions of several variables at our disposal, we can form all sorts of composite functions. To find the derivatives of these composite functions, we must develop the proper chain rules. In the case of functions of one variable we know that if $w = f(u)$, where $u = g(x)$, then the Chain Rule Equation is

$$D_x w = f'(u) D_x u \tag{97-6}$$

or, in differential notation,

$$\frac{dw}{dx} = \frac{dw}{du}\frac{du}{dx}. \tag{97-7}$$

In the preceding section we pointed out that if g is a function of two variables, say $u = g(x, y)$, then we have the Chain Rule Equations

$$\frac{\partial w}{\partial x} = f'(u)\frac{\partial u}{\partial x} \quad \text{and} \quad \frac{\partial w}{\partial y} = f'(u)\frac{\partial u}{\partial y}.$$

Now we will derive the equation that is analogous to Equation 97-6 if f rather than g is a function of two variables.

Suppose that f is a function of two variables such that the derived functions f_1 and f_2 are continuous. Let $u = g(x)$ and $v = h(x)$, where g and h are differentiable functions, and consider the problem of finding

$F'(x)$, where

$$F(x) = f(u, v) = f(g(x), h(x)).$$

According to the definition of the derivative,

$$F'(x) = \lim_{t \to 0} \frac{F(x + t) - F(x)}{t}.$$

Thus $F'(x)$ is the limit of the difference quotient

$$\frac{f(g(x + t), h(x + t)) - f(g(x), h(x))}{t}.$$

We can use Equation 97-2, with $c = g(x + t)$, $d = h(x + t)$, $a = g(x)$, and $b = h(x)$ to rewrite this difference quotient in the form

(97-8) $$\frac{F(x + t) - F(x)}{t} = f_1(m(t), h(x + t)) \frac{g(x + t) - g(x)}{t} + f_2(g(x), n(t)) \frac{h(x + t) - h(x)}{t},$$

where $m(t)$ is a number between $g(x)$ and $g(x + t)$, and $n(t)$ is a number between $h(x)$ and $h(x + t)$. Because g and h are continuous functions,

$$\lim_{t \to 0} g(x + t) = g(x) \quad \text{and} \quad \lim_{t \to 0} h(x + t) = h(x).$$

Since $m(t)$ is "trapped" between $g(x)$ and $g(x + t)$, and $n(t)$ is "trapped" between $h(x)$ and $h(x + t)$, we see that

$$\lim_{t \to 0} m(t) = g(x) \quad \text{and} \quad \lim_{t \to 0} n(t) = h(x).$$

Since we are assuming that f_1 and f_2 are continuous,

(97-9) $$\lim_{t \to 0} f_1(m(t), h(x + t)) = f_1(g(x), h(x)),$$

and

(97-10) $$\lim_{t \to 0} f_2(g(x), n(t)) = f_2(g(x), h(x)).$$

Finally, from the definition of the derivative we see that

(97-11)

$$\lim_{t \to 0} \frac{g(x + t) - g(x)}{t} = g'(x), \quad \text{and} \quad \lim_{t \to 0} \frac{h(x + t) - h(x)}{t} = h'(x).$$

Now we use Equations 97-8, 97-9, 97-10, and 97-11 to calculate $F'(x)$, and we find that

(97-12) $$F'(x) = f_1(g(x), h(x))g'(x) + f_2(g(x), h(x))h'(x).$$

We have just derived the following Chain Rule:
If $w = f(u, v)$, *where* $u = g(x)$ *and* $v = h(x)$, *then*

$$D_x w = f_1(u, v)D_x u + f_2(u, v)D_x v. \tag{97-13}$$

Notice that Equation 97-13 is analogous to Equation 97-6. In the notation that is analogous to the notation of Equation 97-7, our new Chain Rule Equation reads

$$\frac{dw}{dx} = \frac{\partial w}{\partial u}\frac{du}{dx} + \frac{\partial w}{\partial v}\frac{dv}{dx}. \tag{97-14}$$

Example 97-2. Show that Equation 97-14 gives the correct value of $\frac{dw}{dx}$ if

$w = u^2 + v^2$ and $u = x, v = e^x$.

Solution. We see that $w = x^2 + (e^x)^2 = x^2 + e^{2x}$. Hence

$$\frac{dw}{dx} = 2x + 2e^{2x}.$$

Now we will obtain the same result from Equation 97-14. We have

$$\frac{\partial w}{\partial u} = 2u, \quad \frac{\partial w}{\partial v} = 2v, \quad \frac{du}{dx} = 1, \quad \text{and } \frac{dv}{dx} = e^x.$$

When we substitute these numbers in Equation 97-14, we get

$$\frac{dw}{dx} = 2u \cdot 1 + 2v \cdot e^x = 2x + 2e^x e^x = 2x + 2e^{2x},$$

the correct result.

Example 97-3. Find $\frac{dz}{dx}$ if $z = (\sin x)^{e^x}$.

Solution. We can write $z = u^v$, where $u = \sin x$ and $v = e^x$. Therefore, according to the Chain Rule Equation 97-14,

$$\begin{aligned}\frac{dz}{dx} &= vu^{v-1}\cos x + (u^v \ln u)e^x \\ &= e^x(\sin x)^{e^x-1}\cos x + (\sin x)^{e^x}(\ln \sin x)e^x \\ &= e^x(\sin x)^{e^x}(\cot x + \ln \sin x).\end{aligned}$$

Suppose that f is a function of two variables and h is a function of one variable, and let us set $w = f(x, h(x))$. Thus $w = f(x, y)$, where $y = h(x)$. To find $D_x w$ we use Equation 97-13. We simply replace u with x and v with y. Then $D_x u = D_x x = 1$ and $D_x v = D_x y$, and Equation

97-13 gives us $D_xw = f_1(x, y) + f_2(x, y)D_xy$. Thus we have shown that: *If* $w = f(x, y)$, *where* $y = h(x)$, *then*

$$D_xw = f_1(x, y) + f_2(x, y)D_xy. \tag{97-15}$$

In particular, if h is a function such that $f(x, h(x)) = c$, where c is a number that is independent of x, then $D_xw = D_xc = 0$, and

$$0 = f_1(x, y) + f_2(x, y)D_xy.$$

Thus: *If* $f(x, y) = c$, *then*

$$D_xy = -\frac{f_1(x, y)}{f_2(x, y)}. \tag{97-16}$$

Example 97-4. Find the slope of the line tangent to the graph of the equation $x^2 - 3xy + y + 3 = 0$ at the point $(1, 2)$.

Solution. If we write $f(x, y) = x^2 - 3xy + y + 3$, then our equation can be written $f(x, y) = 0$. Then Equation 97-16 tells us that the desired slope is

$$D_xy = -\frac{f_1(1, 2)}{f_2(1, 2)} = \frac{-(2 - 3 \cdot 2)}{-3 + 1} = -2.$$

You should be able to recognize the Chain Rule Equation if different letters are used. For example, if $w = F(r, s)$, where $r = f(x)$ and $s = g(x)$, then

$$\frac{dw}{dx} = \frac{\partial w}{\partial r}\frac{dr}{dx} + \frac{\partial w}{\partial s}\frac{ds}{dx},$$

or in other words,

$$D_xw = F_1(r, s)D_xr + F_2(r, s)D_xs.$$

You should also be able to recognize the generalizations of this Chain Rule Equation that apply to functions of more than two variables. For example, if $w = F(r, s, t)$, where $r = f(x)$, $s = g(x)$, and $t = h(x)$, then

$$\frac{dw}{dx} = \frac{\partial w}{\partial r}\frac{dr}{dx} + \frac{\partial w}{\partial s}\frac{ds}{dx} + \frac{\partial w}{\partial t}\frac{dt}{dx}, \tag{97-17}$$

or in other words,

$$D_xw = F_1(r, s, t)D_xr + F_2(r, s, t)D_xs + F_3(r, s, t)D_xt. \tag{97-18}$$

Example 97-5. Suppose $w = f(x, y, z)$ and $x = a + \alpha t$, $y = b + \beta t$, and $z = c + \gamma t$. Write a formula for D_tw.

Solution. Since $D_tx = \alpha$, $D_ty = \beta$, and $D_tz = \gamma$, we have

$$D_tw = \alpha f_1(x, y, z) + \beta f_2(x, y, z) + \gamma f_3(x, y, z).$$

Problems 97

1. Verify the Chain Rule Equation 97-13 by the procedure used in Example 97-2 if:
   (a) $w = \ln u + e^v$, $u = e^x$, $v = \ln x$
   (b) $w = u^2v$, $u = x$, $v = \dfrac{1}{x^2}$
   (c) $w = \sin uv$, $u = \sqrt{x}$, $v = \sqrt{x}$
   (d) $w = \text{Tan}^{-1} uv$, $u = \sin x$, $v = 2 \cos x$
2. Write out the Chain Rule Equation corresponding to Equation 97-13 if $w = g(p, q)$, $p = f(t)$, and $q = h(t)$.
3. Suppose that $f(x, y) = e^{xy}$ and that g and h are functions such that $g(2) = 3$, $g'(2) = 4$, $h(2) = 5$, and $h'(2) = 6$. Find $F'(2)$ if $F(t) = f(g(t), h(t))$.
4. Write out the Chain Rule Equation corresponding to Equation 97-13 if $u = F(w, x, y, z)$, $x = f(t)$, $y = g(t)$, $z = h(t)$, and $w = G(t)$.
5. Write out the Chain Rule Equation corresponding to Equation 97-13 if $u = F(x, y, z)$, $x = f(t)$, $y = t$, and $z = t^2$.
6. Differentiate both sides of Equation 97-13 to show that

$$D_x^2w = f_1(u, v)D_x^2u + f_2(u, v)D_x^2v + f_{11}(u, v)(D_xu)^2 + 2f_{12}(u, v)D_xuD_xv + f_{22}(u, v)(D_xv)^2$$

7. Show that if $f_{11}(x, y) = f_{12}(x, y) = f_{22}(x, y) = 0$ at every point (x, y), then there are numbers a, b, and c such that $f(x, y) = ax + by + c$.
8. Let f be a function of two variables with the property that $f_1(x, x) = f_2(x, x)$. Let $w = f(\sin x, \cos x) = F(x)$. Find the slope of the tangent line to the graph of the equation $w = F(x)$ at the point where $x = \dfrac{\pi}{4}$.
9. Use Equation 97-16 to find formulas for the slopes of the tangent lines to the graphs of the following equations.
   (a) $2x^2 + 3xy + 4y^2 = 5$
   (b) $\sin xy + e^{xy} = 2$
   (c) $x^y + y^x = 5$
   (d) $\text{Tan}^{-1} xy + \ln xy = 17$.
10. Show that the tangent lines to the graph of the equation $f(x, y) = c$ are horizontal at points where $f_1(x, y) = 0$ and $f_2(x, y) \neq 0$, and are vertical at points where $f_2(x, y) = 0$ and $f_1(x, y) \neq 0$. What can you say about the tangent lines at points where $f_1(x, y) = f_2(x, y) \neq 0$?
11. Let $u = g(x)$, $v = h(x)$, and $w = f(u, v)$. Use the result in Question 6 to find an expression for D_x^2w if:
   (a) $f(u, v) = u^2 + v$
   (b) $f(u, v) = uv - \ln uv$.
12. Suppose that f is a function such that $f(tx, ty) = t^3f(x, y)$ for all x, y, and positive t. Differentiate both sides of this equation with respect to t and then set $t = 1$ to obtain the equation $xf_1(x, y) + yf_2(x, y) = 3f(x, y)$. (The function f is said to be **homogeneous of degree three.** An example is the function defined by the equation $f(x, y) = x^3 \sin \dfrac{x}{y} + xy^2$.)

98. Additional Chain Rule Equations

In the preceding section we developed the following Chain Rule: If $w = f(u, v)$, where $u = g(x)$ and $v = h(x)$, then

$$\frac{dw}{dx} = f_1(u, v)\frac{du}{dx} + f_2(u, v)\frac{dv}{dx}. \tag{98-1}$$

This Chain Rule can be modified to deal with the case in which g and h are functions of two or more variables by replacing the ordinary derivatives with the appropriate partial derivatives. Thus suppose that

$$w = f(u, v), \text{ where } u = g(x, y), \text{ and } v = h(x, y).$$

Then we have

$$\begin{aligned} \frac{\partial w}{\partial x} &= f_1(u, v)\frac{\partial u}{\partial x} + f_2(u, v)\frac{\partial v}{\partial x}, \\ \frac{\partial w}{\partial y} &= f_1(u, v)\frac{\partial u}{\partial y} + f_2(u, v)\frac{\partial v}{\partial y}. \end{aligned} \tag{98-2}$$

These equations can also be written as

$$\begin{aligned} \frac{\partial w}{\partial x} &= \frac{\partial w}{\partial u}\frac{\partial u}{\partial x} + \frac{\partial w}{\partial v}\frac{\partial v}{\partial x} \\ \frac{\partial w}{\partial y} &= \frac{\partial w}{\partial u}\frac{\partial u}{\partial y} + \frac{\partial w}{\partial v}\frac{\partial v}{\partial y}. \end{aligned} \tag{98-3}$$

Example 98-1. Verify the second of Equations 98-2 if $f(u, v) = u \sin v$, where $u = x + y$ and $v = x - y$.

Solution. If we let $w = f(u, v)$ and substitute for u and v, we obtain $w = (x + y) \sin (x - y)$. Then by partial differentiation we find that

$$\frac{\partial w}{\partial y} = \sin (x - y) - (x + y) \cos (x - y).$$

On the other hand, $f_1(u, v) = \sin v$, $f_2(u, v) = u \cos v$, $\frac{\partial u}{\partial y} = 1$, and $\frac{\partial v}{\partial y} = -1$.

Equations 98-2 then give us

$$\frac{\partial w}{\partial y} = 1 \cdot \sin v + (-1)u \cos v = \sin (x - y) - (x + y) \cos (x - y),$$

the same result as before.

Of course, the choice of letters we use to write a Chain Rule Equation is unimportant. It's the "form" that counts! You should practice writing the Chain Rule Equations with letters that are different from the ones that we have used.

The next example illustrates how we can use a Chain Rule to find derivatives of orders higher than the first.

Example 98-2. Suppose that $w = f(u, v)$, where $u = \frac{x+y}{2}$ and $v = \frac{x-y}{2}$. Find $\frac{\partial^2 w}{\partial x\, \partial y}$.

Solution. Since $\frac{\partial^2 w}{\partial x\, \partial y} = \frac{\partial}{\partial x}\left(\frac{\partial w}{\partial y}\right)$, we will first find $\frac{\partial w}{\partial y}$ and then calculate its derivative with respect to x. Since

$$\frac{\partial u}{\partial x} = \frac{1}{2}, \quad \frac{\partial u}{\partial y} = \frac{1}{2}, \quad \frac{\partial v}{\partial x} = \frac{1}{2}, \text{ and } \frac{\partial v}{\partial y} = -\frac{1}{2},$$

Equations 98-3 become

$$\text{(98-4)} \qquad \begin{aligned} \frac{\partial w}{\partial x} &= \frac{1}{2}\frac{\partial w}{\partial u} + \frac{1}{2}\frac{\partial w}{\partial v}, \\ \frac{\partial w}{\partial y} &= \frac{1}{2}\frac{\partial w}{\partial u} - \frac{1}{2}\frac{\partial w}{\partial v}. \end{aligned}$$

The second of these equations gives us $\frac{\partial w}{\partial y}$, and therefore

$$\text{(98-5)} \qquad \frac{\partial^2 w}{\partial x\, \partial y} = \frac{\partial}{\partial x}\left(\frac{1}{2}\frac{\partial w}{\partial u} - \frac{1}{2}\frac{\partial w}{\partial v}\right) = \frac{1}{2}\frac{\partial}{\partial x}\left(\frac{\partial w}{\partial u}\right) - \frac{1}{2}\frac{\partial}{\partial x}\left(\frac{\partial w}{\partial v}\right).$$

We find the derivatives $\frac{\partial}{\partial x}\left(\frac{\partial w}{\partial u}\right)$ and $\frac{\partial}{\partial x}\left(\frac{\partial w}{\partial v}\right)$ by replacing w with $\frac{\partial w}{\partial u}$ and $\frac{\partial w}{\partial v}$ in the first of Equations 98-4:

$$\text{(98-6)} \qquad \begin{aligned} \frac{\partial}{\partial x}\left(\frac{\partial w}{\partial u}\right) &= \frac{1}{2}\frac{\partial}{\partial u}\left(\frac{\partial w}{\partial u}\right) + \frac{1}{2}\frac{\partial}{\partial v}\left(\frac{\partial w}{\partial u}\right) = \frac{1}{2}\left(\frac{\partial^2 w}{\partial u^2} + \frac{\partial^2 w}{\partial v\, \partial u}\right), \\ \frac{\partial}{\partial x}\left(\frac{\partial w}{\partial v}\right) &= \frac{1}{2}\frac{\partial}{\partial u}\left(\frac{\partial w}{\partial v}\right) + \frac{1}{2}\frac{\partial}{\partial v}\left(\frac{\partial w}{\partial v}\right) = \frac{1}{2}\left(\frac{\partial^2 w}{\partial u\, \partial v} + \frac{\partial^2 w}{\partial v^2}\right). \end{aligned}$$

Now we substitute these results in Equation 98-5 to obtain

$$\begin{aligned} \frac{\partial^2 w}{\partial x\, \partial y} &= \frac{1}{4}\left(\frac{\partial^2 w}{\partial u^2} + \frac{\partial^2 w}{\partial v\, \partial u}\right) - \frac{1}{4}\left(\frac{\partial^2 w}{\partial u\, \partial v} + \frac{\partial^2 w}{\partial v^2}\right) \\ &= \frac{1}{4}\left(\frac{\partial^2 w}{\partial u^2} - \frac{\partial^2 w}{\partial v^2}\right). \end{aligned}$$

The next example illustrates another important application of a Chain Rule.

Example 98-3. The transformation equations

$$x = r\cos\theta \qquad (98\text{-}7)$$
$$y = r\sin\theta$$

express x and y in terms of r and θ. Find $\frac{\partial r}{\partial x}$ and $\frac{\partial \theta}{\partial x}$ without first expressing r and θ in terms of x and y.

Solution. We differentiate both sides of Equations 98-7 with respect to x:

$$\frac{\partial x}{\partial x} = \frac{\partial}{\partial x}(r\cos\theta) \quad \text{and} \quad \frac{\partial y}{\partial x} = \frac{\partial}{\partial x}(r\sin\theta). \qquad (98\text{-}8)$$

Clearly, $\frac{\partial x}{\partial x} = 1$, and since we are to treat y as "fixed," we have $\frac{\partial y}{\partial x} = 0$. We can use our Chain Rule to find

$$\frac{\partial}{\partial x}(r\cos\theta) \quad \text{and} \quad \frac{\partial}{\partial x}(r\sin\theta).$$

Thus if $z = f(r, \theta)$, where $r = g(x, y)$ and $\theta = h(x, y)$, then the first of the Chain Rule Equations 98-3 becomes

$$\frac{\partial z}{\partial x} = \frac{\partial z}{\partial r}\frac{\partial r}{\partial x} + \frac{\partial z}{\partial \theta}\frac{\partial \theta}{\partial x}.$$

We successively replace z with $r\cos\theta$ and $r\sin\theta$, and we see that

$$\begin{aligned}\frac{\partial(r\cos\theta)}{\partial x} &= \frac{\partial(r\cos\theta)}{\partial r}\frac{\partial r}{\partial x} + \frac{\partial(r\cos\theta)}{\partial \theta}\frac{\partial \theta}{\partial x}\\ &= \cos\theta\frac{\partial r}{\partial x} - r\sin\theta\frac{\partial \theta}{\partial x}\end{aligned}$$

and

$$\begin{aligned}\frac{\partial(r\sin\theta)}{\partial x} &= \frac{\partial(r\sin\theta)}{\partial r}\frac{\partial r}{\partial x} + \frac{\partial(r\sin\theta)}{\partial \theta}\frac{\partial \theta}{\partial x}\\ &= \sin\theta\frac{\partial r}{\partial x} + r\cos\theta\frac{\partial \theta}{\partial x}.\end{aligned}$$

Therefore, Equations 98-8 become

$$1 = \cos\theta\frac{\partial r}{\partial x} - r\sin\theta\frac{\partial \theta}{\partial x}$$

$$0 = \sin\theta\frac{\partial r}{\partial x} + r\cos\theta\frac{\partial \theta}{\partial x}.$$

These last two equations are simply a pair of linear equations in the two unknowns $\frac{\partial r}{\partial x}$ and $\frac{\partial \theta}{\partial x}$. We solve them by the usual algebraic methods and find

$$\frac{\partial r}{\partial x} = \cos\theta \quad \text{and} \quad \frac{\partial \theta}{\partial x} = \frac{-\sin\theta}{r}.$$

Problems 98

1. In the following cases verify Equations 98-3 by the method used in Example 98-1.
   (a) $w = u^2(3 + 2v)$, $u = x^2$, $v = 3x + 2y$
   (b) $w = e^{uv}$, $u = x + y$, $v = x - y$
   (c) $w = \sin(u + v)$, $u = x + y$, $v = x - y$
   (d) $w = \text{Tan}^{-1} uv$, $u = e^x$, $v = \ln y$

2. Let $w = (\sin x)^{e^y} + e^y \ln \sin x$. Compute $\frac{\partial w}{\partial x}$ and $\frac{\partial w}{\partial y}$ by writing $w = u^v + v \ln u$, where $u = \sin x$ and $v = e^y$, and using the Chain Rule Equations 98-3.

3. Suppose that $w = f(u, v)$ and that $a\frac{\partial u}{\partial x} + b\frac{\partial u}{\partial y} = 0$, and $a\frac{\partial v}{\partial x} + b\frac{\partial v}{\partial y} = 0$. Show that $a\frac{\partial w}{\partial x} + b\frac{\partial w}{\partial y} = 0$.

4. Let $w = f(x - y, y - x)$. Compute $\frac{\partial w}{\partial x} + \frac{\partial w}{\partial y}$.

5. Suppose that $z = f(x + y, x - y)$. Find:
   (a) $\frac{\partial^2 z}{\partial x^2} + \frac{\partial^2 z}{\partial y^2}$
   (b) $\frac{\partial^2 z}{\partial x^2} - \frac{\partial^2 z}{\partial y^2}$

6. Let $g(x, y) = f(3x^2 - 2xy, 2x - y^2)$. Find:
   (a) $g_1(1, -2)$
   (b) $g_{11}(1, -2)$
   (c) $g_{12}(1, -2)$
   (d) $g_{112}(1, -2)$

7. In Example 98-3 we found that $\frac{\partial r}{\partial x} = \cos\theta = \frac{x}{\sqrt{x^2 + y^2}}$. Check this result by solving Equations 98-7 for r in terms of x and y and then calculating $\frac{\partial r}{\partial x}$.

8. If we consider the coordinate transformation defined by the equations $u = x^2 - y^2$ and $v = 2xy$, then $f(u, v)$ is transformed into $g(x, y)$. Set $w = f(u, v) = g(x, y)$ and find $\frac{\partial w}{\partial y}$ in terms of $\frac{\partial w}{\partial u}$ and $\frac{\partial w}{\partial v}$.

9. Find $\frac{\partial u}{\partial x}$ and $\frac{\partial v}{\partial x}$ if $x = 2u + v$, and $y = 3u + 2v$.

10. Find $\frac{\partial u}{\partial x}$ and $\frac{\partial v}{\partial x}$ if $x = 2u^2v + v^3$ and $y = 3uv^2 - uv$.

11. Let $w = \int_x^y f(t)\,dt$, where $x = r - s$ and $y = r + s$. Find $\frac{\partial w}{\partial r} + \frac{\partial w}{\partial s}$.

99. Directional Derivatives. The Gradient

Suppose that f is a function of three variables and that (x, y, z) is a point in the domain of f. If $w = f(x, y, z)$, then the numbers

$$\frac{\partial w}{\partial x} = f_1(x, y, z), \quad \frac{\partial w}{\partial y} = f_2(x, y, z), \quad \text{and } \frac{\partial w}{\partial z} = f_3(x, y, z)$$

measure the (instantaneous) rate of change of the functional value w with respect to distance (at the point (x, y, z)) in the direction of the positive X-, Y-, and Z-axes, respectively.

Example 99-1. Suppose that the temperature at a point (x, y, z) in a region in space is given by the formula $w = e^{-x^2-y^2-z^2}$. What is the rate of change of temperature in the direction of the positive coordinate axes at the point (1, 2, 3)? (Let us suppose that temperature is measured in degrees F. and that distance is measured in feet.)

Solution. We have

$$\frac{\partial w}{\partial x} = -2xe^{-x^2-y^2-z^2}, \quad \frac{\partial w}{\partial y} = -2ye^{-x^2-y^2-z^2}, \quad \text{and } \frac{\partial w}{\partial z} = -2ze^{-x^2-y^2-z^2}.$$

Therefore, at the point (1, 2, 3) these derivatives are the numbers

$$-2e^{-14}, \quad -4e^{-14}, \quad \text{and } -6e^{-14}.$$

Thus at the point (1, 2, 3) the temperature is decreasing at the rate of $2e^{-14}$ degrees per foot in the direction of the positive X-axis. At this point (1, 2, 3) the temperature is also decreasing in the direction of the positive Y- and Z-axes, and the rate of decrease is $4e^{-14}$ degrees per foot in the direction of the positive Y-axis and $6e^{-14}$ degrees per foot in the direction of the positive Z-axis.

Notice that we speak of the rate of change of w *at a point* and *in a direction*. A good way of specifying a direction in space is by means of a vector $\boldsymbol{u} = u_x\boldsymbol{i} + u_y\boldsymbol{j} + u_z\boldsymbol{k}$ that is 1 unit long. Thus the vectors $\boldsymbol{i}$, $\boldsymbol{j}$, and $\boldsymbol{k}$ give us the directions of the positive coordinate axes, for example.

In order to find the derivative of $w = f(x, y, z)$ at the point (x, y, z) and in the direction of a unit vector $\boldsymbol{u}$ (which need not be parallel to one of the coordinate axes), we proceed as follows. A point s units from the point (x, y, z) in the direction of $\boldsymbol{u}$ has coordinates $(x + su_x, y + su_y, z + su_z)$, as we have shown in Fig. 99-1. Now we define $F(s)$ by the equation

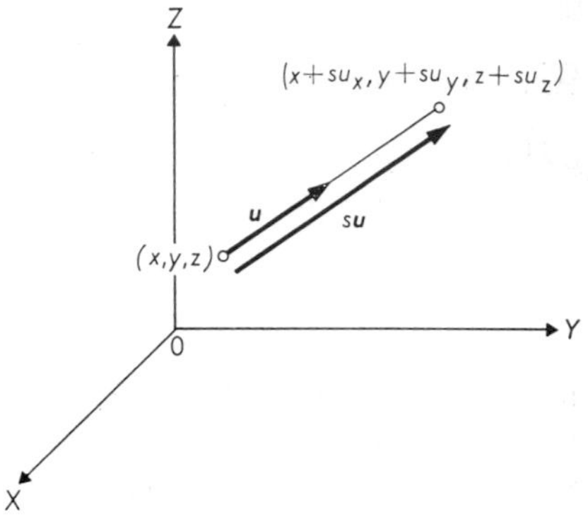

Figure 99-1

(99-1) $$F(s) = f(x + su_x, y + su_y, z + su_z).$$

This new function F of one variable gives us the values of our original function f that correspond to points of the line that contains the point (x, y, z) and has the direction of $\boldsymbol{u}$. For example, $F(0) = f(x, y, z)$ is the value of f at the point (x, y, z). Therefore, the derivative $F'(s)$ is the rate at which these functional values change in the direction determined by $\boldsymbol{u}$; in particular, $F'(0)$ is the rate at which they change at the point (x, y, z). Since $w = f(x, y, z)$, we say that $F'(0)$ is the **directional derivative** of w *at the point* (x, y, z) and *in the direction of the unit vector* $\boldsymbol{u}$. We denote this directional derivative by the symbol $D_{\boldsymbol{u}}w$, and thus we have

$$D_{\boldsymbol{u}}w = F'(0).$$

We calculate $F'(0)$ by applying a Chain Rule to the right side of Equation 99-1. Thus

$$\begin{aligned} F'(s) &= f_1(x + su_x, y + su_y, z + su_z)D_s(x + su_x) \\ &\quad + f_2(x + su_x, y + su_y, z + su_z)D_s(y + su_y) \\ &\quad + f_3(x + su_x, y + su_y, z + su_z)D_s(z + su_z) \\ &= f_1(x + su_x, y + su_y, z + su_z)u_x \\ &\quad + f_2(x + su_x, y + su_y, z + su_z)u_y \\ &\quad + f_3(x + su_x, y + su_y, z + su_z)u_z. \end{aligned}$$

Now when we replace s with 0 we find that

$$F'(0) = f_1(x, y, z)u_x + f_2(x, y, z)u_y + f_3(x, y, z)u_z.$$

Thus we have

(99-2) $$D_{\boldsymbol{u}}w = f_1(x, y, z)u_x + f_2(x, y, z)u_y + f_3(x, y, z)u_z.$$

An analogous formula holds for functions of two variables.

Notice that if $\boldsymbol{u} = \boldsymbol{i}$, then $u_x = 1$, and $u_y = u_z = 0$, so Equation 99-2 tells us that $D_{\boldsymbol{i}}w = f_1(x, y, z) = \frac{\partial w}{\partial x}$. Similarly, $D_{\boldsymbol{j}}w = f_2(x, y, z) = \frac{\partial w}{\partial y}$ and $D_{\boldsymbol{k}}w = f_3(x, y, z) = \frac{\partial w}{\partial z}$. The directional derivative $D_{\boldsymbol{u}}w$ can be considered a partial derivative in the direction of $\boldsymbol{u}$.

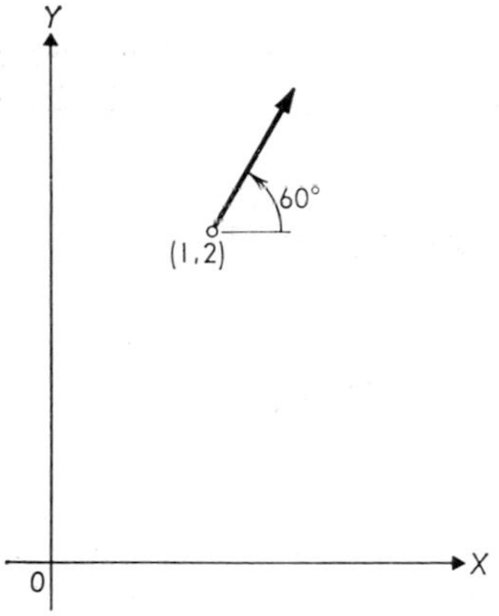

Figure 99-2

Example 99-1. Find $D_{\boldsymbol{u}}w$ at the point (1, 2) if $w = f(x, y) = x^2 + y^2$ and $\boldsymbol{u}$ makes an angle of 60° with the positive X-axis.

Solution. Figure 99-2 shows the point (1, 2) and the vector $\boldsymbol{u}$. Since $\boldsymbol{u}$ is 1 unit long, we see that $\boldsymbol{u} = \cos 60°\, \boldsymbol{i} + \sin 60°\, \boldsymbol{j} = \frac{1}{2}\boldsymbol{i} + \frac{\sqrt{3}}{2}\boldsymbol{j}$. Furthermore, $f_1(1, 2) = 2$ and $f_2(1, 2) = 4$, so Equation 99-2 (adjusted to the case of functions of two variables) gives us

$$D_{\boldsymbol{u}}w = 2\frac{1}{2} + 4\frac{\sqrt{3}}{2} = 1 + 2\sqrt{3}.$$

Equation 99-2 can be simplified by introducing the vector

(99-3) $$\begin{aligned}\nabla w &= f_1(x, y, z)\boldsymbol{i} + f_2(x, y, z)\boldsymbol{j} + f_3(x, y, z)\boldsymbol{k}\\ &= \frac{\partial w}{\partial x}\boldsymbol{i} + \frac{\partial w}{\partial y}\boldsymbol{j} + \frac{\partial w}{\partial z}\boldsymbol{k}.\end{aligned}$$

This vector is called the **gradient** of w. Now we observe that the right side of Equation 99-2 is simply the dot product of the vectors ∇w and $\boldsymbol{u}$. Thus we have the following simple formula for the directional derivative of w:

(99-4) $$D_{\boldsymbol{u}}w = \nabla w \cdot \boldsymbol{u}.$$

Equation 99-4 also applies to functions of two variables. In that case

$$\nabla w = \frac{\partial w}{\partial x}\boldsymbol{i} + \frac{\partial w}{\partial y}\boldsymbol{j}, \quad \text{and} \quad \boldsymbol{u} = u_x\boldsymbol{i} + u_y\boldsymbol{j}.$$

Example 99-2. Find $D_{\boldsymbol{u}}w$ at the point (2, −1, 2) and in the direction from the point (2, − 1, 2) to the origin, if $w = 2x^2y + 3z$.

Solution. We must find the vectors ∇w and $\boldsymbol{u}$ and then compute their dot product. First, we see that

$$\nabla w = \frac{\partial w}{\partial x}\boldsymbol{i} + \frac{\partial w}{\partial y}\boldsymbol{j} + \frac{\partial w}{\partial z}\boldsymbol{k} = 4xy\boldsymbol{i} + 2x^2\boldsymbol{j} + 3\boldsymbol{k}.$$

Therefore, at the point (2, −1, 2) we have

$$\nabla w = -8\boldsymbol{i} + 8\boldsymbol{j} + 3\boldsymbol{k}.$$

The vector $\boldsymbol{u}$ is 1 unit long and its direction is that of the vector $\boldsymbol{v} = -2\boldsymbol{i} + \boldsymbol{j} - 2\boldsymbol{k}$ whose initial point is the point (2, −1, 2) and whose terminal point is the origin. Hence

$$\boldsymbol{u} = \frac{\boldsymbol{v}}{|\boldsymbol{v}|} = \frac{-2\boldsymbol{i} + \boldsymbol{j} - 2\boldsymbol{k}}{3} = -\frac{2}{3}\boldsymbol{i} + \frac{1}{3}\boldsymbol{j} - \frac{2}{3}\boldsymbol{k}.$$

Thus we finally have

$$\begin{aligned} D_{\boldsymbol{u}}w &= (-8\boldsymbol{i} + 8\boldsymbol{j} + 3\boldsymbol{k}) \cdot (-\tfrac{2}{3}\boldsymbol{i} + \tfrac{1}{3}\boldsymbol{j} - \tfrac{2}{3}\boldsymbol{k}) \\ &= \tfrac{16}{3} + \tfrac{8}{3} - \tfrac{6}{3} = 6. \end{aligned}$$

When we calculate the directional derivatives of w at a point (x, y, z) by means of the formula $D_{\boldsymbol{u}}w = \nabla w \cdot \boldsymbol{u}$, we use the same vector ∇w for each direction vector $\boldsymbol{u}$. For different direction vectors this formula yields different directional derivatives, and it is natural to wonder what direction gives us the *greatest* directional derivative. To answer this question, we write the dot product $\nabla w \cdot \boldsymbol{u}$ as $|\nabla w|\,|\boldsymbol{u}| \cos \theta$, where θ is the angle between the vectors ∇w and $\boldsymbol{u}$. Since $\boldsymbol{u}$ is a *unit* vector, then $|\boldsymbol{u}| = 1$, and hence our formula for the directional derivative becomes

$$D_{\boldsymbol{u}}w = |\nabla w| \cos \theta. \tag{99-5}$$

Since the number $\cos \theta$ is a maximum when $\theta = 0$, we see that the number $D_{\boldsymbol{u}}w$ is largest when $\boldsymbol{u}$ is selected as the unit vector in the direction of ∇w; that is, $\boldsymbol{u} = \dfrac{\nabla w}{|\nabla w|}$. Then the maximum directional derivative is the number $(D_{\boldsymbol{u}}w)_{\max} = |\nabla w| \cos 0 = |\nabla w|$. Thus we see that *the maximum rate of change of w at a point occurs in the direction of the gradient vector calculated at that point, and the magnitude of the gradient of w is the maximum value of the rate of change of w with respect to distance.* Equation 99-5 also tells us that the rate of change of w with respect to distance is 0 in directions perpendicular to the gradient, and that w decreases with distance most rapidly along the vector $-\nabla w$.

Example 99-3. The electric potential (voltage) at a point (x, y, z) in a certain region in space is given by the formula $V = x^2 - y^2 + 2xz$. If we put a unit positive charge at the point (1, 2, 3), which way will it start to move?

Solution. It is a fact from electric field theory that the charge will start to move in the direction of the greatest potential *drop;* that is, in the direction in which V decreases most rapidly. Therefore, the charge will move in the direction $-\nabla V$. At the point (1, 2, 3), $\nabla V = 8\boldsymbol{i} - 4\boldsymbol{j} + 2\boldsymbol{k}$, and hence the charge will start to move in the direction of the vector $-8\boldsymbol{i} + 4\boldsymbol{j} - 2\boldsymbol{k}$.

The gradient vector can be used to express Chain Rule Equations in vector notation. Thus suppose that f is a function of three variables. Instead of writing $w = f(x, y, z)$, we can write $w = f(\boldsymbol{R})$, where $\boldsymbol{R}$ is the position vector $\boldsymbol{R} = x\boldsymbol{i} + y\boldsymbol{j} + z\boldsymbol{k}$. If $\boldsymbol{R} = \boldsymbol{F}(t) = a(t)\boldsymbol{i} + b(t)\boldsymbol{j} + c(t)\boldsymbol{k}$, we have $x = a(t)$, $y = b(t)$, and $z = c(t)$, and the derivative $\dfrac{dw}{dt}$ is given by the Chain Rule Equation

$$\frac{dw}{dt} = \frac{\partial w}{\partial x}\frac{dx}{dt} + \frac{\partial w}{\partial y}\frac{dy}{dt} + \frac{\partial w}{\partial z}\frac{dz}{dt}. \tag{99-6}$$

Using the vectors ∇w and $\dfrac{d\boldsymbol{R}}{dt} = \dfrac{dx}{dt}\boldsymbol{i} + \dfrac{dy}{dt}\boldsymbol{j} + \dfrac{dz}{dt}\boldsymbol{k}$, we can write Equation 99-6 in the compact form

$$\frac{dw}{dt} = \nabla w \cdot \frac{d\boldsymbol{R}}{dt}. \tag{99-7}$$

Similarly, if the vector-valued function $\boldsymbol{F}$ is a function of several variables, the Chain Rule Equations can be written in vector form. For example, if $w = f(\boldsymbol{R})$ and $\boldsymbol{R} = \boldsymbol{F}(r, s)$, then the Chain Rule Equations for the partial derivatives of w can be written (see Equations 98-3) as

$$\frac{\partial w}{\partial r} = \nabla w \cdot \frac{\partial \boldsymbol{R}}{\partial r} \quad \text{and} \quad \frac{\partial w}{\partial s} = \nabla w \cdot \frac{\partial \boldsymbol{R}}{\partial s}. \tag{99-8}$$

Example 99-4. Suppose that the temperature w at each point (x, y, z) in space is given by the equation $w = f(x, y, z)$, and suppose that a rocket travels along the path whose vector equation is $\boldsymbol{R} = \boldsymbol{F}(t)$. If P is the coldest point through which the rocket passes, show that the path of the rocket is perpendicular to the gradient of w at P.

Solution. The temperature encountered by the rocket at the point whose position vector is $\boldsymbol{R} = \boldsymbol{F}(t)$ is given by the equation $w = f(\boldsymbol{R})$. We know that at a minimum point, $\dfrac{dw}{dt} = 0$. Therefore, according to Equation 99-7, at a minimum point $\nabla w \cdot \frac{d\mathbf{R}}{dt} = 0$. But this equation says that ∇w is perpendicular to the tangent vector $\frac{d\mathbf{R}}{dt}$, as was to be shown.

Problems 99

1. Find $D_{\mathbf{u}}w$ at the point (3, 2) if $\mathbf{u} = \frac{1}{\sqrt{2}}\mathbf{i} - \frac{1}{\sqrt{2}}\mathbf{j}$ and:
   (a) $w = x - y^2$ (b) $w = \sin \pi xy$
   (c) $w = \ln xy$ (d) $w = \mathrm{Tan}^{-1} \frac{\pi y}{x}$
2. Find $D_{\mathbf{u}}w$ at the point $(4, -1, 2)$ if $w = z(x^2 + y^3)$ and $\mathbf{u}$ is a unit vector in the direction of the given vector.
   (a) $2\mathbf{i} - 2\mathbf{j} + \mathbf{k}$ (b) $\mathbf{i} + 2\mathbf{j} - 2\mathbf{k}$
   (c) $-\mathbf{j}$ (d) $-\mathbf{i} - \mathbf{k}$
3. Find the directional derivative of w at the given point and in the given direction.
   (a) $w = e^{2x+3y}$, (0, 0), direction: $\mathbf{u} = \frac{3}{5}\mathbf{i} - \frac{4}{5}\mathbf{j}$
   (b) $w = 2xy^2$, $(-1, 2)$, direction: $\mathbf{v} = \mathbf{i} - 2\mathbf{j}$
   (c) $w = e^x \sin (y + z)$, (0, 0, 0), in the direction of the line from the origin to the point $(-1, 2, -2)$.
   (d) $w = x^2 + y^2$, (2, 1), in the direction of a vector that makes a positive angle of 60° with the positive X-axis.
   (e) $w = (y + x)/(y - x)$, (1, 2), direction: normal to the line $3x + 4y = 11$.
   (f) $w = \ln xyz^2$, (1, 2, 1), direction: $\frac{1}{3}\mathbf{i} - \frac{2}{3}\mathbf{j} + \frac{2}{3}\mathbf{k}$.
4. Find a unit vector in the direction in which the maximum rate of change of w at the given point occurs if $w = \mathrm{Tan}^{-1} xy + z$.
   (a) (0, 0, 0) (b) (1, 0, 0) (c) (0, 1, 0) (d) (0, 0, 1)
5. Let A_x, A_y, and A_z be given numbers, and let $\mathbf{A} = A_x\mathbf{i} + A_y\mathbf{j} + A_z\mathbf{k}$. Let $\mathbf{R}$ be the position vector, $\mathbf{R} = x\mathbf{i} + y\mathbf{j} + z\mathbf{k}$. Show that $\nabla(\mathbf{A} \cdot \mathbf{R}) = \mathbf{A}$.
6. Let $u = f(x, y)$ and $v = g(x, y)$. Show that $\nabla(uv) = u \nabla v + v \nabla u$.
7. Let $w = \int_x^y e^{-t^2}\, dt$. Find ∇w.
8. Show that if $w = f(x, y)$ and $\nabla w = \mathbf{0}$ for all points in the domain of f, then f is a constant function.
9. Suppose you are standing at the point $(-1, 5, 8)$ on a hill whose equation is $z = 74 - x^2 - 7xy - 4y^2$. Suppose the Y-axis points North and the X-axis East.
   (a) In what direction is the steepest downward path?
   (b) In what directions is the path level?
10. If $w = f(u)$, where $u = g(x, y, z)$, show that $\nabla w = f'(u) \nabla u$.
11. Suppose that $w = f(x, y, z, t)$ and $x = a(t)$, $y = b(t)$, and $z = c(t)$. Show that $D_t w = \frac{\partial w}{\partial t} + \nabla w \cdot \frac{d\mathbf{R}}{dt}$.

12. Let $w = f(\mathbf{R})$, where $\mathbf{R} = \mathbf{F}(t)$. Show that $D_t^2 w = \nabla w \cdot D_t^2 \mathbf{R} + D_t(\nabla w) \cdot D_t \mathbf{R}$.

13. Suppose that $w = f(\mathbf{R})$ and that $z = g(x, y)$. Show that $\dfrac{\partial w}{\partial x} = \nabla w \cdot \left(\mathbf{i} + \dfrac{\partial z}{\partial x}\mathbf{k}\right)$.

100. Normals to Surfaces

Suppose that C is a number in the range of a function f of two variables and that the graph of the equation $f(x, y) = C$ is a curve in the plane. Then this curve is called a **level curve** of the function f. At each

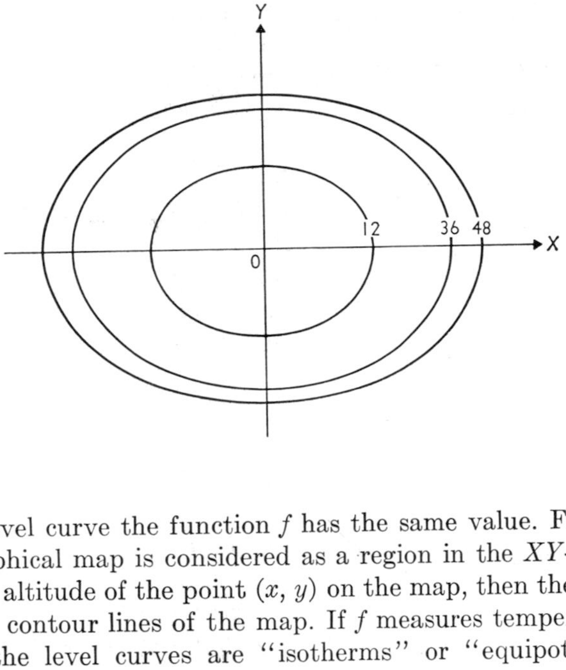

Figure 100-1

point of a given level curve the function f has the same value. For example, if a geographical map is considered as a region in the XY-plane and if $f(x, y)$ is the altitude of the point (x, y) on the map, then the level curves of f are the contour lines of the map. If f measures temperature or voltage, then the level curves are "isotherms" or "equipotential lines," and so on.

Example 100-1. Let $f(x, y) = 9x^2 + 16y^2$. Sketch the level curves that correspond to the functional values 12, 36, and 48.

Solution. The level curves are ellipses whose equations are $9x^2 + 16y^2 = C$, where C is replaced by 12, 36, and 48. They are shown in Fig. 100-1.

The situation in three dimensions is analogous to the two dimensional case. If C is a number in the range of a function f of three variables and the graph of the equation $f(x, y, z) = C$ is a surface in space, then this surface is called a **level surface** of f. Every surface in space can be regarded as a level surface of some function of three variables.

Example 100-2. Find a function f for which the paraboloid of revolution $z + 4 = x^2 + y^2$ is a level surface.

Solution. Since our given equation is equivalent to the equation $z - x^2 - y^2 + 4 = 0$, we see that its graph is a level surface (corresponding to the choice $C = 0$) of the function defined by the equation $f(x, y, z) = z - x^2 - y^2 + 4$. Or we might define the function g by means of the equation $g(x, y, z) = x^2 + y^2 - z$, and then the graph of our given equation is the level surface whose equation is $g(x, y, z) = 4$. There is no end to the number of functions for which our given surface is a level surface.

Let f be a function of three variables and let us consider a curve in the level surface $f(x, y, z) = C$. A curve in space is given by a vector

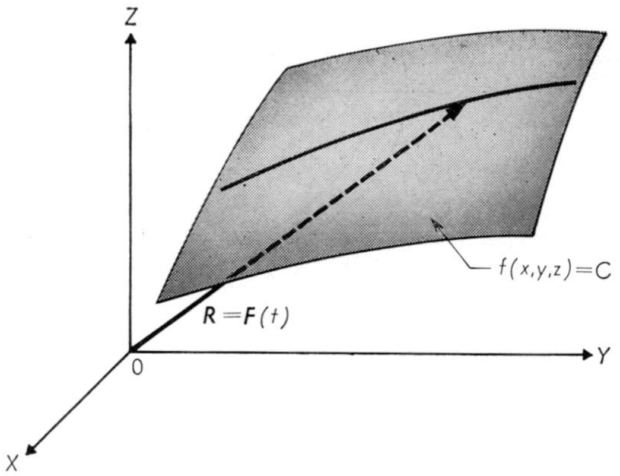

Figure 100-2

equation $\boldsymbol{R} = \boldsymbol{F}(t)$, and to say that the curve lies in the given level surface is to say that $\boldsymbol{R}$ satisfies the equation $f(\boldsymbol{R}) = C$ for each t (see Fig. 100-2). Now we will differentiate both sides of this equation with respect to t. Equation 99-7 tells us that the derivative of the left side is $\nabla w \cdot \boldsymbol{R}'$ (where $w = f(x, y, z)$), and, of course, the derivative of the right side is 0. Therefore, we have the equation

$$\nabla w \cdot \boldsymbol{R}' = 0. \qquad (100\text{-}1)$$

The vector $\boldsymbol{R}'$ is tangent to the graph of the vector equation $\boldsymbol{R} = \boldsymbol{F}(t)$. Therefore, the geometrical interpretation of Equation 100-1 is as follows: *If P is any point of our level surface, then the gradient ∇w at P is perpendicular to the tangent line (at P) to any curve that lies in the surface and* *contains P*. Of course, there are infinitely many curves that lie in the surface and contain P, but Equation 100-1 says that their tangents at P all lie in the same plane, the plane that contains P and has the vector ∇w as a normal. This plane is called the **tangent plane** to our surface at the point P. A vector that is normal to this plane is said to be normal to the surface at P. Thus *the vector* ∇w, *where* $w = f(x, y, z)$, *is normal to the surface* $f(x, y, z) = C$.

Example 100-3. Show that the position vector to a point $P(x, y, z)$ of the sphere whose equation is $x^2 + y^2 + z^2 = 4$ is normal to the sphere.

Solution. Let $w = x^2 + y^2 + z^2$. As we have just said, the vector ∇w is normal to our sphere. Since $\nabla w = 2x\boldsymbol{i} + 2y\boldsymbol{j} + 2z\boldsymbol{k} = 2\boldsymbol{OP}$, where $\boldsymbol{OP}$ is the position vector to $P(x, y, z)$, we see that $\boldsymbol{OP}$ is also normal to our sphere. Thus we see that our definition of a normal vector to a surface leads to the natural result that a radius is normal to a sphere.

Example 100-4. The graph of a function f of two variables is the surface that is the graph of the equation $z = f(x, y)$. Find a vector normal to this surface.

Solution. If we write the equation of our surface as $f(x, y) - z = 0$ and let $w = f(x, y) - z$, then the vector ∇w is normal to our surface. Therefore, a normal vector is $\nabla w = f_1(x, y)\boldsymbol{i} + f_2(x, y)\boldsymbol{j} - \boldsymbol{k}$.

If the vector $\boldsymbol{N} = a\boldsymbol{i} + b\boldsymbol{j} + c\boldsymbol{k}$ is normal to a surface at a point (x_0, y_0, z_0) of the surface, then we recall from our study of analytic geometry (Section 80) that the equation of the tangent plane at (x_0, y_0, z_0) is $a(x - x_0) + b(y - y_0) + c(z - z_0) = 0$. Since the gradient vector $f_1(x_0, y_0, z_0)\boldsymbol{i} + f_2(x_0, y_0, z_0)\boldsymbol{j} + f_3(x_0, y_0, z_0)\boldsymbol{k}$ is normal to the surface $f(x, y, z) = C$ at the point (x_0, y_0, z_0), we see that the equation of our tangent plane can be written as

$$(100\text{-}2)\quad f_1(x_0, y_0, z_0)(x - x_0) + f_2(x_0, y_0, z_0)(y - y_0) + f_3(x_0, y_0, z_0)(z - z_0) = 0.$$

Example 100-5. Find the equation of the plane that is tangent, at the point (1, 1, 5), to the graph of the equation $x^2y^3z = 4 + x$.

Solution. Before we use Equation 100-2 we should write our equation as the equation of a level surface; for example, as $x^2y^3z - x = 4$. Then we use Equation 100-2 with $f(x, y, z) = x^2y^3z - x$ and $(x_0, y_0, z_0) = (1, 1, 5)$. We find that $f_1(x, y, z) = 2xy^3z - 1$, and so $f_1(1, 1, 5) = 9$. Similarly, $f_2(1, 1, 5) = 15$, and $f_3(1, 1, 5) = 1$, and therefore the desired tangent plane has the equation

$$9(x - 1) + 15(y - 1) + (z - 5) = 0,$$

$$9x + 15y + z = 29.$$

Our remarks concerning surfaces in space can be modified so as to apply to curves in the plane. In particular, if $\mathbf{R} = \mathbf{F}(t)$ is a level curve of the function defined by the equation $w = f(x, y)$, then $f(\mathbf{R}) = C$ for each t. Equation 100-1 tells us that at any point P of the level curve the vector ∇w is perpendicular to the tangent line to the level curve at P.

Example 100-6. Find the equation of the tangent line to the level curve $f(x, y) = C$ at the point (x_0, y_0).

Solution. The tangent line plays the same role in the plane as the tangent plane plays in space. We simply drop the last term on the left side of Equation 100-2 to obtain the equation of the desired tangent:

$$f_1(x_0, y_0)(x - x_0) + f_2(x_0, y_0)(y - y_0) = 0.$$

Notice that the slope of this tangent line is $-\dfrac{f_1(x_0, y_0)}{f_2(x_0, y_0)}$, which agrees with Equation 97-16 for the slope of the graph of the equation $f(x, y) = C$.

Problems 100

1. Describe the level curves of the function f and sketch the level curve that contains the point (1, 1). Sketch the gradient vector at the point (1, 1).
(a) $f(x, y) = x^2 + y^2 - 1$
(b) $f(x, y) = x^2 + y$
(c) $f(x, y) = 2x^2 + y^2 - 4$
(d) $f(x, y) = 4x^2 - y^2 - 8x + 4y$

2. Describe the level surfaces of the function f.
(a) $f(x, y, z) = x^2 + y^2 + z^2$
(b) $f(x, y, z) = x^2 + y^2$
(c) $f(x, y, z) = 2x - 3y + 4z$
(d) $f(x, y, z) = 2x^2 + 3y^2 + 4z^2$
(e) $f(x, y, z) = 4x^2 - y^2 - z$
(f) $f(x, y, z) = 4x^2 + y^2 - z$

3. Find a vector normal to the surface at the given point.
(a) $x^2 + y^2 + z^2 = 2$, (0, 1, 1)
(b) $4x^2 + y^2 + z^2 = 6$, (1, 1, 1)
(c) $4x^2 + 9y^2 = 10z$, (1, 2, 4)
(d) $x^3 + y^2z - xyz^2 = 3$, (1, 2, 1)

4. At what point is the normal to the surface $z = 3x^2 - 2y^2$ parallel to the vector $2\mathbf{i} + 4\mathbf{j} + \frac{1}{3}\mathbf{k}$?

5. Show that the equation of the line that is normal at the point (x_0, y_0, z_0) to the surface given by the equation $f(x, y, z) = C$ has parametric equations

$$x = f_1(x_0, y_0, z_0)t + x_0$$
$$y = f_2(x_0, y_0, z_0)t + y_0$$
$$z = f_3(x_0, y_0, z_0)t + z_0.$$

6. Find $\mathbf{M}$ and $\mathbf{B}$ such that the vector equation of the line that is perpendicular to the surface $3x^2 - 4yz + xz^2 = 12$ at the point $(1, -2, 1)$ is $\mathbf{R} = \mathbf{M}t + \mathbf{B}$.

7. Let $w = f(x, y) = (x^2 + y^2)^{3/2}$. Describe the level curves of f. Show that $\nabla w = 3|\mathbf{R}|\mathbf{R}$, where $\mathbf{R}$ is the position vector.

8. Find the equation of the tangent plane at the given point.
(a) $2x^2 - 3xy + 4y^2 = z$, $(-1, 1, 9)$.
(b) $x^2y + y^2z + z^2x + 4 = 0$, $(2, -1, 0)$.
(c) $e^{xy} - 2 \sin z = 1$, $(0, 0, 0)$.
(d) $4 \operatorname{Tan}^{-1} \dfrac{y}{x} = \pi \ln xyz$, $(1, 1, e)$

9. At what points of the graph of the equation $x^2 + 4y^2 + 16z^2 - 2xy = 12$ are the tangent planes parallel to the XZ-plane?

10. Find the directional derivative of $w = 3x^2yz + 2yz^2$ at the point $(1, 1, 1)$ in a direction normal to the surface $x^2 - y + z^2 = 1$ at $(1, 1, 1)$.

11. Find a vector tangent to the line of intersection of the surfaces whose equations are $x^2 - 2xz + y^2z = 1$ and $3xy + 2yz + 6 = 0$ at the point $(1, -2, 0)$. (*Hint:* This vector must be perpendicular to normals to both surfaces).

101. Maxima and Minima of Functions of Several Variables

If a differentiable function g of one variable takes a maximum (or a minimum) value at an interior point a of its domain, then we know that

$$g'(a) = 0. \tag{101-1}$$

Now we will find the analogous equations for functions of several variables.

Geometrically speaking, the equation $g'(a) = 0$ states that the tangent line to the graph of g at the point $(a, g(a))$ is parallel to the X-axis,

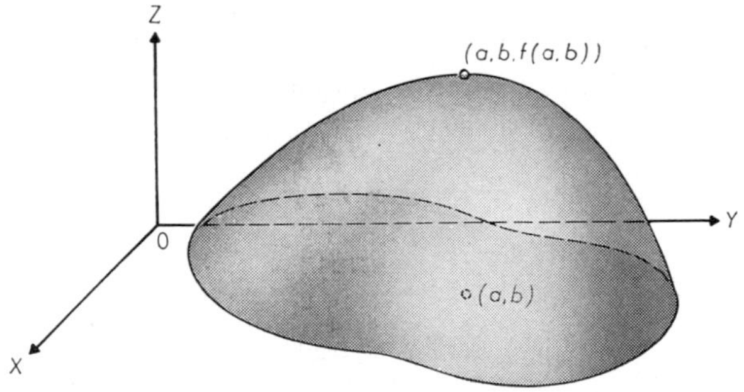

Figure 101-1

and a similar geometric interpretation leads us to the corresponding equations in the case of functions of two variables. Thus Fig. 101-1 shows the graph of a function of two variables with a maximum value at the point (a, b) of its domain; that is, $f(x, y) \leq f(a, b)$ for each point (x, y) in some circle with center (a, b). In Section 96 we noticed that the numbers $f_1(a, b)$ and $f_2(a, b)$ are the slopes of the tangents to the "profile" curves that we obtain by cutting the surface $z = f(x, y)$ with the planes $y = b$ and $x = a$. At our maximum point these tangent lines are clearly parallel to the XY-plane, and so we see that

$$f_1(a, b) = 0 \quad \text{and} \quad f_2(a, b) = 0. \tag{101-2}$$

Similarly we would find that these same equations would hold if $f(a, b)$ were a minimum value of f.

We cannot draw pictures of the situation for functions of more than two variables, but the results are the same. Thus suppose that f is a function of three variables that takes a maximum value at a point (a, b, c) at which its three first partial derivatives exist. To say that f takes a maximum value at (a, b, c) means that there is a sphere with center (a, b, c) such that for each point (x, y, z) inside the sphere we have the inequality

$$f(x, y, z) \leq f(a, b, c). \tag{101-3}$$

Now we let the equation $g(x) = f(x, b, c)$ define a function g of one variable. From Inequality 101-3 we see that for every number x in some interval containing a we have $g(x) \leq g(a)$; that is, g takes a maximum value at a. Therefore, according to the theory of maxima and minima of functions of one variable, $g'(a) = 0$. Thus since $g'(a) = f_1(a, b, c)$, we see that $f_1(a, b, c) = 0$. In a similar way we can show that the other first partial derivatives of f are also zero at (a, b, c). In formal terms, we have the following theorem.

THEOREM 101-1. *If a function f of three variables takes a maximum (or minimum) value at a point (a, b, c) at which its first partial derivatives exist, then*

$$\boldsymbol{f_1(a, b, c) = f_2(a, b, c) = f_3(a, b, c) = 0.} \tag{101-4}$$

If we write $w = f(x, y, z)$, then these equations state that $\dfrac{\partial w}{\partial x} = 0$, $\dfrac{\partial w}{\partial y} = 0$, and $\dfrac{\partial w}{\partial z} = 0$ at (a, b, c). Corresponding theorems hold, of course, for functions of more than three variables.

We know that the equation $g'(a) = 0$ alone does not guarantee that $g(a)$ is a maximum or minimum value of g. For example, if $g(x) = x^3$, then $g'(0) = 0$, but $g(0) = 0$ is not an extreme value of g. Similarly, the fact that the first partial derivatives of a function of several variables are 0 at some point does not guarantee that the function takes an extreme value at that point, as the following example shows.

Example 101-1. Show that there are no maximum or minimum points of the surface whose equation is $z = y^2 - \frac{1}{4}x^2$. In other words, show that the function f defined by the equation $f(x, y) = y^2 - \frac{1}{4}x^2$ has no maximum or minimum values.

Solution. At a maximum or a minimum point, $\frac{\partial z}{\partial x}$ must equal 0 and $\frac{\partial z}{\partial y}$ must equal 0. Since $\frac{\partial z}{\partial x} = -\frac{1}{2}x$ and $\frac{\partial z}{\partial y} = 2y$, we see that $x = 0$ and $y = 0$ at a maximum or minimum point. Hence (0, 0, 0) is the only possible

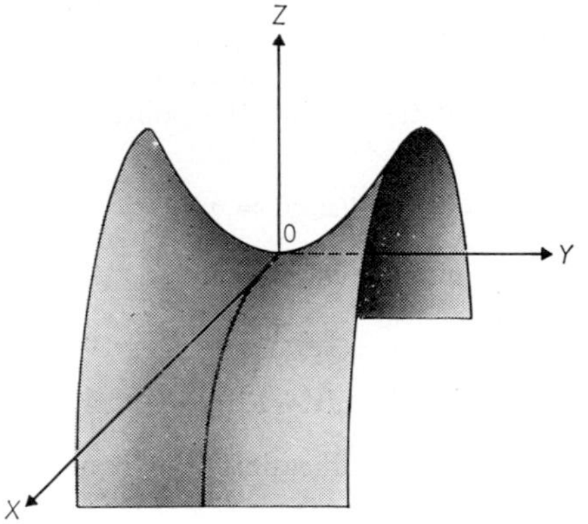

Figure 101-2

maximum or minimum point of our surface. But with the aid of Fig. 101-2 you can see that the point (0, 0, 0) is neither a maximum nor a minimum point, and therefore our surface has no such points.

We will not take up the various analytic tests for selecting maximum and minimum points from among the points at which the first partial derivatives of a function are zero. In our examples we can use geometrical or physical reasoning to decide when we have maxima and minima. It will pay you to proceed by the following sequence of steps as you solve the "word problems" of this section:

(i) Decide what quantity is to be maximized (or minimized).

(ii) Express this quantity as the value of a function of several variables; use the smallest number of variables you can.

(iii) Find the points at which the first partial derivatives of this function are zero and determine whether or not the corresponding functional value is a maximum or a minimum.

(iv) Re-read the question, and use the information from Step (iii) to answer it.

Example 101-2. Find the point of the plane whose equation is $3x + 2y + z = 14$ that is nearest the origin.

Solution. The quantity that must be minimized is the distance d between the origin and a point (x, y, z) of the plane. According to the distance formula, we see that $d = \sqrt{x^2 + y^2 + z^2}$. Since our point (x, y, z) belongs to the given plane, $z = 14 - 3x - 2y$, and therefore we can express d in terms of x and y only:

$$d = \sqrt{x^2 + y^2 + (14 - 3x - 2y)^2}.$$

Since our problem is to locate the point at which the function defined by this equation takes its minimum value, we might now take partial derivatives, find where they are 0, and so on. Actually, it will simplify our differentiation if we recognize that d is a minimum where d^2 is a minimum, and hence we will try to find the point at which the function defined by the equation

$$f(x, y) = x^2 + y^2 + (14 - 3x - 2y)^2$$

takes its minimum value. Here

$$f_1(x, y) = 2x - 6(14 - 3x - 2y),$$

$$f_2(x, y) = 2y - 4(14 - 3x - 2y).$$

After a little simplification, the equations $f_1(x, y) = 0$ and $f_2(x, y) = 0$ become

$$5x + 3y = 21$$

$$6x + 5y = 28.$$

We solve this system of linear equations and find that $x = 3$ and $y = 2$. Since the equations $f_1(x, y) = 0$ and $f_2(x, y) = 0$ have the single solution $(x, y) = (3, 2)$, it follows that *if* our function f has a minimum value, *then* that value must be the number $f(3, 2) = 14$. Now the geometry of the situation makes it clear that there *is* a point of the plane that is nearest the origin, and hence the point $(3, 2)$ *does* give a minimum value for f. Therefore, the X- and Y-coordinates of the nearest point are $x = 3$ and $y = 2$. We obtain the Z-coordinate from the equation of the plane, $z = 14 - 3 \cdot 3 - 2 \cdot 2 = 1$, and so we have found that the point $(3, 2, 1)$ is the point of the given plane that is nearest the origin.

Example 101-3. A rectangular box without a top is to be constructed from 900 square feet of material. What should its dimensions be in order that its volume be a maximum?

Solution. We must maximize the volume V of the box. If the base of the box is x feet by y feet and it is h feet high, then

$$V = xyh.$$

Since we may use only 900 square feet of material, we can express one of the quantities x, y, or h in terms of the other two. For it requires $xy + 2xh + 2yh$ square feet of material to construct an x by y by h box without a top, and therefore

$$xy + 2xh + 2yh = 900.$$

From this equation we find that

$$h = \frac{900 - xy}{2(x + y)}, \tag{101-5}$$

and hence

$$V = \frac{xy(900 - xy)}{2(x + y)}.$$

Now we must find the points at which $\dfrac{\partial V}{\partial x} = 0$ and $\dfrac{\partial V}{\partial y} = 0$. After differentiating and simplifying, we have

$$\frac{\partial V}{\partial x} = \frac{900y^2 - 2xy^3 - x^2y^2}{2(x + y)^2}$$

and

$$\frac{\partial V}{\partial y} = \frac{900x^2 - 2x^3y - x^2y^2}{2(x + y)^2}.$$

When we equate these derivatives to 0 and simplify, we arrive at the system of equations

$$900 - 2xy - x^2 = 0$$
$$900 - 2xy - y^2 = 0.$$

From these equations we see at once that $x^2 = y^2$, and therefore that $x = y$, since both these numbers must be positive. So we can replace y with x in the first equation and find that $x^2 = 300$. Therefore, $x = 10\sqrt{3}$ and $y = 10\sqrt{3}$. From Equation 101-5 we find that $h = 5\sqrt{3}$. Thus the box with the largest volume has a square base measuring $10\sqrt{3}$ by $10\sqrt{3}$ feet, and it is $5\sqrt{3}$ feet high.

Problems 101

1. Find the point of the plane $2x + y + z = 6$ that has positive coordinates and is such that:
   (a) The product of the coordinates is a maximum.
   (b) The sum of the squares of the coordinates is a minimum.
2. Find the lowest point of the surface whose equation is:
   (a) $z = x^2 - 3xy + y^2 + 2x$.
   (b) $9x^2 + 36y^2 + 4z^2 - 18x + 144y + 99 = 0$.

3. Find the highest point of the surface whose equation is:
   (a) $z = 6y - 2x - x^2 - y^2$.
   (b) $9x^2 + 36y^2 + 4z^2 - 18x + 144y + 99 = 0$.
4. Use calculus to find the distance from the point $(2, -1, 3)$ to the plane whose equation is $2x - y + 2z = 5$. (Find the point of the plane that is nearest the point $(2, -1, 3)$).
5. Find the distance between the lines with parametric equations $x = t$, $y = 2t$, $z = t + 1$, and $x = s$, $y = s + 3$, $z = s$.
6. Find the point of the surface whose equation is $z^2 = xy - 3x + 9$ that is closest to the origin.
7. One side of a house is to be built of glass in the shape of a rectangle surmounted by an isosceles triangle and is to have a given perimeter p. Find the slope of the roof if the house is constructed to admit a maximum amount of light.
8. Show that a rectangular box (with a top) made out of S square feet of material has a maximum volume if it is a cube.
9. Find the equation of the plane that contains the point $(1, 2, 1)$ and cuts off the least volume from the first octant.
10. Show that a rectangular box (without a top) made out of S square feet of material has a maximum volume if it has a square base and an altitude that is one-half the length of one side of the base.
11. Let f be the function whose domain is the unit sphere whose equation is $x^2 + y^2 + z^2 = 1$, and whose rule of correspondence is $f(x, y, z) = x^2y^2z^2$. What are the maximum and minimum values of f?
12. Show that the product of the sines of the angles of a triangle is a maximum when the triangle is equilateral.
13. Suppose that we wish to make a rectangular box to hold 20 cubic feet of gold dust. The material used for the sides costs \$1 per square foot, the material used for the bottom costs \$2 per square foot, and the material used for the top costs \$3 per square foot. What are the dimensions of the cheapest box?
14. A long piece of tin 12 inches wide is to be made into a trough by bending up strips of equal width along the edges at equal angles with the horizontal. How wide should these strips be, and what angle must they make with the horizontal if the trough is to have a maximum carrying capacity?

Review Problems, Chapter Eleven

You may use the following questions to test yourself on the material covered in this chapter.

1. If $f(x, y) = |x| + |y|$:
   (a) Find $3f(4, 5) - 5f(-3, -4)$.
   (b) Find $f_1(2, 3) - f_2(-1, -2)$.
   (c) Describe the graph of f.
2. What does the graph of the function defined by the equation $f(x, y) = \sin(x^2 + y^2)$ look like? What are the level curves of this function?

3. Suppose that $F(x) = f(3x, 4x)$, where f is a function of two variables such that $f_1(u, v) = u$ and $f_2(u, v) = 3v$. Find $F'(2)$, $F''(2)$, and $F'''(2)$.

4. If f is a function of two variables such that $f_1(0, 0) = 5$ and $f_2(0, 0) = 8$ and we write $F(x, y) = f(x - y, y - x)$, find the number $F_2(3, 3)$.

5. What is the relation between $f(x, y)$ and $g(x, y)$ if f and g are functions such that $f_1(x, y) = g_1(x, y)$ and $f_2(x, y) = g_2(x, y)$ at every point (x, y)?

6. Give an example of a function f that is not a constant function and that has the property that $\frac{\partial}{\partial x} f(x^2, y^2) = f_1(x^2, y^2)$. Give an example of a function that does not have this property.

7. Find the directional derivative of $w = (x + y)e^{xy}$ at the origin and along the part of the line $y = \sqrt{3}\, x$ that lies in the first quadrant.

8. If $\boldsymbol{R} = x\boldsymbol{i} + y\boldsymbol{j} + z\boldsymbol{k}$ and $w = |\boldsymbol{R}|^n$, where n is a given number, show that $\nabla w = n|\boldsymbol{R}|^{n-2}\boldsymbol{R}$.

9. The domain of a certain function f of three variables consists of the points of the plane $x + 2y + 3z = 4$, and the rule of correspondence of f is given by the equation $f(x, y, z) = x^2 + y^2 + z^2 - \frac{8}{7}$. What is the least value of f?

10. Show that if x, y, and z are positive numbers then

$$\frac{\sqrt[4]{2xyz}}{2 + x + y + z} \leq \frac{1}{4}.$$

When does equality hold?

12 MULTIPLE INTEGRATION

The two basic operations in the calculus of functions of one variable are differentiation and integration. These same operations also play fundamental roles when we come to functions of several variables. In the last chapter we considered some aspects of the differential calculus of functions of several variables, and now we will take up integration of functions of two and three variables.

102. Double Integrals

To start with, we will introduce the concept of the integral of a function of two variables over a region R in the plane. This concept is completely analogous to the concept of the integral of a function of one variable over an interval $[a, b]$ of the line that we encountered in Chapter 5, so a brief review of that situation is in order. The integral $\int_a^b f(x)\,dx$

of a function f over an interval $[a, b]$ is the limit of approximating sums that are formed as follows. The interval of integration $[a, b]$ is first *partitioned* into a set of n subintervals. Then in each subinterval we select a point, the point in the ith interval being denoted by x_i^*. At the point x_i^* the value of our function f is $f(x_i^*)$, and we multiply this number by

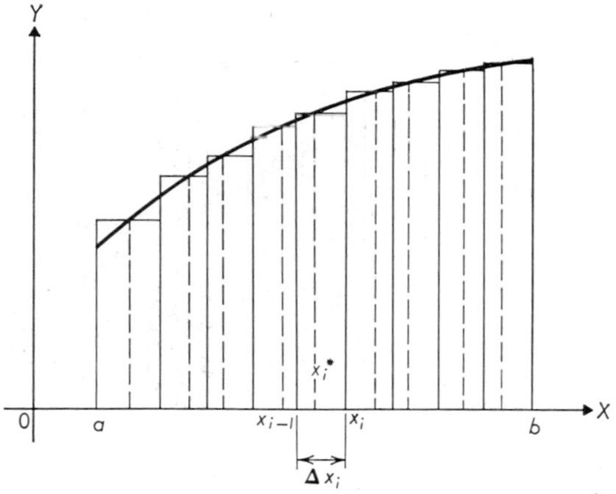

Figure 102-1

the length Δx_i of the ith subinterval to obtain the product $f(x_i^*)\,\Delta x_i$. The sum $\sum_{i=1}^{n} f(x_i^*)\,\Delta x_i$ is a close approximation of the integral $\int_a^b f(x)\,dx$ if the partition of $[a, b]$ is sufficiently fine, that is, if the norm of the partition is close to zero. Graphically, the approximating sum $\sum_{i=1}^{n} f(x_i^*)\,\Delta x_i$ is the area of the region made up of the rectangular strips shown in Fig. 102-1, and we naturally define the area of the region that is bounded by the graph of f, the X-axis, and the lines $x = a$ and $x = b$ to be the limit of these sums; that is, the integral $\int_a^b f(x)\,dx$.

We define the integral of functions of two variables in much the same way that we define the integral of functions of one variable. Suppose f is a function of two variables whose domain contains a region R of the XY-plane, such as the region we have shown in Fig. 102-2, and let us define what we mean by the integral of f over R. The **region of integration R** corresponds to the interval of integration $[a, b]$ for a function of one variable, and our first step is to partition this region R. By drawing lines parallel to the coordinate axes, we construct a rectangular network that covers R. Each rectangle that lies entirely inside R bounds a **rectangular subregion** of R, and the collection of all these subregions (shown shaded in Fig. 102-2) constitutes our **partition** of R. The **norm** of this partition is the length of the longest of the diagonals of the rectangular subregions of the partition. Now we number the subregions of the partition from 1 to n. For each index i we denote by Δx_i the width

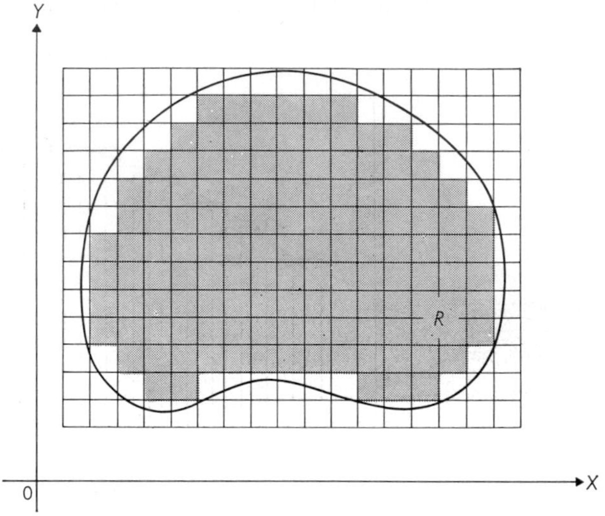

Figure 102-2

of the ith subregion and by Δy_i its height. Thus the product $\Delta x_i \, \Delta y_i$ is the area of the ith rectangular subregion, and we write

$$\boldsymbol{\Delta A_i = \Delta x_i \, \Delta y_i}.$$

Now let us select a point (x_i^*, y_i^*) in the ith subregion, compute the number $f(x_i^*, y_i^*) \, \Delta A_i$, and then add all these products to obtain the sum

(102-1) $$S = \sum_{i=1}^{n} f(x_i^*, y_i^*) \, \Delta A_i.$$

We can, of course, compute many such sums, depending on how we partition the region R and choose the points (x_i^*, y_i^*). But if the function f is a "reasonable" function, all the sums that we can form using partitions with small norms will be close to one particular number, the limit of S as the norm of the partition of R approaches 0. This number is called the **double integral of f over R,** and we will denote it by one of the symbols

$$\iint_R \boldsymbol{f(x, y) \, dA}, \quad \iint_R \boldsymbol{f(x, y) \, dx \, dy}, \text{ or } \iint_R \boldsymbol{f(x, y) \, dy \, dx}.$$

Thus, in rough terms, *the double integral* $\iint_R f(x, y) \, dA$ *is the number that is approximated by every sum S that we can form using a partition with a small norm.*

We will now formulate a definition of the double integral of f over R that puts what we were just trying to say into more precise language. This definition is identical with the definition of the (single) integral that we set down in Section 37. Let r be a positive number and consider the interval $I = (0, r)$. Now let $J(I)$ denote the smallest closed interval that contains every approximating sum S (defined by Equation 102-1) that can be formed using a partition whose norm is a number in the interval I. Thus if h is any number in the interval I, then the set of all approximating sums formed using partitions of norm h belongs to $J(I)$. These J-intervals "squeeze down" on the number $\iint_R f(x, y)\, dA$ as I "shrinks." Thus we have the following definition.

Definition 102-1. *If there is exactly one number that is contained in every interval $J(I)$ described above, then we say that f is* **integrable** *on R and that the number common to all the J-intervals is the* **integral** $\iint_R f(x, y)\, dA$ *of f over R.*

Example 102-1. Let f be the constant function defined by the equation $f(x, y) = 4$, and suppose that R is the circular disk with a radius of 3 whose center is the origin. Find $\iint_R f(x, y)\, dA$.

Solution. The region R is the set of points such that $x^2 + y^2 \leq 9$. In Fig. 102-3 we have partitioned this region into a number of rectangular

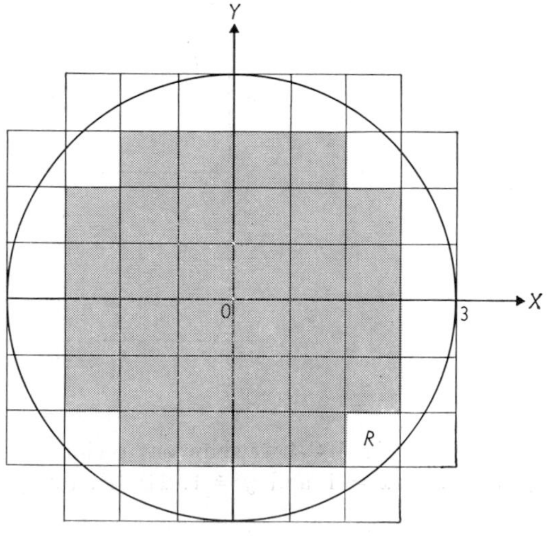

Figure 102-3

subregions. In each of these subregions we are to select a point and then form the approximating Sum 102-1. Since f is the constant function with value 4, $f(x_i^*, y_i^*) = 4$ no matter what point (x_i^*, y_i^*) we select, and so our approximating sum will be

$$S = \sum_{i=1}^{n} 4\,\Delta A_i = 4 \sum_{i=1}^{n} \Delta A_i.$$

Now the number $\sum_{i=1}^{n} \Delta A_i$ is simply the area of the shaded region in our figure, so geometrically we have

$$S = 4 \cdot (\text{the area of the shaded region}).$$

If we choose a partition of small norm (that is, use small rectangles), then our rectangular regions nearly fill up the circular disk. Hence the area of the shaded region approximates the area of the disk. Therefore, the number that is approximated by S is the number

$$4 \cdot (\text{the area of the disk of radius 3}) = 36\pi.$$

This number is, by definition, the integral we are seeking; that is,

$$\iint_R 4\,dA = 36\pi.$$

Example 102-2. Let R be the square region whose vertices are the points (0, 0), (0, 2), (2, 2), and (2, 0). Approximate the number $\iint_R (8x^2 + 2y)\,dA$.

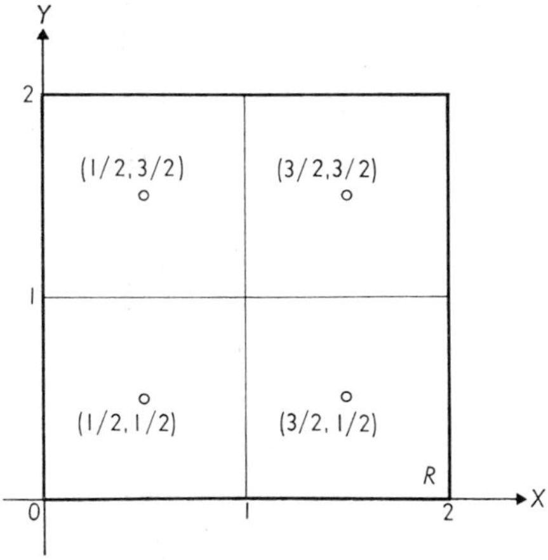

Figure 102-4

Solution. In Fig. 102-4 we show our region R partitioned into 4 subregions by the lines $x = 1$ and $y = 1$. Each subregion is square and measures

1 by 1. Therefore $\Delta A_i = 1$ for each index i. In each square we have selected the center as our point (x_i^*, y_i^*). Thus, since $f(x, y) = 8x^2 + 2y$, a sum that approximates the desired integral is

$$\begin{aligned} S &= f(\tfrac{1}{2}, \tfrac{1}{2}) \cdot 1 + f(\tfrac{1}{2}, \tfrac{3}{2}) \cdot 1 + f(\tfrac{3}{2}, \tfrac{3}{2}) \cdot 1 + f(\tfrac{3}{2}, \tfrac{1}{2}) \cdot 1 \\ &= 3 \cdot 1 + 5 \cdot 1 + 21 \cdot 1 + 19 \cdot 1 \\ &= 48. \end{aligned}$$

We therefore have discovered that

$$\iint_R (8x^2 + 2y)\, dA \approx 48.$$

We shall see in the next section (Example 103-1) that the actual value of the integral is $\frac{152}{3} = 50\frac{2}{3}$.

As we have already mentioned, an integral of a function of one variable can be interpreted as the area of a plane region. Even though the integral itself may have arisen in a non-geometrical problem, this geometrical interpretation may help us to evaluate the integral. Now let us see how we can interpret a double integral as a volume. Suppose that f is a function of two variables and that $f(x, y) > 0$ for each point (x, y) in a region R of the XY-plane. Then the graph of the equation $z = f(x, y)$ for (x, y) in R is a surface that lies above the XY-plane (Fig. 102-5). In this figure we have also shown one of the rectangular sub-

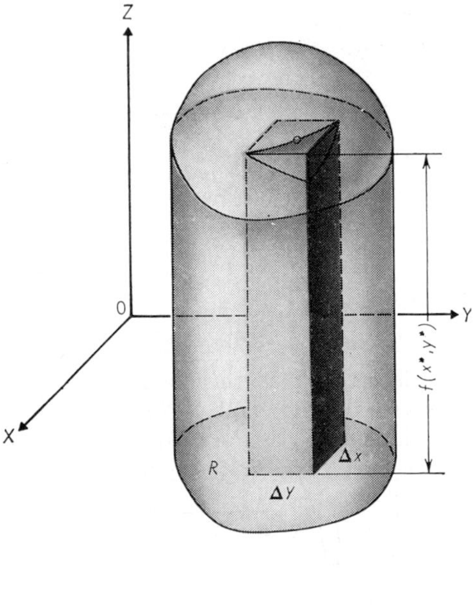

Figure 102-5

regions into which R is partitioned when we form the Approximating Sum 102-1. A typical term of this sum has the form

$$f(x^*, y^*)\,\Delta A = f(x^*, y^*)\,\Delta x\,\Delta y,$$

and this number is the volume of the rectangular block whose base measures Δx by Δy and whose altitude is $f(x^*, y^*)$. The Approximating Sum 102-1 is the sum of such volumes, and it appears from the figure that this sum is an approximation of the volume of the three-dimensional region that is bounded by the cylinder erected on the boundary of R, the plane region R, and the graph of f. Since our approximating sum also approximates the number $\iint_R f(x, y)\,dA$, it is natural to *define* the volume under the graph of f as the integral. The concept of volume as so defined has all the "expected" properties of a volume, and in particular we can use our knowledge of volume to compute double integrals in exactly the same way that we use our knowledge of area to compute single integrals.

Example 102-3. Evaluate $\iint_R \sqrt{a^2 - x^2 - y^2}\,dA$, where a is a given positive number and R is the quarter of the disk that lies in the first quadrant and is bounded by the circle whose equation is $x^2 + y^2 = a^2$.

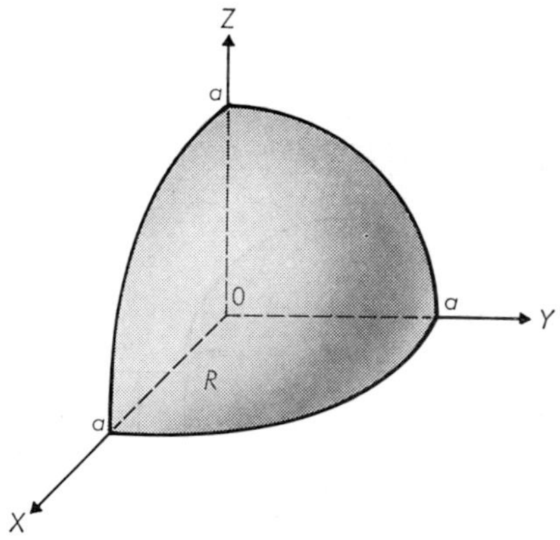

Figure 102-6

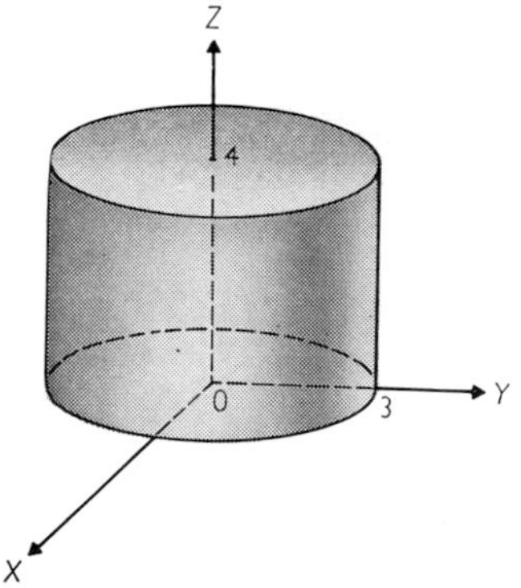

Figure 102-7

Solution. Since the equation $z = \sqrt{a^2 - x^2 - y^2}$ implies that $x^2 + y^2 + z^2 = a^2$, we see that its graph is the upper half of the sphere whose radius is a and whose center is the origin. Thus the desired integral is $\frac{1}{8}$th the volume of the region inside the sphere (see Fig. 102-6), and so

$$\iint_R \sqrt{a^2 - x^2 - y^2}\,dA = \frac{1}{8}\,\frac{4\pi a^3}{3} = \frac{\pi a^3}{6}.$$

Example 102-4. Use the volume interpretation of the double integral to evaluate the integral $\iint_R 4\,dA$ if R is the circular disk whose radius is 3 and whose center is the origin (see Example 102-1).

Solution. The graph of the equation $z = 4$ is a plane parallel to the XY-plane and 4 units above it. The volume of the solid bounded by the plane $z = 4$, the XY-plane, and the circular cylinder $x^2 + y^2 = 9$ (see Fig. 102-7) is $\pi 3^2 \cdot 4 = 36\pi$. This volume is the value of the double integral we were to compute.

Some of the most important properties of integrals are possessed by multiple as well as single integrals. For example, if f and g are integrable functions on a region R, and if m and n are any numbers, then

$$\text{(102-2)} \quad \iint_R [mf(x, y) + ng(x, y)]\,dA = m\iint_R f(x, y)\,dA + n\iint_R g(x, y)\,dA.$$

Furthermore, if R_1 and R_2 are two non-overlapping regions (two halves of a circular disk, for example) which together add up to the region R, then

$$\text{(102-3)} \quad \iint_R f(x, y)\,dA = \iint_{R_1} f(x, y)\,dA + \iint_{R_2} f(x, y)\,dA.$$

Problems 102

1. Suppose we consider the net of rectangles formed by lines parallel to the Y-axis that meet the X-axis at the points 0, 1, -1, 2, -2, and so on, and lines parallel to the X-axis that meet the Y-axis at the points 0, $\frac{1}{2}$, $-\frac{1}{2}$, 1, -1, $\frac{3}{2}$, $-\frac{3}{2}$, and so on. This net determines partitions of each of the regions described below. How many rectangular subregions are contained in each partition?
   (a) The circular disk with a radius of 3 whose center is the origin.
   (b) The triangular region whose vertices are the points (0, 0), (4, 0), and (4, 4).
   (c) The rectangular region whose vertices are (π, π), $(\pi, 0)$, $(-e, 0)$, $(-e, \pi)$.
   (d) The region bounded by the ellipse whose equation is $x^2/9 + y^2/4 = 1$.
2. Use inequalities to define the region R of Example 102-3.
3. Approximate the number $\iint_R (3x^2 - 2y)\,dA$, where R is the circular disk $x^2 + y^2 \leq 8$, as follows. Form a partition of R by using 4 squares, one of which has vertices (0, 0), (0, 2), (2, 2), and (2, 0) and the others of which are symmetrically located in the other 3 quadrants. In each square choose the midpoint as the point (x^*, y^*) and form Sum 102-1.

4. Let R be the rectangular region with vertices (0, 0), (4, 0), (4, 2), and (0, 2). Use the volume interpretation of the integral (and Equation 102-2 if necessary) to evaluate $\iint_R f(x, y)\, dA$ in each case.

(a) $f(x, y) = 6$ (b) $f(x, y) = y$ (c) $f(x, y) = x$
(d) $f(x, y) = 3x + 4y + 5$

5. Use the volume interpretation of the double integral to find $\iint_R f(x, y)\, dA$ if $f(x, y) = 2$ and R is the set of points in the XY-plane such that $|x| + |y| \leq 1$.

6. Use the volume interpretation of the double integral to evaluate $\iint_R \sqrt{x^2 + y^2}\, dA$, where R is the circular disk $x^2 + y^2 \leq 1$. (*Hint:* Recall that the graph of the equation $z = \sqrt{x^2 + y^2}$ is a cone.)

7. Use the volume interpretation of the double integral to evaluate $\iint_R (4 - x^2)\, dA$, where R is the rectangular region bounded by the lines $x = 2$, $x = -2$, $y = 0$, and $y = 5$.

8. Explain why it seems reasonable that $\iint_R 1\, dA$ = area of R. If c is a number, what is $\iint_R c\, dA$?

9. Suppose $f(x, y) = 1$ if $x < y$ and $f(x, y) = 2$ if $x \geq y$. Find $\iint_R f(x, y)\, dA$, where R is the square region with vertices (0, 0), (1, 0), (0, 1), and (1, 1). (*Hint:* Use Equation 102-3).

10. Evaluate $\iint_R ([\![x]\!] + [\![y]\!])\, dA$, where R is the rectangular region with vertices (0, 0), (2, 0), (2, 4), and (0, 4).

103. Evaluating Double Integrals

We shall now use our interpretation of a double integral as a volume to find a method for calculating such integrals. This method will enable us to reduce the problem of evaluating a double integral to the problem of evaluating successive single integrals, and hence we will be able to use all the tricks for evaluating integrals that we developed in earlier chapters.

In Section 44 we found the volumes of various solids by considering the solids as "sums of narrow slices." Let us apply this method to find the volume of the solid that is bounded by the graph of a function f and a cylinder based on the boundary of a plane region R as shown in Fig. 103-1. Suppose that the "shadow" or projection of R on the X-axis is the interval $[a, b]$. Let x be a number in this interval, and consider the plane containing x that is parallel to the YZ-plane. This plane will intersect our solid in the region shown in the figure. If the area of this plane region is $A(x)$, then on the basis of the argument we developed in Section 44 we see that the volume of the solid is $\int_a^b A(x)\,dx$; that is,

$$\iint_R f(x, y)\,dA = \int_a^b A(x)\,dx. \tag{103-1}$$

Therefore, we can evaluate the double integral of f over R by finding a single integral of $A(x)$. Our problem is now reduced to finding $A(x)$.

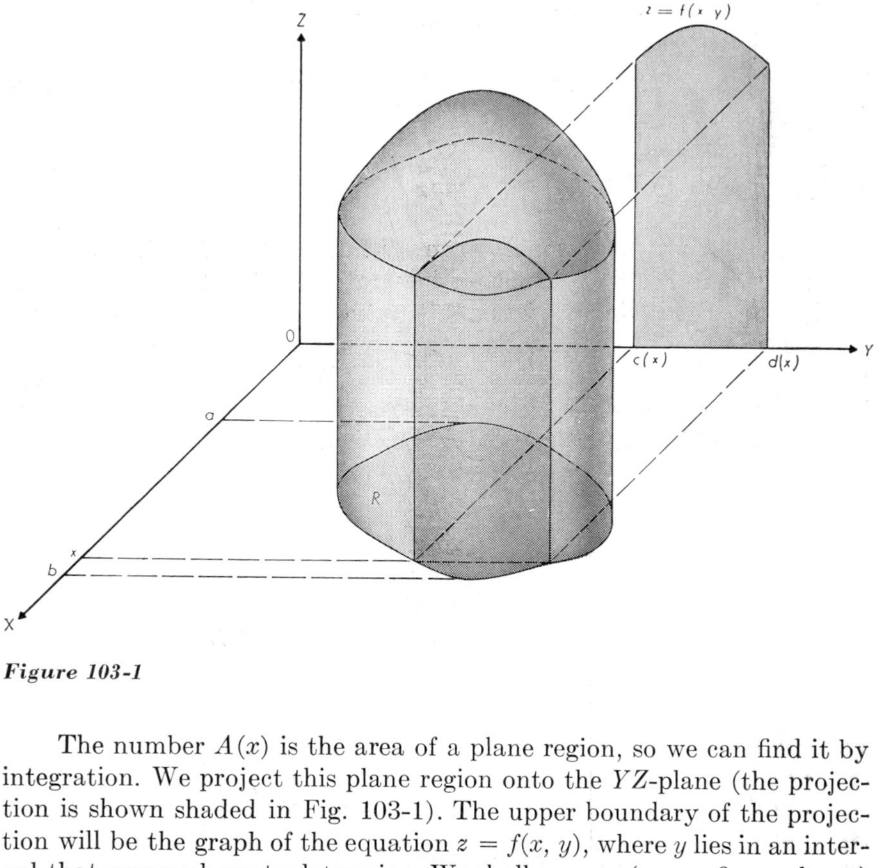

Figure 103-1

The number $A(x)$ is the area of a plane region, so we can find it by integration. We project this plane region onto the YZ-plane (the projection is shown shaded in Fig. 103-1). The upper boundary of the projection will be the graph of the equation $z = f(x, y)$, where y lies in an interval that we now have to determine. We shall assume (as our figure shows) that every line in the XY-plane that is perpendicular to the interval (a, b) intersects the boundary of R in exactly two points. Therefore, when we cut our solid with the plane through x we determine two numbers $c(x)$ and $d(x)$, where $c(x) < d(x)$, the Y-coordinates of the points at which the plane cuts the boundary of R. Thus we see that our shaded projection on the YZ-plane is bounded by the graph of the equation $z = f(x, y)$, the Y-axis, and the lines with equations $y = c(x)$ and $y = d(x)$. It follows that the area of the shaded region is given by the formula

$$A(x) = \int_{c(x)}^{d(x)} f(x, y)\, dy. \tag{103-2}$$

When we substitute this result in Equation 103-1 we obtain the fundamental formula for evaluating double integrals:

$$\iint_R f(x, y)\, dA = \int_a^b \left[\int_{c(x)}^{d(x)} f(x, y)\, dy\right] dx. \tag{103-3}$$

We usually omit the brackets in the **iterated integral** on the right side of Equation 103-3 and write this equation as

$$\boldsymbol{\iint_R f(x, y)\, dA = \int_a^b \int_{c(x)}^{d(x)} f(x, y)\, dy\, dx.} \tag{103-4}$$

When we evaluate the "inner integral" in Equation 103-4, we should remember that y is the variable of integration, not x. The number x is considered "fixed" in this inner integration. Our geometric argument is not a real proof that Equation 103-4 is valid, it merely *suggests* that this equation is true. We leave a proof that it *is* true to more advanced books. In our geometric argument we assumed that $f(x, y) > 0$, but Formula 103-4 is true without this restriction.

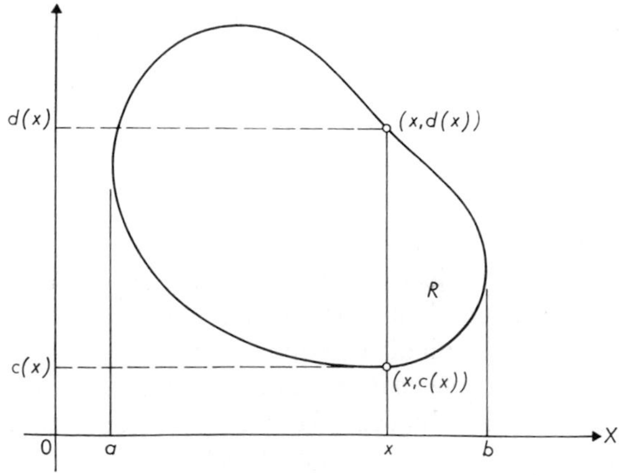

Figure 103-2

The limits of integration of the iterated integral of Equation 103-4 are determined by the region R and are independent of the function f. To determine these limits in a particular problem, we draw our region R in the XY-plane as shown in Fig. 103-2. Then a and b are the endpoints of the interval of the X-axis onto which R projects. Now we pick a point x in the interval (a, b) and draw a line containing x and parallel to the Y-axis. Then $c(x)$ is the Y-coordinate of the lower point of intersection of this line and the boundary of R, and $d(x)$ is the Y-coordinate of the higher point of intersection.

Example 103-1. Evaluate the integral $\iint\limits_R (8x^2 + 2y)\, dA$, where R is the square region whose vertices are the points (0, 0), (0, 2), (2, 0), and (2, 2) (see Example 102-2).

Solution. In this case Equation 103-4 becomes

$$\iint\limits_R (8x^2 + 2y)\, dA = \int_a^b \int_{c(x)}^{d(x)} (8x^2 + 2y)\, dy\, dx,$$

and so we must now determine the limits of integration a, b, $c(x)$, and $d(x)$. We will determine these numbers by examining the region R (Fig. 103-3). Projecting R onto the X-axis gives us the numbers $a = 0$ and $b = 2$. Now we choose a point x in the interval (0, 2) and draw a line containing x and parallel to the Y-axis. This line intersects the boundary of R at the points $(x, c(x))$ and $(x, d(x))$, and from our figure we see that $c(x) = 0$ and $d(x) = 2$ for each choice of x. Hence

$$\begin{aligned}\iint\limits_R (8x^2 + 2y)\, dA &= \int_0^2 \int_0^2 (8x^2 + 2y)\, dy\, dx \\ &= \int_0^2 \left[\int_0^2 (8x^2 + 2y)\, dy\right] dx \\ &= \int_0^2 [8x^2y + y^2]\Big|_0^2\, dx \\ &= \int_0^2 (16x^2 + 4)\, dx \\ &= 50\tfrac{2}{3}.\end{aligned}$$

Example 103-2. Evaluate $\iint\limits_R x\, dA$, where R is the region that is bounded by the Y-axis and the half of the circle whose equation is $x^2 + y^2 = 4$ that lies to the right of the Y-axis.

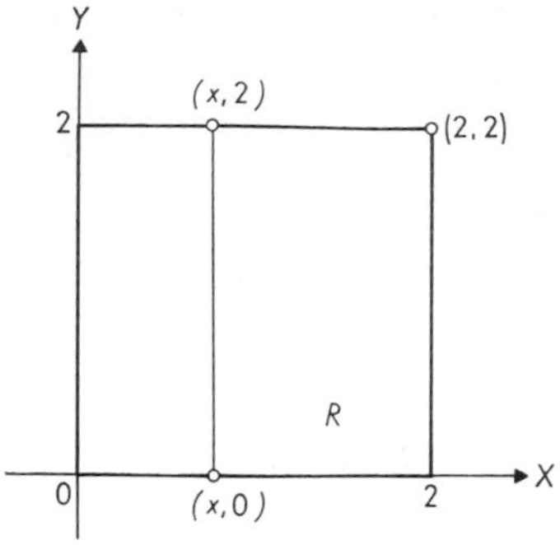

Figure 103-3

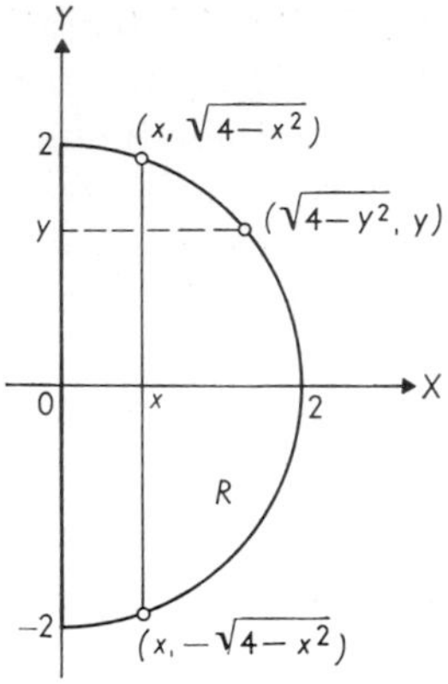

Figure 103-4

Solution. The given region is shown in Fig. 103-4. In order to apply Equation 103-4 we first observe that the projection of R onto the X-axis is the interval $[0, 2]$, so $a = 0$ and $b = 2$. Now if x is any number between 0 and 2, a line that contains x and is parallel to the Y-axis intersects the boundary of R at the points $(x, -\sqrt{4 - x^2})$ and $(x, \sqrt{4 - x^2})$. Hence the numbers $c(x)$ and $d(x)$ are

$$c(x) = -\sqrt{4 - x^2} \quad \text{and} \quad d(x) = \sqrt{4 - x^2}.$$

Thus Equation 103-4 becomes

$$\iint_R x\,dA = \int_0^2 \int_{-\sqrt{4-x^2}}^{\sqrt{4-x^2}} x\,dy\,dx = \int_0^2 x\left[y\,\Big|_{-\sqrt{4-x^2}}^{\sqrt{4-x^2}}\right]dx$$

$$= \int_0^2 2x\sqrt{4 - x^2}\,dx = \tfrac{16}{3}.$$

According to Equation 103-4, we can express a double integral as an iterated integral in which we first consider y as the variable of integration and then x. Of course, the roles of x and y can be interchanged (if R is of the right shape) and we have

$$(103\text{-}5) \qquad \iint_R f(x, y)\,dA = \int_c^d \int_{a(y)}^{b(y)} f(x, y)\,dx\,dy.$$

The method we use to find the limits of integration c, d, $a(y)$, and $b(y)$ is completely analogous to the method we used to find the limits of integration in Equation 103-4. Thus we project our region of integration R onto the Y-axis, and we obtain the interval $[c, d]$. Then at a point y in the interval (c, d) we draw a line parallel to the X-axis. We assume that

R is a region whose shape is such that this line will intersect the boundary of R at just two points for any choice of y in (c, d). These points will be the points $(a(y), y)$ and $(b(y), y)$, and so $a(y)$ and $b(y)$ are determined.

Example 103-3. Use Equation 103-5 to evaluate the integral in Example 103-2.

Solution. We find the numbers c and d from the projection of the region R shown in Fig. 103-4 onto the Y-axis. Thus we see that $c = -2$ and $d = 2$. Now we notice that a line parallel to the X-axis and y units from it cuts the boundary of R at the points $(0, y)$ and $(\sqrt{4 - y^2}, y)$. Hence $a(y) = 0$ and $b(y) = \sqrt{4 - y^2}$, so Equation 103-5 becomes

$$\iint_R x\, dA = \int_{-2}^{2} \int_0^{\sqrt{4-y^2}} x\, dx\, dy = \int_{-2}^{2} \frac{x^2}{2}\Big|_0^{\sqrt{4-y^2}} dy$$

$$= \tfrac{1}{2} \int_{-2}^{2} (4 - y^2)\, dy = \tfrac{16}{3}.$$

The region of integration R determines the limits of integration on an iterated integral used to evaluate a double integral, and, conversely,

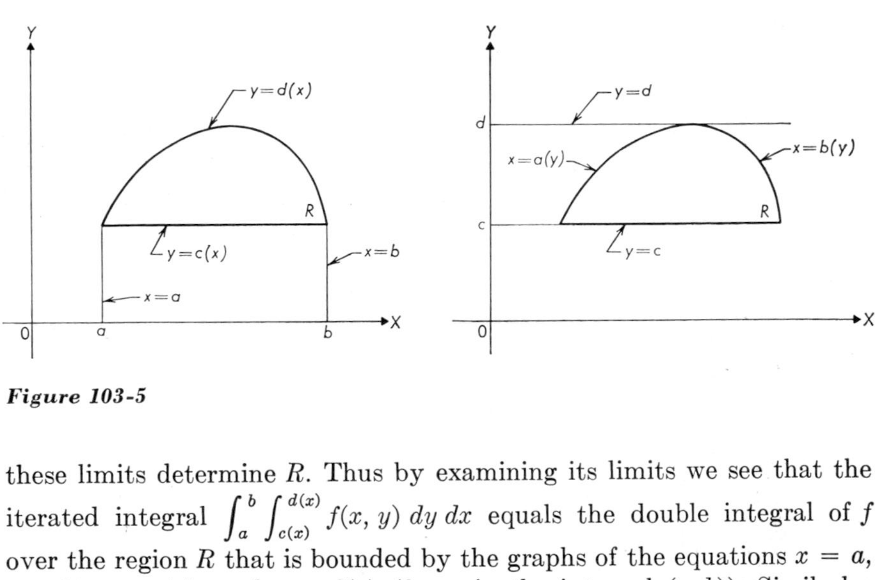

Figure 103-5

these limits determine R. Thus by examining its limits we see that the iterated integral $\int_a^b \int_{c(x)}^{d(x)} f(x, y)\, dy\, dx$ equals the double integral of f over the region R that is bounded by the graphs of the equations $x = a$, $x = b$, $y = c(x)$, and $y = d(x)$ (for x in the interval (a, b)). Similarly, the limits on the iterated integral $\int_c^d \int_{a(y)}^{b(y)} f(x, y)\, dx\, dy$ tell us that our region of integration is bounded by the graphs of the equations $y = c$, $y = d$, $x = a(y)$, and $x = b(y)$ (for y in the interval (c, d)). Figure 103-5 shows us how the boundary of the same region of integration looks from these two points of view. It may be important to have both pictures in mind because sometimes we may want to shift from one iterated integral to the other, as the following example shows.

Example 103-6. Evaluate the iterated integral $\int_0^1 \int_y^1 \tan x^2 \, dx \, dy$.

Solution. In order to evaluate the integral as written, our first task would be to find $\int_y^1 \tan x^2 \, dx$. But none of our integration formulas applies, so we will see if a change of order of integration will help. Our given iterated

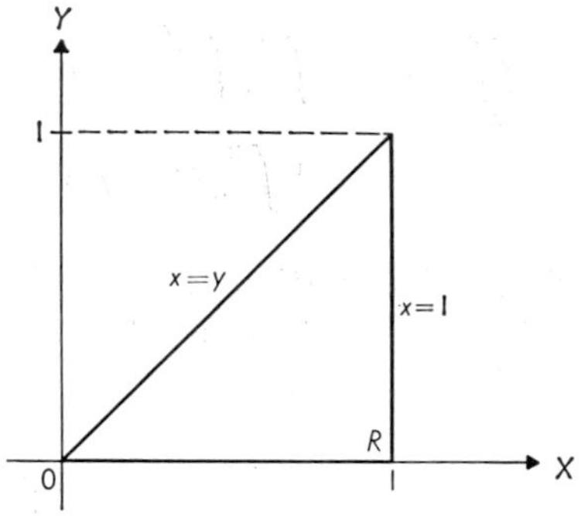

Figure 103-6

integral equals the double integral of $\tan x^2$ over the region R that is bounded by the lines $y = 0$ and $y = 1$, and the graphs of the equations $x = y$ and $x = 1$, as shown in Fig. 103-6. Now we write this double integral $\iint_R \tan x^2 \, dA$ as the iterated integral in reverse order:

$$\iint_R \tan x^2 \, dA = \int_0^1 \int_0^x \tan x^2 \, dy \, dx.$$

Therefore,

$$\begin{aligned} \int_0^1 \int_y^1 \tan x^2 \, dx \, dy &= \int_0^1 \int_0^x \tan x^2 \, dy \, dx \\ &= \int_0^1 x \tan x^2 \, dx = \tfrac{1}{2} \ln \sec x^2 \Big|_0^1 \\ &= \tfrac{1}{2} \ln \sec 1 \approx .308. \end{aligned}$$

Problems 103

1. Let R be the rectangular region whose vertices are (0, 0), (2, 0), (2, 1), and (0, 1). Evaluate $\iint_R f(x, y) \, dA$ if:

(a) $f(x, y) = xy^2$ (b) $f(x, y) = x^2 + y^2$
(c) $f(x, y) = y \ln (1 + x)$ (d) $f(x, y) = e^x \cos y$

2. Evaluate the following iterated integrals.

(a) $\int_1^2 \int_0^1 (1 - y)x^2 \, dy \, dx$ (b) $\int_0^2 \int_0^1 x(x + y) \, dy \, dx$
(c) $\int_0^1 \int_0^2 (x + 2) \, dy \, dx$ (d) $\int_{-1}^1 \int_{-1}^2 x(xy + \sin x) \, dy \, dx$
(e) $\int_0^{\pi/2} \int_0^1 xy \cos x^2 y \, dx \, dy$ (f) $\int_0^{\pi} \int_0^{\pi/2} \sin u \cos (v - \pi) \, du \, dv$

3. Evaluate the following iterated integrals.

(a) $\int_0^4 \int_0^x x \, dy \, dx$ (b) $\int_1^2 \int_{-x}^0 x \, dy \, dx$
(c) $\int_0^1 \int_0^{\sqrt{x}} dy \, dx$ (d) $\int_{-1}^0 \int_0^{-y} x^2 \, dx \, dy$
(e) $\int_0^2 \int_0^x (x^2 + y^2) \, dy \, dx$ (f) $\int_0^1 \int_0^{x^2} \sin \pi x^3 \, dy \, dx$
(g) $\int_0^1 \int_{y^2}^{1-y} (10x + 4y) \, dx \, dy$ (h) $\int_{-1}^1 \int_{x^2}^{2-x^2} y \, dy \, dx$
(i) $\int_0^1 \int_{2x}^{3x} e^{x+y} \, dy \, dx$ (j) $\int_1^2 \int_0^{\sqrt{x}} y \ln x^2 \, dy \, dx$
(k) $\int_0^2 \int_{\sqrt{4-x^2}}^{3e^{x^2}} x \, dy \, dx$ (l) $\int_0^{\pi/2} \int_0^{\sin y} \frac{dx \, dy}{\sqrt{1 - x^2}}$

4. Evaluate the integral $\iint_R xy \, dA$ if R is the region described.

(a) The rectangular region with vertices (0, 0), (4, 0), (4, 2), (0, 2).
(b) The triangular region with vertices (0, 0), (4, 0), (4, 4).
(c) $x \geq 0$, $y \geq 0$, $x^2 + y^2 \leq 1$.
(d) The region in the first quadrant bounded by the parabola $y = x^2$, the Y-axis, and the line $y = 4$.

5. Describe the region of integration R if the double integral $\iint_R f(x, y) \, dA$ can be expressed as the iterated integral:

(a) $\int_4^5 \int_2^3 f(x, y) \, dx \, dy$ (b) $\int_4^5 \int_2^3 f(x, y) \, dy \, dx$
(c) $\int_0^1 \int_0^{1-y} f(x, y) \, dx \, dy$ (d) $\int_{-2}^2 \int_{-3\sqrt{4-x^2}}^{3\sqrt{4-x^2}} f(x, y) \, dy \, dx$

6. Suppose that f is a function such that $f(-x, -y) = -f(x, y)$, and R is the disk $x^2 + y^2 \leq 1$. What is the value of $\iint_R f(x, y) \, dA$?

7. Evaluate $\iint_R f(x, y) \, dA$ if:

(a) $f(x, y) = 2x$; R bounded by the parabola $4y = x^2$ and the line $x - 2y + 4 = 0$.
(b) $f(x, y) = x \sin xy$; R bounded by the coordinate axes, the line $x = 1$, and the line $y = \pi/2$.

(c) $f(x, y) = (1 - x^4)^{-1/2}$; R bounded by the X-axis, the line $y = x$, and the line $x = \dfrac{1}{\sqrt{2}}$.

(d) $f(x, y) = x$; R bounded by the coordinate axes, the line $y = \pi/2$, and the curve $y = \operatorname{Arccos} x$.

(e) $f(x, y) = \dfrac{\sin x}{4 - \sin^2 y}$; R bounded by the X-axis, the line $y = x$, and the line $x = \pi/2$.

(f) $f(x, y) = y^2$; R bounded by the X-axis, the lines $x = 1$ and $x = e$, and the curve $y = -\ln x$.

(g) $f(x, y) = \dfrac{1}{4 - x}$; R bounded by the X-axis, the lines $x = 2$ and $x = 3$, and the hyperbola $xy = 1$.

(h) $f(x, y) = \sec y$; R bounded by the Y-axis, the lines $x = 1$ and $y = \pi/4$, and the curve $y = \operatorname{Arctan} x$.

8. By changing the order of integration, evaluate the following integrals.

(a) $\displaystyle\int_0^2 \int_{2y}^4 e^{x^2}\, dx\, dy$ (b) $\displaystyle\int_0^1 \int_y^1 \sin x^2\, dx\, dy$

9. Invert the order of integration in the iterated integral

$$\int_a^b \int_0^x f(x, y)\, dy\, dx, \quad (0 < a < b).$$

10. Evaluate: $\displaystyle\int_{-1}^0 \int_{\operatorname{Arccos} x}^{2\pi} e^y\, dy\, dx$

104. Finding Volumes and Areas by Double Integration

Double integrals are widely used in science and engineering to calculate such things as work, force, and so on. Because we do not want to take up the background material that would be necessary to understand these physical applications, we shall restrict our applications of multiple integrals to geometrical problems. This restriction is purely a matter of convenience, and you should realize that double integrals are not simply devices for finding volumes, areas, and the like, even though that is the only use we will make of them. These relatively minor applications will, however, give you experience in setting up and evaluating double integrals, and this experience will come in handy when you are faced with a double integral in some other context.

If $f(x, y) > 0$ at each point (x, y) of a region R of the XY-plane, then the region R, the cylinder based on the boundary of R, and the graph of the equation $z = f(x, y)$ bound a region in space like the one shown in Fig. 102-5. We will speak of this region as the "region under the graph of f and above the plane region R," and we have already defined its volume as the number

(104-1) $$V = \iint_R f(x, y)\, dA.$$

Example 104-1. Find the volume of the region under the surface whose equation is $z = 4y$ and above the plane region R that is bounded by the graphs of the equations $y = x^2$ and $x + y = 2$ in the XY-plane.

Solution. The desired volume is the number

$$V = \iint_R 4y\, dA,$$

where R is the plane region that is shown in Fig. 104-1. (We find the intersection points $(-2, 4)$ and $(1, 1)$ by simultaneously solving the equations

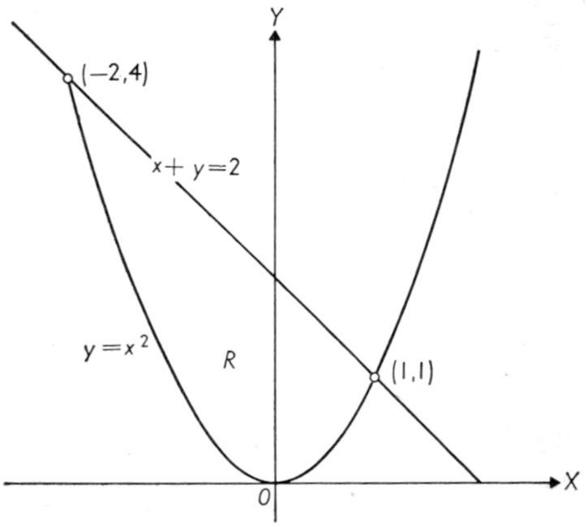

Figure 104-1

$y = x^2$ and $x + y = 2$.) To evaluate this double integral we will replace it with an iterated integral:

$$\iint_R 4y\, dA = \int_{-2}^{1} \int_{x^2}^{2-x} 4y\, dy\, dx.$$

We found the "outer" limits of integration of this iterated integral by projecting the region R onto the interval $[-2, 1]$ of the X-axis. A line perpendicular to this interval at a point x intersects the boundary of R at points with Y-coordinates x^2 and $2 - x$, and hence these numbers are the "inner" limits of integration. Thus

$$V = \int_{-2}^{1} \int_{x^2}^{2-x} 4y\, dy\, dx = \int_{-2}^{1} 2y^2 \Big|_{x^2}^{2-x} dx$$
$$= \int_{-2}^{1} (8 - 8x + 2x^2 - 2x^4)\, dx = \tfrac{144}{5}.$$

Let us review the reasoning that led us to define the volume of the region under the graph of the equation $z = f(x, y)$ and above the plane region R to be the integral $\iint_R f(x, y)\, dA$. We noticed that this double integral is the number that is approximated by a sum of terms of the form

$$\Sigma f(x^*, y^*)\, \Delta A = \Sigma f(x^*, y^*)\, \Delta x\, \Delta y$$

(for simplicity we have omitted the index of summation). Each term

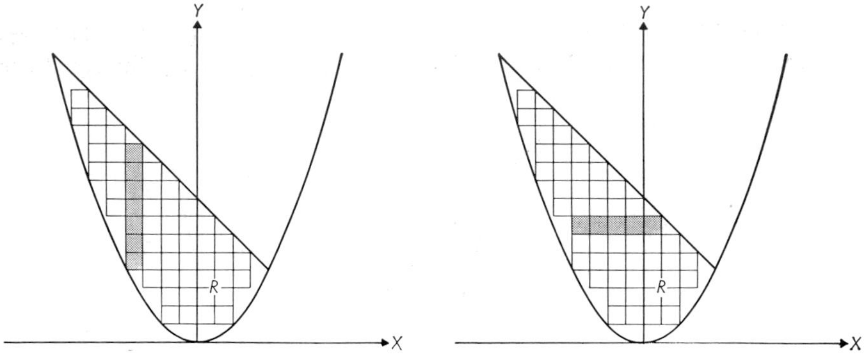

Figure 104-2

in this sum is the volume of a rectangular column like the one shown in Fig. 102-5. Although the set of such columns only approximates the solid region under our surface, it is often convenient to think of the process of evaluating the integral $\iint_R f(x, y)\, dA$ as adding up the volumes of the columns. We can consider an iterated integral as a device by which this addition is performed systematically. Let us return to Example 104-1 to see what we mean. To compute a sum that approximates the double integral $\iint_R 4y\, dA$, we partition our region R into rectangular subregions, as shown in Fig. 104-2. Corresponding to each subregion in the partition there is a term $4y^*\, \Delta x\, \Delta y$ in the approximating sum $\Sigma 4y^*\, \Delta x\, \Delta y$. When we evaluate the iterated integral in which the first integration is with respect to y, we are finding the limit of a sum that is obtained by first adding the terms that correspond to rectangular subregions that form a column parallel to the Y-axis, such as the shaded column on the left side of Fig. 104-2. Then our second integration (with respect to x) adds up the contributions that correspond to the columns.

If we set up our iterated integral so that we must first integrate with respect to x, then we reverse the procedure—we first add terms that correspond to a horizontal row of rectangular subregions and then we add up the contributions of these rows. Thus we evaluate a double integral by using an iterated integral to "sweep out" the region R, first in one direction and then in the other.

Example 104-2. Find the double integral $\iint_R 4y\, dA$ that we evaluated in Example 104-1, this time using an iterated integral in which you integrate first with respect to x.

Solution. We are to write our given integral as an iterated integral of the form $\int_c^d \int_{a(y)}^{b(y)} 4y\, dx\, dy$. Here we must first add up the terms that correspond to horizontal strips, such as the shaded region on the right side of Fig. 104-2. To find the limits of integration on y, we project R onto the interval $[0, 4]$ of the Y-axis. Therefore,

$$\iint_R 4y\, dA = \int_0^4 \int_{a(y)}^{b(y)} 4y\, dx\, dy, \tag{104-2}$$

where the equations $x = a(y)$ and $x = b(y)$ give the left and right boundaries of R. It is clear from Fig. 104-1 that $a(y) = -\sqrt{y}$ for every number y in the interval $(0, 4)$, but that the formula for $b(y)$ depends on the value of y. Thus we see that $b(y) = \sqrt{y}$ if $y \leq 1$, and $b(y) = 2 - y$ if $y \geq 1$. Therefore, we write Equation 104-2 as

$$\begin{aligned}\iint_R 4y\, dA &= \int_0^1 \int_{a(y)}^{b(y)} 4y\, dx\, dy + \int_1^4 \int_{a(y)}^{b(y)} 4y\, dx\, dy \\ &= \int_0^1 \int_{-\sqrt{y}}^{\sqrt{y}} 4y\, dx\, dy + \int_1^4 \int_{-\sqrt{y}}^{2-y} 4y\, dx\, dy \\ &= \int_0^1 8y\sqrt{y}\, dy + \int_1^4 (8y - 4y^2 + 4y\sqrt{y})\, dy \\ &= \tfrac{16}{5} + \tfrac{128}{5} = \tfrac{144}{5}.\end{aligned}$$

Writing our iterated integral as a sum of two iterated integrals is the same as writing

$$\iint_R 4y\, dA = \iint_{R_1} 4y\, dA + \iint_{R_2} 4y\, dA,$$

where R_1 is the part of R that lies below the line $y = 1$ and R_2 is the part of R that lies above this line, and then evaluating the double integrals over R_1 and R_2 by calculating the corresponding iterated integrals.

The integral $\iint_R 1\, dA = \iint_R dA$ of the constant function with a value of 1 over a region R is the limit of sums of the form $\Sigma\,\Delta A$. Such an approximating sum is simply the sum of the areas of the rectangular subregions that make up a partition of R. If the norm of the partition is small, then those subregions nearly fill R and hence the sum $\Sigma\,\Delta A$ approximates the area of R. Thus since both the area of R and the integral $\iint_R dA$ are numbers that are approximated by the same sums, it is apparent that the area A of R is given by the formula

$$A = \iint_R dA. \tag{104-3}$$

Example 104-3. Find the area of the plane region that lies in the first quadrant and is bounded by the X-axis, the circle $x^2 + y^2 = 18$, and the parabola $y^2 = 3x$.

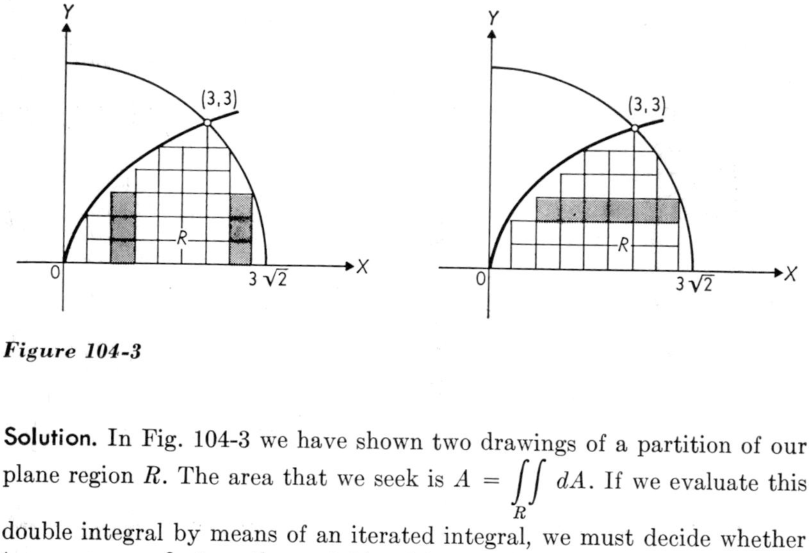

Figure 104-3

Solution. In Fig. 104-3 we have shown two drawings of a partition of our plane region R. The area that we seek is $A = \iint_R dA$. If we evaluate this double integral by means of an iterated integral, we must decide whether to use x or y first as the variable of integration. Intuitively, if we first integrate with respect to y, then we are first finding the area of a vertical strip (see the shaded strips in the picture on the left in Fig. 104-3). The disadvantage of using vertical strips first lies in the fact that two different equations describe the curve that forms the upper boundary of our region. If we first integrate with respect to x, then we are first finding the area of a horizontal strip such as the one that is shaded in the diagram on the right in Fig. 104-3. In this case the right-boundary curve is given by the equation $x = \sqrt{18 - y^2}$ and the left-boundary curve is given by the equation $x = y^2/3$. Thus our iterated integral in this case (which appears to be the simpler case) is

$$A = \int_0^3 \int_{y^2/3}^{\sqrt{18-y^2}} dx\,dy = \int_0^3 (\sqrt{18 - y^2} - \tfrac{1}{3}y^2)\,dy$$

$$= \left[\frac{y\sqrt{18 - y^2}}{2} + 9\,\mathrm{Sin}^{-1}\left(\frac{y}{3\sqrt{2}}\right) - \frac{y^3}{9}\right]_0^3$$

$$= \frac{6 + 9\pi}{4}.$$

Problems 104

1. Use double integration to find the areas of the following regions:
   (a) The region bounded by the curves $y^2 = x + 1$ and $x + y = 1$.
   (b) The first quadrant region bounded by the curves $x^2 = 4 - 2y$, $x = 0$, $y = 0$.
   (c) The region bounded by the curves $xy = 4$ and $x + y = 5$.
   (d) The region bounded by the curves $y^2 = x^3$ and $y = x$.
   (e) The region bounded by the curves $y = 2x - x^2$ and $y = 2x^3 - x^2$.
   (f) The region bounded by the curves $y^2 = 4x$ and $y^2 = 5 - x$.
2. Use double integration to find the area of the triangular region whose vertices are the points (0, 0), (6, 4), and (2, 8).
3. Use double integration to find the volume of the solid tetrahedron whose vertices are the points (0, 0, 0), $(a, 0, 0)$, $(0, b, 0)$, and $(0, 0, c)$.
4. Use double integration to find the volume of the region in the first octant and bounded by the following surfaces:
   (a) The planes $z = x$, $x = 0$, $x = 1$, $y = 0$, $y = 1$, $z = 0$.
   (b) The planes $x = 0$, $y = 0$, $z = 0$, $z = y$, and the cylinder $x^2 + y^2 = 4$.
   (c) The planes $x = 0$, $y = 0$, $z = 0$, $x + z = 4$, and the cylinder $y = 4 - x^2$.
5. Use double integration to find the volume of one of the wedges bounded by the cylinder whose equation is $x^2 + y^2 = a^2$, the XY-plane, and the plane whose equation is $z = mx$.
6. Find the volume of the region bounded by the cylinder $x^2 + z = 1$ and by the planes $x + y = 1$, $y = 0$, and $z = 0$.
7. Find the volume of the region bounded by the ellipsoid whose equation is $\dfrac{x^2}{a^2} + \dfrac{y^2}{b^2} + \dfrac{z^2}{c^2} = 1$.
8. Find the volume of the wedge that is bounded by the cylinder $y^2 = x$, the XY-plane, and the plane $x + z = 1$.
9. The XY-plane and the surface whose equation is $y^2 = 16 - 4z$ cut the cylinder whose equation is $x^2 + y^2 = 4x$. Find the volume of the region bounded by these surfaces.
10. The nose cone of a certain missile has the shape of the region bounded by the XY-plane and the paraboloid $x^2 + y^2 + z = 1$. Use double integration to find the volume of the nose cone.

105. Moments and Moments of Inertia of Plane Regions

Let us consider a rectangular region whose sides are parallel to the coordinate axes (Fig. 105-1). Suppose that the coordinates of its geometrical center (the intersection of the diagonals of the rectangle) are

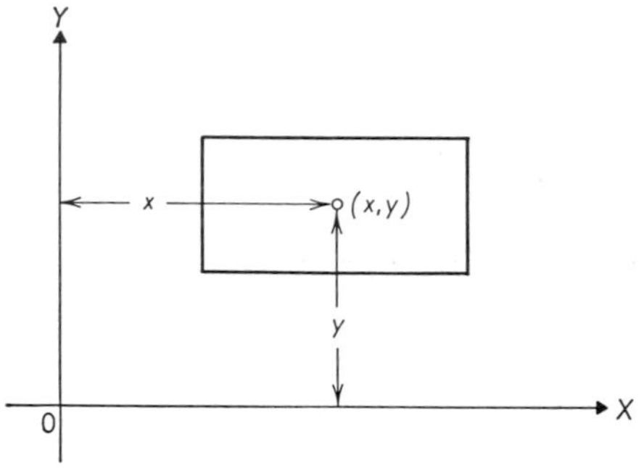

Figure 105-1

(x, y) and that its area is A square units. Then the numbers

(105-1) $$\boldsymbol{M_X = yA} \text{ and } \boldsymbol{M_Y = xA}$$

are called the **moments** of the region about the X- and Y-axis, respectively. Notice that we have defined the moment of a rectangular region; that is, of a geometrical object. However, if we think of our region as a plate made of some material of uniform density, then its mass will be proportional to its area A. Thus if we suppose that gravity acts in a direction perpendicular to the XY-plane, we can find the moments of the plate in the usual mechanical sense of force times lever arm by multiplying the right-hand sides of Equations 105-1 by a factor of proportionality.

In general, we define the moment of a region R such as the one shown in Fig. 105-2 as follows. We first partition R into rectangular subregions, such as the "typical" one shown in the figure. The point (x^*, y^*) is the center of this subregion, and its area is $\Delta A = \Delta x\, \Delta y$. Therefore, its moment about the X-axis is $y^*\, \Delta A$. We define the moment of the partition of R about the X-axis to be the sum $\Sigma y^*\, \Delta A$ of the moments of the rectangular subregions that make up the partition, and the moment of R itself to be the limit of these sums as the norm of the partition of R approaches 0. Since this number is the integral of y over R, then

(105-2) $$\boldsymbol{M_X = \iint_R y\, dA.}$$

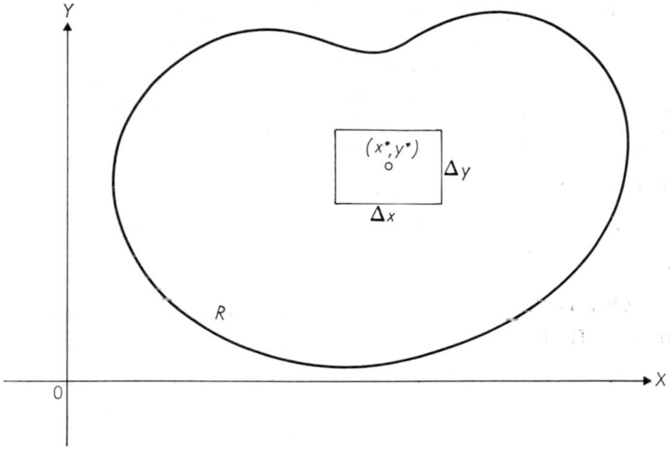

Figure 105-2

Similarly, the moment of R about the Y-axis is defined to be the number

(105-3) $$\boldsymbol{M_Y = \iint_R x\,dA.}$$

Example 105-1. Find the moments M_X and M_Y of the region that is bounded by the upper half of the circle whose equation is $x^2 + y^2 = a^2$ and the X-axis.

Solution. Our region R is shown in Fig. 105-3. According to Equation 105-2,

$$M_X = \iint_R y\,dA = \int_{-a}^{a}\int_0^{\sqrt{a^2-x^2}} y\,dy\,dx$$
$$= \int_{-a}^{a} \frac{a^2 - x^2}{2}\,dx = \frac{2a^3}{3}.$$

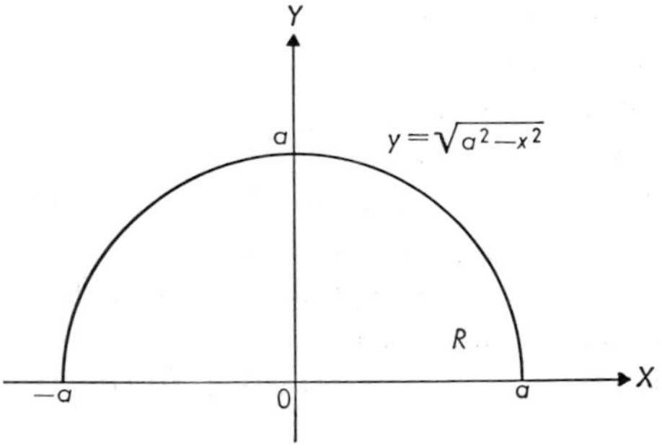

Figure 105-3

We use Equation 105-3 to find M_Y. Thus

$$M_Y = \iint_R x\,dA = \int_0^a \int_{-\sqrt{a^2-y^2}}^{\sqrt{a^2-y^2}} x\,dx\,dy$$
$$= \int_0^a 0\,dy = 0.$$

You will notice that, for ease of calculation, we used different orders of integration when we replaced the double integrals giving M_X and M_Y with iterated integrals.

Our concept of moment gives us a "net moment" of a region about an axis. If the axis is vertical, for example, the moment of the part of the

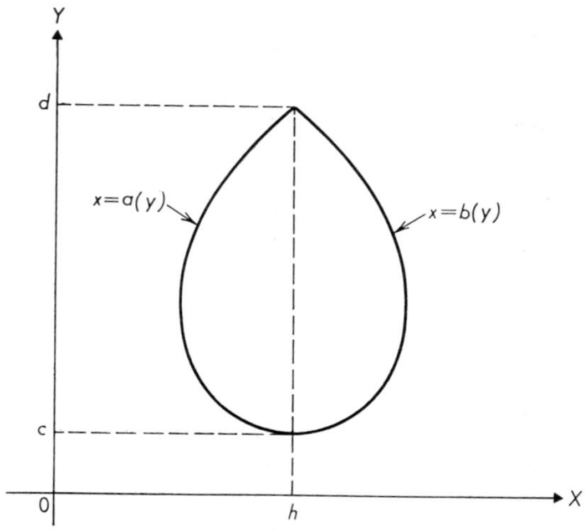

Figure 105-4

region to the right of the axis is positive and the moment of the part to the left is negative. In Example 105-1 we saw how these moments cancelled each other when we calculated the moment about the Y-axis and found that $M_Y = 0$.

It is easy to find the moment of a region about a line that is parallel to a line of symmetry of the region. Thus suppose that we have a region R, such as the one shown in Fig. 105-4, that is symmetric about the line $x = h$. This symmetry means that the average of the X-coordinates of the two boundary points with the same Y-coordinate is always h. Thus if the equations $x = a(y)$ and $x = b(y)$ represent the left and right boundaries of R, we have

$$\frac{a(y) + b(y)}{2} = h$$

for each y. Therefore

$$M_Y = \int_c^d \int_{a(y)}^{b(y)} x\,dx\,dy = \int_c^d \left[\frac{b(y)^2 - a(y)^2}{2}\right] dy$$

$$= \int_c^d \left(\frac{b(y) + a(y)}{2}\right)(b(y) - a(y))\,dy = h \int_c^d (b(y) - a(y))\,dy.$$

On the other hand, the area A of R is given by the equation

$$A = \int_c^d \int_{a(y)}^{b(y)} dx\,dy = \int_c^d (b(y) - a(y))\,dy,$$

and so $\boldsymbol{M_Y = hA}$. Similarly, if our region were symmetric with respect to a line $y = k$, then we would have $\boldsymbol{M_X = kA}$.

In mechanics we define the **center of gravity** of a body as being "the point at which we can imagine the mass of the body to be concentrated." By this statement we mean that if we replace a given body with a "point mass" at the center of gravity, then the moment of this new system about an axis will be the same as the moment of the original body about that axis. The concept of the centroid of a plane region is similar. The **centroid** of a region R that has an area of A is the point $(\bar{x}, \bar{y})$ such that the "moments" $\bar{y}A$ and $\bar{x}A$ equal the moments of R about the X- and Y-axes. Thus $\bar{x}$ and $\bar{y}$ are numbers such that

(105-4) $$\boldsymbol{\bar{x}A = M_Y} \quad \text{and} \quad \boldsymbol{\bar{y}A = M_X}.$$

We can rewrite these equations for $\bar{x}$ and $\bar{y}$ in the form

(105-5) $$\boldsymbol{\bar{x} = \frac{\iint_R x\,dA}{A}} \quad \text{and} \quad \boldsymbol{\bar{y} = \frac{\iint_R y\,dA}{A}}.$$

Example 105-2. Find the centroid of the region shown in Fig. 105-3.

Solution. In Example 105-1 we found that $M_X = 2a^3/3$ and $M_Y = 0$. The area of our semi-circular region whose radius is a is $A = \pi a^2/2$. Therefore, according to Equations 105-4, we have

$$\bar{x} = \frac{0}{A} = 0 \quad \text{and} \quad \bar{y} = \frac{2a^3/3}{\pi a^2/2} = \frac{4a}{3\pi}.$$

Thus the centroid of R is the point $(0, 4a/3\pi)$. If we make a cardboard model of R, it will balance on a pin placed at the point $(0, 4a/3\pi)$.

If a region R with an area of A square units is symmetric with respect to the line $x = h$, then we have seen that $M_Y = hA$, and hence $\bar{x}A = M_Y = hA$. Thus $\bar{x} = h$; that is, the centroid is in the line of symmetry, as illustrated by the preceding example. Similarly, if a region is symmetric with respect to the line $y = k$, then $\bar{y} = k$. You should take advantage of symmetry when you calculate moments and centroids.

Example 105-3. Find the centroid of the region that is bounded by the X-axis and one arch of the sine curve.

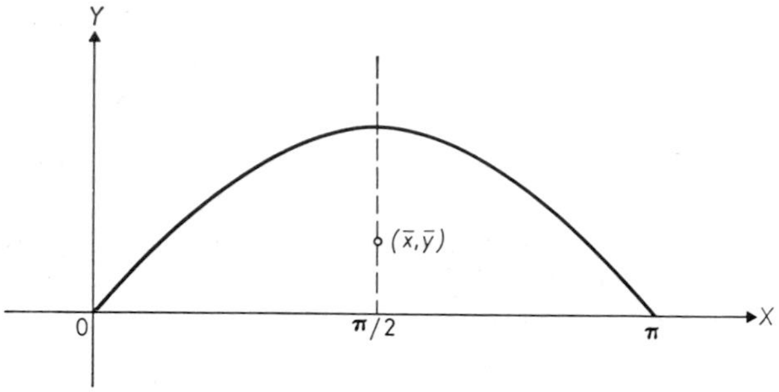

Figure 105-5

Solution. Since the region (shown in Fig. 105-5) is symmetric about the line $x = \pi/2$, we know immediately that $\bar{x} = \pi/2$. Furthermore,

$$A = \int_0^\pi \sin x \, dx = 2,$$

and

$$M_X = \int_0^\pi \int_0^{\sin x} y \, dy \, dx = \frac{1}{2} \int_0^\pi \sin^2 x \, dx = \frac{\pi}{4}.$$

Thus

$$\bar{y} = \frac{M_X}{A} = \frac{\pi}{8},$$

so our centroid is the point $(\pi/2, \pi/8)$.

We can define moments of a region R about lines other than the coordinate axes. For example, the moment about the line L whose equation is $x = h$ is

$$M_L = \iint_R (x - h) \, dA.$$

Since

$$\iint_R (x - h) \, dA = \iint_R x \, dA - h \iint_R dA = M_Y - hA,$$

we have the equation

(105-6) $$M_L = M_Y - hA.$$

Similarly, the moment M_L of a region R about the line L whose equation is $y = k$ is

(105-7) $$M_L = M_X - kA.$$

Example 105-4. Find the centroid of the region R that consists of a circular disk whose radius is 1 and a 2 by 2 square region that touches it, as shown in Fig. 105-6.

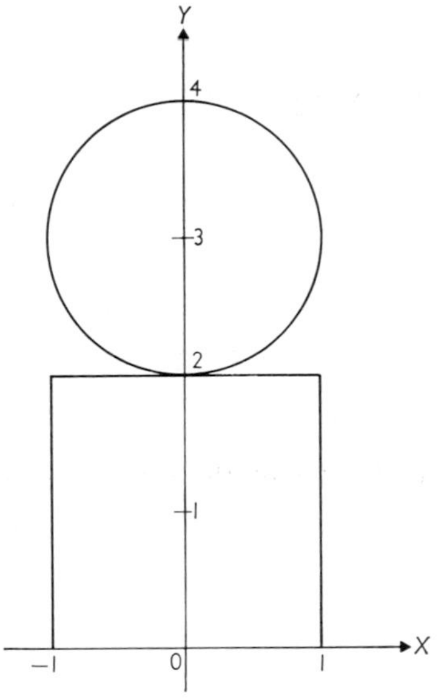

Figure 105-6

Solution. Since our figure is symmetric about the Y-axis, the X-coordinate of its centroid is 0. By definition, $M_X = \iint_R y\,dA$. Since our given region is the sum of the disk R_1 and the square region R_2, we may use Equation 102-3 to write

$$M_X = \iint_R y\,dA = \iint_{R_1} y\,dA + \iint_{R_2} y\,dA.$$

The two integrals on the right of this equation yield the moments M_{1X} and M_{2X} of the disk and the square region about the X-axis, so $M_X = M_{1X} + M_{2X}$. We find these moments by multiplying the areas of R_1 and R_2 by the distances of their lines of symmetry from the X-axis; thus $M_{1X} = 3\pi$, and $M_{2X} = 1 \cdot 4 = 4$. Therefore, $M_X = 3\pi + 4$. The area of R is $A = \pi + 4$, so $\bar{y} = \dfrac{M_X}{A} = \dfrac{3\pi + 4}{\pi + 4} \approx 1.85$. The coordinates of the centroid of our region are therefore approximately (0, 1.85).

Example 105-5. Find the moment of the region R of the preceding example about the line L whose equation is $y = 1$.

Solution. In the preceding example we found that $M_X = 3\pi + 4$ and $A = \pi + 4$. Then, according to Equation 105-7, with $k = 1$,

$$M_L = (3\pi + 4) - (\pi + 4) = 2\pi.$$

Another concept encountered in mechanics is the concept of the **moment of inertia** of a body. The moment of inertia about the X-axis of the rectangular region shown in Fig. 105-1 is the number y^2A, the moment of inertia about the Y-axis is the number x^2A, and the moment of inertia about the origin is the number $(x^2 + y^2)A$. In general, if I_X, I_Y, and I_O are the moments of inertia of the region shown in Fig. 105-2 about the X-axis, the Y-axis, and the origin, then by definition

$$I_X = \iint_R y^2\, dA$$

(105-8)
$$I_Y = \iint_R x^2\, dA$$

$$I_O = \iint_R (x^2 + y^2)\, dA.$$

We immediately see that $I_O = I_X + I_Y$. If our region R were a plate made of material of uniform density, then its moments of inertia (as the term is used in mechanics) are obtained by multiplying our numbers I_X, I_Y, and I_O by the density. The moment of inertia of a body plays a role in rotational motion that is analogous to the role played by the mass of the body in linear motion.

Example 105-6. Find the moment of inertia of the interior of a right triangle about the vertex of the 90° angle.

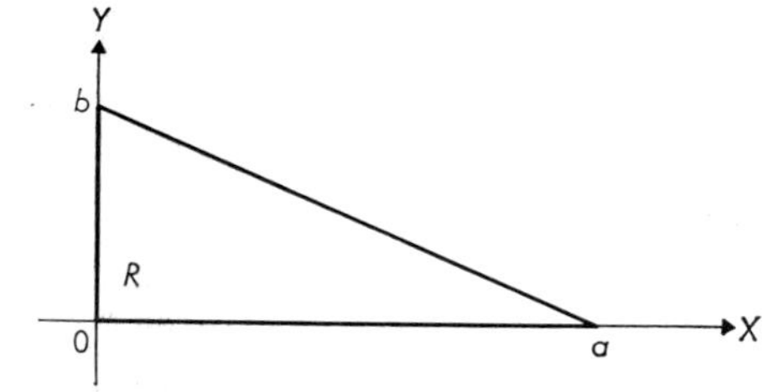

Figure 105-7

Solution. Suppose that the legs of our triangle are a and b units long and that we place it in a coordinate system as in Fig. 105-7. We must compute I_O, which is given by the formula

$$I_O = \iint_R (x^2 + y^2)\, dA.$$

The equation of the hypotenuse of our triangle is $\frac{x}{a} + \frac{y}{b} = 1$, and therefore,

$$I_O = \iint_R (x^2 + y^2)\, dA = \int_0^b \int_0^{a - \frac{ay}{b}} (x^2 + y^2)\, dx\, dy = \frac{ab}{12}(a^2 + b^2).$$

Example 105-7. Find I_X and I_Y for the region R shown in Fig. 105-3.

Solution. According to Equations 105-8,

$$I_X = \iint_R y^2\,dA = \int_{-a}^{a}\int_0^{\sqrt{a^2-x^2}} y^2\,dy\,dx$$

$$= \tfrac{1}{3}\int_{-a}^{a} (a^2 - x^2)^{3/2}\,dx$$

$$= \tfrac{1}{3}\int_{-a}^{a} a^2\sqrt{a^2 - x^2}\,dx - \tfrac{1}{3}\int_{-a}^{a} x^2\sqrt{a^2 - x^2}\,dx$$

$$= \frac{\pi a^4}{8} \quad \text{(see Integration Formulas V-30 and V-32).}$$

Similarly,

$$I_Y = \iint_R x^2\,dA = \int_0^a \int_{-\sqrt{a^2-y^2}}^{\sqrt{a^2-y^2}} x^2\,dx\,dy$$

$$= \frac{2}{3}\int_0^a (a^2 - y^2)^{3/2}\,dy = \frac{\pi a^4}{8}.$$

Problems 105

1. Find the centroids of the following plane regions:
   (a) The first quadrant quarter of the disk $x^2 + y^2 \leq a^2$.
   (b) The upper half of the region bounded by the ellipse $4x^2 + 9y^2 = 36$.
   (c) The first quadrant region bounded by the coordinate axes and the parabola $y^2 = 4 - x$.
   (d) The region bounded by the curve $x^2 = 4y$ and the line $y = 1$.
   (e) The triangular region whose vertices are the points $(0, 0)$, (a, b) and $(c, 0)$, where $b > 0$ and $c > 0$.
   (f) The region bounded by the curves $\sqrt{x} + \sqrt{y} = \sqrt{a}$, $x = 0$, and $y = 0$.
2. Find the centroid of the region bounded by the X-axis, the line $x = \pi/2$, and the sine curve.
3. Show that the centroid of the interior of a triangle is the intersection of its medians (see Question 1e).
4. Find the centroid of the region bounded by the parabolas $x^2 = y$ and $y^2 = x$.
5. Show that if a region R is symmetric about a line L whose equation is $x = h$, then $M_L = 0$.
6. Show that the moments of a region R about lines that contain its centroid and are parallel to the axes are 0.
7. Use the result of the preceding problem to find the moment of the given region R about the given line.
   (a) $R: x^2 + y^2 \leq a^2$, $L: x = 5a$.
   (b) R: The region bounded by the ellipse $b^2x^2 + a^2y^2 = a^2b^2$, L: A latus rectum of the ellipse.

(c) R: The region bounded by the parabolas $x^2 = 4y$ and $x^2 = 5 - y$, L: A vertical line containing the right-hand intersection point of the given curves.

8. Find the moment of inertia about one corner of a rectangular region that is a units long and b units wide.
9. Find I_X, I_Y, and I_O for the region bounded by the parabola $y^2 = 8x$, and the line $x = 2$.
10. Find I_X, I_Y, and I_O for the region bounded by the ellipse $b^2x^2 + a^2y^2 = a^2b^2$.
11. The moment of inertia of a region R about the line L whose equation is $x = h$ is defined by the equation

$$I_L = \iint_R (x - h)^2 \, dA.$$

(a) Show that

$$I_L = I_Y - 2hM_Y + h^2A,$$

where A is the area of R.

(b) What can you conclude from the equation in part (a) if R is symmetric about the Y-axis?

(c) What can you conclude from the equation in part (a) if R is symmetric about the line L?

(d) If L_1 is a line whose equation is $x = k$, show that

$$I_{L_1} = I_L - 2M_Y(k - h) + (k^2 - h^2)A.$$

12. The moment of a region about a line through its centroid is zero. Can you find a line such that the moment of inertia of the region about the line is zero?
13. Use the results of Questions 10 and 11 to find the moment of inertia of the region bounded by the ellipse $b^2x^2 + a^2y^2 = a^2b^2$ about a latus rectum of the ellipse.

106. Double Integrals in Polar Coordinates

The double integral of a function f over a plane region R is defined as the limit of sums of the form

$$S = \Sigma f(x^*, y^*) \, \Delta A. \tag{106-1}$$

Here the number ΔA is the area of a rectangular subregion of the partition of R. It does not matter at what point (x^*, y^*) in this subregion we evaluate f; if the maximum dimension of the subregions is small, then the Sum 106-1 is close to the number $\iint_R f(x, y) \, dA$. It can be shown that even if the region R is partitioned into subregions of non-rectangular shape, then the limit of S will still be the integral of f over R. In this section we are going to investigate the non-rectangular partitioning that we get when we use polar coordinates.

Suppose that we introduce a polar coordinate system into our plane. As usual, we shall take as the pole of this coordinate system the origin of the cartesian coordinate system and as the polar axis the positive X-axis. We form a "polar partition" of a region R by drawing a network of radial lines and concentric circles, as shown in Fig. 106-1. The actual

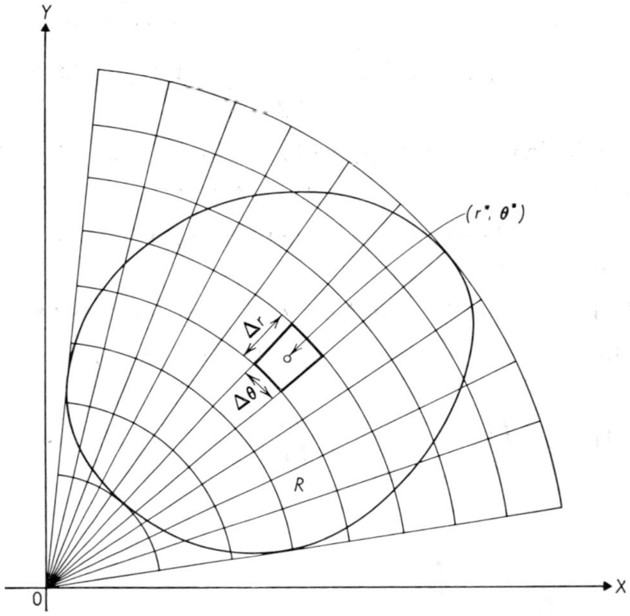

Figure 106-1

partition of R consists of the subregions bounded by the "curved rectangles" that lie entirely in R. The norm of this partition is the length of the longest line segment that is contained in any of the subregions (that is, the norm is the length of the longest "diagonal" of any of the "curved rectangles"). Now we assert that if we start with such a partition whose norm is small, evaluate f at a point in each subregion, multiply this value of f by the area of the subregion, and add up the resulting numbers, then the sum that we obtain will approximate the integral of f over R. Let us see what one such approximating sum looks like. We have singled out a "typical" subregion in Fig. 106-1. We shall suppose that the two radial lines that form the sides of this subregion make an angle of $\Delta\theta$ at the origin and that the concentric circles that form its ends are Δr units apart. Now let (r^*, θ^*) be polar coordinates of the point of the bisector of $\Delta\theta$ that is halfway between the two concentric circles. The XY-coordinates of this point are $(r^* \cos \theta^*, r^* \sin \theta^*)$, so the value of f there is $f(r^* \cos \theta^*, r^* \sin \theta^*)$. Our typical subregion can be considered to be the difference between two circular "wedges," both with a central angle of $\Delta\theta$, but one having a radius of $r^* - \frac{\Delta r}{2}$ and the other a radius of $r^* + \frac{\Delta r}{2}$. The area of a circular wedge is one-half the product of the radian measure of its central angle and the square of its radius (see Appendix A). Therefore, the area of our typical subregion is

$$\Delta A = \frac{1}{2}\left(r^* + \frac{\Delta r}{2}\right)^2 \Delta\theta - \frac{1}{2}\left(r^* - \frac{\Delta r}{2}\right)^2 \Delta\theta.$$

After a little simplification, we find that this formula reduces to

(106-2) $$\Delta A = r^* \Delta r \, \Delta\theta.$$

Therefore, we have an approximating sum that is expressed in terms of polar coordinates as

(106-3) $$S = \Sigma f(r^* \cos \theta^*, r^* \sin \theta^*) r^* \Delta r \, \Delta\theta.$$

The limit of such sums is the double integral of f over R, and their form suggests that we write

(106-4) $$\iint_R \mathbf{f(x, y)\, dA} = \iint_R \mathbf{f(r \cos \theta, r \sin \theta) r \, dr \, d\theta.}$$

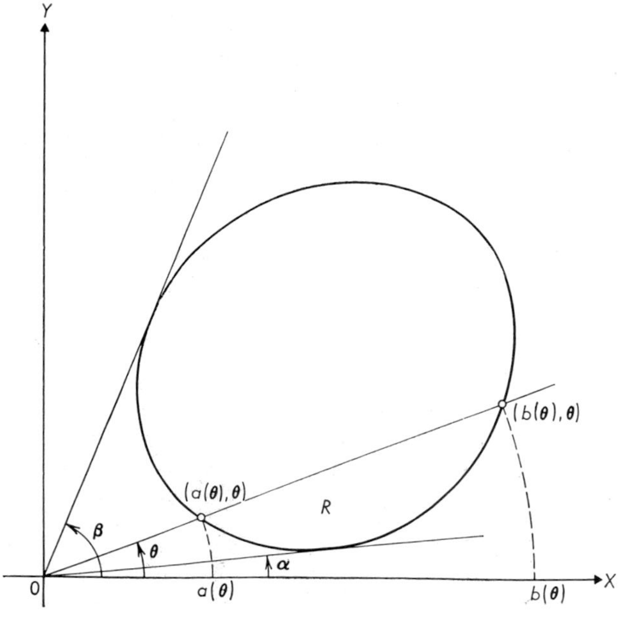

Figure 106-2

It is convenient to think that we obtain the right side of this equation from the left by replacing x with $r \cos \theta$, y with $r \sin \theta$, and dA with $r\, dr\, d\theta$ (see Equation 106-2).

To evaluate our double integral we use iterated integrals. Let us first assume that our region R lies between, and is tangent to, two radial lines $\theta = \alpha$ and $\theta = \beta$, and that any radial line between these two lines cuts the boundary of R in exactly two points (see Fig. 106-2). If the radial line that makes an angle of θ with the polar axis cuts the boundary in points with radial coordinates $a(\theta)$ and $b(\theta)$, then

$$\text{(106-5)} \quad \iint_R \boldsymbol{f(r \cos \theta, r \sin \theta) r\, dr\, d\theta} = \int_\alpha^\beta \int_{a(\theta)}^{b(\theta)} \boldsymbol{f(r \cos \theta, r \sin \theta)\, r\, dr\, d\theta}.$$

Now let us suppose that our region R is between, and tangent to, circles of radii a and b whose center is the origin, and that any other circle whose center is the origin and that lies between these two circles cuts

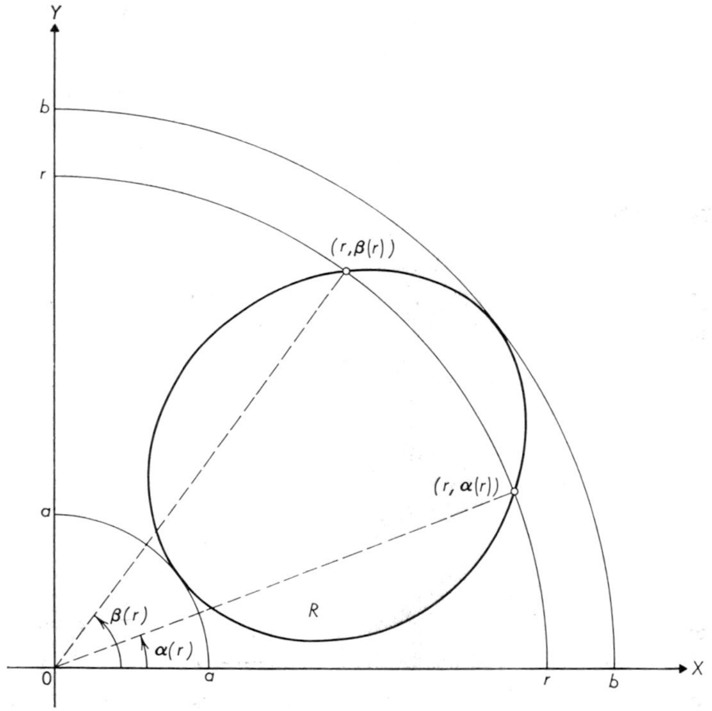

Figure 106-3

the boundary of R in exactly two points (see Fig. 106-3). Then we may integrate with respect to θ first. Thus we suppose that the circle whose radius is r cuts the boundary of R at points with angular coordinates $\alpha(r)$ and $\beta(r)$. Then

$$\text{(106-6)} \quad \iint_R f(r\cos\theta, r\sin\theta)r\,dr\,d\theta = \int_a^b \int_{\alpha(r)}^{\beta(r)} f(r\cos\theta, r\sin\theta)r\,d\theta\,dr.$$

Example 106-1. Find the moment of inertia about the origin of the region bounded by two concentric circles of radius a and b, where $a < b$.

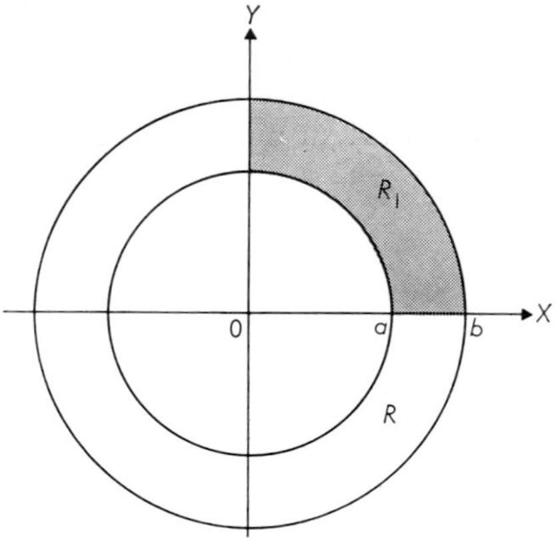

Figure 106-4

Solution. The given region is shown in Fig. 106-4. Using Equations 106-4 and 106-5 we see that the required moment of inertia is

$$\begin{aligned} I_O &= \iint_R (x^2 + y^2)\,dA \\ &= \iint_R r^2 r\,dr\,d\theta \\ &= \int_0^{2\pi} \int_a^b r^3\,dr\,d\theta = \frac{\pi}{2}(b^4 - a^4). \end{aligned}$$

Example 106-2. Find the centroid of the part of the "washer" described in the last example that lies in the first quadrant.

Solution. Our region, we will label it R_1 in this example, is the shaded quarter of the region R of Fig. 106-4. If we denote the coordinates of the required centroid by $(\bar{x}, \bar{y})$, considerations of symmetry tell us that $\bar{x} = \bar{y}$. So we need only compute $\bar{y}$. According to Equation 105-5,

$$(106\text{-}7) \qquad \bar{y} = \frac{\iint_{R_1} y\, dA}{A}.$$

Now, using Equations 106-4 and 106-5, we have

$$\iint_{R_1} y\, dA = \iint_{R_1} r \sin\theta\, r\, dr\, d\theta = \int_0^{\pi/2} \int_a^b r^2 \sin\theta\, dr\, d\theta$$
$$= \int_0^{\pi/2} \frac{b^3 - a^3}{3} \sin\theta\, d\theta = \frac{b^3 - a^3}{3}.$$

It is a matter of simple geometry to show that the area A of the region R_1 is $\frac{\pi}{4}(b^2 - a^2)$. Hence Equation 106-7 tells us that

$$\bar{y} = \frac{4(b^3 - a^3)}{3\pi(b^2 - a^2)}.$$

Problems 106

1. Use an iterated integral and polar coordinates to find the area of the region that lies inside the graph of each of the following equations.
   (a) $r = 2\cos 3\theta$ (b) $r^2 = \cos 2\theta$ (c) $r = 1 + \sin\theta$
2. Use an iterated integral and polar coordinates to find the area of the first quadrant region that lies inside the rose petal $r = 2\sin 2\theta$ and outside the circle $r = \sqrt{3}$.
3. Use polar coordinates to evaluate the integral $\iint_R \sqrt{x^2 + y^2}\, dA$ over the given region R:
   (a) The circular disk $x^2 + y^2 \leq a^2$.
   (b) The circular disk bounded by the graph of the equation $r = \sin\theta$.
   (c) The interior of the cardioid $r = 1 - \cos\theta$.
4. Replace the given iterated integral with an iterated integral in polar coordinates and evaluate.
   (a) $\int_0^2 \int_0^{\sqrt{4-x^2}} e^{-x^2-y^2}\, dy\, dx.$
   (b) $\int_0^1 \int_y^{\sqrt{2-y^2}} x^4\, dx\, dy$
5. Use polar coordinates to calculate the volume of the region cut from the solid sphere $x^2 + y^2 + z^2 \leqq 4a^2$ by the cylinder $x^2 + y^2 = a^2$.
6. Find the moment of inertia about its vertex of a pie-shaped wedge whose radius is a and whose arclength is S.

7. Use polar coordinates to find the volume of the wedge cut by the XY-plane and the plane $z = mx$ from the solid cylinder whose radius is a and whose axis is the Z-axis.
8. The part of the graph of the equation $z/h + r/a = 1$ (in cylindrical coordinates) that lies between the planes $z = 0$ and $z = h$ is a cone whose altitude is h and whose base radius is a. Find its volume.
9. Use polar coordinates to find the moment of inertia about a diameter of a circular disk whose radius is a.
10. Find I_X for the disk bounded by the circle $r = 4 \sin \theta$.
11. Find the centroid of the plane region described:
    (a) The interior of the cardioid $r = a(1 - \cos \theta)$.
    (b) The region in the upper half plane that is bounded by the graph of the equation $r^2 = a \cos \theta$.
    (c) The interior of one loop of the graph of the equation $r = 4 \sin 2\theta$.
    (d) The region bounded by the rays $\theta = 0$ and $\theta = \frac{\pi}{4}$, and the curve $r = \cos 2\theta$.
12. Examine the formula for the coordinates of the centroid of the region R of Example 106-2. (a) Where is the centroid if $a = 0$? (b) What is $\lim_{a \to b} \bar{x}$? (c) Can we choose a so that the centroid of R is a point on the inner boundary of R? outside R?

107. Triple Integrals

The concept of the triple integral of a function of three variables over a region in three-dimensional space is a straightforward generalization of the idea of the double integral of a function of two variables over a plane region. Thus suppose that f is a function of three variables whose domain contains a region R like the one shown in Fig. 107-1. By slicing it with planes parallel to the coordinate planes, we cut R into subregions. The set of rectangular "blocks" formed by these planes and contained in R constitutes a *partition* of R. The *norm* of this partition is the length of the longest diagonal of any of the blocks. A typical block is shown in Fig. 107-1. We have labeled its dimensions Δx, Δy, and Δz. We will denote its volume by ΔV, and so we

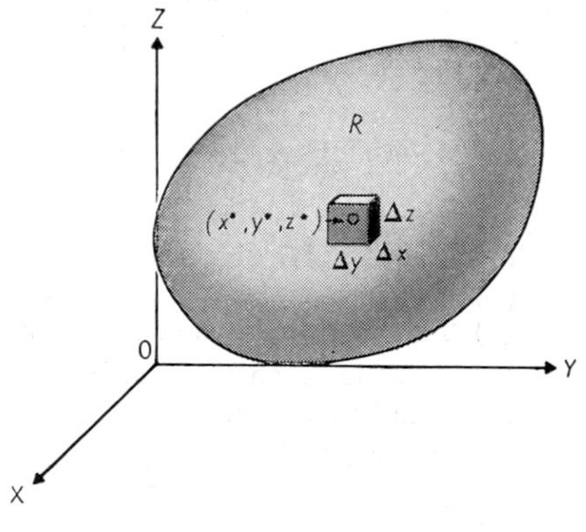

Figure 107-1

have $\Delta V = \Delta x\, \Delta y\, \Delta z$. In each block of the partition we pick a point (x^*, y^*, z^*) and consider sums of the form

$$S = \Sigma f(x^*, y^*, z^*)\, \Delta V, \tag{107-1}$$

where the sum has a term for each block of the partition of R. If S has a limit as the norm of our partition goes to 0, then we say that f is *integrable* over R and we call the limit of S the **triple integral of f over R.** We denote this integral by one of the symbols

$$\iiint_R f(x, y, z)\, dV \quad \text{or} \quad \iiint_R f(x, y, z)\, dx\, dy\, dz.$$

As in the case of double integrals, triple integrals can be evaluated by iteration, and we will now describe an iterated integration in which

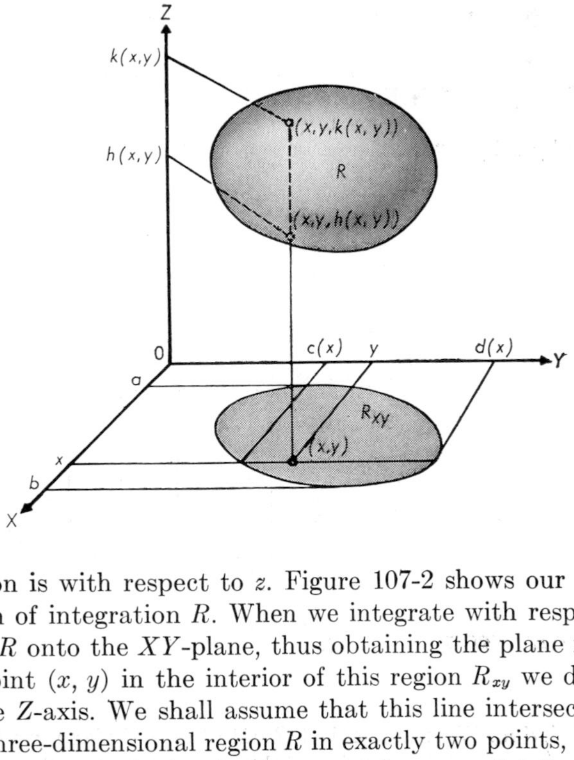

Figure 107-2

the first integration is with respect to z. Figure 107-2 shows our three-dimensional region of integration R. When we integrate with respect to z first, we project R onto the XY-plane, thus obtaining the plane region R_{xy}. Through a point (x, y) in the interior of this region R_{xy} we draw a line parallel to the Z-axis. We shall assume that this line intersects the boundary of our three-dimensional region R in exactly two points, whose Z-coordinates are $h(x, y)$ and $k(x, y)$. These numbers are the limits on the variable of integration z, and we have

$$\iiint_R f(x, y, z)\, dV = \iint_{R_{xy}} \left(\int_{h(x,y)}^{k(x,y)} f(x, y, z)\, dz \right) dA. \tag{107-2}$$

By this equation we mean that the triple integral on the left is the double integral over R_{xy} of the function g that is defined by the equation

$$g(x, y) = \int_{h(x,y)}^{k(x,y)} f(x, y, z)\, dz.$$

This double integral, in turn, can be evaluated as an iterated integral. If we integrate first with respect to y and then x, our figure shows that the limits of integration on y are $c(x)$ and $d(x)$, and the limits on x are a and b. Thus

$$\text{(107-3)} \quad \iiint_R f(x, y, z)\, dV = \int_a^b \int_{c(x)}^{d(x)} \int_{h(x,y)}^{k(x,y)} f(x, y, z)\, dz\, dy\, dx.$$

If our region is of a suitable shape, we might integrate in some other order, using limits that are appropriate to the order of integration.

Example 107-1. Evaluate the integral $\iiint_R xy \sin yz\, dV$, where R is the π by π by π cube shown in Fig. 107-3.

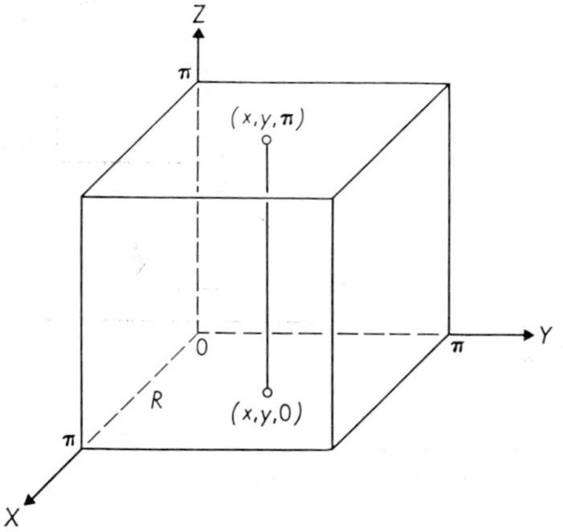

Figure 107-3

Solution. When we project R onto the XY-plane, we get a π by π square. A line containing a point of this square and parallel to the Z-axis cuts the boundary of our cube at points with Z-coordinates 0 and π. Hence our limits of integration on z are 0 and π. Now we must integrate over the square in the plane, and we see that the limits of integration on x and y

are also 0 and π. Thus

$$\iiint_R xy \sin yz \, dV = \int_0^\pi \int_0^\pi \int_0^\pi xy \sin yz \, dz \, dy \, dx$$

$$= \int_0^\pi \int_0^\pi -x \cos yz \Big|_0^\pi dy \, dx$$

$$= \int_0^\pi \int_0^\pi x(1 - \cos \pi y) \, dy \, dx$$

$$= \int_0^\pi x\left(y - \frac{1}{\pi} \sin \pi y\right)\Big|_0^\pi dx$$

$$= \int_0^\pi x\left(\pi - \frac{\sin \pi^2}{\pi}\right) dx = \frac{\pi^3 - \pi \sin \pi^2}{2}.$$

Example 107-2. Evaluate the integral $\iiint_R e^{x+y+z} \, dV$, where R is the region that is bounded by the plane whose equation is $2x + y + z = 4$ and the coordinate planes.

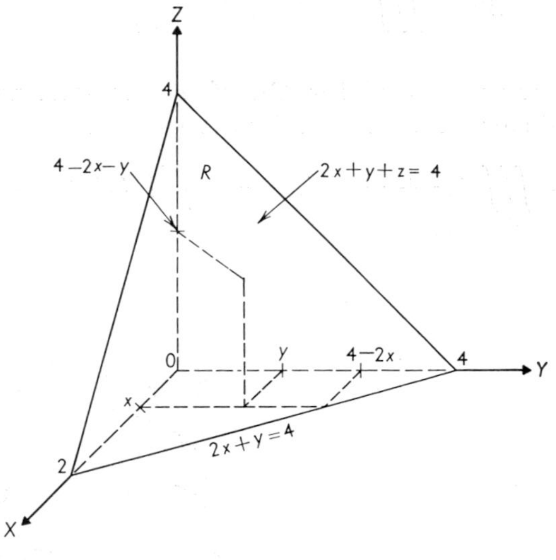

Figure 107-4

Solution. The region R is shown in Fig. 107-4. When we project R onto the XY-plane, we obtain the triangular region bounded by the coordinate axes and the line whose equation is $2x + y = 4$. A line containing a point of this triangular region and parallel to the Z-axis cuts the boundary of our three-dimensional region R in points with Z-coordinates 0 and $4 - 2x - y$. These numbers are the limits of integration with respect to z. After we integrate with respect to z, we must integrate the result over the triangular plane region. We may first integrate with respect to y between the limits 0 and $4 - 2x$ and then integrate with respect to x between the limits 0 and 2. Thus

$$\iiint\limits_R e^{x+y+z}\,dV = \int_0^2 \int_0^{4-2x} \int_0^{4-2x-y} e^{x+y+z}\,dz\,dy\,dx.$$

We leave it to you to carry out the details of finding that the answer is the number $e^4 + 4e^2 - 1$.

The sum $\Sigma\,\Delta V$ is the sum of volumes of the rectangular blocks of a partition of R, and the limit of these sums is the volume of R. Thus the volume V of R is given by the integral

$$V = \iiint\limits_R dV.$$

We define the **centroid** of R to be the point $(\bar{x}, \bar{y}, \bar{z})$, where

$$\bar{x}V = \iiint\limits_R x\,dV, \quad \bar{y}V = \iiint\limits_R y\,dV, \quad \bar{z}V = \iiint\limits_R z\,dV.$$

The **moments of inertia** of a three-dimensional region about the coordinate axes are given by the equations

$$I_X = \iiint\limits_R (y^2 + z^2)\,dV, \quad I_Y = \iiint\limits_R (x^2 + z^2)\,dV,$$

$$I_Z = \iiint\limits_R (x^2 + y^2)\,dV.$$

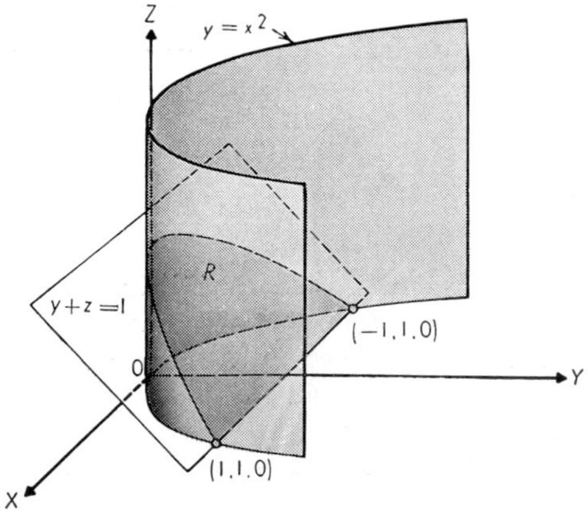

Figure 107-5

Example 107-3. Let R be the "wedge" that is bounded by the cylinder $y = x^2$, the XY-plane, and the plane $y + z = 1$, as shown in Fig. 107-5. Find the moment of inertia of R about the Z-axis.

Solution. We will replace the triple integral $I_Z = \iiint_R (x^2 + y^2)\, dV$ with an iterated integral in which we first integrate with respect to z and then integrate the result over the projection of R onto the XY-plane. A vertical line containing the point (x, y) of this projected region intersects R in points with Z-coordinates 0 and $1 - y$, so these numbers are our inner limits of integration. For the integration over the plane projection of R, we can integrate with respect to y from x^2 to 1, and then with respect to x from -1 to 1. Thus

$$\begin{aligned} I_Z &= \int_{-1}^{1}\int_{x^2}^{1}\int_{0}^{1-y} (x^2 + y^2)\, dz\, dy\, dx \\ &= \int_{-1}^{1}\int_{x^2}^{1} (x^2 + y^2 - x^2y - y^3)\, dy\, dx \\ &= \int_{-1}^{1}\left(\frac{x^8}{4} + \frac{x^6}{6} - x^4 + \frac{x^2}{2} + \frac{1}{12}\right) dx \\ &= \tfrac{64}{315}. \end{aligned}$$

Problems 107

1. Evaluate the following iterated integrals.
   (a) $\int_0^1\int_1^0\int_0^1 (x + y)\, dy\, dz\, dx$
   (b) $\int_{-2}^{0}\int_{-1}^{3}\int_0^2 (6x^2y + 2z)\, dx\, dy\, dz$
   (c) $\int_0^a\int_0^b\int_0^c (x^2 + y^2 + z^2)\, dx\, dy\, dz$
   (d) $\int_{-1}^{0}\int_{e}^{2e}\int_0^{\pi/3} x \ln y \tan z\, dz\, dy\, dx$
2. Evaluate the following iterated integrals.
   (a) $\int_0^2\int_1^z\int_1^y xz\, dx\, dy\, dz$
   (b) $\int_0^2\int_0^z\int_0^{y+z} 24\, xyz\, dx\, dy\, dz$
   (c) $\int_0^2\int_0^x\int_0^{xy} dz\, dy\, dx$
   (d) $\int_0^2\int_0^{\sqrt{4-z^2}}\int_0^{2-z} y\, dx\, dy\, dz$
3. Evaluate the integral $\iiint_R xy\, dV$ if R is the region described:
   (a) The rectangular block whose faces are the coordinate planes and the planes $x = 2$, $y = 3$, and $z = 4$.
   (b) The prism bounded by the coordinate planes, the plane $z = 2$, and the plane $x + y = 1$.

(c) The first octant region cut from the cylinder $x^2 + y^2 = 1$ by the coordinate planes and the plane $z = x$.

4. Describe the region of integration R if the triple integral $\iiint_R f(x, y, z)\, dV$ can be expressed as the given iterated integral.
(a) $\int_0^4 \int_0^3 \int_0^2 f(x, y, z)\, dz\, dy\, dx$
(b) $\int_0^3 \int_0^2 \int_0^x f(x, y, z)\, dz\, dy\, dx$
(c) $\int_0^2 \int_0^x \int_0^y f(x, y, z)\, dz\, dy\, dx$
(d) $\int_{-1}^1 \int_0^{1-x^2} \int_0^y f(x, y, z)\, dz\, dy\, dx$

5. Use triple integration to find the volume of the region bounded by the given surfaces.
(a) The planes $y + z = 1$, $z = 0$, and the cylinder $x^2 = 4y$.
(b) The plane $\frac{x}{a} + \frac{y}{b} + \frac{z}{c} = 1$ and the coordinate planes.
(c) The plane $z = 1$ and the paraboloid $4z = x^2 + 4y^2$.

6. Find the moment of inertia about the edge of length b of a brick whose dimensions are a units by b units by c units.

7. Find the centroid of the region in Question 5a.

8. Find the centroid of the tetrahedron in Question 5b.

9. Find I_Z for the tetrahedron that is bounded by the coordinate planes and the plane $x + y + z = 1$.

10. The moment of inertia of a region R, whose volume is V cubic units, about the line L formed by the intersection of the planes $x = a$ and $y = b$ is defined by the equation

$$I_L = \iiint_R [(x - a)^2 + (y - b)^2]\, dV.$$

Show that if the region R is symmetric with respect to the Z-axis, then $I_L = I_Z + (a^2 + b^2)V$. (Compare with Question 11, Problems 105.)

11. Find the moment of inertia of an ellipsoid whose diameters are $2a$, $2b$, and $2c$ about the diameter whose length is $2a$.

12. Show that the moment of inertia about its axis of a solid right-circular cylinder whose altitude is h, whose base radius is a, and whose volume is V is $\frac{a^2V}{2}$.

108. Triple Integrals in Cylindrical and Spherical Coordinates

In Section 106 we considered double integrals in polar coordinates, and in this section we shall discuss triple integrals in cylindrical and spherical coordinates. The triple integral of a function f of three variables over a three-dimensional region R is defined as the limit of sums of the form

(108-1) $$S = \Sigma f(x^*, y^*, z^*)\,\Delta V.$$

The number ΔV is the volume of a "typical" subregion of the partition of R on which this sum is based. This partition is formed by slicing R with coordinate surfaces. When we use rectangular coordinates these coordinate surfaces are simply planes parallel to the XY-plane, the YZ-plane,

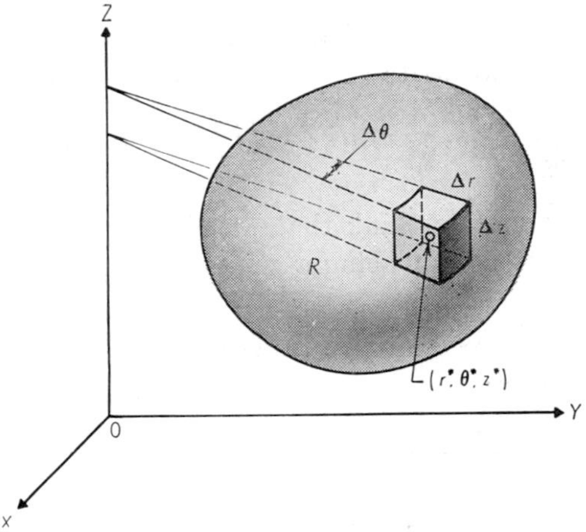

Figure 108-1

and the XZ-plane. Then the resulting elements of our partition of R are rectangular blocks. In other coordinate systems the coordinate surfaces are not all planes and so the elements of the resulting partition are not rectangular blocks. Therefore we cannot calculate the volume ΔV of a typical one of these subdivisions by multiplying the lengths of its edges; we must develop, for each coordinate system that we use, an appropriate formula for ΔV. The key to integration in cylindrical or spherical coordinates is the proper formula for ΔV.

Let us introduce a cylindrical coordinate system into our space as we did in Section 85. We form a "polar partition" of the region R by slicing it with coordinate surfaces, here cylinders whose common axis is the Z-axis, planes that intersect along the Z-axis, and planes parallel to the XY-plane. A typical subregion of such a partition is shown in Fig. 108-1. Its dimensions are indicated on the figure. Planes parallel to the XY-plane cut this subregion in figures that are congruent to its base. Therefore, the volume of our typical subregion is given by the formula

$$\Delta V = (\text{Area of the base})\ \Delta z.$$

The base of this subregion has the form of one of the polar subregions that are illustrated in Fig. 106-1. In Section 106 we found that the area of such a subregion is $r^*\ \Delta r\ \Delta\theta$, where r^* is the radial coordinate of a suitably chosen point inside the region. Let us suppose that the coordinates of such a point are (r^*, θ^*, z^*). Then $\Delta V = r^*\ \Delta r\ \Delta\theta\ \Delta z$, and so one of our approximating sums is

$$\Sigma f(r^* \cos \theta^*, r^* \sin \theta^*, z^*) r^*\ \Delta r\ \Delta\theta\ \Delta z.$$

The limit of such sums is the triple integral of f over R, and their form suggests that we write

$$\text{(108-2)} \quad \boldsymbol{\iiint\limits_R f(x, y, z)\ dV = \iiint\limits_R f(r \cos \theta, r \sin \theta, z) r\ dr\ d\theta\ dz.}$$

It is convenient to think that we obtain the right side of this equation from the left by replacing x with $r \cos \theta$, y with $r \sin \theta$, z with z, and dV with $r\ dr\ d\theta\ dz$.

We evaluate such integrals as iterated integrals, as the following examples show.

Example 108-1. Evaluate the integral $\iiint\limits_R x^2\ dV$, where R is the region that is bounded by the cylinders whose radii are 3 and 4 and the planes $z = 0$ and $z = 3$, as shown in Fig. 108-2.

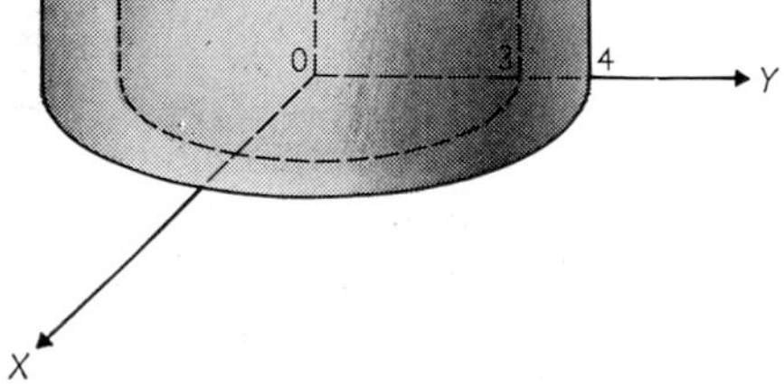

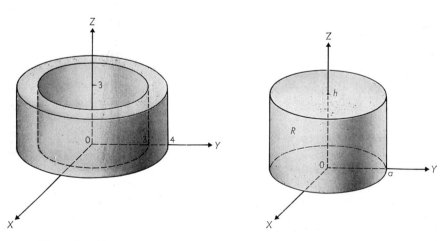

Figure 108-2

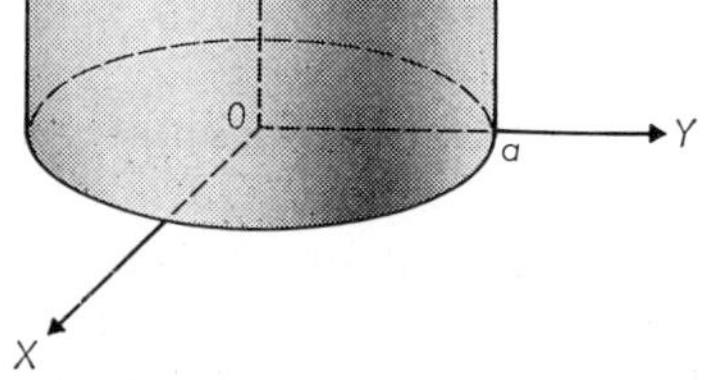

Figure 108-3

Solution. In this case the limits of integration on r are 3 and 4, the limits on θ are 0 and 2π, and the limits on z are 0 and 3. Thus

$$\iiint_R x^2\, dV = \iiint_R r^2 \cos^2 \theta\, r\, dr\, d\theta\, dz$$

$$= \int_0^3 \int_0^{2\pi} \int_3^4 r^3 \cos^2 \theta\, dr\, d\theta\, dz = \frac{525\pi}{4}.$$

Example 108-2. Use cylindrical coordinates to find the moment of inertia about its axis of a solid right-circular cylinder whose altitude is h and whose base radius is a.

Solution. We introduce a cylindrical coordinate system (Fig. 108-3) so that our cylinder is the region R that is bounded by the planes $z = h$ and $z = 0$ and the surface whose equation in cylindrical coordinates is $r = a$. Then

$$I_Z = \iiint_R (x^2 + y^2)\, dV = \iiint_R r^2\, dV.$$

Now we express this integral as an iterated integral in cylindrical coordinates:

$$I_Z = \int_0^a \int_0^{2\pi} \int_0^h r^3\, dz\, d\theta\, dr$$

$$= h \int_0^a \int_0^{2\pi} r^3\, d\theta\, dr = 2\pi h \int_0^a r^3\, dr = \frac{\pi h a^4}{2} = \frac{a^2 V}{2}.$$

If you use cartesian coordinates to find this moment of inertia (see Question 12, Problems 107) you can appreciate the simplicity of the calculations in this example.

The role of spherical coordinates in the study of triple integrals is similar to the role of cylindrical coordinates. Let us introduce a spherical coordinate system into our space and form a partition of a three-dimensional region R by slicing it with coordinate surfaces, here concentric spheres whose center is the origin, planes containing the Z-axis, and cones whose axis is the Z-axis and whose vertex is the origin. One of the subregions that results is shown in Fig. 108-4. We have labeled one corner of this region P, and let us suppose that the coordinates of this point P are (ρ, θ, ϕ). The three edges of the subregion that meet at P have lengths $\Delta\rho$, $\rho\, \Delta\phi$, and $\rho \sin \phi\, \Delta\theta$, where the meaning of the symbols $\Delta\rho$, $\Delta\theta$, and $\Delta\phi$ is indicated on the figure. If our region were rectangular, then its volume would be the product of the lengths of these edges; that is, the number

$$\rho^2 \sin \phi\, \Delta\rho\, \Delta\theta\, \Delta\phi.$$

Actually, this number is not quite equal to ΔV, but it can be shown that there is a point $(\rho^*, \theta^*, \phi^*)$ inside our region for which

$$\Delta V = \rho^{*2} \sin \phi^* \, \Delta\rho \, \Delta\theta \, \Delta\phi.$$

Furthermore, we know that $x^* = \rho^* \sin \phi^* \cos \theta^*$, $y^* = \rho^* \sin \phi^* \sin \theta^*$, and $z^* = \rho^* \cos \phi^*$ are the cartesian coordinates of our point $(\rho^*, \theta^*, \phi^*)$. Therefore, one of the partial sums (Equation 108-1) that approximate the integral of f over R takes the form

$$\Sigma f(\rho^* \sin \phi^* \cos \theta^*, \rho^* \sin \phi^* \sin \theta^*, \rho^* \cos \phi^*)\rho^{*2} \sin \phi^* \, \Delta\rho \, \Delta\theta \, \Delta\phi.$$

This sum suggests that we write

$$\text{(108-3)} \quad \iiint_R f(x, y, z) \, dV = \iiint_R f(\rho \sin \phi \cos \theta, \rho \sin \phi \sin \theta, \rho \cos \phi) \, \rho^2 \sin \phi \, d\rho \, d\theta \, d\phi.$$

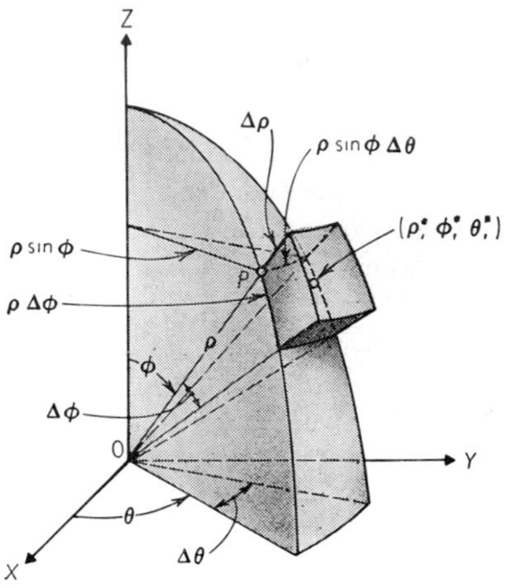

Figure 108-4

It is convenient to think that we obtain the right side of this equation from the left by replacing x with $\rho \sin \phi \cos \theta$, y with $\rho \sin \phi \sin \theta$, z with $\rho \cos \phi$, and dV with $\rho^2 \sin \phi \, d\rho \, d\theta \, d\phi$.

The following examples show how we evaluate such integrals by replacing them with iterated integrals.

Example 108-3. Find the volume of the "ice cream cone" that is cut from a sphere whose radius is 6 by a cone with a half-angle of 30°, as shown in Fig. 108-5.

Solution. The volume of R is the integral $V = \iiint_R dV$. From the figure we see that the limits on the variable of integration ρ are 0 and 6, the limits on θ are 0 and 2π, and the limits on ϕ are 0 and $\pi/6$. Thus

$$V = \int_0^{\pi/6} \int_0^{2\pi} \int_0^6 \rho^2 \sin \phi \, d\rho \, d\theta \, d\phi = 72\pi[2 - \sqrt{3}].$$

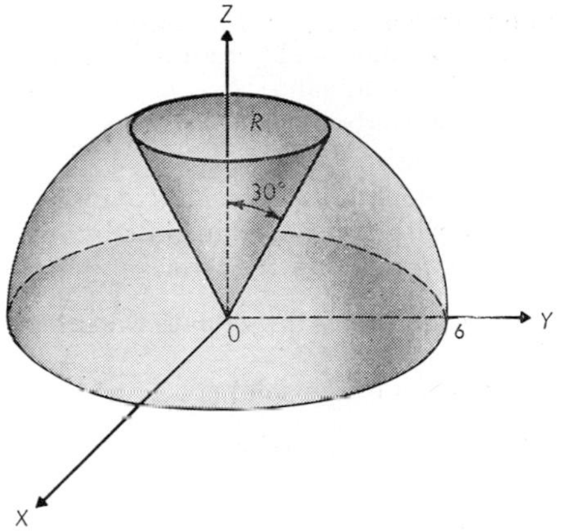

Figure 108-5

Example 108-4. Find the moment of inertia about a diameter of a solid sphere whose radius is a.

Solution. Let the sphere be represented in spherical coordinates by the inequality $\rho \leq a$, and let us compute I_Z. Then

$$\begin{aligned} I_Z &= \iiint_R (x^2 + y^2)\, dV = \iiint_R \rho^2 \sin^2 \phi \, dV \\ &= \int_0^\pi \int_0^{2\pi} \int_0^a \rho^4 \sin^3 \phi \, d\rho \, d\theta \, d\phi \\ &= \frac{a^5}{5} \int_0^\pi \int_0^{2\pi} \sin^3 \phi \, d\theta \, d\phi \\ &= \frac{2\pi a^5}{5} \int_0^\pi \sin^3 \phi \, d\phi \\ &= \frac{8\pi a^5}{15}. \end{aligned}$$

To appreciate the simplicity of this calculation, you should use cartesian coordinates to find this moment of inertia.

Problems 108

1. Use spherical coordinates to find the volume of a sphere whose radius is a.
2. Use cylindrical coordinates to evaluate $\iiint_R x^4 y z^2 \, dV$, where R is the first octant region bounded by the plane $z = 2$ and the cylinder $x^2 + y^2 = 9$.

3. Find the moment of inertia of a circular cylindrical shell whose length is L, inside radius is a, and outside radius is b:
   (a) About its longitudinal axis.
   (b) About a line containing its center and perpendicular to its longitudinal axis.
4. Find approximations to the moments of inertia in the preceding question for a very thin shell with a mean radius of c by setting $b = c + h$ and $a = c - h$, and considering h to be nearly zero.
5. Use spherical coordinates to evaluate the integral $\iiint\limits_R xyz\,dV$, where R is the first octant portion of the solid sphere $x^2 + y^2 + z^2 \leq 9$.
6. Find $\iiint\limits_R (x^2 + y^2 + z^2)\,dV$ if:
   (a) R is bounded by the cylinder $x^2 + y^2 = 1$ and the planes $z = 0$ and $z = 2$.
   (b) R is bounded by a sphere whose radius is 2 and whose center is the origin.
7. Find the moment of inertia about a diameter of a spherical shell bounded by two concentric spheres of radii a and b where $a < b$.
8. Find I_Z for the region bounded by the XY-plane, the sphere $x^2 + y^2 + z^2 = 4$, and the cylinder $x^2 + y^2 = 1$.
9. Use cylindrical coordinates to find the moment of inertia about the axis of a solid right-circular cone whose base radius is a and whose altitude is h.
10. How far above the base of a solid right-circular cone whose altitude is h is the centroid of the cone?
11. A solid hemisphere with a radius of a is lying face down on the XY-plane. What is the Z-coordinate of its centroid?
12. Let a and b be positive numbers with $a < b$, and consider the region between the spheres of radii a and b whose center is the origin. The upper half of the region forms an inverted bowl lying on the XY-plane. Find the Z-coordinate of the centroid of this bowl. Can the centroid lie outside the region?

Review Problems, Chapter Twelve

You can use the following problems to test yourself on the material covered in this chapter.

1. Evaluate the integral $\iint\limits_R (|x| + |y|)\,dA$, where R is the rectangular region whose vertices are the points $(-1, 0)$, $(-1, 1)$, $(2, 0)$, and $(2, 1)$.
2. Use polar coordinates to evaluate the integral $\iint\limits_R [r]\,dA$, where R is the circular disk whose radius is 3 and whose center is the origin.
3. Show that the volume V of the region under the plane $z = ax + by + c$ and above a plane region R is given by the equation $V = aM_Y + bM_X + cA$, where M_X and M_Y are the moments of R about the X- and Y-axes, and A is the area of R.

4. Suppose that $f(x, y) = 1$ when $x < 0$ and $f(x, y) = 2$ when $x \geq 0$ and let R be the region that is bounded by the graph of the equation $y = \sin x$ and the interval $[-\pi, \pi]$. Find $\iint_R f(x, y)\, dA$.

5. Express the iterated integral $\int_0^{\pi} \int_0^{\sin x} f(x, y)\, dy\, dx$ as an iterated integral in which we must first integrate with respect to x.

6. Find in two ways the moment about the Y-axis of the region that is bounded by the graph of the equation $y = \sin x$ and the interval $[0, 2\pi]$.

7. Show that, for any positive number R,

$$\int_0^{\frac{R}{\sqrt{2}}} \int_0^{\frac{R}{\sqrt{2}}} e^{-x^2-y^2}\, dx\, dy < \int_0^{\frac{\pi}{2}} \int_0^{R} e^{-r^2} r\, dr\, d\theta < \int_0^{R} \int_0^{R} e^{-x^2-y^2}\, dx\, dy.$$

8. The moment of a solid region R about a line L in space is given by the integral $M_L = \iint_R D(x, y, z)\, dV$, where $D(x, y, z)$ is the distance between the point (x, y, z) and the line L. Find the moment of an a by a by a cube about one edge.

9. Find the moment about a diameter of a solid hemisphere whose radius is a. (Refer to Question 8 for the definition of the moment of a solid about a line.)

10. Describe the region of integration R if

$$\iiint_R f(x, y, z)\, dV = \int_0^1 \int_{x^2}^1 \int_0^{\sqrt{1-y^2}} f(x, y, z)\, dz\, dy\, dx.$$

13 l'HOSPITAL'S RULE. IMPROPER INTEGRALS

In one way or another, everything in calculus is based on the notion of a limit. The definitions of the derivative and the integral, for example, are stated in terms of limits. In this chapter we will learn a very useful rule for calculating limits, and we shall also use limits to extend the idea of the integral. The techniques that we learn here will be used in the next chapter, too.

109. Extensions of the Theorem of the Mean

We will devote this section to deriving two useful extensions of the Theorem of the Mean (Theorem 21-2). You will recall that this theorem tells us that if f is a differentiable function in an interval (a, b) and is continuous in the closed interval $[a, b]$, then there is a number c in the interval (a, b) such that

(109-1) $$\frac{f(b) - f(a)}{b - a} = f'(c).$$

Geometrically (see Section 21), Equation 109-1 says that the tangent to the graph of f at the point $(c, f(c))$ is parallel to the chord that joins the points $(a, f(a))$ and $(b, f(b))$. If $f(a) = f(b)$, then $f'(c) = 0$, and this special case of the Theorem of the Mean is called Rolle's Theorem (Theorem 21-3).

Example 109-1. Suppose that g is a continuous function in an interval $[a, b]$ and that $g'(x) \neq 0$ for x in the interval (a, b). Show that $g(b) \neq g(a)$.

Solution. If $g(b) = g(a)$, then according to Rolle's Theorem, there would be a point c in the interval (a, b) such that $g'(c) = 0$. But we are assuming that the function g' does *not* take the value 0, so $g(b) \neq g(a)$.

We will use the following extension of the Theorem of the Mean in the next section.

THEOREM 109-1. *Suppose that f and g are functions that are differentiable in an open interval (a, b) and continuous in the closed interval $[a, b]$. Furthermore, suppose that $g'(x) \neq 0$ for x in the open interval (a, b). Then there is a point c in the open interval (a, b) such that*

(109-2) $$\frac{f(b) - f(a)}{g(b) - g(a)} = \frac{f'(c)}{g'(c)}.$$

(Notice that Equation 109-2 reduces to Equation 109-1 if $g(x) = x$.)

Proof. To prove this theorem we define the function h by the equation

$$h(x) = [f(b) - f(a)]g(x) - [g(b) - g(a)]f(x).$$

Now we see that $h(b) = f(b)g(a) - g(b)f(a)$ and $h(a) = f(b)g(a) - g(b)f(a)$, so that $h(b) = h(a)$. Therefore, Rolle's Theorem tells us that there is a number c in the interval (a, b) such that $h'(c) = 0$. But

$$h'(x) = [f(b) - f(a)]g'(x) - [g(b) - g(a)]f'(x),$$

and therefore the equation $h'(c) = 0$ can be written as

(109-3) $$[f(b) - f(a)]g'(c) = [g(b) - g(a)]f'(c).$$

Dividing by $g'(c)[g(b) - g(a)]$ now yields Equation 109-2. The hypothesis that $g'(x) \neq 0$ guarantees that we are not dividing by 0, for it implies that $g'(c) \neq 0$ and (see Example 109-1) that $g(b) - g(a) \neq 0$.

To interpret Equation 109-2 geometrically, let us consider the vector equation $\boldsymbol{R} = f(t)\boldsymbol{i} + g(t)\boldsymbol{j}$ for t in the interval $[a, b]$. The graph of this vector equation is an arc that joins the terminal points of the vectors $f(a)\boldsymbol{i} + g(a)\boldsymbol{j}$ and $f(b)\boldsymbol{i} + g(b)\boldsymbol{j}$. If we denote by $\boldsymbol{C}$ the "chord-vector"

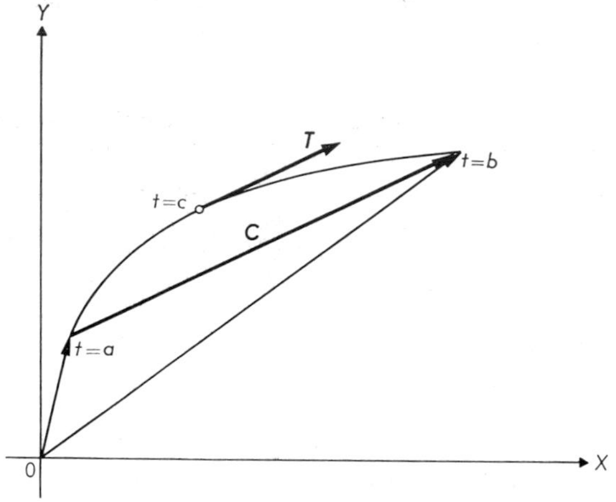

Figure 109-1

from the first of these points to the second, (See Fig. 109-1), then

$$\boldsymbol{C} = [f(b) - f(a)]\boldsymbol{i} + [g(b) - g(a)]\boldsymbol{j}.$$

The vector

$$\boldsymbol{T} = f'(c)\boldsymbol{i} + g'(c)\boldsymbol{j}$$

is tangent to the arc at the point that corresponds to c. A little reflection will convince you that Equation 109-2 says that the chord-vector $\boldsymbol{C}$ and the tangent $\boldsymbol{T}$ are parallel. Thus the geometric interpretation of our first extension of the Theorem of the Mean is the same as the interpretation of the "ordinary" Theorem of the Mean; that is, that there is a point of the arc at which the tangent is parallel to the chord that joins the endpoints.

Now we will extend the Theorem of the Mean in another direction.

THEOREM 109-2. *Let n be an integer that is greater than or equal to 0, and suppose that f is a function for which the derived functions $f', f'', \ldots, f^{(n)}$ are continuous in the closed interval $[a, b]$. Furthermore, suppose that $f^{(n+1)}(x)$ exists at each point x in the open interval (a, b). Then there is a number c in* *the interval* (a, b) *such that*

$$(109\text{-}4)\quad \boldsymbol{f(b) = f(a) + f'(a)(b - a) + f''(a)\frac{(b-a)^2}{2!} + \cdots + f^{(n)}(a)\frac{(b-a)^n}{n!} + f^{(n+1)}(c)\frac{(b-a)^{n+1}}{(n+1)!}}.$$

Equation 109-4 is known as **Taylor's Formula.** Notice that it reduces to the ordinary Theorem of the Mean when $n = 0$.

Before we give a proof of Taylor's Formula, let us look at some examples.

Example 109-2. Express the polynomial $f(x) = x^3 + 2x^2 - x + 5$ as a polynomial in $x - 2$.

Solution. We will set $n = 3$, $b = x$, and $a = 2$. Then $f(a) = f(2) = 19$, $f'(a) = f'(2) = 19$, $f''(a) = f''(2) = 16$, $f'''(a) = f'''(2) = 6$, and Taylor's Formula reads

$$f(x) = 19 + 19(x-2) + 16\frac{(x-2)^2}{2!} + 6\frac{(x-2)^3}{3!} + f^{\text{iv}}(c)\frac{(x-2)^4}{4!},$$

where c is some number (Theorem 109-2 doesn't tell us which) between 2 and x. Because our function f is defined by a polynomial of degree 3, we don't have to know the value of c to know that the $f^{\text{iv}}(c) = 0$. Therefore, after some simplification and rearrangement, our expression for $f(x)$ in powers of $(x - 2)$ is

$$f(x) = (x-2)^3 + 8(x-2)^2 + 19(x-2) + 19.$$

Example 109-3. Use Taylor's Formula with $f(x) = e^x$, $a = 0$, $b = 1$, and $n = 5$ to approximate e. How close is this approximation?

Solution. Here $f(a) = e^0 = 1$, $f'(a) = e^0 = 1$, and so on. Therefore, Equation 109-4 is

$$e = 1 + 1\cdot(1-0) + 1\cdot\frac{(1-0)^2}{2!} + 1\cdot\frac{(1-0)^3}{3!} + 1\cdot\frac{(1-0)^4}{4!} + 1\cdot\frac{(1-0)^5}{5!} + e^c\frac{(1-0)^6}{6!}$$

$$= 1 + 1 + \frac{1}{2!} + \frac{1}{3!} + \frac{1}{4!} + \frac{1}{5!} + \frac{e^c}{6!},$$

where c is a number between 0 and 1. Thus the sum

$$2 + \frac{1}{2!} + \frac{1}{3!} + \frac{1}{4!} + \frac{1}{5!} \approx 2.717$$

approximates e with an error of $\frac{e^c}{6!}$. Since $0 < c < 1$, then $e^c < e^1 < 3$, and so our error is less than $\frac{3}{6!} = \frac{1}{240} < .005$.

Example 109-4. Show how Taylor's Formula could be used to compute the entries in a 5-place table of values of the sine function.

Solution. We set $f(x) = \sin x$, $a = 0$, and $n = 10$ in Taylor's Formula. Then $f(a) = \sin 0 = 0$, $f'(a) = \cos 0 = 1$, $f''(a) = -\sin 0 = 0$, $f'''(a) = -\cos 0 = -1, \ldots, f^{(10)}(a) = -\sin 0 = 0$, and $f^{(11)}(c) = -\cos c$. Thus for any number b, Taylor's Formula becomes

$$\sin b = 0 + 1(b - 0) + 0\frac{(b-0)^2}{2!} + \cdots + 0\frac{(b-0)^{10}}{10!} + (-\cos c)\frac{(b-0)^{11}}{11!},$$

where c is a number between 0 and b. If we drop the last term and simplify, then we obtain the approximation formula

$$\text{(109-5)} \qquad \sin b \approx b - \frac{b^3}{3!} + \frac{b^5}{5!} - \frac{b^7}{7!} + \frac{b^9}{9!}.$$

The accuracy of this approximation can be judged by examining the size of the term that we dropped. The error that we make by using the right side of Formula 109-5 as an approximation to the left side is $(-\cos c)\frac{b^{11}}{11!}$. All we know about c is that it is a number between 0 and b, but whatever it is, $|\cos c| \leq 1$, and so the absolute error that we make by using Formula 109-5 is certainly no greater than $\frac{|b|^{11}}{11!}$. A table of trigonometric values need only contain values of the sine function that correspond to b in the interval $\left(0, \frac{\pi}{2}\right)$, and therefore our absolute error will be less than $\frac{(\pi/2)^{11}}{11!}$. We will leave it to you to show that this number is less than .000004. Hence Formula 109-5 can be used to compute values of the sine function for a five-place table and the error (from rounding off) in any particular value would be, at worst, .00001.

We conclude this section with a proof of Theorem 109-2.

Proof. For a given function f, given numbers a and b, and a given positive integer n, the equation

$$\text{(109-6)} \quad f(b) = f(a) + f'(a)(b-a) + f''(a)\frac{(b-a)^2}{2!} + \cdots + f^{(n)}(a)\frac{(b-a)^n}{n!} + K\frac{(b-a)^{n+1}}{(n+1)!}$$

determines a number K. We will have verified Equation 109-4 and thereby proved Theorem 109-2 as soon as we show that there is a number c in the interval (a, b) such that $K = f^{(n+1)}(c)$. We will demonstrate the existence of this number c by applying Rolle's Theorem to the function g defined by the equation

$$\text{(109-7)} \quad g(x) = f(x) + f'(x)(b - x) + f''(x)\frac{(b - x)^2}{2!} + \cdots + f^{(n)}(x)\frac{(b - x)^n}{n!} + K\frac{(b - x)^{n+1}}{(n + 1)!}.$$

We immediately see that $g(b) = f(b)$, and Equation 109-6 tells us that $g(a) = f(b)$. Therefore, $g(b) = g(a)$, and so it follows from Rolle's Theorem that there is a number c in the interval (a, b) such that $g'(c) = 0$. From Equation 109-7,

$$g'(x) = f'(x) - f'(x) + f''(x)(b - x) - f''(x)(b - x) + f'''(x)\frac{(b - x)^2}{2!} - \cdots + f^{(n+1)}(x)\frac{(b - x)^n}{n!} - K\frac{(b - x)^n}{n!}.$$

The sum on the right "collapses" and leaves us with the equation

$$g'(x) = f^{(n+1)}(x)\frac{(b - x)^n}{n!} - K\frac{(b - x)^n}{n!}.$$

Now we replace x with c and solve the resulting equation for K. Since $g'(c) = 0$ and $c \neq b$, we find that $K = f^{(n+1)}(c)$, as we were to show.

Problems 109

1. Solve Equation 109-2 for c if $a = 0$, $b = 2$, and
   (a) $f(x) = x^3 + 12$, $g(x) = x^2 - 2$.
   (b) $f(x) = \sin x + 3$, $g(x) = \cos x + 7$.
   (c) $f(x) = \sin x + 3$, $g(x) = \cos^2 x$.
   (d) $f(x) = \ln (x + 1)$, $g(x) = x^2$.
2. Let $f(t) = 2 \cos t$, $g(t) = \sin t$, $a = 0$, and $b = \frac{\pi}{2}$. Find c in Equation 109-2 and draw a picture illustrating your result.
3. Let h be a differentiable function such that $h(a) = h(b) = 0$. Let $f(x) = e^{-x}h(x)$. Apply Rolle's Theorem to f to show that there is a number c between a and b such that $h'(c) = h(c)$. Interpret this result geometrically.
4. Let $a = 0$, $b = 1$, and $n = 2$ in Taylor's Formula. Find c if:
   (a) $f(x) = e^x$ (b) $f(x) = \sin x$ (c) $f(x) = \ln (1 + x)$ (d) $f(x) = \sinh x$

5. Show that Taylor's Formula can be written as the equation

$$f(a+h) = f(a) + f'(a)h + f''(a)\frac{h^2}{2!} + \cdots + f^{(n)}(a)\frac{h^n}{n!} + f^{(n+1)}(c)\frac{h^{n+1}}{(n+1)!}.$$

6. Use $a = 0$ and the given value of n and approximate $f(b)$ by dropping the last term in Taylor's Formula.

(a) $f(x) = \ln(1+x)$, $n = 5$ (b) $f(x) = (1-x)^{-1/2}$, $n = 3$
(c) $f(x) = (1+e^x)^{-1}$, $n = 3$ (d) $f(x) = \cos x$, $n = 4$.

7. Use the approximation formulas that you found in the preceding question to determine three-place decimal approximations of the following numbers. Compare your results with tabular values where possible.

(a) $\ln 2$ (b) $\ln 1.4$ (c) $\dfrac{1}{\sqrt{2}}$ (d) $\sqrt{2}$

(e) $\dfrac{1}{1+e}$ (f) $\dfrac{e}{1+e}$ (g) $\cos .1$ (h) $\cos \frac{1}{2}$

8. Express the polynomial $x^4 + x^2$ as a polynomial in $x + 1$.

9. Find an upper bound for the error incurred when using the approximation $\tan x \approx x$ for x in the interval $[0, .1]$.

10. Use Taylor's Formula with $a = 0$, $b = t$, and $n = 4$, to write

$$e^t = 1 + t + \frac{t^2}{2!} + \frac{t^3}{3!} + \frac{t^4}{4!} + \frac{t^5}{5!}\cdot e^c.$$

Use the first five terms as an approximation of e^t and then approximate the integral $\int_0^1 e^{x^2}\,dx$. Show that the error E that you incur satisfies the inequalities $\dfrac{1}{6!} < E < \dfrac{3}{6!}$.

11. Suppose that $f'(a) = f''(a) = \cdots = f^{(n)}(a) = 0$, and that $f^{(n+1)}(x) > 0$ for x in an interval about a. Then if b is any point in this interval, Taylor's Formula tells us that $f(b) - f(a) = f^{(n+1)}(c)\dfrac{(b-a)^{n+1}}{(n+1)!}$, where c is a number between a and b. Use this equation to show that $f(a)$ is a minimum value of f if n is odd.

12. Use the result in the preceding question to show that if $f(x) = x^3 \sin x$, then f has a minimum value at 0.

110. l'Hospital's Rule

In this section we are going to take up a new method of calculating limits, but before we do let us briefly review, and slightly extend, our ideas about limits. Roughly speaking, the equations

$$\lim_{x\to a} f(x) = L, \quad \lim_{x\to a^+} f(x) = L, \quad \text{and} \quad \lim_{x\to a^-} f(x) = L$$

say that L is the number that is approximated by $f(x)$ when x is close to a. In the first equation we only ask that x be close to a, in the second equation we also require that x be greater than a, while in the third equation we ask that x be close to, but less than, a. The technical definitions of these limits are given in Section 13, and the limit concept is discussed further in Appendix B. Notice that we can replace the letter x in these limit equations with any other letter. Thus

$$\lim_{x \to a} f(x) = \lim_{t \to a} f(t) = \lim_{h \to a} f(h),$$

and so on.

The "slight extension" of our ideas about limits follows. The domain of a given function f may contain arbitrarily large numbers. Furthermore, it may be that there is a number L such that we can guarantee that $f(x)$ approximates L with any specified degree of accuracy by taking x large enough. Then we say that "$f(x)$ approaches L as x becomes infinite," and we write

$$\lim_{x \to \infty} f(x) = L.$$

For example, it is easy to see that the quotient $\dfrac{x^2 + 2x - 1}{3x^2 - 5}$ approximates $\frac{1}{3}$ when x is large. We simply divide the numerator and the denominator of this fraction by x^2 and our quotient becomes $\left(1 + \dfrac{2}{x} - \dfrac{1}{x^2}\right) \Big/ \left(3 - \dfrac{5}{x^2}\right)$. From this expression it is clear that if we want to be sure that our quotient approximates $\frac{1}{3}$ with any specified degree of accuracy, we need only take x correspondingly large. Thus we write

$$\lim_{x \to \infty} \frac{x^2 + 2x - 1}{3x^2 - 5} = \frac{1}{3}.$$

Similarly, the equation $\lim_{x \to -\infty} f(x) = L$ means that L is the number that is approximated by $f(x)$ when x is a number that is far to the left on the number scale; that is, when x is negative and $|x|$ is large. These limits may be more formally defined by the equations

$$\lim_{x \to \infty} f(x) = \lim_{h \to 0^+} f\left(\frac{1}{h}\right) \quad \text{and} \quad \lim_{x \to -\infty} f(x) = \lim_{h \to 0^-} f\left(\frac{1}{h}\right).$$

If f and g are functions with limits at a point a, then (see Equation 13-5)

(110-1) $$\lim_{x \to a} \frac{f(x)}{g(x)} = \frac{\lim_{x \to a} f(x)}{\lim_{x \to a} g(x)}$$

if $\lim_{x \to a} g(x) \neq 0$. If $\lim_{x \to a} g(x) = 0$, the right side of Equation 110-1 is meaningless, although the left side may be a perfectly definite number. The prime example of this breakdown of Equation 110-1 is furnished by the limit of the difference quotient used to define a derivative. Thus $\lim_{h\to 0} \frac{f(x+h)-f(x)}{h} = f'(x)$, but we cannot find $f'(x)$ by dividing $\lim_{h\to 0} [f(x+h) - f(x)]$ by $\lim_{h\to 0} h$ since both of these limits are 0. Another simple example is furnished by the quotient

$$\frac{\sin^2 x}{1 - \cos x}$$

As x approaches 0, both $\sin^2 x$ and $1 - \cos x$ approach 0, and hence we cannot use Equation 110-1 to find the limit of this quotient as x approaches 0. However, if we write the given quotient as

$$\frac{\sin^2 x}{1 - \cos x} = \frac{1 - \cos^2 x}{1 - \cos x} = \frac{(1 - \cos x)(1 + \cos x)}{1 - \cos x} = 1 + \cos x,$$

we see that

$$\lim_{x\to 0} \frac{\sin^2 x}{1 - \cos x} = \lim_{x\to 0} (1 + \cos x) = 1 + 1 = 2.$$

Equation 110-1 fails when $\lim_{x\to a} g(x) = 0$, and then the only possibility that $\lim_{x\to a} \frac{f(x)}{g(x)}$ exists is that $\lim_{x\to a} f(x) = 0$, also. The following theorem tells us that we should then look at the limit of the quotient $\frac{f'(x)}{g'(x)}$ in order to find the limit of the given quotient $\frac{f(x)}{g(x)}$.

THEOREM 110-1 (**l'Hospital's Rule**). *Let f and g be differentiable functions in a deleted interval about the point a and suppose that $\lim_{x\to a} f(x) = 0$ and $\lim_{x\to a} g(x) = 0$. Suppose further that $g'(x) \neq 0$ in this interval. Then*

$$\lim_{x\to a} \frac{f(x)}{g(x)} = \lim_{x\to a} \frac{f'(x)}{g'(x)}, \tag{110-2}$$

if the limit on the right side of this equation exists.

We will postpone the proof of l'Hospital's Rule until after we have looked at some examples that illustrate how we use it.

Example 110-1. Use l'Hospital's Rule to find $\lim_{x\to 0} \frac{\sin^2 x}{1 - \cos x}$.

Solution. We notice that $\lim_{x\to0} \sin^2 x = \lim_{x\to0} (1 - \cos x) = 0$, so l'Hospital's Rule applies and

$$\lim_{x\to0} \frac{\sin^2 x}{1 - \cos x} = \lim_{x\to0} \frac{D_x \sin^2 x}{D_x(1 - \cos x)} = \lim_{x\to0} \frac{2 \sin x \cos x}{\sin x}$$
$$= \lim_{x\to0} 2 \cos x = 2,$$

as we found earlier.

Example 110-2. Find $\lim_{x\to\frac{\pi}{2}} \frac{(2x - \pi)(\sin x - 1)}{\cos^2 x}$.

Solution. When we apply l'Hospital's Rule we get

$$\lim_{x\to\frac{\pi}{2}} \frac{(2x - \pi)(\sin x - 1)}{\cos^2 x} = \lim_{x\to\frac{\pi}{2}} \frac{(2x - \pi)\cos x + 2(\sin x - 1)}{-2 \cos x \sin x}.$$

Again, both the numerator and denominator have the limit 0 at $\pi/2$, so we apply l'Hospital's Rule once more, and we have

$$\lim_{x\to\frac{\pi}{2}} \frac{(2x - \pi)\cos x + 2(\sin x - 1)}{-2 \cos x \sin x}$$
$$= \lim_{x\to\frac{\pi}{2}} \frac{4 \cos x - (2x - \pi)\sin x}{2(\sin^2 x - \cos^2 x)} = \frac{0}{2} = 0.$$

l'Hospital's Rule is also valid if we replace a in Equation 110-2 with a^+, a^-, or even ∞ or $-\infty$. The following examples show how we use it in some of these cases.

Example 110-3. Find $\lim_{x\to\infty} \frac{1 - \cos \frac{1}{x}}{\tan^2 \frac{1}{x}}$.

Solution. Since both the numerator and the denominator of our fraction go to zero, l'Hospital's Rule tells us that the limit of the given quotient is the limit of the quotient

$$\frac{D_x\left(1 - \cos \frac{1}{x}\right)}{D_x \tan^2 \frac{1}{x}} = \frac{-\frac{1}{x^2} \sin \frac{1}{x}}{-\frac{1}{x^2}\, 2 \tan \frac{1}{x} \sec^2 \frac{1}{x}} = \frac{\cos^3 \frac{1}{x}}{2}.$$

Thus

$$\lim_{x\to\infty} \frac{1 - \cos\frac{1}{x}}{\tan^2\frac{1}{x}} = \lim_{x\to\infty} \frac{\cos^3\frac{1}{x}}{2} = \frac{1}{2}.$$

Example 110-4. Find $\lim_{x\to 0^+} \frac{\sin x}{\sqrt{x}}$.

Solution. Since $\lim_{x\to 0^+} \sin x = 0$ and $\lim_{x\to 0^+} \sqrt{x} = 0$, we apply l'Hospital's Rule:

$$\lim_{x\to 0^+} \frac{\sin x}{\sqrt{x}} = \lim_{x\to 0^+} \frac{\cos x}{\frac{1}{2\sqrt{x}}} = \lim_{x\to 0^+} 2\sqrt{x}\cos x = 0.$$

There is another form of l'Hospital's Rule that is also very useful. We have been supposing that $\lim_{x\to a} f(x) = 0$ and $\lim_{x\to a} g(x) = 0$. The rule remains valid if these hypotheses are replaced with the assumption that $\lim_{x\to a} f(x) = \infty$ (or $-\infty$) and $\lim_{x\to a} g(x) = \infty$ (or $-\infty$). The "equation" $\lim_{x\to a} f(x) = \infty$ does not mean that the limit of $f(x)$ exists. In graphical terms, it means that the graph of f runs off the top of the graph paper as x approaches a. In other words, no matter how large a number k is, $f(x) > k$ for each number x sufficiently close to a.

THEOREM 110-2 (**Second case of l'Hospital's Rule**). *Let f and g be differentiable functions in a deleted interval about some given point a, and suppose that $\lim_{x\to a} f(x) = \infty$ (or $-\infty$) and $\lim_{x\to a} g(x) = \infty$ (or $-\infty$). Suppose further that $g'(x) \neq 0$ in this interval. Then*

$$\lim_{x\to a} \frac{f(x)}{g(x)} = \lim_{x\to a} \frac{f'(x)}{g'(x)},$$

if the limit on the right side of this equation exists. The number a can be replaced with any one of the symbols a^+, a^-, ∞, or $-\infty$.

The proof of this theorem is more complicated than the proof of Theorem 110-1 and can be left to an advanced calculus course. We will be content to give examples of the way it is used.

Example 110-5. Find $\lim_{x \to \infty} \dfrac{x^2}{e^x}\cdot$

Solution. Here $f(x) = x^2$ and $g(x) = e^x$, and so $\lim_{x \to \infty} f(x) = \infty$ and $\lim_{x \to \infty} g(x) = \infty$. Then according to Theorem 110-2,

$$\lim_{x \to \infty} \frac{x^2}{e^x} = \lim_{x \to \infty} \frac{D_x x^2}{D_x e^x} = \lim_{x \to \infty} \frac{2x}{e^x}\cdot$$

Again, both the numerator and denominator become infinite, so we apply the theorem once more:

$$\lim_{x \to \infty} \frac{2x}{e^x} = \lim_{x \to \infty} \frac{2}{e^x} = 0.$$

Therefore, we get the final result:

$$\lim_{x \to \infty} \frac{x^2}{e^x} = 0.$$

This result can be interpreted to mean that e^x "grows faster" than x^2 as x becomes large.

The following example shows us that it does not always pay to apply l'Hospital's Rule blindly.

Example 110-6. Find $\lim_{x \to \frac{\pi}{2}^+} \dfrac{\tan x}{\sec x}\cdot$

Solution. We notice that $\lim_{x \to \frac{\pi}{2}^+} \sec x = -\infty$ and $\lim_{x \to \frac{\pi}{2}^+} \tan x = -\infty$, so we apply l'Hospital's Rule:

$$\lim_{x \to \frac{\pi}{2}^+} \frac{\tan x}{\sec x} = \lim_{x \to \frac{\pi}{2}^+} \frac{\sec^2 x}{\sec x \tan x} = \lim_{x \to \frac{\pi}{2}^+} \frac{\sec x}{\tan x}\cdot$$

Once again we apply l'Hospital's Rule to get:

$$\lim_{x \to \frac{\pi}{2}^+} \frac{\sec x}{\tan x} = \lim_{x \to \frac{\pi}{2}^+} \frac{\sec x \tan x}{\sec^2 x} = \lim_{x \to \frac{\pi}{2}^+} \frac{\tan x}{\sec x}\cdot$$

Now we are back at our starting point, and we see that it is useless to apply the rule again. An easy trigonometric simplification tells us that $\dfrac{\tan x}{\sec x} = \sin x$, so we see, without using l'Hospital's Rule, that

$$\lim_{x \to \frac{\pi}{2}^+} \frac{\tan x}{\sec x} = \lim_{x \to \frac{\pi}{2}^+} \sin x = 1.$$

We conclude this section with a proof of Theorem 110-1.

Proof. We are to show that if $\lim_{x\to a} f(x) = 0$ and $\lim_{x\to a} g(x) = 0$, then $\lim_{x\to a} \frac{f(x)}{g(x)} = \lim_{x\to a} \frac{f'(x)}{g'(x)}$, if this latter limit exists. Our hypotheses say nothing about the values of the functions f and g *at* the point a and therefore we introduce two new functions, F and G, defined by the equations $F(x) = f(x)$ and $G(x) = g(x)$ if $x \neq a$, and $F(a) = G(a) = 0$. These new functions satisfy the hypotheses of the Extended Theorem of the Mean (Theorem 109-1). Thus suppose that b is some number, different from a, in the interval in which we are now working. Because $F(a) = G(a) = 0$, Equation 109-2 for F and G reduces to

$$\frac{F(b)}{G(b)} = \frac{F'(c)}{G'(c)},$$

where c is a number between a and b. Since $F(x) = f(x)$, $F'(x) = f'(x)$, $G(x) = g(x)$, and $G'(x) = g'(x)$ when $x \neq a$, we can write this equation as

$$\frac{f(b)}{g(b)} = \frac{f'(c)}{g'(c)}.$$

Now c is "trapped" between a and b, so c approaches a as b approaches a. It follows that

$$\lim_{b\to a} \frac{f(b)}{g(b)} = \lim_{c\to a} \frac{f'(c)}{g'(c)},$$

if the limit on the right side of the equation exists, which is the conclusion of our theorem.

Problems 110

1. Find the following limits by "inspection."

(a) $\lim_{x\to 0^+} \exp \frac{1}{x}$ (b) $\lim_{x\to 0^-} \exp \frac{1}{x}$

(c) $\lim_{x\to \infty} \frac{3x^3 - 2x^2 + 1}{7x^3 + \pi x - 3}$ (d) $\lim_{x\to -\infty} \text{Arctan } x$

(e) $\lim_{x\to \infty} \tanh x$ (f) $\lim_{x\to -\infty} \tanh x$

(g) $\lim_{x\to 3^+} ([\![x]\!] - x)$ (h) $\lim_{x\to 3^-} ([\![x]\!] - x)$

2. Find the following limits.

(a) $\lim_{x\to 0} \frac{e^{3x} - \cos x}{x}$ (b) $\lim_{x\to 0} \frac{x + \tan x}{\sin 3x}$

(c) $\lim_{x \to \pi} \frac{\ln x - \ln \pi}{\sin 2x}$

(d) $\lim_{x \to 3} \frac{x^3 + x^2 - 7x - 15}{x^3 - 5x^2 + 8x - 6}$

(e) $\lim_{x \to 0} \frac{\tan x - x}{x - \sin x}$

(f) $\lim_{x \to \pi/2} \frac{\ln(\sin x)}{(\pi - 2x)^2}$

(g) $\lim_{x \to 0} \frac{\sin^2 x}{\sin x^2}$

(h) $\lim_{x \to 0^+} \frac{1 - \cos \sqrt{x}}{x + \sqrt{x}}$

3. Find the following limits.

(a) $\lim_{x \to \infty} \frac{\ln x}{x}$

(b) $\lim_{x \to \infty} \frac{\ln x}{\sqrt{x}}$

(c) $\lim_{x \to \infty} \frac{x^{234}}{e^x}$

(d) $\lim_{x \to \infty} \frac{\sin e^{-x}}{\sin (1/x)}$

(e) $\lim_{x \to \infty} \frac{x - \sin x}{2x}$

(f) $\lim_{t \to \infty} \frac{\ln (kt + 1)}{\ln t}$

4. Find the following limits.

(a) $\lim_{x \to \infty} \frac{\int_0^x \exp t^2 \, dt}{\exp x^2}$

(b) $\lim_{x \to \infty} \frac{\int_3^x e^t(4t^2 + 3t - 1) \, dt}{\int_5^x e^t(2t^2 + 5t + 6) \, dt}$

(c) $\lim_{x \to 0} \frac{\int_0^x \exp(-t^2) \, dt}{\int_0^x (\cos t^3 + \cos^3 t) \, dt}$

(d) $\lim_{x \to 0} \frac{1}{x^3} \int_0^x \sin t^2 \, dt$

5. Find the following limits.

(a) $\lim_{x \to 0} \frac{\cot x}{\cot 2x}$

(b) $\lim_{x \to 0} \frac{\sqrt[3]{1 + x} - \sqrt[3]{1 - x}}{\sqrt[5]{1 + x} - \sqrt[5]{1 - x}}$

(c) $\lim_{x \to 0} \frac{\sinh x - \sin x}{\sin^3 x}$

(d) $\lim_{x \to \infty} \frac{\ln (e^{3x} + x)}{x}$

(e) $\lim_{x \to \pi/2} \frac{1 - \sin x}{1 + \cos 2x}$

(f) $\lim_{x \to 0} \frac{\sec x - 1}{x \sin x}$

6. Let $h(\theta)$ be the vertical distance from the polar axis to a point of the spiral whose polar coordinate equation is $r\sqrt{\theta} = 5$. Find $\lim_{\theta \to 0} h(\theta)$.

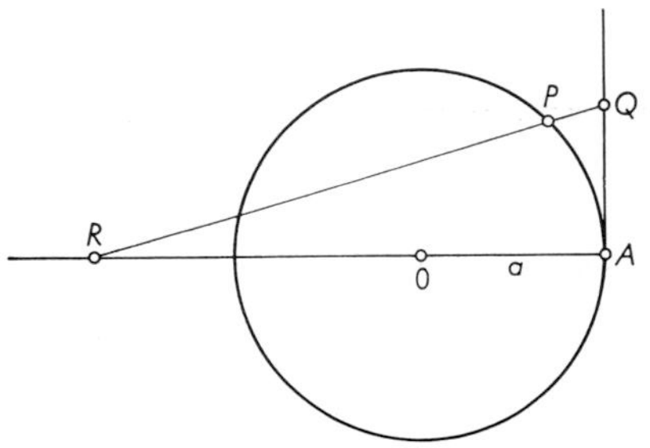

Figure 110-1

7. At a point A of a circle with a radius of a (see Fig. 110-1) we draw a tangent line and a diameter. Next we pick a point P, different from A, of the circle.

Then we choose a point Q of the tangent line so that the distance $\overline{AQ}$ equals the length of the arc AP. The line that contains P and Q intersects the diameter at a point R. Find the limiting position of R as P approaches A.

8. The current flowing t seconds after a switch is thrown in a series circuit containing a resistor of R ohms resistance and a coil of L henries inductance connected to a battery of E volts, is given by the equation $I = (E/R)(1 - e^{-Rt/L})$. Find the limit of I as R approaches zero.

111. Additional Applications of l'Hospital's Rule

We have used l'Hospital's Rule (Theorems 110-1 and 110-2) to find the limits of certain quotients. Often a little elementary algebra will reduce the problem of finding the limit of a product, a sum, or a power to the problem of finding the limit of a quotient. Then we can apply l'Hospital's Rule. The following examples show what we mean.

Example 111-1. Find $\lim_{x \to 0^+} x \ln x$.

Solution. Since $\lim_{x \to 0^+} x = 0$ and $\lim_{x \to 0^+} \ln x = -\infty$, the limit of the product $x \ln x$ is not immediately obvious. However, if we write the product $x \ln x$ as the quotient $\dfrac{\ln x}{1/x}$, then we can apply l'Hospital's Rule:

$$\lim_{x \to 0^+} x \ln x = \lim_{x \to 0^+} \frac{\ln x}{1/x} = \lim_{x \to 0^+} \frac{1/x}{-1/x^2} = \lim_{x \to 0^+} (-x) = 0.$$

Example 111-2. Find $\lim_{x \to 0} \left(\csc x - \dfrac{1}{x}\right)$.

Solution. If x is a number that is near 0, both $\csc x$ and $1/x$ have large absolute values. But, as we shall see, their difference is small. To find the required limit, we write

$$\csc x - \frac{1}{x} = \frac{1}{\sin x} - \frac{1}{x} = \frac{x - \sin x}{x \sin x}$$

and apply l'Hospital's Rule twice. Thus we have

$$\begin{aligned}
\lim_{x \to 0} \left(\csc x - \frac{1}{x}\right) &= \lim_{x \to 0} \frac{x - \sin x}{x \sin x} \\
&= \lim_{x \to 0} \frac{1 - \cos x}{\sin x + x \cos x} \\
&= \lim_{x \to 0} \frac{\sin x}{2 \cos x - x \sin x} \\
&= \tfrac{0}{2} = 0.
\end{aligned}$$

We sometimes are called on to evaluate limits of exponential expressions of the form $\lim_{x \to a} f(x)^{g(x)}$, where the "natural" formula $(\lim_{x \to a} f(x))^{\lim_{x \to a} g(x)}$ does not apply. For example, both $f(x)$ and $g(x)$ may approach 0 or $f(x)$ may approach 1 while $g(x)$ becomes infinite. In such cases we set $y = f(x)^{g(x)}$. Therefore, $\ln y = g(x) \ln f(x)$. Then we write $g(x) \ln f(x)$ as a quotient and apply l'Hospital's Rule to find

$$\lim_{x \to a} \ln y = L.$$

Since $y = e^{\ln y}$, and because the exponential function is continuous, we have

$$\lim_{x \to a} y = e^{(\lim_{x \to a} \ln y)} = e^L.$$

Thus the limit of our original exponential expression is e^L.

Example 111-3. Find $\lim_{x \to 0^+} x^x$.

Solution. We wish to find the number approximated by x^x for a small positive number x. If we choose $x = .001$, we can see what we are up against. Do we conclude that $(.001)^{.001}$ is near zero because its base is near 0, or do we conclude that it is near 1 because its exponent is near 0? Perhaps neither of these possibilities is correct. To find the desired limit, we set $y = x^x$. Then $\ln y = x \ln x$, and we saw in Example 111-1 that $\lim_{x \to 0^+} x \ln x = 0$. Therefore, $\lim_{x \to 0^+} \ln y = 0$, so $\lim_{x \to 0^+} y = e^0 = 1$. Thus we have shown that

$$\lim_{x \to 0^+} x^x = 1.$$

Example 111-4. Find $\lim_{x \to \pi/2} (1 + \cos x)^{\sec x}$.

Solution. If x is near $\pi/2$, it is not obvious what number is approximated by the exponential $(1 + \cos x)^{\sec x}$. For example, if $x = 1.57$, then $1 + \cos x = 1.0008$ and $\sec x = 1256$. Are we to conclude that $(1.0008)^{1256}$ is near 1 because 1.0008 is near 1, or is it large because 1256 is large? Perhaps there is some middle ground. To find the required limit, we set

$$y = (1 + \cos x)^{\sec x}.$$

Then

$$\ln y = \sec x \ln (1 + \cos x) = \frac{\ln (1 + \cos x)}{\cos x}.$$

Therefore,

$$\lim_{x\to\pi/2} \ln y = \lim_{x\to\pi/2} \frac{\ln(1+\cos x)}{\cos x}$$
$$= \lim_{x\to\pi/2} \frac{-\sin x/(1+\cos x)}{-\sin x}$$
$$= \lim_{x\to\pi/2} \frac{1}{(1+\cos x)} = 1.$$

Thus we see that $\lim_{x\to\pi/2} y = e^1 = e$, and so we have shown that

$$\lim_{x\to\pi/2} (1+\cos x)^{\sec x} = e.$$

Some limit problems require a little thought in addition to l'Hospital's Rule.

Example 111-5. Let f be the function that is defined by the equations $f(x) = e^{-1/x^2}$ if $x \neq 0$ and $f(0) = 0$. Find $f'(0)$.

Solution. By definition,

$$f'(0) = \lim_{h\to 0} \frac{f(h) - f(0)}{h} = \lim_{h\to 0} \frac{e^{-1/h^2} - 0}{h}$$
$$= \lim_{h\to 0} \frac{e^{-1/h^2}}{h}.$$

Both the numerator and the denominator of this fraction approach 0 as h approaches 0, so we apply l'Hospital's Rule:

$$\lim_{h\to 0} \frac{e^{-1/h^2}}{h} = \lim_{h\to 0} \frac{(2/h^3)e^{-1/h^2}}{1} = \lim_{h\to 0} \frac{2e^{-1/h^2}}{h^3}.$$

Since this last limit is at least as hard to evaluate as the original, we must change our tactics. We set $x = 1/h$. Then $|x| \to \infty$ as h approaches 0, so

$$\lim_{h\to 0} \frac{e^{-1/h^2}}{h} = \lim_{|x|\to\infty} xe^{-x^2} = \lim_{|x|\to\infty} \frac{x}{e^{x^2}}.$$

Now we fare better when we apply l'Hospital's Rule:

$$\lim_{|x|\to\infty} \frac{x}{e^{x^2}} = \lim_{|x|\to\infty} \frac{1}{2xe^{x^2}} = 0.$$

Thus we have shown that $f'(0) = 0$.

Problems 111

1. Find the following limits.

(a) $\lim_{x \to 0^+} \tan x \ln x$

(b) $\lim_{x \to 1} (\tan \pi x/2)(\ln x)$

(c) $\lim_{x \to 0^+} xe^{\frac{1}{x}}$

(d) $\lim_{x \to 0^-} xe^{\frac{1}{x}}$

(e) $\lim_{x \to \infty} xe^{\frac{1}{x}}$

(f) $\lim_{x \to -\infty} xe^{\frac{1}{x}}$

(g) $\lim_{x \to \infty} e^{-x} \int_0^x e^{\sin t}\, dt$

(h) $\lim_{x \to -\infty} x^2 e^x$

2. Find the following limits.

(a) $\lim_{x \to 0} \left[\frac{1}{x} - \frac{1}{(e^x - 1)}\right]$

(b) $\lim_{x \to \pi/2} \left(x - \frac{\pi}{2}\right) \tan x$

(c) $\lim_{\theta \to \pi/2} (\sec \theta - \tan \theta)$

(d) $\lim_{x \to 0^+} (\cot x - \csc 2x)$

(e) $\lim_{x \to 0} (x^{-2} - \csc^2 x)$

(f) $\lim_{x \to 0} (x^{-3} - \csc^3 x)$

3. Find the following limits.

(a) $\lim_{x \to \infty} x^{1/x}$

(b) $\lim_{x \to 0} (1 + x^{12})^{1/x}$

(c) $\lim_{x \to 0} (\sec x + \tan x)^{\csc x}$

(d) $\lim_{x \to 0} (1 + \sin x)^{1/x}$

(e) $\lim_{x \to \infty} \left(\cos \frac{2}{x}\right)^x$

(f) $\lim_{x \to \infty} \left(1 + \frac{r}{x}\right)^x$

(g) $\lim_{x \to 0} (1 - x)^{1/x}$

(h) $\lim_{x \to \pi/2} (\sin x)^{\tan x}$

4. Show that $\lim_{x \to 0^+} (1 + x^n)^{1/x} = 1$ if $n > 1$. What is the limit if $n = 1$? If $0 \leq n < 1$?

5. Show that $\lim_{x \to \infty} (1 + r^x)^{1/x} = 1$ if $0 \leq r \leq 1$. What is the limit if $r > 1$?

6. Let $0 < h < 1$ and let $A(h)$ be the area of the rectangle whose sides lie along the Y-axis, the line $x = 1$, and the two horizontal lines through the points of the curves $y = 1/(1 - x)$ and $y = 2/(1 - x^2)$ with X-coordinates of h. Find the limiting area of the rectangle as h approaches 1.

112. Improper Integrals

If R is any positive number, then

$$\int_1^R \frac{1}{x^2}\, dx = -\frac{1}{x}\bigg|_1^R = 1 - \frac{1}{R}.$$

Thus since $\lim_{R \to \infty} \left(1 - \frac{1}{R}\right) = 1$, we have the equation $\lim_{R \to \infty} \int_1^R \frac{1}{x^2}\, dx = 1$.

We write this equation in the abbreviated form $\int_1^\infty \frac{1}{x^2}\,dx = 1$. Because the interval of integration is not a finite interval, the "integral" $\int_1^\infty \frac{1}{x^2}\,dx$ is not a proper integral as we defined the concept in Chapter 5. Nevertheless, such "improper integrals," if correctly interpreted, can be useful and do arise in mathematical applications. For example, suppose that the force between two unit charges x centimeters apart is F dynes, where the relation between force and distance is the inverse square law $F = \frac{1}{x^2}$. Then if the charges were initially 1 centimeter apart, our improper integral $\int_1^\infty \frac{1}{x^2}\,dx$ represents the amount of work (in ergs) that is necessary to move one of the charges "infinitely" far away from the other.

In general, suppose that a function f is integrable on the interval $[a, R]$ for every number $R > a$. Then we say that the **improper integral** $\int_a^\infty f(x)\,dx$ is **convergent** if $\lim_{R\to\infty} \int_a^R f(x)\,dx$ exists, and that it is **divergent** if $\lim_{R\to\infty} \int_a^R f(x)\,dx$ does not exist. The limit is called the **value** of a convergent improper integral. Thus

$$\int_a^\infty \boldsymbol{f(x)\,dx} = \boldsymbol{I} \quad \textit{if, and only if,} \quad \lim_{R\to\infty} \int_a^R \boldsymbol{f(x)\,dx} = \boldsymbol{I}.$$

Example 112-1. Test the integrals $\int_0^\infty e^{-x}\,dx$ and $\int_{\pi/2}^\infty \cos x\,dx$ for convergence.

Solution. We have

$$\int_0^R e^{-x}\,dx = 1 - e^{-R},$$

and so

$$\lim_{R\to\infty} \int_0^R e^{-x}\,dx = \lim_{R\to\infty} (1 - e^{-R}) = 1.$$

Therefore, the improper integral $\int_0^\infty e^{-x}\,dx$ converges and its value is 1. On the other hand, $\int_{\pi/2}^R \cos x\,dx = \sin R - 1$. Since $\lim_{R\to\infty} (\sin R - 1)$ does not exist, the improper integral $\int_{\pi/2}^\infty \cos x\,dx$ is divergent.

Example 112-2. For what choices of the number p is the integral $\int_1^\infty \frac{dx}{x^p}$ convergent?

Solution. If $p \neq 1$,

$$\int_1^R \frac{dx}{x^p} = \int_1^R x^{-p}\, dx = \left.\frac{x^{1-p}}{1-p}\right|_1^R = \frac{R^{1-p}-1}{1-p}.$$

Therefore, we must investigate

$$\lim_{R \to \infty} \frac{R^{1-p}-1}{1-p}.$$

If $p > 1$, then the exponent of R is negative, so $\lim_{R\to\infty} R^{1-p} = 0$, and hence

$$\lim_{R \to \infty} \frac{R^{1-p}-1}{1-p} = \frac{-1}{1-p} = \frac{1}{p-1}.$$

If $p < 1$, then the exponent of R is positive, and $\lim_{R\to\infty} \dfrac{R^{1-p}-1}{1-p}$ does not exist. If $p = 1$, we have $\int_1^R \dfrac{dx}{x} = \ln x \Big|_1^R = \ln R$, and hence $\lim_{R\to\infty} \int_1^R \dfrac{dx}{x}$ does not exist. Summarizing:

$$\int_1^\infty \frac{dx}{x^p} \begin{cases} = \dfrac{1}{p-1} & \text{if } p > 1, \\ \text{diverges if } p \leq 1. \end{cases}$$

If f is integrable on each interval $[R, a]$, then we talk about the improper integral $\int_{-\infty}^a f(x)\, dx$. This integral converges if, and only if, $\lim_{R\to-\infty} \int_R^a f(x)\, dx$ exists. We may also observe that an improper integral $\int_a^\infty f(x)\, dx$ converges if, and only if, the integral $\int_b^\infty f(x)\, dx$ converges for each number $b \geq a$, and then

(112-1) $$\int_a^\infty f(x)\, dx = \int_a^b f(x)\, dx + \int_b^\infty f(x)\, dx.$$

The integral $\int_a^\infty f(x)\, dx$ is improper because it does not have a finite interval of integration. We will now give an example of another type of improper integral. If t is any number between 0 and 1, then

$$\int_0^t \frac{dx}{\sqrt{1-x^2}} = \text{Arcsin } x \Big|_0^t = \text{Arcsin } t.$$

Therefore,

$$\lim_{t\to 1^-} \int_0^t \frac{dx}{\sqrt{1-x^2}} = \lim_{t\to 1^-} \text{Arcsin } t = \frac{\pi}{2}.$$

Because of this limit relation we will write $\int_0^1 \frac{dx}{\sqrt{1-x^2}} = \frac{\pi}{2}$, but we must note that the "integral" $\int_0^1 \frac{dx}{\sqrt{1-x^2}}$ is not a proper integral as we defined the term in Chapter Five. The integrand $\frac{1}{\sqrt{1-x^2}}$ is unbounded in our interval of integration, and unbounded functions are not integrable. The integral $\int_0^1 \frac{dx}{\sqrt{1-x^2}}$ represents a new type of improper integral. In general, suppose that we have a function f that is integrable on every interval $[a, t]$, where $a < t < b$, but that f is unbounded in the interval $[a, b)$. Then we say that the **improper integral** $\int_a^b f(x)\,dx$ is **convergent** if $\lim_{t \to b^-} \int_a^t f(x)\,dx$ exists, and that it is **divergent** if the limit does not exist. Similarly, if f is integrable on every interval $[t, b]$, where $a < t < b$, but is unbounded in the interval $(a, b]$, then the improper integral $\int_a^b f(x)\,dx$ converges if, and only if, $\lim_{t \to a^+} \int_t^b f(x)\,dx$ exists.

Example 112-3. Test the integral $\int_0^1 \frac{dx}{x}$ for convergence.

Solution. We see that the integrand $\frac{1}{x}$ is unbounded in the interval $(0, 1]$, so we must investigate the limit

$$\lim_{t \to 0^+} \int_t^1 \frac{dx}{x} = \lim_{t \to 0^+} (-\ln t).$$

Since the limit on the right side of this equation does not exist, we see that the integral $\int_0^1 \frac{dx}{x}$ is divergent.

Example 112-4. For what choices of the number p is the integral $\int_0^1 \frac{dx}{x^p}$ convergent?

Solution. We have just seen that this integral is divergent for $p = 1$. Further, it is a proper integral for $p \leq 0$, and its value is $\frac{1}{1-p}$. Therefore, we need only examine the case in which p is a positive number different from 1. In that case, the integrand is unbounded near 0, so we look at the integral

$$\int_t^1 \frac{dx}{x^p} = \left.\frac{x^{1-p}}{1-p}\right|_t^1 = \frac{1-t^{1-p}}{1-p}.$$

If $0 < p < 1$, then the exponent of t is positive, and so t^{1-p} approaches 0. Thus

$$\lim_{t\to 0^+} \frac{1-t^{1-p}}{1-p} = \frac{1}{1-p}.$$

But if $p > 1$, the exponent of t is negative, and so $\lim_{t\to 0^+} \frac{1-t^{1-p}}{1-p}$ does not exist. Hence we see that

$$\int_0^1 \frac{dx}{x^p} \begin{cases} = \dfrac{1}{1-p} \text{ if } p < 1 \\ \text{diverges if } p \geq 1. \end{cases}$$

If a function f is unbounded in a neighborhood of an interior point c of an interval $[a, b]$, we regard the improper integral $\int_a^b f(x)\,dx$ as the sum of two improper integrals, $\int_a^c f(x)\,dx + \int_c^b f(x)\,dx$, and we investigate the convergence of each of these improper integrals separately. For example, we write

$$\int_0^\pi \sec^2 x\,dx = \int_0^{\pi/2} \sec^2 x\,dx + \int_{\pi/2}^\pi \sec^2 x\,dx.$$

Both of the improper integrals on the right side of this equation diverge; for example,

$$\lim_{t\to\frac{\pi}{2}^-} \int_0^t \sec^2 x\,dx = \lim_{t\to\frac{\pi}{2}^-} \tan t = \infty.$$

Because both of the integrals into which the original integral was decomposed diverge, we say that the original integral $\int_0^\pi \sec^2 x\,dx$ is divergent. Notice that if we had ignored the fact that $\sec^2 x$ is not integrable on the interval $[0, \pi]$ and had simply used the Fundamental Theorem of Calculus, we would have obtained the incorrect result: $\int_0^\pi \sec^2 x\,dx$ is the number $\tan x\Big|_0^\pi = 0$.

Problems 112

1. Evaluate the following improper integrals, or show that they diverge.

(a) $\int_4^\infty x^{-3/2}\,dx$ (b) $\int_5^\infty x \sin x^2\,dx$

(c) $\int_5^\infty xe^{-x^2}\,dx$ (d) $\int_0^\infty (1 + x^2)^{-1}\,dx$

(e) $\int_0^\infty x(1 + x^2)^{-1}\,dx$ (f) $\int_0^\infty x^2(1 + x^2)^{-1}\,dx$

2. Test the following improper integrals for convergence.

(a) $\int_0^1 \frac{\cos \sqrt{x}}{\sqrt{x}}\,dx$ (b) $\int_0^{\pi/2} \sec x\,dx$

(c) $\int_0^{\pi/2} \cot x\,dx$ (d) $\int_0^1 \ln x\,dx$

3. Evaluate the following improper integrals, or show that they diverge.

(a) $\int_0^1 x^{-1/3}\,dx$ (b) $\int_0^1 x^{-2}\,dx$

(c) $\int_0^3 (9 - x^2)^{-1/2}\,dx$ (d) $\int_1^3 (x - 1)^{-3/2}\,dx$

(e) $\int_0^{\pi/2} \tan x\,dx$ (f) $\int_0^4 x(16 - x^2)^{-3/2}\,dx$

4. Evaluate the following improper integrals or show that they diverge. Notice that they are improper at both limits of integration.

(a) $\int_1^\infty (x \ln x)^{-1}\,dx$ (b) $\int_{-1}^1 (1 - x^2)^{-1/2}\,dx$

(c) $\int_{-\infty}^\infty (x^2 + 2x + 2)^{-1}\,dx$ (d) $\int_0^\infty x^{-1/2}\, e^{-x^{1/2}}\,dx$

5. (a) Explain why the integral $\int_{-1}^1 x^{-2}\,dx$ is improper. Does it converge?

(b) Is the integral $\int_0^{\pi/2} \frac{\sin \sqrt{t}}{\sqrt{t}}\,dt$ improper?

6. If f is a function such that $\lim_{R\to\infty} f(R)\, e^{-R} = 0$, use integration by parts to derive the formula

$$\int_0^\infty f(x)\, e^{-x}\,dx = f(0) + \int_0^\infty f'(x)\, e^{-x}\,dx.$$

Use this formula to show that:

(a) $\int_0^\infty e^{-x} \sin x\,dx = \int_0^\infty e^{-x} \cos x\,dx$

(b) $\int_0^\infty e^{-x} \cos x\,dx = 1 - \int_0^\infty e^{-x} \sin x\,dx$

(c) Use parts (a) and (b) to compute $\int_0^\infty e^{-x} \sin x\,dx.$

(d) Compute $\int_0^\infty x^n e^{-x}\,dx$ (n a positive integer).

7. Use integration by parts to find $\int_1^\infty x^{-2} \ln x \, dx$.
8. Show that $\int_{-\infty}^\infty x(1 + x^2)^{-2} \, dx = 0$, but that $\int_{-\infty}^\infty x(1 + x^2)^{-1} \, dx$ diverges.
9. The gravitational force of attraction between the earth and a body is inversely proportional to the square of the distance between the body and the center of the earth. Assume that the radius of the earth is 4000 miles, and that the nose cone of a rocket weighs 1 ton on the surface of the earth. Find the work required to propel the nose cone out of the earth's gravitational field.
10. The force of repulsion between two positive charges q_1 and q_2 is given by the equation $F = kq_1q_2/d^2$, where d is the distance between the charges and k is a physical constant. The electric potential at a point is frequently defined as the work required to bring a unit charge from "infinity" to the point. Find a formula for the potential V at a point r units away from a charge of q units.

113. **Testing the Convergence of Improper Integrals**

We will restrict our discussion in this section to improper integrals of the form $\int_a^\infty f(x) \, dx$. Our results can easily be modified to apply to other types of improper integrals. When we are faced with an improper integral $\int_a^\infty f(x) \, dx$, two questions immediately present themselves:

(i) Does the integral converge?

(ii) If the integral does converge, what is its value?

Question (i) should be answered first, for if the answer to this question is "no," then there is no need to raise Question (ii). We will now introduce a test for convergence that helps us answer the first question for many frequently encountered improper integrals. In later courses you may study some of the techniques of evaluating improper integrals.

To verify the convergence of the improper integral $\int_a^\infty f(x) \, dx$, we must show that the proper integrals of the form $\int_a^R f(x) \, dx$ have a limit as R becomes infinite. If $f(x) \geq 0$ for x in the interval (a, ∞), we can interpret these proper integrals as areas of regions such as the shaded region in Fig. 113-1. It is clear that these integrals increase with R; that is, if $R_1 < R_2$, then $\int_a^{R_1} f(x) \, dx \leq \int_a^{R_2} f(x) \, dx$. It is not hard to show that because of this property the question of whether or not the proper integrals have a limit reduces to the question of whether or not they are *bounded;* that is, whether or not there is a number M such that $\int_a^R f(x) \, dx \leq M$ for each number $R > a$. Thus it can be shown that *if $f(x) \geq 0$ for x in the interval (a, ∞), then the improper integral $\int_a^\infty f(x) \, dx$ converges if,* *and only if, there is a number M such that* $\int_a^R f(x)\,dx \le M$ *for each* $R > a$.

Now suppose that g is a function such that $0 \le g(x) \le f(x)$ for x in the interval (a, ∞). Then for each $R > a$,

$$\int_a^R g(x)\,dx \le \int_a^R f(x)\,dx. \tag{113-1}$$

From Inequality 113-1 we see that if the proper integrals of the form $\int_a^R f(x)\,dx$ are bounded, then the proper integrals of the form $\int_a^R g(x)\,dx$

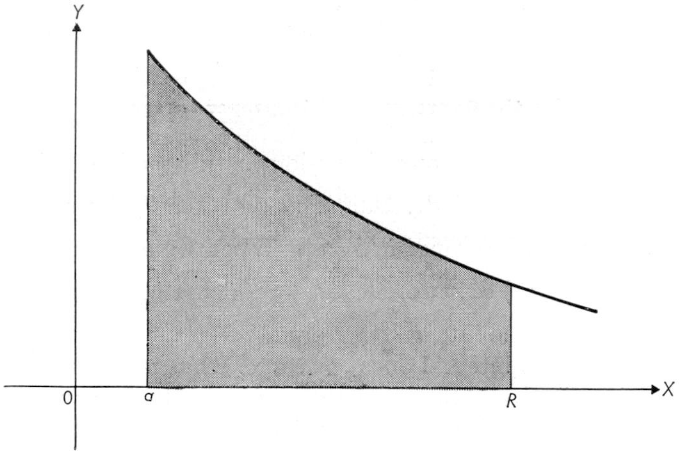

Figure 113-1

are bounded. Therefore, we have the following **comparison test** for the convergence of improper integrals.

THEOREM 113-1. *Suppose that f and g are integrable functions on the interval* $[a, R]$ *for each* $R > a$ *and that* $0 \le g(x) \le f(x)$ *for x in the interval* (a, ∞). *If the improper integral* $\int_a^\infty f(x)\,dx$ *converges, then the improper integral* $\int_a^\infty g(x)\,dx$ *converges. This conclusion also implies that if the integral* $\int_a^\infty g(x)\,dx$ *diverges, then the integral* $\int_a^\infty f(x)\,dx$ *diverges.*

Example 113-1. Test for convergence: $\int_1^\infty \frac{dx}{\sqrt{x^6 + 8x^4 + 5}}$.

Solution. Since

$$\frac{1}{\sqrt{x^6 + 8x^4 + 5}} \le \frac{1}{x^3} \quad \text{(Why?)},$$

and since the improper integral $\int_1^\infty \frac{dx}{x^3}$ converges (see Example 112-2), Theorem 113-1 tells us that the given integral converges.

Example 113-2. Show that the improper integral $\int_0^\infty e^{-x^2}\,dx$ converges. Approximate its value.

Solution. Since $e^{-x^2} \leq e^{-x}$ for $x \geq 1$, and since the integral $\int_1^\infty e^{-x}\,dx$ converges (see Example 112-1), Theorem 113-1 tells us that the integral $\int_1^\infty e^{-x^2}\,dx$ converges. The convergence of this integral, however, implies the convergence of our given integral. To approximate the value of the given integral, we notice that e^{-x^2} is extremely small when x is even moderately large. Thus the integral $\int_0^\infty e^{-x^2}\,dx$ converges very rapidly; that is, $\int_0^R e^{-x^2}\,dx$ approximates its limit $\int_0^\infty e^{-x^2}\,dx$ reasonably well even when R is fairly small. For example,

$$\int_0^\infty e^{-x^2}\,dx = \int_0^3 e^{-x^2}\,dx + \int_3^\infty e^{-x^2}\,dx.$$

If $x \geq 3$, then $e^{-x^2} \leq e^{-3x}$, so

$$\int_3^\infty e^{-x^2}\,dx \leq \int_3^\infty e^{-3x}\,dx \approx .00004.$$

Therefore, you can be sure that the first four decimal places of $\int_0^3 e^{-x^2}\,dx$ and $\int_0^\infty e^{-x^2}\,dx$ differ by no more than one digit in the fourth decimal place. If you use Simpson's Rule with $n = 6$, use 6-place tables, and round off your result to four places, you will find that the number .8862 is an approximation of $\int_0^3 e^{-x^2}\,dx$. Actually, it can be shown that $\int_0^\infty e^{-x^2}\,dx = \frac{\sqrt{\pi}}{2}$, and this number is .8862 with four-place accuracy.

Example 113-3. Show that for each positive integer n

$$\text{(113-2)} \qquad \int_0^\infty x^{n+1}e^{-x}\,dx = (n+1)\int_0^\infty x^n e^{-x}\,dx.$$

Solution. So that we may be sure that the improper integrals that appear in Equation 113-2 converge, let us first show that the integral $\int_0^\infty x^m e^{-x}\,dx$ converges for each integer $m \geq 0$. For this purpose, we consider the limit $\lim_{x\to\infty} \frac{x^{m+2}}{e^x}$. When we apply l'Hospital's Rule $m + 2$ times, we find that this limit is 0. Now since $\frac{x^{m+2}}{e^x}$ approaches 0, there must be a number a such that for $x \geq a$, $\frac{x^{m+2}}{e^x} \leq 1$; that is, $x^m e^{-x} \leq \frac{1}{x^2}\cdot$ We use the comparison test to conclude from this inequality and the fact that the integral $\int_a^\infty \frac{dx}{x^2}$ converges (see Example 112-2) that the integral $\int_a^\infty x^m e^{-x}\, dx$ converges. Hence the integral $\int_0^\infty x^m e^{-x}\, dx$ converges.

Now we return to the verification of Equation 113-2. Integrating by parts yields

$$(113\text{-}3) \qquad \int_0^R x^{n+1}e^{-x}\, dx = -x^{n+1}e^{-x}\Big|_0^R + (n+1)\int_0^R x^n e^{-x}\, dx$$
$$= -R^{n+1}e^{-R} + (n+1)\int_0^R x^n e^{-x}\, dx.$$

We get Equation 113-2 when we take limits in Equation 113-3, using l'Hospital's Rule to show that $\lim_{R\to\infty} (-R^{n+1}e^{-R}) = 0$.

Our comparison test applies only to integrals whose integrands do not change sign. If f takes both positive and negative values, we cannot apply our comparison test directly to the integral $\int_a^\infty f(x)\, dx$. However, we can use the comparison test to test the convergence of the integral $\int_a^\infty |f(x)|\, dx$, and if this integral converges, it is easy to see that the integral $\int_a^\infty f(x)\, dx$ converges. For suppose that $\int_a^\infty |f(x)|\, dx$ converges. Then the integral $\int_a^\infty 2|f(x)|\, dx$ converges. Clearly

$$0 \leq f(x) + |f(x)| \leq 2|f(x)|,$$

and therefore we may use the comparison test to see that the integral $\int_a^\infty (f(x) + |f(x)|)\, dx$ converges. Now we write

$$\int_a^R f(x)\, dx = \int_a^R (f(x) + |f(x)|)\, dx - \int_a^R |f(x)|\, dx,$$

and since the limits of the integrals on the right side of this equation exist, so does the limit of the integral on the left.

Example 113-4. Test the integral $\int_1^\infty \frac{\sin x}{x^2}\, dx$ for convergence.

Solution. Since $\left|\frac{\sin x}{x^2}\right| \leq \frac{1}{x^2}$, and since $\int_1^\infty \frac{dx}{x^2}$ converges, the comparison test tells us that $\int_1^\infty \left|\frac{\sin x}{x^2}\right| dx$ converges. Therefore, from what we have just said, we know that the integral $\int_1^\infty \frac{\sin x}{x^2}\, dx$ converges.

If the integral $\int_a^\infty |f(x)|\, dx$ converges, then we say that the improper integral $\int_a^\infty f(x)\, dx$ **converges absolutely.** It is possible that the integral $\int_a^\infty f(x)\, dx$ converges, but that $\int_a^\infty |f(x)|\, dx$ does not. In this case the integral $\int_a^\infty f(x)\, dx$ is said to **converge conditionally.** For example, we will show in Example 119-5 that the integral $\int_0^\infty \frac{\sin x}{x}\, dx$ converges conditionally. You will be better able to appreciate some of the details concerning the convergence of improper integrals after you have studied sequences and infinite series in the next chapter.

Problems 113

1. Test the following integrals for convergence.
   (a) $\int_2^\infty \frac{x^2}{x^7 + 3}\, dx$
   (b) $\int_4^\infty \frac{x}{x^2 - 3}\, dx$
   (c) $\int_4^\infty \frac{\sqrt{x^3 - 2x}}{\sqrt[3]{2x^5 + 4x - 1}}\, dx$
   (d) $\int_1^\infty x^{123} e^{-x}\, dx$
   (e) $\int_1^\infty \frac{\tanh x}{\sqrt{x}}\, dx$
   (f) $\int_1^\infty e^{-x^2} \sin \frac{1}{\sqrt{x}}\, dx$
   (g) $\int_1^\infty e^{-x} \cos \pi x^2\, dx$
   (h) $\int_2^\infty \frac{\ln x}{x^2}\, dx$
2. Each of the following "infinite" regions has a finite "area." Find the area of the region that lies in the first quadrant and is bounded by the X-axis and:
   (a) The Y-axis and the curve whose equation is $y(x^2 + 4a^2) = 8a^3$.
   (b) The line $x = 3$ and the curve whose equation is $y^2(x^2 - 1)^3 = 4x^2$.
   (c) The Y-axis and the curve whose equation is $xy^2(x + 4)^2 = 1$.
   (d) The line $x = 3$ and the curve whose equation is $yx^2 = 1 + 4y$.
3. Let R be the infinite region bounded by the coordinate axes, the line $x = 1$, and the curve $y = 1/\sqrt{1 - x}$. Express the area of R by means of an integral if you use (a) "vertical strips," and (b) "horizontal strips." Conclude from (a) and (b) that

$$\int_0^1 \frac{dx}{\sqrt{1 - x}} = 1 + \int_1^\infty \frac{dy}{y^2}.$$

Check this equality by actually computing both integrals.

4. Suppose we rotate the region R of the preceding problem about the X-axis to obtain an "infinite" solid. Even though R has a finite area, show that the solid of revolution has an "infinite" volume.
5. As a contrast to the preceding problem, consider the infinite region R that lies in the first quadrant and is bounded by the Y-axis, the line $y = 1$, and the curve $y = 1/x$. Show that R has an "infinite" area, but that the infinite solid obtained by rotating R about the Y-axis has a finite volume. Does the solid have a finite surface area?
6. Use a comparison test that is analagous to Theorem 113-1 to test the following integrals for convergence.
   (a) $\int_0^1 x^{-1}e^x\,dx$ (b) $\int_0^1 x^{-1/2}\cos x\,dx$
   (c) $\int_5^7 \frac{dx}{(x^2+3)\sqrt[3]{7-x}\,\sqrt[5]{x-5}}$ (d) $\int_{-1}^1 x^{-4/3}\sin x\,dx$
   (e) $\int_{-2}^2 x^{-2}\sinh x\,dx$ (f) $\int_0^1 x^{-1/2}\ln x\,dx$
7. Suppose that $f(x)$ and $g(x)$ are both positive for $x > a$, and that $\lim_{x\to\infty} f(x)/g(x) = c$, where $c > 0$. Show that $\int_a^\infty f(x)\,dx$ converges if, and only if, $\int_a^\infty g(x)\,dx$ converges.

Review Problems, Chapter Thirteen

You can use these problems to test yourself on the material covered in this chapter.

1. The Extended Theorem of the Mean (Theorem 109-1) says that if $\boldsymbol{C}$ is the chord vector that joins two points of the graph of the vector equation $\boldsymbol{R} = f(t)\boldsymbol{i} + g(t)\boldsymbol{j}$, then there is a point between them at which the tangent vector is parallel to $\boldsymbol{C}$. Is this theorem also true for curves in three dimensions?
2. Show that $f(x)$ is a polynomial of degree n if, and only if, $f^{(n+1)}(x) = 0$ for all x.
3. Sketch the graph of the equation $y = e^{1/x}$.
4. Suppose that f is a function and a is a point such that $f(a) = 0, f'(a) = 0, \ldots, f^{(n-1)}(a) = 0$ for some integer n. Suppose further that $f^{(n)}$ is continuous at a. Show that $\lim_{x\to a} \frac{f(x)}{(x-a)^n} = \frac{f^{(n)}(a)}{n!}$.
5. Find the following limits.
   (a) $\lim_{x\to 0} \frac{\ln(1+x^2)}{[\ln(1+x)]^2}$ (b) $\lim_{x\to 0} \frac{\sin 3x^2}{\sin^2 x}$
6. When t is very large, the tangent vector to the graph of the equation $\boldsymbol{R} = t\ln t^4\,\boldsymbol{i} + (t^2+2)\boldsymbol{j}$ is "almost parallel" to what unit vector?
7. Evaluate the following limits.
   (a) $\lim_{x\to 0} (1-\cos x)^{\sin x}$ (b) $\lim_{x\to 0^+} (\sin x)^{1-\cos x}$
8. Evaluate the improper integral $\int_0^\infty [\![3e^{-x}]\!]\,dx$.

9. By making the substitution $u = ax$, show that for any positive number a

$$\int_0^\infty \frac{\sin ax}{x}\,dx = \int_0^\infty \frac{\sin u}{u}\,du = \int_0^\infty \frac{\sin x}{x}\,dx.$$

(You may assume that these improper integrals converge.) Can you show that

$$\int_0^\infty \frac{\sin bx}{x}\,dx = -\int_0^\infty \frac{\sin x}{x}\,dx$$

if $b < 0$?

10. Test the following integrals for convergence.

(a) $\displaystyle\int_1^\infty \frac{\cos x}{1 + x^2}\,dx$ (b) $\displaystyle\int_1^\infty \frac{x}{1 + x^2}\,dx$ (c) $\displaystyle\int_1^\infty \frac{[x]}{1 + x^2}\,dx$

14 SEQUENCES AND INFINITE SERIES

You know that the number 3.14159 is only an approximation of the number π. Nevertheless, for most practical applications this approximation is close enough, and if it is not, we can replace the number 3.14159 by a still closer approximation. The number π is the *limit* of the *sequence* of numbers 3, 3.1, 3.14, 3.141, 3.1415, 3.14159, ... Sometimes we express the terms of such a sequence as a sum; for example, we might write 3, $3 + .1$, $3 + .1 + .04$, and so on. Here the more terms we add together, the closer the sum approximates the number π. We are going to study such sequences in this chapter. We will find, for example, that another sequence whose limit is π is the sequence 4, $4 - \frac{4}{3}$, $4 - \frac{4}{3} + \frac{4}{5}$, $4 - \frac{4}{3} + \frac{4}{5} - \frac{4}{7}$, and so on. Thus we can get as accurate an approximation of π as we like by adding together sufficiently many terms in the "sum"

$$4 - \tfrac{4}{3} + \tfrac{4}{5} - \tfrac{4}{7} + \tfrac{4}{9} - \tfrac{4}{11} + \cdots.$$

Similar sums will give us such numbers as e, ln 2, sin .7, and so on.

114. Sequences and their Limits

With each number x in the domain of a function f there is paired the number $f(x)$ in its range. If the domain of f contains a set of integers, we can use this pairing to determine an indexed set that we call a **sequence.** Thus, for example, if the domain of f contains the set of positive integers, we construct the sequence $\{a_n\}$ by setting $a_1 = f(1)$, $a_2 = f(2)$, $a_3 = f(3)$, and so on. The numbers $a_1, a_2, a_3, \ldots$ are called the **terms** of the sequence. These terms are ordered by their subscripts; thus a_1 is the first term of the sequence $\{a_n\}$, a_2 is the second term, and so on. In our work we will be dealing mainly with sequences that are indexed either by the set of all positive integers or the set of all positive integers and zero.

Example 114-1. Let $\{a_n\}$ be the sequence in which $a_n = (-1)^n/(2n - 1)!$. We can write this sequence as $\left\{\dfrac{(-1)^n}{(2n-1)!}\right\}\cdot$ Find a_2, a_5, and a_{14}.

Solution. By direct substitution we obtain

$$a_2 = (-1)^2/3! = \tfrac{1}{6},\ a_5 = (-1)^5/9! = -1/9!,$$

and

$$a_{14} = 1/27!.$$

The terms of a sequence need not be given by a simple arithmetic formula, as in the last example. Any rule that assigns a number a_n to each integer n will define a sequence.

Example 114-2. Let $\{a_n\}$ be the sequence of digits in the decimal representation of $\sin \dfrac{\pi}{3}\cdot$ Find the first four terms of the sequence.

Solution. We know that $\sin \dfrac{\pi}{3} = \dfrac{\sqrt{3}}{2} = .866025 \ldots.$ Thus $a_1 = 8$, $a_2 = 6$, $a_3 = 6$, and $a_4 = 0$. We have no simple algebraic formula to calculate a_n for each n, but the number a_{34}, for example, is completely determined, and we could find it if we cared to.

A sequence may also be given by specifying the first term and then stating a *recursion formula* that tells how to find every other term from the term that precedes it.

Example 114-3. Let $\{a_n\}$ be the sequence in which $a_1 = 1$, and $a_n = 3a_{n-1} - 1$ for $n > 1$. Find a_2, a_3, and a_4.

Solution. Using the recursion formula $a_n = 3a_{n-1} - 1$ and the given fact that $a_1 = 1$, we have $a_2 = 3a_1 - 1 = 3 - 1 = 2$,

$$a_3 = 3a_2 - 1 = 6 - 1 = 5,\ a_4 = 3a_3 - 1 = 14.$$

The terms of the sequence, $\left\{1 - \frac{1}{n}\right\}$ are $0, \frac{1}{2}, \frac{2}{3}, \frac{3}{4}, \frac{4}{5}, \ldots$. Although the number 1 is not in this sequence, it is obvious that terms with very large indices are close to 1. The number 1 is called the *limit of* $1 - \frac{1}{n}$ *as n becomes infinite* and we write $\lim_{n\to\infty} \left(1 - \frac{1}{n}\right) = 1$. The number 1 is also called the *limit of the sequence.* Many times we are able to determine the limit of a sequence by inspection, as in the following examples.

Example 114-4. Find the limit of the sequence of Example 114-1.

Solution. Here $a_n = (-1)^n/(2n - 1)!$. If n is a large number, the denominator is a large number, but the numerator is not. Hence the given fraction is nearly zero, and we conclude that

$$\lim_{n\to\infty} \frac{(-1)^n}{(2n - 1)!} = 0.$$

Example 114-5. Find $\lim_{n\to\infty} (n^2 + 2n - 1)/(2n^2 - n + 3)$.

Solution. When n is large, both the numerator and the denominator of the fraction $(n^2 + 2n - 1)/(2n^2 - n + 3)$ are large numbers, and it may not be immediately obvious what we can say about the quotient. However, if we divide the numerator and denominator of the fraction $\frac{n^2 + 2n - 1}{2n^2 - n + 3}$ by n^2, we obtain the new fraction

$$\frac{1 + 2/n - 1/n^2}{2 - 1/n + 3/n^2}.$$

Here, for large n, the numerator is approximately 1 and the denominator is approximately 2, and so we conclude that the fraction itself is approximately $\frac{1}{2}$. Therefore,

$$\lim_{n\to\infty} \frac{n^2 + 2n - 1}{2n^2 - n + 3} = \frac{1}{2}.$$

Our remarks so far were intended to give some intuitive feeling for the limit concept as it is applied to sequences. Now let us give a more precise definition of the limit. A **final segment** of a sequence $\{a_n\}$ is the set of all terms in the sequence beyond some given term. Thus, for example, the set $\{a_{13}, a_{14}, \ldots\}$ consisting of all the terms beyond a_{12} is a final segment of the sequence $\{a_n\}$. Some final segments of the sequence $\left\{1 - \frac{1}{n}\right\}$ are the sets $\{\frac{4}{5}, \frac{5}{6}, \ldots\}$, $\{\frac{173}{174}, \frac{174}{175}, \ldots\}$, and $\{\frac{1066}{1067}, \frac{1067}{1068}, \ldots\}$. It is not too hard to show that the smallest closed intervals that contain these three final segments are the intervals $[\frac{4}{5}, 1]$, $[\frac{173}{174}, 1]$, and $[\frac{1066}{1067}, 1]$. These three intervals all have the number 1 in common. If we constructed other smallest closed intervals containing final segments of the sequence $\left\{1 - \frac{1}{n}\right\}$, we would find that they all contained the number 1, and in fact it is true that the number 1, the limit of our sequence, is the *only* number that is common to all such smallest closed intervals. This example illustrates the definition of the limit of a sequence $\{a_n\}$. With each integer N we first associate an interval J_N, the smallest closed interval that contains the final segment $\{a_N, a_{N+1}, \ldots\}$. Thus in our example of the sequence $\left\{1 - \frac{1}{n}\right\}$, we have $J_7 = [\frac{6}{7}, 1]$. Then we make the following definition.

DEFINITION 114-1. *If there is a number L that belongs to each of the intervals $J_1, J_2, J_3, \ldots$, and if L is the* **only** *number that is common to all these intervals, then L is called the* **limit** *of a_n as n becomes infinite, and we write*

$$\lim_{n\to\infty} a_n = L.$$

We will also refer to L as the ***limit of the sequence*** $\{a_n\}$.

Not every sequence has a limit. If a sequence has a limit, it is called a **convergent** sequence; otherwise it is **divergent.** Let us consider the sequence $\{(-1)^n\}$. In this case the successive terms are $-1, 1, -1, 1, \ldots$. It is clear that there is no one number L that is approximated by the terms of this sequence for large n. The terms of the sequence "oscillate," being either -1 or 1. The interval J_N for any final segment is $[-1, 1]$, and the sequence is divergent. Another example of a divergent sequence is furnished by the sequence $\{2^n\}$. If n is large, the number 2^n is large, and we see that there is no number L that is approximated by all terms with a sufficiently large index. The interval J_N is the interval $[2^N, \infty]$, and there is no number common to all such intervals. We sometimes write $\lim_{n\to\infty} 2^n = \infty$, but ∞ is not a number, and we do not say that the sequence 2^n converges.

If a sequence $\{a_n\}$ has a limit L, then the intervals $J_1, J_2, J_3, \ldots$ "squeeze down" on L. Thus if we choose any open interval (a, b) that contains L, then we can find an interval J_N that is "squeezed into" the interval (a, b) (see Fig. 114-1). Since every term of the sequence $\{a_n\}$ whose subscript is N or greater is contained in J_N, we see that a_n is contained in the interval (a, b) if $n \geq N$. Thus if we consider any open interval that contains the limit of a sequence, then there is an index N beyond which all the terms of the sequence lie in this interval. We shall later find that this way of looking at the limit of a sequence is very helpful, so we shall state this result as a theorem.

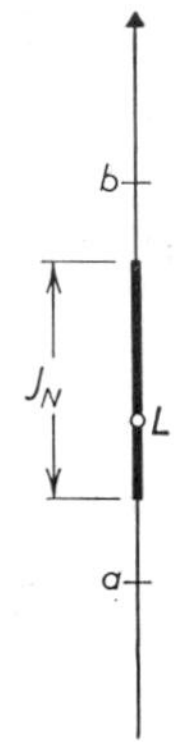

Figure 114-1

THEOREM 114-1. *If* $\lim_{n \to \infty} a_n = L$, *and if* (a, b) *is any open interval that contains* L, *then there is a number* N *such that every element* a_n *with index* $n \geq N$ *is contained in the interval* (a, b).

If we can see at a glance that the limit of a given sequence $\{a_n\}$ is a certain number L, then we can consider ourselves fortunate. In general we would not even expect to be able to tell whether or not a sequence converges, much less what its limit is. The sequence $\left\{\left(\frac{n+1}{n}\right)^n\right\}$ is an example. Is it obvious that this sequence is convergent, and if so, that its limit is the number e? If we set $h = 1/n$ in Equation 50-9, then we see that the sequence does converge to e (or see Question 13 at the end of this section), but this fact is not immediately apparent from a look at the sequence. We will now discuss some simple and useful criteria for determining whether or not sequences of certain types converge.

Suppose that $J_1 = [A, B]$ is the smallest closed interval that contains all the terms of a given sequence $\{a_n\}$. Here the letters A and B stand for numbers, or perhaps A may be the symbol $-\infty$, or B may be the symbol ∞. For example, for the sequence $\{(-1)^n n^2\}$, we have $J_1 = [-\infty, \infty]$, whereas for the sequence $\left\{\frac{(-1)^n}{n^2}\right\}$ we have $J_1 = [-1, 1]$. If B is a number and not the symbol ∞, then we say that the sequence $\{a_n\}$ is **bounded above,** and we call the number B the **least upper bound** of the sequence. Similarly, if A is a number and not the symbol $-\infty$, then the sequence $\{a_n\}$ is said to be **bounded below,** and A is the **greatest lower bound** of the sequence. If both A and B are numbers, then we say that the sequence $\{a_n\}$ is **bounded.** A sequence is bounded if, and only if, there exist *some* numbers C and D such that all the terms of the sequence are contained in the interval $[C, D]$. In that case the *smallest* closed interval $[A, B]$ that contains all the terms of the sequence will itself be contained in $[C, D]$, and we will have $C \leq A$ and $B \leq D$. The number C is called *a lower bound* of the sequence and D is *an upper bound.*

If a sequence $\{a_n\}$ is not bounded above, then the smallest closed intervals that contain final segments of the sequence must be of the form $J_N = [A_N, \infty]$. If all such smallest closed intervals contain a certain number L, then they must contain every number larger than L—for example, $L + 1$. Therefore, the intervals $J_1, J_2, \ldots$ cannot have exactly one number in common, and so the sequence $\{a_n\}$ cannot converge. Similarly, a sequence that is not bounded below cannot be convergent. We can put these two negative statements into positive terms as follows:

If a sequence converges, then it is bounded.

The converse of this statement is *not* true. The sequence $\{(-1)^n\}$, for example, is bounded but it is not convergent.

We say that a sequence $\{a_n\}$ is **non-decreasing** if $a_1 \leq a_2 \leq a_3 \leq \cdots$; that is, if $a_n \leq a_{n+1}$ for each positive integer n. The sequence $\left\{1 - \frac{1}{n}\right\}$, for example, is non-decreasing. If $a_1 \geq a_2 \geq a_3 \geq \cdots$, then the sequence $\{a_n\}$ is said to be **non-increasing.** Notice that non-decreasing sequences are automatically bounded below, and non-increasing sequences are bounded above. If $\{a_n\}$ is a non-decreasing sequence that is bounded above, then the smallest closed interval that contains all its terms is $J_1 = [A, B] = [a_1, B]$, where B is the least upper bound of the sequence and a_1 is its first term. In fact, the intervals $J_2, J_3, \ldots$ that contain the other final segments of the sequence are $J_2 = [a_2, B]$, $J_3 = [a_3, B]$, and so on. All these intervals have the number B in common, and it is not hard to show that B is the only number that they have in common. Therefore, according to Definition 114-1, $\lim_{n \to \infty} a_n = B$. We state this result as a theorem.

THEOREM 114-2. *Let $\{a_n\}$ be a non-decreasing sequence that is bounded above, and let B be its least upper bound. Then the sequence converges, and $\lim_{n \to \infty} a_n = B$.*

The analogous theorem for non-increasing sequences reads as follows.

THEOREM 114-3. *Let $\{a_n\}$ be a non-increasing sequence that is bounded below, and let A be its greatest lower bound. Then the sequence converges, and* $\lim_{n\to\infty} a_n = A$.

Example 114-6. Suppose that $a_1 = \frac{3}{4}$, and $a_n = \frac{4n^2 - 1}{4n^2} a_{n-1}$ for $n \geq 2$. Show that the sequence $\{a_n\}$ converges.

Solution. We have

$$a_1 = \tfrac{3}{4},\ a_2 = \tfrac{3}{4} \cdot \tfrac{15}{16},\ a_3 = \tfrac{3}{4} \cdot \tfrac{15}{16} \cdot \tfrac{35}{36},\ \ldots.$$

In this sequence, each term is the product of positive numbers, so each term is positive. Therefore, the sequence is bounded below, and its greatest lower bound is a number $A \geq 0$. We also notice that each term is obtained from the preceding term by multiplying it by a proper fraction. Therefore, each term is smaller than its predecessor, and so the sequence is non-increasing. Thus we have a non-increasing sequence that is bounded below by 0, and so Theorem 114-3 tells us that it converges to its greatest lower bound A. Actually, the limit of this sequence is the number $2/\pi$. You might calculate a_5 to see what kind of an approximation to the limit it gives.

We bring this section to a close with two more remarks about the limits of sequences. We notice first of all that when calculating the limit of a sequence $\{a_n\}$, we can ignore any *initial segment;* that is, any set of terms in the sequence that precede a given term. For example, the first few terms of the sequence $\{n^3/n!\}$ are 1, 4, $\frac{9}{2}$, $\frac{8}{3}$, $\frac{25}{24}$, ... Therefore, the sequence is neither non-increasing nor non-decreasing. However, if we ignore the first two terms, we will have a non-increasing sequence of positive terms. We can therefore apply Theorem 114-2 to see that this new sequence has a limit. This limit is also the limit of the original sequence. Notice, too, that the limit theorems of Section 13 apply to sequences. The following theorem is the result of rewording Theorem 13-3 in the language of sequences.

THEOREM 114-4. *If $\{a_n\}$ and $\{b_n\}$ are convergent sequences, then*

$$\lim_{n\to\infty} (a_n + b_n) = \lim_{n\to\infty} a_n + \lim_{n\to\infty} b_n, \tag{114-1}$$

$$\lim_{n\to\infty} (a_n b_n) = \lim_{n\to\infty} a_n \lim_{n\to\infty} b_n, \tag{114-2}$$

and

$$\lim_{n\to\infty} \frac{a_n}{b_n} = \frac{\lim_{n\to\infty} a_n}{\lim_{n\to\infty} b_n} \quad \text{(provided that } \lim_{n\to\infty} b_n \neq 0). \tag{114-3}$$

As a special case of Equation 114-2 *we have*

$$\lim_{n \to \infty} ca_n = c \lim_{n \to \infty} a_n, \tag{114-4}$$

where c may be any number.

Suppose the domain of a function f is the set of positive real numbers. Then it certainly contains the positive integers, and the equation $a_n = f(n)$ determines a sequence $\{a_n\}$. Now if $\lim_{x \to \infty} f(x) = L$, then L is the number that is approximated by $f(x)$ when x is large. In particular, if $x = n$, where n is a large integer, then $f(n) = a_n$ approximates L. Thus $\lim_{n \to \infty} a_n = L$. In our examples of sequences of this type we will often find that we can calculate $\lim_{x \to \infty} f(x)$ by means of l'Hospital's Rule. For example, we found in Example 110-3 that

$$\lim_{x \to \infty} \frac{1 - \cos \frac{1}{x}}{\tan^2 \frac{1}{x}} = \frac{1}{2}.$$

Thus the sequence $\left\{\dfrac{1 - \cos \frac{1}{n}}{\tan^2 \frac{1}{n}}\right\}$ converges and its limit is $\frac{1}{2}$.

Problems 114

1. Find and simplify the 5th term of the sequence.
   (a) $\{\cos (n\pi/2)\}$ (b) $\{1 + (-1)^n\}$
   (c) $\{1 \cdot 3 \cdot 5 \cdots (2n - 1)/n!\}$ (d) $\{(2n)!/2^n n!\}$
   (e) $\{n!2^{n+1}/(n + 1)!2^n\}$ (f) $\{\ln n!/4n^2\}$
2. Write the first four terms of the sequence $\{c_n\}$ if:
   (a) $c_1 = 1$, $c_n = (n/2)c_{n-1}$
   (b) $c_1 = 1$, $c_n = \left(1 + \frac{1}{n}\right) c_{n-1}$
   (c) $c_1 = 3$, $c_2 = 2$, $c_n = (c_{n-1} + c_{n-2})/2$
   (d) $c_1 = c_2 = 1$, $c_n = c_{n-1} + c_{n-2}$
3. Find a simple formula for a_n such that the first few terms of the sequence $\{a_n\}$ are:
   (a) 1, 3, 7, 15, 31, ... (b) 1, 0, −1, 0, 1, 0, −1, ...
   (c) 0, 3, 8, 15, 24, ... (d) 1, −1, −1, 1, 1, −1, −1, 1, ...
4. Find a formula for the nth term of the sequence of Example 114-3.

5. If it exists, find $\lim_{n\to\infty} a_n$ if:

(a) $a_n = \dfrac{n^2 + 3n - 2}{2n^2 - n + 14}$ (b) $a_n = \dfrac{(4n + 1)(5n - 2)}{(2n + 3)(3n - 5)}$

(c) $a_n = \dfrac{2^n + 2^{-n}}{5 \cdot 2^n}$ (d) $a_n = n^2 \cos \dfrac{n\pi}{2}$

(e) $a_n = \dfrac{\sin n}{n}$ (f) $a_n = \dfrac{n!2^{n+1}}{(n + 1)!2^n}$

6. Which of the following sequences have limits?
(a) $\{1 + (-1)^n\}$ (b) $\{\cos (n\pi/2)\}$
(c) $\{\ln (1 + 1/n)\}$ (d) $\left\{\int_0^n \cos x\, dx\right\}$
(e) $\{2^{-1/n^2}\}$ (f) $\{n!/100^n\}$

7. Find the limits of the following sequences.

(a) $\{n^2e^{-n}\}$ (b) $\left\{\dfrac{\ln n}{\sqrt{n}}\right\}$

(c) $\left\{\dfrac{\ln (3n + 1)}{\ln n}\right\}$ (d) $\left\{\dfrac{\ln (n + e^{2n})}{n}\right\}$

8. The first few terms of some sequences are given below. Show that these are terms of sequences that satisfy the hypotheses of Theorem 114-3 and hence converge.
(a) $\frac{3}{1}$, $3^2/2!$, $3^3/3!$, $3^4/4!$, ...
(b) 5, $\sqrt{5}$, $\sqrt{\sqrt{5}}$, $\sqrt{\sqrt{\sqrt{5}}}$, ...
(c) 1, $2!/2^2$, $3!/3^3$, $4!/4^4$, $5!/5^5$, ...

9. Find the least upper bound and the greatest lower bound of each of the sequences in the preceding question.

10. Find an index N beyond which all the terms of the given sequence lie in the interval $(-.1, .1)$.
(a) $\{(\cos n)/n\}$
(b) $\{2^{-n}\}$
(c) $\{(n^2 + 3n - 2)/n^3\}$

11. Let a_n be the area of the regular n-sided polygon inscribed in the unit circle. Find a formula for $a_n (n \geq 3)$. What is $\lim_{n\to\infty} a_n$?

12. Let $a_1 = 1$ and $a_n = \dfrac{n^2 - 1}{n^2} a_{n-1}$ for $n \geq 2$. Show that $\{a_n\}$ converges. Show that $\lim_{n\to\infty} a_n = \frac{1}{2}$.

13. Use l'Hospital's Rule to show that the limit of the sequence $\left\{\left(\dfrac{n+1}{n}\right)^n\right\}$ is e.

115. Infinite Series

With each sequence $\{a_n\}$ we can associate another sequence $\{S_n\}$ that is called the sequence of **partial sums** of $\{a_n\}$. The terms of the sequence $\{S_n\}$ are defined by the formula

(115-1) $$S_n = \sum_{k=1}^{n} a_k = a_1 + a_2 + \cdots + a_n.$$

Thus
$$S_1 = a_1,$$
$$S_2 = a_1 + a_2 = S_1 + a_2,$$
$$S_3 = a_1 + a_2 + a_3 = S_2 + a_3,$$

and so on. Clearly

(115-2) $$S_n = S_{n-1} + a_n.$$

Example 115-1. Find the first 5 terms of the sequence of partial sums of the sequence $\{a_n\} = \{1/n(n+1)\}$, and also find a formula that gives S_n for each integer n.

Solution. $S_1 = a_1 = \dfrac{1}{1 \cdot 2} = \dfrac{1}{2}$,

$$S_2 = S_1 + a_2 + \frac{1}{2} + \frac{1}{2 \cdot 3} = \frac{2}{3},$$
$$S_3 = S_2 + a_3 = \frac{2}{3} + \frac{1}{3 \cdot 4} = \frac{3}{4},$$
$$S_4 = S_3 + a_4 = \frac{3}{4} + \frac{1}{4 \cdot 5} = \frac{4}{5},$$
$$S_5 = S_4 + a_5 = \frac{4}{5} + \frac{1}{5 \cdot 6} = \frac{5}{6}.$$

When we look at these terms, we are strongly tempted to conclude that $S_6 = \frac{6}{7}$, $S_7 = \frac{7}{8}$, and in general that $S_n = n/n + 1$. This conclusion is correct, for

$$a_k = \frac{1}{k(k+1)} = \frac{1}{k} - \frac{1}{k+1},$$

and therefore

$$S_n = a_1 + a_2 + a_3 + \cdots + a_n$$
$$= \left(1 - \frac{1}{2}\right) + \left(\frac{1}{2} - \frac{1}{3}\right) + \left(\frac{1}{3} - \frac{1}{4}\right) + \cdots + \left(\frac{1}{n} - \frac{1}{n+1}\right).$$

When we remove the parentheses, this sum "collapses" to

(115-3) $$S_n = 1 - \frac{1}{n+1} = \frac{n}{n+1}.$$

Suppose that S is the limit of the sequence $\{S_n\}$ of partial sums of a sequence $\{a_n\}$. We indicate that the partial sums of the sequence $\{a_n\}$

converge to the number S by writing

(115-4) $$S = \sum_{k=1}^{\infty} a_k + a_1 + a_2 + a_3 + \cdots.$$

Of course, this notation does not mean that we add together all the infinitely many terms of the sequence $\{a_n\}$. It is just another way of saying that $\lim_{n\to\infty} S_n = S$. We call the indicated sum

$$\sum_{k=1}^{\infty} a_k = a_1 + a_2 + a_3 + \cdots$$

an **infinite series.** The numbers a_1, a_2, a_3, ... are its **terms,** and the sequence $\{S_n\}$, where $S_n = \sum_{k=1}^{n} a_n$, is the sequence of **partial sums** of the series. If the sequence $\{S_n\}$ converges, then the series **converges;** otherwise the series is **divergent.** The limit S of S_n (if a limit exists) is called the **sum** of the series.

Example 115-2. Find the sum of the infinite series

$$\sum_{k=1}^{\infty} \frac{1}{k(k+1)} = \frac{1}{1\cdot 2} + \frac{1}{2\cdot 3} + \frac{1}{3\cdot 4} + \frac{1}{4\cdot 5} + \cdots.$$

Solution. In Example 115-1 (Equation 115-3) we found that

$$S_n = \sum_{k=1}^{n} \frac{1}{k(k+1)} = \frac{n}{n+1}.$$

Clearly $\lim_{n\to\infty} \frac{n}{n+1} = 1$, so our given series converges, and its sum is 1.

We are now going to investigate the convergence of a very important series. Suppose that x is some real number, and consider the **geometric series**

(115-5) $$\sum_{k=0}^{\infty} x^k = 1 + x + x^2 + \cdots$$

The terms of this series are the terms of the geometric progression $\{x^k\}$. Notice that our index of summation starts at 0 here. In this case we find it convenient to think of 1 as being the 0th term of the sequence $\{x^k\}$, x as being the first term, and so on. On the other hand we find that it makes our formulas a little simpler if we label the terms in our sequence $\{S_n\}$ of partial sums so that $S_1 = 1$, $S_2 = 1 + x$, and in general

$$S_n = \sum_{k=0}^{n-1} x^k = 1 + x + x^2 + \cdots + x^{n-1}.$$

In this form it is not clear what the limit of S_n is (or even whether S_n has a limit). However, you may remember that there is a simple formula for the partial sums of the terms of a geometric progression. To obtain this formula we write

$$S_n - xS_n = (1 + x + \cdots + x^{n-1}) - (x + x^2 + \cdots + x^n) = 1 - x^n.$$

Then we solve this equation for S_n and find (provided $x \neq 1$) that

$$S_n = \frac{1 - x^n}{1 - x} = \frac{1}{1 - x} - \frac{1}{1 - x} \cdot x^n.$$

From this equation we see that questions about the limit of S_n reduce to questions about the limit of x^n. If $|x| < 1$, then $\lim_{n\to\infty} x^n = 0$ (look at $x = \frac{1}{2}$, for example), and hence $\lim_{n\to\infty} S_n = \frac{1}{1 - x}$. If $|x| > 1$, or if $x = -1$, then $\lim_{n\to\infty} x^n$ does not exist, and hence $\{S_n\}$ is not convergent. If $x = 1$, then $S_n = n$, and so the sequence $\{S_n\}$ is again divergent. Thus the *geometric series is convergent if, and only if, x is a number such that $|x| < 1$*, and we have

$$\text{(115-6)} \qquad \sum_{k=0}^{\infty} x^k = \frac{1}{1 - x}, \quad |x| < 1.$$

Example 115-3. Find the sum of the series $\sum_{k=0}^{\infty} (\frac{2}{3})^k$.

Solution. The sum of this geometric series is obtained by replacing x with $\frac{2}{3}$ in Equation 115-6:

$$\sum_{k=0}^{\infty} \left(\frac{2}{3}\right)^k = \frac{1}{1 - \frac{2}{3}} = 3.$$

Although infinite series are not sums of numbers in the usual sense, they do have some of the properties of ordinary sums. For example, if $\sum_{k=1}^{\infty} a_k$ and $\sum_{k=1}^{\infty} b_k$ are convergent series, then it follows from Equation 114-1 that the series $\sum_{k=1}^{\infty} (a_k + b_k)$ is convergent and that

$$\text{(115-7)} \qquad \sum_{k=1}^{\infty} (a_k + b_k) = \sum_{k=1}^{\infty} a_k + \sum_{k=1}^{\infty} b_k.$$

Similarly, if c is any number and $\sum_{k=1}^{\infty} a_k$ is a convergent series, then it follows from Equation 114-4 that the series $\sum_{k=1}^{\infty} ca_k$ is convergent and that

$$(115\text{-}8) \qquad \sum_{k=1}^{\infty} ca_k = c \sum_{k=1}^{\infty} a_k.$$

Let us illustrate our remarks about sequences and infinite series by considering the decimal notation that we use to represent real numbers. An infinite decimal representation of a real number a determines a sequence of which the number a is the limit. For example, the infinite decimal 1.111 ... represents the number that is the limit of the sequence 1, 1.1, 1.11, 1.111, ... We can regard the terms of this sequence as the partial sums of the infinite series

$$1 + .1 + .01 + .001 + .0001 + \cdots,$$

and then the limit of the sequence is the sum of the series. This series is the geometric series

$$1 + (\tfrac{1}{10}) + (\tfrac{1}{10})^2 + (\tfrac{1}{10})^3 + \cdots = \sum_{k=0}^{\infty} (\tfrac{1}{10})^k.$$

Its sum (Equation 115-6 with $x = \frac{1}{10}$) is therefore

$$\frac{1}{1 - \frac{1}{10}} = \frac{10}{9}.$$

Thus the infinite decimal 1.111 ... represents the number $\frac{10}{9}$.

Example 115-4. Show that 2.999 ... = 3.

Solution. The infinite decimal 2.999 ... represents the sum of the series $2 + .9 + .09 + .009 + \cdots = 2 + \frac{9}{10} + (\frac{9}{10})^2 + (\frac{9}{10})^3 + \cdots$.

According to Equation 115-8, we can factor a common multiplier from each of the terms of a series, so our series can be written

$$2 + (\tfrac{9}{10})[1 + (\tfrac{1}{10}) + (\tfrac{1}{10})^2 + \cdots].$$

The series in brackets is the geometric series whose sum we have just found to be $\frac{10}{9}$. Thus the decimal 2.999 ... represents the number

$$2 + (\tfrac{9}{10})(\tfrac{10}{9}) = 2 + 1 = 3,$$

as was to be shown.

Suppose that the series $\sum_{k=1}^{\infty} a_k$ converges. Then there is a number S such that $\lim_{n \to \infty} S_n = S$, where $\{S_n\}$ is the sequence of partial sums of the series. The equation $\lim_{n\to\infty} S_n = S$ implies that $\lim_{n\to\infty} S_{n-1} = S$, and so

$$\lim_{n\to\infty} (S_n - S_{n-1}) = \lim_{n\to\infty} S_n - \lim_{n\to\infty} S_{n-1} = S - S = 0.$$

Thus, since $S_n - S_{n-1} = a_n$, we have the following theorem.

THEOREM 115-1. *If the series* $\sum_{k=1}^{\infty} a_k$ *converges, then* $\lim_{n\to\infty} a_n = 0$. *In other words, if* a_n *does* ***not*** *approach zero, the series diverges.*

Example 115-5. Test the series

$$1 - \frac{3}{4} + \frac{4}{6} - \frac{5}{8} + \frac{6}{10} - \cdots + (-1)^{n+1}\left(\frac{n+1}{2n}\right) + \cdots$$

for convergence.

Solution. This series is constructed from the terms of the sequence $\left\{\frac{n+1}{2n}\right\}$ by using alternate plus and minus signs. Since $\lim_{n\to\infty} \frac{n+1}{2n} = \frac{1}{2}$, you can see that a term with a large index is close to either $\frac{1}{2}$ or $-\frac{1}{2}$, so a_n does not approach 0. Thus Theorem 115-1 tells us that the series is divergent.

You must be very careful not to read Theorem 115-1 backwards. The theorem says that *if* a series converges, then its terms approach 0. It does *not* say that if its terms approach 0, then a series converges. For example, consider the series $\sum_{k=1}^{\infty} \ln\left(\frac{k+1}{k}\right)$. For this series

$$\lim_{n\to\infty} a_n = \lim_{n\to\infty} \ln\left(\frac{n+1}{n}\right) = \ln 1 = 0.$$

On the other hand,

$$\begin{aligned} S_n &= \sum_{k=1}^{n} \ln\left(\frac{k+1}{k}\right) = \sum_{k=1}^{\infty} [\ln (k+1) - \ln k] \\ &= [\ln 2 - \ln 1] + [\ln 3 - \ln 2] + \cdots + [\ln (n+1) - \ln n] \\ &= \ln (n+1). \end{aligned}$$

Since $\lim_{n\to\infty} S_n = \lim_{n\to\infty} \ln (n+1)$ does not exist, we see that the series $\sum_{k=1}^{\infty} \ln\left(\frac{k+1}{k}\right)$ is divergent.

Problems 115

1. Find the fifth partial sum S_5 of each of the following sequences.

   (a) $\{n\}$ (b) $\{(-1)^{n+1}\}$ (c) $\left\{\dfrac{\cos n\pi}{n}\right\}$ (d) $\{(n+1)! - n!\}$

2. Find the partial sums S_1, S_2, S_3, and S_4 of the sequence $\{(-1)^{n+1} - 1\}$. Does $\lim_{n\to\infty} S_n$ exist?

3. Let $S_n = \sum_{k=1}^{n} a_k$. Find a formula for a_k if S_n is equal to:

   (a) $n(n+1)$ (b) $(-1)^n$ (c) n

   (d) 1 (e) $1 + (-1)^n$ (f) $\sin \dfrac{n\pi}{2}$

4. Find the sum of each of the following infinite series.

   (a) $\sum_{k=0}^{\infty} (\frac{1}{3})^k$ (b) $\sum_{k=0}^{\infty} (-\frac{5}{8})^k$

   (c) $\sum_{k=1}^{\infty} 3^{-k}$ (d) $\sum_{k=4}^{\infty} (\frac{3}{5})^k$

5. Find the sum of the infinite series.

   (a) $\sum_{k=0}^{\infty} [(\frac{1}{2})^k + (-\frac{1}{2})^k]$ (b) $\sum_{k=0}^{\infty} [(\frac{1}{3})^k + (-\frac{1}{4})^k]$

   (c) $\sum_{k=0}^{\infty} [2(\frac{4}{5})^k + 3(\frac{1}{4})^k]$ (d) $\sum_{k=1}^{\infty} [4(\frac{2}{3})^{2k}]$

6. Find the sum of the series

$$\frac{3}{4} + \frac{5}{36} + \frac{7}{144} + \cdots + \frac{2k+1}{k^2(k+1)^2} + \cdots$$

   (Note that $a_k = 1/k^2 - 1/(k+1)^2$).

7. Find an expression for the nth partial sum of the series

$$\ln 2 + \ln \frac{3}{4} + \ln \frac{8}{9} + \cdots + \ln\left(1 - \frac{1}{n^2}\right) + \cdots$$

   What is the sum of this series?

8. Show that the following series diverge.

   (a) $\sum_{k=1}^{\infty} \dfrac{k!}{100^k}$ (b) $\sum_{k=1}^{\infty} \dfrac{k}{k+1}$

   (c) $\sum_{k=1}^{\infty} \dfrac{k^2+k}{4k^2+5k-1}$ (d) $\sum_{k=1}^{\infty} \dfrac{\ln(k+e^k)}{k+\ln k}$

9. Suppose that the series $\sum_{k=1}^{\infty} (a_k + b_k)$ converges. Does it follow that the series $a_1 + b_1 + a_2 + b_2 + a_3 + b_3 + \cdots$ converges? (Examine the situation when $a_k = 1$ and $b_k = -1$ for all k.)

116. Comparison Tests

When we examine an infinite series $\sum_{k=1}^{\infty} a_k$, three questions naturally arise:

(i) Does the series converge?
(ii) If it does converge, what is its sum?
(iii) For a given index n, how well does the partial sum S_n approximate the sum S?

For the geometric series $\sum_{k=0}^{\infty} x^k$, we can answer all of these questions completely. We know that this series converges if $|x| < 1$; we know that if it converges then its sum is $S = \frac{1}{1-x}$; and finally, since the formula for the nth partial sum is $S_n = (1 - x^n)/(1 - x)$, we know that $S - S_n = \frac{x^n}{1-x}$. For most other series, however, we cannot answer all three questions so completely. Most of our attention will be devoted to finding the answer to the first question. For certain kinds of series, we will develop some tools that will help us answer the other two questions as well.

First, we will develop a test for convergence that applies to series with non-negative terms (positive or zero terms). If the terms of the series $\sum_{k=1}^{\infty} a_k$ are all non-negative numbers, then the sequence $\{S_n\}$ of partial sums is a non-decreasing sequence. This sequence will converge if it is bounded (Theorem 114-2), and it will diverge if it is unbounded. Therefore, we have the following theorem.

THEOREM 116-1. *An infinite series of non-negative terms converges if, and only if, its sequence of partial sums is a bounded sequence.*

Example 116-1. Test the following series for convergence.

$$(116\text{-}1) \qquad 1 + \tfrac{1}{2} + \tfrac{1}{4} + \tfrac{1}{4} + \tfrac{1}{8} + \tfrac{1}{8} + \tfrac{1}{8} + \tfrac{1}{8} + \tfrac{1}{16} + \cdots,$$

where there are eight consecutive $\frac{1}{16}$'s, then sixteen consecutive $\frac{1}{32}$'s, and so on.

Solution. We will show that the sequence $\{S_n\}$ of partial sums of this series is unbounded; that is, that there is no limit to the size of its terms. For let us just consider those terms whose indices are powers of 2—S_1, S_2, S_4, S_8, and so on. We have $S_1 = 1 = \frac{2}{2}$, $S_2 = \frac{3}{2}$, $S_4 = \frac{4}{2}$, $S_8 = \frac{5}{2}$, and it is not hard to see that, in general, $S_{2^r} = \frac{r+2}{2}$. There is obviously no limit to the size of such numbers, and so the sequence $\{S_n\}$ is unbounded. Therefore, Theorem 116-1 tells us that our given series of positive terms diverges.

There is a very close analogy between infinite series and improper integrals. Thus the comparison test for the convergence of improper integrals has a counterpart that applies to infinite series.

THEOREM 116-2. *Suppose that $0 \leq a_k \leq b_k$ for each positive integer k. If the series $\sum_{k=1}^{\infty} b_k$ converges, then the series $\sum_{k=1}^{\infty} a_k$ converges. This conclusion also implies that if the series $\sum_{k=1}^{\infty} a_k$ diverges, then the series $\sum_{k=1}^{\infty} b_k$ diverges. We say that the series $\sum_{k=1}^{\infty} b_k$* ***dominates*** *the series $\sum_{k=1}^{\infty} a_k$.*

Proof. By hypothesis, the series of non-negative terms $\sum_{k=1}^{\infty} b_k$ is convergent and therefore, according to Theorem 116-1, its sequence $\{\sum_{k=1}^{n} b_k\}$ of partial sums is a bounded sequence. Now since $a_k \leq b_k$, we see that for each positive integer n, $\sum_{k=1}^{n} a_k \leq \sum_{k=1}^{n} b_k$. Hence it is clear that the sequence $\{\sum_{k=1}^{n} a_k\}$ of partial sums of the series $\sum_{k=1}^{\infty} a_k$ is also bounded, and so Theorem 116-1 tells us that the series $\sum_{k=1}^{\infty} a_k$ converges.

Example 116-2. Test the following series, known as the **harmonic series,** for convergence.

$$\sum_{k=1}^{\infty} \frac{1}{k} = 1 + \frac{1}{2} + \frac{1}{3} + \frac{1}{4} + \cdots. \tag{116-2}$$

Solution. We will compare this series with Series 116-1 of the preceding example. To make this comparison we write Series 116-1 on one line and Series 116-2 below it:

$$1 + \tfrac{1}{2} + \tfrac{1}{4} + \tfrac{1}{4} + \tfrac{1}{8} + \tfrac{1}{8} + \tfrac{1}{8} + \tfrac{1}{8} + \tfrac{1}{16} + \cdots,$$
$$1 + \tfrac{1}{2} + \tfrac{1}{3} + \tfrac{1}{4} + \tfrac{1}{5} + \tfrac{1}{6} + \tfrac{1}{7} + \tfrac{1}{8} + \tfrac{1}{9} + \cdots.$$

Now it is clear that the second series dominates the first. But we found in Example 116-1 that the first series is divergent, and therefore the comparison test tells us that the second series is divergent also.

Example 116-3. Test the following series for convergence.

$$\sum_{k=1}^{\infty} \frac{1}{(k+1)^2} = \frac{1}{2^2} + \frac{1}{3^2} + \frac{1}{4^2} + \cdots.$$

Solution. We already know (Example 115-2) that the series $\sum_{k=1}^{\infty} \frac{1}{k(k+1)}$ is convergent. Each term of this series is larger than the corresponding term of the given series. Therefore, the comparison test tells us that the given series $\sum_{k=1}^{\infty} \frac{1}{(k+1)^2}$ converges. We might notice that since the sum of our comparison series is $\sum_{k=1}^{\infty} \frac{1}{k(k+1)} = 1$, we have $\sum_{k=1}^{\infty} \frac{1}{(k+1)^2} < 1$.

If r is any index, then either both of the series $\sum_{k=1}^{\infty} a_k$ and $\sum_{k=r+1}^{\infty} a_k$ converge, or they both diverge; and if they both converge

$$\sum_{k=1}^{\infty} a_k = \sum_{k=1}^{r} a_k + \sum_{k=r+1}^{\infty} a_k. \tag{116-3}$$

(You should compare this equation with the corresponding result for improper integrals, Equation 112-1). For instance, Example 116-3 shows that the series $\frac{1}{2^2} + \frac{1}{3^2} + \frac{1}{4^2} + \cdots$ converges, and hence the series $\sum_{k=1}^{\infty} \frac{1}{k^2} = 1 + \frac{1}{2^2} + \frac{1}{3^2} + \cdots$ converges. (We will use this series as a comparison series in Example 116-6, and you will use it when you do the problems at the end of the section.)

Example 116-4. Estimate how well the sum of the first 6 terms approximates the sum of the series $\sum_{k=0}^{\infty} \frac{1}{k!} = 1 + \frac{1}{1!} + \frac{1}{2!} + \frac{1}{3!} + \cdots.$

Solution. The sum of our given series is the sum of the first 6 terms plus the "remainder after 6 terms"

$$\sum_{k=6}^{\infty} \frac{1}{k!} = \frac{1}{6!} + \frac{1}{7!} + \frac{1}{8!} + \cdots. \tag{116-4}$$

The remainder Series 116-4 is dominated by the series

$$\frac{1}{6!}+\frac{1}{6!7}+\frac{1}{6!7^2}+\frac{1}{6!7^3}+\cdots=\frac{1}{6!}\left[1+\frac{1}{7}+\left(\frac{1}{7}\right)^2+\cdots\right].$$

The series in the brackets is a geometric series whose sum is $\dfrac{1}{1-\frac{1}{7}}=\dfrac{7}{6}$, so the remainder is less than the number $\dfrac{1}{6!}\dfrac{7}{6}\approx .0016$.

The following "limit comparison test" is a simple consequence of Theorem 116-2. It doesn't do anything that our previous comparison test cannot do, but it is often much easier to apply to particular series.

THEOREM 116-3. *Let* $\sum_{k=1}^{\infty} a_k$ *and* $\sum_{k=1}^{\infty} b_k$ *be series of positive terms. If* $\lim_{k\to\infty}\dfrac{a_k}{b_k}=c$, *where* $c>0$, *then the series* $\sum_{k=1}^{\infty} a_k$ *converges if, and only if, the series* $\sum_{k=1}^{\infty} b_k$ *converges. If* $\lim_{k\to\infty}\dfrac{a_k}{b_k}=0$, *and if* $\sum_{k=1}^{\infty} b_k$ *converges, then the series* $\sum_{k=1}^{\infty} a_k$ *converges. (Notice in the second case—when the limit of the ratio* $\dfrac{a_k}{b_k}$ *is 0—that the divergence of the series* $\sum_{k=1}^{\infty} b_k$ *does* **not** *imply that the series* $\sum_{k\to 1}^{\infty} a_k$ *diverges.)*

Proof. We will write out the proof for the case in which $\lim_{k\to\infty}\dfrac{a_k}{b_k}$ is positive. The other case is treated in practically the same way and is left for the problems.

Since $\lim_{k\to\infty}\dfrac{a_k}{b_k}=c$, Theorem 114-1 tells us that there is an index r such that for $k \geq r$ the quotient $\dfrac{a_k}{b_k}$ is contained in the interval $\left(\dfrac{c}{2}, \dfrac{3c}{2}\right)$. Therefore, $\dfrac{c}{2}<\dfrac{a_k}{b_k}<\dfrac{3c}{2}$, and so $\dfrac{c}{2}b_k<a_k<\dfrac{3c}{2}b_k$. Thus the series $\sum_{k=r}^{\infty} a_k$ dominates the series $\sum_{k=r}^{\infty}\dfrac{c}{2}b_k$ and is dominated by the series $\sum_{k=r}^{\infty}\dfrac{3c}{2}b_k$. Hence, if the series $\sum_{k=1}^{\infty} b_k$ converges, then the series $\sum_{k=r}^{\infty}\dfrac{3c}{2}b_k$ converges, and so the series $\sum_{k=1}^{\infty} a_k$ converges. On the other hand, if the series $\sum_{k=1}^{\infty} b_k$ diverges, then the series $\sum_{k=r}^{\infty} \frac{c}{2} b_k$ diverges, and so the series $\sum_{k=1}^{\infty} a_k$ diverges.

Example 116-5. Test the series $\sum_{k=0}^{\infty} \frac{1}{5 \cdot 2^k + 3 \sin k}$ for convergence.

Solution. We will compare this series with the convergent geometric series $\sum_{k=0}^{\infty} \frac{1}{2^k}$, by investigating the limit of the ratio

$$\frac{\frac{1}{2^k}}{\frac{1}{5 \cdot 2^k + 3 \sin k}} = \frac{5 \cdot 2^k + 3 \sin k}{2^k} = 5 + \frac{3 \sin k}{2^k}.$$

Since $\lim_{k \to \infty} \left(5 + \frac{3 \sin k}{2^k}\right) = 5$, Theorem 116-3 tells us that our given series converges.

Example 116-6. Test for convergence: $\sum_{k=1}^{\infty} \frac{\ln k}{k^3}$.

Solution. Let $b_k = \frac{1}{k^2}$ and $a_k = \frac{\ln k}{k^3}$. With the aid of l'Hospital's Rule, we find that $\lim_{k \to \infty} \frac{a_k}{b_k} = 0$, and since the series $\sum_{k=1}^{\infty} \frac{1}{k^2}$ converges, Theorem 116-3 tells us that our given series converges also.

Problems 116

1. Use a comparison test to test the series for convergence.

(a) $\sum_{k=1}^{\infty} \frac{1}{k!}$ (b) $\sum_{k=1}^{\infty} \frac{1}{2k^2 - k}$

(c) $\sum_{k=1}^{\infty} \operatorname{sech} k$ (d) $\sum_{k=1}^{\infty} \frac{1}{k^k}$

(e) $\sum_{k=1}^{\infty} \frac{k^2 - k}{k + 100}$ (f) $\sum_{k=1}^{\infty} \frac{1}{k^5}$

(g) $\sum_{k=1}^{\infty} \frac{5}{2^k + k}$ (h) $\sum_{k=5}^{\infty} \frac{5}{2^k - k^2}$

2. We know that if $p = 2$, then the series $\sum_{k=1}^{\infty} \frac{1}{k^p}$ converges. Show that this fact implies that the series also converges if $p > 2$.

3. Use the facts mentioned in the preceding question and a comparison test to show that the following series converge.

(a) $\sum_{k=1}^{\infty} \frac{1}{3k^3 + 2k + 5}$ (b) $\sum_{k=1}^{\infty} \frac{4}{3k^3 - 2k - 5}$

(c) $\sum_{k=1}^{\infty} \frac{4k + 3}{3k^3 - 2k - 5}$ (d) $\sum_{k=1}^{\infty} \frac{9k^2}{(k + 1)(k + 2)(k + 3)(k + 4)}$

(e) $\sum_{k=1}^{\infty} \frac{1}{k^2 - 3}$ (f) $\sum_{k=1}^{\infty} \frac{k^2}{k^4 - 3}$

4. Use the fact that $0 < \sin x < x$, if $0 < x \leq 1$, and a comparison test to show that the series $\sum_{k=1}^{\infty} \sin\left(\frac{1}{k^2}\right)$ converges.

5. Use the series $\sum_{k=0}^{\infty} \left(\frac{e}{3}\right)^k$ as a comparison series to show that the following series converge.

(a) $\sum_{k=0}^{\infty} \frac{e^k}{2 + 3^k}$ (b) $\sum_{k=0}^{\infty} \frac{6e^k}{6 + 3^k}$ (c) $\sum_{k=0}^{\infty} \frac{1 + e^k}{k + 3^k}$

6. Estimate how well the sum of the first 11 terms approximates the sum of the series $1 + \frac{1}{1!} + \frac{1}{2!} + \frac{1}{3!} + \cdots$.

7. Prove the second case $\left(\text{when } \lim_{h \to \infty} \frac{a_k}{b_k} = 0\right)$ of Theorem 116-3.

8. Use Theorem 116-3 to prove that a series of positive numbers $\sum_{k=1}^{\infty} a_k$ converges if, and only if, the series $\sum_{k=1}^{\infty} \ln(1 + a_k)$ converges.

117. Alternating Series

Suppose that a series $\sum_{k=1}^{\infty} a_k$ has both positive and negative terms. Many convergence tests, such as the comparison tests of the last section, do not apply directly to such series. However, the comparison tests do apply to the series $\sum_{k=1}^{\infty} |a_k|$, and if this series converges, then the following theorem tells us that our original series converges. We discussed the analogous result for improper integrals in Section 113.

THEOREM 117-1. *If the series $\sum_{k=1}^{\infty} |a_k|$ converges, then the series $\sum_{k=1}^{\infty} a_k$ converges. (If $\sum_{k=1}^{\infty} |a_k|$ converges, we say that the series $\sum_{k=1}^{\infty} a_k$* ***converges absolutely.****)*

Proof. If the series $\sum_{k=1}^{\infty} |a_k|$ converges, then the series $\sum_{k=1}^{\infty} 2|a_k|$ converges. Thus since $0 \leq a_k + |a_k| \leq 2|a_k|$, a comparison test tells us that the series $\sum_{k=1}^{\infty} (a_k + |a_k|)$ converges. Now in Equation 115-7 we replace a_k with $a_k + |a_k|$ and b_k with $-|a_k|$, and we see that the series $\sum_{k=1}^{\infty} (a_k + |a_k| - |a_k|) = \sum_{k=1}^{\infty} a_k$ converges.

Example 117-1. Show that the series $\sum_{k=1}^{\infty} \frac{\sin k}{k^2}$ converges absolutely.

Solution. Since $\left|\frac{\sin k}{k^2}\right| \leq \frac{1}{k^2}$, and since (see Example 116-3) the series $\sum_{k=1}^{\infty} \frac{1}{k^2}$ converges, we see that the series $\sum_{k=1}^{\infty} \left|\frac{\sin k}{k^2}\right|$ converges. Hence our original series converges absolutely.

The converse of Theorem 117-1 is *not* true; that is, just because a series $\sum_{k=1}^{\infty} a_k$ converges, it does not follow that the series of absolute values $\sum_{k=1}^{\infty} |a_k|$ converges. For example, let us change the sign of every other term in Series 116-1 to obtain the series

$$(117\text{-}1) \qquad 1 - \tfrac{1}{2} + \tfrac{1}{4} - \tfrac{1}{4} + \tfrac{1}{8} - \tfrac{1}{8} + \tfrac{1}{8} - \tfrac{1}{8} + \tfrac{1}{16} - \cdots.$$

In Example 116-1 we showed that this series is *not* absolutely convergent. Nevertheless, it is convergent, as we will now see. To investigate the convergence of Series 117-1, we look at its sequence of partial sums and find that

$$S_1 = 1,\ S_2 = \tfrac{1}{2},\ S_3 = \tfrac{3}{4},\ S_4 = \tfrac{1}{2},\ S_5 = \tfrac{5}{8},\ S_6 = \tfrac{1}{2},\ S_7 = \tfrac{5}{8},\ S_8 = \tfrac{1}{2},\ S_9 = \tfrac{7}{16},$$

and so on. We immediately observe that each term with an even index is $\frac{1}{2}$. Therefore, for any index n, one of the numbers S_n and S_{n-1} is $\frac{1}{2}$. Now the difference $S_n - S_{n-1}$ is the nth term of Series 117-1, and since the terms of this series approach 0, we see that S_n and S_{n-1} are close together if n is large. Thus for a large index n, S_n either equals or is close to $\frac{1}{2}$. It is therefore apparent that $\lim_{n\to\infty} S_n = \frac{1}{2}$; that is, $\frac{1}{2}$ is the sum of Series 117-1.

A series such as Series 117-1 which converges, but which does not converge absolutely, is said to be **conditionally convergent.**

Series 117-1 is typical of the class of infinite series that we are now going to study. An **alternating series** is a series that takes the form

$$\sum_{k=1}^{\infty} (-1)^{k+1} a_k = a_1 - a_2 + a_3 - a_4 + \cdots, \tag{117-2}$$

where each of the numbers a_1, a_2, a_3, ... is positive. We will now show that those alternating series for which

$$a_1 \geq a_2 \geq a_3 \geq \cdots \tag{117-3}$$

and

$$\lim_{k \to \infty} a_k = 0 \tag{117-4}$$

are convergent. Series 117-1 is such a series, and you should keep this example in mind as we take up the general case.

To show that Hypotheses 117-3 and 117-4 guarantee the convergence of Series 117-2, we must show that the sequence $\{S_n\}$ of partial sums of this series has a limit. We will find it easy to show that the subsequence that consists of the partial sums with odd indices converges (the subsequence consisting of partial sums with even indices would also serve as a starting point). Then we use the fact, Hypothesis 117-4, that the terms of our series approach 0 to see that the limit of the partial sums with odd indices is the limit of the sequence $\{S_n\}$ itself.

So now let us turn our attention to those partial sums with odd indices:

$$\begin{aligned} S_1 &= a_1, \\ S_3 &= a_1 - a_2 + a_3, \\ S_5 &= a_1 - a_2 + a_3 - a_4 + a_5, \\ &\cdots \\ S_{2k+1} &= a_1 - a_2 + a_3 - a_4 + \cdots + a_{2k-1} - a_{2k} + a_{2k+1}, \\ &\cdots. \end{aligned}$$

We see that $S_1 - S_3 = a_2 - a_3$. According to Hypothesis 117-3, $a_2 - a_3 \geq 0$, and so $S_1 \geq S_3$. Similarly, $S_3 - S_5 = a_4 - a_5 \geq 0$, and hence $S_3 \geq S_5$, and so on. Thus our hypothesis that $\{a_n\}$ is a non-increasing sequence implies that the sequence $S_1, S_3, S_5, S_7, \ldots$ is also non-increasing. Now suppose that we group the terms in the sum S_{2k+1} in pairs as follows:

$$S_{2k+1} = (a_1 - a_2) + (a_3 - a_4) + \cdots + (a_{2k-1} - a_{2k}) + a_{2k+1}.$$

According to our hypotheses, each term in parentheses is greater than or equal to 0, and $a_{2k+1} > 0$. Hence $S_{2k+1} > 0$. Thus the sequence S_1, S_3, S_5, ... is not only non-increasing, but each term is greater than 0, so the sequence is bounded below. Therefore, Theorem 114-3 tells us that this sequence converges, and hence there exists a number S such that $\lim_{k\to\infty} S_{2k+1} = S$. Now we make use of Hypothesis 117-4 to see that the number S is the limit of the sequence $\{S_n\}$ itself. The essence of the argument is this. The difference $S_n - S_{n-1}$ of two consecutive terms in the sequence $\{S_n\}$ is the nth term of our Series 117-2. According to Hypothesis 117-4, the terms of this series approach 0, so if n is large, the numbers S_n and S_{n-1} do not differ by much. Therefore, if one of these numbers is a good approximation to S, so is the other. But we know that either S_n or S_{n-1} approximates S, because one of the indices n or $n - 1$ must be odd. Thus, regardless of whether n is even or odd, S_n approximates S if n is large. It follows that S is the limit of our sequence $\{S_n\}$ of the partial sums of the alternating Series 117-2, and so this series is convergent under the Hypotheses 117-3 and 117-4.

Example 117-2. Test the following series for convergence.

$$1 - \tfrac{1}{2} + \tfrac{1}{3} - \tfrac{1}{4} + \cdots. \tag{117-5}$$

Solution. This series is an alternating series $\sum_{k=1}^{\infty} (-1)^{k+1}a_k$, with $a_k = \frac{1}{k}$. Since $a_{k+1} = \frac{1}{k+1} < \frac{1}{k} = a_k$, we see that Hypothesis 117-3 is satisfied. Furthermore, $\lim_{k\to\infty} a_k = \lim_{k\to\infty} \frac{1}{k} = 0$, and so Hypothesis 117-4 is also fulfilled. Therefore, our series converges. If we replace each term in Series 117-5 with its absolute value, we obtain the harmonic series $1 + \frac{1}{2} + \frac{1}{3} + \frac{1}{4} + \cdots$ which we found to be divergent (Example 116-2). Therefore, our given series is conditionally convergent.

In order to apply our alternating series test to a given series

$$\sum_{k=1}^{\infty} (-1)^{k+1}a_k,$$

we must show that each term of the sequence $\{a_k\}$ is not less than its successor; that is, we must show that

$$a_k \geq a_{k+1}.$$

Sometimes it is more convenient to verify this inequality when it is written in one of the forms

$$a_k - a_{k+1} \geq 0 \quad \text{or} \quad \frac{a_{k+1}}{a_k} \leq 1.$$

We can even use calculus, as the following example shows.

Example 117-3. Test the series $\sum_{k=1}^{\infty} (-1)^{k+1} \frac{k}{1+k^2}$ for convergence.

Solution. It is clear that $\lim_{k \to \infty} \frac{k}{1+k^2} = 0$, so Hypothesis 117-4 is satisfied. To show that the sequence $\left\{\frac{k}{1+k^2}\right\}$ is non-increasing, we will proceed as follows. We note that the terms of this sequence are the values at the positive integers of the function defined by the equation $f(x) = x/(1+x^2)$. We can readily calculate $f'(x) = (1-x^2)/(1+x^2)^2$, and we see that $f'(x) < 0$ if $x > 1$. Hence f is a decreasing function. It follows that $f(k+1) < f(k)$ for each positive integer k, and so our sequence is non-increasing. Thus Hypothesis 117-3, as well as Hypothesis 117-4, is satisfied, and therefore our series converges.

We have seen that a series that satisfies Hypotheses 117-3 and 117-4 converges. But we can say still more about such a series. The partial sums of Series 117-2 which have even subscripts are

$$S_2 = a_1 - a_2,\ S_4 = S_2 + a_3 - a_4,\ S_6 = S_4 + a_5 - a_6,$$

and so on. Thus each even partial sum is obtained from the preceding even sum by adding to it a non-negative number. Therefore, the sequence $S_2, S_4, \ldots$ is non-decreasing, and so we see that the even partial sums approach the limit S from below, whereas the odd sums approach S from above, as illustrated in Fig. 117-1. From the figure it is apparent that the difference between the term S_n and the sum S cannot be greater than the difference between S_n and S_{n+1}; that is,

$$(117\text{-}6) \qquad |S - S_n| \leq |S_n - S_{n+1}| = a_{n+1}.$$

Figure 117-1

For example, for the sequence illustrated in Fig. 117-1

$$|S - S_5| < |S_5 - S_6| = a_6.$$

The number $R_n = S - S_n$ is called the **remainder after n terms** of the series $\sum_{k=1}^{\infty} a_k$. It represents the error that one makes by taking the number S_n as an approximation of the sum S of the series. Inequality 117-6 tells us that if we take S_n as an approximation of the sum of an alternating series that satisfies Hypotheses 117-3 and 117-4, then the remainder will be no larger than the first term that we do not use when we form the partial sum S_n. Let us summarize our results concerning alternating series in a theorem.

THEOREM 117-2. *Let* $\{a_k\}$ *be a non-increasing sequence of positive numbers such that* $\lim_{k\to\infty} a_k = 0$. *Then the alternating series*

$$\sum_{k=1}^{\infty} (-1)^{k+1}a_k = a_1 - a_2 + a_3 - a_4 + a_5 - a_6 + \cdots$$

converges to a sum S, *and for each integer* n,

$$|S - S_n| \leq a_{n+1}.$$

Example 117-4. Show that the series

$$\sum_{k=0}^{\infty} \frac{(-1)^k}{k!} = 1 - \frac{1}{1!} + \frac{1}{2!} - \frac{1}{3!} + \cdots$$

converges, and approximate its sum with an error of less than .01.

Solution. Clearly the terms of the sequence $\left\{\frac{1}{k!}\right\}$ decrease, and their limit is 0. Therefore, our series converges to a sum S. The number

$$S_4 = 1 - 1 + \tfrac{1}{2} - \tfrac{1}{6} + \tfrac{1}{24} = \tfrac{3}{8}$$

will differ (in absolute value) from S by less than the first unused term—namely, $\frac{1}{5!} = \frac{1}{120}$, and this number is less than .01. We will see later that the sum of this series is the number $1/e = .368$, so our actual remainder is the number $\frac{1}{e} - \frac{3}{8} = .368 - .375 = -.007$.

Although infinite series enjoy many of the properties of ordinary sums, series and sums are not the same in all respects. Let us illustrate this statement by performing a few manipulations with Series 117-5. Since this series converges, there is a number S such that

(117-7) $$S = 1 - \tfrac{1}{2} + \tfrac{1}{3} - \tfrac{1}{4} + \tfrac{1}{5} - \tfrac{1}{6} + \tfrac{1}{7} - \tfrac{1}{8} + \cdots.$$

Hence $$\tfrac{1}{2}S = \tfrac{1}{2} - \tfrac{1}{4} + \tfrac{1}{6} - \tfrac{1}{8} + \cdots,$$

and so when we add these two series we obtain

(117-8) $$\tfrac{3}{2}S = 1 + \tfrac{1}{3} - \tfrac{1}{2} + \tfrac{1}{5} + \tfrac{1}{7} - \tfrac{1}{4} + \tfrac{1}{9} + \cdots.$$

If you write out this addition for a large number of terms, you will readily convince yourself that the series on the right side of Equation 117-8 contains the same terms as the series on the right side of Equation 117-7. Since the value of an ordinary sum is independent of the order of its terms, we are naturally tempted to conclude that these series also have the same sum, and thus that $\frac{3}{2}S = S$. It would therefore follow that $S = 0$. But you can easily check (Theorem 117-2) that $\frac{1}{2} < S < 1$, so we must have gone wrong somewhere. We erred when we tried to conclude that just because the series in Equations 117-7 and 117-8 contain the same terms, then they have the same sum. It can be shown that if two series have the same terms, and if one of the series converges absolutely, then the other series also converges absolutely and the two sums are the same. However, in the case of conditionally convergent series (such as the series in Equations 117-7 and 117-8) the sums of two series containing the same terms (but in different orders) need not be equal.

Problems 117

1. Test each series for absolute convergence.

   (a) $\sum_{k=1}^{\infty} \frac{\sin k}{2^k}$ (b) $\sum_{k=1}^{\infty} \frac{e^{\sin k}}{k^2}$

   (c) $\sum_{k=1}^{\infty} \frac{\sin e^k}{e^k}$ (d) $\sum_{k=1}^{\infty} (-1)^{k+1} \frac{(k+2)}{k^3-3}$

2. Does the series $\sum_{k=0}^{\infty} \frac{\cos k\pi}{2k-1}$ converge? Does it converge absolutely?

3. Test each series for convergence and for absolute convergence.

   (a) $\sum_{k=2}^{\infty} \frac{(-1)^k}{\ln k}$ (b) $\sum_{k=1}^{\infty} \frac{(-1)^{k+1}}{\sqrt{k}}$

   (c) $\sum_{k=1}^{\infty} (-1)^{k+1} \frac{\sqrt{3k-2}}{k}$ (d) $\sum_{k=1}^{\infty} (-1)^{k+1} \ln\left(1+\frac{1}{k}\right)$

4. Theorem 117-2 states that the absolute value of the error involved in approximating the sum of the series $1 - \frac{2}{3} + (\frac{2}{3})^2 - (\frac{2}{3})^3 + \cdots$ by taking the sum of the first n terms is no larger than $(\frac{2}{3})^n$. What is the actual absolute value of the error?

5. It can be shown that $\pi = 4(1 - \frac{1}{3} + \frac{1}{5} - \frac{1}{7} + \cdots)$. How many terms must we add together so that Theorem 117-2 will guarantee that the error in our approximation of π is no more than .01?

6. Find an upper bound for the absolute value of the error obtained by approximating the sum of the series by the first 4 terms of the series

   (a) $\sum_{k=1}^{\infty} \frac{(-1)^{k+1}}{k}$ (b) $\sum_{k=1}^{\infty} \frac{(-1)^{k+1}}{k^2 10^k}$ (c) $\sum_{k=0}^{\infty} \frac{(-1)^k}{2^k}$ (d) $\sum_{k=0}^{\infty} \frac{\sin (k+\frac{1}{2})\pi}{k^2}$

7. Approximate the sum of the series with an error whose absolute value is no more than indicated.

(a) $\frac{1}{3} \cdot 2! - \frac{1}{5} \cdot 3! + \frac{1}{7} \cdot 4! - \frac{1}{9} \cdot 5! + \cdots, \ |E| \leq .001$

(b) $1 - \dfrac{1}{2!2^2} + \dfrac{1}{4!2^4} - \dfrac{1}{6!2^6} + \cdots, \ |E| \leq .00005$

(c) $\frac{1}{3} - (\frac{1}{3})(\frac{1}{3})^3 + (\frac{1}{5})(\frac{1}{3})^5 - (\frac{1}{7})(\frac{1}{3})^7 + \cdots, \ |E| \leq .00005$

8. It can be shown that $1/e = \sum_{n=0}^{\infty} (-1)^n/n!$. Approximate $1/e$ correct to 3 decimal places.

9. Show that Hypothesis 117-3 is satisfied for the series $\sum_{k=0}^{\infty} (-1)^{k+1}k/(3k-1)$. Does the series converge?

10. The graph of a certain function f is the polygonal line joining the points (0, 0), (1, 1), $(2, -\frac{1}{2})$, $(3, \frac{1}{3})$, $(4, -\frac{1}{4})$, and so on. Let $a_k = \int_k^{k+1} f(x)\, dx$. Does the series $\sum_{k=0}^{\infty} a_k$ converge? Does the improper integral $\int_0^{\infty} f(x)\, dx$ converge?

118. The Integral Test

We have mentioned the close relationship between improper integrals of the form $\int_a^{\infty} f(x)\, dx$ and infinite series $\sum_{k=1}^{\infty} a_k$, and we will develop some further aspects of this relationship in this section. Suppose that f is a decreasing function such that $f(x) > 0$ for x in the interval $[1, \infty]$. The graph of such a function is shown in Fig. 118-1. Let us investigate

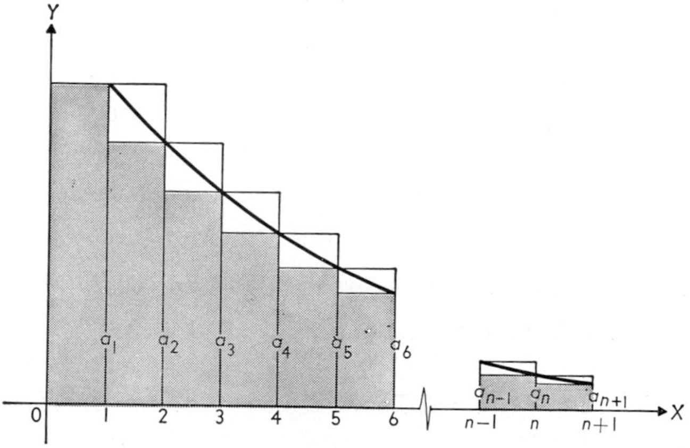

Figure 118-1

the convergence of the series

(118-1) $$\sum_{k=1}^{\infty} a_k = a_1 + a_2 + a_3 + \cdots$$

whose terms are given by the equations

$$a_k = f(k), \quad k = 1, 2, 3, \ldots .$$

In Fig. 118-1 we have constructed rectangles of base 1 and altitudes $a_1, a_2, \ldots$. The areas of these rectangles are the terms of Series 118-1, $a_1, a_2, a_3, \ldots$. Sums of the areas of these rectangles are partial sums of our series. Thus, for example, the sum of the areas of the "interior" (shaded) rectangles that lie between the lines $x = 0$ and $x = n$ is the partial sum $S_n = a_1 + a_2 + \cdots + a_n$. This same partial sum is also the sum of the areas of the "exterior" rectangles that lie between the lines $x = 1$ and $x = n + 1$. Now we observe that this collection of "exterior" rectangles contains the region R that is bounded by the graph of f, the X-axis, and the lines $x = 1$ and $x = n$. This region R, in turn, contains all the shaded interior rectangles that lie to the left of the line $x = n$, except the first. Therefore, since the area of the region R is given by the integral $\int_1^n f(x)\,dx$, we have the inequalities

$$\int_1^n f(x)\,dx \leq S_n \quad \text{and} \quad a_2 + a_3 + \cdots + a_n \leq \int_1^n f(x)\,dx.$$

If we add a_1 to both sides of the second inequality, we get $S_n \leq a_1 + \int_1^n f(x)\,dx$, and so we have

(118-2) $$\int_1^n f(x)\,dx \leq S_n \leq a_1 + \int_1^n f(x)\,dx.$$

Because Series 118-1 is a series of positive terms, the question of whether or not it converges reduces to the question of whether or not its sequence of partial sums is bounded. From Inequalities 118-2 we see that the sequence $\{S_n\}$ is bounded if, and only if, the sequence $\left\{\int_1^n f(x)\,dx\right\}$ is bounded, and, since $f(x) \geq 0$, we know that this sequence is bounded if, and only if, the improper integral $\int_1^\infty f(x)\,dx$ converges. Therefore, we have the following theorem.

THEOREM 118-1 (**The Integral Test**). *An infinite series whose terms are the values at the positive integers of a decreasing, positive function f converges if, and only if, the improper integral $\int_1^\infty f(x)\,dx$ converges.*

Example 118-1. Use the integral test to examine the convergence of the series $\sum_{k=1}^{\infty} \frac{1}{1+k^2}$.

Solution. According to Theorem 118-1, the given series converges if, and only if, the improper integral $\int_1^{\infty} \frac{dx}{1+x^2}$ converges. Therefore, we investigate the limit of the proper integrals of the form

$$\int_1^n \frac{dx}{1+x^2} = \operatorname{Tan}^{-1} x \Big|_1^n = \operatorname{Tan}^{-1} n - \frac{\pi}{4}.$$

Since $\lim_{n\to\infty} \operatorname{Tan}^{-1} n = \frac{\pi}{2}$, we see that the integral $\int_1^{\infty} \frac{dx}{1+x^2}$ is convergent, and so our given series is convergent.

Example 118-2. For what choices of the exponent p is the ***p*-series** $\sum_{k=1}^{\infty} \frac{1}{k^p}$ convergent?

Solution. The integral test says that the p-series will converge if, and only if, the improper integral $\int_1^{\infty} \frac{dx}{x^p}$ converges. We found in Example 112-2 that the improper integral converges if $p > 1$ and diverges if $p \leq 1$. Thus

$$\sum_{k=1}^{\infty} \frac{1}{k^p} \text{ (the } p\text{-series)} \begin{cases} \text{converges if } p > 1. \\ \text{diverges if } p \leq 1. \end{cases}$$

Example 118-3. Use the integral test to test the series $\sum_{k=3}^{\infty} \frac{1}{k^2-4}$ for convergence.

Solution. Just because the index of summation starts with a number other than 1 is, of course, no reason why we cannot use the integral test. This series converges if, and only if, the improper integral $\int_3^{\infty} \frac{dx}{x^2-4}$ converges. Since

$$\lim_{n\to\infty} \int_3^n \frac{dx}{x^2-4} = \lim_{n\to\infty} \frac{1}{4} \ln\left(\frac{x-2}{x+2}\right)\Big|_3^n = \frac{1}{4} \ln 5,$$

we see that the integral, and hence the series, converges.

Theorem 118-1 says that the sequence $\{S_n\}$ of partial sums of Series 118-1 and the sequence $\left\{\int_1^n f(x)\,dx\right\}$ of integrals of f either both converge or both diverge. Of course, if they both converge, we know that the sequence of differences $\{d_n\}$, where $d_n = S_n - \int_1^n f(x)\,dx$, converges. The following example illustrates the fact that the sequence of differences also converges even when the sequence of partial sums and the sequence of integrals diverge. (Also, see Question 10 of the Problems of this section.)

Example 118-4. Suppose that $d_n = 1 + \frac{1}{2} + \frac{1}{3} + \cdots + 1/n - \ln n$. Show that $\lim_{n\to\infty} d_n$ exists.

Solution. If we set $f(x) = 1/x$, Inequalities 118-2 become

$$\ln n \leq 1 + \tfrac{1}{2} + \cdots + 1/n \leq 1 + \ln n.$$

Therefore, $0 \leq 1 + \frac{1}{2} + \cdots + 1/n - \ln n = d_n \leq 1$, and so the sequence $\{d_n\}$ is bounded. Now for each positive integer n,

$$\begin{aligned} d_n - d_{n+1} &= (1 + \tfrac{1}{2} + \cdots + 1/n - \ln n) \\ &\qquad - (1 + \cdots + 1/n + 1/(n+1) - \ln(n+1)) \\ &= \ln(n+1) - \ln n - 1/(n+1). \end{aligned}$$

If we can show that this difference is greater than or equal to 0, then we shall have shown that $d_n \geq d_{n+1}$ and that therefore $\{d_n\}$ is a bounded, non-increasing sequence and so has a limit. Therefore, let us show that

$$\text{(118-3)} \qquad \ln(n+1) - \ln n \geq 1/(n+1).$$

The number $\ln(n+1) - \ln n$ is given by the integral $\int_n^{n+1} \frac{dx}{x}$. For x in the interval $[n, n+1]$, it is clear that $\frac{1}{x} \geq \frac{1}{n+1}$, and hence

$$\int_n^{n+1} \frac{dx}{x} \geq \int_n^{n+1} \frac{dx}{n+1} = \frac{1}{n+1}.$$

Thus we have verified Inequality 118-3, and we now know that the sequence $\{d_n\}$ is convergent. The number $\lim_{n\to\infty} (1 + \frac{1}{2} + \cdots + 1/n - \ln n)$ is called **Euler's Constant,** and it is denoted by the Greek letter γ. It can be shown that $\gamma = .5772156\ldots$.

Not only can we use improper integrals to test the convergence of infinite series, but we can use series to examine the convergence of improper integrals, as the following example illustrates.

Example 118-5. Test the improper integral $\int_0^\infty \frac{\sin x}{x}\,dx$ for convergence.

Solution. If we break up the positive X-axis into the intervals $[0, \pi]$, $[\pi, 2\pi]$, $[2\pi, 3\pi]$, and so on, then our integral converges if, and only if, the following series converges:

$$\int_0^{\pi} \frac{\sin x}{x}\, dx + \int_{\pi}^{2\pi} \frac{\sin x}{x}\, dx + \int_{2\pi}^{3\pi} \frac{\sin x}{x}\, dx + \cdots. \tag{118-4}$$

The nth term of this series is given by the formula

$$a_n = \int_{(n-1)\pi}^{n\pi} \frac{\sin x}{x}\, dx.$$

We see that our series is an alternating series since, for x in the interval $((n - 1)\pi, n\pi)$, $\sin x$ is positive if n is odd and negative if n is even. In either case

$$\frac{|\sin x|}{n\pi} \leq \left| \frac{\sin x}{x} \right| \leq \frac{|\sin x|}{(n-1)\pi},$$

and so

$$\int_{(n-1)\pi}^{n\pi} \frac{|\sin x|}{n\pi}\, dx \leq \int_{(n-1)\pi}^{n\pi} \left| \frac{\sin x}{x} \right| dx \leq \int_{(n-1)\pi}^{n\pi} \frac{|\sin x|}{(n-1)\pi}\, dx. \tag{118-5}$$

Now we observe that $\int_{(n-1)\pi}^{n\pi} |\sin x|\, dx = \int_0^{\pi} \sin x\, dx = 2$, and $|a_n| = \int_{(n-1)\pi}^{n\pi} \left| \frac{\sin x}{x} \right| dx$. Therefore, Inequalities 118-5 give us the inequalities

$$\frac{2}{n\pi} \leq |a_n| \leq \frac{2}{(n-1)\pi}. \tag{118-6}$$

From these inequalities we see that $\lim_{n \to \infty} a_n = 0$. Furthermore, if we replace n with $n + 1$ we have $\frac{2}{(n+1)\pi} \leq |a_{n+1}| \leq \frac{2}{n\pi}$, and hence $|a_{n+1}| \leq |a_n|$. Thus Series 118-4 is an alternating series whose terms decrease in absolute value. According to the alternating series test, this series therefore converges, and so we see that the integral $\int_0^{\infty} \frac{\sin x}{x}\, dx$ converges. The integral $\int_0^{\infty} \left| \frac{\sin x}{x} \right| dx$ converges if, and only if, the Series 118-4 converges absolutely. But Inequalities 118-6 say that the series $\sum_{k=1}^{\infty} |a_k|$ dominates the divergent series $\sum_{k=1}^{\infty} \frac{2}{k\pi}$, so $\sum_{k=1}^{\infty} |a_k|$ diverges, and hence the integral $\int_0^{\infty} \left| \frac{\sin x}{x} \right| dx$ is divergent. Therefore, our given improper integral is conditionally convergent.

Problems 118

1. Use the integral test to test for convergence.

(a) $\sum_{k=1}^{\infty} \frac{1}{k\sqrt{k}}$ (b) $\sum_{n=0}^{\infty} \frac{1}{2^n}$

(c) $\sum_{r=1}^{\infty} \frac{r}{e^{r^2}}$ (d) $\sum_{k=0}^{\infty} \frac{1}{k^2+4}$

(e) $\sum_{n=2}^{\infty} \frac{\ln n}{n}$ (f) $\sum_{k=1}^{\infty} \coth k$

(g) $\sum_{k=1}^{\infty} \frac{1}{k\sqrt{k^2+3}}$ (h) $\sum_{j=0}^{\infty} e^{-j}$

(i) $\sum_{n=1}^{\infty} ne^{-n}$ (j) $\sum_{n=1}^{\infty} \frac{1}{3+\sqrt{n}}$

2. Test the following series for convergence.

(a) $\sum_{n=1}^{\infty} \frac{2+\cos n}{n^2}$ (b) $\sum_{n=1}^{\infty} \frac{1}{\sqrt{n^2+1}}$

(c) $\sum_{n=1}^{\infty} \frac{1}{(2n-1)2n}$ (d) $\sum_{k=2}^{\infty} \frac{1}{k\sqrt{k^2-3}}$

(e) $\sum_{n=3}^{\infty} \frac{\cos n + e^{-n}}{n^3-2n+4}$ (f) $\sum_{n=1}^{\infty} \frac{1}{\sqrt{n(n+1)}}$

3. Can you use the integral test to test the series $\sum_{k=1}^{\infty} \frac{\sin^2 k}{k^2}$? Does the series converge?

4. Let p be a positive number. Show that $\sum_{k=2}^{\infty} 1/k(\ln k)^p$ converges if $p > 1$ and diverges if $0 < p \leq 1$.

5. Let $L = \lim_{n\to\infty} \int_1^n f(x)\,dx$, where $a_k = f(k)$. Conclude from Inequalities 118-2 that $L \leq \sum_{k=1}^{\infty} a_k \leq L + a_1$.

6. Let $\zeta(p)$ be the sum of the p-series for $p > 1$. Clearly $\zeta(p) \geq 1$. Use the result in the preceding question to show that $\zeta(p) \leq p/(p-1)$.

7. Let $0 < r < 1$. Use the integral test to show that the geometric series $\sum_{k=0}^{\infty} r^k$ converges. With the aid of Question 5 show that $-1/\ln r \leq 1/(1-r) \leq -1/\ln r + 1$.

8. In Example 118-1 we found that $\sum_{k=1}^{\infty} \frac{1}{1+k^2}$ converges. Let S be its sum. Use the result in Question 5 to estimate S.

9. Show that if $\lim_{n\to\infty} na_n = L$, then the series $\sum_{k=1}^{\infty} a_k$ is divergent unless $L = 0$. Give an example of a divergent series $\sum_{n=1}^{\infty} a_n$ such that $\lim_{n\to\infty} na_n = 0$, and of a convergent series $\sum_{n=0}^{\infty} b_n$ such that $\lim_{n\to\infty} nb_n = 0$.

10. Suppose that f is a decreasing function that takes only positive values. Show that $\lim_{n\to\infty} \left[f(1) + f(2) + \cdots + f(n) - \int_1^n f(x)\,dx\right]$ exists.

119. Ratio Tests

In this section we shall develop some of the most frequently used tests for the convergence of infinite series, the **ratio tests.** These tests are applied to determine divergence or absolute convergence, so in addition to a given series

(119-1) $$a_1 + a_2 + a_3 + \cdots,$$

we shall consider the series of positive terms

(119-2) $$|a_1| + |a_2| + |a_3| + \cdots.$$

Let us first suppose that, after a certain index, the ratio of any term in the Series 119-2 to the preceding term is less than or equal to a number q which itself is less than 1. For example, if we take the ratio of any term beyond the 5th to the preceding term in the series

$$\frac{3}{1!} + \frac{3^2}{2!} + \frac{3^3}{3!} + \frac{3^4}{4!} + \cdots + \frac{3^n}{n!} + \cdots,$$

we will obtain a number that is less than or equal to $\frac{1}{2}$, and $\frac{1}{2}$, in turn, is less than 1. Thus we are assuming that there is an index N such that for any index $n > N$ we have the inequality

(119-3) $$\frac{|a_{n+1}|}{|a_n|} \leq q < 1.$$

We have already pointed out that the convergence of an infinite series is unaffected if we ignore any initial segment of the series, so we may check on the convergence of our Series 119-2 by investigating the convergence of the series

(119-4) $$|a_{N+1}| + |a_{N+2}| + |a_{N+3}| + \cdots.$$

Now we apply Inequality 119-3. Since $N + 1 > N$, we may replace n

with $N + 1$ in Inequality 119-3 to obtain

$$\frac{|a_{N+2}|}{|a_{N+1}|} \leq q,$$

and so

$$|a_{N+2}| \leq |a_{N+1}|q.$$

Similarly, $\dfrac{|a_{N+3}|}{|a_{N+2}|} \leq q$, and so $|a_{N+3}| \leq |a_{N+2}|q$. But we have just seen that $|a_{N+2}| \leq |a_{N+1}|q$, and therefore

$$|a_{N+3}| \leq |a_{N+1}|q^2.$$

We can continue in this way and show that

$$|a_{N+4}| \leq |a_{N+1}|q^3, \quad |a_{N+5}| \leq |a_{N+1}|q^4, \text{ and so on.}$$

We therefore conclude that the Series 119-4 is dominated by the series

$$|a_{N+1}| + |a_{N+1}|q + |a_{N+1}|q^2 + \cdots = |a_{N+1}|(1 + q + q^2 + \cdots).$$

The series in parentheses is the geometric series with a ratio of q. Since we are assuming that $0 < q < 1$, it follows that this series converges, and (according to the comparison test) its convergence implies the convergence of Series 119-2 and thus the absolute convergence of Series 119-1. We have proved the following theorem.

THEOREM 119-1. *If after some term in the infinite series* $\sum_{n=1}^{\infty} a_n$ *we have* $\dfrac{|a_{n+1}|}{|a_n|} \leq q$, *where* q *is a number that is less than* 1, *then the series is absolutely convergent.*

Example 119-1. Show that the series $\sum_{n=1}^{\infty} \dfrac{1}{n!} = 1 + \dfrac{1}{2!} + \dfrac{1}{3!} + \cdots$ is convergent.

Solution. The nth term of this series is given by the formula $a_n = \dfrac{1}{n!}$.

Hence

$$\frac{|a_{n+1}|}{|a_n|} = \frac{1/(n+1)!}{1/n!} = \frac{n!}{(n+1)!} = \frac{1}{(n+1)}.$$

This quotient is less than or equal to $\frac{1}{2}$ for each index n, so we see that the series converges.

In order to use Theorem 119-1 to show that a series converges, we must show that the ratios of the absolute values of successive terms are ultimately less than or equal to a number q which itself is actually less than 1. The analogous test for divergence does not require us to be so careful. Suppose that after some index N,

$$\frac{|a_{n+1}|}{|a_n|} \geq 1. \tag{119-5}$$

Inequality 119-5 means that the absolute value of a_{n+1} is at least as large as the absolute value of its predecessor. It follows that the terms of our series do not approach 0, and therefore (See Theorem 115-1) the series is divergent. We have the following theorem.

THEOREM 119-2. *If after a certain term in an infinite series* $\sum_{n=1}^{\infty} a_n$ *we have* $\frac{|a_{n+1}|}{|a_n|} \geq 1$, *then the series is divergent.*

In order to apply Theorem 119-1 or Theorem 119-2 we must show that the appropriate one of the Inequalities 119-3 or 119-5 holds for each integer n larger than some particular integer N. Thus we must really verify infinitely many inequalities. One method of showing that these inequalities hold is to calculate the limit of the quotient $\frac{|a_{n+1}|}{|a_n|}$, if this limit exists. Let us suppose that

$$\lim_{n\to\infty} \frac{|a_{n+1}|}{|a_n|} = L,$$

and consider the three cases, $L < 1, L > 1$, and $L = 1$. In the first case we choose q to be any number between L and 1; thus $L < q < 1$. Then the open interval $(L - 1, q)$, for example, contains L, and hence, according to Theorem 114-1, there is a number N such that for $n > N$ the quotient $\frac{|a_{n+1}|}{|a_n|}$ lies in this interval. Thus we have shown that there is an index N beyond which the quotient is less than q. Therefore, if $L < 1$, then the hypotheses of Theorem 119-1 are satisfied, and so our series converges absolutely. Now suppose that $L > 1$. Then the open interval $(1, L + 1)$ contains L, and so there is an index N such that for $n > N$ the quotient $\frac{|a_{n+1}|}{|a_n|}$ lies in this interval. Thus we have shown that there is an index N beyond which the quotient is greater than 1. Therefore, if $L > 1$ the hypotheses of Theorem 119-2 are satisfied, and we see that our series diverges. We have considered the case when $L < 1$ and the case when $L > 1$; there still remains the possibility that $L = 1$. This information is not enough to tell us whether our series converges or diverges, as the example of the p-series $\sum_{n=1}^{\infty} 1/n^p$ shows. Here the ratio $\frac{|a_{n+1}|}{|a_n|}$ is

$$\frac{n^p}{(n+1)^p} = \left(\frac{n}{n+1}\right)^p,$$

and its limit is 1, regardless of the choice of p. But we know that the p-series converges if $p > 1$ and diverges if $p \leq 1$, so we see that there are both convergent and divergent series for which $\lim_{n \to \infty} \frac{|a_{n+1}|}{|a_n|} = 1$. Thus we have the following theorem.

THEOREM 119-3. *Suppose that* $\lim_{n \to \infty} \frac{|a_{n+1}|}{|a_n|} = L$. *Then*

(i) if $L < 1$, *the series* $\sum_{n=1}^{\infty} a_n$ *converges absolutely,*

(ii) if $L > 1$, *the series* $\sum_{n=1}^{\infty} a_n$ *diverges, and*

(iii) if $L = 1$, *we need further information to determine whether or not the series converges.*

Example 119-2. Does the series

$$\frac{10^2}{1!} + \frac{10^4}{2!} + \frac{10^6}{3!} + \cdots + \frac{10^{2n}}{n!} + \cdots$$

converge or diverge?

Solution. If we set $a_n = \frac{10^{2n}}{n!}$, we have

$$\frac{|a_{n+1}|}{|a_n|} = \frac{10^{2n+2}}{(n+1)!} \cdot \frac{n!}{10^{2n}} = \frac{100}{n+1},$$

so that

$$\lim_{n \to \infty} \frac{|a_{n+1}|}{|a_n|} = \lim_{n \to \infty} \frac{100}{(n+1)} = 0.$$

Certainly this limit $L = 0$ is less than 1, so the ratio test of Theorem 119-3 tells us that the series converges.

Example 119-3. For what choices of x does the series $\sum_{n=1}^{\infty} x^n/n$ converge?

Solution. The nth term of this series is given by the formula $a_n = x^n/n$, and so

$$\frac{|a_{n+1}|}{|a_n|} = \frac{|x^{n+1}|}{n+1}\frac{n}{|x^n|} = \frac{n}{n+1}|x|.$$

Clearly $\lim_{n \to 0} \frac{n}{n+1}|x| = 1 \cdot |x| = |x|$, so for this series $L = |x|$. Therefore, we see that if $|x| < 1$, the series is absolutely convergent; if $|x| > 1$, the series is divergent; whereas if $|x| = 1$, we must use some other test for convergence or divergence. There are two possible cases in which $|x| = 1$. If $x = 1$, our series is the divergent harmonic series $1 + \frac{1}{2} + \cdots$, whereas if $x = -1$ our series is the convergent alternating series $-1 + \frac{1}{2} - \frac{1}{3} + \cdots$. Thus we have shown that the series $\sum_{n=1}^{\infty} x^n/n$ converges when x is a number that satisfies the inequalities $-1 \leq x < 1$ and it diverges otherwise.

Problems 119

1. Use a ratio test to test the following series for convergence.

(a) $\sum_{n=1}^{\infty} \frac{n^2}{2^n}$ (b) $\sum_{n=1}^{\infty} n\left(\frac{3}{5}\right)^n$

(c) $\sum_{k=0}^{\infty} \frac{k!}{10^k}$ (d) $\sum_{k=0}^{\infty} \frac{2^k}{k!}$

(e) $\sum_{n=1}^{\infty} \frac{2^n}{n^3}$ (f) $\sum_{n=1}^{\infty} \frac{n^5}{(1.01)^n}$

(g) $\sum_{n=1}^{\infty} \frac{\pi^n}{1+3^n}$ (h) $\sum_{n=0}^{\infty} \frac{2^{2n}}{2n!}$

2. Test for convergence.

(a) $\frac{1}{3} + \frac{2}{5} + \frac{3}{7} + \cdots + \frac{n}{(2n+1)} + \cdots$

(b) $\frac{1}{3} + \frac{1 \cdot 3}{3 \cdot 6} + \frac{1 \cdot 3 \cdot 5}{3 \cdot 6 \cdot 9} + \cdots$

(c) $\frac{1!}{2!} + \frac{2!}{4!} + \frac{3!}{6!} + \frac{4!}{8!}$

(d) $1 + \frac{2!}{1 \cdot 3} + \frac{3!}{1 \cdot 3 \cdot 5} + \frac{4!}{1 \cdot 3 \cdot 5 \cdot 7} + \cdots$

3. Use Theorem 119-3 to test the following series for convergence.

(a) $\sum_{k=1}^{\infty} \frac{k^k}{k!}$ (b) $\sum_{n=0}^{\infty} \frac{(n!)^2}{(2n)!}$

4. Determine which of the following series are absolutely convergent and which are conditionally convergent.

(a) $\sum_{n=0}^{\infty} \frac{(-1)^n 10^n}{(2n)!}$ (b) $\sum_{n=1}^{\infty} \frac{(-1)^{n+1} 3^n}{4^n + 1}$

(c) $\sum_{n=1}^{\infty} \frac{(-1)^{n-1} n}{(n^2 + 1)}$ (d) $\sum_{n=1}^{\infty} \frac{(-1)^{n+1}}{\sqrt{n}}$

5. Suppose that the ratio test (Theorem 119-3) shows that the series $\sum_{n=1}^{\infty} a_n$ is a convergent series. Show that $\sum_{n=1}^{\infty} n a_n$ is also convergent. Is $\sum_{n=1}^{\infty} n^2 a_n$ convergent?

6. Determine x so that the following series are convergent.

(a) $\sum_{n=1}^{\infty} n x^n$ (b) $\sum_{n=1}^{\infty} \frac{e^{nx}}{n}$

(c) $\sum_{n=0}^{\infty} \sin^n x$ (d) $\sum_{n=1}^{\infty} \frac{n^2}{x^n}$

(e) $\sum_{n=0}^{\infty} \frac{(2x)^n}{(x^2 + 1)^n}$ (f) $\sum_{n=1}^{\infty} n^3 x^{3n}$

7. Is the ratio test applicable to the series $\frac{1}{2} + \frac{1 \cdot 3}{2 \cdot 4} + \frac{1 \cdot 3 \cdot 5}{2 \cdot 4 \cdot 6} + \cdots$? Does the series converge?

8. Let $\sum_{n=1}^{\infty} a_n$ be a convergent series of positive terms. Let R_n denote the remainder after n terms and suppose that $a_{n+1}/a_n \leq q < 1$ for all $n > N$. Show that

$$0 \leq R_n \leq \frac{a_{n+1}}{1 - q} \quad \text{for } n \geq N.$$

9. Estimate the sum of the series $\sum_{n=1}^{\infty} 2^n/n!$ by finding the sum of the first 5 terms. Use the result of the preceding question to find an upper bound for the error in your approximation.

10. Show that if $\sqrt[k]{|a_k|} \leq q < 1$ for each k greater than some index K, then the series $\sum_{k=1}^{\infty} a_k$ is absolutely convergent. Show that if $\sqrt[k]{|a_k|} \geq 1$ for each k greater than some index K, then the series $\sum_{k=1}^{\infty} a_k$ diverges.

11. Apply the test of the preceding question to the following series.

(a) $\sum_{k=2}^{\infty} \frac{1}{(\ln k)^k}$ (b) $\sum_{k=1}^{\infty} \frac{1}{k^k}$

(c) $\frac{1}{2} + \frac{1}{3} + (\frac{1}{2})^2 + (\frac{1}{3})^2 + (\frac{1}{2})^3 + (\frac{1}{3})^3 + \cdots$ (d) $\sum_{k=2}^{\infty} \frac{1}{(\ln k)^{\ln k}}$

120. Power Series

Suppose that we select a sequence $\{c_n\}$ of numbers and a number a. Then for each number x we can form the **power series** in $(x - a)$,

$$\sum_{n=0}^{\infty} c_n(x - a)^n = c_0 + c_1(x - a) + c_2(x - a)^2 + \cdots . \tag{120-1}$$

The terms of the sequence $\{c_n\}$ are called the **coefficients** of the series. The series

$$\sum_{n=0}^{\infty} \frac{(x-3)^n}{n!} \quad \text{and} \quad \sum_{n=0}^{\infty} (-1)^n x^n$$

are examples of power series. In the first of these examples $a = 3$, $c_0 = \frac{1}{0!} = \frac{1}{1} = 1$, $c_1 = 1$, $c_2 = \frac{1}{2!}$, and so on; and in the second example $a = 0$, $c_0 = (-1)^0 = 1$, $c_1 = -1$, $c_2 = 1$, and so on. Power series play a central role in mathematical analysis, and they are widely used in applied mathematics. We will see why they are important as we study the next few sections.

We can use any number x when we form a power series, and we naturally want to know which numbers yield convergent series. Many times we can use a ratio test to help us find an interval in which x must lie in order that the series should converge.

Example 120-1. Find the interval in which x must lie for the power series $\sum_{n=1}^{\infty} \frac{(x-3)^n}{n^2}$ to be convergent.

Solution. The nth term of this series is given by the formula $a_n = \frac{(x-3)^n}{n^2}$, so the ratio $|a_{n+1}|/|a_n|$ is

$$\left|\frac{(x-3)^{n+1}}{(n+1)^2}\right| \left|\frac{n^2}{(x-3)^n}\right| = \frac{n^2}{(n+1)^2}|x-3|.$$

Therefore,

$$\lim_{n\to\infty} \frac{|a_{n+1}|}{|a_n|} = \lim_{n\to\infty} \frac{n^2}{(n+1)^2}|x-3| = 1 \cdot |x-3| = |x-3|.$$

Now, according to Theorem 119-3, if this number $L = |x - 3|$ is less than 1, our series converges (absolutely), and if L is greater than 1, the series diverges. Hence the series is convergent if $|x - 3| < 1$; that is, if x is in the interval $(2, 4)$. If $|x - 3| > 1$; that is, if x is outside the closed interval [2, 4], then the series diverges. If $|x - 3| = 1$ (in other words, if $x = 2$ or $x = 4$), then we must make a further investigation of convergence. If $x = 4$, our series becomes the p-series $\sum_{n=1}^{\infty} 1/n^2$ which converges, whereas if $x = 2$, our series is $\sum_{n=1}^{\infty} (-1)^n/n^2$ which also converges. Thus we see that the given series is convergent for each number x such

Figure 120-1

that $|x - 3| \leq 1$ and is divergent otherwise. Figure 120-1 shows a graphical representation of the set of points for which the series converges.

Example 120-2. For which x is the series $\sum_{n=0}^{\infty} x^n/n!$ convergent?

Solution. The ratios of the absolute values of successive terms of this series are given by the formula

$$\left|\frac{x^{n+1}}{(n+1)!}\right|\left|\frac{n!}{x^n}\right| = \frac{n!}{(n+1)!}|x| = \frac{|x|}{n+1}.$$

No matter what number x is, $\lim_{n \to \infty} \frac{|x|}{n+1} = 0$. Since this limit is less than 1, Theorem 119-3 tells us that our series converges for each number x.

Example 120-3. For which x is the series

$$\sum_{n=0}^{\infty} n!x^n = 1 + 1!x + 2!x^2 + \cdots$$

convergent?

Solution. The ratios of the absolute values of successive terms are given by the formula

$$\frac{|(n+1)!x^{n+1}|}{|n!x^n|} = (n+1)|x|.$$

If $x \neq 0$, it is clear that we can find a number N such that, for $n > N$, $(n+1)|x| > 1$. Therefore, according to Theorem 119-2, our series is divergent for each number x that is different from 0. Of course, if $x = 0$, the series converges, for then it is simply the series $1 + 0 + 0 + \cdots = 1$.

These last three examples illustrate different possibilities for the sets of numbers for which a power series $\sum_{n=0}^{\infty} c_n(x - a)^n$ converges. As Example 120-1 shows, there may be an interval centered at the point a and possessing the property that for every x in the interval the series converges, whereas for every x outside the interval the series diverges. Or, as in Example 120-2, the series may converge for every number x. Finally, in Example 120-3 we have a series that converges at only one point. Our three examples illustrate all the possibilities. It can be shown that for any power series $\sum_{n=0}^{\infty} c_n(x - a)^n$ one of the following statements must be true:

(i) *The series converges only for the "trivial choice" $x = a$.*

(ii) *The series converges for every number x.*

(iii) *There is a positive number r such that the series converges for every number x in the open interval $(a - r, a + r)$ and diverges for every number outside the closed interval $[a - r, a + r]$.* Some series converge at both endpoints $a - r$ and $a + r$, some converge at only one endpoint, and some converge at neither endpoint.

The number r is called the **radius of convergence** of the power series, and the open interval $(a - r, a + r)$ is the **interval of convergence.** We say that a series that converges only for $x = a$ has the radius of convergence 0, and we also say that the interval of convergence of a series that converges for all x is the interval $(-\infty, \infty)$.

As in our preceding examples, the ratio test can be used to find the radius of convergence of most of the power series that you are likely to meet.

Example 120-4. Find the radius of convergence of the power series

$$\sum_{n=1}^{\infty} \frac{(-1)^n 2^n (x - 5)^{2n}}{n^2}.$$

Solution. We first find the limit of the ratios of the absolute values of successive terms. Here $a_n = \dfrac{(-1)^n 2^n (x - 5)^{2n}}{n^2}$, so

$$\lim_{n\to\infty} \left| \frac{a_{n+1}}{a_n} \right| = \lim_{n\to\infty} \frac{2^{n+1}(x - 5)^{2n+2}}{(n + 1)^2} \cdot \frac{n^2}{2^n (x - 5)^{2n}}$$

$$= \lim_{n\to\infty} 2(x - 5)^2 \left(\frac{n}{n + 1}\right)^2 = 2(x - 5)^2.$$

Our series will converge if the number $2(x - 5)^2$ is less than 1, and it will diverge if $2(x - 5)^2 > 1$. The inequality $2(x - 5)^2 < 1$ is equivalent to the inequality $|x - 5| < \frac{1}{\sqrt{2}}$. This inequality says that x is less than $\frac{1}{\sqrt{2}}$ units from the point 5. Thus the radius of convergence of our series is the number $\frac{1}{\sqrt{2}}$, and its interval of convergence is the interval $\left(5 - \frac{1}{\sqrt{2}}, 5 + \frac{1}{\sqrt{2}}\right)$. If we replace x with $5 - \frac{1}{\sqrt{2}}$ or with $5 + \frac{1}{\sqrt{2}}$, we get the series $\sum_{n=1}^{\infty} \frac{(-1)^n}{n^2}$, which is convergent. Therefore, our given series converges for x in the closed interval $\left[5 - \frac{1}{\sqrt{2}}, 5 + \frac{1}{\sqrt{2}}\right]$, and it diverges for x outside this interval.

It is not always possible to use the ratio test to find the radius of convergence of a power series. For example, consider the series

$$(120\text{-}1) \qquad 1 + 2x + x^2 + 2x^3 + x^4 + 2x^5 + \cdots.$$

Here the ratios of the absolute values of successive terms of the series are alternately the numbers $2|x|$ and $\frac{1}{2}|x|$, and this sequence does not have a limit unless $x = 0$. Nevertheless, the series has a positive radius of convergence, as we show in the following example.

Example 120-5. Show that the radius of convergence of Series 120-1 is the number 1.

Solution. The radius of convergence of our series is the number r such that the series is convergent at every point of the open interval $(-r, r)$ and divergent at every point outside the closed interval $[-r, r]$. If we replace x with 1 in Series 120-1, we obtain the divergent series $1 + 2 + 1 + 2 + \cdots$, and hence the number 1 cannot be in the interval of convergence; that is, 1 cannot be less than r. Thus we see that $r \leq 1$. Now we will show that r cannot be less than 1. For suppose that t is any number such that $0 < t < 1$. Then if we replace x with t in Series 120-1, we obtain the series $1 + 2t + t^2 + 2t^3 + \cdots$, which is dominated by the convergent geometric series $2 + 2t + 2t^2 + \cdots = 2(1 + t + t^2 + \cdots)$. Thus the interval of convergence $(-r, r)$ of Series 120-1 must contain every number t such that $0 < t < 1$. It follows that r cannot be less than 1 and therefore $r = 1$, since we have already shown that r cannot be greater than 1.

Problems 120

1. Find the radius of convergence, the interval of convergence, and the set of points for which the following power series converge.

(a) $\sum_{n=0}^{\infty} \frac{x^n}{2^n}$ (b) $\sum_{n=1}^{\infty} n(x-2)^n$

(c) $\sum_{n=0}^{\infty} \frac{(-1)^n}{3^n+n}(x+1)^n$ (d) $\sum_{n=1}^{\infty} \frac{x^n}{\sqrt{n}}$

(e) $\sum_{n=1}^{\infty} \frac{(x-4)^n}{\sqrt{3n}}$ (f) $\sum_{n=1}^{\infty} \frac{x^n}{n(n+1)}$

2. Find the interval of convergence of the following power series.

(a) $\sum_{n=0}^{\infty} \frac{n^2+3n-2}{n+1}(x-3)^n$ (b) $\sum_{n=1}^{\infty} (\operatorname{csch} n)x^n$

(c) $\sum_{n=1}^{\infty} (\operatorname{Arctan} n)(x-2)^n$ (d) $\sum_{n=1}^{\infty} \frac{n^5}{5^n}(x-5)^n$

(e) $\sum_{n=1}^{\infty} \frac{n^n}{n!}x^n$ (f) $\sum_{n=0}^{\infty} \frac{(x-2)^n}{2^n\sqrt{n+1}}$

3. Find the interval of convergence of the following power series.

(a) $\sum_{n=1}^{\infty} \frac{(-1)^{n+1}}{(2n-1)!}x^{2n-1}$ (b) $\sum_{n=1}^{\infty} \frac{(-1)^n 5 \cdot 6 \cdots (n+4)}{n!}x^{2n}$

(c) $\sum_{n=0}^{\infty} \frac{(x-2)^{4n}}{2^n}$ (d) $\sum_{n=1}^{\infty} (3^n+3^{-n})(x+1)^{3n-2}$

(e) $\sum_{n=0}^{\infty} \frac{(-1)^n}{2^{2n+k}n!(n+k)!}x^{2n+k}$

where k is a positive integer.

4. Show that if $\lim_{n\to\infty}\left|\frac{c_{n+1}}{c_n}\right| = L > 0$, then the radius of convergence of the power series $\sum_{n=0}^{\infty} c_n(x-a)^n$ is $\frac{1}{L}$. What if $L = 0$?

5. Use the result of Question 9, Problems 119, to show that if $\lim_{n\to\infty}\sqrt[n]{|c_n|} = L > 0$, then the radius of convergence of the power series $\sum_{n=0}^{\infty} c_n(x-a)^n$ is $\frac{1}{L}$.

6. Show that the radius of convergence of the following power series is 2:

$$1 + x + \frac{x^2}{2^2} + \frac{x^3}{2^2} + \frac{x^4}{2^4} + \frac{x^5}{2^4} + \cdots.$$

7. Show that if a power series $\sum_{n=0}^{\infty} c_n x^n$ converges for $x = R$, then it converges (absolutely) at every point in the interval $(-|R|, |R|)$. (If $|x| < |R|$, then the geometric series $\sum_{n=0}^{\infty}\left(\frac{|x|}{|R|}\right)^n$ converges because $\frac{|x|}{|R|} < 1$. Now apply the limit comparison test (Theorem 116-3).)

8. Show that if a power series $\sum_{n=0}^{\infty} c_n x^n$ diverges when $x = R$, then it diverges at every point outside the interval $[-|R|, |R|]$. (See the preceding question.)

121. Functions Defined by Power Series

Let us agree not to bother with "trivial" power series that converge at only one point. Then the interval of convergence of a power series

$$\sum_{n=0}^{\infty} c_n(x - a)^n \tag{121-1}$$

is either the infinite interval $(-\infty, \infty)$ or else it is a finite interval $(a - r, a + r)$. In the latter case we may also have to add one or both of the endpoints $x = a - r$ or $x = a + r$ to obtain the set of points for which the series is convergent. Let us denote by I the *interval of convergence* of our series and by D the *set of points for which the series converges*. These two sets of points may coincide, and at worst D can be obtained from I by adding two more points. So the difference between the two sets is small. Nevertheless, in the statements of the various theorems that follow it is necessary to distinguish between the sets D and I, even though it looks as if we are splitting hairs.

Corresponding to each number x in the set D we obtain a number, the sum of the Series 121-1. Thus our power series defines a function f. The domain of f is the convergence set D, and the values of f are the sums of the series. So we have

$$\boldsymbol{f(x) = \sum_{n=0}^{\infty} c_n(x - a)^n.} \tag{121-2}$$

Among the functions whose values can be expressed as sums of power series are most of the important functions of mathematics. For example, the trigonometric, logarithmic, and exponential functions belong to this class, as we shall see. Therefore, this class of functions has been studied extensively. We shall now state, without proof, three important theorems that apply to functions of this class.

Our first theorem tells us that functions defined by power series are continuous.

THEOREM 121-1. *The function f defined by the equation $f(x) = \sum_{n=0}^{\infty} c_n(x - a)^n$ is continuous at each point of the convergence set D of the defining infinite* *series. That is, if b is any point of the convergence set, then*

(121-3) $$\lim_{x \to b} f(x) = f(b) = \sum_{n=0}^{\infty} c_n(b - a)^n.$$

We shall give an application of this theorem after we have stated the theorems about differentiation and integration of series.

If $f(x)$ were an ordinary sum of terms of the form $c_n(x - a)^n$, then we could find its derivative by differentiating each term in the sum and then adding. But $f(x)$ is *not* an ordinary sum; it is the "sum" of an infinite series. On the face of it, therefore, it is not obvious that we can obtain derivatives or integrals of $f(x)$ by differentiating or integrating each term of the series that defines f. Such "term-by-term" differentiation or integration is not always possible in the case of functions defined by some kinds of infinite series. When a function is defined by a *power series*, however, we may differentiate or integrate "under the summation sign" according to the following theorems that are proved in advanced calculus.

THEOREM 121-2. *The function f defined by the equation* $f(x) = \sum_{n=0}^{\infty} c_n(x - a)^n$ *is differentiable at every point of the interval of convergence I of the defining series, and at each point x of I we have*

(121-4) $$f'(x) = \sum_{n=1}^{\infty} nc_n(x - a)^{n-1}.$$

The interval of convergence of the series in Equation 121-4 is the interval of convergence of the original series.

THEOREM 121-3. *If x is any point of the convergence set D of the infinite series of Equation* 121-2, *then*

(121-5) $$\int_a^x f(t)\, dt = \sum_{n=0}^{\infty} \frac{c_n(x - a)^{n+1}}{n + 1}.$$

The interval of convergence of the series in Equation 121-5 is the interval of convergence of the original series.

Let us now consider some applications of these theorems. The only power series whose sum we know at the moment is the geometric series. Thus

(121-6) $$\frac{1}{1 - x} = \sum_{n=0}^{\infty} x^n,$$

where $D = I = (-1, 1)$. According to Equation 121-5, if x is any point of the interval $(-1, 1)$, then

$$\int_0^x \frac{dt}{1-t} = \sum_{n=0}^{\infty} \frac{x^{n+1}}{n+1} = x + \frac{x^2}{2} + \frac{x^3}{3} + \cdots.$$

But

$$\int_0^x \frac{dt}{1-t} = -\ln(1-t)\Big|_0^x = -\ln(1-x),$$

so we have the following equation, valid for $-1 < x < 1$:

$$(121\text{-}7) \qquad -\ln(1-x) = x + \frac{x^2}{2} + \frac{x^3}{3} + \frac{x^4}{4} + \cdots.$$

Thus, for example, if we set $x = \frac{1}{2}$, and recall that $-\ln\frac{1}{2} = \ln 2$, then we see that

$$\ln 2 = \tfrac{1}{2} + \tfrac{1}{8} + \tfrac{1}{24} + \tfrac{1}{64} + \cdots.$$

The sum of the first 4 terms of this series is .68, which is a close approximation of the value $\ln 2 = .69$. Of course, the more terms we add, the more nearly we will approximate $\ln 2$, and *we can approximate* $\ln 2$ *with any degree of accuracy we wish simply by adding together enough terms.* In practice we would probably use a machine to help us with the computation.

We are only sure that Equation 121-7 is valid for $|x| < 1$, but it is not hard to develop a series that will give us the logarithm of any positive number. In Equation 121-7 we replace x with $-x$ and obtain the equation

$$(121\text{-}8) \qquad -\ln(1+x) = -x + \frac{x^2}{2} - \frac{x^3}{3} + \frac{x^4}{4} - \cdots.$$

Then we subtract the corresponding sides of Equations 121-7 and 121-8:

$$\ln(1+x) - \ln(1-x) = 2\left(x + \frac{x^3}{3} + \frac{x^5}{5} + \cdots\right).$$

Thus, since $\ln(1+x) - \ln(1-x) = \ln\frac{1+x}{1-x}$, we have

$$(121\text{-}9) \qquad \ln\frac{1+x}{1-x} = 2\left(x + \frac{x^3}{3} + \frac{x^5}{5} + \cdots\right).$$

Now we have a series that will give us the logarithm of any positive number. If we are given a positive number N, then we solve the equation $\frac{1+x}{1-x} = N$ for x. We find that $x = \frac{N-1}{N+1}$ and therefore $|x| < 1$. Thus we may replace x in Equation 121-9 with the number $\frac{N-1}{N+1}$ and we will obtain a convergent series whose sum is $\ln N$:

$$\text{(121-10)} \qquad \ln N = 2\left[\left(\frac{N-1}{N+1}\right) + \frac{1}{3}\left(\frac{N-1}{N+1}\right)^3 + \frac{1}{5}\left(\frac{N-1}{N+1}\right)^5 + \cdots\right].$$

Let us now return to Equation 121-7. Theorem 121-3 guarantees that this equation is valid for x in the interval $(-1, 1)$. But now we observe that the series in Equation 121-7 also converges at the point $x = -1$; that is, the convergence set for this series is the interval $D = [-1, 1)$. Now Theorem 121-1 says that a function defined by a power series is continuous on its convergence set D. In this case, Equation 121-3 with b replaced by -1^+ and $f(x) = -\ln(1-x)$ becomes

$$\lim_{x \to -1^+} [-\ln(1-x)] = -\ln 2 = -1 + \tfrac{1}{2} - \tfrac{1}{3} + \tfrac{1}{4} - \cdots.$$

Thus we get the interesting equation

$$\text{(121-11)} \qquad \ln 2 = 1 - \tfrac{1}{2} + \tfrac{1}{3} - \tfrac{1}{4} + \tfrac{1}{5} - \cdots.$$

Example 121-1. Obtain a series representation of $\frac{1}{(1-x)^2}$.

Solution. From our knowledge of the geometric series we know that $\frac{1}{1-x} = \sum_{n=0}^{\infty} x^n$ if $|x| < 1$. It is easy to see that $D_x\left[\frac{1}{1-x}\right] = \frac{1}{(1-x)^2}$. Now term-by-term differentiation of the geometric series, in accordance with Theorem 121-2, yields

$$\frac{1}{(1-x)^2} = \sum_{n=1}^{\infty} nx^{n-1} = 1 + 2x + 3x^2 + 4x^3 + \cdots,$$

and this equation is valid if $|x| < 1$.

We close this section with some remarks on the algebra of power series. If we add the corresponding terms of two given convergent infinite series, then the resulting series is also convergent and we can obtain its sum by adding the sums of the given series. Similar remarks apply to subtraction. Thus to add or subtract power series, we simply add or subtract the coefficients of like powers of $x - a$ in the "natural way." We can also multiply and divide power series "naturally." Thus the product of two power series is again a power series. To obtain the initial segment of the product series that ends with the term containing $(x-a)^n$, we multiply the initial segments of the factor series that end with the terms containing $(x-a)^n$ and then discard all terms that contain $(x-a)$ to a power larger than n. We use the corresponding procedure to obtain the quotient of two power series, except that then we also require that the first coefficient c_0 of the divisor series be different from 0.

Example 121-2. Find the initial segment that ends with the term containing x^3 in the product of the series $\sum_{n=0}^{\infty} x^n$ and $\sum_{n=1}^{\infty} nx^{n-1}$.

Solution. We multiply the initial segments of the factor series as shown:

$$\begin{array}{l} 1 + x + x^2 + x^3 \\ 1 + 2x + 3x^2 + 4x^3 \\ \hline 1 + 3x + 6x^2 + 10x^3 + 9x^4 + 7x^5 + 4x^6. \end{array}$$

Then we discard the terms that contain x to a power higher than 3, and we are left with the desired initial segment of the product:

$$\left(\sum_{n=0}^{\infty} x^n\right)\left(\sum_{n=1}^{\infty} nx^{n-1}\right) = 1 + 3x + 6x^2 + 10x^3 + \cdots.$$

If you carry out the process one more step, you will find that the next term in the product series is $15x^4$.

Problems 121

1. Calculate a two-place decimal approximation to $f(\frac{1}{2})$ if:
   (a) $f(x) = \sum_{n=0}^{\infty} \frac{(-1)^n}{(2n)!} x^n$ (b) $f(x) = \sum_{x=0}^{\infty} \frac{(-1)^n}{n!} (x - 1)^n$
   (c) $f(x) = \sum_{n=0}^{\infty} (-1)^n \frac{5 \cdot 6 \cdots (n + 4)}{n!} x^{2n}$
   (d) $f(x) = 1 + x - \frac{x^2}{2!} - \frac{x^3}{3!} + \frac{x^4}{4!} + \frac{x^5}{5!} - \cdots$
2. Let $f(x) = 1 + 2x - x^2 + 2x^3 - x^4 + 2x^5 - \cdots$. Explain how you know that $\lim_{x \to 0} f(x) = 1$.
3. Use a power series to find an approximation to $\ln N$ and check your result with Table II if:
   (a) $N = .9$ (b) $N = 1.1$ (c) $N = 5$ (d) $N = .3$
4. Use the equation developed in Example 121-1 to find the sum of the series $\sum_{n=1}^{\infty} \frac{n}{2^n}$.
5. If we replace x with $-t^2$, Equation 121-6 becomes $\frac{1}{1 + t^2} = \sum_{n=0}^{\infty} (-1)^n t^{2n}$ for t in the interval $(-1, 1)$. Use this equation and Theorem 121-3 to show that

$$\text{Arctan } x = \sum_{n=0}^{\infty} \frac{(-1)^n x^{2n+1}}{2n + 1} \text{ for } x \text{ in the interval } (-1, 1).$$

6. Use the result of the preceding question to show that

$$\frac{\pi}{4} = 1 - \frac{1}{3} + \frac{1}{5} - \frac{1}{7} + \cdots.$$

7. Find a two-place approximation to $\int_0^{1/2} g(x)\,dx$ if

$$g(x) = 1 - \tfrac{1}{2}x^3 - \tfrac{1}{8}x^6 - \tfrac{1}{16}x^9 - \cdots.$$

8. Integrate each side of the equation $\dfrac{1}{1 - t^2} = \sum_{n=0}^{\infty} t^{2n}$ between the limits 0 and x to obtain Equation 121-9.

9. Let $g(x) = \sum_{n=0}^{\infty} (-1)^n \dfrac{x^{2n}}{(2n)!}$. Show that $g''(x) + g(x) = 0$.

10. Use power series to show that

$$\int_0^x \text{Arctan}\, t\, dt = x \text{ Arctan } x - \tfrac{1}{2} \ln(1 + x^2) \text{ (see Question 5).}$$

11. Multiply the series in powers of x whose sums are $\dfrac{1}{1 - x}$ and $\dfrac{1}{1 + x}$ to obtain a power series whose sum is $\dfrac{1}{1 - x^2}$.

12. Compare the results obtained by squaring the series in powers of x whose sum is $\dfrac{1}{1 - x}$ and by differentiating this series.

13. Use long division to express $\dfrac{1}{2 - x}$ as the sum of a series in powers of x.

14. Use the series obtained in the preceding question and the series in powers of x whose sum is $\dfrac{1}{1 - x}$ to obtain a power series whose sum is $\dfrac{1}{(1 - x)(2 - x)}$ by:

(a) Multiplying the two power series.

(b) First writing $\dfrac{1}{(1 - x)(2 - x)}$ in the form $\dfrac{A}{1 - x} + \dfrac{B}{2 - x}$ and then adding two power series that have these terms as sums.

122. Taylor's Series

A power series $\sum_{n=0}^{\infty} c_n(x - a)^n$ determines a function f whose domain is the set of points for which the series converges, and whose values are the sums of the series; that is,

$$f(x) = c_0 + c_1(x - a) + c_2(x - a)^2 + \cdots. \tag{122-1}$$

Thus we see, for example, that $f(a) = c_0$. We will now show how to express the derivatives of f at a in terms of the other coefficients of our series.

According to Theorem 121-2, the derivative $f'(x)$ is the sum of the series that results from differentiating the given series term-by-term; that is,

$$f'(x) = c_1 + 2c_2(x - a) + 3c_3(x - a)^2 + \cdots.$$

We may apply Theorem 121-2 again and again to obtain the equations

$$f''(x) = 2c_2 + 2 \cdot 3c_3(x - a) + 3 \cdot 4c_4(x - a)^2 + \cdots,$$
$$f'''(x) = 2 \cdot 3c_3 + 2 \cdot 3 \cdot 4c_4(x - a) + 3 \cdot 4 \cdot 5c_5(x - a)^2 + \cdots,$$

and so on. You can easily convince yourself that in general

$$(122\text{-}2) \quad f^{(n)}(x) = n!c_n + (n + 1)!c_{n+1}(x - a) + \frac{(n + 2)!}{2}(x - a)^2 + \cdots,$$

for $n = 0, 1, 2, \ldots$. (We will agree that $f^{(0)}(x) = f(x)$, and that $0! = 1$.) When we replace x with a in Equation 122-2, we obtain the following formula for the derivatives of f at a in terms of the coefficients of our given series:

$$(122\text{-}3) \qquad \boldsymbol{f^{(n)}(a) = n!c_n}, \ n = 0, 1, 2, 3, \ldots.$$

Example 122-1. Let $f(x) = \dfrac{1}{1 - x^2}$. Find $f^{(14)}(0)$.

Solution. We will find a power series for which our given $f(x)$ is the sum, and then we will use Equation 122-3. If we simply divide 1 by $1 - x^2$, or replace x with x^2 in Equation 121-6, we find that

$$\frac{1}{1 - x^2} = 1 + x^2 + x^4 + x^6 + \cdots.$$

Here $a = 0$ and it is clear that $c_{14} = 1$, and so Equation 122-3 shows us that $f^{(14)}(0) = 14!$. You might try to calculate this number by starting with the given quotient and differentiating 14 times.

Suppose that the sum $f(x)$ in Equation 122-1 is the number 0 for each x in an interval $(a - r, a + r)$. Then all the derivatives of $f(x)$ are 0 in this interval, and hence Equation 122-3 tells us that all the coefficients of our power series are 0. Thus the only power series whose sum is 0 is the one with zero coefficients. This result leads to the following theorem.

THEOREM 122-1. *If* $\sum_{n=0}^{\infty} a_n(x - a)^n = \sum_{n=0}^{\infty} b_n(x - a)^n$ *for each number* x *in an interval* $(a - r, a + r)$, *then* $a_n = b_n$ *for each integer* $n = 0, 1, 2, 3, \ldots$. *Thus one equation between power series is equivalent to infinitely many equations between their coefficients.*

Proof. To prove this theorem we simply note that the equation

$$\sum_{n=0}^{\infty} a_n(x - a)^n = \sum_{n=0}^{\infty} b_n(x - a)^n$$

implies that

$$\sum_{n=0}^{\infty} (a_n - b_n)(x - a)^n = 0,$$

and we have just seen that if the sum of a power series is 0 in an interval, then all its coefficients must be 0. Therefore, $a_0 - b_0 = 0$, $a_1 - b_1 = 0$, and so on, as the theorem claims.

If we start with a power series $\sum_{n=0}^{\infty} c_n(x - a)^n$, then Equation 122-1 defines a function f that has derivatives of all orders at the point a. Now let us proceed in the opposite direction. Suppose we start with a function f that has derivatives of all orders at a point a and see if we can find a power series in $x - a$ of which $f(x)$ is the sum. From what we have said in the preceding paragraphs, we see that the coefficients of such a power series (if there is one) must be the numbers given by Equation 122-3. That is, we must have $c_n = \dfrac{f^{(n)}(a)}{n!}$. So let us form the power series in $x - a$ that has these numbers as coefficients,

$$\text{(122-4)} \quad \sum_{n=0}^{\infty} \frac{f^{(n)}(a)}{n!}(x - a)^n = f(a) + f'(a)(x - a) + \frac{f''(a)}{2!}(x - a)^2 + \cdots,$$

and see whether or not it converges to $f(x)$. Series 122-4 is called **Taylor's Series** for $f(x)$ about the point a. We can form Taylor's Series for any function that has derivatives of all orders at a, and it turns out that for many of the familiar functions of mathematics Taylor's Series converges to the value of the function at each point x in some interval centered at a.

Example 122-2. Find Taylor's Series for e^x about the origin.

Solution. Here $f(x) = e^x$ and $a = 0$. Since $f(x)$ and all its derivatives equal e^x, we have $f(0) = f'(0) = f''(0) = \cdots = 1$. Thus in this case, $f^{(n)}(a) = 1$ for each index n, and so Taylor's Series for e^x about the origin is

$$\sum_{n=0}^{\infty} \frac{x^n}{n!} = 1 + x + \frac{x^2}{2!} + \frac{x^3}{3!} + \cdots.$$

The ratio test shows (see Example 120-2) that this series converges absolutely for every number x.

We have just seen that Taylor's Series for e^x about the origin converges. Now we want to go one step farther and show that its sum is e^x. To find out whether or not Taylor's Series for $f(x)$ converges to $f(x)$, we use Taylor's Formula. Thus in Section 109 we saw that for each integer m we can write

$$\text{(122-5)}\quad \begin{aligned} f(x) &= f(a) + f'(a)(x - a) + \cdots + \frac{f^{(m)}(a)}{m!}(x - a)^m + R_m(x) \\ &= S_m(x) + R_m(x), \end{aligned}$$

where $S_m(x)$ is the mth partial sum of Taylor's Series, and the remainder $R_m(x)$ is given by the formula

$$\text{(122-6)}\qquad R_m(x) = \frac{f^{(m+1)}(c)}{(m+1)!}(x - a)^{m+1},$$

where c is some number between a and x. Since $S_m(x) = f(x) - R_m(x)$, we see that $\lim_{m\to\infty} S_m(x) = f(x)$ if, and only if, $\lim_{m\to\infty} R_m(x) = 0$. *Thus Taylor's Series for $f(x)$ has $f(x)$ as its sum if, and only if,* $\lim_{m\to\infty} R_m(x) = 0$.

Example 122-3. Show that Taylor's Series for e^x about the origin converges to e^x.

Solution. If x is any number other than 0, we have $R_m(x) = \dfrac{e^c x^{m+1}}{(m+1)!}$, where c is a number such that $|c| < |x|$. Thus we see that

$$|R_m(x)| \leq \frac{e^{|x|}|x|^{m+1}}{(m+1)!}.$$

Now since the series $\sum_{n=0}^{\infty} \dfrac{|x|^n}{n!}$ converges, its terms approach 0. Therefore,

$$\text{(122-7)}\qquad \lim_{m\to\infty} \frac{|x|^{m+1}}{(m+1)!} = 0,$$

and so

$$\lim_{m\to\infty} e^{|x|} \frac{|x|^{m+1}}{(m+1)!} = e^{|x|} \lim_{m\to\infty} \frac{|x|^{m+1}}{(m+1)!} = 0.$$

It follows that $\lim_{m\to\infty} R_m(x) = 0$, and we have therefore derived the important equation

$$\text{(122-8)}\qquad \boldsymbol{e^x = \sum_{n=0}^{\infty} \frac{x^n}{n!} = 1 + x + \frac{x^2}{2!} + \frac{x^3}{3!} + \cdots.}$$

Example 122-4. Find Taylor's Series for $\cos x$ about an arbitrary point a and use the result to calculate $\cos 3$.

Solution. Here $f(x) = \cos x$, and so $f(a) = \cos a$, $f'(a) = -\sin a$, $f''(a) = -\cos a$, $f'''(a) = \sin a$, and so on. Depending on m, the derivative $f^{(m+1)}(c)$ will be one of the numbers $\cos c$, $\sin c$, $-\cos c$, or $-\sin c$. In any event, $|f^{(m+1)}(c)| \leq 1$, and so $|R_m(x)| \leq \dfrac{|x-a|^{m+1}}{(m+1)!}$. Now if we replace x in Equation 122-7 with $x - a$, we see that $\displaystyle\lim_{m\to\infty} \frac{|x-a|^{m+1}}{(m+1)!} = 0$. Therefore, $\displaystyle\lim_{m\to\infty} R_m(x) = 0$, and Taylor's Series for $\cos x$ has $\cos x$ as its sum. Thus

$$\text{(122-9)} \qquad \cos x = \cos a - \sin a\,(x-a) - \cos a\,\frac{(x-a)^2}{2!} + \sin a\,\frac{(x-a)^3}{3!} + \cdots.$$

To use this formula to find $\cos 3$, we must choose a "suitable" number a. This choice is governed by two considerations:

(i) We must be able to find $f(a)$, $f'(a)$, and so on; in this case we must know what the numbers $\cos a$ and $\sin a$ are.

(ii) The number a should be close to 3 so that when we set $x = 3$ in Formula 122-9 the number $(x - a)$ will be small and we can use a reasonably short initial segment of our series to approximate its sum. These considerations suggest that we take $a = \pi$. Then

$$\cos 3 = -1 + \frac{(\pi-3)^2}{2!} - \frac{(\pi-3)^4}{4!} + \frac{(\pi-3)^6}{6!} - \cdots.$$

This series is an alternating series, so the error that we make by taking the sum of the first three terms as an approximation of $\cos 3$ is less than the fourth term. It is not hard to show that the fourth term is less than .0000001. Then we find that the sum of the first three terms gives us $\cos 3 = -.989992$ with 6-place accuracy.

It would have been perfectly correct to set $a = 0$ in Equation 122-9 to obtain the equation

$$\text{(122-10)} \qquad \cos x = 1 - \frac{x^2}{2!} + \frac{x^4}{4!} - \frac{x^6}{6!} + \cdots.$$

When we put $x = 3$ in this series, we get a series whose sum is $\cos 3$, but to be sure of an error of less than .0000001 (according to our rule for alternating series) we would have to take the sum of the first 9 terms. Equation 122-10 would be more suitable for calculating a number such as $\cos .1$.

Problems 122

1. Find $f^{(9)}(0)$ if:
(a) $f(x) = 1/(1 - x)$ (b) $f(x) = \ln(1 + x)$ (c) $f(x) = \text{Arctan}\, x$
2. Find Taylor's Series for $f(x)$ about 0 if:
(a) $f(x) = \sin x$ (b) $f(x) = \sinh x$
(c) $f(x) = \cosh x$ (d) $f(x) = 2 - 3x + 4x^3$
(e) $f(x) = \ln(a + x)$ (f) $f(x) = \sinh^{-1} x$
3. Use the series you found in the preceding question to compute:
(a) $\sin .1$ (b) $\sinh .1$ (c) $\cosh .1$ (d) $\cosh 1$
4. Show that Taylor's Series can be written in the form

$$f(a + h) = f(a) + f'(a)h + \frac{f''(a)}{2} h^2 + \frac{f'''(a)}{3!} h^3 + \cdots.$$

5. Find the first four terms in Taylor's Series for $f(x)$ about $\pi/4$ if:
(a) $f(x) = \sin x$ (b) $f(x) = \cos x$ (c) $f(x) = \tan x$ (d) $f(x) = \csc x$
6. Find Taylor's Series for $f(x)$ about 4 if:
(a) $f(x) = 1/x$ (b) $f(x) = \sqrt{x}$ (c) $f(x) = x^2 - 2x + 3$ (d) $f(x) = \sqrt[3]{x}$
7. Find Taylor's Series for $\ln x$ about 1.
8. Calculate the following numbers using series and compare your results with tabulated values.
(a) $\sin 3°$ (b) $\sin 3$ (c) $\cos 31°$ (d) $\ln 1.1$
9. Find the first three non-vanishing terms in Taylor's Series for $\text{Sin}^{-1} x$ about 0.
10. Show that if $|x| < \pi/2$, then the sum of the first 5 non-vanishing terms of the series for $\sin x$ (in powers of x) gives the number $\sin x$ with an error less than .00005.
11. Let x and y be any given numbers. Show that

$$\sin(x + y) = \sin y + (\cos y)x - (\sin y)x^2/2! - (\cos y)x^3/3! + \cdots$$

Now group the terms that contain $\sin y$ and those that contain $\cos y$ to find the addition formula for $\sin(x + y)$.

123. Using Taylor's Series. The Binomial Series

The straightforward way to find Taylor's Series for $f(x)$ about a point a is to calculate $f(a)$ and the derivatives $f'(a)$, $f''(a)$, and so on, and substitute these numbers in Formula 122-4. Even if the resulting series converges, we must still investigate the limit of the remainder $R_m(x)$ to see if the sum of the series is $f(x)$. Often, however, it is easier to find a desired Taylor's Series by "operating on"—with calculus or algebra—some series we already know, such as the series for e^x, $\frac{1}{1-x}$, and $\cos x$. The following examples illustrate this point, and they also show some of the uses of Taylor's Series.

Example 123-1. Find Taylor's Series for $\sin x$ about 0.

Solution. Equation 122-10 gives us Taylor's Series for $\cos x$ about 0, and we may differentiate both sides of this equation and then multiply by -1 to see that

$$\text{(123-1)} \qquad \sin x = x - \frac{x^3}{3!} + \frac{x^5}{5!} - \frac{x^7}{7!} + \cdots.$$

Example 123-2. Find Taylor's Series for $\tan x$ about 0.

Solution. If we calculate a few derivatives of $\tan x$, we soon see that they become quite complicated. A simpler way to obtain Taylor's Series for $\tan x = \dfrac{\sin x}{\cos x}$ is to divide the series for $\sin x$ by the series for $\cos x$. Thus

$$\tan x = \frac{x - \dfrac{x^3}{3!} + \dfrac{x^5}{5!} - \cdots}{1 - \dfrac{x^2}{2!} + \dfrac{x^4}{4!} - \cdots},$$

and we see, for example, that the initial segment $c_0 + c_1x + c_2x^2 + c_3x^3 + c_4x^4 + c_5x^5$ of the series for $\tan x$ is the corresponding initial segment of the quotient that we obtain by dividing the polynomial $x - \dfrac{x^3}{3!} + \dfrac{x^5}{5!}$ by the polynomial $1 - \dfrac{x^2}{2!} + \dfrac{x^4}{4!}$. When we perform this division, we find that

$$\tan x = x + \frac{x^3}{3} + \frac{2x^5}{15} + \cdots.$$

Example 123-3. Approximate the integral $\int_0^1 e^{-x^2}\,dx$ with an error of no more than .005.

Solution. We will not find an antiderivative of e^{-x^2} in any table of integrals, so we must evaluate this integral by some means other than the Fundamental Theorem of Calculus. We will use series. To find Taylor's Series for e^{-x^2}, recall (Equation 122-8) that

$$\text{(123-2)} \qquad e^t = 1 + t + \frac{t^2}{2!} + \frac{t^3}{3!} + \cdots,$$

and when we replace t with $-x^2$ in this equation, we get

$$e^{-x^2} = 1 - x^2 + \frac{x^4}{2!} - \frac{x^6}{3!} + \cdots.$$

Term-by-term integration gives us

$$\int_0^1 e^{-x^2}\,dx = 1 - \frac{1}{3} + \frac{1}{5 \cdot 2!} - \frac{1}{7 \cdot 3!} + \frac{1}{9 \cdot 4!} - \cdots.$$

Since $\frac{1}{9 \cdot 4!} < .005$, the error incurred by using the sum of the first four terms of this alternating series as an approximation to the sum of the series itself is less than .005. Hence we can take

$$\int_0^1 e^{-x^2}\,dx = .74$$

and be sure that at worst we have made an error of one digit in the second decimal place.

In elementary algebra we learned the Binomial Theorem, which is a rule for writing a power of a sum as a sum of powers. Thus we can use the Binomial Theorem to write the expression $(1 + x)^p$ as a sum of powers of x. In our elementary work we had to assume that the exponent p is a positive integer, but even though p is not a positive integer we can still formally apply the rules of the Binomial Theorem to the expression $(1 + x)^p$. In that case, however, the rules generate an infinite series rather than a finite sum. If we assume that the sum of this **binomial series** is really $(1 + x)^p$, then we have the equation

$$\text{(123-3)} \quad \mathbf{(1 + x)^p = 1 + px + \frac{p(p-1)}{2!}x^2 + \cdots + \frac{p(p-1)\cdots(p-n+1)}{n!}x^n + \cdots.}$$

Now let us see if we can justify this use of the equals sign.

We can write the series on the right side of Equation 123-3 as $\sum_{n=0}^{\infty} c_n x^n$, where the coefficients are determined by the recursion formulas

$$\text{(123-4)} \qquad c_0 = 1 \quad \text{and} \quad c_{n+1} = \frac{p-n}{n+1} c_n,\ n = 0, 1, 2, \ldots.$$

Thus we see that

$$\left| \frac{c_{n+1}x^{n+1}}{c_n x^n} \right| = \frac{|p-n|}{n+1} |x|.$$

Since p is independent of n, $\lim_{n \to \infty} \frac{|p-n|}{n+1} = 1$, and hence the limit of the ratios of consecutive terms of the series is $|x|$. It follows from the ratio test that the binomial series converges if $|x| < 1$. Let us denote the sum of the series by $f(x)$. Then

(123-5) $$f(x) = \sum_{n=0}^{\infty} c_n x^n$$

for x in the interval $(-1, 1)$.

We have found the interval of convergence of the binomial series, and now there remains the task of showing that its sum, which we have denoted by $f(x)$, is really $(1 + x)^p$. Thus we must show that the quotient $\frac{f(x)}{(1 + x)^p}$ is the number 1 for each number x in the interval $(-1, 1)$. Let us first show that this quotient is independent of x, which we will do by showing that its derivative is 0. Since the derivative of $\frac{f(x)}{(1 + x)^p}$ is

$$\frac{(1 + x)^p f'(x) - p(1 + x)^{p-1} f(x)}{(1 + x)^{2p}} = \frac{(1 + x)f'(x) - pf(x)}{(1 + x)^{p+1}},$$

we see that if it is to be 0, then

(123-6) $$(1 + x)f'(x) = pf(x),$$

so let us verify this equation. From Equation 123-5 we see that

(123-7) $$f'(x) = \sum_{n=0}^{\infty} nc_n x^{n-1} = 0 \cdot c_0 + 1 \cdot c_1 + 2 \cdot c_2 x + 3 \cdot c_3 x^2 + \cdots.$$

You will notice that we can also write this series as $\sum_{n=0}^{\infty} (n + 1)c_{n+1}x^n$, and so

(123-8) $$f'(x) = \sum_{n=0}^{\infty} (n + 1)c_{n+1}x^n.$$

To express the left side of Equation 123-6 as a series, we multiply both sides of Equation 123-7 by x and add corresponding sides of the resulting equation and Equation 123-8:

$$(1 + x)f'(x) = \sum_{n=0}^{\infty} [(n + 1)c_{n+1} + nc_n]x^n.$$

From Equation 123-4 we see that $(n + 1)c_{n+1} + nc_n = pc_n$. Thus

$$(1 + x)f'(x) = \sum_{n=0}^{\infty} pc_n x^n = p \sum_{n=0}^{\infty} c_n x^n = pf(x),$$

and hence Equation 123-6 is verified. Since the derivative of $\frac{f(x)}{(1 + x)^p}$ is 0 at each point of the interval $(-1, 1)$, it follows that the value of this quotient at any point x of the interval is the same as its value at 0; that is $\dfrac{f(x)}{(1+x)^p} = \dfrac{f(0)}{(1+0)^p} = f(0)$. But Equations 123-4 and 123-5 tell us that $f(0) = c_0 = 1$, and so we have finally shown that $\dfrac{f(x)}{(1+x)^p} = 1$. Therefore, we see that the Binomial Theorem, Equation 123-3, is valid for any real number p as long as x is in the interval $(-1, 1)$. Of course, if p is a positive integer, then Equation 123-3 is valid for every number x.

Example 123-4. Find $\sqrt{105}$.

Solution. We write $\sqrt{105} = \sqrt{100 + 5} = 10\sqrt{1 + \frac{1}{20}}$, and expand $\sqrt{1 + \frac{1}{20}} = (1 + \frac{1}{20})^{1/2}$ by the Binomial Theorem:

$$\left(1 + \frac{1}{20}\right)^{1/2} = 1 + \frac{1}{2}\left(\frac{1}{20}\right) + \frac{\frac{1}{2}(\frac{1}{2} - 1)}{2!}\left(\frac{1}{20}\right)^2 + \frac{\frac{1}{2}(\frac{1}{2} - 1)(\frac{1}{2} - 2)}{3!}\left(\frac{1}{20}\right)^3 + \cdots$$

$$= 1 + \frac{1}{40} - \frac{1}{3200} + \frac{1}{128{,}000} - \cdots.$$

Thus

$$\sqrt{105} = 10 + \frac{1}{4} - \frac{1}{320} + \frac{1}{12{,}800} - \cdots.$$

Since we have an alternating series, it is easy to estimate the error incurred in taking a partial sum of this series as an approximation of the sum. For example, if we add the first three terms of this series, we obtain the partial sum $S_3 = 10.246875$. This sum approximates $\sqrt{105}$ with an error of less than $\dfrac{1}{12{,}800} < .0001$. Therefore, the equation $\sqrt{105} = 10.247$ is surely correct to three decimal places.

Example 123-5. Find an approximation to the circumference C of an ellipse.

Solution. An ellipse with major and minor diameters of lengths $2a$ and $2b$ can be represented by the parametric equations

$$x = a\cos t \quad \text{and} \quad y = b\sin t, \quad 0 \le t \le 2\pi.$$

Thus (see Equation 75-10)

$$C = \int_0^{2\pi} \sqrt{a^2 \sin^2 t + b^2 \cos^2 t}\, dt$$

$$= a\int_0^{2\pi} \sqrt{1 - e^2 \cos^2 t}\, dt,$$

where $e = \dfrac{\sqrt{a^2 - b^2}}{a}$ is the eccentricity of the ellipse. Now we use the binomial series Formula 123-3 with $p = \frac{1}{2}$ and $x = -e^2 \cos^2 t$, and we have

$$C = a \int_0^{2\pi} \left(1 - \frac{e^2}{2}\cos^2 t - \frac{e^4}{8}\cos^4 t + \cdots\right) dt.$$

The first two terms of this expansion give us the following approximation of the circumference of the ellipse:

$$C \approx a\left[t - \frac{e^2}{2}\left(\frac{t}{2} + \frac{\sin 2t}{4}\right)\right]\Bigg|_0^{2\pi} = 2\pi a\left(1 - \frac{e^2}{4}\right).$$

Problems 123

1. Multiply or divide known series to find Taylor's Series about 0 for the following:
   (a) $e^x \sin x$ (b) $e^x \cos x$
   (c) $\sec x$ (d) e^{-x}
   (e) $\dfrac{e^x}{(1 + x)}$ (f) $e^x \sec x$
2. Use series and term-by-term integration to evaluate:
   (a) $\int_0^1 \cos \sqrt{x}\, dx$ (b) $\int_0^{.5} x \ln (1 + x)\, dx$
   (c) $\int_0^{2/5} \sin x^2\, dx$ (d) $\int_0^{.25} \sec x \ln (1 + x)\, dx$
3. Use the binomial series to compute:
   (a) $\sqrt{1.02}$ (b) $\sqrt{3.92}$
   (c) $\sqrt[3]{.98}$ (d) $\sqrt[3]{30}$
   (e) $10^{-2/3}$ (f) $\sqrt[4]{17}$
4. Use the binomial series and term-by-term integration to compute:
   (a) $\int_0^1 \sqrt[3]{8 + x^3}\, dx$ (b) $\int_0^{.4} t\sqrt{1 - t^3}\, dt$
   (c) $\int_0^{.1} (1 + x^2)^{.9}\, dx$ (d) $\int_0^{\pi/2} \sqrt{1 - (\frac{1}{2}) \sin^2 u}\, du$
5. Expand $(1 - t^2)^{-1/2}$ by the binomial formula and integrate from 0 to x, term-by-term, to obtain a series for Arcsin x.
6. Does the binomial series converge if $|x| = 1$ and $p = -1$?
7. Use the series in Example 123-2 and term-by-term integration to find a series in powers of x whose sum is $\ln \cos x$.
8. Use the identity $\sin^2 x = \frac{1}{2}(1 - \cos 2x)$ to find the series for $\sin^2 x$ in powers of x.
9. Find the area of the region bounded by the X-axis, the lines $x = 1$ and $x = 2$, and the curve whose equation is $xy = \sin x$.
10. Find the area of the region bounded by the coordinate axes, the line $x = 1$, and the curve whose equation is $xy = \sinh x$.

Review Problems, Chapter Fourteen

You can use the following problems to test yourself on the material covered in this chapter.

1. The terms of a certain sequence $\{a_n\}$ are given by the following rule: The first term is 1 and each of the other terms is the square of one-half of its predecessor. Express a_n in terms of n. What is $\lim_{n\to\infty} a_n$?
2. Find a formula for the nth partial sum S_n of the infinite series
$$\sum_{k=1}^{\infty} \ln\left(\frac{\text{Arctan } (k+1)}{\text{Arctan } k}\right).$$
What is the sum of this series?
3. Test the following series for convergence.
(a) $\sum_{k=1}^{\infty} \sin \frac{1}{k}$ (b) $\sum_{k=1}^{\infty} \sin^2 \frac{1}{k}$ (c) $\sum_{k=1}^{\infty} \sqrt{\sin \frac{1}{k^2}}$
4. Show that if a series of positive terms $\sum_{k=1}^{\infty} a_k$ converges, then the series $\sum_{k=1}^{\infty} a_k^2$ converges. Does it necessarily follow that the series $\sum_{k=1}^{\infty} \sqrt{a_k}$ converges?
5. Suppose that $\sum_{k=1}^{\infty} a_k$ and $\sum_{k=1}^{\infty} b_k$ are convergent series of positive terms. Show that the series $\sum_{k=1}^{\infty} a_k b_k$ is also convergent.
6. Test the following series for convergence.
(a) $\sum_{k=1}^{\infty} \frac{\sin \frac{1}{2}k\pi}{k}$ (b) $\sum_{k=1}^{\infty} \frac{\sin \frac{1}{3}k\pi}{k}$
7. Use integration to show that the error that results from using the first K terms of the series $\sum_{k=1}^{\infty} \left(\frac{1}{1+k^2}\right)$ to approximate its sum is less than $\frac{\pi}{2} - \text{Tan}^{-1} K$ and more than $\frac{\pi}{2} - \text{Tan}^{-1} (K+1)$.
8. Give an example of a divergent series $\sum_{n=1}^{\infty} a_n$ of positive terms such that $\frac{a_{n+1}}{a_n} < 1$ for each integer n. Does this example contradict Theorem 119-1?
9. Find the set of points for which the power series $\sum_{n=1}^{\infty} \sin n\, x^n$ converges.
10. Suppose that $f(x) = 1 + c_1x + c_2x^2 + c_3x^3 + \cdots$ and that $f'(x) = f(x)$. Show that then c_n is given by the formula $c_n = \frac{1}{n!}$.
11. What is the product of the series $\sum_{n=0}^{\infty} \frac{x^n}{n!}$ and $\sum_{n=0}^{\infty} \frac{(-1)^n x^n}{n!}$?
12. Show that we can use the Binomial Theorem to expand $(a+b)^p$, where p is any real number, if $|b| < |a|$.

APPENDIX

A TRIGONOMETRIC FORMULAS

The following trigonometric identities are valid for any numbers t, u, and v for which the functions involved are defined.

(A-1)
$$\csc t = \frac{1}{\sin t} \qquad \tan t = \frac{\sin t}{\cos t} \qquad \tan^2 t + 1 = \sec^2 t$$
$$\sec t = \frac{1}{\cos t} \qquad \cot t = \frac{\cos t}{\sin t} \qquad \cot^2 t + 1 = \csc^2 t$$
$$\cot t = \frac{1}{\tan t} \qquad \sin^2 t + \cos^2 t = 1$$

(A-2)
$$\sin (u \pm v) = \sin u \cos v \pm \cos u \sin v$$
$$\cos (u \pm v) = \cos u \cos v \mp \sin u \sin v$$
$$\tan (u \pm v) = \frac{\tan u \pm \tan v}{1 \mp \tan u \tan v}$$

$$\text{(A-3)} \qquad \begin{aligned} \sin(-t) &= -\sin t \\ \cos(-t) &= \cos t \\ \tan(-t) &= -\tan t \end{aligned}$$

$$\text{(A-4)} \qquad \begin{aligned} \sin 2t &= 2 \sin t \cos t \\ \cos 2t &= \cos^2 t - \sin^2 t = 1 - 2\sin^2 t = 2\cos^2 t - 1 \\ \tan 2t &= \frac{2 \tan t}{1 - \tan^2 t} \end{aligned}$$

$$\text{(A-5)} \qquad \begin{aligned} \sin^2 t &= \tfrac{1}{2}(1 - \cos 2t) \\ \cos^2 t &= \tfrac{1}{2}(1 + \cos 2t) \end{aligned}$$

The length s of the arc of a circle of radius r that is intercepted by a central angle that measures t radians is given by the formula

$$\boldsymbol{s = rt.}$$

The area of the wedge that this angle cuts from the interior of this circle is given by the formula

$$\boldsymbol{K = \tfrac{1}{2}rs = \tfrac{1}{2}r^2t.}$$

If an angle measures A degrees and t radians, then

$$\boldsymbol{\frac{A}{180} = \frac{t}{\pi}.}$$

The following brief table of values of the trigonometric functions is often useful.

t	$\cos t$	$\sin t$	$\tan t$
0	1	0	0
$\pi/6$	$\sqrt{3}/2$	$\frac{1}{2}$	$1/\sqrt{3}$
$\pi/4$	$\sqrt{2}/2$	$\sqrt{2}/2$	1
$\pi/3$	$\frac{1}{2}$	$\sqrt{3}/2$	$\sqrt{3}$
$\pi/2$	0	1	—
$2\pi/3$	$-\frac{1}{2}$	$\sqrt{3}/2$	$-\sqrt{3}$
$3\pi/4$	$-\sqrt{2}/2$	$\sqrt{2}/2$	-1
$5\pi/6$	$-\sqrt{3}/2$	$\frac{1}{2}$	$-1/\sqrt{3}$
π	-1	0	0

APPENDIX

B LIMITS

In Section 13 we defined what we mean by the limit at a point a of a function f and stated (without proof) some of the basic limit theorems. Here we shall say a few words about how such theorems may be proved. When proving limit theorems, it is convenient to use a definition of the limit that looks different but is equivalent to the definition given in Section 13.

Let us use Fig. B-1 to recall what we mean by the symbols

$$\lim_{x \to a} f(x) = L.$$

The interval I is a deleted open interval about a. The interval $J(I)$ is the smallest closed interval that contains the set of numbers that correspond (under f) to the numbers in I. Thus if x is in I, then the corresponding number $f(x)$ is in $J(I)$. Then as I "squeezes down" on the point a, $J(I)$ "squeezes down" on the point L. More precisely, L is the one and only number that belongs to every interval $J(I)$. Suppose that r is a given positive number and that we construct the interval $(L - r, L + r)$ of length $2r$ with L as center. Then for a sufficiently short interval I, say all points except a of the interval $(a - d, a + d)$ for a suitably small positive number d, the corresponding J-interval will be contained in the interval $(L - r, L + r)$. Thus for any given positive number r there is a positive number d such that if x is in the interval $(a - d, a + d)$, but $x \neq a$, then $f(x)$ is in the interval $(L - r, L + r)$. This property can be used to define the limit concept

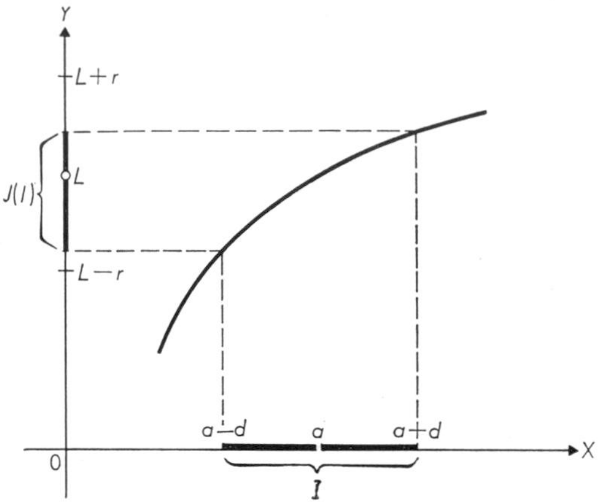

Figure B-1

and we get the definition of limit that is found in most calculus books. This new definition is equivalent to Definition 13-1 and reads as follows.

DEFINITION B-1. *The number L is the limit of the function f at the point a, in symbols*

$$\lim_{x \to a} f(x) = L,$$

if, and only if, for each positive number r there is a positive number d such that $f(x)$ is in the interval $(L - r, L + r)$ whenever x is a number different from a in the interval $(a - d, a + d)$. In terms of inequalities and absolute values,

$$|f(x) - L| < r \quad \textit{whenever} \quad 0 < |x - a| < d.$$

The key idea of Definition B-1 is that if we pick *any* interval about L (of length $2r$), then there is an interval about a (of width $2d$) such that our inequalities hold when x is a number (other than a) in the second interval. In general, if we pick a very narrow interval about L, then we will be forced to choose a narrow interval about a. But no matter how narrow the interval about L, if L really is the limit there will always be a corresponding interval about a.

Example B-1. Show that $\lim_{t \to 0} \cos t = 1$.

Solution. We are to show that for any given positive number r there is a positive number d such that whenever $0 < |t| < d$,

(B-1) $$|\cos t - 1| < r.$$

In Example 10-2 we showed that if we proceed t units along the unit circle from the point (1, 0) to the point ($\cos t$, $\sin t$), then the length c of the chord joining these points satisfies the equation

$$|\cos t - 1| = \frac{c^2}{2}.$$

Since the length c of this chord is less than the length $|t|$ of the arc, we have the inequality

$$\text{(B-2)} \qquad |\cos t - 1| < \frac{t^2}{2}.$$

If t is a number such that $|t| < \sqrt{2r}$, then we may replace t^2 in Inequality B-2 with $2r$ and obtain Inequality B-1. Thus for any given positive number r, we may take $d = \sqrt{2r}$, and then

$$|\cos t - 1| < r \quad \text{whenever} \quad 0 < |t| < d.$$

We will now use Definition B-1 to prove two limit theorems. The proofs of the other fundamental limit theorems listed in Section 13 are quite similar. You can find them in any advanced calculus book.

THEOREM B-1. *Suppose that* $\lim_{x \to a} f(x) = L$ *and that* c *is any number. Then*

$$\lim_{x \to a} cf(x) = cL.$$

Proof. If $c = 0$, the theorem reduces to the obvious equation $\lim_{x \to a} 0 = 0$, so let us suppose that $c \neq 0$. Then we may divide by c in the following calculations. We are to show that for each positive number r there is a number d such that

$$\text{(B-3)} \qquad |cf(x) - cL| < r \quad \text{whenever} \quad 0 < |x - a| < d.$$

Now our hypothesis that $\lim_{x \to a} f(x) = L$ means that for each positive number r_1 there is a number d_1 such that $|f(x) - L| < r_1$ whenever $0 < |x - a| < d_1$. In particular, therefore, for the positive number $r_1 = \frac{r}{|c|}$ there is a number d_1 such that

$$\text{(B-4)} \qquad |f(x) - L| < \frac{r}{|c|} \quad \text{whenever} \quad 0 < |x - a| < d_1.$$

If we choose $d = d_1$, then Inequalities B-4 are equivalent to Inequalities B-3. Thus we have demonstrated the existence of the required number d and our proof is complete.

THEOREM B-2 (*see Equation* 13-3). *If* $\lim_{x \to a} f(x) = L$ *and* $\lim_{x \to a} g(x) = M$, *then*

$$\lim_{x \to a} [f(x) + g(x)] = L + M.$$

Proof. We are to show that for any given positive number r there is a number d such that

(B-5) $|f(x) + g(x) - (L + M)| < r \quad \text{whenever} \quad 0 < |x - a| < d.$

Since $\lim_{x \to a} f(x) = L$ and $\lim_{x \to a} g(x) = M$, we know that for the positive number $\frac{r}{2}$ there are numbers d_1 and d_2 such that

$$|f(x) - L| < \frac{r}{2} \quad \text{whenever} \quad 0 < |x - a| < d_1$$

and

$$|g(x) - M| < \frac{r}{2} \quad \text{whenever} \quad 0 < |x - a| < d_2.$$

Therefore, let us choose d to be the smaller of the numbers d_1 and d_2. Then if $0 < |x - a| < d$, both $|f(x) - L| < \frac{r}{2}$ and $|g(x) - M| < \frac{r}{2}$, and hence

$$\begin{aligned} |f(x) + g(x) - (L + M)| &= |(f(x) - L) + (g(x) - M)| \\ &\leq |f(x) - L| + |g(x) - M| \\ &< \frac{r}{2} + \frac{r}{2} = r. \end{aligned}$$

Thus Inequalities B-5 hold, and our proof is complete.

TABLE I

Trigonometric Functions

t	sin t	cos t	tan t	cot t	sec t	csc t
0.0	.0000	1.0000	.0000	......	1.000	......
0.1	.0998	.9950	.1003	9.967	1.005	10.02
0.2	.1987	.9801	.2027	4.933	1.020	5.033
0.3	.2955	.9553	.3093	3.233	1.047	3.384
0.4	.3894	.9211	.4228	2.365	1.086	2.568
0.5	.4794	.8776	.5463	1.830	1.139	2.086
0.6	.5646	.8253	.6841	1.462	1.212	1.771
0.7	.6442	.7648	.8423	1.187	1.307	1.552
0.8	.7174	.6967	1.030	.9712	1.435	1.394
0.9	.7833	.6216	1.260	.7936	1.609	1.277
1.0	.8415	.5403	1.557	.6421	1.851	1.188
1.1	.8912	.4536	1.965	.5090	2.205	1.122
1.2	.9320	.3624	2.572	.3888	2.760	1.073
1.3	.9636	.2675	3.602	.2776	3.738	1.038
1.4	.9854	.1700	5.798	.1725	5.883	1.015
1.5	.9975	.0707	14.101	.0709	14.137	1.003
1.6	.9996	−.0292	−34.233	−.0292	−34.25	1.000

TABLE II

Natural Logarithms

x	$\ln x$	x	$\ln x$	x	$\ln x$
0.0	......	3.5	1.2528	7.0	1.9459
0.1	−2.303	3.6	1.2809	7.1	1.9601
0.2	−1.609	3.7	1.3083	7.2	1.9741
0.3	−1.204	3.8	1.3350	7.3	1.9879
0.4	−.916	3.9	1.3610	7.4	2.0015
0.5	−.693	4.0	1.3863	7.5	2.0149
0.6	−.511	4.1	1.4110	7.6	2.0282
0.7	−.357	4.2	1.4351	7.7	2.0412
0.8	−.223	4.3	1.4586	7.8	2.0541
0.9	−.105	4.4	1.4816	7.9	2.0669
1.0	0.0000	4.5	1.5041	8.0	2.0794
1.1	0.0953	4.6	1.5261	8.1	2.0919
1.2	0.1823	4.7	1.5476	8.2	2.1041
1.3	0.2624	4.8	1.5686	8.3	2.1163
1.4	0.3365	4.9	1.5892	8.4	2.1282
1.5	0.4055	5.0	1.6094	8.5	2.1401
1.6	0.4700	5.1	1.6292	8.6	2.1518
1.7	0.5306	5.2	1.6487	8.7	2.1633
1.8	0.5878	5.3	1.6677	8.8	2.1748
1.9	0.6419	5.4	1.6864	8.9	2.1861
2.0	0.6931	5.5	1.7047	9.0	2.1972
2.1	0.7419	5.6	1.7228	9.1	2.2083
2.2	0.7885	5.7	1.7405	9.2	2.2192
2.3	0.8329	5.8	1.7579	9.3	2.2300
2.4	0.8755	5.9	1.7750	9.4	2.2407
2.5	0.9163	6.0	1.7918	9.5	2.2513
2.6	0.9555	6.1	1.8083	9.6	2.2618
2.7	0.9933	6.2	1.8245	9.7	2.2721
2.8	1.0296	6.3	1.8406	9.8	2.2824
2.9	1.0647	6.4	1.8563	9.9	2.2925
3.0	1.0986	6.5	1.8718	10.0	2.3026
3.1	1.1314	6.6	1.8871		
3.2	1.1632	6.7	1.9021		
3.3	1.1939	6.8	1.9169		
3.4	1.2238	6.9	1.9315		

TABLE III

Exponential and Hyperbolic Functions

x	e^x	e^{-x}	$\sinh x$	$\cosh x$	$\tanh x$
0.0	1.0000	1.0000	0.0000	1.0000	0.0000
0.1	1.1052	.9048	.1002	1.0050	.0997
0.2	1.2214	.8187	.2013	1.0201	.1974
0.3	1.3499	.7408	.3045	1.0453	.2913
0.4	1.4918	.6703	.4108	1.0811	.3799
0.5	1.6487	.6065	.5211	1.1276	.4621
0.6	1.8221	.5488	.6367	1.1855	.5370
0.7	2.0138	.4966	.7586	1.2552	.6044
0.8	2.2255	.4493	.8881	1.3374	.6640
0.9	2.4596	.4066	1.0265	1.4331	.7163
1.0	2.7183	.3679	1.1752	1.5431	.7616
1.1	3.0042	.3329	1.3356	1.6685	.8005
1.2	3.3201	.3012	1.5095	1.8107	.8337
1.3	3.6693	.2725	1.6984	1.9709	.8617
1.4	4.0552	.2466	1.9043	2.1509	.8854
1.5	4.4817	.2231	2.1293	2.3524	.9051
1.6	4.9530	.2019	2.3756	2.5775	.9217
1.7	5.4739	.1827	2.6456	2.8283	.9354
1.8	6.0496	.1653	2.9422	3.1075	.9468
1.9	6.6859	.1496	3.2682	3.4177	.9562
2.0	7.3891	.1353	3.6269	3.7622	.9640
2.1	8.1662	.1225	4.0219	4.1443	.9705
2.2	9.0250	.1108	4.4571	4.5679	.9757
2.3	9.9742	1003	4.9370	5.0372	.9801
2.4	11.023	.0907	5.4662	5.5569	.9837
2.5	12.182	.0821	6.0502	6.1323	.9866
2.6	13.464	.0743	6.6947	6.7690	.9890
2.7	14.880	.0672	7.4063	7.4735	.9910
2.8	16.445	.0608	8.1919	8.2527	.9926
2.9	18.174	.0550	9.0596	9.1146	.9940
3.0	20.086	.0498	10.018	10.068	.9951

TABLE IV

Differentiation Formulas

IV-1	$D_x u^r = r u^{r-1} D_x u$
IV-2	$D_x \sin u = \cos u \, D_x u$
IV-3	$D_x \cos u = - \sin u \, D_x u$
IV-4	$D_x \tan u = \sec^2 u \, D_x u$
IV-5	$D_x \cot u = - \csc^2 u \, D_x u$
IV-6	$D_x \sec u = \sec u \tan u \, D_x u$
IV-7	$D_x \csc u = - \csc u \cot u \, D_x u$
IV-8	$D_x e^u = e^u D_x u$
IV-9	$D_x \ln\|u\| = \frac{1}{u} D_x u$
IV-10	$D_x a^u = a^u \ln a \, D_x u$
IV-11	$D_x \log_b \|u\| = \frac{\log_b e}{u} D_x u$
IV-12	$D_x \text{Arcsin } u = \frac{1}{\sqrt{1 - u^2}} D_x u$
IV-13	$D_x \text{Arccos } u = - \frac{1}{\sqrt{1 - u^2}} D_x u$
IV-14	$D_x \text{Arctan } u = \frac{1}{1 + u^2} D_x u$
IV-15	$D_x \cosh u = \sinh u \, D_x u$
IV-16	$D_x \sinh u = \cosh u \, D_x u$
IV-17	$D_x \tanh u = \text{sech}^2 u \, D_x u$
IV-18	$D_x \coth u = - \text{csch}^2 u \, D_x u$
IV-19	$D_x \text{sech } u = - \text{sech } u \tanh u \, D_x u$
IV-20	$D_x \text{csch } u = - \text{csch } u \coth u \, D_x u$
IV-21	$D_x \sinh^{-1} u = \frac{1}{\sqrt{u^2 + 1}} D_x u$
IV-22	$D_x \text{Cosh}^{-1} u = \frac{1}{\sqrt{u^2 - 1}} D_x u$
IV-23	$D_x \tanh^{-1} u = \frac{1}{1 - u^2} D_x u$
IV-24	$D_x \coth^{-1} u = \frac{-1}{u^2 - 1} D_x u$
IV-25	$D_x \text{Sech}^{-1} u = \frac{-1}{u \sqrt{1 - u^2}} D_x u$
IV-26	$D_x \text{csch}^{-1} u = \frac{-1}{u \sqrt{1 + u^2}} D_x u$

TABLE V

Basic Integration Formulas

(Note: The number a is assumed to be positive in the following 25 basic formulas.)

V-1 $\int u^r\,du = \dfrac{u^{r+1}}{r+1} \qquad (r \neq -1)$

V-2 $\int \cos u\,du = \sin u$

V-3 $\int \sin u\,du = -\cos u$

V-4 $\int \sec^2 u\,du = \tan u$

V-5 $\int \csc^2 u\,du = -\cot u$

V-6 $\int \sec u \tan u\,du = \sec u$

V-7 $\int \csc u \cot u\,du = -\csc u$

V-8 $\int e^u\,du = e^u$

V-9 $\int \dfrac{du}{u} = \ln |u|$

V-10 $\int a^u\,du = a^u/\ln a$

V-11 $\int \ln |u|\,du = u(\ln |u| - 1)$

V-12 $\int \dfrac{du}{\sqrt{a^2 - u^2}} = \text{Arcsin}\left(\dfrac{u}{a}\right)$

V-13 $\int \dfrac{du}{a^2 + u^2} = \left(\dfrac{1}{a}\right) \text{Arctan}\left(\dfrac{u}{a}\right)$

V-14 $\int \sinh u\,du = \cosh u$

V-15 $\int \cosh u\,du = \sinh u$

V-16 $\int \operatorname{sech}^2 u\,du = \tanh u$

V-17 $\int \operatorname{csch}^2 u\,du = -\coth u$

V-18 $\int \operatorname{sech} u \tanh u\,du = -\operatorname{sech} u$

V-19 $\int \operatorname{csch} u \coth u\,du = -\operatorname{csch} u$

V-20 $\int \dfrac{du}{\sqrt{u^2 + a^2}} = \sinh^{-1}\left(\dfrac{u}{a}\right) = \ln\left(\dfrac{u + \sqrt{u^2 + a^2}}{a}\right)$

V-21 $\int \dfrac{du}{\sqrt{u^2 - a^2}} = \text{Cosh}^{-1}\left(\dfrac{u}{a}\right) = \ln\left(\dfrac{u + \sqrt{u^2 - a^2}}{a}\right)$

V-22 $\int \dfrac{du}{a^2 - u^2} = \dfrac{1}{a}\tanh^{-1}\left(\dfrac{u}{a}\right) = \dfrac{1}{2a}\ln\left(\dfrac{a+u}{a-u}\right), \ (u^2 < a^2)$

TABLE V *(Continued)*

V-23 $\int \frac{du}{u^2 - a^2} = -\frac{1}{a}\coth^{-1}\left(\frac{u}{a}\right) = -\frac{1}{2a}\ln\left(\frac{u+a}{u-a}\right), \ (u^2 > a^2)$

V-24 $\int \frac{du}{u\sqrt{a^2 - u^2}} = -\frac{1}{a}\operatorname{Sech}^{-1}\left(\frac{u}{a}\right)$

$= -\frac{1}{a}\ln\left(\frac{a + \sqrt{a^2 - u^2}}{u}\right), \ 0 < u < a$

V-25 $\int \frac{du}{u\sqrt{a^2 + u^2}} = -\frac{1}{a}\operatorname{csch}^{-1}\left(\frac{|u|}{a}\right)$

$= -\frac{1}{a}\ln\left(\frac{a + \sqrt{a^2 + u^2}}{|u|}\right)$

Additional Integration Formulas

V-26 $\int \frac{u\,du}{au + b} = \frac{u}{a} - \frac{b}{a^2}\ln|au + b|$

V-27 $\int \frac{u\,du}{(au + b)^2} = \frac{b}{a^2(au + b)} + \frac{1}{a^2}\ln|au + b|$

V-28 $\int \frac{du}{u(au + b)} = \frac{1}{b}\ln\left|\frac{u}{au + b}\right|$

V-29 $\int \frac{du}{u(au + b)^2} = \frac{1}{b(au + b)} + \frac{1}{b^2}\ln\left|\frac{u}{au + b}\right|$

V-30 $\int \sqrt{a^2 - u^2}\,du = \frac{u}{2}\sqrt{a^2 - u^2} + \frac{a^2}{2}\operatorname{Arcsin}\frac{u}{a},$

V-31 $\int \sqrt{u^2 \pm a^2}\,du = \frac{u}{2}\sqrt{u^2 \pm a^2} \pm \frac{a^2}{2}\ln|u + \sqrt{u^2 \pm a^2}|$

V-32 $\int u^2\sqrt{a^2 - u^2}\,du = -\frac{1}{4}u(a^2 - u^2)^{3/2} + \frac{a^2u}{8}\sqrt{a^2 - u^2} + \frac{a^4}{8}\operatorname{Arcsin}\frac{u}{a},$

V-33 $\int \sec u\,du = \ln|\sec u + \tan u|$

V-34 $\int \csc u\,du = \ln|\csc u - \cot u|$

V-35 $\int e^{au}\sin bu\,du = \frac{e^{au}(a\sin bu - b\cos bu)}{a^2 + b^2}$

V-36 $\int e^{au}\cos bu\,du = \frac{e^{au}(b\sin bu + a\cos bu)}{a^2 + b^2}$

V-37 $\int u^n\ln u\,du = u^{n+1}\left[\frac{\ln u}{n + 1} - \frac{1}{(n + 1)^2}\right]$

V-38 $\int \sin^n u\,du = \frac{-\sin^{n-1}u\cos u}{n} + \frac{n - 1}{n}\int \sin^{n-2}u\,du$

V-39 $\int \cos^n u\,du = \frac{\cos^{n-1}u\sin u}{n} + \frac{n - 1}{n}\int \cos^{n-2}u\,du$

V-40 $\int \tan^n u\,du = \frac{\tan^{n-1}u}{n - 1} - \int \tan^{n-2}u\,du$

V-41 $\int u^ne^{au}\,du = \frac{u^ne^{au}}{a} - \frac{n}{a}\int u^{n-1}e^{au}\,du$

TABLE V *(Continued)*

V-42 $$\int u^n \sin au\,du = \frac{-u^n}{a}\cos au + \frac{n}{a}\int u^{n-1}\cos au\,du$$

V-43 $$\int u^n \cos au\,du = \frac{u^n}{a}\sin au - \frac{n}{a}\int u^{n-1}\sin au\,du$$

V-44 $$\int \frac{du}{au^2+bu+c} = \frac{2}{\sqrt{4ac-b^2}}\operatorname{Tan}^{-1}\left(\frac{2au+b}{\sqrt{4ac-b^2}}\right), \qquad (b^2 < 4ac)$$

V-45 $$\int \frac{udu}{au^2+bu+c} = \frac{1}{2a}\ln|au^2+bu+c| - \frac{b}{a\sqrt{4ac-b^2}}\operatorname{Tan}^{-1}\left(\frac{2au+b}{\sqrt{4ac-b^2}}\right), \qquad (b^2 < 4ac)$$

V-46 $$\int \frac{du}{(au^2+bu+c)^r} = \frac{2au+b}{(r-1)(4ac-b^2)(au^2+bu+c)^{r-1}} + \frac{2(2r-3)a}{(r-1)(4ac-b^2)}\int \frac{du}{(au^2+bu+c)^{r-1}}$$

V-47 $$\int \frac{u\,du}{(au^2+bu+c)^r} = \frac{-(2c+bu)}{(r-1)(4ac-b^2)(au^2+bu+c)^{r-1}} - \frac{b(2r-3)}{(r-1)(4ac-b^2)}\int \frac{du}{(au^2+bu+c)^{r-1}}$$

SELECTED ANSWERS

Problems 1. *Page 5*

1. (a) $\frac{7}{3}$; (b) $\frac{-21}{4}$; (c) -2; (d) $\frac{1}{2}$. **2.** $-1, 0, 1, 2$. **3.** (a), (b), and (c) are true. **7.** $\frac{61}{21}$. **8.** (a) $x = 4$ or $x = -4$; (b) $x = 4$ or $x = -2$; (c) $x \geq 0$; (d) $x \leq 1$. **9.** (a) No; (b) Yes; (c) No. **10.** (a) $x < y$; (b) $|x| < |y|$; (c) $|x - 3| < \frac{1}{2}$; (d) $|x - y| < 1$. **11.** (a) 3.141 and 3.142; (b) 1.73 and 1.74.

Problems 2. *Page 9*

1. (a) $m = 2, d = 4$; (b) $m = 1, d = 4$; (c) $m = -3, d = 4$; (d) $m = \frac{49}{12}, d = \frac{5}{6}$. **5.** (a) $[-1, 1]$; (b) $(-2, 2)$; (c) $(2, 4)$; (d) $[-4, -2]$; (e) $(-2, -1)$; (f) $[-1, -1]$. **6.** (a) $(3, \infty)$ or $(-\infty, -3)$; (b) $[3, \infty]$ or $[-\infty, -1]$; (c) $[-1, \infty]$ or $[-\infty, -5]$; (d) $(6, \infty)$ or $(-\infty, -2)$. **7.** (a) $|x - 4| < 1$; (b) $|x - \frac{7}{2}| < \frac{7}{2}$; (c) $|x - 1| < 2$; (d) $|x - 7| \leq 3$; (e) $|x + \frac{9}{2}| \leq \frac{5}{2}$; (f) $|x - \frac{7}{2}| \leq \frac{11}{2}$. **8.** (a) $[2, 3]$; (b) $[-1, 5]$; (c) $[-1, 1]$; (d) $[-1, 1]$; (e) $[-\infty, \infty]$; (f) $[-\infty, \infty]$.

Problems 3. *Page 14*

1. (a) Domain is the set of positive integers, range is the set of positive integers that are greater than 1, and $f(n) = n + 1$; (b) Domain is the interval $(-\infty, \infty)$, range is the interval $[0, \infty]$, and $g(x) = 3x^2$; (c) Domain is the interval $(0, \infty)$, range is the interval $(0, \infty)$, and $h(x) = x^2 + \sqrt{x}$. **3.** (a) $(0, \infty)$; (b) $(0, \infty)$; (c) $(-\infty, -1)$ and $(-1, \infty)$; (d) $(-\infty, 0)$ and $(0, \infty)$; (e) $(-\infty, -1)$ and $(1, \infty)$; (f) $[-\infty, -1]$ and $(1, \infty)$. **5.** (a) 1; (b) 5; (c) 36; (d) 12; (e) 2; (f) 2. **7.** (a) 4; (b) 0; (c) 0; (d) 0. **9.** Domain is the set of positive integers that are less than 14, $f(1) = 1, f(4) = 2, f(5) = 2$, and the range is the set consisting of the integers 0, 1, and 2. **11.** $c = 22x^2$. **13.** $c = .1\pi r^2 + \dfrac{.01\pi\sqrt{r^6 + 81}}{r}$.

Problems 4. *Page 19*

1. (a) $\sqrt{29}$; (c) 5; (e) $\sqrt{16 + 2\sqrt{10}}$. **3.** (a) $2\sqrt{a^2 + b^2}$; (b) $2\sqrt{a + b}$. **5.** Not a right triangle. **7.** $(-2, -1)$. **9.** (4, 0). **11.** (a) Not collinear; (b) Collinear.

Problems 5. *Page 24*

3. $(-3, 2)$. **5.** $\sqrt{37}$. **7.** $[2, \infty]$.

Problems 6. *Page 28*

3. Center $(-3, 1)$ and radius 1. **5.** $\sqrt{2}$.

Problems 7. *Page 32*

1. (a) $y = \dfrac{3}{2}x$; (b) $y = -7x$; (c) $y = -\dfrac{3}{4}x$. **2.** (a) $y = \dfrac{12}{x^2}$; (b) $y = \dfrac{-2}{x^2}$; (c) $y = \dfrac{9}{x^2}$. **3.** (b) No; (c) No; (d) No; (e) No. **4.** (b) No; (c) No; (d) No; (e) No. **5.** (a) 129 miles; (b) 4 hours and 38 minutes. **7.** $h = 2$ feet. **9.** $y = x^m$.

Problems 8. *Page 36*

1. (a) $f(x) = 3x - 2$; (c) $f(x) = \dfrac{\pi}{3}(1 - x)$. **3.** (a) $f(x) = mx$; (b) $f(x) = x + b$; (c) $f(x) = mx + m - 1$; (d) $f(x) = mx + (2 - 3m)$; (e) $f(x) = \frac{1}{4}x + \frac{5}{4}$; (f) $f(x) = -\frac{8}{3}x + \frac{4}{3}$. **5.** 80 calories. **7.** They are parallel.

Problems 9. *Page 42*

1. (a) $m = 3$, $b = -1$; (c) $m = 2$, $b = \frac{7}{2}$; (e) $m = -3$, $b = 7$; (g) $m = -\frac{1}{2}$, $b = -\frac{1}{4}$. **3.** (a) $y = 4x - 1$; (c) $x + y = 2$; (e) $y = 2x$; (g) $y = \frac{22}{7}x + (\pi - \frac{22}{7})$. **5.** (a) 1; (c) $-\frac{1}{2}$; (e) 0; (g) No slope. **7.** $3x + 5y - 7 = 0$. **9.** $x + \sqrt{3}\,y - 4 = 0$. **13.** (3, 1) and $(-27, 41)$.

Problems 10. *Page 49*

1. (a) .84; (b) .54; (c) .07; (d) .48. **3.** (a) $\frac{\sqrt{2}}{2}$; (b) $\frac{\sqrt{2}}{2}$; (c) 1; (d) $\frac{\sqrt{3}}{2}$; (e) $\frac{1}{2}$; (f) $\frac{1}{2}$. **5.** (a), (c), and (f) are positive. **7.** (a) $\sqrt{2}$; (c) $\sqrt{2}$; (e) 1. **9.** (a) 1; (c) $-\cos 4t$; (e) $-\cot 2t$; (g) 1. **11.** $\frac{42\pi}{5}$ inches.

Review Problems, Chapter 1. *Page 50*

1. 2.5. **3.** x is between -3 and 3, x is to the right of 4 or to the left of -2, x is between the numbers 2 and -4 or it may be one of the numbers 2 or -4. **5.** $-1 < x \leq 7$. **6.** (b) and (d). **7.** (a) (0, 6); (c) $f(2) = 1.5$, $f(\pi) = 2.5$. **9.** $f(x) = 2x + 1$, $(-\frac{1}{2}, 0)$. **13.** (5, 2). **16.** (a) $x = k\pi$, k any integer; (b) No solution.

Problems 11. *Page 58*

1. (a) $f'(1) = 2$, $f'(2) = 4$; (c) $f'(1) = -\frac{3}{5}$, $f'(2) = -\frac{12}{5}$; (e) $f'(1) = -\frac{1}{2}$, $f'(2) = -.4$. **3.** The constant function with value zero. **7.** (a) $f'(1) = 2.1$; (c) $f'(1) = -.662$; (e) $f'(1) = -.5289$. **9.** (a) $y' = \frac{1}{2}$; (c) $y' = 2$.

Problems 12. *Page 65*

1. Slopes of chords: -1, $-\frac{3}{2}$, and $-\frac{5}{2}$. Slope of tangent is -2. **3.** (a) $f'(x) = 2$; (b) $f'(x) = -1$; (c) $f'(x) = 2x - 4$; (d) $f'(x) = 3x^2 - 7$; (e) $f'(x) = 2x - 2$; (f) $f'(x) = -2/(1 + x)^2$. **5.** (a) $y + x - 1 = 0$; (c) $y + 2x - 2 = 0$; (e) $y - x + 1 = 0$. **7.** (a) 1; (b) -1; (c) $f'(0)$ does not exist. **9.** (a) 0; (b) 0; (c) $f'(0) = 0$. **11.** (a) 0; (b) 0; (c) $f'(0) = 0$.

Problems 13. *Page 74*

3. (a) -4; (b) 2; (c) 1; (d) 3. **4.** (a) -4; (c) 11; (e) 7; (g) 3; (i) 2; (k) 0. **5.** (a) $y' = 2(x - 2)$; (c) $y' = -2/x^3$; (e) $y' = 2/(1 - x)^2$; (g) $y' = 4x(x^2 + 1)$. **6.** (a) f is not differentiable at 2; (c) f is not differentiable at 2. **7.** $q(h) = (\sin h)/h$ and $f'(0) = 1$. **9.** (a) 0; (b) -1; (c) No. **11.** (a) 0; (b) 1.

Problems 14. *Page 77*

1. (a) $D_x y = 6x$; (b) $D_x y = -3x^2$; (c) $D_x y = -1/(1 + x)^2$; (d) $D_x y = 1/2\sqrt{1 + x}$; (e) $D_x y = x/\sqrt{1 + x^2}$; (f) $D_x y = 3\sqrt{x}/2$. **3.** Velocities are approximately 1, .88, and .54. **5.** $D_r A = 2\pi r$. **7.** (a) $v = -1/(1 + t)^2$; (b) $v = 1 - 1/t^2$; (c) $v = 2/(1 + t)^3$; (d) $v = 1/(t + 2)^2$.

Problems 15. *Page 82*

1. (a) $y' = 7x^6$; (b) $y' = 1/4\sqrt[4]{x^3}$; (c) $y' = 1/5\sqrt[5]{t^4}$; (d) $y' = 3u^2$; (e) $y' = 1/6\sqrt[6]{v^5}$; (f) $y' = 9w^8$. **3.** (a) $3y - x - 2 = 0$; (c) $4x - y - 3 = 0$. **7.** (a) $3x + y - 4 = 0$; (c) $x + 4y - 5 = 0$. **10.** $|ra^r + 1/ra^{r-2}|$.

Problems 16. *Page 87*

1. (a) $y' = x$; (c) $y' = 6x$; (e) $y' = 6t^2 + 1$; (g) $y' = 1/\sqrt{2x}$; (i) $y' = 2v^3 - 1$; (k) $y' = x^{-2/3} - 1$. **2.** (a) -2; (c) 11; (e) -5; (g) $\sqrt[3]{2}/3$; (i) $(\sqrt[3]{2} + \sqrt[5]{2})/2$; (k) -1. **3.** (a) $4x^3 - \dfrac{x^{-3/4}}{12} + 17$; (c) $6t^2 - 6t + 7$. **5.** (a) $2x + 4$; (c) $4t^3 + 4t$; (e) $3x^2 + 6x + 3$; (g) $2(2x + 3)(x^2 + 3x - 1)$. **6.** (a) $4y - 5x - 4 = 0$; (c) $y - 16x + 65 = 0$. **7.** (a) $12y - x - 134 = 0$; (c) $x - 3y + 8 = 0$. **8.** $D_rV = 4\pi r^2$, $D_rV = 2\pi rh$, $D_rV = 2\pi rh/3$. **9.** (a) $(\frac{9}{2}, -\frac{5}{4})$; (b) $(3, -35)$ and $(-3, 49)$; (c) $(1, \frac{163}{15})$ and $(-1, \frac{107}{15})$; (d) No points. **10.** When $t = 1$, $v = 448$ feet per second, max height 15 seconds after firing.

Problems 17. *Page 91*

1. (a) $y' = 1/2\sqrt{x + 1}$; (b) $y' = -1/3\sqrt[3]{(4 - x)^2}$; (c) $y' = 1/\sqrt{2x - 7}$; (d) $y' = -1/2\sqrt[4]{(1 - 2x)^3}$; (e) $y' = 6(x + 1)(x^2 + 2x - 1)^2$; (f) $y' = 2x/3\sqrt[3]{(x^2 - 3)^2}$; (g) $y' = -8x(2 - x^2)^3$; (h) $y' = -x/\sqrt{25 - x^2}$; (i) $y' = 12(3x^2 - 1)(1 - x + x^3)^3$; (j) $y' = (1 - 2x)/2\sqrt{x - x^2}$. **3.** (a) $y' = (x + 2)/\sqrt{x^2 + 4x - 3}$; (b) $y' = (3x^2 - 5)/2\sqrt{x(x^2 - 5)}$; (c) $y' = (3x^2 - 2x + 1)/2\sqrt{(x - 1)(x^2 + 1)}$; (d) $y' = 1/4\sqrt{x(\sqrt{x} + 1)}$. **5.** (a) $(2x^2 + 1)/\sqrt{x^2 + 1}$; (b) $-t/\sqrt{1 - t^2}$; (c) $x(\sqrt{x^2 - 7} - \sqrt{x^2 + 7})/\sqrt{x^4 - 49}$; (d) $2t(t^2 - 1)^3(5t^2 - 1)$; (e) $2(2x - 1)^2(2x + 1)(10x + 1)$; (f) $x(\sqrt{1 - x^2} - \sqrt{1 + x^2})/\sqrt{1 - x^4}$. **7.** (a) $9/\sqrt{23}$; (b) $-3\sqrt{2}$; (c) $2\sqrt[3]{2}/3\sqrt[3]{3}$; (d) $3\sqrt[4]{2}/4\sqrt[4]{3}$. **9.** Slopes are: undefined, zero, 1, zero, undefined. **11.** (a) 12; (b) 2; (c) 2; (d) $\frac{10}{3}$. **12.** Velocity zero when $t = \frac{1}{2}$.

Problems 18. *Page 96*

1. (a) $y' = 5/7x^{2/7}$; (b) $y' = 4x^{-3/5}$; (c) $y' = 3/4\sqrt[4]{x}$; (d) $y' = 2\sqrt[3]{2}/3\sqrt[3]{z}$; (e) $y' = -2/3x\sqrt[3]{x^2}$; (f) $y' = -4/3t^{13/9}$; (g) $y' = -3\sqrt{1 - x/2}$; (h) $y' = 2/3(1 - w)^{5/3}$; (i) $y' = x/(1 - x^2)^{3/2}$; (j) $y' = -30x(5x^2 + 7)^{-4}$. **2.** (a) $-2/(x - 1)^2$; (b) $4t/(1 - t^2)^2$; (c) $4x(x^2 + 3)/(1 - x^2)^3$; (d) $(1 + 2z - 2z^2)/(1 - 2z)^2$; (e) $(y^2 - 25)/8y^2$; (f) $-3(1 + 2/x)^{1/2}/x^2$. **3.** (a) $-\frac{80}{27}$; (b) $2\sqrt{3}/9$; (c) $\sqrt{6}/36$; (d) $-36\sqrt{65}/845$. **5.** (a) $-x/\sqrt{1 - x^2}$; (b) $y' = (t + \sqrt{t^2 + 4})^{1/2}/2\sqrt{t^2 + 4}$; (c) $y' = -x^{-1/3}(1 - x^{2/3})^{1/2}$; (d) $y' = -(x^2 + x + 3)/\sqrt{(2x + 1)(x^2 - 3)^3}$. **7.** (a) $v = (-1 + t + 3t^2)/2t\sqrt{t}$; (b) $v = 1 - t^{-2}$. **8.** $D_xy = \frac{1}{2}$. **9.** (a) $(0, 2)$; (b) $(-1, \frac{1}{3})$. **10.** $3x + 4y - 20 = 0$.

Problems 19. *Page 100*

1. (a) $(\cos\sqrt{x})/2\sqrt{x}$; (c) $(\cos x)/2\sqrt{\sin x}$; (e) $3\cos(3t + 2)$; (g) $(\cos\sqrt{2t + 3})/\sqrt{2t + 3}$; (i) $2\cos 2x + \cos x$; (k) $3\cos 3x$. **2.** (a) -1, (c) $-\sqrt{3}/2$; (e) $\frac{1}{2}$; (g) $-\frac{2}{3}$. **3.** 0. **4.** (a) $y = x$ and $y = -x$; (c) $y = 1$ and $x = \pi/2$. **5.** One point is $(2\pi/3, \sqrt{3}/2)$. **8.** $v = bA\cos(bt + c)$. **9.** $f'(x) = -\cos x$ in $(-\pi/2, 0)$ and $f'(x) = \cos x$ in $(0, \pi/2)$. 0 is not in the domain of f'.

Problems 20. *Page 104*

1. (a) $-2 \sin (2x - 3)$; (c) $2x \sec x^2 \tan x^2$; (e) $-(\csc^2 \sqrt{x})/2\sqrt{x}$; (g) $\sec x \tan^2 x + \sec^3 x$; (i) $6(\sin 2x - \sin 3x)$; (k) $\sec^2 2x - \cos 2x$; (m) $-\sin 2x/\sqrt{\cos 2x}$; (o) $-4x \csc^2 x^2 \cot x^2$; (q) $x \cos x$; (s) $-\sin x \cos (\cos x)$. **5.** (a) 0; (b) $\sin 2x$; (c) $2 \sec^2 2x$; (d) $-2 \sin 2x$. **8.** $x = 4/\pi + k$, where k is any integer, $y = 0$. **9.** $4\pi\sqrt{3}$.

Problems 21. *Page 111*

1. (a) Continuous; (b) Continuous; (c) Not continuous; (d) Not continuous. **2.** (a) $c = \pi/2$; (b) c is any number in $(0, 1)$; (c) $c = \frac{1}{2}$; (d) $c = 2\sqrt{3}/3$; (e) $c = \frac{5}{3}$; (f) $c = \pi/4$. **4.** $f'(x) = g'(x)$. **5.** $f(\frac{1}{2}) = 3$. **6.** $f(x) = 3 \cdot 10^{-x}$. **7.** No. **8.** No. Yes.

Problems 22. *Page 114*

1. (a) $6x - 4$; (c) $4/(1 + x)^3$; (e) $1/2x\sqrt{x}$; (g) $(3 - x)/4x^{5/2}$; (i) $2x(x^2 + 3)/(x^2 - 1)^3$; (k) $(4 - x)/4(x - 1)^{5/2}$. **2.** (a) $-4 \sin 2x$; (b) $-2 \cos 2x$; (c) $(6x - x^3) \cos x - 6x^2 \sin x$; (d) $\dfrac{(2 \sin x - x^2 \sin x - 2x \cos x)}{x^3}$; (e) $-\dfrac{[\sin (1/x)]}{x^3}$; (f) $(2 - 4x^{-4}) \sin (1/x^2) - 2x^{-2} \cos (1/x^2)$. **4.** $f(x) = ax^2 + bx + c$. **9.** Replace f with f' and f' with f'' in Theorem 21-3.

Problems 23. *Page 121*

1. (a) Increasing in $(-\infty, 1)$ and $(3, \infty)$, decreasing in $(1, 3)$; (c) Increasing in $(-\pi/4 + k\pi, \pi/4 + k\pi)$, decreasing in $(\pi/4 + k\pi, 3\pi/4 + k\pi)$; (e) Decreasing in $(-\infty, 0)$ and $(0, \infty)$; (g) Increasing in $(-\pi/4 + k\pi/2, \pi/4 + k\pi/2)$; (i) Increasing in $(-\infty, -1)$ and $(1, \infty)$, decreasing in $(-1, 0)$ and $(0, 1)$; (k) Increasing in $(-\infty, -1)$ and $(1, \infty)$, decreasing in $(-1, 1)$. **3.** (a) Concave up for $x > \frac{2}{3}$, concave down for $x < \frac{2}{3}$; (c) Concave up for all x; (e) Concave up if $x > \sqrt{3}/3$ or $x < -\sqrt{3}/3$. Concave down for x in $(-\sqrt{3}/3, \sqrt{3}/3)$; (g) Concave up if $x > 3$ or $x < -1$. Concave down for x in $(-1, 3)$. **4.** (a) Increasing for all x, concave up if $x < 0$, concave down if $x > 0$; (c) Decreasing in $(-2, 0)$, increasing in $(0, 2)$, concave up in $(-2, 2)$; (e) Decreasing in $(-1, -\sqrt{2}/2)$ and $(\sqrt{2}/2, 1)$, increasing in $(-\sqrt{2}/2, \sqrt{2}/2)$, concave up in $(-1, 0)$, concave down in $(0, 1)$; (g) f is periodic with period 2π. Answers for interval $(0, 2\pi)$ are: Increasing in $(0, .936)$, $(2.574, 3.710)$, and $(5.347, 2\pi)$, decreasing in $(.936, 2.574)$ and $(3.710, 5.347)$, concave up in $(1.697, \pi)$ and $(4.587, 2\pi)$, concave down in $(0, 1.697)$ and $(\pi, 4.587)$.

Review Problems, Chapter 2. *Page 122*

1. (a). **2.** (b). **3.** (c). **4.** (d). **5.** 0, -1. **7.** (a). **9.** (d). **10.** (d). **12.** (d). **14.** $x = 0$. **15.** $f(a) = f(b), f'(c) = 0$. **17.** $-\dfrac{\sqrt{\cos x}}{4}[\tan^2 x + 2]$. **19.** Decreasing in the interval $[-\infty, 1]$, concave down in the interval $(0, 1)$.

Problems 24. *Page 130*

1. (a) $y = -\frac{5}{2}, -2, -\frac{5}{2}, \frac{5}{2}, 2, \frac{5}{2}, y' = \frac{3}{4}, 0, -3, -3, 0, \frac{3}{4}$; (b) Concave up for $x > 0$, concave down for $x < 0$; (c) Maximum point $(-1, -2)$, minimum point $(1, 2)$. **3.** (a) Increasing function and concave up in $(0, 2)$, minimum point $(0, 0)$; (b) Minimum point $(1, 3)$, concave up for $x < -\sqrt[3]{2}$ and $x > 0$, concave down for $-\sqrt[3]{2} < x < 0$; (c) Minimum point $(\frac{5}{2}, -\frac{27}{16})$, concave up for $x < 1$ and $x > 2$, concave down for $1 < x < 2$; (d) Minimum point $(1, 0)$, concave up for $x < 0$ and $x > \frac{2}{3}$, concave down for $0 < x < \frac{2}{3}$; (e) Minimum point $(\frac{1}{2}, -\frac{1}{3})$, concave down if $x > \frac{5}{4}$, concave up if $x < \frac{5}{4}$; (f) Minimum point $(1, 0)$, concave down for all x. **5.** (a) Maximum points $(\pi/2, 3)$ and $(2\pi, 0)$, minimum points $(0, 0)$ and $(3\pi/2, -1)$, concave down in the interval $(\pi/6, 5\pi/6)$ concave up in the intervals $(0, \pi/6)$ and $(5\pi/6, 2\pi)$; (b) Minimum point $(\pi, -1)$, maximum points $(0, 3)$ and $(2\pi, 3)$, concave down in the intervals $(0, \pi/3)$ and $(5\pi/3, 2\pi)$, concave up in the interval $(\pi/3, 5\pi/3)$. **8.** Maximum point $(1, 0)$, minimum points when $x = (1 - \sqrt{105})/4$ and $x = (1 + \sqrt{105})/4$, concave up for $x < -1$ or $x > 2$, concave down for $-1 < x < 2$.

Problems 25. *Page 135*

1. (a) Maximum value $f(-2) = 33$, minimum value $f(\frac{1}{2}) = \frac{7}{4}$; (b) Maximum values $f(2k\pi) = 1$, minimum values $f(2k\pi + \pi) = -1$; (c) Minimum value $f(1) = 0$; (d) No maximum or minimum values; (e) Maximum value $f(-1) = -6$, minimum value $f(1) = -10$; (f) Maximum value $f(2) = 1$. **3.** (a) Minimum at $x = 1$, maximum at $x = \frac{1}{5}$; (b) No maximum or minimum values; (c) No maximum or minimum values; (d) Minimum at $x = 27$. **4.** (a) Maximum values are all 1, minimum values are all -1; (c) Maximum values are all 0, minimum values are all 0; (e) Maximum value $2\sqrt{37}$, minimum value 11 and minimum value 0; (g) Maximum value $\frac{1}{2}$, minimum value $-\frac{1}{2}$.

Problems 26. *Page 141*

1. $10 \times 10 \times 5$. **3.** 16 cubic inches. **7.** (b) 60°. **9.** 6 inches by 9 inches. **11.** $k^2/2$ square inches. **13.** (b) $8(\sqrt[3]{9} + 1)^{3/2}$.

Problems 27. *Page 146*

1. (a) $v = 20, r = 20, a = 16$; (b) $v = -31, r = 31, a = 192$; (c) $v = -\pi/2\sqrt{3}$, $r = \pi/2\sqrt{3}$, $a = -\pi^2/18$; (d) $v = 1.38$, $r = 1.38$, $a = .239$. **3.** (a) 256 feet; (b) 400 feet; (c) 160 feet per second. **5.** (a) 100 miles; (b) $400\sqrt{3}$ miles per minute; (c) $\pi/3$ minutes; (d) $400\sqrt{3}$ miles per minute. **7.** $v = 8\sqrt{s}$, $D_s v = 4/\sqrt{s}$. **9.** $\sqrt{3} < t < 2\sqrt{2 + \sqrt{5}}$. **11.** No. $D_t S = gT$.

Problems 28. *Page 150*

1. 60 cubic inches per minute, $\frac{1}{3}$ inch per minute. **3.** $\frac{24}{5}$ feet per second. **5.** 800 feet per second, 400 feet per second. **7.** $8\frac{1}{3}$ feet per second, $3\frac{1}{3}$ feet per second. **9.** $.07\pi/8 = .0275$ square inches per minute. **11.** $D_t h = 12$ inches per minute.

Problems 29. *Page 158*

1. (a) 5.1; (c) $\frac{81}{40}$; (e) $\frac{191}{768}$; (g) $\frac{80}{243}$. **2.** $A_1 = 2\pi a(b - a)$, $A = \pi(b^2 - a^2)$, 5% error. **3.** .7033. **4.** $V \approx 2\pi hrt$. **5.** $V \approx 4\pi r^2 t$. **6.** (a) 1.04; (c) $-.515$; (e) 1.722; (g) 0, 1.896, -1.896. **7.** 3.14′. **9.** $x_2 = [(n - 1)x_1^n + a]/nx_1^{n-1}$.

Problems 30. *Page 164*

1. (a) $(1 + y^2 + y^4)^{-1}$; (b) $2x/5y$; (c) $(20 - 3x^2)/3y^2$; (d) $-2xy/(x^2 + 3y^2)$; (e) $(2y - y^3)/(3xy^2 - 2x + 2y)$; (f) $-(y + 8x^{7/2}y^{3/2})/(x + 2x^{9/2}y^{1/2})$; (g) $y/x - (x + y)^2$; (h) $(x^4 - 1)/x^3y$; (i) $x(y^2 - 1)/y(1 - x^2)$; (j) $(2x - 1)/2y$. **2.** (a) $-\frac{1}{2}$; (b) $-\frac{3}{5}$; (c) $-b^2x_0/a^2y_0$; (d) $\frac{1}{3}$. **4.** $my_0(x - x_0) + nx_0(y - y_0) = 0$. **6.** $2x + y = 12$ and $14x + y = 60$. **8.** (a) $-1/y^3$; (b) $-2x/y^5$; (c) $-4a^2/y^3$; (d) $(2y^4 - x^2y^2 - x^4)/x^2y^3$.

Review Problems, Chapter 3. *Page 164*

3. Maximum value 2, minimum value -18, concave down $(-\infty, 0)$. **7.** $10\sqrt{5}$. **9.** $y' = \dfrac{2xy^2}{1 - 2x^2y}$, $(0, -4)$ is a minimum point. **11.** $y' = \frac{5}{8}$. **13.** $(\frac{3}{4}, \frac{4}{5})$. **15.** $t = \sqrt{(2k - 1)\pi}$. **17.** $\sqrt[3]{3}$.

Problems 31. *Page 172*

1. (a) $(x - 3)^2 + (y + 2)^2 = 25$; (c) $(x + 1)^2 + (y + 1)^2 = 4$; (e) $x^2 + y^2 = \frac{1}{4}$. **2.** (a) $(2, -1)$, 3; (c) $(-3, 0)$, 2; (e) $(-2, 2)$, $2\sqrt{2}$; (g) $(1, -2)$, $\frac{1}{3}$. **3.** (a) $(x - \frac{1}{2})^2 + (y - \frac{1}{2})^2 = \frac{1}{2}$; (c) Either $(x - 4)^2 + y^2 = 17$ or $(x + 4)^2 + y^2 = 17$. **4.** (a) $(-2, 3)$; (c) $(-7, 4)$; (e) $(0, 0)$. **5.** (a) $(2, -3)$; (c) $(-3, -2)$; (e) $(4, -6)$. **6.** One choice is $h = 0$ and $k = -2$. In every case $m = 3$. **7.** $(h, k) = (-1, 2)$. The lines are $\bar{x} - 3\bar{y} = 0$ and $2\bar{x} - \bar{y} = 0$. **8.** $\bar{x} = x + \frac{3}{2}$, $\bar{y} = y - 1$. **9.** $x^2 + y^2 - 10y + 16 = 0$. Translate origin to $(0, 5)$. **11.** $a^2 + b^2 > 4c$.

Problems 32. *Page 180*

1. (a) $\dfrac{x^2}{9} + \dfrac{y^2}{4} = 1$; (c) $(x - 2)^2 + 4(y + 1)^2 = 4$. **2.** Tacks should be placed on a line parallel to the 11-inch edge through the center of the paper and at points $\sqrt{195}/4 \approx \frac{7}{2}$ inch from the center. String should be approximately 18 inches long. **3.** (a) $\dfrac{x^2}{16} + \dfrac{y^2}{12} = 1$; (c) $\dfrac{(x - 2)^2}{4} + \dfrac{(y - 4)^2}{3} = 1$. **4.** (a) $\dfrac{x^2}{9} + \dfrac{y^2}{25} = 1$; (c) $\dfrac{(x - 6)^2}{36} + \dfrac{(y + 1)^2}{9} = 1$. **5.** (a) $(-3, -2)$ and $(5, -2)$; (c) $(-4, 0)$ and $(-2, 0)$. **6.** (a) Tangent line: $2x + 3y = 12$, normal line: $3x - 2y = 5$; (c) Tangent line: $x + 2y + 1 = 0$, normal line: $2x - y + 7 = 0$. **9.** Slope is $-c/a$. **11.** Curve is a circle, the given points are end points of diameter. **13.** Curve is an ellipse, given points are two of the vertices of the ellipse.

Problems 33. *Page 188*

1. (a) Vertices: $(-2, 0)$, $(2, 0)$, foci: $(-\sqrt{5}, 0)$, $(\sqrt{5}, 0)$, asymptotes: $y = (\frac{1}{2})x$ and $y = (-\frac{1}{2})x$; (c) Vertices: $(0, -1)$, $(0, 1)$, foci: $(0, -\sqrt{5})$, $(0, \sqrt{5})$, asymptotes: $y = (\frac{1}{2})x$ and $y = (-\frac{1}{2})x$; (e) Vertices: $(-5, 2)$, $(3, 2)$, foci: $(-6, 2)$, $(4, 2)$, asymptotes: $3x - 4y - 5 = 0$ and $3x - 4y + 11 = 0$; (g) Vertices: $(1, -5)$, $(1, 1)$, foci: $(1, -7)$, $(1, 3)$, asymptotes: $3x - 4y = 11$ and $3x + 4y + 5 = 0$. **2.** $\frac{x^2}{a^2 - b^2} - \frac{y^2}{b^2} = 1$. **3.** $11x^2 + 18y^2 = 198$. **4.** (a) $5x^2 - 4y^2 = 20$; (c) $\frac{(x-1)^2}{16} - \frac{(y-1)^2}{20} = 1$. **5.** No. **6.** (a) Tangent line: $2x - y - 4 = 0$, normal: $x + 2y - 7 = 0$; (c) Tangent line: $2x - y + 9 = 0$, normal: $x + 2y - 13 = 0$. **7.** (a) $4x^2 - y^2 = 3$; (c) $(y - 2)^2 - (x - 1)^2 = 3$. **9.** Slope is c/a. **10.** Point traces out a hyperbola.

Problems 34. *Page 193*

1. (a) $(2, 0)$, $x = -2$; (c) $(-3, 8)$, $y = -4$; (e) $(1, -2)$, $y = 0$. **2.** (a) $y^2 = 12x$; (c) $(y - 3)^2 = 12(x + 2)$. **3.** $(x + 1)^2 = -2(y - 3)$. **7.** (a) 12; (c) 12. **8.** The tangents are perpendicular. **9.** $(x - 5c/2)^2 + y^2 = 25c^2/4$. **11.** $y^2 = 4(c - a)(x - a)$, where $c^2 = a^2 + b^2$. **13.** $y^2 = 4(c - a)(x - a)$, where $c^2 = a^2 - b^2$.

Problems 35. *Page 201*

1. c/b. **3.** (a) $3x^2 - y^2 + 20x + 12 = 0$; (c) $3x^2 + 4y^2 - 20x + 12 = 0$; (e) $x^2 - 8y^2 - 8y + 16 = 0$; (g) $9x^2 + 8y^2 - 18x - 40y + 41 = 0$. **4.** (a) $e = \frac{1}{2}$, $x = 4$ and $x = -4$; (c) $e = \sqrt{21}/3$, $x = 3\sqrt{21}/7$ and $x = -3\sqrt{21}/7$; (e) $e = \sqrt{3}$, $x = 2\sqrt{3}/3$ and $x = -2\sqrt{3}/3$; (g) $e = \sqrt{2}/2$, $x = 4\sqrt{2}$ and $x = -4\sqrt{2}$. **5.** $e = \frac{1}{2}$, $x = 7$ and $x = -9$. **6.** (a) An ellipse with eccentricity near zero is relatively circular, an ellipse with eccentricity near 1 is relatively flat or narrow; (b) A hyperbola with eccentricity near 1 is relatively narrow, a hyperbola with a large eccentricity is relatively open or wide. **7.** $e = \sqrt{2}$. **9.** $e = \sqrt{2}/2$. **11.** $e = \sqrt{2} - 1$. **13.** $e = \sqrt{2} + 1$.

Review Problems. Chapter 4. *Page 202*

1. $\frac{x^2}{8} + \frac{y^2}{4} = 1$, $e = \frac{\sqrt{2}}{2}$. **3.** $(x - 2)^2 + (y - 6)^2 = 25$. **5.** Length of major diameter is 1, eccentricity is $\sqrt{5}/3$. **7.** $x + y + 2 = 0$. **8.** $\frac{d_2 - d_1}{d_2 + d_1}$. **9.** $y' = -e$.

Problems 36. *Page 211*

1. (a) 4, 6, 8, 10; (c) $-\frac{7}{5}, \frac{1}{5}, \frac{9}{5}, \frac{17}{5}$. **2.** True areas are (a) 48; (c) 64; (e) $\frac{128}{3}$. **5.** True areas are (a) .7; (c) 2. **6.** (a) $\frac{1}{2}(2 + \sqrt{2} + \sqrt{3})$; (c) $F(100) - F(0)$. **7.** $A \approx 17.3$. **9.** 164.

Problems 37. *Page 219*

1. Norm is 1. 1, 2, 3 give minimum sum 2; 2, 3, 4 give maximum sum 3. If the norm is $\frac{1}{3}$, then $\frac{7}{3} \le S \le \frac{8}{3}$. The limit of the approximating sum is $\frac{5}{2}$. **11.** $c = 1$.

Problems 38. *Page 223*

2. (a) 24; (c) -4; (e) 24; (g) $\frac{28}{3}$. **3.** (a) $-\frac{26}{3}$; (c) 39; (e) $\frac{2}{3}$; (g) 0. **4.** (a) $\frac{4}{3}$; (c) 21; (e) $2a$; (g) 0. **7.** (a) $\frac{1295}{4}$; (c) 0. **8.** (a) 2; (c) $\frac{56}{3}$. **9.** (a) 2.

Problems 39. *Page 231*

1. 6. **3.** (a) 3; (c) 17; (e) 4. **4.** (a) $\frac{10}{3}$; (b) 3.25. **5.** (a) 6.25; (c) 1.82. **7.** (a) 2.004; (c) .78; (e) 1.8538. **11.** 2.

Problems 40. *Page 236*

1. (a) 64; (c) $\frac{1}{4}$; (e) 2; (g) $15(2\sqrt[3]{2} - \frac{1}{16})$. **2.** (a) $-\frac{7}{15}$; (c) $\frac{32}{3}$; (e) 16; (g) $\frac{16}{5}$. **3.** (a) 16; (c) $2\sqrt{2}/3$. **4.** (a) $\frac{256}{3}$; (c) $\frac{4}{3}$. **5.** $x = 2$. **7.** No. **8.** (a) $3 - 2\sqrt{2}$; (c) 1.

Problems 41. *Page 240*

1. (a) 3; (c) .9597; (e) 0. **2.** (a) $\frac{1}{2}$; (c) 1.683. **3.** (a) $(-1)^n$; (c) $-\dfrac{1}{\pi}\sin\dfrac{n\pi}{2}$. **4.** (a) 4; (c) 4. **5.** (a) 2; (c) $\sqrt{2}$. **6.** $x = \pi/6$.

Problems 42. *Page 249*

1. $\frac{9}{2}$. **3.** (a) 4; (c) $\frac{1}{2}$; (e) 2. **4.** (a) 9; (c) 18; (e) $\frac{28}{3}$, and $\frac{23}{12}$.

Problems 43. *Page 254*

1. $4\pi ab^2/3$. **2.** (a) $128\pi/7$; (c) $\pi a^3/15$. **3.** $\pi/2$. **4.** (a) $96\pi/5$; (c) $64\pi/7$. **5.** $2n$ and $2/n$. **6.** $\pi h(b^2 + ab + a^2)/3$. **7.** (a) $125\pi/12$; (c) $3456\pi/35$. **9.** $2\pi^2a^2b$.

Problems 44. *Page 259*

1. $256\sqrt{3}/3$. **3.** π. **5.** $4\pi r^3/3k$. **7.** $\frac{1}{3}$ cubic inch. **9.** $16r^3/3$.

Problems 45. *Page 264*

1. $\frac{25}{6}$ foot pounds. **3.** 112,500 foot pounds. **5.** 875π foot pounds. **7.** $6.9\pi 10^4$ foot pounds. **9.** $16 \cdot 10^6$ mi. lbs.

Review Problems, Chapter 5. *Page 265*

1. .5. **3.** $\frac{4}{3}$, exact. **4.** (a) -2; (c) 278/8; (e) $\frac{279}{8}$. **5.** $\frac{8}{3}$. **7.** $36\pi/5$. **9.** $\frac{4}{3}$. **10.** $2\pi a^3/3$.

Problems 46. *Page 271*

2. Maximum when $x = \pi$; minimum when $x = -\pi$. **7.** (a) $5^x + x^5$; (c) $-(1 + x^2)^{-1}$. **8.** (a) $2x^5$; (c) $f(-x)$. **11.** Maximum when $x = 0$; minimum when $x = 1$.

Problems 47. *Page 276*

1. (a) $\frac{67}{60}$. **3.** (a) 1.79; (c) 3.3; (e) .83. **4.** (a) 3.9890; (c) $-.6144$. **6.** (a) $1/2x$; (c) $2 \tan x$; (e) $x^{-1} \cos (\ln x)$; (g) $-1/x(\ln x)^2$. **7.** $G(2) = .4$, $G(\frac{1}{2}) = .15$. **11.** .3567.

Problems 48. *Page 282*

1. (a) $f^{-1}(x) = \dfrac{1 - x}{3}$; (c) $f^{-1}(x) = \dfrac{1}{x}$. **3.** (c) and (d). **4.** (a) $\dfrac{1}{5y^4 + 3y^2}$; (c) $\dfrac{1}{2 - \cos y}$.

Problems 49. *Page 288*

1. $x = e$. **2.** (a) 9.9742; (c) .04979; (e) 2.32. **5.** (a) e^{x+2}; (c) $2xe^{x^2}$; (e) $2e^{2x}$; (g) $\cos x \exp (\sin x)$. **7.** $\pi/4$. **8.** $-1/e$.

Problems 50. *Page 292*

3. (a) xe^x; (c) $xe^x/(1 + x)^2$. **5.** (a) $(5 \ln 2 - 3)/2$; (c) $\frac{7}{3}$; (e) $\frac{15}{2} + \ln 16$; (g) 3; (i) $(3 \ln 2 - 1)/2$. **7.** $\pi(1 - e^{-10})/2 \approx 1.57$. **9.** (a) 4.87. **11.** $1/e$. **13.** $\ln(e - 1)$.

Problems 51. *Page 296*

1. (a) $3^x \ln 3$; (c) $4^x \ln 2$; (e) $2^{5x^2} 10x \ln 2$; (g) $\dfrac{(1 - x^2) \log_{10} e}{x(1 + x^2)}$; (i) $x^x(1 + \ln x)$; (k) $(x + 1)^{x-1}[(x + 1) \ln (x + 1) + x]$; (m) $y(2 + \ln x)/2\sqrt{x}$. **3.** $\pi^e \approx 22.5$, $e^\pi \approx 23.1$. **5.** $e^{-1/e}$. **6.** (a) e^π; (c) $\dfrac{3}{\ln 4}$; (e) $\dfrac{8}{\ln 9}$; (g) $\dfrac{3}{\ln 2} + \dfrac{8}{3}$. **7.** 4. **9.** 2.2. **11.** $\dfrac{-\ln 3}{x(\ln x)^2}$.

Problems 52. *Page 302*

1. (a) $\pi/3$; (c) $\pi/2$; (e) .2. **3.** (a) x; (c) $\text{Sin}^{-1} x$. **4.** (a) Positive; (c) Positive; (e) Negative. **5.** (a) $\dfrac{\pi}{2} - 1$; (c) $\dfrac{\pi}{12} + \dfrac{\sqrt{3}}{2} - 1$. **7.** $\dfrac{\sqrt{2}}{2}$.

Problems 53. *Page 306*

1. (a) $\dfrac{2ax}{(1 + a^2x^4)}$; (c) $\dfrac{1}{2\sqrt{x - x^2}}$; (e) $\dfrac{1}{2x\sqrt{x - 1}}$; (g) $\dfrac{-1}{(\text{Cos}^{-1} x)\sqrt{1 - x^2}}$. **2.** (a) $-\sqrt{\dfrac{1 - y^2}{1 - x^2}}$; (c) $-\dfrac{1 + y^2}{\sqrt{1 - x^2}}$. **3.** $\dfrac{-1}{1 + x^2}$ and $\dfrac{2x}{(1 + x^2)^2}$. **5.** (a) Yes; (c) Yes. **7.** 12 feet. **9.** 1.

Problems 54. *Page 310*

1. Approximately 63.2. **3.** (a) $\dfrac{\pi}{3}$; (c) $\dfrac{7\pi}{6\sqrt{3}}$; (e) .23. **4.** (a) $\dfrac{\pi}{2} - 2x$. **7.** $4\pi - 3\sqrt{3}$.

Problems 55. *Page 316*

3. (a) $e^x \sinh e^x$; (c) $-x^{-2} \cosh x^{-1}$; (e) $2x \operatorname{sech}^2 x^2$; (g) $-2 \operatorname{sech}^2 x \tanh x$; (i) $-\coth x$; (k) $-2(x^2 + 1)/(x^2 - 1)^2$. **7.** 1.4067π. **11.** No. $2 \operatorname{Tan}^{-1} e^x = \operatorname{Tan}^{-1} (\sinh x) + \pi/2$. **12.** $\int \operatorname{sech} x \, dx = 2 \operatorname{Tan}^{-1} e^x$ and $\int \operatorname{sech} x \, dx = \operatorname{Tan}^{-1} (\sinh x)$.

Problems 56. *Page 320*

5. 1. **6.** (a) $\dfrac{-|x|}{x^2\sqrt{1 + x^2}}$; (c) $\dfrac{1}{2\sqrt{x(x - 1)}}$; (e) $-\csc x$; (g) $-\operatorname{csch} x$; (i) $\operatorname{Cosh}^{-1} (\cos x)$ is not defined on an interval. **7.** (a) .9; (c) .5; (e) ln 3; (g) .0933.

Review Problems, Chapter 6. *Page 321*

1. (a) $a^2x^{a^2-1}$; (c) $\dfrac{1}{2\sqrt{x - x^2}}$; (e) $\dfrac{1}{x \ln x} + e^x \exp (e^x)$. **3.** $\dfrac{1}{2e}$. **5.** e^2. **7.** (a) $\pi/3$; (c) $\dfrac{e^{-3} + 3e - 4}{6}$. **9.** $x = 1$. **10.** (b) $F(0) = 0$, $F(1) = 2$, $F(2) = 3$, $F(3) = 5$; (c) $F'(1) = 1$, $F'(3) = 3$. **11.** Domain $[-1, 1]$, always concave up.

Problems 57. *Page 326*

1. (a) $\frac{1}{6}$; (c) -1; (e) 2. **3.** (a) $-3 \cos x - 2 \sin x$; (c) $\dfrac{2x^3}{3} - \ln |x|$; (e) $\dfrac{1}{2} \operatorname{Arctan} \dfrac{u}{2} - \sinh^{-1} \dfrac{u}{2}$; (g) $4w (\ln |w| - 1)$. **5.** $4\pi\sqrt{3}$. **7.** Maximum when $x = \dfrac{\pi}{2} + 2k\pi$; minimum when $x = \dfrac{3\pi}{2} + 2k\pi$.

Problems 58. *Page 330*

1. (a) e^{x^3}; (c) $-\frac{1}{3}\cos x^3$; (e) $\frac{1}{6}$ Arctan $\frac{3x}{2}$; (g) $\frac{1}{4}(\ln x)^4$; (i) $\ln|\sec x|$. **2.** (a) $\frac{(x^2+1)^{3/2}}{3}$; (c) $\sqrt{x^2+1}$; (e) $\frac{-1}{2(t^2+8t+3)}$; (g) $\ln(\cosh v)$. **3.** (a) $\exp(\sin x)$; (c) $\frac{1}{2}\tan(2x+3)$; (e) $\frac{2}{3}\sqrt{x^3-5}$; (g) $\sec e^x$. **4.** (a) $\frac{1}{3}\sec^3 x$; (c) $\ln\sqrt[8]{|3+4\sin 2x|}$; (e) x^3; (g) $e^t - \ln(e^t+1)$. **5.** (a) 0; (c) $\frac{7}{340}$. **7.** $\frac{32}{3}$.

Problems 59. *Page 336*

1. (a) $\frac{\sqrt{3}}{4}$; (c) $\frac{1}{3}(2\sqrt{2}-1)$; (e) $2e(e-1)$; (g) $-\frac{2}{3}(5^{3/2}-3^{3/2})$. **3.** (a) $\frac{1}{2}\ln\frac{5}{2}$; (c) $1-\ln\frac{3}{2}$; (e) $\ln\frac{3}{2}+\frac{1}{6}$. **7.** $\frac{8\pi}{3}$. **9.** π.

Problems 60. *Page 340*

1. (a) $\sin x - x\cos x$; (c) $\frac{xe^{2x}}{2}-\frac{e^{2x}}{4}$; (e) $\frac{x^6}{6}\ln x - \frac{x^6}{36}$; (g) $x\,\mathrm{Sin}^{-1}x + \sqrt{1-x^2}$; (i) $\frac{1}{101\cdot 102}(x+25)^{101}(101x-25)$. **2.** (a) $\frac{32}{15}$; (c) $\frac{\pi}{2}-1$; (e) $2(\ln 2-1)^2$. **3.** (a) $x^2\sin x + 2x\cos x - 2\sin x$; (c) $\frac{1}{4}(x^4-1)\,\mathrm{Tan}^{-1}x - \frac{x^3}{12}+\frac{x}{4}$; (e) $\pi - 2$. **6.** (a) $\frac{1}{2}x^2\sin x^2 + \frac{1}{2}\cos x^2$. **9.** (c) $\frac{4}{5}\cdot\frac{2}{3}$ and $\frac{5}{6}\cdot\frac{3}{4}\cdot\frac{1}{2}\cdot\frac{\pi}{2}$.

Problems 61. *Page 344*

1. (a) $\frac{x^4(4\ln x - 1)}{16}$; (c) $\ln\sqrt{u^2+1}$; (e) $\frac{1}{2}\mathrm{Tan}^{-1}\frac{u}{2}$; (g) $\frac{e^{x^2}(\sin 2x^2 - 2\cos 2x^2)}{10}$. **2.** (a) $\ln(\sec\sqrt{x}+\tan\sqrt{x})^2$; (c) $\frac{1}{3}\ln\left|\frac{\sin x}{2\sin x+3}\right|$; (e) $\ln\sqrt{\cosh x + 2}$. **3.** (a) $\frac{e^{3x}(9x^3-9x^2+6x-2)}{27}$; (c) $\frac{\tan^6 x}{6}-\frac{\tan^4 x}{4}+\frac{\tan^2 x}{2}+\ln|\cos x|$; (e) $\frac{xe^{2x}}{2}-\frac{e^{2x}}{4}$. **4.** (a) $\frac{105\pi}{768}$; (c) $\frac{16}{45}$; (e) $\frac{1}{2}\ln\frac{2}{5}+2\left(\mathrm{Tan}^{-1}2-\frac{\pi}{4}\right)$. **5.** $\ln\frac{4}{3}$.

Problems 62. *Page 351*

1. (a) $x^2 - x + 1 - \frac{1}{x+1}$; (c) $\frac{2}{x+2}+\frac{3}{x-2}$; (e) $\frac{5x+2}{x^2+4}$. **2.** (a) $\frac{x^3}{3}-\frac{x^2}{2}+x-\ln|x+1|$; (c) $\ln(x+2)^2+\ln|x-2|^3$; (e) $\frac{5}{2}\ln(x^2+4)+\mathrm{Tan}^{-1}\frac{x}{2}$.

3. (a) $\ln\left(\frac{x^2(x+2)^4}{|x+1|^3}\right)$; (c) $\frac{x^2}{2} - 2x + \frac{1}{x+1} + 3\ln|x+1|$; (e) $\ln|x| - \frac{2}{x} - \frac{1}{2x^2}$; (g) $\frac{t^2}{2} - 2t + \frac{4}{t} + \ln(t^2+2t)^2$. **6.** (a) $\ln[(x+1)^2\sqrt{x^2+x+1}] - \sqrt{3}\,\text{Tan}^{-1}\frac{2x+1}{\sqrt{3}}$; (c) $\ln|x-1| + \text{Arctan}\,x$; (e) $\ln\sqrt{\frac{z-1}{z+1}} - \text{Tan}^{-1} z$. **7.** (a) $\ln\left(\frac{4}{3}\right)^4 - \frac{3}{2} \approx -.3492$; (c) $\frac{1}{3}\left(\ln 2 + \frac{\pi}{\sqrt{3}}\right)$; (e) $\ln\left[\frac{12}{5}\left(\frac{20}{13}\right)^{3/2}\right] \approx 1.522$.

Problems 63. *Page 356*

1. (a) $-x - \cot x$; (c) $\frac{1}{3}\sin^3 x - \frac{1}{5}\sin^5 x$; (e) $\frac{-2}{3}(\cos x)^{3/2}$. **2.** (a) $\frac{x}{2} + \frac{\sin 6x}{12}$; (c) $\frac{3x}{8} - \frac{\sin 2x}{4} + \frac{\sin 4x}{32}$. **4.** (a) $\frac{1}{4}\sec^4 x$; (c) $\ln|\sec x + \tan x| - \sin x$. **7.** (a) $\frac{1}{2}\sin x + \frac{1}{14}\sin 7x$; (c) $\frac{1}{2}\sin x - \frac{1}{14}\sin 7x$. **9.** $\frac{\pi}{2}$. **10.** (a) $\frac{4}{3}$.

Problems 64. *Page 361*

1. (a) $y = 3x - 4$; (c) $y = \frac{1}{2}(3 - \cos x^2)$. **2.** (a) $f(x) = \frac{(2x)^{3/2}}{3} - \frac{2}{3}$; (c) $f(x) = 2 + \sin\ln x$. **3.** $f(x) = 2x + 3 - 3\sin x - 2\cos x$. **5.** (a) $y = \int_1^x |t|\,dt + 2$. **7.** (a) 3.283. **9.** Maximum *at* $t = \sqrt{k\pi}$, k an odd integer. **11.** No.

Problems 65. *Page 366*

1. (a) $6(x^{-3} - x^{-4})$; (c) $\frac{1-\ln x}{x^2}$. **4.** (a) $2(x+1) + \Delta x$, $2(x+1)$; (c) $\frac{1}{\Delta x}\ln\left(\frac{x+\Delta x}{x}\right)$, $\frac{1}{x}$. **5.** (a) $\frac{1}{2(x+1)}$; (c) x. **6.** (a) $\frac{-4}{y^3}$; (c) $\frac{2xy + 2y\cos y + y^2\sin y}{(x+\cos y)^3}$.
7. 0.

Review Problems, Chapter 7. *Page 367*

1. (a) $\frac{e^{x^3}}{3}$; (b) $\frac{x^2-1}{2}e^{x^2}$. **3.** (a) $\frac{2}{9}(x^3+1)^{3/2}$; (b) $\frac{x^2(x^2-1)^{3/2}}{3} - \frac{2}{15}(x^2-1)^{5/2}$.
5. $\ln\left(1 + \frac{2}{\sqrt{3}}\right)$. **6.** (a) 0; (c) $\frac{3\pi}{16}$.

Problems 66. *Page 374*

1. (a) $(2\sqrt{3}, 2)$; (c) $(3\sqrt{2}, -3\sqrt{2})$; (e) $(0, 90)$. **2.** (a) $(4, 180°)$; (c) $(12, 120°)$; (e) $(270, 270°)$. **3.** No. **4.** (a) $x^2 + y^2 = 2x$; (c) $y = 5x$. **7.** No. **9.** Symmetric with respect to (a) pole; (c) line on pole perpendicular to polar axis; (e) line containing polar axis. **11.** (a) (2, 30°) and 7 other points; (c) (0, 0), $\left(1, \frac{\pi}{4}\right)$, $\left(1, \frac{5\pi}{4}\right)$.

Problems 67. *Page 382*

1. 6. **3.** $r = 2\sqrt{2}\cos(\theta - 135°)$. **5.** (a) Hyperbola, vertices $\left(2, \frac{\pi}{2}\right)$ and $\left(-8, \frac{3\pi}{2}\right)$, foci (0, 0) and $\left(10, \frac{\pi}{2}\right)$; (c) Parabola, vertex $\left(2, \frac{\pi}{2}\right)$, focus (0, 0); (e) Parabola, vertex $\left(\frac{1}{2}, \frac{\pi}{2}\right)$, focus (0, 0). **6.** (a) Hyperbola; (c) Ellipse. **9.** Practically a circle of radius 5.

Problems 68. *Page 388*

1. $\psi \approx 81°$. **2.** (a) Undefined; (c) $\frac{-1}{\sqrt{3}}$. **3.** (a) and (c) $\theta = \frac{\pi}{4}$, $\theta = \frac{-\pi}{4}$. **4.** (a) -2; (c) $\sqrt{\pi} + 2\pi$. **7.** $\left(3, \frac{2\pi}{3}\right)$. **13.** (a) 30°, 30°, and 90°.

Problems 69. *Page 393*

1. $\frac{\pi}{2}$. **2.** (a) $\frac{4\pi^3}{3}$; (c) $\frac{\pi}{2} + \frac{\sinh 4\pi}{8}$. **3.** 25π. **7.** 11π. **9.** π. **11.** $\frac{32}{3}$.

Problems 70. *Page 398*

2. (a) $(2 - \sqrt{3}, 2\sqrt{3} + 1)$; (c) $(1 - 2\sqrt{3}, -2 - \sqrt{3})$; (e) $(2, -4)$; (g) $(-2, 4)$. **3.** (a) $\left(\frac{1}{2}, \frac{\sqrt{3}}{2}\right)$; (c) $\left(\frac{1 - \sqrt{3}}{2}, \frac{1 + \sqrt{3}}{2}\right)$. **5.** $-m$. **7.** (a) 6; (c) $4\sqrt{2}$. **9.** $\bar{x} = (x - h)\cos\alpha + (y - k)\sin\alpha$, $\bar{y} = -(x - h)\sin\alpha + (y - k)\cos\alpha$.

Problems 71. *Page 404*

1. (a) $3\bar{x}^2 - \bar{y}^2$; (c) $5\bar{x}^2$. **2.** (a) $4\bar{x}^2 - \bar{y}^2 = 4$; (c) $4\bar{x}^2 - \bar{y}^2 = 4$. **3.** (a) $4\bar{\bar{x}}^2 + \bar{\bar{y}}^2 = 16$; (c) $\bar{\bar{y}}^2 = 4\bar{\bar{x}}$. **5.** $3x^2 - 2xy + 3y^2 = 8$, $\bar{x}^2 + 2\bar{y}^2 = 4$. **9.** (a) Parabola; (b) Ellipse; (c) Hyperbola.

Problems 72. *Page 411*

1. (a) (1, 2); (c) (1, 3). **2.** (a) 0 and $2\sqrt{5}$. **3.** (a) $\sqrt{|\boldsymbol{A}|^2 + |\boldsymbol{B}|^2}$; (c) $\sqrt{9|\boldsymbol{A}|^2 + 16|\boldsymbol{B}|^2}$; (e) $\sqrt{2}\,|\boldsymbol{A}|\,|\boldsymbol{B}|$. **4.** (a) $\boldsymbol{AC}$; (c) $\boldsymbol{BA}$. **5.** $\boldsymbol{A} - \boldsymbol{B}$. **7.** (a) $t = 2$.

Problems 73. *Page 417*

1. (a) $3\boldsymbol{i} + 4\boldsymbol{j}$, 5; (c) $-5\boldsymbol{j}$, 5. **2.** (a) $(4, -6)$; (c) $(6, -2)$; (e) $(16, -3)$. **3.** $\left(\frac{x_1 + x_2}{2}, \frac{y_1 + y_2}{2}\right)$. **4.** (a) $(4, 3)$; (c) $(19, 23)$. **5.** 45°, 45°, 90°. **7.** $2x + 3y = 0$, $\frac{1}{\sqrt{13}}(-3\boldsymbol{i} + 2\boldsymbol{j})$.

Problems 74. *Page 424*

1. (a) Semicircle; (c) Line segment; (e) One branch of a hyperbola. **5.** (a) $x = 1 - t$, $y = 10 - 3t$; (c) $x = 5$, $y = t$. **6.** (a) $x = t^2$, $y = t^3$; $x = t^{2/3}$, $y = t$; (c) $x = \sec t$, $y = \tan t$; $x = \coth t$, $y = \operatorname{csch} t$. **7.** (a) $\boldsymbol{R} = (3t + 2)\boldsymbol{i} + (3 - t)\boldsymbol{j}$; (c) $\boldsymbol{R} = (t - 1)\boldsymbol{i} + (3t + 1)\boldsymbol{j}$.

Problems 75. *Page 431*

1. (a) $\boldsymbol{i} + \boldsymbol{j}$; (c) $\sin 2\,(-\boldsymbol{i} + \boldsymbol{j})$. **3.** (a) $\frac{3}{5}\boldsymbol{i} + \frac{4}{5}\boldsymbol{j}$; (c) $\frac{e\boldsymbol{i} + \boldsymbol{j}}{\sqrt{1 + e^2}}$; (e) $\frac{\boldsymbol{i} - \boldsymbol{j}}{\sqrt{2}}$. **5.** $\boldsymbol{R} = (t + 1)e\boldsymbol{i} + t\boldsymbol{j}$. **7.** $8a$. **9.** 6. **11.** $\frac{61}{27}$. **13.** $\frac{17}{12}$.

Problems 76. *Page 439*

2. (a) 2; (c) $\frac{1}{\sqrt{2}}$. **3.** (a) 2; (c) 0. **7.** (a) $b\boldsymbol{j}$; (c) $\boldsymbol{A} = -\boldsymbol{R}$. **9.** (a) $\frac{\sqrt{10}}{30}$ and $\frac{\sqrt{10}}{10}$. **10.** (a) $\boldsymbol{V} = 8\pi\boldsymbol{i}$, $\boldsymbol{A} = -8\pi^2\boldsymbol{j}$.

Problems 77. *Page 444*

3. $\pi r\sqrt{h^2 + r^2}$. **4.** (a) $\frac{49\pi}{4}$. **5.** $\pi\left[18 + \frac{75}{2}\operatorname{Sin}^{-1}\frac{4}{5}\right]$. **7.** (a) $\frac{208\pi}{3}$; (c) $\frac{\pi}{2}[2 + \sinh 2]$. **9.** $\frac{13\pi}{3}$.

Review Problems, Chapter 8. *Page 445*

1. $Q(r, \pi - \theta)$, $R(-r, \theta)$, $S(r, -\theta)$. **2.** $r = \frac{4}{1 - \cos\left(\theta - \frac{\pi}{4}\right)}$. **4.** $r = 2\sqrt{2}\,e^{\theta}$. **5.** Any integral multiple of $\frac{\pi}{2}$. **7.** $\frac{\boldsymbol{A} \cdot \boldsymbol{B}}{|\boldsymbol{B}|^2}$. **9.** $\boldsymbol{R} = \boldsymbol{F}'(a)t + \boldsymbol{F}(a)$. **11.** $2/(1 + 4t^2)^{3/2}$.

Problems 78. *Page 452*

2. (a) $10\boldsymbol{k}$; (c) $3\boldsymbol{j} + 10\boldsymbol{k}$. **3.** (a) $12\boldsymbol{i} + 9\boldsymbol{j} + 6\boldsymbol{k}$; (c) $3\sqrt{29}$; (e) $(11, 11, -3)$, for example. **7.** $\boldsymbol{A} + \boldsymbol{B}$ and $\frac{1}{2}(\boldsymbol{A} + \boldsymbol{B})$. **9.** $|\boldsymbol{A} + \boldsymbol{X}| \leq |\boldsymbol{A}| + |\boldsymbol{X}|$, equality when $\boldsymbol{X} = \dfrac{x\boldsymbol{A}}{|\boldsymbol{A}|}$.

Problems 79. *Page 458*

2. (a) -5; (c) $11\boldsymbol{i} + 7\boldsymbol{j} + 6\boldsymbol{k}$; (e) 145. **3.** $\dfrac{-4}{9}$. **7.** $\boldsymbol{A} \times \boldsymbol{B} = -\boldsymbol{i} + 4\boldsymbol{j} + 6\boldsymbol{k}$.

Problems 80. *Page 462*

1. (a) $\dfrac{1}{3}(2\boldsymbol{i} + \boldsymbol{j} - 2\boldsymbol{k})$; (c) $\dfrac{1}{\sqrt{3}}(\boldsymbol{i} + \boldsymbol{j} + \boldsymbol{k})$. **2.** (a) $2x - 3y + z + 1 = 0$; (c) $x = 0$. **3.** A set of parallel planes. **5.** $2x - 3z + 7 = 0$. **7.** $3x + 4y - z - 16 = 0$. **9.** 3. **11.** $x - 7y + 5\sqrt{2}\,z = 0$ or $x - 7y - 5\sqrt{2}\,z = 0$.

Problems 81. *Page 467*

2. (a) $z = x^2 + y^2$; (c) $\dfrac{y^2}{4} + \dfrac{x^2 + z^2}{9} = 1$; (e) $y^2 + z^2 = x^4$. **5.** $4b^2(x^2 + z^2) = (x^2 + y^2 + z^2 + b^2 - r^2)^2$. **7.** A parabolic cylinder.

Problems 82. *Page 473*

1. (a) Ellipsoid; (c) Hyperboloid of one sheet; (e) Elliptical cone. **2.** (a) Parabola, $(0, 0, 0)$; (c) Parabola, $(0, 3, -1)$; (e) Parabola, $(4, 0, 4)$. **3.** (a) $x^2 - 2y^2 + 3z^2 - 2 = 0$; (c) $12x^2 + 5y^2 - 27z^2 - 5 = 0$. **4.** (a) $(1, -1, 0)$, 2. **5.** (a) $x + 2y + 2z = 9$. **6.** (a) Hyperboloid of one sheet; (c) Hyperboloid of two sheets. **7.** (a) $8y = x^2 + z^2$; (c) $4x^2 + 4z^2 + 3y^2 - 20y + 12 = 0$. **8.** (a) $5x^2 + 5z^2 = 2y$.

Problems 83. *Page 479*

1. (a) $\dfrac{1}{\sqrt{3}}(-\boldsymbol{i} + \boldsymbol{j} + \boldsymbol{k})$, $\sqrt{3}\,(e^\pi - 1)$; (c) $\dfrac{2}{\sqrt{9\pi^2 + 100}}\left(\dfrac{-3\pi}{2}\boldsymbol{i} + 3\boldsymbol{j} + 4\boldsymbol{k}\right)$, $\dfrac{\pi\sqrt{9\pi^2 + 25}}{2} + \dfrac{25}{6}\ln\left(\dfrac{3\pi + \sqrt{9\pi^2 + 25}}{5}\right)$. **3.** $\dfrac{1}{\sqrt{26}}(\boldsymbol{i} + 3\boldsymbol{j} + 4\boldsymbol{k})$. **5.** $\dfrac{14}{3}$.

9. $\boldsymbol{T} = \dfrac{1}{\sqrt{2}}(\tanh t\boldsymbol{i} + \boldsymbol{j} + \operatorname{sech} t\boldsymbol{k})$, $\boldsymbol{N} = \operatorname{sech} t\boldsymbol{i} - \tanh t\boldsymbol{j}$, $\boldsymbol{B} = \dfrac{1}{\sqrt{2}}(-\tanh t\boldsymbol{i} + \boldsymbol{j} - \operatorname{sech} t\boldsymbol{k})$. **10.** (a) $\boldsymbol{F}(t) \times \boldsymbol{F}''(t)$; (c) $\dfrac{\boldsymbol{F}(t) \cdot \boldsymbol{F}'(t)}{|\boldsymbol{F}(t)|}$. **11.** $\sqrt{\kappa^2 + \tau^2}$.

13. (a) $-\kappa\tau$; (c) $-\kappa^2$; (e) $\kappa^2\tau$.

Problems 84. *Page 483*

1. (a) $\boldsymbol{R} = (3t + 2)\boldsymbol{i} - 2t\boldsymbol{j} + (7t + 3)\boldsymbol{k}$; (c) $\boldsymbol{R} = (2t + 1)\boldsymbol{i} + (5t + 2)\boldsymbol{j} + (t + 3)\boldsymbol{k}$. **3.** $\boldsymbol{R} = (3t + 2)\boldsymbol{i} + (2t - 1)\boldsymbol{j} + (3 - t)\boldsymbol{k}$. **4.** (a) $\boldsymbol{R} = (2t - 2)\boldsymbol{i} + (t + 1)\boldsymbol{j} + (2t + 2)\boldsymbol{k}$. **5.** $\frac{10}{3\sqrt{14}}$. **7.** $(-1, 2, 1)$. **9.** Yes. **11.** $\frac{-1}{\sqrt{11}}, \frac{3}{\sqrt{11}}, \frac{1}{\sqrt{11}}$, and $\frac{7}{\sqrt{59}}, \frac{-3}{\sqrt{59}}, \frac{1}{\sqrt{59}}$.

Problems 85. *Page 489*

1. (a) $(\sqrt{3}, 1, -1)$; (c) $(\sqrt{2}, \sqrt{2}, 1)$; (e) $(0, -1, -1)$. **2.** (a) $\left(\frac{3}{2}, \frac{\sqrt{3}}{2}, 1\right)$; (c) $(0, 5, 0)$; (e) $(0, 0, 1)$. **3.** (a) $z = 2(x^2 + y^2)$; (c) $3x + 4y + z = 2$. **4.** (a) $x^2 + y^2 + z^2 = 9$; (c) $x^2 + y^2 = 25$. **5.** (a) $z = r^2$; (c) $r \sin \theta = 5$. **6.** (a) $\theta = 60°$; (c) $\rho = 4 \cos \theta$. **7.** (a) $\frac{5}{2} \ln 3$. **11.** $\frac{\pi}{2}\sqrt{1 + k^2}$.

Review Problems, Chapter 9. *Page 490*

1. $Q(3, 4, -3)$, $R(-7, 4, 5)$, $S(-1, 0, 1)$, $T(-4, -3, 5)$. **3.** $\frac{4}{7}$. **5.** $\frac{x}{a} + \frac{y}{b} + \frac{z}{c} = 1$. **9.** $\boldsymbol{R} = \boldsymbol{F}'(a)t + \boldsymbol{F}(a)$.

Problems 86. *Page 497*

1. (a) $(2, -1)$; (c) $(0, 1)$; (e) $(\frac{3}{5}, \frac{4}{5})$. **2.** (a) $(1, 2, -1)$; (c) $(2, 0, 1)$; (e) $(1, -1, 0, 2)$. **3.** $x = \frac{ud - vb}{ad - bc}$, $y = \frac{av - uc}{ad - bc}$. **4.** (a) $(0, 0, 0)$. **7.** 80°, 85°, 15°.

Problems 87. *Page 502*

1. (a) $(2, 1)$; (c) $(-1, 1)$; (e) $(4, 3)$. **2.** (a) $(1, -1, 1)$; (c) $(0, 0, 0)$; (e) $(2, 0, -1, 1)$. **3.** (a) $(5t, 3t, -7t)$. **4.** Yes. **5.** (a) $(7t, 1 + 3t, -1 - 5t)$; (b) $(7t, -1 + 3t, 1 - 5t)$; (c) No solution; (d) $(7t, 3t, -5t)$. **6.** 374. **7.** No.

Problems 88. *Page 509*

1. (a) $(12, 3, -5)$; (c) 14. **2.** (a) 10; (c) 70. **3.** (a) $(t, -2t)$; (b) $\left(\frac{1}{\sqrt{5}}, \frac{-2}{\sqrt{5}}\right)$ or $\left(\frac{-1}{\sqrt{5}}, \frac{2}{\sqrt{5}}\right)$. **5.** $\begin{bmatrix} 0 & 0 & 0 & 1 \\ 0 & 0 & 1 & 0 \\ 0 & 1 & 0 & 0 \\ 1 & 0 & 0 & 0 \end{bmatrix}$. **6.** Zero matrix. **7.** (a) $(2, -2)$; (b) $\begin{bmatrix} 13 & 0 \\ 2 & 0 \end{bmatrix}$; (c) $(-5, 10, 6)$; (d) $\begin{bmatrix} 2 & 0 & -5 \\ 14 & -7 & 9 \\ 2 & 5 & 23 \end{bmatrix}$.

8. (a) $\begin{bmatrix} 8 & 4 \\ 1 & 9 \end{bmatrix}$; (c) $\begin{bmatrix} 2 & 14 \\ -2 & 11 \end{bmatrix}$. **11.** 3^9S.

Problems 89. *Page 515*

2. (a) $\begin{bmatrix} 0 & -1 \\ 1 & 0 \end{bmatrix}$; (c) $\begin{bmatrix} 0 & 1 & 0 \\ 1 & 0 & 0 \\ 0 & 0 & 1 \end{bmatrix}$; (e) $\begin{bmatrix} 1 & 0 & 0 \\ 0 & 3 & -1 \\ 0 & -5 & 2 \end{bmatrix}$.

3. $x = 3u - v$, $y = -5u + 2v$.

4. (a) $\begin{bmatrix} 2 & -1 \\ -7 & 4 \end{bmatrix}$; (c) $\begin{bmatrix} -5 & -1 & 6 \\ 1 & 0 & -1 \\ 9 & 2 & -10 \end{bmatrix}$; (e) $\begin{bmatrix} 9 & -2 & 0 & 0 \\ -4 & 1 & 0 & 0 \\ 0 & 0 & -3 & 1 \\ 0 & 0 & -8 & 3 \end{bmatrix}$.

5. $(-11, 2, 20)$.

6. (a) $\begin{bmatrix} -2 & 1 \\ \frac{3}{2} & \frac{-1}{2} \end{bmatrix}$; (c) $\begin{bmatrix} \frac{1}{2} & \frac{1}{2} & \frac{-1}{2} \\ \frac{-1}{10} & \frac{-3}{10} & \frac{1}{2} \\ \frac{-3}{10} & \frac{1}{10} & \frac{1}{2} \end{bmatrix}$; (e) $\begin{bmatrix} \frac{2}{7} & \frac{3}{7} & \frac{-4}{7} \\ \frac{1}{7} & \frac{-2}{7} & \frac{5}{7} \\ \frac{-3}{7} & \frac{-1}{7} & \frac{6}{7} \end{bmatrix}$.

7. $\dfrac{1}{a_{11}a_{22} - a_{12}a_{21}} \begin{bmatrix} a_{22} & -a_{12} \\ -a_{21} & a_{11} \end{bmatrix}$.

Problems 90. *Page 520*

1. (a) -2; (c) 0. **4.** (a) -7; (c) 0; (e) -24. **6.** Yes. **7.** $x = 1$ or $x = 6$. **8.** $k = 2$ or $k = 7$.

Problems 91. *Page 524*

8. No. **9.** v, x, and y must be 0, u, w, and z must be either $+1$ or -1.

Problems 92. *Page 528*

1. (a) $\lambda^2 - 4\lambda + 3 = 0$; (b) 3, 1; (c) (1, 1) and $(-1, 1)$; (d) $\begin{bmatrix} \frac{1}{\sqrt{2}} & \frac{-1}{\sqrt{2}} \\ \frac{1}{\sqrt{2}} & \frac{1}{\sqrt{2}} \end{bmatrix}$.

3. (a) $\begin{bmatrix} 5 & 0 \\ 0 & 3 \end{bmatrix}$; (c) $\begin{bmatrix} 1 & 0 \\ 0 & -1 \end{bmatrix}$; (e) $\begin{bmatrix} \sqrt{13} & 0 \\ 0 & -\sqrt{13} \end{bmatrix}$.

5. (a) $\lambda^3 - 5\lambda^2 + 6\lambda = 0$; (b) 3, 2, 0; (c) (1, 1, 1), $(0, 1, -1)$, $(2, -1, -1)$; (d) $\begin{bmatrix} \frac{1}{\sqrt{3}} & 0 & \frac{2}{\sqrt{6}} \\ \frac{1}{\sqrt{3}} & \frac{1}{\sqrt{2}} & \frac{-1}{\sqrt{6}} \\ \frac{1}{\sqrt{3}} & \frac{-1}{\sqrt{2}} & \frac{-1}{\sqrt{6}} \end{bmatrix}$. **7.** (a) $\begin{bmatrix} 2 & 0 & 0 \\ 0 & 1 & 0 \\ 0 & 0 & -2 \end{bmatrix}$; (b) $\begin{bmatrix} 5 & 0 & 0 \\ 0 & 3 & 0 \\ 0 & 0 & 2 \end{bmatrix}$;

(c) $\begin{bmatrix} 3 & 0 & 0 \\ 0 & 1 & 0 \\ 0 & 0 & 1 \end{bmatrix}$; (d) $\begin{bmatrix} \sqrt{2} & 0 & 0 \\ 0 & 0 & 0 \\ 0 & 0 & -\sqrt{2} \end{bmatrix}$; (e) $\begin{bmatrix} 6 & 0 & 0 \\ 0 & 3 & 0 \\ 0 & 0 & 2 \end{bmatrix}$.

Problems 93. *Page 534*

3. 30°. **5.** (a) (−6, 3, 9); (c) $\bar{x} + 2\bar{y} - 11\bar{z} - 1 = 0$.

Problems 94. *Page 539*

1. (a) $3\bar{x}^2 + \bar{y}^2 = 1$; (b) $\begin{bmatrix} \frac{1}{\sqrt{2}} & \frac{1}{\sqrt{2}} \\ \frac{-1}{\sqrt{2}} & \frac{1}{\sqrt{2}} \end{bmatrix}$; (c) 45°. **3.** (a) $5\bar{x}^2 + 3\bar{y}^2 = 3$; (c) $\bar{x}^2 - \bar{y}^2 = 1$; (e) $\bar{x}^2 = 1$. **4.** (a) $3\bar{x}^2 + 2\bar{y}^2 = 1$; (b) $\begin{bmatrix} \frac{1}{\sqrt{3}} & \frac{1}{\sqrt{3}} & \frac{1}{\sqrt{3}} \\ 0 & \frac{1}{\sqrt{2}} & \frac{-1}{\sqrt{2}} \\ \frac{2}{\sqrt{6}} & \frac{-1}{\sqrt{6}} & \frac{-1}{\sqrt{6}} \end{bmatrix}$.
6. (a) $5\bar{x}^2 + 3\bar{y}^2 + 2\bar{z}^2 = 2$; (c) $\bar{x}^2 - \bar{z}^2 = \sqrt{2}$; (e) $\bar{x}^2 + \frac{\bar{y}^2}{2} + \frac{\bar{z}^2}{3} = 1$.

Review Problems, Chapter 10. *Page 540*

1. 4 nickels, 3 dimes, and 3 quarters or 1 nickel, 7 dimes, and 2 quarters. **5.** Either $b = c$ or if $b \neq c$, then $b = -c$ and $a = d$. **6.** (a) and (c) are true.

9. $P = \begin{bmatrix} \frac{1}{\sqrt{3}} & \frac{2}{\sqrt{6}} & 0 \\ \frac{1}{\sqrt{3}} & \frac{-1}{\sqrt{6}} & \frac{1}{\sqrt{2}} \\ \frac{1}{\sqrt{3}} & \frac{-1}{\sqrt{6}} & \frac{-1}{\sqrt{2}} \end{bmatrix}$.

Problems 95. *Page 545*

1. (a) 12; (c) 0. **2.** (a) $e^{x^2} \sin yz$; (c) x^2yz^2. **3.** (a) $(4 + h) \ln 3$; (c) $12 + 6h + h^2$. **5.** (a) $e^u e^v \sin (u - v)$. **6.** (a) All points of the plane except the line $y = x$; (c) "Square" defined by the inequality $|x + y| \leq 1$. **7.** $f(x, y) = \frac{y}{x}$.
9. $R = \frac{l}{25r^2}$, R ohms, l centimeters, r millimeters. **11.** The plane $2x - 3y + 4z = 7$.

Problems 96. *Page 552*

1. (a) $6e^{-2}$; (c) $-2 \cos 6$; (e) $\frac{-2}{27}$; (g) $\frac{1}{4}$; (i) $g(3)$. **2.** (a) $2xe^y$; (c) $\cos xy - xy \sin xy$; (e) $x^{y-1} + yx^{y-1} \ln x$; (g) $\frac{2}{(2x-y)^2}$; (i) 0. **3.** (a) $2e^x y \cos y^2$; (c) $2ye^{x^2+y^2}$; (e) $\frac{1}{y}$; (g) $x \cos xy$. **9.** $8x(x^2 - 2y)e^{-(x^2-2y)^2}$. **11.** No.

Problems 97. *Page 558*

3. $38e^{15}$. **5.** $D_t u = F_1(x, y, z)D_t x + F_2(x, y, z) + 2tF_3(x, y, z)$. **9.** (a) $\frac{-(4x+3y)}{3x+8y}$; (c) $\frac{-(yx^{y-1} + y^x \ln y)}{x^y \ln x + xy^{x-1}}$. **11.** (a) $2uD_x^2 u + D_x^2 v + 2(D_x u)^2$.

Problems 98. *Page 562*

5. (a) $2[f_{11}(x+y, x-y) + f_{22}(x+y, x-y)]$. **6.** (a) $10f_1(7, -2) + 2f_2(7, -2)$; (c) $-20f_{11}(7, -2) + 36f_{12}(7, -2) + 8f_{22}(7, -2) - 2f_1(7, -2)$. **9.** 2 and -3. **11.** $2f(r+s)$.

Problems 99. *Page 568*

1. (a) $\frac{5}{\sqrt{2}}$; (c) $\frac{-1}{6\sqrt{2}}$. **2.** (a) $\frac{35}{3}$; (c) -6. **3.** (a) $\frac{-6}{5}$; (c) 0; (e) $\frac{4}{5}$ or $\frac{-4}{5}$. **4.** (a) $\boldsymbol{k}$; (c) $\frac{1}{\sqrt{2}}(\boldsymbol{i} + \boldsymbol{k})$. **7.** $-e^{-x^2}\boldsymbol{i} + e^{-y^2}\boldsymbol{j}$. **9.** (a) N. E.; (b) N. W. and S. E.

Problems 100. *Page 572*

1. (a) Circles; (c) Ellipses. **2.** (a) Spheres; (c) Planes; (e) Hyperbolic paraboloids. **3.** (a) $\boldsymbol{j} + \boldsymbol{k}$; (c) $4\boldsymbol{i} + 18\boldsymbol{j} - 5\boldsymbol{k}$. **7.** Circles. **8.** (a) $7x - 11y + z + 9 = 0$; (c) $z = 0$. **9.** (2, 2, 0) and $(-2, -2, 0)$. **11.** $3\boldsymbol{i} + 2\boldsymbol{j} - 3\boldsymbol{k}$.

Problems 101. *Page 577*

1. (a) (1, 2, 2). **2.** (a) (8, 12, -64). **3.** (a) (-1, 3, 10). **5.** $\frac{\sqrt{2}}{2}$. **7.** $\frac{1}{\sqrt{3}}$. **9.** $2x + y + 2z = 6$. **11.** $\frac{1}{27}$ and 0. **13.** 2 feet by 2 feet by 2 feet.

Review Problems, Chapter 11. *Page 578*

1. (a) -8; (b) 2. **3.** 114, 57, 0. **7.** $\frac{1+\sqrt{3}}{2}$. **9.** 0.

Problems 102. *Page 587*

1. (a) 36; (c) 30. **3.** 48. **4.** (a) 48; (c) 16. **5.** 4. **7.** $\frac{160}{3}$. **9.** $\frac{3}{2}$.

Problems 103. *Page 594*

1. (a) $\frac{2}{3}$; (c) $\frac{3}{2}\ln 3 - 1$. **2.** (a) $\frac{7}{6}$; (c) 5; (e) $\frac{1}{2}$. **3.** (a) $\frac{32}{3}$; (c) $\frac{2}{3}$; (e) $\frac{16}{3}$; (g) 1; (i) $\frac{e^4}{4} - \frac{e^3}{3} + \frac{1}{12}$; (k) $\frac{3}{2}e^4 - \frac{41}{6}$. **4.** (a) 16; (c) $\frac{1}{8}$. **5.** (a) Rectangle: (2, 4), (3, 4), (3, 5), (2, 5); (c) Triangle: (0, 0), (1, 0), (0, 1). **8.** (a) $\frac{1}{4}(e^{16} - 1)$. **9.** $\int_0^a \int_a^b f(x, y)\,dx\,dy + \int_a^b \int_y^b f(x, y)\,dx\,dy$.

Problems 104. *Page 601*

1. (a) $\frac{9}{2}$; (c) $\frac{15}{2} - \ln 256$; (e) 1. **3.** $\frac{abc}{6}$. **4.** (a) $\frac{1}{2}$; (c) $\frac{52}{3}$. **5.** $\frac{2ma^3}{3}$. **7.** $\frac{4\pi abc}{3}$. **9.** 15π.

Problems 105. *Page 609*

1. (a) $\left(\frac{4a}{3\pi}, \frac{4a}{3\pi}\right)$; (c) $\left(\frac{8}{5}, \frac{3}{4}\right)$; (e) $\left(\frac{a+c}{3}, b\right)$. **7.** (a) $5\pi a^3$; (c) $\frac{80}{3}$. **9.** $I_X = \frac{512}{15}$, $I_Y = \frac{128}{7}$; $I_0 = \frac{5504}{105}$. **11.** (c) $I_L = I_Y - h^2A$. **13.** $\frac{\pi ab(5a^2 - 4b^2)}{4}$.

Problems 106. *Page 615*

1. (a) π; (c) $\frac{3\pi}{2}$. **3.** (a) $\frac{2\pi a^3}{3}$; (c) $\frac{5\pi}{3}$. **4.** (a) $\frac{\pi}{4}(1 - e^{-4})$. **5.** $\frac{4\pi a^3}{3}(8 - 3\sqrt{3})$. **7.** $\frac{2ma^3}{3}$. **9.** $\frac{\pi a^4}{4}$. **11.** (a) $\left(\frac{-5a}{6}, 0\right)$; (c) $\left(\frac{512}{105\pi}, \frac{512}{105\pi}\right)$. **12.** (a) $\bar{x} = \frac{4b}{3\pi}$; (c) Yes. Yes.

Problems 107. *Page 621*

1. (a) -1; (c) $\frac{abc}{3}(a^2 + b^2 + c^2)$. **2.** (a) $\frac{2}{5}$; (c) 2. **3.** (a) 36; (c) $\frac{1}{15}$. **4.** (a) Brick whose faces are the coordinate planes and the planes $x = 4$, $y = 3$, and $z = 2$. (c) Tetrahedron with vertices (0, 0, 0), (2, 0, 0), (2, 2, 0), and (2, 2, 2). **5.** (a) $\frac{16}{15}$; (c) π. **7.** $\left(0, \frac{3}{7}, \frac{2}{7}\right)$. **9.** $\frac{1}{30}$. **11.** $\frac{V(b^2 + c^2)}{5}$.

Problems 108. *Page 627*

1. $\frac{4\pi a^3}{3}$. **3.** (a) $\frac{V}{2}(a^2 + b^2)$. **4.** (a) Vc^2. **5.** $\frac{243}{16}$. **6.** (a) $\frac{11\pi}{3}$. **7.** $\frac{8\pi}{15}(b^5 - a^5)$. **9.** $\frac{\pi a^4 h}{10} = \frac{3a^2V}{10}$. **11.** $\frac{3a}{8}$.

Review Problems, Chapter 12. *Page 628*

1. 4. **2.** 13π. **5.** $\int_0^1 \int_{\text{Arcsin } y}^{\pi - \text{Arcsin } y} f(x, y)\, dx\, dy$. **9.** $\frac{\pi^2}{8} a^4$.

Problems 109. *Page 635*

1. (a) $\frac{4}{3}$; (c) $\frac{\pi}{6}$. **4.** (a) $\ln(6e - 15) \approx .27$; (c) $\frac{1}{\sqrt[3]{\ln 8 - 3/2}} - 1 \approx .2$. **6.** (a) $b - \frac{b^2}{2} + \frac{b^3}{3} - \frac{b^4}{4} + \frac{b^5}{5}$; (c) $\frac{1}{2} - \frac{b}{4} + \frac{b^3}{48}$. **7.** (a) .783; (c) .5625; (e) .271; (g) .995. **9.** .00034.

Problems 110. *Page 642*

1. (a) ∞; (c) $\frac{3}{7}$; (e) 1; (g) 0. **2.** (a) 3; (c) $\frac{1}{2\pi}$; (e) 2; (g) 1. **3.** (a) 0; (c) 0; (e) $\frac{1}{2}$. **4.** (a) 0; (c) $\frac{1}{2}$. **5.** (a) 2; (c) $\frac{1}{3}$; (e) $\frac{1}{2}$. **7.** $3a$ units to the left of A.

Problems 111. *Page 647*

1. (a) 0; (c) ∞; (e) 1; (g) 0. **2.** (a) $\frac{1}{2}$; (c) 0; (e) $\frac{-1}{3}$. **3.** (a) 1; (c) e; (e) 1; (g) $\frac{1}{e}$. **5.** r.

Problems 112. *Page 652*

1. (a) 1; (c) $\frac{1}{2e^{25}}$; (e) Divergent. **2.** (a) Convergent; (c) Divergent. **3.** (a) $\frac{3}{2}$; (c) $\frac{\pi}{2}$; (e) Divergent. **4.** (a) Divergent. (c) π. **5.** (a) No. **6.** (c) $\frac{1}{2}$. **7.** 1. **9.** 42.24×10^9 foot pounds.

Problems 113. *Page 657*

1. (a) Convergent; (c) Convergent; (e) Divergent; (g) Convergent. **2.** (a) $2\pi a^2$; (c) $\frac{\pi}{8}$. **5.** No. **6.** (a) Divergent; (c) Convergent; (e) Divergent.

Review Problems, Chapter 13. *Page 658*

1. No. **5.** (a) 1. **7.** (a) 1. **8.** ln 4.5.

Problems 114. *Page 667*

1. (a) 0; (c) $\frac{63}{8}$; (e) $\frac{1}{3}$. **2.** (a) 1, 1, $\frac{3}{2}$, 3; (c) 3, 2, $\frac{5}{2}$, $\frac{9}{4}$. **3.** (a) $2^n - 1$; (c) $n^2 - 1$. **5.** (a) $\frac{1}{2}$; (c) $\frac{1}{5}$; (e) 0. **6.** (c) and (e) converge. **7.** (a) 0; (c) 1. **9.** (a) $\frac{9}{2}$ and 0; (c) 1 and 0. **11.** $\left(\sin \frac{2\pi}{n}\right) \Big/ \frac{2}{n}$, π.

Problems 115. *Page 674*

1. (a) 15; (c) $\frac{-47}{60}$. **3.** (a) $2n$; (c) 1; (e) $a_1 = 0$, $a_n = 2(-1)^n$. **4.** (a) $\frac{3}{2}$; (c) $\frac{1}{2}$. **5.** (a) $\frac{8}{3}$; (c) 14. **7.** $S_n = \ln\left(1 + \frac{1}{n}\right)$, $S = 0$. **9.** No.

Problems 116. *Page 679*

1. (a) Convergent; (c) Convergent; (e) Divergent; (g) Convergent.

Problems 117. *Page 686*

1. All absolutely convergent. **3.** (a) Conditionally convergent; (c) Conditionally convergent. **5.** 200. **6.** (a) .2; (c) $\frac{1}{32}$. **7.** (a) .139; (c) $\frac{24{,}628}{76{,}545} \approx .3217$. **9.** No.

Problems 118. *Page 692*

1. (a) Convergent; (c) Convergent; (e) Divergent; (g) Convergent; (i) Convergent. **2.** (a) Convergent; (c) Convergent; (e) Convergent. **3.** No. Yes. **9.** $a_n = \frac{1}{n \ln n}$, $b_n = \frac{1}{n^2}$.

Problems 119. *Page 697*

1. (a) Convergent; (c) Divergent; (e) Divergent; (g) Divergent. **2.** (a) Divergent; (c) Convergent. **3.** (a) Divergent. **4.** (a) Absolutely convergent; (c) Conditionally convergent. **5.** Yes. **6.** (a) $-1 < x < 1$; (c) $x = (2n + 1)\pi$; (e) $x \neq 1$. **7.** No. No. **9.** $\frac{64}{15}$. $0 \leq R_5 \leq \frac{28}{225}$. **11.** (a) Convergent; (c) Convergent.

Problems 120. *Page 703*

1. (a) 2, $(-2, 2)$, $(-2, 2)$; (c) 3, $(-4, 2)$, $(-4, 2)$; (e) 1, $(3, 5)$, $[3, 5)$. **2.** (a) $(2, 4)$; (c) $(1, 3)$; (e) $\left(-\frac{1}{e}, \frac{1}{e}\right)$. **3.** (a) $(-\infty, \infty)$; (c) $(2 - \sqrt[4]{2}, 2 + \sqrt[4]{2})$; (e) $(-\infty, \infty)$.

Problems 121. *Page 708*

1. (a) .76; (c) $-.67$. **7.** .49. **13.** $\frac{1}{2} + \frac{x}{2^2} + \frac{x^2}{2^3} + \cdots$. **14.** (a) $\frac{1}{2} + \frac{3}{4}x + \frac{7}{8}x^2 + \cdots$.

Problems 122. *Page 714*

1. (a) 9!; (c) 8!. **2.** (a) $x - \frac{x^3}{3!} + \frac{x^5}{5!} - \cdots$; (c) $1 + \frac{x^2}{2!} + \frac{x^4}{4!} + \cdots$; (e) $\ln a + \frac{x}{a} - \frac{x^2}{2a^2} + \frac{x^3}{3a^3} - \cdots$. **3.** (a) .0998; (c) 1.0050. **5.** (a) $\frac{1}{\sqrt{2}}\left[1 + \left(x - \frac{\pi}{4}\right) - \frac{\left(x - \frac{\pi}{4}\right)^2}{2!} - \frac{\left(x - \frac{\pi}{4}\right)^3}{3!} - \cdots\right]$. (c) $1 + 2\left(x - \frac{\pi}{4}\right) + \frac{4\left(x - \frac{\pi}{4}\right)^2}{2!} + \frac{16\left(x - \frac{\pi}{4}\right)^3}{3!} + \cdots$. **6.** (a) $\frac{1}{4}\left[1 - \frac{(x-4)}{4} + \frac{(x-4)^2}{4^2} - \frac{(x-4)^3}{4^3} + \cdots\right]$; (c) $11 + 6(x - 4) + (x - 4)^2$. **7.** $(x - 1) - \frac{1}{2}(x - 1)^2 + \frac{1}{3}(x - 1)^3 - \cdots$. **9.** $x + \frac{1}{2}\frac{x^3}{3} + \frac{1 \cdot 3}{2 \cdot 4}\frac{x^5}{5} + \cdots$.

Problems 123. *Page 719*

1. (a) $x + x^2 + \frac{x^3}{3} - \frac{x^5}{30} + \cdots$; (c) $1 + \frac{x^2}{2} + \frac{5x^4}{24} + \frac{61x^6}{720} + \cdots$; (e) $1 + \frac{x^2}{2} - \frac{x^3}{3} + \frac{3x^4}{8} - \cdots$. **2.** (a) .764; (c) .0214. **3.** (a) 1.01; (c) .99; (e). 22. **4.** (a) 2.02; (c) .1003. **5.** $x + \frac{1}{2}\frac{x^3}{3} + \frac{1 \cdot 3}{2 \cdot 4}\frac{x^5}{5} + \cdots$. **7.** $-\frac{x^2}{2} - \frac{x^4}{12} - \frac{x^6}{45} - \cdots$. **9.** .659.

Review Problems, Chapter 14. *Page 720*

1. $a_n = 2^{(2-2^n)}$, $\lim_{n\to\infty} a_n = 0$. **2.** $\ln\frac{\pi}{2}$. **3.** (a) Divergent; (c) Divergent. **6.** (a) Conditionally convergent. **9.** $-1 < x < 1$. **11.** 1.

INDEX

INDEX

A

C